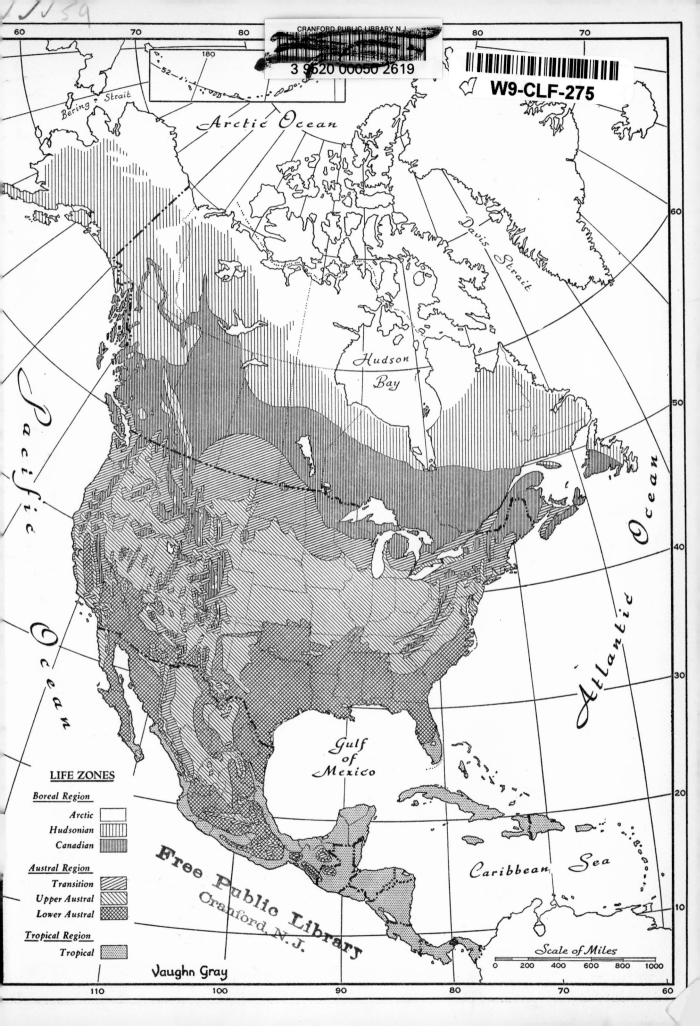

LIFE ZONES

Boreal Region

Arctic

Hudsonian

Canadian

Austral Region

Transition

Upper Austral

Lower Austral

Tropical Region

Tropical

Scale of Miles

0   200   400   600   800   1000

Vaughn Gray

THE MAMMALS

OF

NORTH AMERICA

E. RAYMOND HALL, PH.D.

SUMMERFIELD DISTINGUISHED PROFESSOR, CHAIRMAN OF THE DEPARTMENT OF ZOOLOGY,
AND DIRECTOR OF THE MUSEUM OF NATURAL HISTORY,
UNIVERSITY OF KANSAS

and

KEITH R. KELSON, PH.D.

DIVISION OF SCIENTIFIC PERSONNEL AND EDUCATION,
NATIONAL SCIENCE FOUNDATION

VOLUME I

THE RONALD PRESS COMPANY   NEW YORK

Published March 31, 1959

Library of Congress Catalog Card Number: 58-5832

Dedicated to the Memory of

CARL VON LINNÉ

author of *Systema Naturae*, 10th ed., published in 1758

and to the Memory of

SPENCER FULLERTON BAIRD

author of *Mammals* [of North America], published in 1858

PREFACE

In preparing the following account, we have assumed that all mammals have had a common ancestor. The Class Mammalia can be thought of, in a general way, as a "tree," the "limbs" of which extend upward in time with the still-growing "twig-tips" reaching into the present; the base of the trunk immediately below the first "fork" could be thought of as the common ancestral stock that lived millions of years ago in Mesozoic time. The still-growing twig-tips are the existing species. The Order Marsupialia can be thought of as one of the first limbs—low down near the base of the trunk—and the Order Carnivora as a limb that appeared later, higher up on the principal trunk. Accordingly, in the following account, we treat the Marsupialia first and the Carnivora later on. For families within each order, for genera within each family, and for species within each genus, we have followed the same system. As an example: In each genus we list first the species that we estimate to be the oldest; the other species in that genus are treated in order of what we judge to be decreasing age. Subspecies of any given species are arranged alphabetically.

The taxonomic limits here assigned to any order or genus or intermediate taxonomic category reflect our own personal judgment. For the specific *versus* subspecific status of any given kind of mammal, we have accepted the last-published opinion that was supported by evidence obtained from examination of specimens.

For any given record of occurrence, the authority is cited. His, or her, published identification reflects what was last written and not necessarily what we think should have been written. Any departure from this practice is clearly indicated as such and information is provided that will permit the reader to go to the original source and by independent study make his own decision. Similarly, means are provided whereby the reader himself can locate and appraise such new material as we have contributed; the new material consists almost entirely of identifications of specimens not heretofore reported in the literature. Each identification of that sort is followed by an entry (in parentheses) giving the catalogue number of the specimen and the "initials" of the museum in which the specimen is housed. For these identifications we, of course, assume responsibility, but only in the sense illustrated by the following example: According to the last-published account, *acutus* and *jaliscensis* are two of the recognized subspecies of the species *Liomys irroratus*; among the subspecies of *Liomys irroratus*, specimen No. 39906 KU, in our judgment, is referable to the subspecies *Liomys irroratus acutus* and not to *L. i. jaliscensis* or any other currently recognized subspecies of the species *Liomys irroratus*. The user of this book should understand that our identification of the specimen signifies nothing at all as to our opinion—or even that we had one—concerning whether *Liomys irroratus jaliscensis* and *Liomys irroratus acutus* were subjectively (in the zoological sense) tenable subspecies or whether the morphological differences were so slight between *Liomys irroratus jaliscensis* and *Liomys irroratus acutus* that the latter name should be arranged as a synonym of the earlier proposed *jaliscensis*.

Lest the reader infer that we have attempted to escape responsibility in instances where the literature contained conflicting statements and obviously improbable identifications, we remind him that within the limits of our time and opportunities we have obtained specimens, studied them, and published our findings (see under the terminal listing of literature cited—for example, Hall and Kelson, 1952). Indirectly, therefore, the accounts of a few species and subspecies in the present work do reflect our personal views, but these views are previously published judgments (except where we cite catalogue numbers of specimens) supported by evidence obtained from study of specimens and are not unsupported assumptions simply thought by us to be probabilities. Unsupported assumptions that we have made are clearly labeled as such, and we have kept them to a minimum because of our conviction that study of the actual mammals is the surest means for understanding what species there are and what the geographic range is of each species.

The number of species of mammals recognized in 1923 (Miller, 1924) was 1399 (2554 species and subspecies); in 1953 (Miller and Kellogg, 1955) the number of species was 1065 (3622 species and subspecies); in 1957 (on the pages that follow) there are only 1003 species (3679 species and subspecies). The decrease in number of species results from many of the named kinds having been reduced from specific to subspecific status in the past thirty years. Certainly the number of species listed in the present work is still too large; many geographically adjacent pairs of nominal species will prove to be only subspecies of one and the same species when adequate specimens are studied from geographic areas between the known areas of occurrence of the two kinds.

For example, we would not be surprised if collections, that ought to be obtained, of voles from between Nelson River of Manitoba and Burntside Lake of Minnesota would reveal intergradation between the yellow-cheeked vole, *Microtus xanthognathus*, and the rock vole, *Microtus chrotorrhinus* (Map 413). Such proof that the two kinds are only subspecies of a single species would reduce the number of species by one. Scores of other instances in which corresponding results can be expected will be apparent from inspection of the maps beyond and we hope that they will be an impetus to taxonomic study of American mammals. Of the 1003 species listed beyond for North America, at least 8 (for instance *Mus* and *Rattus*) have been introduced by modern man, leaving 995 that are native. When adequate materials of all 995 have been carefully studied, it may turn out that about 125 are only subspecies of other species, thus leaving about 870 species. For example, there may be only one instead of 77 species of the subgenus *Ursus*; there may be only one instead of two species of the genus *Aotus*. Of the 870 species, each of approximately 170 of them is confined to some island (for example, *Peromyscus seguis*) or to some isolated mountain mass (for example, *Eutamias palmeri*). Each of these species clearly is a close relative of some second species that ordinarily occurs in a neighboring district separated from the first by a barrier of some sort. Were these isolated species eliminated from the list, we would be left with approximately 700 species. Most of the mentioned isolated species, however, have distinctive morphological features and probably would not crossbreed in nature with their relatives of neighboring districts if afforded an opportunity to do so. Consequently, we would consider these isolated kinds to be valid species and would guess that there are approximately 800 Recent (in the geological sense) species of North American mammals. Of these, it should be remembered, some occur also in Eurasia (for example, *Spermophilus undulatus*) and a larger number occur also in South America (for example, *Didelphis marsupialis*).

Studies that reveal how many species there are, and that make known the geographic range of each kind—whether referred to as taxonomy, classification, speciation, extent of gene-flow, introgressive hybridization, geographic variation, systematics, or by some other term—are basic, important in themselves, and an aid in advancing knowledge in related fields of science. In explanation of the last point: About 45 years ago the lure of the "new" field of genetics, later of experimental embryology, and still later of virology, attracted so many beginning biologists that only a few persons took the places of the many systematists who were removed by time. Consequently, systematics languished. Meanwhile expanding frontiers of knowledge in several of the newer fields caught up with that in systematics and pushed ahead of it. Now progress has slowed down in some of these newer fields for want of adequately precise and detailed knowledge of systematics. An example is the study of disease: When, in experimental work, mammals are used as hosts of vectors or disease-causing parasites (viruses, bacteria, fungi, and invertebrates), it is found that physiological responses vary little or none between subspecies of a single species of host but may vary greatly between hosts that are of different species. By way of illustration, a particular strain of fungus multiplies so rapidly that it causes 90 per cent of one species of rabbit to die, but causes only moderate illness in another species of rabbit and seems unable to live at all in a third species of rabbit. To advance the knowledge of the disease organism, it is obviously necessary to know which kinds of rabbits are different species and which are subspecies of the same species. Knowledge in taxonomy is necessary also for purely theoretical research—for example, in correlating extents of Pleistocene sheets of ice with speciation of mammals. The correlation is close, but to discover the correlation we must ascertain which of the residual kinds of mammals are species and which are only subspecies of a single species.

In choosing zoological names we have taken as a starting point the 10th edition of *Systema Naturae*, 1758, by Linnaeus and have adhered to the law of priority. Names employed on other grounds are few, and each of them is identified as an exception at the place where the name is first used in the following account—see, for example, the generic name *Lasiurus* on page 188. In retrospect, we feel that a 100-per-cent adherence by us to the law of priority would have been desirable as a means of achieving stability of nomenclature at the earliest date possible.

Our aim was to include all pertinent taxonomic and distributional information that came to our attention up to October 31, 1957.

In the synonymy of each subspecies and each monotypic species (a species that is not divided into subspecies), the aim is to cite: first, the name first proposed for that kind of mammal; second, the accepted (first available) name in the form in which it originally was used by the proposer; third, the first usage of the current name-combination if it differs from the combination as originally proposed; and fourth, in chronological order, synonyms having type localities that fall within the geographic range of the subspecies or monotypic species concerned.

Parentheses enclosing an author's name signify that the immediately preceding scientific name was originally proposed in combination with a generic name other than the one now used. A comma is interposed between a scientific name and the name of the authority if the authority did not originally propose the name.

For each subspecies, and for each monotypic species, that is known by specimens from more than one locality, peripheral record-stations of occurrence are given under the heading of *"Marginal records."* The occurrences are arranged in clockwise order, beginning with the northernmost locality. If more than one of the marginal localities lies on the line of latitude that is northernmost for a given kind of mammal, the westernmost of those on that line is recorded first. The marginal localities that are represented by symbols on the corresponding distribution map are in roman type; those that are not represented on the map, in most instances because undue crowding or overlapping of symbols would have occurred, are in italic type.

Where a dot on a map is "split" by the boundary separating two subspecies, two specimens labeled as two subspecies are recorded from the same place; the assumption is that the two specimens actually were obtained some distance apart. Users of the maps should understand that the black dots represent actual geographic occurrences, and that the shaded areas are our guesses as to the probable North American ranges of the kinds of mammals concerned. A shaded arrow projecting into South America signifies our understanding that the species, but not necessarily the subspecies, occurs in South America.

Descriptions of mammals and artificial keys are designed to permit the identification of a specimen to species and to each "higher" taxonomic category (taxon) up to and including the Class. In constructing the keys, the aim was to use qualitative characters insofar as possible; wherever this was not possible and quantitative characters (for example, "broader skull" *versus* "narrower skull") are used, it is to be understood that reference is to be made to the illustrations of the skulls. Identification of a specimen to subspecies will not be achieved by reference to the following pages; the person making the subspecific identification will have to consult the original description of the subspecies and/or such literature as is cited immediately following the name of the genus or species. Such literature is prefaced with the words "Revised by" (for example, see under *Scapanus* on page 67 and *Scapanus latimanus* on page 69), and some by the words "Reviewed by."

Linear measurements, unless otherwise specified, are in millimeters. External measurements are given in this order: Total length; length of tail; length of hind foot, including the longest claw; height of ear from notch. Capitalized color designations are in the terms of Ridgway (Color Standards and Color Nomenclature, Washington, D.C., 1912); non-capitalized designations are not related to any particular standard, except that some of these color terms were taken *verbatim* from the early literature on mammals and may refer to unknown color charts.

North America, as here delimited, includes Greenland, all of Panamá, the entire continent between these areas, the Greater Antilles, and the Lesser Antilles south to and including Grenada.

A large share of the financial assistance used in organizing the following accounts came from the Office of Naval Research, United States Department of the Navy, through a contract (NR 160–187) between that Office and the University of Kansas. Some funds from the National Science Foundation were used in the final stages of the work. Funds for out-of-state field work were received from the Atomic Energy Commission and in larger measure from the Kansas University Endowment Association. This field work yielded specimens that provide many of the marginal records of occurrence. Grateful acknowledgment is made to the University of California Press for permission to use here certain illustrations that appeared in "The Mammals of Nevada" in 1946.

The senior author began work on the present account of the mammals of North America in 1945 and continued it as a principal project until the time of publication. The junior author worked full-time on the account from September 15, 1949, to August 5, 1954. Remington Kellogg greatly assisted us by making available proof sheets of the "List of North American Recent Mammals," Bulletin 205 of the United States National Museum. We are grateful to Sydney Anderson, Rollin H.

Baker, Mary F. Hall, Charles O. Handley, Jr., Philip Hershkovitz, David H. Johnson, and Henry W. Setzer for assistance with different parts of the account.

In decreasing order of total time devoted to the preparation of the present volume, the persons named below participated in its preparation.

J. Knox Jones, Jr.
Richard G. Van Gelder
Victor Hogg *
E. Lendell Cockrum
Robert J. Russell
Lucy Remple *
Virginia (Cassell) Unruh *
James W. Bee
James S. Findley
Norma Janes †
W. Gene Frum
George C. Rinker
Robert L. Packard
Donald J. Nash
Philip H. Krutzsch
Janet Luckfield †
Thane S. Robinson
Lottie Roscoe †
Nora Mason
Sheila Miller †
Richard B. Loomis
Walter C. Biggs
Ina Harding †
Mary Jane Rowland †

Robert E. Delphia
Austin B. Williams
Louise Brunk *
Sushil Bhatia
Artie L. Metcalf
W. Jackson Davis
Robert G. Webb
William N. Berg
Walter W. Dalquest
Richard P. Grossenheider *
Jean Bullock
Johanna Fichter †
Claremont G. Pritchard *
Robert M. Hankins
Terry A. Vaughan *
Alice Brown
John W. Twente, Jr.
Sylvia C. Robinson
William L. Cutter
Mary Lou (Hanson) Pritchard
Gene Pacheco *
Lorna Cordonnier *
Constances M. Spitz *
Louise E. Farrell †

E. Raymond Hall
Keith R. Kelson

Lawrence, Kansas
December, 1958

* Assisted primarily with drawings.
† Assisted primarily with typing.

CONTENTS

Volume I

CONTENTS

VOLUME II

ZOOGEOGRAPHY

What patterns emerge from the 500 maps showing the geographic distribution of North American mammals? What factors account for these patterns? Why are there fewer kinds of mammals in one area than in another?

The most common pattern is well illustrated in Volume 2 by Maps 484 (page 968) of the lynx, 485 (page 970) of the bobcat, and 480 (page 960) of the ocelot, Boreal, Temperate, and Tropical species, respectively. Actually, few mammals in the Temperate region of North America range from the Atlantic Coast to the Pacific Coast, as does the bobcat, and a more nearly typical illustration of distribution in the Temperate region is shown in Volume 1 by Map 229 (page 353) of the rock squirrel and Map 249 (page 388) of the fox squirrel, western and eastern species, respectively. More will be said about eastern and western distributions within the Temperate region farther on.

One of the factors responsible for the pattern of distribution outlined immediately above is temperature. The late C. Hart Merriam [1] postulated that "the northward distribution of terrestrial animals and plants is governed by the sum of the positive temperatures for the entire season of growth and reproduction, and the southward distribution is governed by the mean temperature of a brief period during the hottest part of the year." Presence or absence of moisture and uniformity *versus* variety in soil also determine the presence or absence of some species.

Another one of the factors important in accounting for the geographic distribution of a taxon [2] is its paleontological history. For example, paleontological evidence is to the effect that the Family Antilocapridae evolved in, and never radiated to any area outside of, North America; [3] consequently the pattern of its present geographic distribution probably would be otherwise had its paleontological history differed.

Before attempting to explain why any given region contains fewer or more kinds than another, it is helpful to consider the actual numbers recorded in Table 1 on the following page.

As shown in Table 1, almost three times as many species of mammals—four times as many endemic species—live in the Tropical region as in the Boreal region. The greater size range in plants and the greater number of kinds of plants in the Tropical region are partly responsible. Mammals depend on plants not only for shelter but for food directly or indirectly—rodents and ungulates are directly dependent; insectivorous bats and carnivorous mammals are indirectly dependent, since their prey is phytophagous. Not long ago it was pointed out that in, say,

[1] Life-zones and crop-zones, U.S. Dept. Agric. Div. Biol. Surv., Bull. No. 10, pp. 7–79, 1899; and, Science, n.s., 9:116, 1899.

[2] A taxon (plural, taxa) is a taxonomic unit, as, for example, the Order Rodentia, or Family Mustelidae, or genus *Cervus*, or species *Felis concolor*, or subspecies *Peromyscus maniculatus bairdii*, or any other taxonomic unit.

[3] The other strictly North American families of continental North America are rodents: Geomyidae and Heteromyidae. In the tropical West Indies, endemic families are: Solenodontidae, Nesophontidae (McDowell, Bull. Amer. Mus. Nat. Hist., 115:203, May 5, 1958, I think correctly places the Nesophontidae in the Solenodontidae), and Heptaxodontidae. The last, now extinct, seems to have lived until Recent time.

TABLE 1

ORDERS, FAMILIES, GENERA, AND SPECIES OF NORTH AMERICAN MAMMALS
ARRANGED BY REGIONS

Taxa[1]	Total Number	Boreal Region			Temperate Region			Tropical Region		
		Number in Boreal Region	Number confined to Boreal Region	Number in Boreal Region that range into Temperate Region, and *vice versa*	Number in Temperate Region	Number confined to Temperate Region	Number in Temperate Region that range into Tropical Region, and *vice versa*	Number in Tropical Region	Number confined to Tropical Region	Number that range into South America
Orders	11	7	0	7	9	0	9	11	2	11
Families ...	45	13	1	12	24	3	18	39	21	34
Genera	233	53	17	36	82	28	31	165	134	107
Species[2] ...	850	147	89	58	379	292	24	407	383	136

[1] Exclusive of Cetacea and Pinnipedia.
[2] Nominal species of bears of Subgenus *Ursus* are reckoned as one species.

an area 25 miles square, fewer than 17 species of land mammals live in the Arctic Life-zone of the Boreal region immediately south of Point Barrow, Alaska, as contrasted with about 55 at Lawrence, Kansas, in the Temperate region, and more than 140 in the Tropical region immediately adjacent to Panama City, Panamá. In attempting to account for the small number of kinds in the Arctic region, it was written [4] that

> Continuous cold for a long part of each year so shortens the growing season that there are few kinds of foods readily available and but few places to live and so only a few species can exist. Bats, for example, subsist mostly on insects; but at Point Barrow insects are readily obtained in only two of the twelve months and so no bats live there. There are no trees there and consequently no arboreal mammals such as make up a sizable part of the mammalian fauna farther south. There are not even any bushes five to ten feet tall that provide habitat for such mammals as chipmunks and wood rats farther south. The permafrost, several hundred to more than a thousand feet deep, excludes the variety of species that burrow and live in holes in the ground farther south. Lakes and streams . . . are open only briefly in the short summer and for most of the year are frozen solid; fresh-water mammals, therefore, have no place to live and so the river otter, mink, muskrat, and water shrew are missing.
>
> It is only the surface of the ground that is available to mammals, and of course, for a brief period in summer, the upper six to eight inches of soil that thaws out.

It seems, therefore, that there are fewer kinds of mammals in the Boreal region than in either of the two more southern regions because there are fewer kinds of places in which to live.

Zonation of the mammalian fauna of North America is clearly evident on the maps beyond. From north to south the life-zones, in the terminology of Merriam, are Arctic, Hudsonian, Canadian, Transition, Upper Austral, Lower Austral, Upper Tropical, and Lower Tropical. The first three are in the Boreal region, the next three are in the Temperate region, and the last two are in the Tropical region. The number of species is progressively larger from north to south. The most pronounced "breaks" are between the Canadian and Upper Austral life-zones (in the Transition Life-zone, where it occurs—see Hall,[5] p. 43), and between the Lower

[4] Mammals of northern Alaska, by James W. Bee and E. Raymond Hall, Univ. Kansas, Mus. Nat. Hist., Miscl. Publ. No. 8, p. 9, March 10, 1956.

[5] Hall, E. R. Mammals of Nevada. Univ. California Press, Berkeley, California, xi + 710 pp., col. frontispiece, 11 pls., 485 figs., plus unnumbered silhouettes, July 1, 1956.

Sonoran and Upper Tropical life-zones. The reader desiring detailed information on the zonation of North American mammals can profitably consult Hall [5] and Grinnell and Storer,[6] but the gist of the matter is indicated in Table 1 on p. xxiv, from which it can be ascertained that 61 per cent of the species occurring in the Boreal region are confined to that region and that corresponding percentages in the Temperate region and Tropical region are, respectively, 77 and 94. Analysis of faunas by regions and subregions irrespective of life-zones can be instructive, as shown in a recent paper by Hershkovitz.[7]

On a continental basis, North America has contributed a little to the fauna of Eurasia and has received much from Eurasia. North America has contributed much to the fauna of South America and has received less from South America.

For the geologically short period of the past few thousand years, North America has been separated from Eurasia, as the two are now by salt water in Bering Strait; this water barrier is thought to have existed intermittently in the Tertiary.[8] The fossil record indicates that throughout most of Tertiary time, Eurasia and North America were connected, in the region of Alaska, by land and by chains of islands, too. Therefore, for most of the time in which existing orders of mammals have been dominant, North America and Eurasia might properly be thought of as one continuous region—the Holarctic region. Because the existing saltwater barrier was only recently re-established, it is understandable that the existing mammals in the Boreal regions of Eurasia and North America closely resemble one another. Indeed, the ermine, Arctic ground squirrel, tundra vole, and wolf seem to be specifically the same on the two sides of Bering Strait. Almost every one of the other Boreal mammals has a species in North America so closely resembling one on the Eurasian side of Bering Strait that the common origin of the two species is evident.

In an instance where animals on the two sides of a barrier are so closely related as those just described, possibly few or no kinds from one side would be expected to establish themselves on the other side because competition would be so intense as ordinarily to eliminate the non-native strain. But, at times in the past, when the climate was Temperate there, as opposed to times when it was Boreal as it is now, more kinds of animals crossed from one continent to the other and established permanent populations in the newly invaded terrain. This crossing and establishment of populations on the other continent occurred because more kinds lived at each end of the land bridge in periods of Temperate climate than in times of Boreal climate and possibly because each kind differed markedly from its counterpart on the other continent.

As concerns the existing land connection between North and South America, it seems to have been established in late Pliocene time. Shortly before that time, North America had approximately 27 and South America 29 families [9] of terres-

---

[5] See footnote at bottom of page xxiv.

[6] Grinnell, J., and Storer, T. I. Animal life in the Yosemite. Univ. California Press, Berkeley, California, xviii + 752 pp., 62 pls., 65 figs., 1924.

[7] A geographical classification of Neotropical mammals. Fieldiana: Zool., 36:579–620, July 11, 1958.

[8] Paleontologists and geologists reckon time in the divisions of the Tertiary Period approximately as follows: Paleocene Epoch, 75 million years to 60 mllion years ago, embracing a span of 15 million years; Eocene Epoch, 60 to 40 million years ago; Oligocene Epoch, 40 to 30 million years ago; Miocene Epoch, 30 to 10 million years ago; Pliocene Epoch, 10 to 1 million years ago. The Quaternary Period that follows is divided into the Pleistocene Epoch, 1 million to 20,000 years ago; and the Recent Epoch, 20,000 years ago until now.

[9] Simpson, G. G. Mammals and land bridges. Jour. Washington Acad. Sci., 30:158, 1940.

trial mammals (excluding bats), but only one or possibly two of these families occurred on both continents. In the Pleistocene, not long after the connection, the admittedly incomplete fossil record shows that at least 22 families occurred on both continents. Today, 27 families occur on both continents. To judge from present-day distributions of species of the 38 families of North American terrestrial mammals and 34 families in South America, two more probably will be on both continents soon; the interchange seems still to be going on.

The only South American (strictly terrestrial) mammals of modern time that have extended for any great distance [10] into North America are the opossum (*Didelphis marsupialis*) and the porcupine (*Erethizon dorsatum*). Neither seems to have entirely replaced any North American competitor. North American mammals of modern times that have extended for significant distances into South America are many. They include leporids, sciurids, cricetids, canids, mustelids, felids, and cervids. The Carnivora have long since gone all the way to the Straits of Magellan and completely replaced the South American carnivorous marsupials. North American ungulates likewise have pushed to extinction the strictly South American ungulates. North American lagomorphs have now passed the equator and seem to be pushing on south, possibly at the expense of their South American ecological counterparts. Some North American rodents are pushing southward, probably at the expense of some South American rodents, but I lack data on competition between rodents there, say, between some heteromyids and echimyids.

North America has been a pathway along which mammals reached South America. Nevertheless, almost every stock that made the journey did so by separate stages; whether a stock started from the Old World and traveled *via* the Bering land bridge to the New World or instead only from the Nearctic part of the Boreal region, that stock seems ordinarily to have resided for a considerable time in the Temperate region where the stock changed to a specific or generic or even familial degree before moving on to the brink of the Tropical region. Once into it, many lingered and radiated into the varied habitats where they diversified and evolved into new genera. A few pushed on, with but short pauses, reaching one montane area after another of a Temperate sort. But even they were slightly altered in the process, and, if they retained vigor to push on to challenging lands south of the equator, the vigor of only a very few sufficed to permit a return journey. Pressures from the new immigrants coming down the old path possibly were too great and several of the hardiest of those early arrivals fought a rear guard action as they moved into the narrow wedge of southern South America.

Even if the Old World Tropical region spawned vigorous stocks that radiated to, and persisted in, adjoining regions [11]—and I am not convinced that such was generally the case—the New World Tropical region seems in general to have been a dead end for mammals that got there—a dead end in the sense that movement from their region and survival elsewhere have not been achieved by anywhere

[10] Hershkovitz's (A geographic classification of Neotropical mammals, Fieldiana: Zoology, 36(No. 6):594, July 11, 1958) statement that "the greater faunal flow in Recent time is from south to north [South America to North America], not the reverse" might be questioned and upon first consideration seems to negate the statement above. Actually Hershkovitz's statement is correct. The flow is between Tropical regions. The South American Tropical region is vast and that of Central America is small. If the same proportion of the numerous truly South American tropical species flows into Central America that flows from the small number of truly Central American tropical species into South America, the actual number of species in the northward flow would be much the larger. His statement is not contradictory because few, if any, of the species do or will extend far into North America—no farther than the Tropical region itself.

[11] See Darlington, P. J., Jr. Zoogeography, p. 618. John Wiley & Sons, Inc., 1957.

nearly so large a percentage of the species or of the genera as has been the case with the mammals of the Boreal region or those of the Temperate region.[12]

Allusion was made above to the tendency of modern species in the North American Temperate region to occur only in some part of that region instead of all across it from west to east. The geographic ranges of *Sorex longirostris*, Map 14 (page 29), and *Scalopus aquaticus*, Map 41 (page 73) in the eastern area, and *Sorex merriami*, Map 25 (page 47) and *Scapanus latimanus*, Map 39 (page 69) in the west illustrate this tendency. Of the 379 species that occur in the Temperate region, 308 occur in the west, 86 occur in the east, and 50 are in the central part. Of the 286 species that occur only in the Temperate region, 239 occur in the west, 48 occur in the east, and 15 occur in the central part. Many of the pairs of species —one in the west and the other in the east—seem to owe their existence to the extensions southward and recessions northward in the noncoastal parts of North America of glaciers of Pleistocene time. More directly, the alternation of dry and moist periods, corresponding to recessions and extensions of the glaciers, seem to have isolated eastern and western segments of more than one species. For example, *Sylvilagus floridanus* now in the eastern area that supports shrubs and trees is a cottontail that probably was conspecific with *Sylvilagus nuttallii* now in the western area (see Map 185 on page 261) that supports shrubs and trees. In one period of the Pleistocene this particular cottontail stock probably withdrew from most of the area that we now designate as the Great Plains because of increasing aridity associated with recession of a glacial front. On the now still arid Great Plains, albeit less arid than at some times in the past, the two stocks again occur, but only in the few ribbonlike riparian plant associations that extend from west to east across the grassy plains. Where the two stocks of cottontails now meet, they do not intergrade (crossbreed), having evolved, while separated from each other, along different physiological and physical lines.

Probably another example of the effect of aridity in an interglacial period, in this instance in the Great Basin of the western part of the United States, is the shrew, *Sorex vagrans*.[13] During the time when the two stocks of *Sorex vagrans* presumably were separated, evolution seems not to have proceeded quite so far as in the cottontails and so the two stocks of shrews crossbreed at a few of the places where their geographic ranges ultimately met again. At other places they do not crossbreed. Indeed, the geographic ranges of two parts of the species broadly overlap and provide one of the few examples in mammals of two subspecies of the same species occurring together over a considerable geographic area.

Incidentally, it seems to me that the effectiveness of the grasslands of the Great Plains (extending from Canada to México) in isolating closely related stocks of land vertebrates from each other has not been so often taken into account by zoogeographers as it should have been and certainly has not been accurately assessed.

For mammals, tabulation of the number of eastern and western species that stop short at the border of the Great Plains, allowance being made for other factors, would be one measure of the grasslands' effectiveness as a barrier to dispersal. In this connection see Map 196 (page 294) of *Tamias striatus*. Uncertainty in allowing for the "other factors" permits only an estimate of how many of the

---

[12] See Matthew, W. D. Climate and evolution. Annals New York Acad. Sci., 24:171–318, 33 figs., February 18, 1915.
[13] Speciation of the wandering shrew. By James S. Findley. Univ. Kansas Publ., Mus. Nat. Hist., 9:1–68, December 10, 1955.

eastern species and their western counterparts find the grasslands to be a barrier to dispersal. Probably more than 50 per cent of those pairs of species do so.

The occurrence of 86 species in the eastern part of the Temperate region and 308 in the west reflect the relatively uniform nature of the eastern part and the relatively diversified nature of the larger, western part. In the latter, four areas have separately spawned and/or preserved species and even genera peculiar to it. Of these four areas, the Pacific Coastal one,[14] set off by the Cascade–Sierra Nevada Mountain Chain has the largest number of endemic species—more than 30.[15] The Great Basin, bounded by the Sierra Nevada–Cascade Mountain Chain on the west and the Rocky Mountains and Wasatch Range on the east, has 15 endemic species. See Maps 181 (page 254), 218 (p. 337), 291 (p. 489), 304 (p. 509), 305 (p. 510), and 307 (p. 518). The Great Plains, referred to above as a barrier to dispersal of mammals, also has 15 or so species restricted to it.[16] The fourth unit that has spawned a notable number of species of its own is made up of the southwestern United States and the tableland of México. That unit is in the Sonoran life-zones. Many living species seem to have differentiated there, one from another, and several remain as endemics.[17]

Turning our attention for a moment to subspeciation that is a step toward the formation of species, the southwestern quarter of the United States of America, and especially the region made up of Utah, Arizona and some adjacent parts of California, Nevada, and New Mexico, has a larger number of subspecies than any other continental area of equal size in the world. Maps 262–265, 289, and 306 illustrate the large number. The reasons seem to be high degree of relief caused by alternating mountain ranges and valleys or inclosed basins, great range in elevation (below sea level in Death Valley to more than 14,000 feet on nearby Mount Whitney), deeply cut, steep, rock-walled cañons (the Grand Cañon of the Colorado for one), resultant wide range in temperature, sharply marked zonation of plants, and tremendous diversity of types of soil. Natural selection frequently aided by isolation caused by natural barriers has resulted in truly amazing geographic variation in animal morphology and coloration. Adequate series of specimens from closely spaced collecting stations in parts of this region reveal uniformity in size, shape, and color throughout most of the geographic range of any one of scores of subspecies, and reveal also that intergradation frequently occurs in narrow belts.

One of the principal reasons for applying subspecific names to these geographic variants is, of course, to prepare maps that allow comparisons of the geographic variation in all species of a major taxon, say, within the Class Mammalia. Comparisons of the subspecific patterns with patterns of elevation, temperature, flora, soil, and other features of the environment can reasonably be expected to reveal parts of the process of species-formation in nature while the process is going on at the twig-ends of the tree of mammalian life. For the Utahan [18] and Nevadan [19] parts of this region some findings are on record.

[14] See A. B. Howell. On the faunal position of the Pacific Coast of the United States. Ecology, 8:18–26, January, 1927.

[15] See Maps 183 (page 257), 200 (p. 307), 230 (p. 355), 312 (p. 525), 394 (p. 700), 408 (p. 733), and 409 (p. 734).

[16] For examples, see Maps 228 (page 351), 236 (p. 365), 272 (p. 451), 285 (p. 476), 294 (p. 496), 340 (p. 583), and 466 (p. 915).

[17] For probable examples see Maps 234 (page 359), 281–283 (pp. 464–469), 293 (p. 494), 295 (p. 497), 298–300 (pp. 501–503), 354 (p. 607), 381 (p. 666), 389 (p. 687), and 392 (p. 695).

[18] Mammals of Utah, taxonomy and distribution. By Stephen D. Durrant. Univ. Kansas Publ., Mus. Nat. Hist., 6:1–549, 91 figs., August 10, 1952.

[19] Mammals of Nevada. See footnote 5.

Thinking now of taxa above the level of subspecies, the West Indies [20] present, for the Americas at least, an unusual case. That insular area supports: the large insectivores, *Solenodon* and *Atopogale*, frequently referred to, with some reason, as living fossils; the small insectivore, *Nesophontes*, also known from no other place; several genera of rodents of the family Capromyidae and the endemic family Heptaxodontidae; and many phyllostomid bats, including those of the endemic subfamily Phyllonycterinae. Indeed nearly seven-tenths of the genera of mammals still living there are bats. Although none of the five orders occurring there within historic time is endemic, one-fourth (3 of 11) of the families are endemic, as also are half (27 of 46) of the genera and four-fifths (87 of 109) of the species. Considering (1) the kinds of mammals that are there, (2) their differing degrees of morphological resemblance to continental relatives, (3) paleontology of the West Indies, (4) kinds of continental mammals that are not in the West Indies, and (5) other information, it seems that the ancestral stocks arrived accidentally by rafting (the bats, of course, are presumed to have flown). The number of kinds present is small. The fauna resembles that of South America slightly more than that of Central America. Mammals that reached the West Indies, even after undergoing considerable evolution there, remain; none is known to have gone on, or back, from there and established itself elsewhere.

In summary and review: Mammals evolved from reptiles in the Triassic Period of the Mesozoic Era. Relative to reptiles, mammals were insignificant throughout the Mesozoic. They were a significant part of the vertebrate fauna at the beginning of the Cenozoic Era, played a dominant role in the Tertiary Period by radiating into all lands and seas and by adapting themselves to different habitats, and in the Recent Epoch they seem as a class to be declining.

Submergence at irregular intervals of land bridges between continents retarded terrestrial mammals in reaching some major land areas and, indeed, prevented a number of kinds from reaching several areas. Aerial locomotion notwithstanding, bats distributed themselves in approximately the same patterns as did terrestrial mammals.

Emergence of land in the Bering Strait region has made North America continuous with Eurasia at some times, and at other times submergence has made North America, as it is now, a separate continent. Eurasia has a much larger land area than does North America. Mammals of a large land area more often than not prevail over their counterparts of a small land area when the two are brought into competition. Many Recent North American mammals came from Eurasia and fewer North American mammals invaded and survived in Eurasia. Most North American mammals seem to have come from the north, whether they were immigrants from Eurasia or were from the Boreal region of North America when it and Eurasia were so effectively connected by land that their northern parts constituted a single faunal region.

The mammalian fauna of North America supplied South America with its mammals principally in two separate invasions—first seemingly in Paleocene time and second for a much shorter period beginning in late Pliocene time and continuing still.

In North America the principal patterns of geographic distribution are three: one related to the Boreal (northern) region, another related to the Temperate region, and a third related to the Tropical (southern) region. Different ranges of temperatures that are optimum for different species of mammals cause this pattern and cause also evident zonation within each of the three principal patterns.

[20] Zoogeography of West Indian land mammals. By G. G. Simpson. Amer. Mus. Novitates, No. 1759:1–28, March 8, 1956.

Taxa that evolved from subspecific to familial rank wholly within the limits of the North American mainland seem to have done so in what is now the Temperate region, and during a period when, I guess, the climate there was Temperate rather than Boreal or Lower Tropical.

The number of genera and species is proportional to the number of habitats. The Boreal region has the fewest genera and species, the Tropical region has the most, and the Temperate region has an intermediate number.

The Tropical region of North America (and of the Americas) seems to be a dead end for mammals in as much as but few move out and survive elsewhere. From the West Indian subregion of the North American Tropics, none is known to have moved out and survived elsewhere.

Many (292) species of mammals are restricted to the Temperate region. Few now range entirely across it from west to east, probably because alternating dry and moist climates in the central part of the continent, corresponding to extensions and recessions of continental glaciers, isolated the eastern and western segments of original stocks long enough for the segments to have evolved into two or more species.

The western three-fifths of the Temperate region can conveniently be divided into four faunal units. They are Pacific Coastal, Great Basin, Great Plains, and Southwestern (Sonoran). In the last, subspeciation is more pronounced than in any other area of equal size in the world.

Studies in the Southwestern unit have greatly increased our understanding of how species are formed, and well-planned investigations there can be expected to yield much additional information on the formation of species in nature as this process goes on at the twig-ends of the tree of mammalian life.

                                                                    E. R. H.

THE MAMMALS
OF
NORTH AMERICA

CLASS MAMMALIA

Beings especially notable for possessing mammary glands (mammae) that permit the female to nourish the new-born young with milk; hair present although confined to early stages of development in most of the Cetacea; mandibular ramus of lower jaw made up of single bone (dentary); lower jaw articulating directly with skull without intervention of quadrate bone; two exoccipital condyles; differing from both Aves and Reptilia in possessing diaphragm and in having non-nucleated red blood corpuscles; resembling Aves and differing from Reptilia in having "warm blood," complete double circulation, and 4-chambered heart; differing from Amphibia and Pisces in presence of amnion and allantois and in absence of gills.

Mammals generally are considered by man to be the pinnacle of development of animal life—a consideration difficult to divorce entirely from self interest since man is a mammal. In many particulars birds also are complex and highly developed morphologically. Considered as a whole, however, the Mammalia seem to have achieved the highest point in physical organization of any of the five great classes of the Subphylum Vertebrata, and, except for the birds (Class Aves), were the last to develop on earth. Both the mammals and the birds had their beginnings in the much older Class Reptilia.

The name mammal and the idea that it expresses both are comparatively recent. The English naturalist, John Ray, 263 years ago in his "*Synopsis Methodica Animalium Quadrupedum et Serpentini Generis*" (1695) bracketed the terrestrial or quadrupedal mammals with the aquatic as "vivipara" in contrast to the "ovipara" or birds. Thus the idea was first expressed, but 63 years elapsed before it was adopted. This was done by the great Swedish naturalist, Linnaeus, in preparing the 10th edition of his "*Systema Naturae*," published in 1758. He caught on to John Ray's idea, removed from the fishes the cetaceans (whales and porpoises), combined them and hairy quadrupeds in a special class, and coined for it the word "Mammalia." The essential component is the Latin *mamma*, meaning breast. By analogy with *anima* (animal) and the derived technical term Animalia, Linnaeus, just 200 years ago, coined the word Mammalia. From this the English-speaking peoples subsequently derived the vernacular name mammal and its plural, mammals.

Subclass THERIA

Young developing to point of being recognizable as mammals in reproductive tract of female instead of developing in egg outside female as, for example, in Order Monotremata of Subclass Prototheria; members of the extinct Subclass Allotheria, comprising orders Multituberculata and Triconodonta, having, in general, platelike teeth and triconodont teeth (talon and talonid absent or poorly developed) respectively, also may have laid eggs.

Infraclass METATHERIA

Differs from Infraclass Pantotheria (extinct orders Pantotheria and Symmetrodonta) in presence of inflected angle on lower jaw instead of lacking angle (Order Symmetrodonta) or having noninflected angle (Order Pantotheria); differs from Infraclass Eutheria in that placenta is absent or incomplete, in presence of epipubic bones, and in other characters as are listed below for the Order Marsupialia.

ORDER **MARSUPIALIA**—Marsupials

Monographed by A. Cabrera, Genera Mammalium: Monotremata, Marsupialia, Mus. Nac. Ciencias Nat., Madrid, pp. 1–177, 18 pls., June 23, 1919.

Nonplacental (loose allantoic placenta in some; in *Dasyurus* a yolk-sac placenta; chorionic placenta, lacking villi, in the peramelidae); young extruded from bifid reproductive tract of female in notably undeveloped condition, undergoing further development (corresponding to terminal part of embryonic development in a placental mammal) while firmly attached for some time after birth to mammae through which milk is injected; in several genera mammae are in an abdominal pouch (= marsupium); long epipubic bones, or their rudiments, present in both sexes; skull with small braincase and large preorbital region; brain lacking corpus callosum; nasals expanded posteriorly; jugal bone contributing to glenoid fossa; tympanic bone small, annular, or tubular and but rarely fused with other bones of skull; auditory bulla, if present, formed entirely or principally from alisphenoid.

SUBORDER **POLYPROTODONTIA**

Incisors $\frac{4}{3}$ or more, subequal and smaller than canines; molars with sharp cusps (not bluntly tuberculated or with transversely ridged crowns).

SUPERFAMILY **DIDELPHOIDEA**

Incisor teeth $\frac{5}{4}$ All living members of this superfamily belong to the one Family Didelphidae.

FAMILY **DIDELPHIDAE**—Opossums

Differs from extinct Family Caroloameghiniidae (Lower Eocene of South America) in tuberculosectorial, instead of bunodont, lower molars. Other characters, not necessarily distinctive as compared with Caroloameghiniidae, are as follows: 5 subequal incisors above and 4 below; long pointed snout; tail more or less prehensile; in species of North America and Central America less than proximal half of tail furred, remainder of tail being naked; stomach simple; 5 toes on each foot; clawless hallux of hind foot opposable to other digits; marsupial pouch in *Didelphis, Chironectes* and *Philander* and represented in other genera by rudimentary traces, such as two folds of skin; precranial part of skull long and pointed; braincase small; zygomatic arches large; hard palate with fenestrae opposite molars; upper molars tritubercular; lower molars tritubercular with well-developed trigonids; epipubic bones present; dental formula uniform throughout family, being i. $\frac{5}{4}$; c. $\frac{1}{1}$; p. $\frac{3}{3}$; m. $\frac{4}{4}$, 50 teeth in all.

All living members of the family are confined to the Americas; fossils are known from the Tertiary of Europe. Probably all species are omnivorous to a degree; some are primarily insectivorous and some are primarily carnivorous. The careful comparisons of the Central American genera by Miss Mary E. Works, in an unpublished manuscript (1950) at the University of Kansas, show that *Didelphis, Chironectes,* and *Philander* form a natural group of genera, whereas another natural group is made up of *Marmosa, Caluromys,* and *Metachirus.* In this latter group the teeth are unlike in the different genera but do agree in having the 2nd post-canine tooth in the upper jaw larger than the 3rd. There is more uniformity in the teeth of the first group, composed of the three genera *Didelphis, Chironectes,* and *Philander,* in which the two mentioned teeth are subequal.

KEY TO NORTH AMERICAN GENERA OF DIDELPHIDAE

1. Hind feet with toes fully webbed; zygomatic breadth ⅗ or more of basal length. . . *Chironectes,* p. 9
1'. Hind feet with toes not webbed; zygomatic breadth less than ⅗ of basal length.
   2. More than basal third of tail haired; more than 33 caudal vertebrae; upper tooth-rows prominently bowed outward. . . . . *Caluromys,* p. 16
   2'. Less than proximal third of tail haired; fewer than 33 caudal vertebrae; upper tooth-rows not prominently bowed outward (relatively straight and convergent anteriorly).
      3. Tail less than ¾ as long as head and body. . . . . *Monodelphis,* p. 18
      3'. Tail more than ¾ as long as head and body.
         4. Pelage of two distinct types of hair, underfur and coarse, long, white-tipped guard-hair; sternum of 8 segments. *Didelphis,* p. 5
         4'. Pelage of one principal type of hair, the long, white-tipped guard-hairs being absent; sternum of 7 segments.

5. Hind foot more than 33; greatest length of skull more than 50; total length more than 465.
    6. Color dark grayish; clearly marked light spot above each eye; more than basal 15 per cent of tail densely haired; gland on throat; postorbital processes prominent; 4 vacuities in posterior part of hard palate. . . . . *Philander*, p. 10
    6'. Color brownish; faintly marked light spot above each eye; less than basal 15 per cent of tail densely haired; no gland on throat; no postorbital processes; only 2 vacuities in posterior part of hard palate. . . . . *Metachirus*, p. 19
5'. Hind foot less than 33; greatest length of skull less than 50; total length less than 465. . *Marmosa*, p. 11

Genus **Didelphis** Linnaeus—Opossums

Revised by J. A. Allen, Bull. Amer. Mus. Nat. Hist., 14:149–188, June 15, 1901.

1758. *Didelphis* Linnaeus, Syst. nat., ed. 10, 1:54. Type, *Didelphis marsupialis* Linnaeus.
1777. *Didelphys* Schreber, Die Säugthiere . . . , fasc. 3, p. 532.
1819. *Sarigua* Muirhead, Brewster's Encyclopaedia, 13:429 (under Mazology).
1853. *Didelphus* Lapham, Trans. Wisconsin Agric. Soc., 2:337.

External measurements (in North America): 645–1017; 255–535; 48–80. Total length of skull, 80–139. Pelage consisting of underfur and white-tipped over-hairs (which are wanting or few in the other genera of the family); color gray, black, reddish, or rarely white; basal tenth or so of tail furred, remainder naked; 1st digit (hallux) on hind foot clawless and opposed to the other toes for grasping; sagittal and occipital crests high in old individuals; postorbital processes present; palate fenestrated (see Fig. 1); female having well-developed marsupium in which the mammae are situated; 8 separate bones in sternum (in *D. m. virginiana*) as contrasted with only 7 bones in other genera examined.

Didelphis marsupialis
Opossum

See characters of the genus. The species ranges from southern Canada well into South America, where there is also a second species that does not occur in Panamá or any other part of North America. The habit of feigning death when injured or in a dangerous position can cause an enemy to turn its attention elsewhere long enough for the "possum"

to scramble to a place of safety. The Great Plains of southern Canada and the United States together with the more southern desertlike country of southern New Mexico and northwestern Mexico constituted a barrier for the opossum; it did not occur on the plains or to the westward, but after the species was introduced in the first part of the twentieth century on the Pacific Coast of the United States the opossum multiplied amazingly and at this writing is well established in nearly all of the coastal country from Canada to Mexico.

Didelphis marsupialis battyi Thomas

1902. *Didelphis marsupialis battyi* Thomas, Nov. Zool., 9:137, April 10, type from Coiba Island, Panamá. Known only from Coiba Island.

Didelphis marsupialis californica Bennett

1816. *Did[elphys]. mes-americana* Oken, Lehrbuch der Naturgeschichte, 2(3):1152, type locality in northern México. Oken's names are non-Linnaean.
1833. *Didelphis Californica* Bennett, Proc. Zool. Soc. London, p. 40, May 17, type probably from northern, or northwestern, part of Republic of Mexico; restricted to Sonora by Hershkovitz (Fieldiana-Zool., Chicago Nat. Hist. Mus., 31(47):548. July 10, 1951).
1951. *Didelphis marsupialis californica,* Hershkovitz Fieldiana-Zool., Chicago Nat. Hist. Mus., 31(47):548, July 10.
1833. *Didelphis breviceps* Bennett, Proc. Zool. Soc. London, p. 40, May 17, type probably from northern, or northwestern, part of Republic of Mexico.

MARGINAL RECORDS.—Sonora (Burt, 1938:18): Llano; Oputo. Chihuahua: Batopilas (J. A. Allen, 1901:167). Durango: Chacala (*ibid.*). Zacatecas: San Juan de Capistrano (*ibid.*). Jalisco: Atemajac (*ibid.*). Guanajuato: Celaya (*ibid.*). Querétaro: Jalpan (*ibid.*). Coahuila: 1 mi. SW San Pedro de las Colonias, 3700 ft. (40194 KU); 1 mi. N San Lorenzo, 4200 ft. (40195 KU). Nuevo León: Monterrey (J. A. Allen, 1901:167). Tamaulipas: 36 km. N, 10 km. W Ciudad Victoria (Baker, 1951:209); Alta Mira, near Tampico (J. A. Allen, 1901:167). Puebla: Metlaltoyuca (J. A. Allen, 1901:168). Veracruz (*ibid.*): Las Vegas [= Vigas]; Jico; Orizaba. Oaxaca (*ibid.*): Tuxtepec; San Domingo; Tehuantepec; thence west and north along coast at least to Sinaloa: Culiacán (J. A. Allen, 1901:167). Sonora (Burt, 1938:18): Tesia; Hermosillo.

Didelphis marsupialis cozumelae Merriam

1901. *Didelphis yucatanensis cozumelae* Merriam, Proc. Biol. Soc. Washington, 14:101, July 19, type from Cozumel Island, Yucatán. Known only from Cozumel Island.
1952. *Didelphis marsupialis cozumelae,* Hall and Kelson, Univ. Kansas Publ., Mus. Nat. Hist., 5:324, December 5.

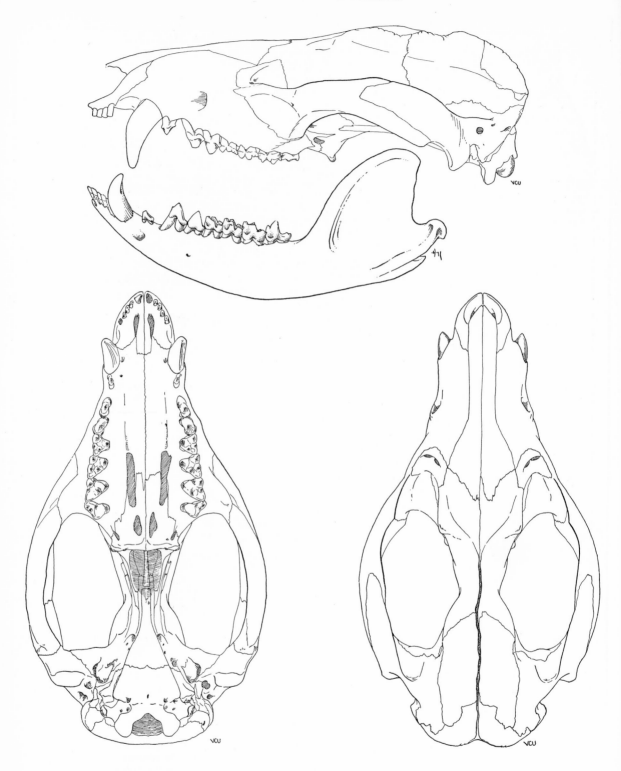

Fig. 1. *Didelphis marsupialis virginiana*, 1 mi. N Lawrence, Douglas Co., Kansas, No. 3780 K.U., ♂, X 1.

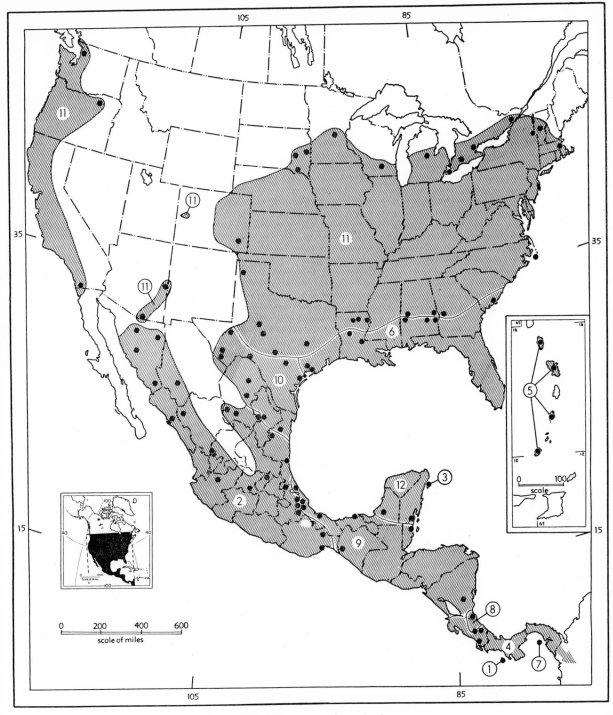

Map 1. *Didelphis marsupialis* and subspecies.

1. *D. m. battyi*
2. *D. m. californica*
3. *D. m. cozumelae*
4. *D. m. etensis*
5. *D. m. insularis*
6. *D. m. pigra*
7. *D. m. particeps*
8. *D. m. richmondi*
9. *D. m. tabascensis*
10. *D. m. texensis*
11. *D. m. virginiana*
12. *D. m. yucatanensis*

Didelphis marsupialis etensis J. A. Allen

1902. *Didelphis marsupialis etensis* J. A. Allen, Bull. Amer. Mus. Nat. Hist., 16:262, August 18, type from Eten, Piura, Perú.

MARGINAL RECORDS (Goodwin, 1946:282).—Costa Rica: Santa Teresa Perálta, thence E to coast and along same into South America, and up Pacific Coast from South America to latitude of Costa Rica: Palmar; San José.

Didelphis marsupialis insularis J. A. Allen

1902. *Didelphis marsupialis insularis* J. A. Allen, Bull. Amer. Mus. Nat. Hist., 16:259, August 18, type from Caparo, Trinidad.

MARGINAL RECORDS (Miller, 1924:4).—Island of Dominica; Martinique Island; St. Vincent Island; Granada Island, and in the South American area on Trinidad Island.

Didelphis marsupialis pigra Bangs

1898. *Didelphis virginiana pigra* Bangs, Proc. Boston Soc. Nat. Hist., 28:172, March, type from Oak Lodge, opposite Micco, Brevard Co., Florida.
1952. *Didelphis marsupialis pigra*, Hall and Kelson, Univ. Kansas Publ., Mus. Nat. Hist., 5:323, December 5.

MARGINAL RECORDS.—South Carolina: Charleston (Penney, 1950:83), thence south and west along Atlantic Coast and Gulf of Mexico to Texas (Hall and Kelson, 1952:323): Matagordo; Deming Station. Louisiana (Lowery, 1943:216): Natchitoches Parish; Pointe Coupee Parish. Alabama (A. H. Howell, 1921:20): Myrtlewood; Catoma Creek; Seale.

Didelphis marsupialis particeps Goldman

1917. *Didelphis marsupialis particeps* Goldman, Proc. Biol. Soc. Washington, 30:107, May 23, type from San Miguel Island, Golfo de Panamá, Panamá. Known only from San Miguel Island.

Didelphis marsupialis richmondi J. A. Allen

1901. *Didelphis richmondi* J. A. Allen, Bull. Amer. Mus. Nat. Hist., 14:175, June 15, type from Greytown, Nicaragua.
1920. *D[idelphis]. m[arsupialis]. richmondi*, Goldman, Smiths. Miscl. Coll., 69(5):46, April 24.

MARGINAL RECORDS.—Nicaragua: type locality. Costa Rica: San José (J. A. Allen, 1901:175).

Didelphis marsupialis tabascensis J. A. Allen

1901. *Didelphis marsupialis tabascensis* J. A. Allen, Bull. Amer. Mus. Nat. Hist., 14:173, June 15, type from Teapa, Tabasco.

MARGINAL RECORDS (J. A. Allen, 1901:173, unless otherwise noted).—Veracruz: Papantla, thence to coast and south along coast at least to Tabasco: Frontera. British Honduras: Belize (A. Murie, 1935:15), thence down coast approximately to Nicaragua: Peña Blanca (J. A. Allen, 1910:93), thence westerly to Pacific Coast and north to Chiapas: Ocuilapa. Veracruz: Catemaco; Mirador; 5 km. N Jalapa (Davis, 1944:374).

Didelphis marsupialis texensis J. A. Allen

1901. *Didelphis marsupialis texensis* J. A. Allen, Bull. Amer. Mus. Nat. Hist., 14:172, June 15, type from Brownsville, Cameron Co., Texas.

MARGINAL RECORDS.—Texas: Monahans (V. Bailey, 1932:7); mouth of Pecos River (Strecker, 1926:7); San Antonio (*ibid.*); Rockport (J. A. Allen, 1901:172). Tamaulipas: near El Mulato, San Carlos Mts. (Dice, 1937:249). Nuevo León: Río Ramos, 20 km. NW Montemorelos, 1000 ft. (Davis, 1944:374). Coahuila: Monclova, 2000 ft. (34890 KU); ½ mi. S Sabinas, 100 ft. (34545 KU). Texas: Pinnacle Spring (Borell and Bryant, 1942:6); Rosillas Mts. (*ibid.*).

Didelphis marsupialis virginiana Kerr

1792. *Didelphis virginiana* Kerr, The animal kingdom . . . , p. 193. Type locality, Virginia.
1952. *Didelphis marsupialis virginiana*, Hall and Kelson, Univ. Kansas Publ., Mus. Nat. Hist., 5:322, December 5.
1795. *D[idelphys]. pilosissima* Link, Beyträge zur Naturgeschichte, p. 67, based on Sarique à longs poils Buff[on]., V. 4. T. 29.
1795. *D[idelphys]. illinensium* Link, Beyträge zur Naturgeschichte, p. 67, based on Sarique à longs poils Buff[on]., V. 4. T. 29.
1806. *Didelphis woapink* Barton, Facts, observations, and conjectures relative to the generation of the opossum of North America, p. 2.

MARGINAL RECORDS.—Minnesota: St. Cloud (Swanson, 1945:53). Wisconsin: near Beaver Dam (Cory, 1912:17). Michigan: Isabella Co. (Burt, 1946:82). Ontario: Lot 10, Concession 2, Chatham Twp., Kent Co. (Wood, 1949:199); Middlesex County (Anderson, 1947:11); Toronto (Peterson and Downing, 1956:431); near Morrisburg (*op. cit.*: 433). New York (Miller, 1899:294): Crown Point. Vermont: Rochester (F. W. Osgood, 1938:435). Massachusetts: Newton Center (Crane, 1931:268), thence southward along Atlantic Coast at least to North Carolina: Hatteras (J. A. Allen, 1901:162). Georgia: 1½ mi. W Junction City (14602 KU). Alabama (A. H. Howell, 1921:19): Auburn; Greensboro. Louisiana (Lowery, 1943:216): Tallula; Monroe; Ruston. Texas: Washington County (J. A. Allen, 1901:162); Kerrville (*ibid.*); in 1907, Mearns (p. 153) reported specimens from these last two localities as *D. virginianus* without indication of subspecies; San Angelo (V. Bailey, 1905:56); Colorado (*ibid.*); Tascosa (*ibid.*). Colorado (*widespread over nearly all of Colorado east of the Divide* [Rodeck, 1952:69]): near head Caddoa Creek, 12 mi. N Gaume's Ranch (Warren, 1942:4). South Dakota (Over and Churchill, 1945:4): Bon Homme County; Sanborn County; Brookings County. Introduced now and established on Pacific Coast, inland to Washington: Clear Lake (Dalquest, 1948:121). Oregon: Birch Creek, below Pilot Rock (Jewett and Dobyns, 1929:351). California: San Diego County (Grinnell *et al.*, 1937:51, fig. 10). Introduced also in Arizona (Hock, 1952:465): Alpine; Nogales. Introduced also in Colorado (R. G. Beidelman, MS): *vicinity of Grand Junction.*

Didelphis marsupialis yucatanensis J. A. Allen

1901. *Didelphis yucatanensis* J. A. Allen, Bull. Amer. Mus. Nat. Hist., 14:178, June 15, type from Chichén-Itzá, Yucatán. *Didelphis nelsoni* (J. A. Allen, *op. cit.*:160), a *nomen nudum,* may have been intended to apply to this subspecies.

1946. *Didelphis marsupialis yucatanensis,* Goldman and Moore, Jour. Mamm., 26:360, February 12.

MARGINAL RECORDS.—Campeche: Apazote (J. A. Allen, 1901:178), west to coast, thence along coast of Yucatán Peninsula to British Honduras: Orange Walk (Gaumer, 1917:13), thence to point of beginning.

Genus **Chironectes** Illiger—Water Opossum

1811. *Chironectes* Illiger, Prodromus systematis mammalium et avium . . . , p. 76. Type *Lutra minima* Zimmermann.

External measurements: 651–685; 380–386; 70–72. Greatest length of skull, 74.2–76.5. Pelage relatively short, fine and dense; color marbled black and gray, rounded black areas being confluent along mid-line of back. Toes webbed; pisiform area of forefoot enlarged and simulating, in some respects, a 6th digit; sole of hind foot granular and without plantar tubercles; tail furred only at base; marsupium present; skull with notably broad braincase; only 2 fenestrae in posterior part of bony palate; sagittal and lambdoidal crests present in adults. Although specialized for aquatic life and consequently superficially unlike *Didelphis, Chironectes* agrees in deep-seated parts of its anatomy with *Didelphis* and *Philander* and is closely related to those genera.

Chironectes panamensis
Water Opossum

See characters of the genus. At this writing no fewer than 4 nominal species of the genus, 3 of them in South America, are recognized. We have made no study designed to show if the kinds are anything more than subspecies of one species.

C.G.Pritchard

X 1/5

Chironectes panamensis argyrodytes Dickey

1928. *Chironectes argyrodytes* Dickey, Proc. Biol. Soc. Washington, 41:15, February 4, type caught in Río Sucio at Hda. Zapotitán, 1500 ft., La Libertad, El Salvador.

1942. *Chironectes panamensis argyrodytes,* Goodwin, Bull. Amer. Mus. Nat. Hist., 79:112, May 29.

MARGINAL RECORDS.—Honduras (Goodwin, 1942: 112): Las Flores; Minas de Oro; Tegucigalpa. El Salvador: type locality.

Chironectes panamensis panamensis Goldman

1914. *Chironectes panamensis* Goldman, Smiths. Misc. Coll., 63(5):1, March 14, type from Cana, 2000 ft., Darién, Panamá.

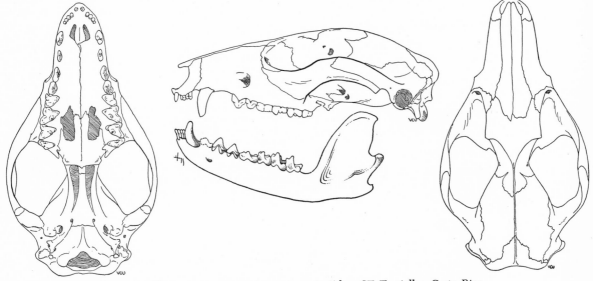

Fig. 2. *Chironectes panamensis panamensis,* 5 km. SE Turrialba, Costa Rica, No. 26928 K.U., ♂, X 1.

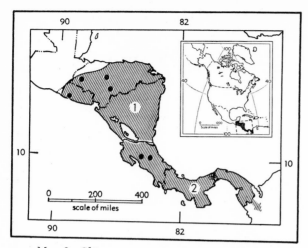

Map 2. *Chironectes panamensis* and subspecies.
1. *C. p. argyrodytes*   2. *C. p. panamensis*

MARGINAL RECORDS.—Costa Rica (Goodwin, 1946: 283): Vijagual; Carillo, thence eastward throughout Panamá to South America.

Genus **Philander** Tiedemann—Four-eyed Opossum

For use of this name rather than *Metachirops* Matschie see Hershkovitz, Proc. Biol. Soc. Washington, 62:11, March 17, 1949.

1808. *Philander* Tiedemann, Zoologie . . . , 1:426. Type, P[hilander]. *virginianus* Tiedemann [= *Didelphis opossum* Linnaeus].

1916. *Metachirops* Matschie, Sitzungsb. Gesell. naturforsch. Freunde, Berlin, p. 262, October. Type *Didelphis quica* Temminck.

1919. *Holothylax* Cabrera, Genera Mammalium: Monotremata, Marsupialia, Mus. Nac. Cienc. Nat., Madrid, p. 47, June 23. Type, *Didelphis opossum* Linnaeus.

External measurements: 534–610; 283–300; 39–50. Greatest length of skull, 66–80; color dark gray; white spot above each eye; tail furred at base and naked distally; marsupium present; 4 fenestrae in bony palate.

This is a smaller and more agile animal than *Didelphis*; the agility is reflected in the looser attachments of the vertebrae and in the longer neural spines than in *Didelphis*.

Philander opossum

Four-eyed Opossum

See characters of the genus. This species ranges into South America.

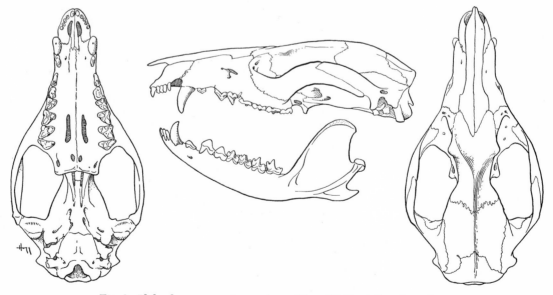

Fig. 3. *Philander opossum fuscogriseus*, 5 km. SE Turrialba, Costa Rica, No. 26923 K.U., ♂, X 1.

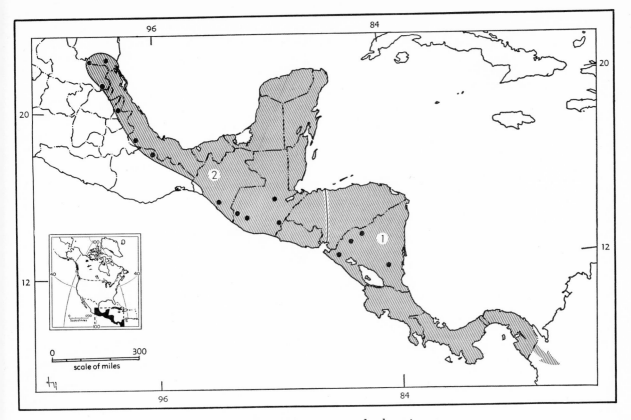

Map 3. *Philander opossum* and subspecies.

1. *P. o. fuscogriseus*   2. *P. o. pallidus*

Philander opossum fuscogriseus (J. A. Allen)

1900. *Metachirus fuscogriseus* J. A. Allen, Bull. Amer. Mus. Nat. Hist., 13:194, October 23, type from Greytown, Nicaragua (see J. A. Allen, Bull. Amer. Mus. Nat. Hist., 30:247, December 2, 1911).

1946. *Philander opossum fuscogriseus,* Goodwin, Bull. Amer. Mus. Nat. Hist., 87:283, December 31.

MARGINAL RECORDS.—Nicaragua: Río Coco (J. A. Allen, 1910:93); Escondido River, 50 mi. above Bluefields (J. A. Allen, 1901:214), thence along Caribbean Coast to South America and then northward along Pacific Coast to Nicaragua (J. A. Allen, 1910:93): Volcán de Chinandega [= Volcán el Viejo]; San Juan [= San Juan Telpaneca, 3500 ft.].

Philander opossum pallidus (J. A. Allen)

1901. *Metachirus fuscogriseus pallidus* J. A. Allen, Bull. Amer. Mus. Nat. Hist., 14:215, July 3, type from Orizaba, Veracruz.

1955. *Philander opossum pallidus,* Miller and Kellogg, Bull. U.S. Nat. Mus., 205:8, March 3.

MARGINAL RECORDS.—Tamaulipas: 2 km. W El Carrizo (Baker, 1951:210), thence along Caribbean Coast to Guatemala: Finca Sepacuite (Goodwin, 1934:5); Lake Atescatempa (Handley, 1950:143); Finca Cipres (Goodwin, 1934:5); Finca Carolina (*ibid.*). Chiapas: 1 km. S Mapastepec (Villa, 1949:497). Oaxaca: Tuxtepec (J. A. Allen, 1901:216). Veracruz: Orizaba (*ibid.*). Puebla: Metlaltoyuca (*ibid.*). San Luis Potosí (Dalquest, 1953b: 19): Xilitla; El Salto.

Genus Marmosa Gray—Murine Opossums

Revised by Tate, Bull. Amer. Mus. Nat. Hist., 66:1–250, pls. 1–26, 29 figs. in text, August 10, 1933.

1821. *Marmosa* Gray, London Med. Repos., 15:308, April 1. Type, *Didelphis murina* Linneaus.

1842. *Asagis* Gloger, Gemeinnütziges Hand- und Hilfsbuch der Naturgeschichte, 1:82. Type not designated; according to Thomas the type is *Didelphis murina* Linnaeus.

1842. *Notagogus* Gloger, *loc. cit.* Type not designated; according to Thomas the type is *Didelphis murina* Linnaeus.

1842. *Micoureus* Lesson, Nouveau tableau du règne animal . . . mammifères, p. 186. Type by subsequent designation (Thomas, Catalogue of the Marsupialia and Monotremata, p. 340, 1888), *Didelphis cinerea* Temminck.

1843. *Thylamys* Gray, List of the . . . Mammalia in the . . . British Museum, p. 101. Type by monotypy, *Didelphis elegans* Waterhouse.

1854. *Grymaeomys* Burmeister, Systematische Uebersicht der Thiere Brasiliens . . . , 1:138. Type by subsequent designation (Thomas, Catalogue of the Marsupialia and Monotremata, p. 340, 1888), *Didelphis murina*.
1856. *Microdelphis* Burmeister, Erläuterungen zur Fauna Brasiliens . . . , p. 83. Type by subsequent designation (Thomas, Catalogue of the Marsupialia and Monotremata, p. 354, 1888), *Didelphis tristriata* Kuhl.
1916. *Marmosops* Matschie, Sitzungsb. Gesell. naturforsch. Freunde, Berlin, p. 267, December 15. Type *Didelphis incana* Lund.

Maximum external measurements, 450, 281, 33.

Greatest length of skull, 47. Grayish or brownish above, some individuals having black markings on face. Tail longer than head and body, underside of tip modified for grasping; 6 plantar tubercles, 2 exterior, 2 interior, 2 divided by base of 3rd digit; external pads united in some species; marsupium absent; temporal ridges not uniting into a sagittal crest; postorbital processes present or absent according to species; tooth-rows convergent anteriorly; M3 usually larger than M1.

KEY TO NORTH AMERICAN SPECIES OF MARMOSA

1. Fur grayish and often wooly; external anterior and posterior pads of hind foot united; 9 to 14 spirals of scales per centimeter of tail-length; greatest length of skull more than 44. . . . . . . *M. alstoni,* p. 12
1'. Fur rarely (in *M. canescens*) grayish and never wooly; external posterior pads of hind foot separate; 16 or more spiral rows of scales per centimeter of tail-length; greatest length of skull less than 44.
  2. Plantar pad between digits 3 and 4 smaller than that between digits 2 and 3; the 3 minute hairs accompanying each scale of the tail flattened, appressed, provided with median dorsal keel, somewhat petiolate at insertion, and often black; nasals exceeding premaxillae when skull is in norma verticalis, no pointed supraorbital processes; tympanic bulla with anteromedial process. . *M. invicta,* p. 16
  2'. Plantar pad between digits 3 and 4 approximately same size as that between digits 2 and 3; the 3 minute hairs accompanying each scale of the tail not flattened, not appressed, lacking a median dorsal keel, not petiolate at insertion, and rarely black; nasals not exceeding premaxillae when skull is in norma verticalis; pointed supraorbital processes present; anteromedial process of tympanic bulla lacking or represented by only a minute spine.
    3. Upper parts gray, rarely with faint wash of cinnamon; small openings between palatal slit and molars. . . . . *M. canescens,* p. 15
    3'. Upper parts brown or cinnamon; no small openings between palatal slits and molars.
      4. Supraorbital processes reduced and scarcely pointed; no trace of postorbital constriction; temporal ridges widely separated. *M. mexicana,* p. 14
      4'. Supraorbital processes large and grooved; postorbital constriction marked; temporal ridges often approximated. . . . . *M. mitis,* p. 13

---

cinerea-group

Marmosa alstoni

Alston's Opossum

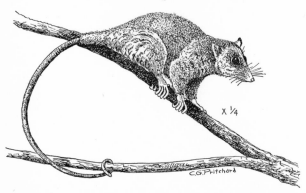

X ¼

External measurements: 385–450; 195–281; 27–33. Greatest length of skull, 44.9–45.7. One of the largest species of the genus; upper parts grayish brown; underparts, and in some individuals face, cream-buff; basal 25–50 mm. of tail furred, often

frizzled and longer than elsewhere on animal; braincase broad; postorbital region slightly, if at all, constricted; supraorbital processes without dorsal grooves; palatal fenestrae smaller than in other species of approximately equal size.

Marmosa alstoni alstoni (J. A. Allen)

1900. *Caluromys alstoni* J. A. Allen, Bull. Amer. Mus. Nat. Hist., 13:189, October 12, type from Tres Ríos, Cartago, Costa Rica.
1905. [*Marmosa*] *alstoni,* Trouessart, Catalogus Mammalium . . . , Suppl., fasc., 4, p. 855.

MARGINAL RECORDS.—Honduras: Segovia River (Goodwin, 1942:115). Costa Rica: Cubre (Goodwin, 1946:286); A. Caliente, 1300 m., Cartago (26922 KU); Escazú (Goodwin, 1946:285). Occurs also in Colombia, S. Amer.

Marmosa alstoni nicaraguae Thomas

1905. *Marmosa cinerea nicaraguae* Thomas, Ann. Mag. Nat. Hist., ser. 7, 16:313, September, type from Bluefields, sea level, Nicaragua.

1933. *Marmosa alstoni nicaraguae,* Tate, Bull. Amer. Mus. Nat. Hist., 66:69, August 10.

MARGINAL RECORDS.—British Honduras: Double Falls (Hershkovitz, 1951:550). Nicaragua: type locality. Costa Rica: Siguirres, Río Pacuare (Goodwin, 1946:287).

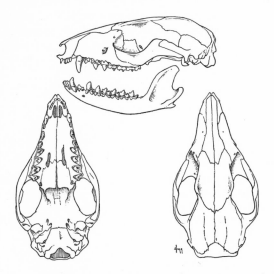

Fig. 4. *Marmosa alstoni alstoni,* A. Caliente, Cartago, Costa Rica, No. 26922 K.U., ♂, X 1.

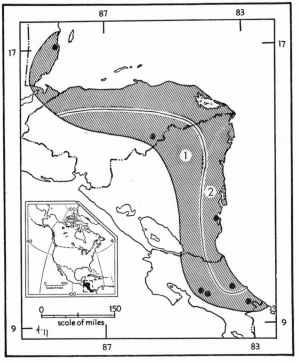

Map 4. *Marmosa alstoni* and subspecies.

1. *M. a. alstoni*   2. *M. a. nicaraguae*

murina-group
Marmosa mitis
South American Mouse-opossum

Total length up to 421, tail as long as 230, hind foot 22–29. Greatest length of skull, 33.5–43.5. Upper parts some shade of cinnamon or russet; face paler; tail densely clothed with fine hairs that almost conceal scales and give tail whitish appearance; posterior border of nasals rounded; supraorbital ridges well developed, moderately pointed and with pronounced dorsal grooves; a pronounced constriction postorbitally.

Marmosa mitis chapmani J. A. Allen

1900. *Marmosa chapmani* J. A. Allen, Bull. Amer. Mus. Nat. Hist., 13:197, October 23, type from Caura, head of Caura Valley, 500 ft., northern range, Trinidad.
1951. *Marmosa mitis chapmani,* Hershkovitz, Fieldiana-Zool., Chicago Nat. Hist. Mus., 31:552, July 10.
1911. *Marmosa grenadae* Thomas, Ann. Mag. Nat. Hist., ser. 8, 7:514, May, type from Annandale, Grenada. (Indistinguishable from *M. chapmani* according to G. M. Allen, Bull. Mus. Comp. Zool., 54:194, July, 1911.)
1911. *Marmosa tobagi* Thomas, Ann. Mag. Nat. Hist., ser. 8, 7:515, type from Waterloo (see Tate, Bull. Amer. Mus. Nat. Hist., 66:120, August 10, 1933), Tobago.
1911. *Marmosa nesaea* Thomas, Ann. Mag. Nat. Hist., ser. 8, 7:515, type from Savanna Grande (see Tate, Bull. Amer. Mus. Nat. Hist., 66:120, August 10, 1933), Trinidad.

MARGINAL RECORDS.—Known, within the geographic limits of this work, only from Grenada.

Marmosa mitis fulviventer Bangs

1901. *Marmosa fulviventer* Bangs, Amer. Nat., 35:632, August, type from San Miguel Island, Golfo de Panamá, Panamá.
1933. *Marmosa mitis fulviventer,* Tate, Bull. Amer. Mus. Nat. Hist., 66:117, August 10.

MARGINAL RECORDS.—Panamá: Saboga Island; type locality.

Marmosa mitis isthmica Goldman

1912. *Marmosa isthmica* Goldman, Smiths. Miscl. Coll., 56(36):1, February 19, type from Río Indio, near Gatún, Canal Zone, Panamá.
1951. *Marmosa mitis isthmica,* Hershkovitz, Fieldiana-Zool., Chicago Nat. Hist. Mus., 31:552, July 10.

MARGINAL RECORDS.—Panamá: From Boquéte (Tate, 1933:125) east over at least northern half of Panamá into South America.

Marmosa mitis ruatanica Goldman

1911. *Marmosa ruatanica* Goldman, Proc. Biol. Soc. Washington, 24:237, November 28, type from Ruatán Island, Caribbean Coast of Honduras.

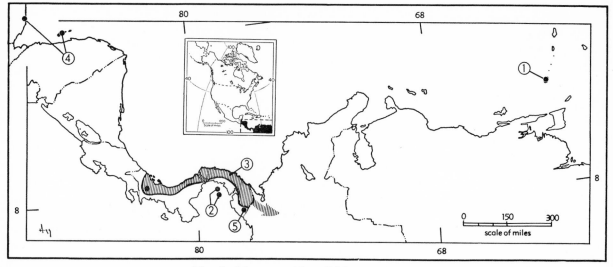

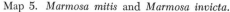

Map 5. *Marmosa mitis* and *Marmosa invicta*.

Guide to kinds		
1. *M. mitis chapmani*	2. *M. mitis fulviventer*	4. *M. mitis ruatanica*
	3. *M. mitis isthmica*	5. *M. invicta*

1951. *Marmosa mitis ruatanica*, Hershkovitz, Fieldiana-Zool., Chicago Nat. Hist. Mus., 31:551, July 10.

MARGINAL RECORDS (Hershkovitz, 1951:551).—British Honduras: Silkgrass; *Bokowina*. Honduras: type locality.

Marmosa mexicana
Mexican Mouse-opossum

External measurements: 290–386; 150–190; 20–27. Greatest length of skull, 32.4–40.8. Upper parts reddish brown; underparts yellowish to buffy; eye-rings intensely black; tail having thin growth of fine hair throughout its length and faintly bicolor; skull not constricted postorbitally, supraorbital ridges projecting laterally only slightly; no accessory fenestra between M2 and normal palatal fenestra. Comparison with *M. canescens* made in account of that species.

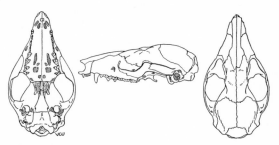

Fig. 5. *Marmosa mexicana mexicana*, 5 km. N Jalapa, 4500 ft., Veracruz, No. 19067 K.U., ♀, X 1.

Marmosa mexicana mayensis Osgood

1913. *Marmosa mayensis* Osgood, Proc. Biol. Soc. Washington, 26:176, August 8, type from Izamal, east of Mérida, Yucatán.
1917. *Marmosa mexicana mayensis*, Goldman, Proc. Biol. Soc. Washington, 30:109, May 23.

MARGINAL RECORDS.—Yucatán: type locality; Chichén-Itzá (Tate, 1933:135). British Honduras: Bokowina (Hershkovitz, 1951:551).

Marmosa mexicana mexicana Merriam

1897. *Marmosa murina mexicana* Merriam, Proc. Biol. Soc. Washington, 11:44, March 16, type from Juquila, 1500 m., Oaxaca.

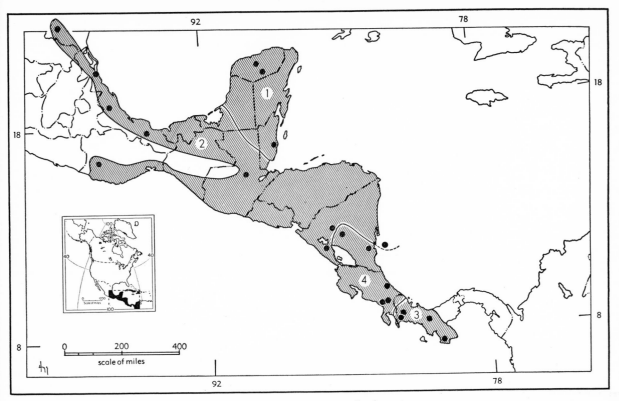

Map 6. *Marmosa mexicana* and subspecies.

1. *M. m. mayensis*
2. *M. m. mexicana*
3. *M. m. savannarum*
4. *M. m. zeledoni*

1902. *Marmosa mexicana*, Bangs, Bull. Mus. Comp. Zool., 39:19, April.

MARGINAL RECORDS (Tate, 1933:133–134, unless otherwise noted).—Tamaulipas: Aserradero del Infernillo (Goodwin, 1954:3). Veracruz: Truxpan [= Tuxpan] southward along coast to base of Yucatán Peninsula, across base of peninsula, and southward to Corn Islands. Nicaragua: Matagalpa; Chinandega, thence northwestward up coast approximately to Oaxaca: type locality. Guatemala: Cajabon [= Cahabon]. Veracruz: Pasa Nueva; Texolo [probably Barranca of Texolo at Puebla of Teocelo].

Marmosa mexicana savannarum Goldman

1917. *Marmosa mexicana savannarum* Goldman, Proc. Biol. Soc. Washington, 30:108, May 23, type from Boquerón, Chiriquí, Panamá. Regarded by Tate (Bull. Amer. Mus. Nat. Hist., 64:133, August 10, 1933) as indistinguishable from *M. m. mexicana*.

MARGINAL RECORDS.—Panamá: type locality; Province of Veragua west of Colón and Coclé (Tate, 1933:134); Mariato (Bole, 1937:145); Bogava (Tate, 1933:134).

Marmosa mexicana zeledoni Goldman

1911. *Marmosa zeledoni* Goldman, Proc. Biol. Soc. Washington, 24:238, November 28, type from Navarro, near Orosi, Caribbean slope, between 2500 and 3000 ft., Cartago, Costa Rica.
1917. *Marmosa mexicana zeledoni* Goldman, Proc. Biol. Soc. Washington, 30:109, May 23.

MARGINAL RECORDS.—Nicaragua (Tate, 1933:136): Río Tuma east of Matagalpa below 1000 ft.; Bluefields. Costa Rica (Goodwin, 1946:287): Río Pacuare; Agua Buena; Boruca.

Marmosa canescens
Grayish Mouse-opossum

External measurements: 261–285; 135–167; 18–21. Greatest length of skull, 31.3–36.1. Dorsally distinctly gray and in this feature unique among Mexican members of the genus, rarely with a faint wash of cinnamon; underparts yellowish-buff or cream-buff; skull with prominent, winglike supraorbital processes, which, in adults, continue posteriorly as converging temporal ridges; palate ordinarily having an accessory fenestra on each side between M2 and the normal palatal fenestra. The accessory fenestrae, the gray instead of red color, and the sharp and much produced supraorbital ridges (as opposed to low blunt ridges, or absence of ridges) are differences from *M. mexicana*.

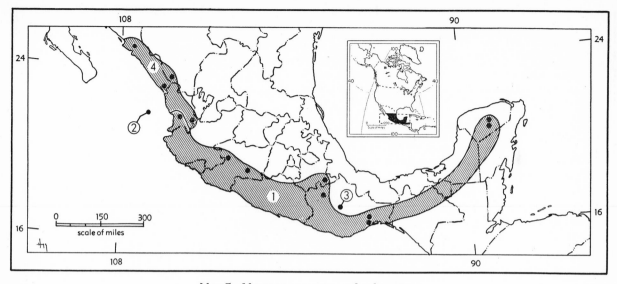

Map 7. *Marmosa canescens* and subspecies.

1. *M. c. canescens*   3. *M. c. oaxacae*
2. *M. c. insularis*   4. *M. c. sinaloae*

Marmosa canescens canescens (J. A. Allen)

1893. *Didelphis* (*Micoureus*) *canescens* J. A. Allen, Bull. Amer. Mus. Nat. Hist., 5:235, September 22, type from Santo Domingo de Guzmán, Isthmus of Tehuantepec, Oaxaca.
1897. *Marmosa canescens* J. A. Allen, Bull. Amer. Mus. Nat. Hist., 9:58, March 15.
1913. *Marmosa gaumeri* Osgood, Proc. Biol. Soc. Washington, 26:175, August 8, type from Yaxcaba, SW of Chichén-Itzá, Yucatán.

MARGINAL RECORDS (Tate, 1933:141, unless otherwise noted).—Nayarit: *3½ mi. E San Blas* (Hooper, 1955:7); Tepic. Michoacán: Los Reyes; 1 mi. E and 6 mi. S Tacámbaro, 4000 ft. (Hall and Villa, 1950:164). Puebla: Tehuacán, 1700 m. (Hooper, 1947:43). Oaxaca: Tlapacingo; type locality. Yucatán: Yaxcaba; Chichén-Itzá (Hershkovitz, 1951:551). Oaxaca: Tehuantepec, thence up coast to point of beginning.

Marmosa canescens insularis Merriam

1898. *Marmosa insularis* Merriam, Proc. Biol. Soc. Washington, 12:14, January 27, type from María Madre Island, Tres Marías Islands, Nayarit. Known only from Tres Marías Islands.
1933. *Marmosa canescens insularis*, Tate, Bull. Amer. Mus. Nat. Hist., 66:144, August 10.

Marmosa canescens oaxacae Merriam

1897. *Marmosa oaxacae* Merriam, Proc. Biol. Soc. Washington, 11:43, March 16, type from City of Oaxaca, 4600 ft., Oaxaca. Known only from the type locality.
1933. *Marmosa canescens oaxacae*, Tate, Bull. Amer. Mus. Nat. Hist., 66:143, August 10.

Marmosa canescens sinaloae J. A. Allen

1898. *Marmosa sinaloae* J. A. Allen, Bull. Amer. Mus. Nat. Hist., 10:143, April 12, type from Tatamales, Sinaloa.

1933. *Marmosa canescens sinaloae*, Tate, Bull. Amer. Mus. Nat. Hist., 66:142, August 10.

MARGINAL RECORDS (Tate, 1933:142–143).—Sinaloa: Culiacán. Durango: Ventanas. Nayarit ?: Rancho Palo Amarillo. Sinaloa: Esquinapa; *Mazatlán*.

noctivaga-group
Marmosa invicta Goldman
Panamá Mouse-opossum

1912. *Marmosa invicta* Goldman, Smiths. Miscl. Coll., 60(2):3, September 20, type from Cana, 2000 ft., Darién, Panamá. Known only from the type locality.

External measurements of the two known specimens, adult male and adult female, are: 248, 240; 137, 136; 19, 17.5. Greatest length of skull, 27.2, 27.0. Upper parts bone brown; underparts silvery-gray; tympanic bulla triangular and having process; supraorbital region smooth; palatal length less than zygomatic breadth; pronounced median frontal depression; palatal fenestrae small with second minute pair behind first.

This small species is a relative of a South American group (*fuscata*-section of the *noctivaga*-group), of species and subspecies, that reaches its northern limit of known occurrence in Panamá.

Genus **Caluromys** J. A. Allen—Wooly Opossums

For use of *Caluromys* J. A. Allen in place of *Philander* authors (not Tiedemann, 1808), see Hershkovitz, Proc. Biol. Soc. Washington, 62:12, March 17, 1949; and Hopwood, Proc. Zool. Soc. London, 117:533, October 30, 1947.

1856. *Philander* Burmeister, Erläuterungen zur Fauna Brasiliens . . . , Berlin, p. 74. Type, *Philander cayopollin*
Burmeister [= *Didelphis philander* Linnaeus]. Not *Philander* Tiedemann, 1808.

1900. *Caluromys* J. A. Allen, Bull. Amer. Mus. Nat. Hist.,
13:189, October 12. Type, *Didelphis philander* Linnaeus.

1916. *Micoureus* Matschie, Sitzungsb. Gesell. naturforsch.
Freunde, Berlin, 8:259, 269, December 15, and *op. cit.*,
p. 281 (September 10, 1917). Type, *Didelphis laniger*
Desmarest [= *Didelphis lanata* Olfers]. Not *Micoureus*
Lesson, 1842 [= *Marmosa* Gray, 1821].

1920. *Mallodelphys* Thomas, Ann. Mag. Nat. Hist., ser. 9,
5:195, February. Substitute name for *Micoureus* Matschie,
1916, preoccupied.

External measurements: 587–760; 395–490; 45–47.
Greatest length of skull, 58.7–61.0. Pelage long, fine
and wooly; hair extending along almost all of, or
more than, basal half of tail; color-pattern ornate,
including dark stripe on face and in some subspecies reddish and blackish on body; tail longer
than head and body and having 37 instead of 28 to
30 caudal vertebrae as in the other Central American genera except possibly *Monodelphis*, in which
the number is unknown to us; marsupium rudimentary; temporal ridges infrequently uniting to form
sagittal crest; postorbital processes well developed;
maxillary tooth-rows curved and converging anteriorly; M3 not larger than M1; posterior part of
palate lacking fenestrae. Reig (1955:121–130)
presents evidence that *Caluromys* belongs in the
subfamily Microbiotheriinae whereas the other
genera of Recent opossums that occur in North
America belong in the subfamily Didelphinae.

The wooly opossum is nocturnal. Although slow
by day the animal is more agile when night comes
on than are other kinds of Central American opossums; furthermore it is less often on the ground
than they are. A captive that Walter Dalquest had
at Potrero Viejo, Veracruz, readily ate bananas, insects including cockroaches, and young mice.

Caluromys derbianus
Wooly Opossum

X ¼

See account of the genus.

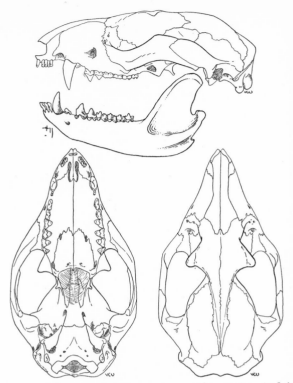

Fig. 6. *Caluromys derbianus aztecus*, 3 km. E San Andrés
Tuxtla, Veracruz, No. 23367 K.U., ♀, X 1.

Caluromys derbianus aztecus (Thomas)

1913. *Philander laniger aztecus* Thomas, Ann. Mag. Nat.
Hist., ser. 8, 12:359, October, type from San Juan de la
Punta, Veracruz.

1955. *Caluromys derbianus aztecus,* Miller and Kellogg,
Bull. U.S. Nat. Mus., 205:10, March 3.

MARGINAL RECORDS.—Veracruz: type locality. Ta-
basco: Teapa (Thomas, 1913:359). Veracruz: 20 km. E
Jesús Carranza, 300 ft. (23373 KU); 20 km. ENE Jesús
Carranza (32052 KU).

Caluromys derbianus canus (Matschie)

1917. *Micoureus canus* Matschie, Sitzungsb. Gesell. naturforsch. Freunde, Berlin, 4:284, September, type from
Nicaragua. Recorded only from the type locality.

1952. *Caluromys derbianus canus,* Hall and Kelson, Univ.
Kansas Publ., Mus. Nat. Hist., 5:324, December 5.

Caluromys derbianus centralis (Hollister)

1914. *Philander centralis* Hollister, Proc. Biol. Soc. Washington, 27:103, May 11, type from Talamanca, Costa Rica.

1946. *Caluromys derbianus centralis,* Goodwin, Bull. Amer.
Mus. Nat. Hist., 87:285, December 31.

MARGINAL RECORDS.—Costa Rica: 5 km. SE Turrialba,
1950 ft. (26923 KU); type locality.

Caluromys derbianus derbianus (Waterhouse)

1841. *Didelphys derbianus* Waterhouse, *in* The naturalist's
library (edit. Jardine), 30(Mammals, 11):97, type locality, Cauca Valley, Colombia, South America.

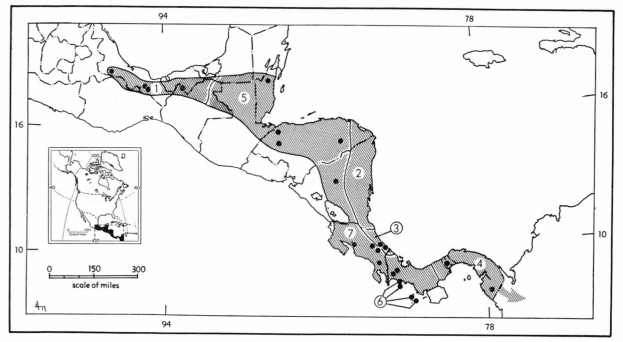

Map 8. *Caluromys derbianus* and subspecies.

Guide to	2. *C. d. canus*	5. *C. d. fervidus*
subspecies	3. *C. d. centralis*	6. *C. d. nauticus*
1. *C. d. aztecus*	4. *C. d. derbianus*	7. *C. d. pallidus*

1955. *Caluromys derbianus derbianus,* Miller and Kellogg, Bull. U.S. Nat. Mus., 205:9, March 3.

MARGINAL RECORDS (Goldman, 1920:54).—Panamá: Tabernilla; Cana, thence southeastward into South America.

Caluromys derbianus fervidus (Thomas)

1913. *Philander laniger fervidus* Thomas, Ann. Mag. Nat. Hist., ser. 8, 12:359 October type probably from "Guatemala," lowlands of east-central Guatemala or northern Honduras according to Goodwin (Bull. Amer. Mus. Nat. Hist., 79:114, May 29, 1942).
1942. *Caluromys derbianus fervidus,* Goodwin, Bull. Amer. Mus. Nat. Hist., 79:114, May 29.

MARGINAL RECORDS.—British Honduras: Kates Lagoon (Hershkovitz, 1951:552), thence along Caribbean Coast at least to Honduras: San Pedro Sula (Hall and Kelson, 1952:325); Catacamas (Goodwin, 1942:114); Ilama (*ibid.*).

Caluromys derbianus nauticus (Thomas)

1913. *Philander laniger nauticus* Thomas, Ann. Mag. Nat. Hist., ser. 8, 12:359, October, type from Gobernadora Island, off west coast of Panamá.
1955. *Caluromys derbianus nauticus,* Miller and Kellogg, Bull. U.S. Nat. Mus., 205:10, March 3.

MARGINAL RECORDS (Goldman, 1920:55).—Panamá: Brava Island; Parida Island; type locality; Cebaco Island.

Caluromys derbianus pallidus (Thomas)

1899. *Philander laniger pallidus* Thomas, Ann. Mag. Nat. Hist., ser. 7, 4:286, October, type from Bogava [=Bugaba], 2500 m., Chiriquí, Panamá.
1946. *Caluromys derbianus pallidus,* Goodwin, Bull. Amer. Mus. Nat. Hist., 87:285, December 31.

MARGINAL RECORDS (Goodwin, 1946:285, unless otherwise noted).—Nicaragua: Matagalpa (J. A. Allen, 1910:92). Costa Rica: Fuentes; Irazú. Panamá: Boquerón; type locality. Costa Rica: Puerto Cortez; Puntarenas.

Genus **Monodelphis** Burnett
Short-tailed Opossums

1830. *Monodelphis* Burnett, Quart. Jour. Sci. Lit. Art, 28:351. Type by subsequent selection (Matschie, Sitzungsb. Gesell. naturforsch. Freunde, Berlin, 1916, p. 271), *Didelphis brevicaudata* Erxleben.
1842. *Peramys* Lesson, Nouveau tableau règne animal, Mamm., p. 187. Type, *Didelphys brachyura* Schreber [= *D. brevicaudata* Erxleben].
1856. *Microdelphys* Burmeister, Erläuterungen zur Fauna Brasiliens . . . , Berlin, p. 83. Type, *Sorex americanus* Müller.
1919. *Minuania* Cabrera, Genera mammalium: Monotremata, Marsupialia, Mus. Nac. Ciencias Nat., Madrid, p. 43, June 23. Type, *Didelphis dimidiata* Wagner.

External measurements of the type of *M. melanops,* an adult male, are: 168, 60, 16.5. Condylobasal length of skull, 28. Pelage short, dense, and rather stiff; tail approximately half as long as head and body (always shorter than body alone), only slightly prehensile, its basal tenth haired as is body; remainder of tail thinly provided with fine hairs; hind foot having 5 toes and 5 plantar tubercles; skull resembling that of *Marmosa* but lacking supraorbital crests, although some specimens have rudiments of postorbital processes; in some species, old animals have indications of sagittal crest; palate having only one pair of fenestrae; marsupium absent.

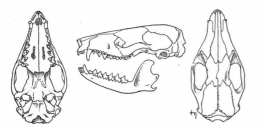

Fig. 7. *Monodelphis peruvianus?*, Mera, Ecuador, No. 67274, A.M., ♂, X 1.

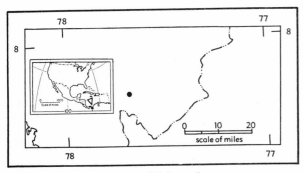

Map 9. *Monodelphis melanops*.

Monodelphis melanops (Goldman)
Short-tailed Murine Opossum

1912. *Peramys melanops* Goldman, Smiths. Miscl. Coll., 60(2):2, September 20, type from Cana, 2000 ft., Darién, Panamá. Known only from the type locality.
1924. *Monodelphis melanops*, Miller, Bull. U.S. Nat. Mus., 128:7, April 29.

External measurements small (see account of genus); upper parts dark brown (lacking stripes or spots that are present in some of the South American members of the genus), suffused with cinnamon on cheeks and sides of neck; face, shoulders, and lower part of back black; throat and sides of abdomen mouse-gray; underparts slightly grayer and with median buffy-white stripe extending from white pectoral region to buffy inguinal region; feet and tail black all around. The short tail is a diagnostic character among American opossums.

Genus Metachirus Burmeister
Brown-masked Opossums

1854. *Metachirus* Burmeister, Systematische Uebersicht der Thiere Brasiliens . . ., 1:135. Type, *Didelphys myosurus* Temminck [= *D. nudicaudata* É. Geoffroy St.-Hilaire].

External measurements of holotype of *Metachirus nudicaudatus dentaneus*: 597, 332, 48. Greatest length of skull, 63. Pelage brown (gray in genus *Philander*); ratio of haired part of tail to naked part of tail less than in other Central American genera; entire tail merely pale in contrast to white-tipped tails of other genera; no marsupium; no postorbital processes; posterior palatine vacuities only 2 (rarely indications of 2 more); interparietal rectangular; in upper jaw, 2nd post-canine tooth larger than 3rd.

Metachirus nudicaudatus
Brown Opossum

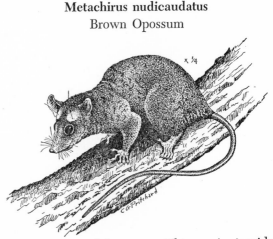

See characters of the genus. This species is widely distributed in South America.

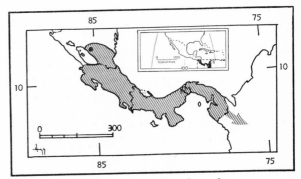

Map 10. *Metachirus nudicaudatus dentaneus*.

Metachirus nudicaudatus dentaneus Goldman

1912. *Metachirus nudicaudatus dentaneus* Goldman, Smiths. Miscl. Coll., 56(36):2, February 19, type from Gatún, Canal Zone, Panamá.

MARGINAL RECORDS.—Nicaragua: [district of] Chontales (Goodwin, 1946:284), thence southward at least throughout Panamá.

Infraclass EUTHERIA

Placenta complete; epipubic bones absent; skull of most members having large braincase and small preorbital region; corpus callosum present in brain; jugal bone not forming part of glenoid fossa; tympanic annulus (in Insectivora and some Chiroptera) and tympanic bulla (in other orders) formed by tympanic bone.

Order INSECTIVORA—Insectivores

Monographed by A. Cabrera, Genera Mammalium: Insectivora, Galeopithecia, Mus. Nac. Ciencias Nat., Madrid, pp. 1–232, 19 pls., November 29, 1925.

Size generally small; feet plantigrade, pentadactyl; digits with claws; snout usually long and pointed; placenta deciduous and discoidal; uterus bicornuate; cerebral hemispheres smooth and short, exposing cerebellum and often corpora quadrigemina; form of skull primitive; braincase low; orbital and temporal fossae confluent; tympanic bone usually annular, either entirely free or enclosed in an entotympanic bulla; or incorporated into the structure of the bulla; basisphenoid and petrosal both taking part in enclosure of tympanic cavity; vertical portion of palatine excluded from orbit by maxilla; angular process of mandible typically not inflected; dental formula primitively i. $\frac{3}{3}$, c. $\frac{1}{1}$, p. $\frac{4}{4}$, m. $\frac{3-4}{3-4}$; incisors may be reduced to $\frac{2}{1}$ and enlarged or reduced; canine either caniniform or, more commonly, incisiform or premolariform, two-rooted; premolars acuminate, the posteriormost frequently sectorial; molars lophodont or bunodont; lower molars usually with 5 sharp tubercles, and the uppers tri- or quadri-tubercular; teeth always rooted, diphyodont; milk dentition usually shed early and seldom functional; clavicle present (except in *Potomogale*); interclavicle vestigial, sometimes absent; pollex and hallux not opposable; entepicondyloid foramen and centrale usually present; distal ends of tibia and fibula usually fused; glenoid fossa for humerus widely separated from sternum; prespinous fossa present; testes abdominal, inguinal, or in a prepenile scrotum; predominantly insectivorous or carnivorous; usually nocturnal; terrestrial, fossorial, or amphibious.

The order has served as a catch-all for a number of groups of mammals of doubtful relationships and is a loose, and possibly unnatural, assemblage. Many of the members show no close relationship except that they are all primitive placentals. The description of the order here given is conservatively framed to include the following Recent families: Solenodontidae, Potomogalidae, Chrysochloridae, Erinaceidae, Macroscelididae, Soricidae, and Talpidae.

Key to North American Families of Insectivora

1. Paracone and metacone of each of first two upper molars forming a W-shaped loph.
    2. Zygomatic arch present. . . Talpidae, p. 66
    2′. Zygomatic arch absent.
        3. First upper incisor hooked and with a second point that resembles a talon; crown surface of M3 less than half that of M2; M1 and M2 with a hypocone. . . . . . Soricidae, p. 22
        3′. First upper incisor simple and without talonlike cusp; crown surface of M3 half or more of the area of M2; M1 and M2 without a hypocone.
                                   Nesophontidae, p. 77
1′. Amphicone of each of first two upper molars together with labial cusplets forming a V-shaped loph. . . . . . Solenodontidae, p. 20

Family SOLENODONTIDAE—Solenodons

External measurements: 500; 215; 65. Greatest length of skull, 90; general form of body that of a large shrew; snout elongate, tip bare, nostrils opening laterally; eyes small; ears visible above pelage; tail so sparsely haired as to seem naked; pelage composed of hair of two lengths; claws of forefeet longer than those of hind feet; axillary and inguinal odoriferous glands; one pair of inguinal mammae; cranium elongate; sagittal and especially lambdoidal crests pronounced; rostrum tubular; zygomatic arches absent, although maxillary and squamosal

20

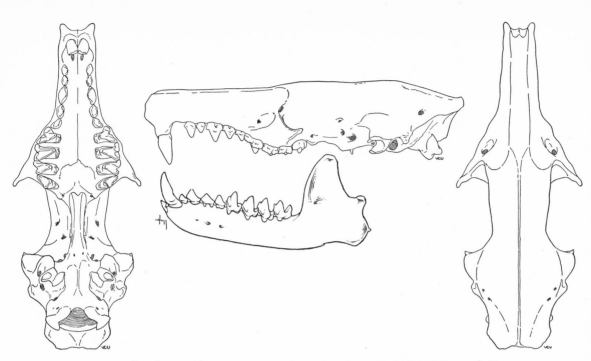

Fig. 8. *Solenodon paradoxus*, Las Vegas, Santo Domingo, No. 29502 K.U., sex ?, X 1.

roots are present; I1 and i2 greatly enlarged, the latter with a hollow groove on medial surface; occlusal surface of upper molars consisting of high, V-shaped amphicone and low, internal protocone and hypocone. Dentition, i. $\frac{3}{3}$, c. $\frac{1}{1}$, p. $\frac{3}{3}$, m. $\frac{3}{3}$.

Members of this family are found only on Cuba and Haiti. The animals are mainly nocturnal, live in burrows and caves, have 1 to 3 young, and eat a variety of food, mostly animal.

KEY TO GENERA OF SOLENODONTIDAE

1. Claws on forefeet approximately same length as toes; I3 in contact with C; P3 with base oval; prenasal bone present.   .   *Solenodon*, p. 21
1'. Claws on forefeet considerably longer than toes; I3 separated from C by small diastema; P3 with base triangular; prenasal bone absent.   .   .   .   .   *Atopogale*, p. 22

Genus **Solenodon** Brandt—Haitian Solenodon

1833. *Solenodon* Brandt, Mém. Acad. Imp. Sci., St. Pétersbourg, ser. 6, Sci. Math. Phys. et Nat., 2:459. Type, *Solenodon paradoxus* Brandt.

Pelage coarse; claws on forefeet as long as toes; skull with small, rounded, prenasal bone placed horizontally in front of premaxillae; mesopterygoid space wider anteriorly than posteriorly; tympanic rings farther apart posteriorly than anteriorly; I3 in contact with canine; C with small anterior cusp

formed by cingulum; P3 simple with oval base; 16 thoracic vertebrae.

Solenodon paradoxus Brandt
Haitian Solenodon

1833. [*Solenodon*] *paradoxus* Brandt, Mém. Acad. Imp. Sci., St. Pétersbourg, ser. 6, Sci. Math. Phys. et Nat., 2:459, type from Hispaniola. Known only from Island of Haiti. Characters as for the genus.

Still living, according to G. M. Allen (1942:12), in areas of stony forest in northeastern part of Dominican Republic, Island of Haiti.

MARGINAL RECORDS.—Dominican Republic: kilometer 2 Site (Miller, 1929c:4); Río San Juan (*ibid.*); Naranjo Abajo (*ibid.*); La Vega (Allen, 1942a:1J); vicinity of San José de las Matas (*ibid.*).

Genus **Atopogale** Cabrera—Cuban Solenodon

1925. *Atopogale* Cabrera, Genera Mammalium: Insectivora, Galeopithecia, Mus. Nac. Ciencias Nat., Madrid, p. 177, November 29. Type, *Solenodon cubanus* Peters. Used as a subgenus by Aguayo, Bol. Hist. Nat. Soc. Felipe Poey, 1:131, November 1950.

Pelage longer and finer than in *Solenodon*; claws more delicate but considerably longer than toes; no prenasal bone; tympanic rings separated more widely anteriorly than posteriorly; mesopterygoid space narrower anteriorly than posteriorly; pterygoid ending in large hamular process; teeth generally smaller than in *Solenodon*; I3 separated from canine by short diastema; C lacking small anterior cusp; P3 relatively large and with posterior prolongation giving base triangular outline; 15 thoracic vertebrae.

Atopogale cubana
Cuban Solenodon

See characters of the genus. Barbour (Proc. New England Zool. Club, 23:4, 1944) suggests that the subspecies in southeastern and south-central Cuba is extinct.

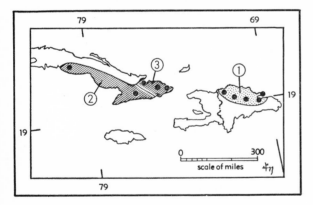

Map 11. *Solenodon* and *Atopogale*.

1. *Solenodon paradoxus*
2. *Atopogale cubana cubana*
3. *Atopogale cubana poeyana*

Atopogale cubana cubana (Peters)

1861. *Solenodon cubanus* Peters, Monatsb. preuss. Akad. Wiss., Berlin, 169, type from Bayamo, Cuba.

1925. *Atopogale cubana*, Cabrera, Genera Mammalium: Insectivora, Galeopithecia, Mus. Nac. Ciencias Nat., Madrid, p. 177, November 29.

MARGINAL RECORDS (G. M. Allen, 1942a:13).—Cuba: near Trinidad; mountains east of Bayamo.

Atopogale cubana poeyana (Barbour)

1944. *Solenodon poeyanus* Barbour, Proc. New England Zool. Club, 23:6, March 7, type from vicinity of Nipe Bay, Cuba. Known only from mountains of northeastern Cuba.
1950. *Solenodon* (*Atopogale*) *cubanus poeyanus*, Aguayo, Bol. Hist. Nat. Soc. Felipe Poey, 1(3):131, November.

MARGINAL RECORDS.—Cuba: type locality; Sierra de Toar (Barbour, 1944:4); Nabuiabo Swamp, Finca La Caridad, between Baracoa and Duaba (*op. cit.*:4–5).

FAMILY **SORICIDAE**—Shrews

External measurements: 71–174; 12–80; 8.5–21.2. Condylobasal length of skull, 13–23.8. Shape generally mouselike; nose long and pointed; eyes small and often partly hidden in fur; ears provided with pinnae which may be reduced (*Blarina*) or well developed (*Notiosorex*); feet pentadactyl and normally developed. Skull triangular; zygomatic arches and auditory bullae lacking; tympanic bone annular; first upper incisors procumbent with tips curved or hooked ventrad and in addition possessing a second, posterior, ventrally projecting, unicuspidlike conule which seems to serve as an additional unicuspid tooth; other incisors, canines, and all premolars except p4 and P4 simple and unicuspid; crowns of upper molars W-shaped; M3 markedly smaller than M1 or M2.

Most shrews are suited to a secretive life spent beneath leaf litter, grass, fallen logs, and in the runways of other small mammals. The species *Sorex palustris* is highly specialized for amphibious life. Food is mainly animal matter though occasionally vegetable food is accepted by most species.

The family has been divided into 2 subfamilies, Crocidurinae and Soricinae, based, respectively, on the absence or presence of pigment in the teeth. The division is of doubtful validity. Presumably all Recent North American shrews are soricines.

KEY TO NORTH AMERICAN GENERA OF SORICIDAE

In the upper jaw the first tooth (I1) has two large cusps and therefore is not counted as a unicuspid. The last four grinding teeth (P4–M3) of the upper jaw are not unicuspids but the teeth intervening between the first tooth (I1) and the anterior grinding tooth (P4) are so termed. In some shrews certain of the unicuspids are not visible in lateral view. Therefore, it is necessary to examine the teeth from the crown (occlusal) surface with a hand lens or lower-power dissecting microscope to be certain of the number of unicuspids. In *Microsorex* the 3rd and 5th unicuspids are reduced to minute pegs partly hidden between the adjoining teeth; thus, at first glance, *Microsorex* seems to possess only 3 unicuspids.

1. Three unicuspid teeth in each side of upper jaw. . . . . *Notiosorex*, p. 64
1'. Four or 5 unicuspid teeth in each side of upper jaw.
   2. Four unicuspid teeth in each side of upper jaw. . . . . *Cryptotis*, p. 55
   2'. Five unicuspid teeth in each side of upper jaw.
      3. Tail less than two-fifths of length of head and body; viewed from the side, 3rd and 4th unicuspids subequal and each one less than a fourth as large as the 1st or 2nd unicuspid; lateral edge of braincase produced into a sharp, pointed angle, even in young specimens. . . . *Blarina*, p. 52
      3'. Tail more than two-fifths of length of head and body; viewed from the side, 3rd and 4th unicuspids unequal in size and one or both more than a fourth as large as the 1st or 2nd unicuspid; lateral edge of braincase not produced into a sharp, pointed angle, even in old specimens.
         4. At least 4, and usually all 5, of the upper unicuspids easily visible in lateral view; ridge extending from apex medially to cingulum of 2nd and 3rd upper teeth without a distinct caudad bend near terminus when viewed occlusally; in lateral view base of lower incisor and premolar separated by space nearly equal to anteroposterior diameter of canine. *Sorex*, p. 23
         4'. Only 3 upper unicuspids easily visible in lateral view; ridge extending from apex medially to cingulum of 2nd and 3rd upper unicuspidate teeth with a distinct caudad bend near terminus when viewed occlusally; in lateral view base of lower incisor and premolar separated by space equal to less than two-fifths (usually one-fourth) of anteroposterior diameter of canine. . . . . *Microsorex*, p. 50

Genus **Sorex** Linnaeus—Long-tailed Shrews

North American species revised by Jackson, *in* N. Amer. Fauna, 51:vi + 238, 13 pls., 24 figs., July 24, 1928.

1758. *Sorex* Linnaeus, Syst. Nat., ed. 10, 1:53. Type, *Sorex araneus* Linnaeus.
1762. *Musaraneus* Brisson, Regnum animale, p. 126. Type, Musaraneus (type); included also *M. aquaticus* from Europe and *M. brasiliensis* from Brazil.
1829. *Oxyrhin* Kaup, Skizzirte Entwickelungs-Geschichte und natürliches System der europäischen Thierwelt, p. 120. Type, *Sorex tetragonurus* Hermann by subsequent designation (Miller, Catalogue of the mammals of western Europe, p. 29, November 23, 1912).
1835. *Amphiosorex* Duvernoy, Mém. Soc. Mus. d'Hist. Nat. Strasbourg, 2:23. Type, *Sorex hermanni* Duvernoy [= *Neomys fodiens* (Pennant) skull plus *Sorex araneus tetragonurus* Hermann skin].
1838. *Corsira* Gray, Proc. Zool. Soc. London, for 1837, p. 123. Type, *Sorex araneus* Linnaeus.
1842. *Otisorex* De Kay, Zoology of New-York . . . , pt. 1, Mammalia, p. 22 and pl. 5, fig. 1. Type, *Otisorex platyrhinus* De Kay [= *Sorex cinereus* Kerr].
1848. *Hydrogale Pomel*, Arch. Sci. Phys. et Nat., Genève, 9:248, November. Type, *Sorex fimbripes* Bachman [= *Sorex cinereus* Kerr]. Not *Hydrogale* Kaup, 1829.
1858. *Neosorex* Baird, Mammals, *in* Repts. Expl. Surv. . . . , 8(1):11, July 14. Type, *Neosorex navigator* Baird.

1884. *Atophyrax* Merriam, Trans. Linnaean Soc. New York, 2:217, August. Type, *Atophyrax bendirii* Merriam.
1890. *Homalurus* Schulze, Schriften des Naturwissenschaft. Vereins des Harzes in Wernigerode, 5:28. Type, *Sorex alpinus* Schinz.
1927. *Soricidus* Altobello, Rev. Franc. Mamm., 1:6. Type *Soricidus monsvairani* Altobello [= *Sorex araneus tetragonurus* Hermann].

External measurements: 71–174; 25–80; 10–21. Condylobasal length of skull, 14.2–23.8. Body slender; tail a third to more than a half of total length, hairy in young, glabrous in old adults; snout long and slender, having well-developed vibrissae; eyes minute but visible; pinnae of ears usually projecting slightly above pelage; 3 pairs of inguinal mammae; color varying from tan to black; uni-, bi-, or tri-colored; skull triangular; sagittal and lambdoidal crests present on older individuals. Five upper unicuspid teeth; pigmentation varying according to species: 1st, 2nd, and 4th well developed with pigmented apices; 3rd variable in size; 5th smaller than any other, often an unpigmented peg difficult to see in lateral view; articular process of mandible having 2 horizontal articular facets; angular process long and slender. Dentition, i. $\frac{3}{1}$, c. $\frac{1}{1}$, p. $\frac{3}{1}$, m. $\frac{3}{3}$.

Key to North American Species of Sorex

1. Hind foot more than 18; pelage grayish, never distinctly brown.
   2. Rostrum short and slightly downcurved; anterior part of premaxilla scarcely shallower dorsoventrally than middle part; vertical depth of rostrum at level of 3rd unicuspid equal to approximately half the distance from anterior border of infraorbital foramen to posterior border of first incisor; posterior end of internal cutting edge of anterior portion of internal basal shelf of first and 2nd upper molars usually without cusplike lobe; hind foot distinctly fimbriated.
      3. Skull having well-developed sagittal and lambdoidal crests; condylobasal length averaging less than 19.3; known only from Point Gustavus, Glacier Bay, Alaska. . . . . . *S. alaskanus*, p. 40
      3'. Skull smooth, lacking well-developed sagittal and lambdoidal crests; condylobasal length averaging more than 19.3; not occurring at Point Gustavus, Glacier Bay, Alaska. . *S. palustris*, p. 38

    2'. Rostrum long and much curved downward; anterior part of premaxilla much shallower dorsoventrally than middle part; vertical depth of rostrum at 3rd unicuspid less than half the distance from anterior border of infraorbital formen to posterior border of first incisor; posterior end of internal cutting edge of anterior portion of internal basal shelf of 1st and 2nd upper molars usually with distinct cusplike lobe; hind foot slightly fimbriated. . . . . *S. bendirii,*   p. 40

1'. Hind foot less than 18, or, when more than 18, pelage brownish.
  4. Third unicuspid not smaller than 4th.
    5. Known geographic range north of United States–Mexico boundary.
      6. Posterior border of infraorbital foramen posterior to plane of space between M1 and M2.
        7. Total length more than 115; hind foot more than 13; condylobasal length more than 16.8. . . . . *S. dispar,*   p. 45
        7'. Total length less than 115; hind foot less than 13; condylobasal length less than 16.8.   *S. gaspensis,*   p. 44
      6'. Posterior border of infraorbital foramen even with, or anterior to, plane of space between M1 and M2.
        8. Maxillary breadth less than 4.6.
          9. Condylobasal length 14.7 or more; not occurring in eastern Oregon.
            10. Known geographic range confined to Sierra Nevada of California. . *S. lyelli,*   p. 28
            10'. Known geographic range outside of California.
              11. Confined to St. Lawrence Island, Alaska; color of back sharply darker than that of sides; tricolored in summer pelage. . . . . . . *S. jacksoni,*   p. 43
              11'. Not occurring on St. Lawrence Island; color of back not sharply darker than that of sides; bicolored in summer pelage. . . . . *S. cinereus,*   p. 25
          9'. Condylobasal length less than 14.7; occurring in eastern Oregon. . . *S. preblei,*   p. 28
        8'. Maxillary breadth more than 4.6.
          12. Occurring on Unalaska Island, Alaska. . . . . *S. hydrodromus,*   p. 43
          12'. Not occurring on Unalaska Island, Alaska.
            13. Condylobasal length more than 17.5; cranial breadth 8.5 or more; maxillary tooth-row 6.1 or more.
              14. Distinctly tricolored (back sharply darker than sides); tail less than 45.   *S. arcticus,*   p. 43
              14'. Distinctly bicolored (back same as sides); tail 45 or more. . *S. fumeus,*   p. 41
            13'. Condylobasal length less than 17.5; cranial breadth no more than 8.5; maxillary tooth-row 6.1 or less.
              15. Hind foot 13 or more; palatal length less than 6.0; maxillary breadth less than 5.0; occurring on Pribilof Islands, Alaska. . . . *S. pribilofensis,*   p. 41
              15'. Hind foot less than 13; palatal length more than 6.0; maxillary breadth 5.0 or more; not occcurring on Pribilof Islands. . . . . *S. merriami,*   p. 47
  5'. Known geographic range south of United States–Mexican boundary.
    16. Occurring in Guatemala. . . . . *S. saussurei,*   p. 48
    16'. Occurring in México.
      17. Condylobasal length more than 17.9; maxillary tooth-row 6.5 or more.
        18. Hind foot 16 or more; condylobasal length 19.0 or more. . . . . *S. sclateri,*   p. 49
        18'. Hind foot less than 16; condylobasal length less than 19. . . . *S. saussurei,*   p. 48
      17'. Condylobasal length less than 17.9; maxillary tooth-row less than 6.5.
        19. Condylobasal length less than 17.4; maxillary tooth-row less than 6.3.
          20. Cranial breadth less than 7.7; maxillary breadth less than 4.7; underparts paler than upper parts. . . . . *S. milleri,*   p. 28
          20'. Cranial breadth more than 7.7; maxillary breadth more than 4.7; underparts essentially as dark as upper parts. . . . . *S. oreopolus,*   p. 49
        19'. Condylobasal length more than 17.4; maxillary tooth-row more than 6.3.
          21. Cranial breadth less than 8.5; maxillary breadth less than 5.2. *S. oreopolus,*   p. 49
          21'. Cranial breadth more than 8.5; maxillary breadth more than 5.2. *S. stizodon,*   p. 50
 4'. Third unicuspid smaller than 4th.
    22. Occurring in United States east of 95° longitude. . . . . *S. longirostris,*   p. 29
    22'. Occurring in México, and west of 95° longitude in the more northern parts of the continent.
      23. Occurring north of United States–Mexican boundary but including Baja California.
        24. Tail sharply bicolor; underparts of body scarcely, if any, paler than upper parts; ridge extending from apex of unicuspid toward interior edge of cingulum but slightly pigmented, and rarely pigmented to cingulum, separated from cingulum by longitudinal groove, and never ending in distinct cusplet. . . . . *S. trowbridgii,*   p. 46

24'. Tail not sharply bicolor; underparts of body paler than upper parts; ridge extending from apex of unicuspid toward interior edge of cingulum well pigmented usually to cingulum, not separated from cingulum by longitudinal groove, and usually ending in a distinct cusplet more or less pigmented.

Subgenus Otisorex De Kay

1842. *Otisorex* De Kay, Zoology of New York . . . , pt. 1, Mammalia, p. 22, and pl. 5, fig. 1. Type, *Otisorex platyrhinus* De Kay [= *Sorex cinereus* Kerr].

Postmandibular foramen absent in most species; upper unicuspids usually having pigmented ridge, extending from apex of tooth to cingulum and uninterrupted by anteroposterior groove.

Sorex cinereus
Masked Shrew

External measurements: 71–111; 25–50; 10–14. Condylobasal length of skull, 14.6–16.9. Color grayish or tan to brownish, bicolor or tricolor in some subspecies; paler in winter, darker in summer. Skull with relatively narrow rostrum and relatively high braincase; teeth narrow in exterointernal diameter; 3rd unicuspid tooth larger than or, less commonly,

equal to 4th (in some individuals of *S. c. ohionensis* 3rd unicuspid may actually be smaller than 4th); unicuspids with distinctly pigmented internal ridge extending from apex medially to cingulum, sometimes ending in small internal cusplet.

This species prefers moist open areas near water but is often found in other habitats including dry forest floors in the eastern United States. Four to 10 young are born between April and October. Food consists mostly of arthropods with smaller amounts of vertebrates, annelids, mollusks, and vegetable matter.

According to van den Brink (1953:96) this species has a circumboreal distribution and should bear the specific name *Sorex caecutiens*.

Sorex cinereus acadicus Gilpin

1867. *Sorex acadicus* Gilpin, Proc. and Trans. Nova Scotian Inst. Nat. Sci., 1(2):2. Type locality, Nova Scotia, assumed to be near Halifax, Halifax Co.

1940. *Sorex cinereus acadicus,* R. W. Smith, Amer. Midl. Nat., 24:219, July 31.

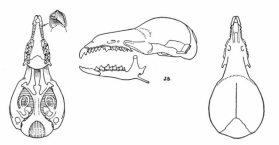

Fig. 9. *Sorex cinereus ugyunak,* Kaolak, 69° 56′ 00″, 160° 14′ 51″, 178 ft., Alaska, No. 43166 K.U., ♀, X 2.

MARGINAL RECORDS (Smith, 1940:220).—Nova Scotia: Cape North; Newport. [Possibly the geographic range of *acadicus* is more extensive than shown on Map 12.

Without mentioning record stations of occurrence, Smith (1940:219) includes "New Brunswick, and eastern Quebec" in the range of *acadicus.* Miller and Kellogg (1955:13) do likewise and include also Prince Edward Island in the range of *acadicus.* Cameron (1953:31) assigns "eastern Quebec south of the St. Lawrence River" to the range of *S. c. cinereus.*]

Sorex cinereus cinereus Kerr

1792. *Sorex arcticus cinereus* Kerr, The animal kingdom . . . , p. 206. Type locality, Fort Severn, Ontario.
1925. *Sorex cinereus cinereus,* Jackson, Jour. Mamm., 6:56, February 9.
1827. *Sorex personatus* I. Geoffroy St.-Hilaire, Mém. Mus. Hist. Nat., Paris, 15:122. Type locality, eastern United States.
1828. *Sorex forsteri* Richardson, Zool. Jour., 3:516, April, type from "Hudson's Bay countries."
1837. *Sorex cooperi* Bachman, Jour. Acad. Nat. Sci. Philadelphia, 7(2):388, type from "North Western Territory."

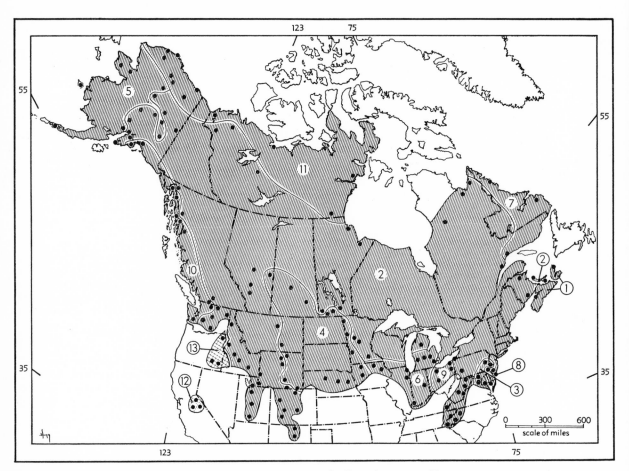

Map 12. *Sorex cinereus, Sorex lyelli,* and *Sorex preblei.*

1. *S. c. acadicus*
2. *S. c. cinereus*
3. *S. c. fontinalis*
4. *S. c. haydeni*
5. *S. c. hollisteri*
6. *S. c. lesueurii*
7. *S. c. miscix*
8. *S. c. nigriculus*
9. *S. c. ohionensis*
10. *S. c. streatori*
11. *S. c. ugyunak*
12. *S. lyelli*
13. *S. preblei*

1837. *Sorex fimbripes* Bachman, Jour. Acad. Nat. Sci. Philadelphia, 7(2):391, type from Drury Run, Pennsylvania.

1842. *Otisorex platyrhinus* De Kay, Zoology of New York . . . , pt. 1, Mammalia, p. 22, type from Tappan, Rockland Co., New York.

1891. *Sorex idahoensis* Merriam, N. Amer. Fauna, 5:32, July 30, type from Timber Creek, 8200 ft., Salmon River Mts. [now Lemhi Mts.], Lemhi Co., Idaho.

1926. *Sorex frankstounensis* Peterson, Ann. Carnegie Mus., 16:292, March, type from Frankstown Cave, near Hollidaysburg, Blair Co., Pennsylvania.

MARGINAL RECORDS (Jackson, 1928:46–50, unless otherwise noted).—Northwest Territories: Anderson River Region (Fort Anderson); Lake St. Croix. Manitoba: Churchill (Bole and Moulthrop, 1942:95); York Factory. Quebec: Seal Lake; Fort Chimo; George River Hudson's Bay Post (Hildebrand, 1949:310); Godbout. New Brunswick: Bathurst, 15 mi. from Miramichi Rd. Prince Edward Island: Alberton; Georgetown. New Brunswick: Hampton. New Jersey: Mauricetown. Pennsylvania: Kennett Square. West Virginia: Cheat Bridge (Bole and Moulthrop, 1942:95); Cranberry Glades (*ibid.*). North Carolina: Grandfather Mtn. (*ibid.*); Mt. Mitchell (*ibid.*); Highlands Plateau on main Blue Ridge of Appalachian Mts., a few mi. from both Georgia and South Carolina (Odum, 1949:187). Tennessee: Buck Fork, Little Pigeon River (Kellogg, 1939:249). Kentucky: Big Black Mtn. (Barbour, 1941:195). West Virginia: Jobs Knob (Kellogg, 1937:446). Maryland: Bittinger. Pennsylvania: Westmoreland County (Grimm and Roberts, 1950:42); Erie County (Richmond and Rosland, 1949:38). Michigan: Roscommon County (Burt, 1946:93). Minnesota: Steele County; Long Prairie; Ottertail County. Manitoba: Winnipeg (Soper, 1946:134); Oak Lake. Alberta: South Edmonton; forks of Blindmans and Red Deer rivers; Calgary. Montana: Zortman. Wyoming: head Trapper Creek, Bighorn Mts., 9500 ft.; head N fork Powder River, Big Horn Mts.; S base Bridger Peak, 8800 ft., Sierra Madre Mts. Colorado: *Fort Collins* (Beidleman, 1950:459); Loveland; Summit House, Pikes Peak (Warren, 1942:9). New Mexico: Twining; Pecos Baldy. Colorado: Hermit; Ruby Lake; Mud Springs (V. Bailey, 1932:370). Wyoming: Evanston. Utah (Durrant and Newey, 1953:117): Wildcat Ranger Station, 8000 ft.; ½ mi. S Mt. Nebo Ranger Station, 6125 ft.; head Lamb's Canyon, 9000 ft.; Beaver Creek, S fork Ogden River, 6500 ft. Wyoming: Cokeville. Idaho (Davis, 1939:101): American Falls; Ketchum; Sawtooth Lake; ½ mi. E Black Lake; Cedar Mtn. Washington: Loon Lake; Signal Peak, 4000 ft., Yakima Indian Reservation; Mt. Rainier; Lake Keechelus; Bauerman Ridge. British Columbia: Hope; *Hazleton*; Stikine River at Great Glacier. Alaska: White Pass; Seldovia; Hope; Tyonek; S fork Kuskokwim River, 10 mi. above mouth Post River; Mt. Sischoo; Nenana; Eagle; Fairbanks; Tanana. Northwest Territories: near Old Fort Good Hope. [See remarks on geographic range under *S. c. acadicus.*]

Sorex cinereus fontinalis Hollister

1911. *Sorex fontinalis* Hollister, Proc. U.S. Nat. Mus., 40:378, April 17, type from Cold Spring Swamp, near Beltsville, Prince Georges Co., Maryland.

1937. *Sorex cinereus fontinalis*, Poole, Jour. Mamm., 18:96, February 11.

MARGINAL RECORDS (Jackson, 1928:57, unless otherwise noted).—Pennsylvania: Ridgewood near Reading (Poole, 1937:96); 3 mi. N Swarthmore (Pearson and Pearson, 1947:142). Delaware: *Keeny* (Poole, 1937:96). Maryland: Cambridge; Hollywood. Virginia: 6 mi. from Washington, D.C. (Bray, 1939:102). Maryland: Cabin John.

Sorex cinereus haydeni Baird

1858. *Sorex haydeni* Baird, Mammals, *in* Repts. Expl. Surv. . . . , 8(1):29, July 14, type from Fort Union, Nebraska [later Fort Buford, now Mondak, Montana, near Buford, Williams Co., North Dakota].

1925. *Sorex cinereus haydeni*, Jackson, Jour. Mamm., 6:56, February 9.

MARGINAL RECORDS (Jackson, 1928:52–53, unless otherwise noted).—Alberta: Islay. Saskatchewan: Osler; Indian Head. Manitoba: Killarney; Carberry. Minnesota: Kittson County; Moorhead; Madison. Iowa: Arnold's Park (Scott, 1937:54); *2 mi. W Sac City*; Wall Lake. Nebraska: 4 mi. N and ½ mi. E Octavia (Jones, 1954:481); 2½ mi. N Ord (*ibid.*); Kennedy. Wyoming: Sherman; Fort Steele; Wolf (Eaton's Ranch). Montana: *Crow Agency*; Fort Custer.

Sorex cinereus hollisteri Jackson

1900. *Sorex personatus arcticus* Merriam, Proc. Washington Acad. Sci., 2:17, March 14, type from St. Michael, Alaska. Not *Sorex arcticus* Kerr, 1792.

1925. *Sorex cinereus hollisteri* Jackson, Jour. Mamm., 6:55, February 9, a renaming of *Sorex personatus arcticus* Merriam.

MARGINAL RECORDS (Jackson, 1928:56, unless otherwise noted).—Alaska: Bettles; Richardson, Tanana River; Swede Lake (Strecker, *et al.*, 1952:476); Lake Clark, head Nogheling River; Kings Cove, Alaska Peninsula; Nunivak Island; Sawtooth Mts.; Cloud Lake (Quay, 1951:90).

Sorex cinereus lesueurii (Duvernoy)

1842. *Amphisorex lesueurii* Duvernoy, Mag. Zool. d'Anat. Comp. et Paleont., 1842, livr. 25, p. 33, pl. 50, type from Wabash River Valley, Indiana.

1942. *Sorex cinereus lesueurii*, Bole and Moulthrop, Sci. Publs., Cleveland Mus. Nat. Hist., 5:95, September 11.

MARGINAL RECORDS (Burt, 1943:1–2, unless otherwise noted).—Michigan: Clinton County (Burt, 1946:93); Livingston County; Washtenaw County. Indiana: Randolph County (Lyon, 1936:42); New Harmony (Jackson, 1928:47). Illinois: St. Anne (Necker and Hatfield, 1941:42). Iowa: Buchanan County (Scott, 1937:53); Winnebago County. Illinois: Chicago (Necker and Hatfield, 1941:42). Michigan: Allegan County (Burt, 1946:93).

Sorex cinereus miscix Bangs

1899. *Sorex personatus miscix* Bangs, Proc. New England Zool. Club, 1:15, February 28, type from Black Bay, Labrador.

1925. *Sorex cinereus miscix*, Jackson, Jour. Mamm., 6:56, February 9.

MARGINAL RECORDS.—Labrador: Okak (Jackson, 1928:51); 20 mi. above mouth Paradise River (*ibid*). Quebec: Bay of Seven Islands (Anderson, 1947:14).

Sorex cinereus nigriculus Green

1932. *Sorex cinereus nigriculus* Green, Univ. California Publ. Zool., 38:387, June 9, type from alluvial tidewater marsh on Tuckahoe River, east of Tuckahoe, Cape May Co., New Jersey. Known only from the type locality.

Sorex cinereus ohionensis Bole and Moulthrop

1942. *Sorex cinereus ohionensis* Bole and Moulthrop, Sci. Publs., Cleveland Mus. Nat. Hist., 5:89, September 11, type from Hunting Valley, Cuyahoga Co., Ohio.

MARGINAL RECORDS.—Ohio: Mechanicsville (Bole and Moulthrop, 1942:94); Ellsworth (70566 USBS); Milford Center (19434 NM); Maple Grove (Bole and Moulthrop, 1942:95).

Sorex cinereus streatori Merriam

1895. *Sorex personatus streatori* Merriam, N. Amer. Fauna, 10:62, December 31, type from Yakutat, Alaska.
1925. *Sorex cinereus streatori*, Jackson, Jour. Mamm., 6:56, February 9.

MARGINAL RECORDS (Jackson, 1928:54–55, unless otherwise noted).—Alaska: Port Nell Juan (head Prince William Sound); Valdez Narrows (Prince William Sound); Skagway; Taku River; Thomas Bay; Anan Creek. British Columbia: Observatory Inlet (Anderson, 1947:15); Mt. Baker Range, 49th parallel, 6000 ft. Washington: Whatcom Pass, 5200 ft.; Cedarville (Dalquest, 1948:134).

Sorex cinereus ugyunak Anderson and Rand

1945. *Sorex cinereus ugyunak* Anderson and Rand, Canadian Field-Nat., 59:62, October 16, type from Tuktoyaktok (Tuktak), about 20 mi. SW Toker Point, on Arctic coast near NE corner of Mackenzie River Delta, Mackenzie.

MARGINAL RECORDS.—Alaska: Point Barrow (50404 KU); Okpilak River, near Bater Island (Anderson, 1947:15). Northwest Territories: type locality; Coronation Gulf (*ibid.*); Chesterfield (*ibid.*); Padley Post (*ibid.*). Alaska: Brooks Range, about 80 mi. W Alaska-Yukon boundary (*ibid.*); Anaktuvuk Pass (Rausch, 1951:165); Chandler Lake (43185 KU); Kaolak, 160° 14′ 51″, 69° 56′ 00″, 178 ft. (43170 KU); Wainwright (Bee and Hall, 1956:22).

Sorex lyelli Merriam
Mt. Lyell Shrew

1902. *Sorex tenellus lyelli* Merriam, Proc. Biol. Soc. Washington, 15:75, March 22, type from Mount Lyell [near head Lyell Fork of Tuolumne River], Tuolumne Co., California.
1928. *Sorex lyelli*, Jackson, N. Amer. Fauna, 51:57, July 24.

External measurements: 102–103; 39–41; 11.0–12.0. Condylobasal length of skull, 15.2–15.4. Upper parts brownish; underparts pale olive-gray or smoke-gray; tail bicolored; 3rd unicuspid tooth equal to or larger than 4th; skull similar to that of *S. cinereus* but wider interorbitally and having more nearly flat braincase.

MARGINAL RECORDS (Grinnell, 1933:79).—California: near Williams Butte, Mono Co.; Mammoth; Vogelsang Lake.

Fig. 10. *Sorex lyelli*, Vogelsang Lake, Mariposa Co., California, No. 23001 M.V.Z., ♀, X 2.

Sorex preblei Jackson
Preble's Shrew

1922. *Sorex preblei* Jackson, Jour. Washington Acad. Sci., 12:263, June 4, type from Jordan Valley, 4200 ft., Malheur Co., Oregon.

External measurements: 85–95; 35–36; 11–11. Condylobasal length of skull, 14.2–14.6. Upper parts brownish; underparts paler; tail bicolor. Skull resembling that of *S. lyelli* but smaller and with relatively shorter tooth-row.

MARGINAL RECORDS (Jackson, 1928:59).—Oregon: Sled Springs, 25 mi. N Enterprise, 4600 ft.; Jordan Valley, 4200 ft.; Diamond, 4300 ft.

Sorex milleri Jackson
Carmen Mountain Shrew

1947. *Sorex milleri* Jackson, Proc. Biol. Soc. Washington, 60:131, October 9, type from Madera Camp, 8000 ft., Sierra del Carmen, Coahuila.

External measurements: 95; 44; 11. Condylobasal length of skull, 15.5. Summer pelage unknown; upper parts brownish; underparts paler; unicuspids with internal ridges pigmented to cingula; 3rd unicuspid approximately equal to 4th.

MARGINAL RECORDS.—Coahuila: type locality; *13 mi. E San Antonio de las Alazanas, 9350 ft.* (Baker, 1956:168). Nuevo León: Cerro Potosí, near La Jolla (Findley, 1955a:617).

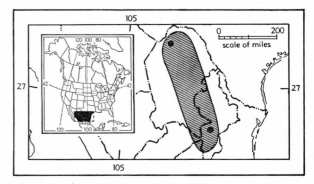

Map 13. *Sorex milleri.*

Sorex longirostris
Southeastern Shrew

External measurements: 79–108; 27–40; 10–13. Condylobasal length of skull, 13.9–16.4. Reddish brown or brownish above, paler below; 3rd unicuspid smaller than or equal to 4th; unicuspids broader than long and having internal ridge that is not pigmented; skull relatively broad and top flattened.

Most southeastern shrews have been taken in bogs, marshy or swampy areas, or in dense ground cover in woods. Four or 5 young comprise a litter.

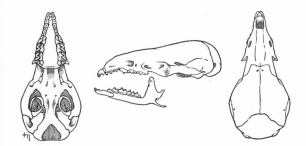

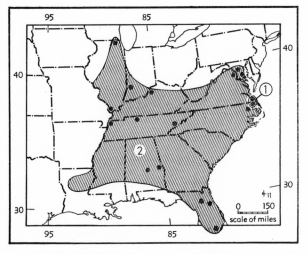

Fig. 11. *Sorex longirostris fisheri*, Dismal Swamp, Virginia, No. 75167 U.S.N.M., ♀, X 2.

Map 14. *Sorex longirostris* and subspecies.

1. *S. l. fisheri*   2. *S. l. longirostris*

Sorex longirostris fisheri Merriam

1895. *Sorex fisheri* Merriam, N. Amer. Fauna, 10:86, December 31, type from Lake Drummond, Dismal Swamp, Virginia.
1928. *Sorex longirostris fisheri*, Jackson, N. Amer. Fauna, 51:87, July 24.

MARGINAL RECORDS.—Virginia: type locality. North Carolina: Chapanoke (Jackson, 1928:87).

Sorex longirostris longirostris Bachman

1837. *Sorex longirostris* Bachman, Jour. Acad. Nat. Sci. Philadelphia, ser. 1, 7(2):370, type locality, Hume Plantation, swamps of the Santee River [=Cat Island, mouth of Santee River], South Carolina.
1848. [*Musar[aneus]. (Croc[idura].)] Bachmani (longirostris junior* Bachm[an]), Pomel, Arch. Sci. Phys. et Nat., 9:249.
1868. *Sorex wagneri* Fitzinger, Sitzungsb. k. Akad. Wiss., Wien, 57:512.

MARGINAL RECORDS (Kellogg, 1939:250–251, unless otherwise noted).—Illinois: Pistakee Lake (a misidentification?, Necker and Hatfield, 1941:42). Indiana: Bicknell (Jackson, 1928:86). Kentucky: Bernheim Forest (Barbour, 1956:110). Tennessee: Greenbrier; C.C.C. Camp, Great Smoky Mts. National Park. Virginia: Falls Church. Maryland: Sandy Spring; *Laurel*; Chesapeake Beach. North Carolina: Bertie County (Miller, 1895:52). Florida: Welaka (Moore, 1946:53); near Davenport (Hill, 1945:88); 5 mi. E Gainesville (Moore, 1943:405). Alabama: Auburn (Dusi, 1951:223); Bear Swamp, 4 mi. NE Autaugaville (Jackson, 1928:86). Tennessee: Reelfoot Lake. Illinois: Olive Branch (Necker and Hatfield, 1941:42).

Sorex vagrans
Vagrant Shrew

Subspecies revised by Findley, Univ. Kansas Publ., Mus. Nat. Hist., 9:1–68, 18 figs., December 10, 1955.

External measurements: 90–153; 31–67; 11–17.5. Condylobasal length of skull, 16.1–23.0. Tail a little more than a third to almost a half of total length; color pattern tricolored through bicolored to almost unicolored; color reddish (Sayal- or Snuff-Brown) to grayish in summer pelage, and black to pale gray in winter; 3rd unicuspid smaller than 4th; and unicuspids, except 5th, with a pigmented ridge extending from near apex of each tooth medially to cingulum and sometimes ending as internal cusplet. *S. vagrans* differs from members of the *ornatus*-group in less flattened skull, and in more ventrally situated foramen magnum that encroaches more on the basioccipital and less on the supraoccipital. The dental features mentioned above distinguish *S. vagrans* from *S. trowbridgii, S. saussurei, S. cinereus, S. merriami,* and *S. arcticus*—kinds which occur where *vagrans* occurs. The large *S. palustris* and *S. bendirii* can be distinguished from *S. vagrans* by larger size and darker color.

S. vagrans is an intergrading chain of subspecies the end members of which differ so much in size and ecological requirements that two subspecies live together without crossbreeding along the Pacific Coast from southern British Columbia to the Golden Gate in California. The details of this distribution and probable reasons for it have been published by Findley (1955b).

See the account of *Sorex ornatus* on page 34 con-

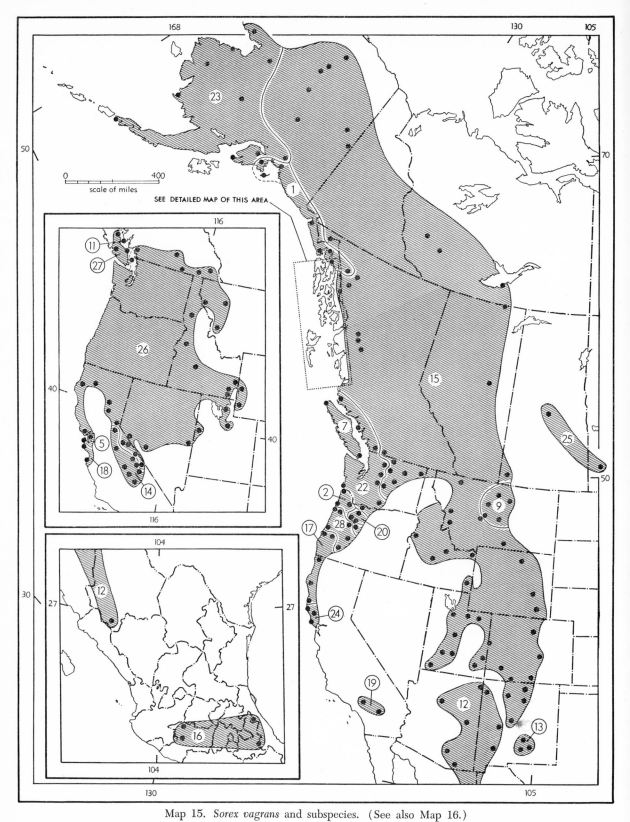

Map 15. *Sorex vagrans* and subspecies. (See also Map 16.)

1. *S. v. alascensis*
2. *S. v. bairdi*
5. *S. v. halicoetes*
7. *S. v. isolatus*
9. *S. v. longiquus*
10. *S. v. malitiosus*

11. *S. v. mixtus*
12. *S. v. monticola*
13. *S. v. neomexicanus*
14. *S. v. obscuroides*
15. *S. v. obscurus*
16. *S. v. orizabae*

17. *S. v. pacificus*
18. *S. v. paludivagus*
19. *S. v. parvidens*
20. *S. v. permiliensis*
21. *S. v. prevostensis*
22. *S. v. setosus*

23. *S. v. shumaginensis*
24. *S. v. sonomae*
25. *S. v. soperi*
26. *S. v. vagrans*
27. *S. v. vancouverensis*
28. *S. v. yaquinae*

30

cerning the possibility that it is only subspecifically distinct from the species *Sorex vagrans*. *S. vagrans vagrans* and *S. ornatus californicus* may intergrade.

Sorex vagrans alascensis Merriam

1895. *Sorex obscurus alascensis* Merriam, N. Amer. Fauna, 10:76, December 31, type from Yakutat, Alaska.
1955. *Sorex vagrans alascensis*, Findley, Univ. Kansas Publ., Mus. Nat. Hist., 9:41, December 10.
1900. *Sorex glacialis* Merriam, Proc. Washington Acad. Sci. 2:16, March 14, type from Point Gustavus, E side of entrance to Glacier Bay, Alaska.

MARGINAL RECORDS (Findley, 1955b:42).—Alaska: Valdez Narrows, Prince William Sound; N shore Yakutat Bay; E side Chilkat River, 100 ft., 9 mi. W, 4 mi. N Haines. British Columbia: Sheslay River. Alaska: Juneau; Glacier Bay; Montague Island, Prince William Sound; Port Nell Juan.

Sorex vagrans bairdi Merriam

1895. *Sorex bairdi* Merriam, N. Amer. Fauna, 10:77, December 31, type from Astoria, Oregon.
1955. *Sorex vagrans bairdi*, Findley, Univ. Kansas Publ., Mus. Nat. Hist., 9:35, December 10.

MARGINAL RECORDS (Findley, 1955b:36).—Oregon: type locality; Portland; N slope Three Sisters; Taft.

Sorex vagrans calvertensis Cowan

1941. *Sorex obscurus calvertensis* Cowan, Proc. Biol. Soc. Washington, 54:103, July 31, type from Safety Cove, Calvert Island, British Columbia.
1955. *Sorex vagrans calvertensis*, Findley, Univ. Kansas Publ., Mus. Nat. Hist., 9:39, December 10.

MARGINAL RECORDS (Findley, 1955b:39).—British Columbia: Larson Harbor, Banks Island; type locality.

Sorex vagrans elassodon Osgood

1901. *Sorex longicauda elassodon* Osgood, N. Amer. Fauna, 21:35, September 26, type from Cumshewa Inlet near old Indian Village of Clew, Moresby Island, Queen Charlotte Islands, British Columbia.
1955. *Sorex vagrans elassodon*, Findley, Univ. Kansas Publ., Mus. Nat. Hist., 9:40, December 10.

MARGINAL RECORDS (Findley, 1955b:41).—Alaska: Hawk Inlet [Admiralty Island]; Kupreanof Island; Mitkof Island; St. John Harbor, Zarembo Island; Kasaan Bay, Prince of Wales Island; Duke Island. British Columbia: Massett, Graham Island, Queen Charlotte Islands; type locality; Langara Island, Queen Charlotte Islands. Alaska: Forester Island; Rocky Bay, Dall Island; Shakan [really on Kosciusko Island]; Point Baker; Kuiu Island; Port Conclusion, Baranof Island.

Sorex vagrans halicoetes Grinnell

1913. *Sorex halicoetes* Grinnell, Univ. California Publ. Zool., 10:183, March 20, type from salt marsh near Palo Alto, Santa Clara Co., California.
1928. *Sorex vagrans halicoetes*, Jackson, N. Amer. Fauna, 51:108, July 24.

MARGINAL RECORDS (Findley, 1955b:59).—California: Berkeley; *Elmhurst; Palo Alto*; San Mateo.

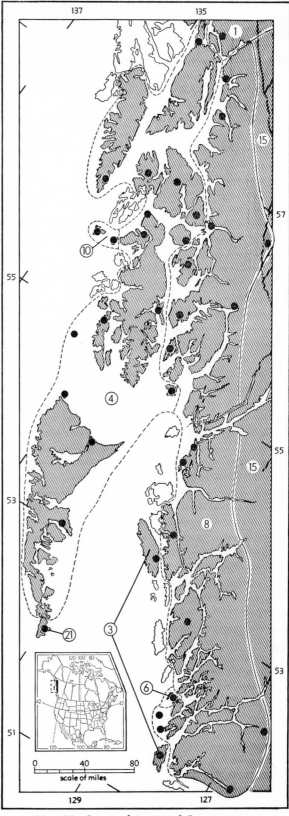

Map 16. Some subspecies of *Sorex vagrans*.
(See also Map 15.)

1. *S. v. alascensis*	8. *S. v. longicauda*
3. *S. v. calvertensis*	10. *S. v. malitiosus*
4. *S. v. elassodon*	15. *S. v. obscurus*
6. *S. v. insularis*	21. *S. v. prevostensis*

31

Sorex vagrans insularis Cowan

1941. *Sorex obscurus insularis* Cowan, Proc. Biol. Soc. Washington, 54:103, July 31, type from Smythe Island, Bardswell Group, British Columbia.
1955. *Sorex vagrans insularis*, Findley, Univ. Kansas Publ., Mus. Nat. Hist., 9:39, December 10.

MARGINAL RECORDS (Findley, 1955b:39).—British Columbia: Bardswell Group: *type locality*; Townsend Island; *Reginald Island*.

Sorex vagrans isolatus Jackson

1922. *Sorex obscurus isolatus* Jackson, Jour. Washington Acad. Sci., 12:263, June 4, type from mouth Millstone Creek, Nanaimo, Vancouver Island, British Columbia.
1955. *Sorex vagrans isolatus*, Findley, Univ. Kansas Publ., Mus. Nat. Hist., 9:38, December 10.

MARGINAL NOTES. (Findley, 1955b:39).—British Columbia: Vancouver Island: Cape Scott; Victoria.

Sorex vagrans longicauda Merriam

1895. *Sorex obscurus longicauda* Merriam, N. Amer. Fauna, 10:74, December 31, type from Wrangell, Alaska.
1955. *Sorex vagrans longicauda*, Findley, Univ. Kansas Publ., Mus. Nat. Hist., 9:37, December 10.

MARGINAL RECORDS (Findley, 1955b:38).—Alaska: Port Snettisham. British Columbia: Great Glacier, Stikine River. Alaska: Burroughs Bay. British Columbia: Bella Coola region; head Rivers Inlet; Spider Island; Goose Island; Princess Royal Island; Pitt Island; Metlakatla; Port Simpson. Alaska: Gravina Island; Helm Bay; Etolin Island; Sergief Island, mouth Stikine River; Sumdum Village.

Sorex vagrans longiquus Findley

1955. *Sorex vagrans longiquus* Findley, Univ. Kansas Publ., Mus. Nat. Hist., 9:49, December 10, type from 25 mi. ESE Big Sandy, Eagle Creek, Chouteau Co., Montana.

MARGINAL RECORDS (Findley, 1955b:50).—Montana: Bearpaw Mts.; Zortman; Big Snowy Mts.; 16 mi. N White Sulphur Springs; Highwood Mts.

Sorex vagrans malitiosus Jackson

1919. *Sorex obscurus malitiosus* Jackson, Proc. Biol. Soc. Washington, 32:23, April 11, type from E side Warren Island, Alaska. Known only from Warren and Coronation islands, Alaska.
1955. *Sorex vagrans malitiosus*, Findley, Univ. Kansas Publ., Mus. Nat. Hist., 9:40, December 10.

Sorex vagrans mixtus Hall

1938. *Sorex obscurus mixtus* Hall, Amer. Nat., 72:462, September 10, type from Vanada, Texada Island, Georgia Strait, British Columbia. Known only from the type locality.
1955. *Sorex vagrans mixtus*, Findley, Univ. Kansas Publ., Mus. Nat. Hist., 9:38, December 10.

Sorex vagrans monticola Merriam

1890. *Sorex monticolus* Merriam, N. Amer. Fauna, 3:43, September 11, type from San Francisco Mtn., 11,500 ft., Coconino Co., Arizona.
1895. *Sorex vagrans monticola* Merriam, N. Amer. Fauna, 10:69, December 31.
1932. *Sorex melanogenys* Hall, Jour. Mamm., 13:260, August 9, type from Marijilda Canyon, 8600 ft., Graham Mts. [= Pinaleno Mts.], Graham Co., Arizona.

MARGINAL RECORDS (Findley, 1955b:51).—Arizona: Tunitcha Mts. New Mexico: Chusca Mts.; Copper Canyon, Magdalena Mts.; Mimbres Mts., near Kingston. Chihuahua: Guadalupe y Calvo. Arizona: Huachuca Mts.; Santa Catalina Mts.; White River, Horseshoe Cienega, 8300 ft., White Mts.; type locality.

Sorex vagrans neomexicanus V. Bailey

1913. *Sorex obscurus neomexicanus* V. Bailey, Proc. Biol. Soc. Washington, 26:133, May 21, type from Cloudcroft, 9000 ft., Sacramento Mts., Otero Co., New Mexico.
1955. *Sorex vagrans neomexicanus*, Findley, Univ. Kansas Publ., Mus. Nat. Hist., 9:50, December 10.

MARGINAL RECORDS (Findley, 1955b:50).—New Mexico: NW slope Capitan Mts.; 10 mi. NE Cloudcroft; type locality.

Sorex vagrans obscuroides Findley

1955. *Sorex vagrans obscuroides* Findley, Univ. Kansas Publ., Mus. Nat. Hist., 9:58, December 10, type from Bishop Creek, 6600 ft., Inyo Co., California.

MARGINAL RECORDS (Findley, 1955b:58).—California: Pyramid Peak; near Mammoth; *Round Valley*; type locality; Mt. Whitney; Kern Lakes; Halstead Meadows; Horse Corral Meadows; E Fork Indian Canyon.

Sorex vagrans obscurus Merriam

1891. *Sorex vagrans similis* Merriam, N. Amer. Fauna, 5:34, July 30, type from near Timber Creek, 8200 ft., Salmon River Mts [now Lehmi Mts.], 10 mi. W Junction [near present town of Leadore], Lemhi Co., Idaho. (Not *S. similis* Hensel, 1855 [= *Neomys similis*], type from bone deposits at Cagliari, Sardinia.)
1895. *Sorex obscurus* Merriam, N. Amer. Fauna, 10:72, December 31, a renaming of *Sorex vagrans similis* Merriam.
1955. *Sorex vagrans obscurus*, Findley, Univ. Kansas Publ., Mus. Nat. Hist., 9:43, December 10.

MARGINAL RECORDS (Findley, 1955b:48, unless otherwise noted).—Alaska: Chandler Lake, 68°12' N, 152°45' W; Yukon River, 20 mi. above Circle; Mountains near Eagle. Mackenzie: Nahanni River Mts.; Fort Simpson; Fort Resolution, Mission Island. Alberta: Wood Buffalo Park; Athabaska River, 30 mi. above Athabaska Landing. Saskatchewan: Cypress Hills. Montana: 4 mi. S Fort Logan; Pryor Mts. Wyoming: 1 mi. W, 1 mi. S Buffalo; Springhill, 12 mi. N Laramie Peak; 5 mi. W, 1 mi. N Horse Creek P.O. Colorado: Boulder; Hunters Creek; 5 mi. S, 1 mi. W Cuchara Camps. New Mexico: 3 mi. N Red River, 10,700 ft.; Pecos Baldy; Manzano Mts.; Jemez Mts. Colorado: Navajo River; Silverton. Utah: *Abajo Mts.* (Durrant, 1955: 71); Elk Ridge (*ibid.*); La Sal Mts., 11,000 ft. Colorado: Baxter Pass. Utah: junction Trout and Ashley creeks,

9700 ft.; Mirror Lake, 10,000 ft.; Mt. Baldy R.S.; Wildcat R.S.; Pine Valley Mts.; Puffer Lake; Butterfield Canyon. Idaho: Preuss Mts.; 4 mi. S Trude; head Pahsimeroi River, Pahsimeroi Mts.; Perkins Lake; 1 mi. NE Heath; ½ mi. E *Black Lake*. Montana: Sula; 8 mi. NE Stevensville; St. Mary. Washington: head Pass Creek; Conconully; Wenatchee; Easton: Stehekin; Pasayten River. British Columbia: Second Summit, Skagit River, 5000 ft.; Babine Mts., 6 mi. N Babine Trail, 5200 ft.; Hazleton; 23 mi. N Hazleton; Flood Glacier, Stikine River; Cheonee Mts.; Level Mtn.; W side Mt. Glave, 4000 ft., 14 mi. S, 2 mi. E Kelsall Lake. Alaska: head Toklat River; Tanana; Alatna; Bettles.

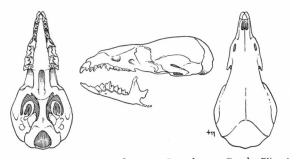

Fig. 12. *Sorex vagrans obscurus*, Stonehouse Creek, 5½ mi. W jct. Stonehouse Creek and Kelsall River, British Columbia, No. 28545 K.U., ♀, X 2.

Sorex vagrans orizabae Merriam

1895. *Sorex orizabae* Merriam, N. Amer. Fauna, 10:71, December 31, type from W slope Mt. Orizaba, 9500 ft., Puebla.
1928. *Sorex vagrans orizabae,* Jackson, N. Amer. Fauna, 51:113, July 24.

MARGINAL RECORDS (Findley, 1955b:52).—Michoacán: Patambán. Veracruz: Cofre de Perote. Puebla: type locality. Michoacán: Mt. Tancítaro.

Sorex vagrans pacificus Coues

1877. *Sorex pacificus* Coues, Bull. U.S. Geol. and Geog. Surv. Terr., 3(3):650, May 15, type from Fort Umpqua, mouth Umpqua River, Douglas Co., Oregon.

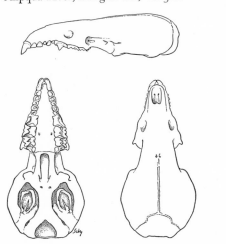

Fig. 13. *Sorex vagrans pacificus,* Russian Gulch State Park, Mendocino Co., California, No. 95645 M.V.Z., ♂, X 2.

1955. *Sorex vagrans pacificus,* Findley, Univ. Kansas Publ., Mus. Nat. Hist., 9:34, December 10.

MARGINAL RECORDS (Findley, 1955b:34).—Oregon: Marsfield; type locality. California: Gasquet; 5 mi. S Dyerville; Mendocino.

Sorex vagrans paludivagus von Bloeker

1939. *Sorex vagrans paludivagus* von Bloeker, Proc. Biol. Soc. Washington, 52:93, June 5, type from salt marsh at mouth Elkhorn Slough, Moss Landing, Monterey Co., California.

MARGINAL RECORDS (Findley, 1955b:60).—California: San Gregorio; Seaside; mouth Salinas River; type locality.

Sorex vagrans parvidens Jackson

1921. *Sorex obscurus parvidens* Jackson, Jour. Mamm., 2:161, August 19, type from spring known as Thurman's Camp, Bluff Lake, about 7500 ft., San Bernardino Mts., California.
1955. *Sorex vagrans parvidens,* Findley, Univ. Kansas Publ., Mus. Nat. Hist., 9:58, December 10.

MARGINAL RECORDS (Findley, 1955b:59).—California: Camp Baldy, San Antonio Canyon, 4200 ft.: type locality.

Sorex vagrans permiliensis Jackson

1918. *Sorex obscurus permiliensis* Jackson, Proc. Biol. Soc. Washington, 31:128, November 29, type from Permilia Lake, W base Mt. Jefferson, Cascade Range, Marion Co., Oregon.
1955. *Sorex vagrans permiliensis,* Findley, Univ. Kansas Publ., Mus. Nat. Hist., 9:36, December 10.

MARGINAL RECORDS (Findley, 1955b:36).—Oregon: Sand Creek, Mt. Hood; type locality; Detroit.

Sorex vagrans prevostensis Osgood

1901. *Sorex longicauda prevostensis* Osgood, N. Amer. Fauna, 21:35, September 26, type from N end Prevost Island [Kunghit Island on some maps], off coast of Houston Stewart Channel, Queen Charlotte Islands, British Columbia. Known only from type locality.
1955. *Sorex vagrans prevostensis,* Findley, Univ. Kansas Publ., Mus. Nat. Hist., 9:41, December 10.

Sorex vagrans setosus Elliot

1899. *Sorex setosus* Elliot, Field Columb. Mus., Publ. 32, Zool. Ser., 1:274, May 19, type from Happy Lake, Olympic Mts., Clallam Co., Washington.
1955. *Sorex vagrans setosus,* Findley, Univ. Kansas Publ., Mus. Nat. Hist., 9:36, December 10.

MARGINAL RECORDS (Findley, 1955b:37, unless otherwise noted).—British Columbia: Rivers Inlet; *Agassiz*; Chilliwack Lake. Washington: Barron; Lyman Lake; Mt. Stuart; Satus Pass (Dalquest, 1948:141). Oregon: 2 mi. W Parkdale, 1500 ft. Washington: Ilwaco. British Columbia: Lund, Malaspina Inlet.

Sorex vagrans shumaginensis Merriam

1900. *Sorex alascensis shumaginensis* Merriam, Proc. Washington Acad. Sci., 2:18, March 14, type from Popof Island, Shumagin Islands, Alaska.
1955. *Sorex vagrans shumaginensis*, Findley, Univ. Kansas Publ., Mus. Nat. Hist., 9:42, December 10.

MARGINAL RECORDS (Findley, 1955b:43, except as otherwise noted).—Alaska: Nome River; Nulato; Kuskokwim River, 200 mi. above Bethel, Crooked Creek; 6 mi. WSW Snowshoe Lake; Seldovia; mountains near Hope; Morhzovoi Bay; Goodnews Bay; Russian Mission (Jackson, 1928:126); St. Michael.

Sorex vagrans sonomae Jackson

1921. *Sorex pacificus sonomae* Jackson, Jour. Mamm., 2:162, August 19, type from Sonoma Co. side of Gualala River, Gualala, California.
1955. *Sorex vagrans sonomae*, Findley, Univ. Kansas Publ., Mus. Nat. Hist., 9:32, December 10.

MARGINAL RECORDS (Findley, 1955b:34).—California: Point Arena; Monte Rio; Inverness.

Sorex vagrans soperi Anderson and Rand

1945. *Sorex obscurus soperi* Anderson and Rand, Canadian Field-Nat., 59:47, October 16, type from 2½ mi. NW Lake Audy, Riding Mtn. National Park, Manitoba.
1955. *Sorex vagrans soperi*, Findley, Univ. Kansas Publ., Mus. Nat. Hist., 9:48, December 10.

MARGINAL RECORDS (Findley, 1955b:49).—Saskatchewan: Prince Albert National Park, 1700 ft. Manitoba: type locality.

Sorex vagrans vagrans Baird

1858. *Sorex vagrans* Baird, Mammals, *in* Repts. Expl. Surv. . . . , 8(1):15, July 14, type from Shoalwater Bay [known also as Willapa Bay], Pacific Co., Washington.
1858. *Sorex suckleyi* Baird, Mammals, *in* Repts. Expl. Surv. . . . , 8(1):18, July 14, type from Steilacoom, Pierce Co., Washington.
1891. *Sorex dobsoni* Merriam, N. Amer. Fauna, 5:33, July 30, type from Alturas or Sawtooth Lake, about 7200 ft., E base Sawtooth Mts., Blaine Co., Idaho.
1895. *Sorex amoenus* Merriam, N. Amer. Fauna, 10:69, December 31, type from near Mammoth, 8000 ft., head Owens River, E slope Sierra Nevada, Mono Co., California.
1895. *Sorex nevadensis* Merriam, N. Amer. Fauna, 10:71, December 31, type from Reese River, 6000 ft., Nye-Lander Co. line, Nevada.
1899. *Sorex shastensis* Merriam, N. Amer. Fauna, 16:87, October 28, type from Wagon Camp, Mt. Shasta, 5700 ft., Siskiyou Co., California.

MARGINAL RECORDS (Findley, 1955b:57).—British Columbia: Okanagan; Westbridge; Kuskonook; Cranbrook. Montana: Flathead Lake; 6 mi. E Hamilton; Prospect Creek. Idaho: Cedar Mtn.; New Meadows; Alturas Lake; 10 mi. SE Irwin. Wyoming: 13 mi. N, 2 mi. W Afton; 6 mi. N, 2 mi. E Sage. Idaho: 1 mi. W Bancroft; Swan Lake. Utah: Beaver Creek, South Fork, Ogden River; Midway Fish Hatchery; west side Deep Creek Mts., Queen of Sheba Canyon, 8000 ft. Nevada: Baker Creek; Reese River; 2 mi.

S Hinds Hot Springs. California: Mono Lake; near Mammoth; Alvord; Mount Conness; Donner; Buck Ranch; Warner Creek, Drake Hot Springs; Canyon Creek; Cuddeback; Novato Point, thence northward along the coast to Washington: Friday Harbor, San Juan Island. British Columbia: Port Moody.

Sorex vagrans vancouverensis Merriam

1895. *Sorex vancouverensis* Merriam, N. Amer. Fauna, 10:70, December 31, type from Goldstream, Vancouver Island, British Columbia.
1928. *Sorex vagrans vancouverensis*, Jackson, N. Amer. Fauna, 51:106, July 24.

MARGINAL RECORDS (Findley, 1955b:60).—British Columbia: Sayward; Bowen Island; Alberni.

Sorex vagrans yaquinae Jackson

1918. *Sorex yaquinae* Jackson, Proc. Biol. Soc. Washington, 31:127, November 29, type from Yaquina Bay, Lincoln Co., Oregon.
1955. *Sorex vagrans yaquinae*, Findley, Univ. Kansas Publ., Mus. Nat. Hist., 9:34, December 10.

MARGINAL RECORDS (Findley, 1955b:35).—Oregon: type locality; Philomath; McKenzie Bridge; Crescent Lake; Prospect; Gardiner.

Sorex ornatus
Ornate Shrew

External measurements: 89–108; 32–44; 12–13. Condylobasal length of skull, 15.9–17.1. Upper parts grayish brown, underparts paler; tail indistinctly bicolored. Braincase flattened on top; foramen magnum placed dorsally, encroaching more into supraoccipital and less into basioccipital; cranium relatively narrow; 3rd unicuspid smaller than 4th; unicuspids relatively narrow; metacone of M1 relatively high.

The ornate shrew inhabits coastal and inland marshes, stream sides, damp earth on hill slopes, and sometimes dry slopes beneath chaparral.

Rudd's (1955:21–34) suggestion that this species, through its subspecies *Sorex ornatus californicus*, intergrades or hybridizes with *Sorex vagrans vagrans* at Tolay Creek on the north side of San Pablo Bay, California, raises the question of whether all of the subspecies of *S. ornatus* should be arranged instead as subspecies of *S. vagrans*, which latter name is the oldest of those concerned. See also under *Sorex sinuosus* beyond.

Sorex ornatus californicus Merriam

1895. *Sorex californicus* Merriam, N. Amer. Fauna, 10:80, December 31, type from Walnut Creek, Contra Costa Co., California.
1922. *Sorex ornatus californicus*, Jackson, Jour. Washington Acad. Sci., 12:264, June 4.

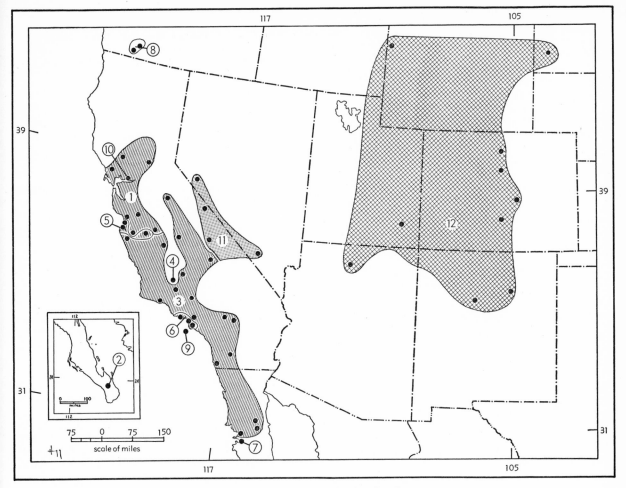

Map 17. *Sorex ornatus* and closely related species.

1. S. *ornatus californicus*	5. S. *ornatus salarius*	9. S. *willetti*
2. S. *ornatus lagunae*	6. S. *ornatus salicornicus*	10. S. *sinuosus*
3. S. *ornatus ornatus*	7. S. *juncensis*	11. S. *tenellus*
4. S. *ornatus relictus*	8. S. *trigonirostris*	12. S. *nanus*

MARGINAL RECORDS (Jackson, 1928:169, unless otherwise noted).—California: Rumsey, 500 ft.; Auburn (Grinnell, 1933:83); summit Pacheco Pass; Mendota (Grinnell, 1933:83); Stonewall Creek, 6.3 mi. NE Soledad, 1300 ft.; Gilroy; Petaluma.

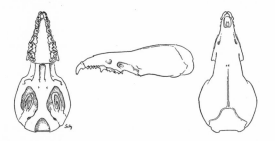

Fig. 14. *Sorex ornatus californicus*, salt marsh, 1 mi. W Avon, Contra Costa Co., California, No. 74572 M.V.Z., ♀, X 2.

Sorex ornatus lagunae Nelson and Goldman

1909. *Sorex lagunae* Nelson and Goldman, Proc. Biol. Soc. Washington, 22:27, March 10, type from La Laguna, 5500 ft., Sierra Laguna, Baja California. Known only from type locality.
1928. *Sorex ornatus lagunae*, Jackson, N. Amer. Fauna, 51:169, July 24.

Sorex ornatus ornatus Merriam

1895. *Sorex ornatus* Merriam, N. Amer. Fauna, 10:79, December 31, type from head San Emigdio Canyon, Mt. Piños, Kern Co., California.
1903. *Sorex oreinus* Elliot, Field Columb. Mus., Publ. 74, Zool. Ser., 3:172, May 7, type from Aguaje de las Fresas, 6000 ft., Sierra San Pedro Mártir, Baja California.

MARGINAL RECORDS (Jackson, 1928:167–168, unless otherwise noted).—California: El Portal, 1800 to 2500 ft.; Little Lake (von Bloeker, 1932:132); Piru Creek; Big Bear

Valley; San Bernardino Mts., 7400 to 7500 ft.; Santa Ysabel. Baja California: Aguaje de las Fresas; La Grulla, Sierra San Pedro Mártir; San Quintín. California: San Diego (Grinnell, 1933:82); Los Angeles; Santa Barbara; Paraiso Springs; Summit Lake, 12 mi. NW Lemoore; San Emigdio Creek (von Bloeker, 1932:132); Bakersfield (*ibid.*); Orosi.

Sorex ornatus relictus Grinnell

1932. *Sorex ornatus relictus* Grinnell, Univ. California Publ. Zool., 38:389, June 9, type from Buena Vista Lake, 290 ft., Kern Co., California. Known only from type locality.

Sorex ornatus salarius von Bloeker

1939. *Sorex ornatus salarius* von Bloeker, Proc. Biol. Soc. Washington, 52:94, June 5, type from salt marsh at mouth Salinas River, Monterey Co., California.

MARGINAL RECORDS (von Bloeker, 1939:95).—California: Moss Landing; Sugarloaf Peak, 3 mi. NNE Natividad; Carmel.

Sorex ornatus salicornicus von Bloeker

1932. *Sorex ornatus salicornicus* von Bloeker, Proc. Biol. Soc. Washington, 45:131, September 9, type from Playa del Rey, Los Angeles Co., California.

MARGINAL RECORDS (Grinnell, 1933:82).—California: Point Mugu; type locality; Nigger Slough.

Sorex tenellus Merriam
Inyo Shrew

1895. *Sorex tenellus* Merriam, N. Amer. Fauna, 10:81, December 31, type from along Lone Pine Creek, at upper edge of Alabama Hills at about 5000 ft. [not "summit of Alabama Hills," as stated by Merriam in original description; see also A. B. Howell, Jour. Mamm., 4:266, November 1, 1923], near Lone Pine, Owens Valley, Inyo Co., California.
1902. *Sorex tenellus myops* Merriam, Proc. Biol. Soc. Washington, 15:76, March 22, type from Pipers Creek (Cottonwood Creek), near main peak of White Mts., 9500 ft., Mono Co., California.

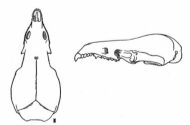

Fig. 15. *Sorex tenellus,* Rainbow Falls, 8200 ft., Kyle Canyon, Clark Co., Nevada, No. 86842 M.V.Z., ♂, X 2.

External measurements: 85–103; 36–42; 9–12.5. Condylobasal length of skull, 15.1–15.2. Upper parts drab, underparts paler; tail bicolored; skull resembling that of S. *ornatus* but smaller with relatively shorter palate and narrower braincase.

MARGINAL RECORDS.—Nevada (Hall, 1946:123): ¼ mi. N Wichman, 5500 ft.; Kyle Canyon, 8000 ft. California (Jackson, 1928:173): type locality; Pipers [= Cottonwood] Creek, 9500 ft.

Sorex trigonirostris Jackson
Ashland Shrew

1922. *Sorex trigonirostris* Jackson, Jour. Washington Acad. Sci., 12:264, June 4, type from Ashland, 1975 ft., Jackson Co., Oregon.

External measurements: 95, 34, 12. Condylobasal length of skull, 15.6. Color as in S. *ornatus;* skull with short angular rostrum; mastoidal region relatively angular and prominent from dorsal aspect; teeth as in S. *ornatus.*

MARGINAL RECORDS (V. Bailey, 1936:367).—Oregon: W slope Grizzly Mts.; type locality.

Sorex nanus Merriam
Dwarf Shrew

1895. *Sorex tenellus nanus* Merriam, N. Amer. Fauna, 10:81, December 31, type from Estes Park, Larimer Co., Colorado.
1928. *Sorex nanus,* Jackson, N. Amer. Fauna, 51:174, July 24.

External measurements: 91–105; 39–42; 10–10.5. Condylobasal length of skull, 14.1–14.5. Upper parts brownish, underparts grayish; tail indistinctly bicolored. Skull resembles that of S. *tenellus* but smaller and relatively slightly narrower.

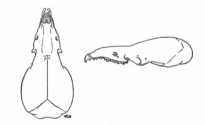

Fig. 16. *Sorex nanus,* North Fork Camp Ground, sec. 28, T. 16 N, R. 78 W, Albany Co., Wyoming, No. 184 A.B. Mickey, ♀, X 2.

MARGINAL RECORDS.—Wyoming: South Cascade Canyon, 10,050 ft., Grand Teton National Park (Durrant and Lee, 1955:560). South Dakota: 2½ mi. N Fairburn (Findley and Baker, 1957:543). Colorado: type locality; Silver Plume (von Bloeker, 1944:312); near Colorado Springs, 7000 to 8000 ft. (Warren, 1942:11); West Cliff, 8300 ft. (Jackson, 1928:175). New Mexico: 13 mi. NW Las Vegas (Koster and Clothier, 1952:250–251); near Capulin R.S., Sandia Mts. (Clothier, 1957:256). Utah: Gooseberry Ranger Station, Elk Ridge, 8560 ft. (Durrant and Lee, 1955:560). Arizona: N rim Grand Canyon, 9 mi. E Swamp Point, within Grand Canyon National Park, near boundary of Kaibab National Forest (Schellbach, 1948:295).

Sorex juncensis Nelson and Goldman
Tule Shrew

1909. *Sorex californicus juncensis* Nelson and Goldman, Proc. Biol. Soc. Washington, 22:27, March 10, type from Socorro, 15 mi. S San Quintín, Baja California. Known only from type locality.
1928. *Sorex juncensis*, Jackson, N. Amer. Fauna, 51:172, July 24.

External measurements: 101, 41, 12.5. Condylobasal length of skull, 15.6. Color as in *S. ornatus*; skull resembles that of *S. ornatus* but is relatively higher and narrower.

Sorex willeti von Bloeker
Santa Catalina Shrew

1942. *Sorex willeti* von Bloeker, Bull. Southern California Acad. Sci., 40:163, January 31, type from Avalon Canyon, Santa Catalina Island, Los Angeles Co., California. Known only from the type locality.

External measurements: 104, 43, 12. Condylobasal length of skull, 17.6. Brown above, gray below; tail bicolored; skull relatively high and narrow; rostrum relatively long and narrow; known from one specimen.

Sorex sinuosus Grinnell
Suisun Shrew

1913. *Sorex sinuosus* Grinnell, Univ. California Publ. Zool., 10:187, March 20, type from Grizzly Island, near Suisun, Solano Co., California. Known only from Grizzly Island and adjacent tidal marshes (see Rudd, Syst. Zool., 4:23, March, 1955).

External measurements: 99, 37, 12. Condylobasal length of skull, 16.4. Almost black both dorsally and ventrally; skull and teeth resemble those of *S. ornatus*. Rudd's (1955:21–34) finding of crossbreeding between *S. sinuosus* and *S. ornatus californicus* suggests that *S. sinuosus* should be arranged as a subspecies of *S. ornatus*.

Sorex veraepacis
Verapaz Shrew

External measurements: 117–128; 45–58; 14.0–16.0. Condylobasal length of skull, 18.0–19.9. Dorsum dark brown, venter but little if any paler; tail unicolored. Cranium relatively deep, broad, and angular; relatively broad interorbitally; 3rd unicuspid smaller than 4th; unicuspids with well-defined internal ridges running from apices to cingula, these ridges more or less pigmented in unworn teeth.

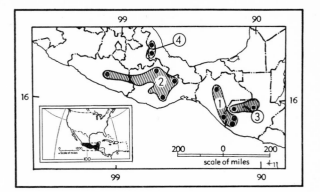

Map 18. *Sorex veraepacis* and *Sorex macrodon*.

1. *S. veraepacis chiapensis*
2. *S. veraepacis mutabilis*
3. *S. veraepacis veraepacis*
4. *S. macrodon*

Sorex veraepacis chiapensis Jackson

1925. *Sorex veraepacis chiapensis* Jackson, Proc. Biol. Soc. Washington, 38:129, November 13, type from San Cristóbal, 9500 ft., Chiapas.

MARGINAL RECORDS (Jackson, 1928:150).—Chiapas: type locality. Guatemala: Calel; Volcano Santa Maria, Quezaltenango. Chiapas: Pinabete.

Sorex veraepacis mutabilis Merriam

1895. *Sorex saussurei caudatus* Merriam, N. Amer. Fauna, 10:84, December 31, type from Reyes (near Cuicatlán), 10,200 ft., Oaxaca. Not *S. caudatus* Hodgson, 1849 (*nomen nudum*) [=*S. caudatus* Horsfield, 1851, from Sikim and Darjeeling, India].
1898. *Sorex saussurei mutabilis* Merriam, Science (n.s.), 8:782, December 2, a renaming of *S. saussurei caudatus* Merriam.
1925. *Sorex veraepacis mutabilis*, Jackson, Proc. Biol. Soc. Washington, 38:130, November 13.

MARGINAL RECORDS (Jackson, 1928:152).—Oaxaca: type locality; Tontontepec [=Totontepec]; Ozolotepec. Guerrero: Omilteme.

Sorex veraepacis veraepacis Alston

1877. *Sorex verae-pacis* Alston, Proc. Zool. Soc. London, p. 445, October, type from Cobán, Guatemala.
1877. *C[orsira]. teculyas* [*sic*] Alston, Proc. Zool. Soc. London, p. 445, October (in synonymy).

MARGINAL RECORDS (Jackson, 1928:150).—Guatemala: type locality; Todos Santos.

Sorex macrodon Merriam
Large-toothed Shrew

1895. *Sorex macrodon* Merriam, N. Amer. Fauna, 10:82, December 31, type from Orizaba, 4200 ft., Veracruz.

External measurements: 128–130; 50–52; 15.0–15.5. Condylobasal length of skull, 19.2–19.6. Upper parts clove brown or sepia, underparts little if any paler; tail essentially unicolored. Skull large and massive; rostrum relatively broad anteriorly; anterior nares broad; borders of premaxillae relatively thick; teeth relatively large; 3rd unicuspid smaller than 4th; unicuspids with well-developed internal ridges.

These shrews have been taken under logs and stones in dense oak-forest from 5500 to 6500 ft., and in the fir zone at 9500 ft. They reportedly make broad runways in the soft earth beneath shelter.

MARGINAL RECORDS (Jackson, 1928:153).—Veracruz: Xico [=Jico]; type locality.

Sorex palustris
Water Shrew

External measurements: 144–158; 63–78; 18–21. Condylobasal length of skull, 18.8–21.5. Black dorsally, white, gray, or brownish ventrally; tail markedly bicolored; hind feet relatively large and with fringe of stiff hairs. Anterior part of rostrum comparatively short, little decurved; anterior part of premaxillae approximately as deep as middle part; depth of rostrum measured at 3rd unicuspid equal to approximately half the distance between anterior border of infraorbital foramen and posterior border of I1; 3rd unicuspid smaller than 4th; protocone of M1 and M2 usually without posterior cusplike lobe.

Water shrews occur along the borders of ponds and streams in meadows, marshes, or woods. These animals reproduce in the spring of their second year, the most common number of young is 6, and several litters may be born in a breeding season.

Sorex palustris albibarbis (Cope)

1862. *Neosorex albibarbis* Cope, Proc. Acad. Nat. Sci. Philadelphia, 14:188, type from Profile Lake, Franconia Mts., Grafton Co., New Hampshire. [Green, A contribution to the mammalogy . . . of Pennsylvania, p. 11, March 31, 1930, believes that *N. albibarbis* is preoccupied by *S. fimbripes* Bachman, 1837, which we have placed as a synonym of *Sorex cinereus cinereus*.]
1903. *Sorex palustris albibarbis*, Rhoads, The mammals of Pennsylvania and New Jersey, p. 191.

MARGINAL RECORDS.—Quebec: Lake Edward (Anderson, 1939:45); St. Rose, Temiscouata Dist. (Jackson,

1928:183). Maine: Lincoln (Miller, 1895:47); Mt. Desert Island, 20 mi. NE Penobscot Bay (Manville, 1942:391); Brunswick (Jackson, 1928:183). Connecticut: South Woodstock (Goodwin, 1935:37); *Sharon Mtn.* (Starrett, Starrett, and Youngman, 1952:398). New York: Beaver Dam Brook (Gierson, 1948:77). Pennsylvania: Bushkill Creek, 7 mi. E Cresco (Hooper, 1942b:4); Mifflin County (Gifford and Whitebread, 1951:51); near Carter Camp P.O., NE slope Mt. Broadhead (Wible, 1946:89). New York: 1 mi. S Red House Lake, Allegheny State Park (Eaton, 1945:194); Tupper Lake (Hooper, 1942b:4). Ontario: North Bay (Jackson, 1928:183).

Sorex palustris brooksi Anderson

1934. *Sorex palustris brooksi* Anderson, Canadian Field-Nat., 48:134, November 1, type from Black Creek, 150 ft., Comox District, E coast Vancouver Island, British Columbia.

MARGINAL RECORDS.—British Columbia (Vancouver Island): type locality; near Victoria (Anderson, 1947:21).

Sorex palustris gloveralleni Jackson

1915. *Neosorex palustris acadicus* G. M. Allen, Proc. Biol. Soc. Washington, 28:15, February 12, type from Digby, Digby Co., Nova Scotia. Not *Sorex acadicus* Gilpin, 1867 [= *Sorex cinereus* Kerr, 1792].
1926. *Sorex palustris gloveralleni* Jackson, Jour. Mamm., 7:57, February 15, a renaming of *Neosorex palustris acadicus* G. M. Allen, 1915.

MARGINAL RECORDS.—Quebec: Point St. Charles and Seal River (Johnson, 1951:112); Mt. Albert (Jackson, 1928:184). Nova Scotia: Cape Breton Island (Anderson, 1947:21). New Brunswick: Charlotte County (Morris, 1948:167). Quebec: Godbout (Johnson, 1951:112).

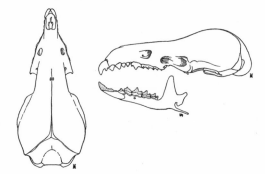

Fig. 17. *Sorex palustris navigator*, Cottonwood Creek, Mt. Grant, 7400 ft., Mineral Co., Nevada, No. 63521 M.V.Z., ♂, X 2.

Sorex palustris hydrobadistes Jackson

1926. *Sorex palustris hydrobadistes* Jackson, Jour. Mamm., 7:57, February 15, type from Withee, Clark Co., Wisconsin.

MARGINAL RECORDS.—Wisconsin: Solon Springs (Jackson, 1928:181). Ontario: *E end Lake Superior* (Anderson, 1947:21). Michigan: Otsego County (Burt, 1946:97). Wisconsin: Marinette County (Jackson, 1928:181); type locality. Minnesota: Elk River (B. Bailey, 1929:153).

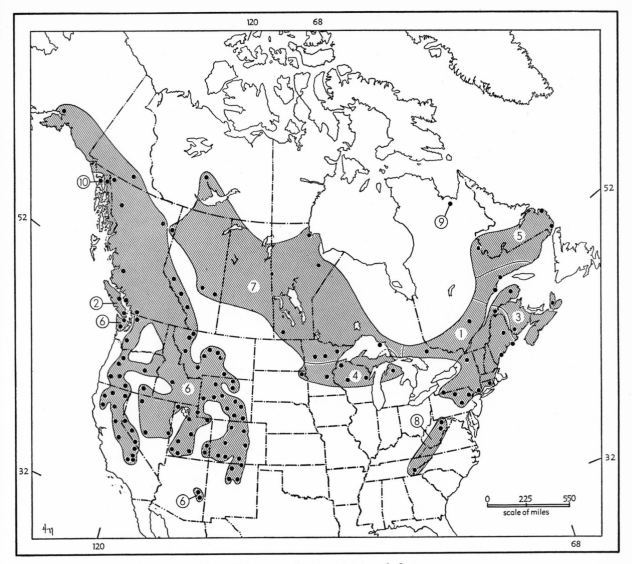

Map 19. *Sorex palustris* and *Sorex alaskanus*.

Guide to	3. *S. p. gloveralleni*	7. *S. p. palustris*
kinds	4. *S. p. hydrobadistes*	8. *S. p. punctulatus*
1. *S. p. albibarbis*	5. *S. p. labradorensis*	9. *S. p. turneri*
2. *S. p. brooksi*	6. *S. p. navigator*	10. *S. alaskanus*

South Dakota: Fort Sisseton (Anderson, 1947:21). Fort Wadsworth in South Dakota (Jackson, 1928:181) not found.

Sorex palustris labradorensis Burt

1938. *Sorex palustris labradorensis* Burt, Occas. Papers Mus. Zool., Univ. Michigan, 383:1, August 27, type from Red Bay, Strait of Belle Isle, Labrador.

MARGINAL RECORDS (Johnson, 1951:111).—Labrador: Cartwright, on coast S of Hamilton Inlet, lat. 53° 48′ N, long. 56° 59′ W; type locality. Quebec: Astray Lake, on the height of land between Ste. Margaret River and Swampy Bay River, approximately lat. 53° N, long. 67° W [F. Harper, *in litt.*, places Astray Lake on Hamilton River].

Sorex palustris navigator (Baird)

1858. *Neosorex navigator* Baird, Mammals, *in* Repts. Expl. Surv. . . . , 8(1):11, July 14, type from near head Yakima River, Cascade Mts., Washington.
1895. *Sorex (Neosorex) palustris navigator*, Merriam, N. Amer. Fauna, 10:92, December 31.

MARGINAL RECORDS (Jackson, 1928:187–189, unless otherwise noted).—Alaska: 20 mi. NE Anchorage (Baker and Findley, 1954:475). Yukon: Nisutlin River (Anderson, 1947:21). British Columbia: Halfway River, 10 mi. N Laurier Pass (Sheldon, 1932:203). Alberta: Smoky Valley, 50 mi. N Jasper House; Brazeau Valley; Banff. Montana: St. Mary's Lake; Paola; Florence; Ward Peak, 6000 ft.;

Sheep Creek, 16 mi. N White Sulphur Springs; Highwood Mts.; Moccasin Mts., 5 mi. NW Hilger; Tyler, 10 mi. W North Fork at Willow Creek; Pryor Mts. Wyoming: Wolf; Bighorn Mts., 8400 ft.; *head Trappers Creek, 8500 ft.*; Valley 7000–7500 ft.; South Pass City; 7 mi. S Casper, 6000 ft.; N slope Laramie Mts., 8000 ft.; 10 mi. E Laramie, 8500 ft. Colorado: Boulder; Lake Moraine; Culebia Canyon, 9100 ft. New Mexico: Costilla Pass, 9000 ft. (V. Bailey, 1932:374); Willis; Santa Clara Canyon; 6 mi. W Hopewell, 9900 ft. Colorado: Hermit; Rico. Utah: North Creek, 7 mi. W Monticello, Abajo Mts., 8000 ft. (Durrant, 1955:71); Warner R.S., 9700 ft., La Sal Mts. (Durrant, 1952:37). Colorado: Crested Butte; Middle Park. Wyoming: Headquarters Park, 10,200 ft., Medicine Bow Mts.; Ferris Mts., 7800–8500 ft.; Lake Fork, Wind River Mts.; 10 mi. SE Afton; Evanston. Utah (Durrant, 1952:37): Carter Creek, 9000 ft.; Mammoth R.S., Manti National Forest; Kaiparowits Plateau; Springdale 3850 ft.; Pine Valley; Beaver; City Creek Canyon; Pine Canyon, 6600 ft., Raft River Mts. Nevada (Hall, 1946:125): Baker Creek, 11,100 ft.; 1 to 2 mi. E Jefferson, 7600–8000 ft.; *Jett Canyon, Toyabe Mts.*; head Big Creek, 8000 ft., Pine Forest Mts. Oregon: Steen Mts. Idaho: Sawtooth City. Oregon: Strawberry Mts.; Anna Creek, 6000 ft., Mt. Mazama; near Drews Creek. California: Parker Creek, Warner Mts. Nevada (Hall, 1946:125): 2 mi. W Mt. Rose summit; Cottonwood Creek, 7400 ft., Mt. Grant; Arlemont, 4900 ft. California: White Mts.; Lone Pine; Whitney Meadows, Mt. Whitney; Halstead Meadows, Sequoia National Park; Merced Grove, 5400 ft.; Blue Canyon, 4700–5000 ft.; Mill Creek, 5000 ft., Mt. Lassen; South Yolla Bolly Mtn., 6000 ft.; Canyon Creek; Upper Ash Creek, Mt. Shasta. Oregon: Prospect; McKenzie Bridge; Permilia Lake, Mt. Jefferson. Washington: Mt. St. Helens, 5500 ft.; Mt. Baker; head N fork, Quinault River, 4000 ft. (Dalquest, 1948:141); Elwha. British Columbia: Chilliwack Valley (Anderson, 1947:21); Powell River (Cowan and Guiguet, 1956:54); Bella Coola region (*ibid.*); Telegraph Creek. Alaska: Haines (Anderson, 1947:21). British Columbia: Bennett. Southern segment of range: Arizona: White River, White Mts.; Prieto Plateau.

Sorex palustris palustris Richardson

1828. *Sorex palustris* Richardson, Zool. Jour., 3(12, January to April):517, April, type from "marshy places, from Hudson's Bay to the Rocky Mountains."

MARGINAL RECORDS (Jackson, 1928:179–180, unless otherwise noted).—Northwest Territories: Grandin River. Manitoba: Aimie Lake, Flin Flon area (Rand, 1948a: 141); Churchill (Smith and Foster, 1957:103); Hill River, near Swampy Lake (Preble, 1902:71). Ontario: Michipicoten Island. Minnesota: Tower; Itasca County; Itasca Park (Quimby, 1943:261). Manitoba: Aweme. Alberta: Ranfurly; Edmonton (Rand, 1948b:52). British Columbia: Tupper Creek, Peace River District (Cowan, 1939:70).

Sorex palustris punctulatus Hooper

1942. *Sorex palustris punctulatus* Hooper, Occas. Papers Mus. Zool., Univ. Michigan, 463:1, September 15, type from 6 mi. NW Durbin, Shavers Fork of Cheat River, 3600 ft., Randolph Co., West Virginia.

MARGINAL RECORDS.—West Virginia: 1 mi. SSE Cranesville, 2600 ft. (Hooper, 1942b:4); Blister Run, 4 mi. NNW Durbin, 3650 ft. (*ibid.*). Tennessee: W Prong, Little Pigeon River, Great Smoky Mts. National Park (Conaway

and Pfitzer, 1952:106; here regarded as S. *p. punctulatus* on geographical grounds). West Virginia: *type locality.*

Sorex palustris turneri Johnson

1951. *Sorex palustris turneri* Johnson, Proc. Biol. Soc. Washington, 64:110, August 24, type from Fort Chimo (on eastern bank Koksoak River, lat. 58° 8′ N, long. 68° 15′ W), Ungava District, Quebec. Known only from the type locality.

Sorex alaskanus Merriam
Glacier Bay Water Shrew

1900. *Sorex navigator alaskanus* Merriam, Proc. Washington Acad. Sci., 2:18, March 14, type from Point Gustavus, Glacier Bay, Alaska. Known only from type locality.
1926. *Sorex alaskanus,* Jackson, Jour. Mamm., 7:58, February 15.

External measurements: 145–160; 65–72; 18.5–19. Condylobasal length of skull, 18.4–19.2. Color as in S. *palustris.* Skull short, heavy, and angular; rostrum and mesopterygoid space relatively short; sagittal and lambdoidal crests much developed; a distinct inframaxillary ridge extending above base of unicuspids. S. *alaskanus* may be only a subspecies of S. *palustris.*

Sorex bendirii
Pacific Water Shrew

External measurements: 147–174; 61–80; 18.5–21. Condylobasal length of skull, 20.8–23.8. The largest North American species of *Sorex*; upper parts dark brown, underparts scarcely paler except in subspecies *albiventer* in which they are whitish; tail unicolored; hind feet weakly fimbriate; anterior part of rostrum relatively long, distinctly curved ventrally; anterior end of premaxilla decidedly shallower than middle part; depth of rostrum measured at 3rd unicuspid less than half the distance between anterior border of infraorbital foramen and posterior border of I1; anteroposterior diameter of upper unicuspids relatively more than in subgenus *Neosorex*; protocone of M1 and M2 usually with distinct posterior cusplike lobe.

These shrews are found about marshes, swamps, in moist areas near water, and in damp woods.

Sorex bendirii albiventer Merriam

1895. *Sorex (Atophyrax) bendirii albiventer* Merriam, N. Amer. Fauna, 10:97, December 31, type from Lake Cushman, Olympic Mts., Mason Co., Washington.

MARGINAL RECORDS (Jackson, 1928:199, unless otherwise noted).—Washington: Neah Bay; Canyon Creek; Duckabush; Harstine Island; Shelton; Quinault Lake (Dalquest, 1948:144); Lapush.

Sorex bendirii bendirii (Merriam)

1884. *Atophyrax bendirii* Merriam, Trans. Linnaean Soc. New York, 2:217, August 28, type from about 1 mile from Williamson River, 18 mi. SE Fort Klamath, Klamath Co., Oregon.

1890. *Sorex bendirii*, Dobson, A monograph of the Insectivora . . . , pt. 3, fasc. 1, pl. 23, fig. 17 and explanation.

MARGINAL RECORDS (Jackson, 1928:196, unless otherwise noted).—British Columbia (Anderson, 1947:22): Port Moody; Chilliwack. Washington: Easton; Signal Peak, 4000 ft. Oregon: type locality. California: Gualala; Carson Camp, Mad River, Humboldt Bay. Oregon: Prospect. Washington: Ilwaco; Oakville (Dalquest, 1948:144); Steilacoom (*ibid.*).

Sorex bendirii palmeri Merriam

1895. *Sorex (Atophyrax) bendirii palmeri* Merriam, N. Amer. Fauna, 10:97, December 31, type from Astoria, Clatsop Co., Oregon.

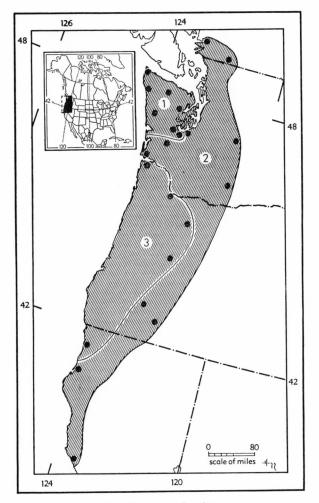

Map 20. *Sorex bendirii.*

1. *S. b. albiventer*   2. *S. b. bendirii*
3. *S. b. palmeri*

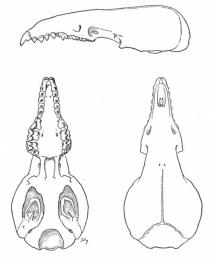

Fig. 18. *Sorex bendirii bendirii*, Russian Gulch State Park, Mendocino Co., 40 ft., California, No. 95649 M.V.Z., ♀, X 2.

MARGINAL RECORDS.—Oregon: type locality; Portland (Jackson, 1928:198); Camas Prairie, E base Cascade Mts. (*ibid.*); McKenzie Bridge (V. Bailey, 1936:358). California: Requa (Grinnell, 1933:84), thence up coast to point of beginning.

Sorex pribilofensis Merriam
Pribilof Shrew

1895. *Sorex pribilofensis* Merriam, N. Amer. Fauna, 10:87, December 31, type from St. Paul Island, Pribilof Group (in Bering Sea), Alaska. Known only from type locality. (See Fig. 22.)

External measurements: 92–103; 32–37; 13–14.5. Condylobasal length of skull, 15.4–16.0. Tricolored (brown, pale brown, gray) in summer pelage, bicolored (brown and gray) in winter; 3rd unicuspid larger than 4th; internal ridges of unicuspids well developed and heavily pigmented.

Subgenus Sorex Linnaeus

1758. *Sorex* Linnaeus, Syst. nat., ed. 10, 1:53. Type, *Sorex araneus* Linnaeus.

Post-mandibular foramen usually present and well developed; each upper unicuspid lacking a pigmented ridge from the apex to the cingulum.

Sorex fumeus
Smoky Shrew

External measurements: 111–127; 45–52; 13–15. Condylobasal length of skull, 17.8–19.0. Color grayish or blackish in winter pelage, brownish in summer pelage, underparts slightly paler than upper parts but general effect unicolor, tail usually bicolor. Unicuspids with ridge extending medially from apex approximately halfway to internal cingulum, this ridge pigmented near apex of tooth; unicuspids broader than long; 3rd unicuspid larger than 4th.

Smoky shrews inhabit moist, deciduous, or coniferous forests. Two and sometimes 3 litters of from 4 to 7 young are born between April and August. The food is mostly insects, although other arthropods, annelids, snails, vertebrates, and parts of some plants are eaten.

Sorex fumeus fumeus Miller

1895. *Sorex fumeus* Miller, N. Amer. Fauna, 10:50, December 31, type from Peterboro, Madison Co., New York.

MARGINAL RECORDS (Jackson, 1928:64–65, unless otherwise noted).—Ontario: Fraserdale (Anderson, 1947: 15). Quebec: Lake Edward (*ibid.*); St. Joachim (*ibid.*). New York: Tupper Lake. Vermont: Mt. Mansfield (Osgood, 1938:436). New Hampshire: Mossy Brook, Mt. Monadnock; Intervale; Ossipee. New Jersey: Greenwood Lake. Pennsylvania: Chester County. Virginia: Paris; Madison County (Handley and Patton, 1947:106). North Carolina: Magnetic City, Roan Mtn. South Carolina: *Jones Gap*

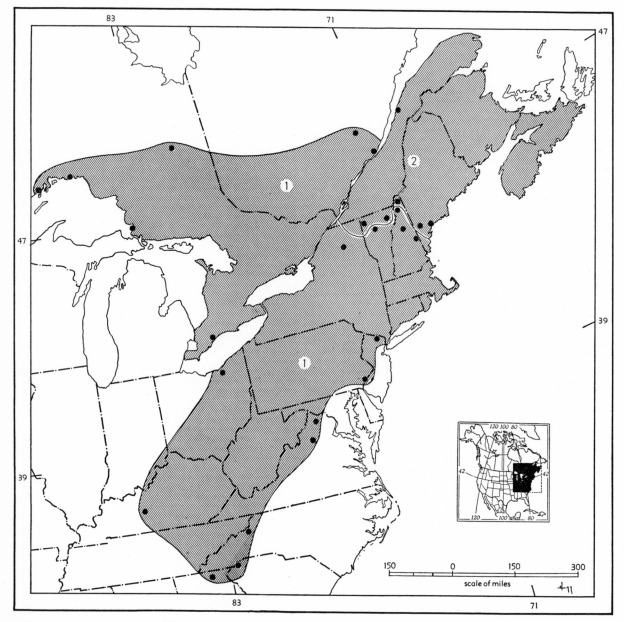

Map 21. *Sorex fumeus*: (1) S. f. *fumeus*; (2) S. f. *umbrosus*.

(Schwartz, 1955:286); Jocassee (*ibid.*). Georgia: Brasstown Bald, 4700 ft. Kentucky: Mammoth Cave (Barbour, 1951:102). Ohio: North Chagrin Metropolitan Park, Cuyahoga Co. (Bole and Moulthrop, 1942:97). Ontario: Elgin County (Anderson, 1947:15); Pancake Bay (Anderson, 1947:15); Schreiber (*ibid.*); Thunder Bay (*ibid.*). The record from Racine, Wisconsin (Jackson, 1928:65) needs verification and is not shown on the distribution map.

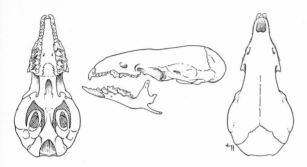

Fig. 19. *Sorex fumeus fumeus*, 1½ mi. W Camden on Gauley, Webster Co., West Virginia, No. 39056 K.U. ♂, X 2.

Sorex fumeus umbrosus Jackson

1917. *Sorex fumeus umbrosus* Jackson, Proc. Biol. Soc. Washington, 30:149, July 27, type from James River, Antigonish Co., Nova Scotia.

MARGINAL RECORDS.—Quebec: Rivière-du-Loup (Anderson, 1947:16). Maine: Brunswick (Jackson, 1928:66); "Lynchtown," Twp. 5, R. 4, Oxford Co. (Palmer, 1947:13). New Hampshire: First Connecticut Lake, 7 mi. N Pittsburg (Preble, 1937:513). Vermont: Brighton (Osgood, 1938:436); St. Albans (*ibid.*).

Sorex jacksoni Hall and Gilmore
St. Lawrence Island Shrew

1932. *Sorex jacksoni* Hall and Gilmore, Univ. California Publ. Zool., 38:392, September 17, type from Sevoonga, 2 mi. E North Cape, St. Lawrence Island, Bering Sea, Alaska. Known only from St. Lawrence Island.

External measurements: 94–107; 32–37; 12–14. Condylobasal length of skull, 15.6–16.3. Tricolored (Clove Brown, paler brown, and Smoke Gray) in summer pelage; 3rd unicuspid equal to or larger than 4th; unicuspids without pigmented internal ridge.

Sorex hydrodromus Dobson
Unalaska Shrew

1889. *Sorex hydrodromus* Dobson, Ann. Mag. Nat. Hist., ser. 6, 4:373, November, type from Unalaska Island, Aleutian Islands, Alaska. Known only from type locality.

There seems to be no specimen of this shew in American museums. According to Jackson (1928:75–76) it may prove to be identical with *Sorex arcticus tundrensis*.

Sorex arcticus
Arctic Shrew

External measurements: 101–117; 30–45; 12.5–15. Condylobasal length of skull, 17.8–19.1. Tricolored in most pelages, dorsal region darkest (grayish to brownish), distinctly set off from brownish (or tan) flanks, and still paler venter; *S. a. tundrensis* bicolored in some pelages, color of sides being scarcely differentiated from that of belly; 3rd unicuspid larger than 4th; ridges extending from apices of unicuspids medially toward cingula but incomplete, weakly pigmented, and not ending in internal cusplets.

This shrew is often taken in bogs in the southern part of its range and occurs on the tundra in the far North. Little is known of its life history. The closely related Palaearctic *S. araneus* has an average of 6.45 embryos and, in England, a breeding season of from May to September or October.

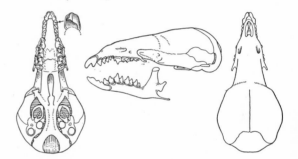

Fig. 20. *Sorex arcticus tundrensis*, 1½ mi. W and ¾ mi. N Umiat, 69° 22' 18", 152° 08' 10", 370 ft., Alaska, No. 43212 K.U., ♂, X 2.

Sorex arcticus arcticus Kerr

1792. *Sorex arcticus* Kerr, The animal kingdom . . . , p. 206. Type locality, settlement on Severn River, Hudson Bay, now known as Fort Severn, mouth of Severn River, Ontario.
1837. *Sorex richardsonii* Bachman, Jour. Acad. Nat. Sci. Philadelphia, 7:383. Type locality, probably plains of Saskatchewan.
1877. *Sorex sphagnicola* Coues, Bull. U.S. Geol. and Geog. Surv. Territories, 3:650, May 15, type from Fort Liard, Mackenzie.

MARGINAL RECORDS (Jackson, 1928:70–71, unless otherwise noted).—Northwest Territories: Fort Norman; Fort Rae; Great Slave Lake. Manitoba: Shamattawa River, tributary of Hayes River. Ontario: type locality. Quebec: Saguenay County (Anderson, 1947:16). Ontario: Macdiarmid, Lake Nipigon. Manitoba: Whitemouth River, S of Reynolds (Soper, 1946:134); Red River Settlement; S end Lake Manitoba. North Dakota: 6 mi. N Lostwood. Saskatchewan: Indian Head. Alberta: Blindmans and Red Deer rivers; Island Lake, 15 mi. W Lake St. Ann. British Columbia: Tupper Creek, Peace River District (Cowan, 1939:69). Northwest Territories: Fort Liard (Preble, 1908:246).

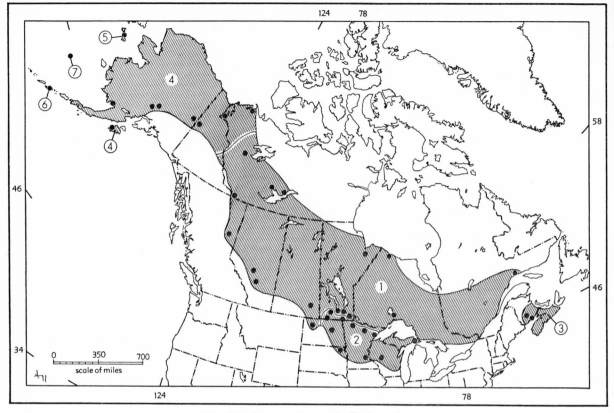

Map 22. *Sorex arcticus* and allied species.

Guide to	2. S. arcticus laricorum	5. S. jacksoni
kinds	3. S. arcticus maritimensis	6. S. hydrodromus
1. S. arcticus arcticus	4. S. arcticus tundrensis	7. S. pribilofensis

Sorex arcticus laricorum Jackson

1858. *Sorex pachyurus* Baird, Mammals, *in* Repts. Expl. Surv. . . . , 8(1):20, July 14, type from Pembina, North Dakota [not Minnesota, as stated by Baird]. Not [S.] *Pachyurus* Küster, 1835, type from Cagliari, Sardinia, *qui Pachyurus etrusca* Savi, 1822, type from Pisa, Italy.
1925. *Sorex arcticus laricorum* Jackson, Proc. Biol. Soc. Washington, 38:127, November 13, type from Elk River, Sherburne Co., Minnesota.

MARGINAL RECORDS (Jackson, 1928:72, unless otherwise noted).—Manitoba: Carberry (Anderson, 1947:16); Emerson (*ibid.*). Minnesota: Lake of the Woods County (Aldous and Manweiler, 1942:250); Winnibigoshish; St. Louis County (Aldous and Manweiler, 1942:250). Michigan: Chippewa County. Wisconsin: Withee. Minnesota: Fort Snelling. South Dakota: Fort Sisseton. North Dakota: Fort Totten. Manitoba: Max Lake, Turtle Mts. (Soper, 1946:134); *Aweme* (Anderson, 1947:16).

Sorex arcticus maritimensis R. W. Smith

1939. *Sorex arcticus maritimensis* R. W. Smith, Jour. Mamm., 20:244, May 15, type from Wolfville, Kings Co., Nova Scotia.

MARGINAL RECORDS.—Nova Scotia and west in New Brunswick to Maugerville and Hampton (Morris, 1948:167).

Sorex arcticus tundrensis Merriam

1900. *Sorex tundrensis* Merriam, Proc. Washington Acad. Sci., 2:16, March 14, type from St. Michael, Alaska.
1956. *Sorex arcticus tundrensis*, Bee and Hall, Univ. Kansas Mus. Nat. Hist., Miscl. Publ., 8:22, March 10.

MARGINAL RECORDS (Jackson, 1928:74, unless otherwise noted).—Mackenzie: Anderson River, near Liverpool Bay (Anderson, 1947:16); Peel River, Mackenzie Delta (*ibid.*). Yukon: Fortymile (*ibid.*). Alaska: near Eagle (Hall, 1929:420); Savage River; Mt. McKinley; Kodiak Island (Orr, 1939:251); Nushagak, thence along coast north and east to point of beginning.

Sorex gaspensis Anthony and Goodwin
Gaspé Shrew

1924. *Sorex gaspensis* Anthony and Goodwin, Amer. Mus. Novit., 109:1, March 10, type from Mt. Albert, 2000 ft., Gaspé Peninsula, Quebec.

External measurements: 95–115; 47–55; 12.0–12.5. Condylobasal length of skull, 15.8–16.3. Mouse-gray or neutral gray, underparts slightly paler; tail bicolor; skull similar to but smaller than that of *S. dispar*.

Most individuals of this species have been cap-tured in the vicinity of streams in coniferous forests. Goodwin (1929:242) suggests that the habits of the Gaspé Shrew are similar to those of *Sorex palustris*.

MARGINAL RECORDS.—Quebec: type locality; Cascapedia Valley at Red Camp, 8 mi. inland (Goodwin, 1929: 242); Big Berry Mtn., 35 mi. inland (*ibid.*).

Sorex dispar
Long-tailed Shrew

External measurements: 103–139; 48–66; 13–16. Condylobasal length of skull, 17.3–18.5. Mouse-gray dorsally, nearly the same ventrally; tail ordinar-ily unicolored; orbital region of skull relatively elongate and depressed; unicuspids relatively nar-row, 1st and 2nd subequal, 3rd and 4th smaller than 1st and 2nd, 3rd equal to or slightly smaller than 4th, 5th relatively large but smaller than 3rd.

Shrews of this species live under and around rock-piles and down-logs in damp forests.

Sorex dispar blitchi Schwartz

1956. *Sorex dispar blitchi* Schwartz, Jour. Elisha Mitchell Sci. Soc., 72(1):26, May 24, type from 2 mi. NE Wagon Road Gap, 4525 ft., Haywood Co., North Carolina.

MARGINAL RECORDS (Schwartz, 1956:29).—Tennes-see: Walker Prong, Great Smoky National Park, 4400–4500 ft.; *bet. Highway 71 and West Prong, Little Pigeon River, 3400 ft.* North Carolina: type locality; *talus above High-way 107, 4400 ft.*; Clingmans Dome, 6400–6642 ft.

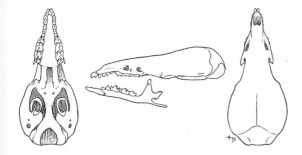

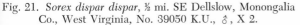

Fig. 21. *Sorex dispar dispar*, ½ mi. SE Dellslow, Monongalia Co., West Virginia, No. 39050 K.U., ♂, X 2.

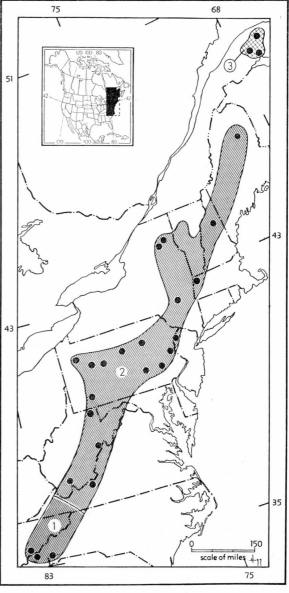

Map 23. Two species of *Sorex*.

Guide to kinds   2. *S. dispar dispar*
1. *S. dispar blitchi*   3. *S. gaspensis*

Sorex dispar dispar Batchelder

1896. *Sorex macrurus* Batchelder, Proc. Biol. Soc. Washing-ton, 10:133, December 8, type from Beedes (some-times called Keene Heights), Essex Co., New York. Not *S. macrourus* Lehmann, 1822.
1911. *Sorex dispar* Batchelder, Proc. Biol. Soc. Washington, 24:97, May 15, a renaming of *S. macrurus* Batchelder.

MARGINAL RECORDS (Jackson, 1928:91, unless other-wise noted).—Maine: SW edge Lower South Branch Pond (Starrett, 1954:583). New Hampshire: Tuckerman's Ravine, Mt. Washington (Preble, 1937:95). Massachusetts: Mt. Graylock. New Jersey: Stillwater Twp., Sussex Co. (J. A.

Davis, 1956:110). Pennsylvania: Northampton County (Roberts and Early, 1952:45); Berks County (Hamilton, 1943:38); Perry County (Gifford and Whitebread, 1951:50). West Virginia: Spruce (Wilson, 1945:96). Virginia: 4²⁄₁₀ mi. NNE Mt. Lake (Schwartz, 1956:29). West Virginia: Winding Gulf, 4 mi. SW Pemberton, 2000 ft. (Kellogg, 1937:446); ½ mi. SE Dellslow (39050 KU). Pennsylvania: 2 mi. SSE Rector (Grimm and Roberts, 1950:43); Jefferson County (Richmond and Roslund, 1949:39); Venango County (ibid.); Clearfield County (Roslund, 1951:39); Lycoming County (ibid.); Lake Leigh. New York: Hunter Mtn.; Mt. Marcy; type locality.

Sorex trowbridgii
Trowbridge's Shrew

External measurements: 110–132; 48–62; 12–15. Condylobasal length of skull, 16.4–18.8. Color dark gray or blackish, sometimes with brownish hue, above and below; tail sharply bicolor; 3rd unicuspid smaller than 4th; internal ridge of unicuspids weakly pigmented, never pigmented to cingulum, not ending in internal cusplet, separated from cingulum by anteroposterior groove.

Dry coniferous forests are the preferred habitat of this species in the north, although it occurs in moist forests when no other shrews are present. In the southern part of the range of this species it occurs in chaparral, moist forested canyons, and thick vegetation near water. Four embryos have been recorded in April. Food consists of insects and their larvae. Seeds of conifers also are eaten, at certain times and places.

Sorex trowbridgii destructioni Scheffer and Dalquest

1942. *Sorex trowbridgii destructioni* Scheffer and Dalquest, Jour. Mamm., 23:334, August 13, type from Destruction Island, Jefferson Co., Washington. Known only from Destruction Island.

Sorex trowbridgii humboldtensis Jackson

1922. *Sorex trowbridgii humboldtensis* Jackson, Jour. Washington Acad. Sci., 12:264, June 4, type from Carsons Camp, Mad River, Humboldt Bay, Humboldt Co., California.

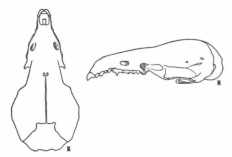

Fig. 22. *Sorex trowbridgii mariposae*, ½ mi. NE Dutch Flat, Placer Co., California, No. 88148 M.V.Z., ♀, X 2.

MARGINAL RECORDS.—California: Orick (Grinnell, 1933:79); Hoopa Valley (*ibid.*); type locality; Dyerville (Jackson, 1928:97); Briceland (*ibid.*); Sherwood (Hall and Kelson, 1952:327); Mendocino (*ibid.*), thence up coast to point of beginning.

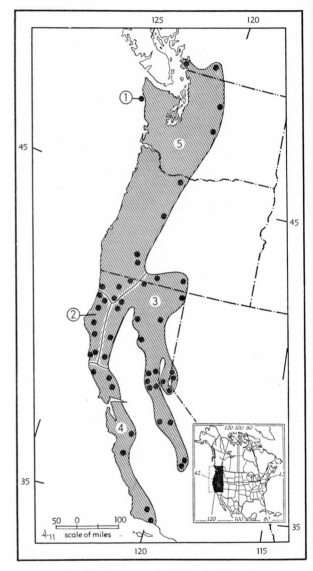

Map 24. *Sorex trowbridgii* and subspecies.

Guide to subspecies
1. *S. t. destructioni*
2. *S. t. humboldtensis*
3. *S. t. mariposae*
4. *S. t. montereyensis*
5. *S. t. trowbridgii*

Sorex trowbridgii mariposae Grinnell

1913. *Sorex montereyensis mariposae* Grinnell, Univ. California Publ. Zool., 10:189, March 20, type from Yosemite Valley, 4000 ft., Mariposa Co., California.
1923. *Sorex trowbridgii mariposae* Grinnell, Univ. California Publ. Zool., 21:314, January 27.

MARGINAL RECORDS (Jackson, 1928:99–100, unless otherwise noted).—Oregon: Lakeview. California: Parker Creek, Warner Mts. (Grinnell, 1933:80); Hayden Hill. Nevada (Hall, 1946:118): Verdi; 3 mi. S Mt. Rose, 8500 ft. California: Myers; Mt. Tallac; Cisco, 6000 ft.; Fyffe, 3600 ft.; type locality; Giant Forest, Sequoia National Park; Kaweah River, east fork; Sweetwater Creek, 3800 ft., 2 mi. E Feliciana Mtn.; Placerville; middle fork American River; Dutch Flat, 3400 ft.; S base Mt. Lassen, Mill Creek, 5000 ft.; Carberry's Ranch; South Yolla Bolly Mtn.; 8 mi. E Hearst; Canyon Creek, 4600 ft.; Jackson Lake; Beswick. Oregon: Swan Lake Valley.

Sorex trowbridgii montereyensis Merriam

1895. *Sorex montereyensis* Merriam, N. Amer. Fauna, 10:79, December 31, type from Monterey, Monterey Co., California.
1922. *Sorex t[rowbridgii]. montereyensis*, Jackson, Jour. Washington Acad. Sci., 12:264, June 4.

MARGINAL RECORDS (Jackson, 1928:98, unless otherwise noted).—California: Gualala; Mt. St. Helena; Mt. Veeder; summit Pacheco Peak; Tassajara Creek, 6 mi. below Tassajara Springs; Peachtree River, San Rafael Mts. (von Bloeker, 1944:311); Santa Barbara Botanic Gardens, Mission Canyon (*ibid.*), thence up coast to point of beginning.

Sorex trowbridgii trowbridgii Baird

1858. *Sorex trowbridgii* Baird, Mammals, *in* Repts. Expl. Surv. . . . , 8(1):13, July 14, type from Astoria, mouth Columbia River, Clatsop Co., Oregon.

MARGINAL RECORDS.—British Columbia: Hope (Anderson, 1947:17). Washington (Jackson, 1928:96); Stehekin; 2 mi. S Blewett Pass. Oregon (Jackson, 1928:95): 2 mi. W Parkdale; Three Sisters; Drew; Prospect. California: Stud Horse Canyon, Siskiyou Mts. (Grinnell, 1933:79); Happy Camp, Klamath River (*ibid.*); Forest Glen, Trinity Mts. (von Bloeker, 1944:311); mouth Klamath River (Anderson, 1947:17), thence northward along coast to Fraser River Delta in British Columbia (*ibid.*).

Sorex merriami
Merriam's Shrew

External measurements: 88–107; 33–41; 11–13. Condylobasal length of skull, 15.8–16.9. Grayish above; feet and underparts whitish; 3rd unicuspid larger than 4th; unicuspid row crowded; unicuspids higher (dorsoventrally) than long (anteroposteriorly), lacking heavily-pigmented internal ridge.

Most specimens of this rare shrew have come from open arid places.

Sorex merriami leucogenys Osgood

1909. *Sorex leucogenys* Osgood, Proc. Biol. Soc. Washington, 22:52, April 17, type from mouth of the canyon of Beaver River, about 3 mi. E Beaver, Beaver Co., Utah.
1939. *Sorex merriami leucogenys*, Benson and Bond, Jour. Mamm., 20:348, August 14.

MARGINAL RECORDS.—Colorado: Owl Canyon (Hoffmeister, 1956c:276). New Mexico: Tree Springs (Findley, 1956c:277). Arizona: Rose Peak (Hall, 1932:261); Saw-

mill Springs, 8 mi. SE Mormon Lake (Hall, 1933:153). Utah: War God Spring (Durrant, 1952:31); type locality. Nevada: ½ mi. SE Indian Spring, 7700 ft., Mt. Magruder (Hall, 1946:117). California: Cottonwood Creek, 9500 ft. (Hoffmann, 1955:561). Nevada: Chiatovich Creek, 8200 ft. (Hall, 1946:117). Colorado: 0.4 mi. S of U.S. 40, beside the road to Juniper Hot Springs (Starrett and Starrett, 1956:276).

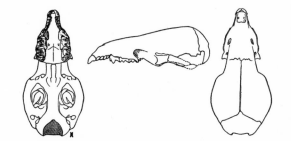

Fig. 23. *Sorex merriami leucogenys*, Chiatovich Creek, 8200 ft., Esmeralda Co., Nevada, No. 38398 M.V.Z., ♀, X 2.

Sorex merriami merriami Dobson

1890. *Sorex merriami* Dobson, A monograph of the Insectivora . . . , pt. 3 (fasc. 1; pl. 23, fig. 6), May, type from Little Bighorn River, about 1 mi. above Fort Custer, Bighorn Co., Montana.

MARGINAL RECORDS (Jackson, 1928:81, unless otherwise noted).—Montana: Eagle Creek, Madison Ranch, 6 mi. NNW Warrick, Bearpaw Mts. (Hooper, 1944:92). North Dakota: Medora. Wyoming: 3.6 mi. SW Laramie (Mickey and Steele, 1947:293). Nevada: Desert Ranch, 100 mi. NE Golconda (Hall, 1946:117). California: Indian Well Cave, Lava Beds National Monument (Benson and Bond, 1939:348). Oregon: 7 mi. SE Antelope. Washington: 17 mi. E Ellensburg (James, 1953:121); near the East Wall, Grand

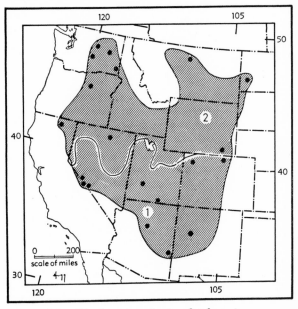

Map 25. *Sorex merriami* and subspecies.

1. *S. m. leucogenys*   2. *S. m. merriami*

Coulee, 16 mi. N Coulee City (Johnson, *et al.*, 1951:39); 5 mi. SE Creston (Hudson and Bacon, 1956:437); Cloverland Grade, about 3½ mi. SW Asotin (*ibid.*).

Sorex saussurei
Saussure's Shrew

External measurements: 104–128; 41–60; 13.5–15.0. Condylobasal length of skull, 17.4–18.5. Upper parts fuscous to clove brown, underparts paler or much the same depending upon subspecies; tail indistinctly bicolored. Skull flattened; braincase rounded laterally; mesopterygoid space relatively narrow; 3rd unicuspid usually equal to 4th in size, sometimes slightly larger or smaller; unicuspids with poorly defined unpigmented internal ridge running from apex of tooth to cingulum; cingula narrow, sloping, and indistinct.

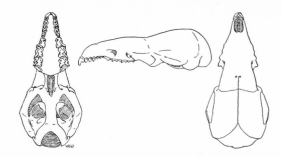

Fig. 24. *Sorex saussurei veraecrucis*, 6 km. SSE Altotonga, 9000 ft., Veracruz, No. 19093 K.U., ♀, X 2.

Sorex saussurei cristobalensis Jackson

1925. *Sorex saussurei cristobalensis* Jackson, Proc. Biol. Soc. Washington, 38:129, November 13, type from San Cristóbal, 8400 ft., Chiapas. Known only from type locality.

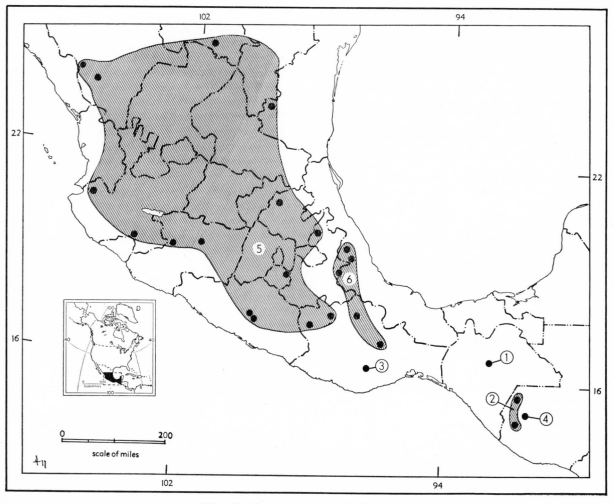

Map 26. *Sorex saussurei* and subspecies.

1. *S. s. cristobalensis*   3. *S. s. oaxacae*   5. *S. s. saussurei*
2. *S. s. godmani*   4. *S. s. salvini*   6. *S. s. veraecrucis*

Sorex saussurei godmani Merriam

1897. *Sorex godmani* Merriam, Proc. Biol. Soc. Washington, 11:229, July 15, type from Volcán Santa María, 9000 ft., Quezaltenango, Guatemala.
1928. *Sorex saussurei godmani,* Jackson, N. Amer. Fauna, 51:158, July 24.

MARGINAL RECORDS (Jackson, 1928:159).—Guatemala: Todos Santos; type locality.

Sorex saussurei oaxacae Jackson

1925. *Sorex saussurei oaxacae* Jackson, Proc. Biol. Soc. Washington, 38:128, November 13, type from mountains near Ozolotepec, 10,000 ft., Oaxaca. Known only from type locality.

Sorex saussurei salvini Merriam

1897. *Sorex salvini* Merriam, Proc. Biol. Soc. Washington, 11:229, July 15, type from Calel, 10,200 ft., Quezaltenango, Guatemala. Known only from type locality.
1928. *Sorex saussurei salvini,* Jackson, N. Amer. Fauna, 51:159, July 24.

Sorex saussurei saussurei Merriam

1892. *Sorex saussurei* Merriam, Proc. Biol. Soc. Washington, 7:173, September 29, type from N slope Sierra Nevada de Colima, approximately 8000 ft., Jalisco.
1925. *Sorex durangae* Jackson, Proc. Biol. Soc. Washington, 38:127, November 13, type from El Salto, Durango (regarded as indistinguishable from *Sorex saussurei saussurei* by Findley, Univ. Kansas Publ., Mus. Nat. Hist., 7:617, June 10, 1955).

MARGINAL RECORDS (Jackson, 1928:156, unless otherwise noted).—Coahuila: Sierra Guadalupe. Tamaulipas: Miquihuana. Hidalgo: Encarnación. Puebla: Huauchinango. México: Mt. Popocatépetl. Oaxaca: Tamazulapan; Tlapancingo. Guerrero: Chilpancingo; Omilteme. Michoacán: Pátzcuaro; Mt. Tancítaro. Jalisco: type locality; San Sebastian. Durango: El Salto (Findley, 1955:617); 1½ mi. W San Luis (Hooper, 1955:7).

Sorex saussurei veraecrucis Jackson

1925. *Sorex saussurei veraecrucis* Jackson, Proc. Biol. Soc. Washington, 38:128, November 13, type from Xico [= Jico], 6000 ft., Veracruz.

MARGINAL RECORDS (Jackson, 1928:157).—Veracruz: *6 km. SSE Altotonga, 9000 ft.* (19093 KU); Las Vegas; type locality. Oaxaca: Mt. Zempoaltepec; [Pápalo Santos] Reyes, near Cuicatlán. Puebla: Mt. Orizaba.

Sorex oreopolus
Mexican Long-tailed Shrew

External measurements: 88–112; 36–46; 12.5–14. Condylobasal length of skull, 16.4–17.8. Upper parts clove brown, sepia, or between sepia and bister; underparts paler, grayish in some; tail bicolored. Skull relatively deep; molars relatively small; 3rd unicuspid smaller than 4th except in S. o.

emarginatus where reverse is true. Resembling *Sorex saussurei* but smaller.

Sorex oreopolus emarginatus Jackson

1925. *Sorex emarginatus* Jackson, Proc. Biol. Soc. Washington, 38:129, November 13, type from Sierra Madre, near Bolaños, 7600 ft., Jalisco.
1955. *Sorex oreopolus emarginatus,* Findley, Univ. Kansas Publ., Mus. Nat. Hist., 7:616, June 10.

MARGINAL RECORDS.—Durango: 7 mi. SW Las Adjuntas, 8900 ft. (Findley, 1955:616). Zacatecas: Plateado, 7600 to 8500 ft. (Jackson, 1928:160). Jalisco: type locality.

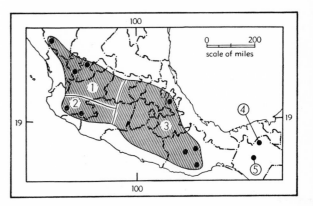

Map 27. *Sorex oreopolus* and allied species.

Guide to kinds	
1. S. o. emarginatus	3. S. o. ventralis
2. S. o. oreopolus	4. S. sclateri
	5. S. stizodon

Sorex oreopolus oreopolus Merriam

1892. *Sorex oreopolus* Merriam, Proc. Biol. Soc. Washington, 7:173, September 29, type from N slope Sierra Nevada de Colima, approximately 10,000 ft., Jalisco.

MARGINAL RECORDS.—Jalisco: 8200 ft., SE of Autlán (Hooper, 1955:7); type locality; *Volcano de Nieve* (Jackson, 1928:162).

Sorex oreopolus ventralis Merriam

1895. *Sorex obscurus ventralis* Merriam, N. Amer. Fauna, 10:75, December 31, type from Cerro San Felipe, 10,000 ft., Oaxaca.
1955. *Sorex oreopolus ventralis* Findley, Univ. Kansas Publ., Mus. Nat. Hist., 7:617, June 10.

MARGINAL RECORDS (Jackson, 1928:162).—Puebla: Huauchinango. Oaxaca: near Cajonos; mountains near Ozolotepec; 15 mi. W Oaxaca.

Sorex sclateri Merriam
Sclater's Shrew

1897. *Sorex sclateri* Merriam, Proc. Biol. Soc. Washington, 11:228, July 15, type from Tumbalá, 5000 ft., Chiapas. Known only from the type locality.

External measurements: 125–126; 52; 16. Condylobasal length of skull, 19.6–19.9. Winter pelage everywhere brown or blackish brown; summer pelage unknown; skull relatively narrow; interorbital region elongate; 3rd unicuspid equal to or larger than 4th; unicuspids without internal pigmented ridges or cusplets.

Sorex stizodon Merriam
San Cristóbal Shrew

1895. *Sorex stizodon* Merriam, N. Amer. Fauna, 10:98, December 31, type from San Cristóbal, 9000 ft., Chiapas. Known only from the type locality.

External measurements: 107; 41; 13.5. Condylobasal length of skull, 17.5. Upper parts bister or a little darker, underparts slightly paler. Skull broad and flattened; rostrum relatively short and wide; teeth with little pigment; 3rd unicuspid approximately equal to 4th in size; width of M1 more than anteroposterior length.

Genus **Microsorex** Coues—Pygmy Shrew

Revised by Jackson, N. Amer. Fauna, 51:200–210, July 24, 1928.

1877. *Microsorex* Coues, Bull. U.S. Geol. and Geog. Surv. Territories, 3:646, May 15. Type, *Sorex hoyi* Baird.

External measurements: 78–98; 27–35; 8.5–12. Condylobasal length of skull, 13.0–15.8. Brownish above, paler below, tail indistinctly bicolored. Skull resembles that of *Sorex* but relatively narrower and more flattened; rostrum relatively short and broad; infraorbital foramen relatively small; mandible short and heavy; 1st and 2nd unicuspids with distinct internal ridge terminating in pronounced internal cusp; apices of unicuspids curved posteriorly; 3rd unicuspid disklike, much compressed anteroposteriorly; 4th unicuspid normal; 5th unicuspid minute; molariform teeth resembling those of *Sorex*; bases of lower incisor and premolar separated by space equal to approximately ¼ anteroposterior diameter of canine.

Microsorex hoyi
Pygmy Shrew

See characters of the genus.
These tiny shrews have boreal predilections; little is known of their habits.

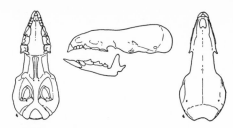

Fig. 25. *Microsorex hoyi washingtoni*, Thompson River, 7 mi. E Thompson Falls, 2250 ft., Sanders Co., Montana, No. 80762 M.V.Z., ♀, X 2.

Microsorex hoyi alnorum (Preble)

1902. *Sorex* (*Microsorex*) *alnorum* Preble, N. Amer. Fauna, 22:72, October 31, type from Robinson Portage, about 35 mi. SW Oxford Lake, Manitoba.
1925. *Microsorex hoyi alnorum*, Jackson, Proc. Biol. Soc. Washington, 38:126, November 13.

MARGINAL RECORDS.—Manitoba: type locality. Ontario: Favourable Lake (Anderson, 1947:22).

Microsorex hoyi eximius (Osgood)

1901. *Sorex* (*Microsorex*) *eximius* Osgood, N. Amer. Fauna, 21:71, September 26, type from Tyonek, Cook Inlet, Alaska.
1925. *Microsorex hoyi eximius*, Jackson, Proc. Biol. Soc. Washington, 38:125, November 13.

MARGINAL RECORDS (Jackson, 1928:209).—Alaska: Tanana; Bear Creek, Mt. McKinley; Moose Camp, Kenai Peninsula; 80 mi. up Kakwok River; Nulato.

Microsorex hoyi hoyi (Baird)

1858. *Sorex hoyi* Baird, Mammals, *in* Repts. Expl. Surv. . . . , 8(1):32, July 14, type from Racine, Wisconsin.
1901. [*Microsorex*] *hoyi*, Elliot, Field Columb. Mus., Publ. 45, Zool. Ser., 2:377, March 6.

MARGINAL RECORDS (Jackson, 1928:204, unless otherwise noted).—Alberta: forks of Blindman and Red Deer rivers (Rand, 1948b:54). Manitoba: Aweme (Soper, 1946:135); Red River Settlement. Minnesota: Itasca Park (Quimby, 1943:261); Elk River (B. Bailey, 1929:154). Ontario: Coldstream. Wisconsin: type locality. Iowa: Clear Lake (Scott, 1937:54); Mud Lake (Scott, 1939:251). South Dakota: ½ mi. E, ¼ mi. N Vermillion (Findley, 1956b:22; overlooked when Map 28 was being prepared); Ft. Sisseton. North Dakota: Devils Lake. British Columbia: Cariboo (referred without comment to *M. h. intervectus* by Cowan and Guiguet, 1956:59).

Microsorex hoyi intervectus Jackson

1925. *Microsorex hoyi intervectus* Jackson, Proc. Biol. Soc. Washington, 38:125, November 13, type from Lakewood, Oconto Co., Wisconsin.

MARGINAL RECORDS (Anderson, 1947:22–23, unless otherwise noted).—Mackenzie: Fort Franklin, Great Bear Lake; Fort Rae; Big Island, Great Slave Lake (Jackson, 1928:208). Alberta: Athabaska Lake. Manitoba: Echimamish River (Jackson, 1928:207). Ontario (Anderson,

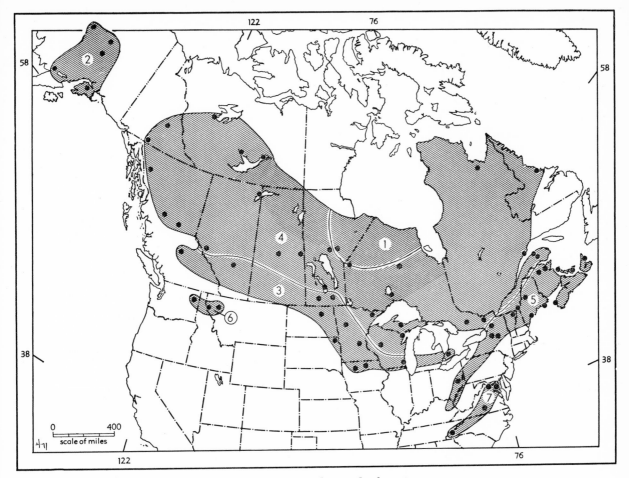

Map 28. *Microsorex hoyi* and subspecies.

Guide to	2. *M. h. eximius*	5. *M. h. thompsoni*
subspecies	3. *M. h. hoyi*	6. *M. h. washingtoni*
1. *M. h. alnorum*	4. *M. h. intervectus*	7. *M. h. winnemana*

1947:22): Favourable Lake; Attawapiscat Lake. Quebec: Chimo. Labrador: Hopedale. Quebec: Godbout; Ste. Anne des Monts (Jackson, 1928:208); Grand Cascapedia (*ibid.*). Ontario: near Leitrim (Rand, 1945c:114); Algonquin Park (Jackson, 1928:208); Macdiarmid, Lake Nipigon (*ibid.*). Michigan: Marquette County (Burt, 1946:98); Menominee County (*ibid.*). Wisconsin: Hewett (Schmidt, 1931:107). Minnesota: Ely (Cahn, 1937:21). Manitoba: Lake Manitoba (Soper, 1946:135). Saskatchewan: Cumberland District; Prince Albert National Park. Alberta: Entrance (Rand, 1948b:54). British Columbia: Fort St. James (Jackson, 1928:207); Hazelton (*ibid.*); Telegraph Creek. Yukon: Haines Road; Sheldon Lake.

Microsorex hoyi thompsoni (Baird)

1858. *Sorex thompsoni* Baird, Mammals, *in* Repts. Expl. Surv. . . . , 8(1):34, July 14, type from Burlington, Chittenden Co., Vermont.
1925. *Microsorex hoyi thompsoni*, Jackson, Proc. Biol. Soc. Washington, 38:126, November 13.

MARGINAL RECORDS (Jackson, 1928:205, unless otherwise noted).—New Brunswick: Trousers Lake; Bathurst, 15 mi. from Miramichi Road. Prince Edward Island: Alberton; Georgetown. Nova Scotia: Ingonish Centre, Cape Breton Island (Smith, 1940:223); Little River, Digby Neck (*ibid.*). Maine: Eagle Lake, Mt. Desert Island (Manville, 1942:393); Brunswick. New York: Northwood. Ohio: Zanesville. New York: Locust Grove; Canton. Vermont: Brighton (F. L. Osgood, 1938:436). New Hampshire: First Connecticut Lake (Preble, 1938:371). Maine: Brassua Lake.

Microsorex hoyi washingtoni Jackson

1925. *Microsorex hoyi washingtoni* Jackson, Proc. Biol. Soc. Washington, 38:125, November 13, type from Loon Lake, Stevens Co., Washington.

MARGINAL RECORDS.—Washington: type locality. Montana: S fork Flathead River, 20 mi. S Hungry Horse Dam (Setzer, 1952:398); 7 mi. E Thompson Falls, Sanders Co. (Koford, 1938:372).

Microsorex hoyi winnemana Preble

1910. *Microsorex winnemana* Preble, Proc. Biol. Soc. Washington, 23:101, June 24, type from bank of Potomac River near Stubblefield Falls, 4 mi. below Great Falls of Potomac River, Fairfax Co., Virginia.
1925. *Microsorex hoyi winnemana,* Jackson, Proc. Biol. Soc. Washington, 38:126, November 13.

MARGINAL RECORDS.—Virginia: type locality. Maryland: Berwyn (Jackson, 1928:206). Virginia: Altavista (Handley and Patton, 1947:109). North Carolina: Pisgah National Forest (Hamilton, 1943:50).

Genus **Blarina** Gray—Short-tailed Shrews

Revised by Merriam, N. Amer. Fauna, 10:9–16, December 31, 1895. See also Bole and Moulthrop, Sci. Publ. Cleveland Mus. Nat. Hist., 5(6):99–113, September 11, 1942.

1838. *Blarina* Gray, Proc. Zool. Soc. London for 1837, p. 124, June 14. Type, *Sorex talpoides* Gapper.

External measurements: 95–134; 17–30; 11.5–17. Condylobasal length of skull, 20.2–24.7. External ear not apparent; eyes minute; tail always less than half length of head and body; color grayish-black, sometimes with silvery or brownish cast; 1st and 2nd upper unicuspids large, 3rd and 4th smaller and subequal; 5th minute. Dentition, i. $\frac{4}{2}$, c. $\frac{1}{1}$, p. $\frac{2}{1}$, m. $\frac{3}{3}$.

KEY TO SPECIES OF BLARINA

1. Occurring in Dismal Swamp, Virginia
   B. telmalestes, p. 55
1′. Not occurring in Dismal Swamp, Virginia
   B. brevicauda, p. 52

Blarina brevicauda
Short-tailed Shrew

x ³⁄₄

For diagnosis see account of the genus.

The short-tailed shrew is commonest in eastern United States and southeastern Canada where it is found in deciduous or coniferous forests and in open fields. In the Great Plains it is limited to westward extensions of the deciduous forests along watercourses or to lush, grassy areas near water.

The short-tailed shrew begins to reproduce in the spring of its 2nd year. Two litters, each of 3 to 7 young, may be produced. The animals usually do

not survive their 2nd year. Food consists of many kinds of invertebrates, some small vertebrates, and some plant material.

Blarina brevicauda aloga Bangs

1902. *Blarina brevicauda aloga* Bangs, Proc. New England Zool. Club, 3:76, March 31, type from West Tisbury, Marthas Vineyard Island, Dukes Co., Massachusetts. Known only from Marthas Vineyard Island.

Blarina brevicauda angusta Anderson

1943. *Blarina brevicauda angusta* Anderson, Ann. Rep. Provancher Soc. Nat. Hist., Quebec, p. 52, September 7, type from Kelly's Camp, Berry Mountain Brook, near head Grand Cascapedia River, Gaspé Co., Quebec.

MARGINAL RECORDS (Anderson, 1947:23, unless otherwise noted).—Quebec: Ste. Anne des Monts (Anderson, 1943:52); type locality. New Brunswick: St. Leonard; Baker Lake.

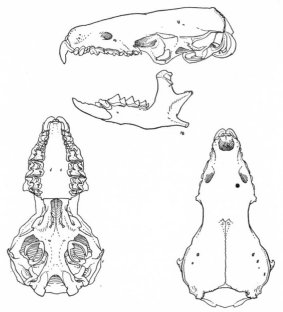

Fig. 26. *Blarina brevicauda kirtlandi,* 1 mi. W Highland Park, Lake Co., Illinois, No. 81749 M.V.Z., ♀, X 2.

Blarina brevicauda brevicauda (Say)

1823. *Sorex brevicaudus* Say, *in* Long, Account of an exped. . . . to the Rocky Mts., 1:164. Type locality, W bank of Missouri River, near Blair, formerly Engineer Cantonment, Washington Co., Nebraska.
1858. *Blarina brevicauda,* Baird, Mammals, *in* Repts. Expl. Surv. . . . , 8(1):42, July 14.
1891. *Blarina costaricensis* J. A. Allen, Bull. Amer. Mus. Nat. Hist., 3:205, April 17, type probably from upper Mississippi Valley, although alleged by describer to be from La Carpintera, Costa Rica.

MARGINAL RECORDS.—Ontario: Rat Portage, Lake of the Woods (Merriam, 1895b:13); Quetico Park (Cahn, 1937:21). Minnesota: Grand Marais (Bole and Moulthrop, 1942:104). Wisconsin: Worden Twp., Clark Co. (*ibid.*);

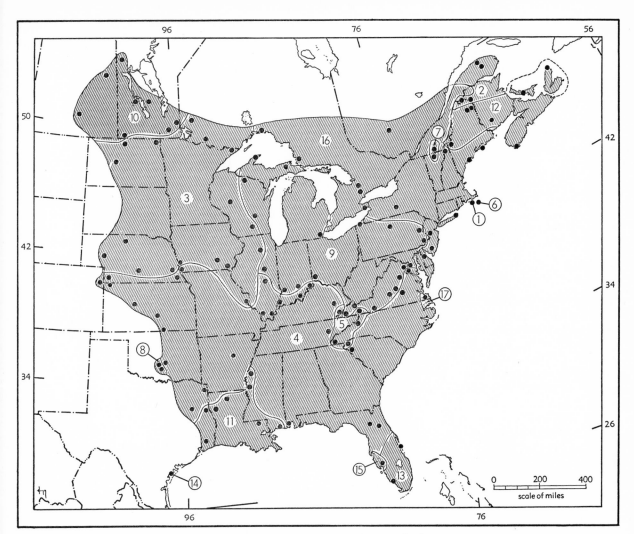

Map 29. *Blarina brevicauda* and *Blarina telmalestes*.

Guide to kinds		
1. *B. b. aloga*	6. *B. b. compacta*	12. *B. b. pallida*
2. *B. b. angusta*	7. *B. b. hooperi*	13. *B. b. peninsulae*
3. *B. b. brevicauda*	8. *B. b. hulophaga*	14. *B. b. plumbea*
4. *B. b. carolinensis*	9. *B. b. kirtlandi*	15. *B. b. shermani*
5. *B. b. churchi*	10. *B. b. manitobensis*	16. *B. b. talpoides*
	11. *B. b. minima*	17. *B. telmalestes*

Prairie du Sac (Cory, 1912:428). Illinois: Dekalb (Merriam, 1895b:13). Missouri: Kimmswick (*ibid.*). Iowa: Hillsboro (Bole and Moulthrop, 1942:104); Knoxville (Scott, 1937:55); Council Bluffs (*ibid.*). Nebraska: 2 mi. NE Crete (Jones and Findley, 1954:210); Kearney (Bole and Moulthrop, 1942:104); 2 mi. N North Platte (76913 KU —dot on Map 29 is 88 mi. too far W and N); Valentine (Bole and Moulthrop, 1942:104). North Dakota (V. Bailey, 1927:205): Fort Berthold; Turtle Mts.; Pembina.

Blarina brevicauda carolinensis (Bachman)

1837. *Sorex carolinensis* Bachman, Jour. Acad. Nat. Sci. Philadelphia, 7(2):366. Type locality, eastern South Carolina.

1895. *Blarina brevicauda carolinensis,* Merriam, N. Amer. Fauna, 10:13, December 31.

MARGINAL RECORDS.—Iowa: 4 mi. S, 9 mi. W Sidney (Findley, Jones and Vaughan, 1954:212). Illinois (Necker and Hatfield, 1941:42): Alto Pass; White Heath. Indiana (Mumford and Handley, 1956:408): New Harmony; Corydon; Bascom. Kentucky: Quicksand (Hamilton, 1930:306). Tennessee: Harriman (Kellogg, 1939:253). South Carolina: Greenville (Penney, 1950:84). Virginia: Amelia County (Handley and Patton, 1947:111). Maryland: Cambridge (Gardner, 1950:67), thence southward along coast (excluding range of *Blarina telmalestes*) to Florida: Welaka (Moore, 1949:57); Gainesville (Bole and Moulthrop, 1942:108). Alabama: Alabama Port (A. H. Howell, 1921:

21). Arkansas: Beebe (Merriam, 1895b:14). Texas: 10 mi. S Texarkana (Strecker and Williams, 1929:259); Cherokee County (McCarley and Bradshaw, 1953:516). Oklahoma (Blair, 1939:99): 7 mi. S Norman; *Norman.* Kansas (Jones and Findley, 1954:210): 3 mi. SE Arkansas City; 1 mi. E, ½ mi. N Halstead; 3½ mi. W, ¾ mi. S Hays; 15 mi. W, 11½ mi. N St. Francis. Colorado: 1 mi. E Laird (*ibid.*). Nebraska (*ibid.*): 5 mi. N, 2 mi. W Parks; 6 mi. W Falls City.

Blarina brevicauda churchi Bole and Moulthrop

1942. *Blarina brevicauda churchi* Bole and Moulthrop, Sci. Publ. Cleveland Mus. Nat. Hist., 5:109, September 11, type from Roan Mtn., Mitchell Co., North Carolina.

MARGINAL RECORDS.—Kentucky: Black Mtn. (Barbour, 1951:103). Virginia: Whitetop Mtn. (Handley and Patton, 1947:111). North Carolina: type locality. South Carolina: 8 mi. E Caesers Head (269932 USNM). North Carolina: 9 mi. SW Murphy (268979 USNM).

Blarina brevicauda compacta Bangs

1902. *Blarina brevicauda compacta* Bangs, Proc. New England Zool. Club, 3:77, March 31, type from Nantucket Island, Nantucket Co., Massachusetts. Known only from the type locality.

Blarina brevicauda hooperi Bole and Moulthrop

1942. *Blarina brevicauda hooperi* Bole and Moulthrop, Sci. Publ. Cleveland Mus. Nat. Hist., 5:110, September 11, type from Lyndon, Caledonia Co., Vermont.

MARGINAL RECORDS.—Quebec: North Hatley (Anderson, 1947:23). Vermont: type locality.

Blarina brevicauda hulophaga Elliot

1899. *Blarina brevicauda hulophaga* Elliot, Field Columb. Mus., Publ. 38, Zool. Ser., 1:287, May 25, type from Dougherty, Murray Co., Oklahoma.

MARGINAL RECORDS.—Oklahoma: Arbuckle Mts. (Blair, 1939:99); type locality.

Blarina brevicauda kirtlandi Bole and Moulthrop

1942. *Blarina brevicauda kirtlandi* Bole and Moulthrop, Sci. Publ. Cleveland Mus. Nat. Hist., 5:99, September 11, type from Holden Arboretum, Kirtland Twp., Lake Co., and Chadron Twp., Geauga Co. (county line bisects type locality), Ohio.

MARGINAL RECORDS (Bole and Moulthrop, 1942:102–103, unless otherwise noted).—Michigan (Burt, 1946:103): Keweenaw County; Luce County; Monroe County, thence eastward along southern shore of Lake Erie to Pennsylvania: McKean; Drury Run; Nazareth; Philadelphia. Maryland: Oxon Hill (Handley and Patton, 1947:111). Virginia (*ibid.*): Fairfax County; Spotsylvania County; Cumberland County; Campbell County; Patrick County; Tazewell County; Scott County. Ohio: Cincinnati. Indiana (Mumford and Handley, 1956:408): Kurtz; Bicknell. Illinois: Bloomington. Wisconsin: Green Lake; Mamie Lake.

Blarina brevicauda manitobensis Anderson

1947. *Blarina brevicauda manitobensis* R. M. Anderson, Bull. Nat. Mus. Canada, 102:23, January 24, type from Max Lake, Manitoba.

MARGINAL RECORDS.—Manitoba (Anderson, 1947:23–24, unless otherwise noted): The Pas (Krivda, 1957:83); Overflowing River, Lake Winnipegosis; Lake St. Martin Reserve; Telford, near Whiteshell Forest Reserve, 10 mi. W Ingoman; Sandilands Forest Reserve, SW Marchand; Max Lake, Turtle Mts., 2100 ft. Saskatchewan: Regina (Nero, 1956:46); Somme (*op. cit.*, 45).

Blarina brevicauda minima Lowery

1943. *Blarina brevicauda minima* Lowery, Occas. Papers Mus. Zool., Louisiana State Univ., 13:218, November 22, type from Comite River, 13 mi. NE Baton Rouge, East Baton Rouge Parish, Louisiana.

MARGINAL RECORDS (Lowery, 1943:219, unless otherwise noted).—Mississippi: Rosedale; Washington. Louisiana: Hackley. Mississippi: Biloxi, thence westward along Gulf Coast to Texas: 7 mi. NE Sour Lake (Hall and Kelson, 1952:329); Joaquin (*ibid.*). Louisiana: Mansfield; Ruston.

Blarina brevicauda pallida R. W. Smith

1940. *Blarina brevicauda pallida* R. W. Smith, Amer. Midl. Nat., 24:223, July 31, type from Wolfville, Kings Co., Nova Scotia.

MARGINAL RECORDS (Bole and Moulthrop, 1942:106, unless otherwise noted).—Nova Scotia: Cape North (Smith, 1940:224); Barrington Passage (Anderson, 1943:50). New Brunswick: Scotch Lake. Maine: Mooselookmeguntic Lake; Ashland; Caribou. Prince Edward Island (Anderson, 1947:24).

Blarina brevicauda peninsulae Merriam

1895. *Blarina carolinensis peninsulae* Merriam, N. Amer. Fauna, 10:14, December 31, type from Miami River, Dade Co., Florida.
1897. [*Blarina brevicauda*] *peninsulae*, Trouessart, Catalogus Mammalium . . . , fasc. 1, p. 188.

MARGINAL RECORDS (Sherman, 1937:106).—Florida: Oak Lodge; Everglade.

Blarina brevicauda plumbea Davis

1941. *Blarina brevicauda plumbea* Davis, Jour. Mamm., 22:317, August 14, type from ½ mi. W Marano Mill, Aransas Co., Texas. Known only from Aransas National Wildlife Refuge, Aransas Co., Texas.

Blarina brevicauda shermani Hamilton

1955. *Blarina brevicauda shermani* Hamilton, Proc. Biol. Soc. Washington, 68:37, May 20, type from 2 mi. N Fort Myers, Lee Co., Florida. Known only from the type locality.

Blarina brevicauda talpoides (Gapper)

1830. *Sorex talpoides* Gapper, Zool. Jour., 5:202. Type locality, between York and Lake Simcoe, Ontario.
1902. *Blarina brevicauda talpoides,* Bangs, Proc. New England Zool. Club, 3:75, March 31.
1858. *Blarina angusticeps* Baird, Mammals, *in* Repts. Expl. Surv. . . . , 8(1):34, July 14, type from Burlington, Chittenden Co., Vermont. Regarded by Merriam, N. Amer. Fauna, 10:10, December 31, 1895, as based on a deformed skull. See also Bole and Moulthrop, Sci. Publs. Cleveland Mus. Nat. Hist., 5(6):111, September 11, 1942.

MARGINAL RECORDS (Bole and Moulthrop, 1942: 105–106, unless otherwise noted).—Ontario: Schrieber (Anderson, 1942:50). Quebec: Bark Lake. New Hampshire: Pittsburg. Maine: Mt. Desert Island (Manville, 1942:391); Small Point Beach. New York: eastern end Long Island at Orient (Hatt, 1930:323). New Jersey: Mays Landing. Delaware: Smyrna (Ulmer, 1940:457). New Jersey: Princeton. New York: Bath (Hamilton, 1939:252); *Elba.* Ontario: Point Abino (Jameson, 1943:194); near Cedardale Mill (Snyder and Logier, 1930:175); Lake Simcoe (Merriam, 1895b:12); Pancake Bay (Anderson, 1942:50).

Blarina telmalestes Merriam
Swamp Short-tailed Shrew

1895. *Blarina telmalestes* Merriam, N. Amer. Fauna, 10:15, December 31, type from Lake Drummond, Dismal Swamp, Norfolk Co., Virginia. Known only from Dismal Swamp, Virginia.

External measurements: 118–119.5; 26.4–28; 16–16. Greatest length of skull, 24. Skull relatively slender; dentition little pigmented. Only slightly differentiated from *Blarina brevicauda talpoides.* The range of *B. telmalestes* is surrounded by that of the smaller darker *B. b. carolinensis.* If the range of *telmalestes* were adjacent to that of the northern *B. b. talpoides,* the two kinds probably would be considered as subspecies of a single species.

Genus Cryptotis Pomel—Small-eared Shrews

Revised by Merriam, under the name *Blarina,* N. Amer. Fauna, 10:16–31, December 31, 1895.

1848. *Cryptotis* Pomel, Arch. Sci. Phys. et Nat. Genève, 9:249, November. Type, *Sorex cinereus* Bachman [= *Sorex parvus* Say].

External measurements: 75–134; 12–42; 9–17. Condylobasal length of skull, 14.4–23.5. Upper parts brownish or blackish, underparts same or paler; eyes minute; pinnae of ears inconspicuous, snout pointed; skull approximately conical; braincase low, laterally angular; rostrum wedge-shaped; unicuspids 4, never in 2 pairs, 4th always smaller than 3rd, usually minute. Dentition, i. $\frac{3}{1}$, c. $\frac{1}{1}$, p. $\frac{2}{1}$, m. $\frac{3}{3} = 30$.

Shrews of this genus ordinarily are dwellers of the forest floor, but *C. parva* inhabits open fields.

KEY TO NORTH AMERICAN SPECIES OF CRYPTOTIS

11′. Not occurring at San Rafael del Norte, Nicaragua.
    12. Venter paler than dorsum; maxillary tooth-row less than 8.1; known geographic range confined to Costa Rica.
        13. Skull less than 47% as broad as long (including incisors). . . . . . . *C. celatus*, p. 58
        13′. Skull more than 47% as broad as long (including incisors). . . . . . . *C. orophila*, p. 63
    12′. Venter same color as dorsum; maxillary tooth-row more than 8.1; known only from Cerro Punta, Panamá. . . . . *C. zeteki*, p. 62
2′. Known geographic range entirely or in part north of southern boundary of Republic of México.
    14. Known geographic range confined to Yucatán. . . . . *C. mayensis*, p. 61
    14′. Not known to occur in Yucatán.
        15. Total length more than 125. . . . . *C. magna*, p. 62
        15′. Total length less than 125.
            16. Condylobasal length of skull less than 18.5; total length less than 96.
                17. Not known south of Altimira, Tamaulipas, or west of Tamaulipas. . . *C. parva*, p. 56
                17′. Occurring south from Boca del Río, Veracruz, or west of Tamaulipas.
                    18. Known only from Distrito Federal, México. . . . . *C. soricina*, p. 63
                    18′. Not known from Distrito Federal, México.
                        19. Occurring in Oaxaca, Chiapas, and central and S. Veracruz. *C. micrura*, p. 62
                        19′. Not occurring in the above-mentioned states.
                            20. Known only from Tulancingo, Hidalgo. . . . . . *C. obscura*, p. 61
                            20′. Not known from Tulancingo, Hidalgo (but rather from northern Puebla, Guanajuato, Jalisco, Michoacán, and Nayarit).
                                    C. pergracilis, p. 58
            16′. Condylobasal length of skull more than 18.5; total length more than 96.
                21. Known geographic range confined to central Chiapas. . . . *C. griseoventris*, p. 60
                21′. Not known from Chiapas.
                    22. Known only from near Tehuantepec, Oaxaca. . . . . . . *C. frontalis*, p. 60
                    22′. Not known from near Tehuantepec, Oaxaca.
                      23. P4 deeply excavated posteriorly.
                        24. Known only from Mt. Zempoaltepec, Oaxaca. . . . . *C. fossor*, p. 62
                        24′. Not known from Oaxaca (but rather from Puebla and State of México). *C. alticola*, p. 60
                    23′. P4 not deeply excavated posteriorly.
                      25. Known only from Volcán de Tuxtla, Veracruz. . . . *C. nelsoni*, p. 61
                      25′. Not known from Volcán de Tuxtla.
                        26. Known only from Omilteme, Guerrero. . . *C. guerrerensis*, p. 60
                        26′. Not known from Omilteme (see Map 31 for geographic occurrence). . . . . *C. mexicana*, p. 58

Cryptotis parva
Least Shrew

External measurements: 75–89; 12–22; 9–12. Condylobasal length of skull, 14.4–18. Brownish or grayish brown above, paler below; tail bicolor; grayer in winter. Differs from *C. micrura* in smaller average size; resembles *C. pergracilis* with which it may be specifically related; much smaller in all dimensions than any of the *C. mexicana* complex.

Least shrews inhabit open fields, coastal marshes or prairies and are much less often found in other situations. Food consists of invertebrates and some vegetable matter. They breed from March to No-

vember in the north and possibly throughout the year in the south. Five or 6 young comprise a litter. Young are blind and naked at birth.

Cryptotis parva berlandieri (Baird)

1858. *Blarina berlandieri* Baird, Mammals, *in* Repts. Expl. Surv. . . . , 8(1):53, July 14, type from Matamoros, Tamaulipas.
1941. *Cryptotis parva berlandieri*, Davis, Jour. Mamm., 22:413, November 13.

Fig. 27. *Cryptotis parva parva*, Monroe, Ouchita Parish, Louisiana, No. 70505 M.V.Z., ♀, X 2.

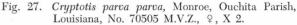

Map 30. *Cryptotis parva* and subspecies.

Guide to subspecies
1. *C. p. berlandieri*
2. *C. p. elasson*
3. *C. p. floridana*
4. *C. p. harlani*
5. *C. p. parva*

MARGINAL RECORDS.—Texas (Davis, 1941:418): Del Rio; Dilley; San Diego. Tamaulipas: Altamira (54924 KU). San Luis Potosí: El Salto (Booth, 1957:9). Tamaulipas: 9 km. N Rancho Tigre (Goodwin, 1954:3).

Cryptotis parva elasson Bole and Moulthrop

1942. *Cryptotis parva elasson* Bole and Moulthrop, Sci. Publ. Cleveland Mus. Nat. Hist., 5:97, September 11, type from Bettsville, Seneca Co., Ohio.

MARGINAL RECORDS.—Ohio (Bole and Moulthrop, 1942:99): Austinburg; Aurora Pond; Smoky Creek in Green Twp.; Antwerp; Evansport; Bay Point.

Cryptotis parva floridana (Merriam)

1895. *Blarina floridana* Merriam, N. Amer. Fauna, 10:19, December 31, type from Chester Shoal, 11 mi. N Cape Canaveral, Brevard Co., Florida.
1927. *Cryptotis parva floridana*, Harper, Proc. Boston Soc. Nat. Hist., 38:270, March.

MARGINAL RECORDS.—Georgia: St. Marys (Harper 1927:270); thence throughout *peninsular Florida*. Georgia: 10 mi. SSW Thomasville, approximately 7 mi. from Florida boundary (Quay, 1949:66).

Cryptotis parva harlani (Duvernoy)

1842. *Brachysorex harlani* Duvernoy, Mag. de Zool., Anat. Comp. et Pal., Paris, livr. 25, p. 40, pl. 53. Type locality, New Harmony, Indiana.
1942. *Cryptotis parva harlani*, Bole and Moulthrop, Sci. Publ. Cleveland Mus. Nat. Hist., 5:97, September 11.

MARGINAL RECORDS (Bole and Moulthrop, 1942:99). —Indiana: Orland; Pleasant Mills; Terre Haute; type locality. Illinois: Bloomington.

Cryptotis parva parva (Say)

1823. *Sorex parvus* Say, *in* Long, Account of an exped. . . . to the Rocky Mts., 1:163, type from west bank of Missouri River, near Blair, formerly Engineer Cantonment, Washington Co., Nebraska.
1912. *Cryptotis parva*, Miller, Bull. U.S. Nat. Mus., 79:24, December 31.
1837. *Sorex cinereus* Bachman, Jour. Acad. Nat. Sci. Philadelphia, 7:373, type from "Goose Creek about twenty-two miles from Charleston," South Carolina. Not *Sorex arcticus cinereus* Kerr, 1792.
1858. *Blarina exilipes* Baird, Mammals, *in* Repts. Expl. Surv. . . . , 8(1):51, July 14, type from Washington, Mississippi.
1858. *B[larina]. eximius* Baird, Mammals, *in* Repts. Expl. Surv. . . . , 8(1):52, July 14. Based on 2 specimens: one from DeKalb Co., Ill., and one from St. Louis, Mo.

MARGINAL RECORDS.—Minnesota: Homer (Swanson, *et al.*, 1945:58). Wisconsin: Prairie du Sac (A. L. Nelson, 1934:252), thence along shores of south quarter of Lake Michigan into Michigan: Allegan County (Burt, 1946:100); Clinton County (*ibid.*); Lake Angelus NE of Pontiac (Hatt, 1938:247), thence east, presumably, to west end of Lake Ontario and along south shore of same to Niagara River, along west bank of Niagara River to Lake Erie and west along north shore of same (as at Long Point in Ontario by Anderson, 1947:215), northern boundary of Ohio, east half of north boundary of Indiana, and southwest to Illinois (Necker and Hatfield, 1941:43): Mason County; Wolf Lake. Thence along southern margins of geographic ranges of *C. p. harlani* and *C. p. elasson* to south shore of Lake Erie and east along same to New York: Depew (C. B. Peterson, 1936:284); 3 mi. E Ithaca (Hamilton, 1934:154). Connecticut: Salisbury (Goodwin, 1932:39); Darien (Goodwin, 1935:39). Thence south along Atlantic Coast to approximately 31°. Georgia: Chesser's Island, Okefinokee Swamp (Harper, 1927:270) and along coast of western Florida to Alabama: Alabama Port (A. H. Howell, 1921:22) and west along Gulf Coast to Texas: Victoria (Bole and Moulthrop, 1942:99); 9 mi. E Pleasanton (Davis, 1941: 417); San Antonio (*ibid.*); Waco (*ibid.*); Gainesville (*ibid.*). Oklahoma (Blair, 1939:98): Wichita National Forest. Texas: 2½ mi. W, 5–6 mi. S Old Mobeetie (Stickel and Stickel, 1948:292); Stinnett (Blair, 1954b:241). Kansas (Cockrum, 1952:47): 17 mi. SW Meade; 2 mi. S Ludell. Colorado: Dry Willow Creek (Warren, 1942:13); 5 mi. W Crook (Beidleman and Remington, 1955:123). Nebraska: *Lincoln County* (Jones, 1957:274); Blair (Bole and Moulthrop, 1942:99). South Dakota: Cottonwood Range Exp. Station, 1½ mi. S Cottonwood (Findley, 1956a:1).
    Cahn (1937:21) recorded the species *Cryptotis parva* from four localities in Quetico Provincial Park, Ontario, but we have chosen not to show any of these on our map.

Cryptotis celatus Goodwin
Goodwin's Short-tailed Shrew

1956. *Cryptotis celatus* Goodwin, Amer. Mus. Novit., 1791: 1, September 28, type from Las Cuevas, Santiago Lachiguiri, District of Tehuantepec, Oaxaca. Known only from the type locality.

External measurements: 67; 14; 11. Greatest length of skull including incisors, 17.7; breadth of cranium, 7.5. Prout's brown above; light buff below; feet flesh-colored. This species is described as closely resembling *Cryptotis parva berlandieri* except that the skull is longer and narrower.

Cryptotis pergracilis
Slender Small-eared Shrew

External measurements: 77–87; 17.4–22; 10–13. Condylobasal length of skull, 16.0–17.0. Upper parts brownish, underparts paler. Smaller on the average than *C. micura*, *C. obscura* or *C. soricina*; much smaller in all dimensions than members of the *C. mexicana*-group.

Cryptotis pergracilis macer Miller

1911. *Cryptotis pergracilis macer* Miller, Proc. Biol. Soc. Washington, 24:223, October 31, type from near Guanajuato City, Guanajuato. Known only from type locality.

Cryptotis pergracilis nayaritensis Jackson

1933. *Cryptotis pergracilis nayaritensis* Jackson, Proc. Biol. Soc. Washington, 46:79, April 27, type from Tepic, 3000 ft., Nayarit.

MARGINAL RECORDS.—Nayarit: type locality. Jalisco: 21 mi. SW Guadalajara (Twente and Baker, 1951:120).

Cryptotis pergracilis pergracilis (Elliot)

1903. *Blarina pergracilis* Elliot, Field Columb. Mus., Publ. 71, Zool. Ser., 3:149, March 20, type from Ocotlán, Jalisco.
1911. *Cryptotis pergracilis pergracilis*, Miller, Proc. Biol. Soc. Washington, 24:223, October 31.

MARGINAL RECORDS.—Jalisco: type locality. Michoacán: Colonia Ibarra, Pátzcuaro (Hall and Villa, 1950:165).

Cryptotis pergracilis pueblensis Jackson

1933. *Cryptotis pergracilis pueblensis* Jackson, Proc. Biol. Soc. Washington, 46:79, April 27, type from Huauchinango, 5000 ft., Puebla.

MARGINAL RECORDS.—Tamaulipas: Aserradero del Paraíso (Goodwin, 1954:3). Puebla: type locality.

Cryptotis mexicana
Mexican Small-eared Shrew

External measurements: 94–108; 20–31; 13–17. Condylobasal length of skull, 17.8–19.35. Blackish above, the same or slightly paler below; feet and tail black; smaller than *C. magna*; differs from *C. alticola* and *C. fossor* in smaller molariform teeth, which are not deeply excavated posteriorly; separated geographically from *C. frontalis* and *C. guerrerensis* with which it may prove to be conspecific.

This species occurs in meadows and forests in the mountains where it makes runways much like those of *Blarina brevicauda*.

Cryptotis mexicana goldmani (Merriam)

1895. *Blarina mexicana goldmani* Merriam, N. Amer. Fauna, 10:25, December 31, type from mountains near Chilpancingo, 10,000 ft., Guerrero. Known only from the type locality.
1912. *Cryptotis mexicana goldmani,* Miller, Bull. U.S. Nat. Mus., 79:27, December 31.

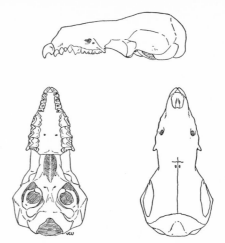

Fig. 28. *Cryptotis mexicana mexicana*, 4 km. W Tlapacoyan, 1700 ft., Veracruz, No. 23413 K.U., ♀, X 2.

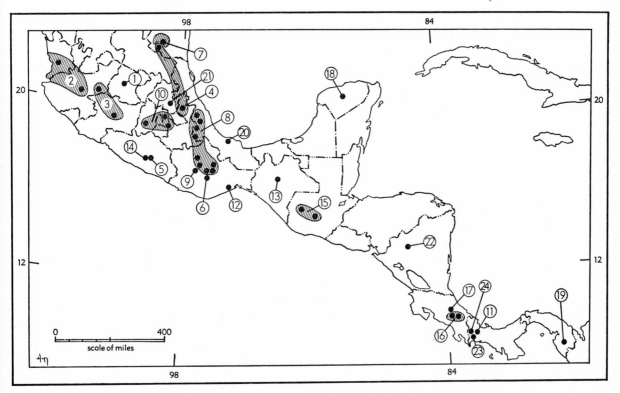

Map 31. *Cryptotis pergracilis* and several related species.

1. *C. pergracilis macer*
2. *C. pergracilis nayaritensis*
3. *C. pergracilis pergracilis*
4. *C. pergracilis pueblensis*
5. *C. mexicana goldmani*
6. *C. mexicana machetes*
7. *C. mexicana madrea*
8. *C. mexicana mexicana*

9. *C. mexicana peregrina*
10. *C. alticola*
11. *C. endersi*
12. *C. frontalis*
13. *C. griseoventris*
14. *C. guerrerensis*
15. *C. goodwini*
16. *C. gracilis*

17. *C. jacksoni*
18. *C. mayensis*
19. *C. mera*
20. *C. nelsoni*
21. *C. obscura*
22. *C. olivacea*
23. *C. zeteki*
24. *C. tersus*

Cryptotis mexicana machetes (Merriam)

1895. *Blarina mexicana machetes* Merriam, N. Amer. Fauna, 10:26, December 31, type from mountains near Ozolotepec, 10,000 ft., Oaxaca. Known only from type locality.
1912. *Cryptotis mexicana machetes,* Miller, Bull. U.S. Nat. Mus., 79:27, December 31.

Cryptotis mexicana madrea Goodwin

1954. *Cryptotis mexicana madrea* Goodwin, Amer. Mus. Novit., 1670:1, June 28, type from 5 mi. NW Gómez Farías, 3500 ft., Tamaulipas.

MARGINAL RECORDS.—Tamaulipas: type locality; *Rancho del Cielo* (Goodwin, 1954:4); Aserradero del Infernillo (*ibid.*).

Cryptotis mexicana mexicana (Coues)

1877. *Blarina* (*Soriciscus*) *mexicana* Coues, Bull. U.S. Geol. and Geog. Surv. Territories, 3:652, May 15, type from Jalapa, Veracruz.
1911. *Cryptotis mexicana,* Miller, Proc. Biol. Soc. Washington, 24:221, October 31.

MARGINAL RECORDS (Merriam, 1895b:24).—Veracruz: *Tlapacoyan, 1700 ft.* (23413 KU); Las Vigas; Jalapa. Oaxaca: Totontepec; Mt. Zempoaltepec; near Cajones; Cerro San Felipe; [Papalo Santos] Reyes. Veracruz: Orizaba; Jico.

Cryptotis mexicana peregrina (Merriam)

1895. *Blarina mexicana peregrina* Merriam, N. Amer. Fauna, 10:24, December 31, type from mountains 15 mi. W Oaxaca, 9500 ft., Oaxaca. Known only from the type locality.
1911. *C*[*ryptotis*]. *mexicana peregrina,* Miller, Proc. Biol. Soc. Washington, 24:222, October 31.

Cryptotis alticola (Merriam)
Popocatépetl Small-eared Shrew

1895. *Blarina alticola* Merriam, N. Amer. Fauna, 10:27, December 31, type from Mt. Popocatépetl, 11,500 ft., México.
1912. *Cryptotis alticola,* Miller, Bull. U.S. Nat. Mus., 79:27, December 31.

External measurements: 104–107; 26–26; 15–15. Greatest length of skull, 21. Blackish above, slightly paler on belly; skull resembles that of *C. mexicana* but molariform teeth larger, especially P4; unicuspids with thicker, blunter crowns; differs from *C. fossor* in possession of well-developed anterointernal angle and cusp on P4; manus and foreclaws relatively large.

This species occurs in forests and areas of sacaton at altitudes of from 9000 to 12,000 ft.

MARGINAL RECORDS.—México: Monte Río Frío, 45 km. ESE Mexico City (Davis, 1944:376); type locality; N slope Volcán Toluca (Merriam, 1895b:28).

Cryptotis endersi Setzer
Enders' Small-eared Shrew

1950. *Cryptotis endersi* Setzer, Jour. Washington Acad. Sci., 40:300, September 29, type from Cylindro, Chiriquí, Panamá. Known only from type locality.

External measurements: 109; 36; 12. Condylobasal length of skull, 20.2. Dorsal surface, belly, tail and feet Chaetura Black; dorsal surface of skull concave above orbits; rostrum relatively long and narrow; maxillary tooth-row relatively straight and uncrowded; 4th unicuspid visible in lateral view; larger than *C. jacksoni, C. gracilis,* or *C. zeteki.* Only one specimen is known.

Cryptotis frontalis Miller
Tehuantepec Small-eared Shrew

1911. *Cryptotis frontalis* Miller, Proc. Biol. Soc. Washington, 24:222, October 31, type from near Tehuantepec City, Oaxaca. Known only from the type locality.

External measurements: 66 (length of head and body); 27; 12. Condylobasal length of skull, 19. Resembling *C. mexicana* in general appearance, but rostrum more robust and braincase unusually deepened posteriorly and rising at much more conspicuous angle from plane of rostrum.

Cryptotis griseoventris Jackson
San Cristóbal Small-eared Shrew

1933. *Cryptotis griseoventris* Jackson, Proc. Biol. Soc. Washington, 46:80, April 27, type from San Cristóbal, 9500 ft., Chiapas. Known only from the type locality.

External measurements: 110; 30; 14.5. Condylobasal length of skull, 20.0. Upper parts near Clove Brown but darker, underparts between Clove Brown and Chaetura Drab; skull larger than in *C. mexicana;* rostrum and braincase relatively narrower than in *C. guerrerensis.*

Cryptotis guerrerensis Jackson
Guerreran Small-eared Shrew

1933. *Cryptotis guerrerensis* Jackson, Proc. Biol. Soc. Washington, 46:80, April 27, type from Omilteme, 8000 ft., Guerrero. Known only from type locality.

External measurements: 110; 32; 14.5. Condylobasal length of skull, 20.0. Upper parts between Sepia and Clove Brown; underparts Hair Brown, or between Hair Brown and Drab; resembles *C. mexicana* but is larger than its nearest geographic representative, *C. m. goldmani,* and with more robust skull that is relatively and actually wider interorbitally and rostrally.

Cryptotis goodwini Jackson
Goodwin's Small-eared Shrew

1933. *Cryptotis goodwini* Jackson, Proc. Biol. Soc. Washington, 46:81, April 27, type from Calel, 10,200 ft., Guatemala.

External measurements: 117; 28; 15.5. Condylobasal length of skull, 21.3. Upper parts somewhat darker than Clove Brown; underparts paler; excepting *C. magna*, the largest species of the genus; cranium deep; cranium and rostrum relatively broad; molariform teeth relatively broad.

MARGINAL RECORDS.—Guatemala: type locality; Tecpam (*sic*) (Goodwin, 1934:6).

Cryptotis gracilis Miller
Talamancan Small-eared Shrew

1911. *Cryptotis gracilis* Miller, Proc. Biol. Soc. Washington, 24:221, October 31, type from head Lari River, 6000 ft., near base of Pico Blanco, Talamanca, Costa Rica.

External measurements: 76 (head and body length); 34–35; 13.6–14.5. Condylobasal length of skull, 18.6–20. Blackish above and below, feet and tail blackish; skull relatively much narrower in all dimensions than in neighboring species (breadth of braincase 48% of condylobasal length); braincase nearly circular when viewed from above.

MARGINAL RECORDS.—Costa Rica: Las Vueltas (Goodwin, 1946:290); type locality.

Cryptotis jacksoni Goodwin
Jackson's Small-eared Shrew

1944. *Cryptotis jacksoni* Goodwin, Amer. Mus. Novit., 1267: 1, December 10, type from Volcán Irazú, Costa Rica. Known only from the type locality.

External measurements: 110; 34.5; 14.5. Condylobasal length of skull, 19.4. Upper parts and underparts dark mummy brown; skull slender, superior outline depressed behind orbits; braincase broad (51% of condylobasal length), its lateral angles well developed; upper unicuspid teeth not crowded; each of 1st 3 upper unicuspids having well-developed keel; 3rd unicuspid smaller than 1st, 4th minute but in line of tooth-row; in P4, posterior border equal to outer border.

Cryptotis mayensis (Merriam)
Yucatán Small-eared Shrew

1901. *Blarina mayensis* Merriam, Proc. Washington Acad. Sci., 3:559, November 29, type from Maya ruin at Chichén-Itzá, Yucatán. Known only from the type locality.

1912. *Cryptotis mayensis,* Miller, Bull. U.S. Nat. Mus., 79: 26, December 31.

External measurements: 102; 29; 13. Upper parts plumbeous with finely grizzled appearance; underparts plumbeous overlaid with ash brown; skull resembles that of *C. mexicana* but slightly longer and less massive, unicuspids larger, braincase shallower, and P4 smaller; 1st and 2nd unicuspids having inner tubercle obsolete.

Cryptotis mera Goldman
Mt. Pirri Small-eared Shrew

1912. *Cryptotis merus* Goldman, Smiths. Miscl. Coll., 60(2):17, September 20, type from near head of Río Limón, 4500 ft., Mt. Pirri, eastern Panamá. Known only from type locality.

External measurements: 91–101; 25–31; 12–12.5. Condylobasal length of skull, 18.8. Black above and below; feet and tail blackish; resembles *C. zeteki* but darker, skull large, braincase more inflated, unicuspids less crowded, skull more concave above orbits; smaller than *C. endersi.*

Cryptotis nelsoni (Merriam)
Nelson's Small-eared Shrew

1895. *Blarina nelsoni* Merriam, N. Amer. Fauna, 10:26, December 31, type from Volcán Tuxtla, 4800 ft., Veracruz. Known only from the type locality.

1912. *Cryptotis nelsoni,* Miller, Bull. U.S. Nat. Mus., 79:27, December 31.

External measurements: 106–110; 29–31; 13.3–14. Greatest length of skull, 20.5. Sooty brown above and below; interpterygoid notch relatively broader and shorter than in *C. mexicana* or *C. alticola;* inner cusplets on unicuspids nearly obsolete; molariform teeth resembling those of *C. mexicana* but larger; P4 relatively broad posteriorly but not excavated, in this respect resembling that of *C. mexicana* and differing from that of *C. alticola.*

This species occurs in the forests of the Tuxtla volcano up to 5400 ft., and makes runways under logs and roots.

Cryptotis obscura (Merriam)
Dusky Small-eared Shrew

1895. *Blarina obscura* Merriam, N. Amer. Fauna, 10:23, December 31, type from Tulancingo, 8500 ft., Hidalgo. Known only from type locality.

1912. *Cryptotis obscura,* Miller, Bull. U.S. Nat. Mus., 79:26, December 31.

External measurements: 89–92; 24–25; 13–13. Greatest length of skull, 18. Upper parts plumbeous, underparts paler plumbeous; skull resembles that of *C. mexicana* but postrostral part relatively smaller.

The two known specimens were caught in runways under logs in fir woods.

Cryptotis olivacea (J. A. Allen)
Olivaceous Small-eared Shrew

1908. *Blarina olivaceus* J. A. Allen, Bull. Amer. Mus. Nat. Hist., 24:669, October 13, type from San Rafael del Norte, 5000 ft., Nicaragua. Known only from type locality.
1912. *Cryptotis olivaceus*, Miller, Bull. U.S. Nat. Mus., 79:26, December 31.

External measurements: 80; 17; 10. Upper parts grayish brown with olivaceous reflection in certain lights; underparts whitish gray; feet whitish; tail bicolor; differs from *C. orophila* in relatively narrower interorbital region and rostrum, tooth-row straight instead of convex outward, and teeth relatively narrower; resembles *C. pergracilis.*

Cryptotis zeteki Setzer
Zetek's Small-eared Shrew

1950. *Cryptotis zeteki* Setzer, Jour. Washington Acad. Sci., 40:299, September 29, type from Cerro Punta (lat. 8° 42′ N, long. 82° 48′ W), 6500 ft., Chiriquí, Panamá. Known only from the type locality.

External measurements: 83; 22; 11. Condylobasal length of skull, 18.1. Upper parts and underparts Mummy Brown; tail paler; feet whitish; maxillary tooth-row, especially unicuspid series, crowded; 4th unicuspid displaced medially from tooth-row; rostrum relatively short and wide; differs from *C. endersi* in smaller size, paler color, and longer, straighter tooth-row.

Cryptotis fossor (Merriam)
Zempoaltepec Small-eared Shrew

1895. *Blarina fossor* Merriam, N. Amer. Fauna, 10:28, December 31, type from Mt. Zempoaltepec, 10,500 ft., Oaxaca. Known only from Mt. Zempoaltepec, 8200 to 10,500 ft.
1912. *Cryptotis fossor*, Miller, Bull. U.S. Nat. Mus., 79:28, December 31.

External measurements: 108–111; 29–29; 14.6–15. Greatest length of skull, 21.2. Upper parts sooty plumbeous, underparts slightly paler; differs from *C. alticola* in lack of anterointernal angle of P4, and narrower molariform teeth; P4, M1, and M2 more deeply excavated posteriorly than in *C. mexicana*; smaller than *C. magna.*

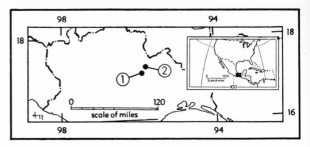

Map 32. *Cryptotis fossor* (1) and *Cryptotis magna* (2).

Cryptotis magna (Merriam)
Big Small-eared Shrew

1895. *Blarina magna* Merriam, N. Amer. Fauna, 10:28, December 31, type from Totontepec, 6800 ft., Oaxaca.
1912. *Cryptotis magna*, Miller, Bull. U.S. Nat. Mus., 79:28, December 31.

External measurements: 134; 42; 17. Greatest length of skull, 24.5. Upper parts and underparts dull sooty brown; molariform teeth not excavated posteriorly; P4 short and broad, with anterointernal angle broadly rounded; unicuspids narrow with minute internal cusplet; largest species of the genus.

The species occurs in dense forests of oaks.

MARGINAL RECORDS.—Oaxaca (Merriam, 1895b:28); type locality; *Zempoaltepec.*

Cryptotis micrura (Tomes)
Guatemalan Small-eared Shrew

1862. *Sorex micrurus* Tomes, Proc. Zool. Soc. London, for 1861, p. 279, April. Type locality, Cobán, 4400 ft., Guatemala.
1924. *Cryptotis micrura*, Miller, Bull. U.S. Nat. Mus., 128:32, April 29.
1895. *Blarina tropicalis* Merriam, N. Amer. Fauna, 10:21, December 31, type from Cobán, Guatemala.

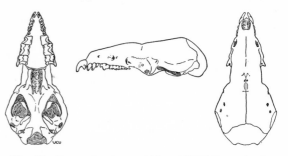

Fig. 29. *Cryptotis micrura*, 7 km. NNW Cerro Gordo, Veracruz, No. 23415 K.U., ♀, × 2.

External measurements: 73–93; 18–28; 11–13. Condylobasal length of skull, 16.6–17.4. Upper parts dark grayish brown or blackish, underparts slightly paler; larger and with larger unicuspid teeth than *C. parva*; smaller and with relatively narrower skull than *C. alticola* or *C. mexicana.* Possibly only subspecifically distinct from *C. obscura* and *C. soricina.*

MARGINAL RECORDS.—Veracruz: 7 km. W El Brinco (29522 KU); Boca del Río (Findley, 1955a:615); Catemaco (Merriam, 1895b:22). British Honduras: Mountain Pine Ridge (Murie, 1935:17). Honduras: Cantoral (Goodwin, 1942:116). Costa Rica (Harris, 1943:7): El Muñeco; *Estrella; Cartago.* Honduras: Belén Guacho (Goodwin, 1942:116). Guatemala: Panajachel (Goodwin, 1934:5). Chiapas: Finca Esperanza (Hooper, 1947:43). Oaxaca: Juquila (Merriam, 1895b:22). Veracruz: Orizaba (Merriam, 1895b:22).

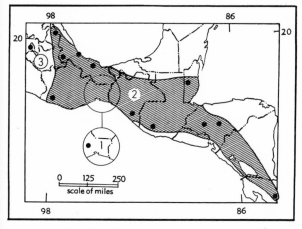

Map 33. Three species of *Cryptotis.*

Guide to species
1. *Cryptotis celatus*
2. *Cryptotis micrura*
3. *Cryptotis soricina*

Cryptotis soricina (Merriam)
Tlalpam Small-eared Shrew

1895. *Blarina soricina* Merriam, N. Amer. Fauna, 10:22, December 31, type from Tlalpam, 10 mi. S Mexico City, 7600 ft., Distrito Federal.
1911. *C[ryptotis]. soricina,* Miller, Proc. Biol. Soc. Washington, 24:221, October 31.

External measurements: 88–91 23.5–26.5; 12.5–12.5. Greatest length of skull, 18. Upper parts sooty black, underparts paler and browner; differs from *C. micrura* in larger 3rd and 4th unicuspids, less deeply excavated P4, and absence of excavation on M1. The relationship of the species to neighboring small species of *Cryptotis* is not clear.

MARGINAL RECORDS (Villa, 1953:320).—Distrito Federal: *Universidad Femenina, near Bosque de Chapultepec; Xochimilco; Cerro de Santa Rosa, Contreras, 3200 m.*

Cryptotis nigrescens (J. A. Allen)
Blackish Small-eared Shrew

1895. *Blarina (Soriciscus) nigrescens* J. A. Allen, Bull. Amer. Mus. Nat. Hist., 7:339, November 8, type from "San Isidro (San José)," Costa Rica.

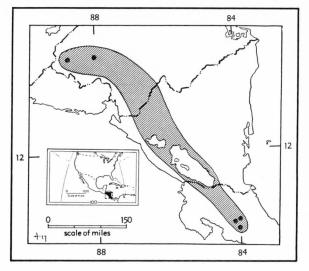

Map 34. *Cryptotis nigrescens.*

1911. *C[ryptotis]. nigrescens,* Miller, Proc. Biol. Soc. Washington, 24:222, October 31.

External measurements: 65–75 (head and body); 22–22; 11.5–12. Condylobasal length of skull, 18.5–19.5. Blackish above and below; blackish feet and tail; larger than *C. orophila;* darker and slightly smaller than *C. jacksoni;* darker and slightly smaller than *C. gracilis* with relatively broader skull.

MARGINAL RECORDS.—Honduras: San José (Goodwin, 1942:117). Costa Rica: Irazú, 9400 ft. (Goodwin, 1946:288); Tablazo (Setzer, 1950:300); type locality. Honduras: Las Flores (Goodwin, 1942:117).

Cryptotis orophila (J. A. Allen)
Costa Rican Small-eared Shrew

1895. *Blarina (Soriciscus) orophila* J. A. Allen, Bull. Amer. Mus. Nat. Hist., 7:340, November 8, type from Volcán Irazú [= Irazú Range], Prov. Cartago, Costa Rica (see Goodwin, Amer. Mus. Novit., 1267:2, December 10, 1954).
1911. *C[ryptotis]. orophila,* Miller, Proc. Biol. Soc. Washington, 24:221, October 31.

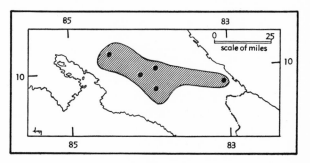

Map 35. *Cryptotis orophila.*

External measurements: 55–63 (head and body); 21–24; 11–13. Greatest length of skull, 17.6–19.4; breadth of braincase, 8.3, 9.4. Brownish above, paler below, feet white; differs from other Costa Rican species of *Cryptotis* in smaller size and different color; probably indistinguishable from *C. olivacea*; supposedly differs from *C. micrura* in narrow and pinched, rather than broadly rounded, profile of 1st and 2nd upper unicuspids.

MARGINAL RECORDS.—Costa Rica (Goodwin, 1946: 289); Zarcéro; type locality; La Estrella; Estrella de Cartago; San José.

Cryptotis tersus Goodwin
Dark Small-eared Shrew

1954. *Cryptotis tersus* Goodwin, Amer. Mus. Novit., 1677:1, June 28, type from Santa Clara, 4200 ft., on the Pan-American Highway, 15 mi. from Costa Rican border, Chiriquí Prov., Panamá. Known only from the type locality.

External measurements: 82; 22.6; 11. Greatest length of skull, approximately 18.9. Pelage darker than Mummy Brown, almost black, with reddish brown sheen on underparts; tail and feet blackish. Except for smaller size, *C. tersus* externally resembles *C. nigrescens* from Costa Rica but has a smaller and narrower skull, and more nearly straight tooth-row (after Goodwin, 1954:2).

Genus Notiosorex Coues—Desert Shrews

Revised by Merriam, N. Amer. Fauna, 10:31–34, December 31, 1895.

1877. *Notiosorex* Coues, Bull. U.S. Geol. and Geog. Surv. Territories, 3:646, May 15. Type, *Sorex* (*Notiosorex*) *crawfordi* Coues.
1950. *Megasorex* Hibbard, Contrib. Mus. Paleo., Univ. Michigan, 8:127, June 29. Type, *Notiosorex gigas* Merriam.

Tail relatively short; pinnae of ears conspicuous; 3 unicuspids forming a uniform series, 3rd more than half as large as 2nd and never minute; unicuspids narrow-based without an internal cusplet. Dentition, i. $\frac{3}{2}$, c. $\frac{1}{0}$, p. $\frac{1}{1}$, m. $\frac{3}{3}$.

KEY TO NORTH AMERICAN SPECIES OF NOTIOSOREX

1. Posterior borders of P4, M1 and M2 nearly straight when viewed from occlusal surface (see Fig. 31). . . . . *N. gigas*, p. 65
1'. Posterior borders of P4, M1, and M2 "excavated" (deeply concave) when viewed from occlusal surface (see Fig. 30)   *N. crawfordi*, p. 64

Notiosorex crawfordi
Crawford's Desert Shrew

External measurements: 87–90; 26–31; 11–11.5. Greatest length of skull, 17.3. Grayish above, the same or paler below; cranial characters those of the genus; differs from *N. gigas* in concave posterior borders of P4, M1, and M2.

This shrew has most often been taken in desert areas and a number have been captured in apiaries. Little is known of its habits.

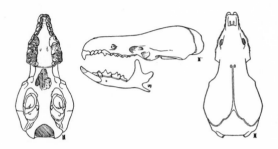

Fig. 30. *Notiosorex crawfordi crawfordi*, 5 mi. E and 1 mi. N Grapevine Peak, 5500 ft., Nye Co., Nevada, No. 92391 M.V.Z., ♂, X 2.

Notiosorex crawfordi crawfordi (Coues)

1877. *Sorex* (*Notiosorex*) *crawfordi* Coues, Bull. U.S. Geol. and Geog. Surv. Territories, 3:651, May 15, type from near old Fort Bliss, approximately 2 mi. above El Paso, El Paso Co., Texas.
1895. *Notiosorex crawfordi*, Merriam, N. Amer. Fauna, 10: 32, December 31.

MARGINAL RECORDS.—Colorado: 3 mi. NW Higbee (Finley, 1954:110). Oklahoma: Tesquite Canyon (Glass, 1953:118). Arkansas: Natural Dam (Sealander, 1952: 105). Oklahoma: northeastern Pushmataha County (Clark, 1953:117). Texas: San Antonio (V. Bailey, 1905:207); Corpus Christi (Hibbard, 1950:128). Tamaulipas: Jaumave (54932 KU); Palmilla (54933 KU). Coahuila: 3 mi. NW Cuatro Ciénegas (Baker, 1953:254). Texas: E base Burro Mesa (Borell and Bryant, 1942:6). *Chihuahua: 3½ mi. ESE Los Lamentos* (Anderson and Ogilvie, 1957:34, only to species). Texas: type locality. Arizona: Chiricahua Mts. (Cahalane, 1939:421); mouth of Miller Canyon, Huachuca Mts. (Hoffmeister and Goodpaster, 1954:46). California: Palo Verde (Grinnell, 1933:85). Baja California: Santa Anita (Merriam, 1895b:33). California: San Diego (Grinnell, 1933:85); El Rincon Creek (von Bloeker, 1944:312). Nevada: 5 mi. E, 1 mi. N Grapevine Peak (Hall, 1946:127). New Mexico: near Juan Tofoya, east base Mt. Taylor Plateau, near Puerco River (V. Bailey, 1932:369).

Notiosorex crawfordi evotis (Coues)

1877. *Sorex* (*Notiosorex*) *evotis* Coues, Bull. U.S. Geol. and Geog. Surv. Territories, 3:652, May 15, type from Mazatlán, Sinaloa.
1895. *Notiosorex crawfordi evotis*, Merriam, N. Amer. Fauna, 10:34, December 31.

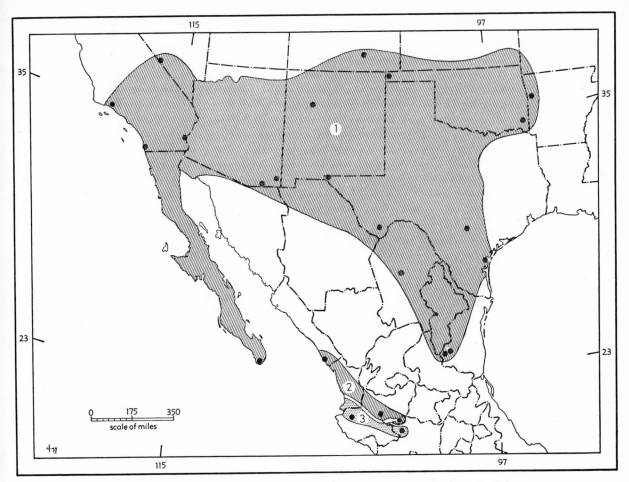

Map 36. *Notiosorex crawfordi crawfordi* (1), *Notiosorex crawfordi evotis* (2), and *Notiosorex gigas* (3).

MARGINAL RECORDS.—Sinaloa: type locality. Michoacán: 2 mi. E La Palma (Baker and Alcorn, 1953:116). Jalisco: 21 mi. SW Guadalajara (Twente and Baker, 1951: 120).

Notiosorex gigas Merriam
Merriam's Desert Shrew

1897. *Notiosorex gigas* Merriam, Proc. Biol. Soc. Washington, 11:227, July 15, type from mountains at Milpillas, near San Sebastián, Jalisco.

External measurements: 127–130; 39–43; 16–17. Condylobasal length, 22.2–22.8; breadth of braincase, 10.5. Pelage plumbeous, barely lighter on underparts than on upper parts. Differs cranially from *C. crawfordi* in straight posterior borders of P4, M1, M2.

MARGINAL RECORDS.—Jalisco: type locality. Michoacán: Los Reyes (Hibbard, 1950:128).

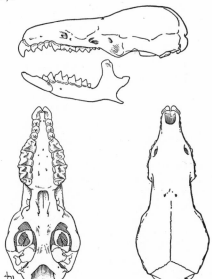

Fig. 31. *Notiosorex gigas*, Los Reyes, Michoacán, No. 125896 U.S.N.M., ♂, X 2.

FAMILY **TALPIDAE**—Moles

The American members of the family have been revised by Jackson (N. Amer. Fauna, 38:1–100, illustrated, September 30, 1915).

External measurements: 100–237; 18–83.5; 13.0–30. Greatest length of skull, 21.1–44.6. Pelage resembling velvet; snout long; opening for eye in skin minute or wanting; forefeet much broader horizontally than thick (vertically); zygomatic arch complete but delicate; crowns of upper molars W-shaped.

From the American shrews, all of which belong to the family Soricidae, the American moles differ as follows: pinna of ear absent, instead of present (small and inconspicuous in *Blarina* and *Cryptotis*); clavicle short and broad instead of long and slender; humerus less, instead of more, than twice as long as wide; pelvis 3, instead of less than 3, times, as long as wide; os falciforme present, instead of absent, on forefoot; terminal phalanges of forefeet bifurcate, instead of simple; zygomata present rather than absent; external pterygoid region rounded and much inflated instead of angular and not inflated; first upper incisor flat and without elongated crown instead of not flat and with elongated crown.

The American members of the family Talpidae all are highly modified for burrowing and for a life underground; one example of this modification is the enlargement of the foreleg and pectoral girdle. All of the species are primarily insectivorous but some, *Scapanus townsendii* for example, eat some plant material. None of the American genera is truly aquatic, but *Condylura* is semiaquatic in that it enters water through burrows of its own making which enter the sides and bottoms of streams under water.

The family has been divided into 5 subfamilies (see Cabrera, 1925:79) of which only two, Condylurinae and Scalopinae, occur in the New World.

KEY TO NORTH AMERICAN GENERA OF TALPIDAE

1. Tail less than one-fourth of total length; width of palm equaling or exceeding its length.
  2. Tail naked or but scantily haired; nostrils superior; auditory bullae complete; interior basal projection of upper molars narrow, simple.
    3. Tail slender, essentially naked; foretoes webbed; 2 lower incisors; geographic range east of Rocky Mts.   *Scalopus*, p. 72
    3'. Tail fleshy and scantily haired; foretoes not webbed; 3 lower incisors; geographic range west of Rocky Mts.   *Scapanus*, p. 67

2'. Tail densely covered with hair; nostrils lateral; auditory bullae incomplete; interior basal projection of upper molars broad, lobed.   *Parascalops*, p. 71
1'. Tail more than one-fourth of total length; width of palm less than its length.
  4. Anterior end of snout with circular fringe of fleshy processes; nostrils circular to oval, and anterior; interior basal projection of first and second upper molars trilobed; premolars $\frac{4}{4}$.   *Condylura*, p. 75
  4'. Anterior end of snout without circular fringe of fleshy processes; nostrils crescentic and lateral; interior basal projection of first and second upper molars bilobed; premolars $\frac{2}{2}$.   *Neürotrichus*, p. 66

SUBFAMILY **SCALOPINAE**

Anterior nasal openings of skull directed anteriorly; snout lacking fleshy appendages.

Genus **Neürotrichus** Günther—Shrew-mole

Revised by Jackson, N. Amer. Fauna, 38:92–98, September 30, 1915.

1880. *Neürotrichus* Günther, Proc. Zool. Soc. London, p. 441, October. Type, *Urotrichus gibbsii* Baird.

Smallest of the American moles; external measurements: 107–126; 33–42; 15.7–17.0. Greatest length of skull, 21.5–24.2. Color dark mouse-gray or blackish mouse-gray. Tail approximately half as long as head and body, moderately fleshy, constricted at base, scaled, annulated, provided with coarse hairs; palms of forefeet longer than broad; toes not webbed; 6 tubercles on sole of hind foot; auditory bullae incomplete; braincase broad and skull scarcely constricted interorbitally; zygomata short; upper molars with bicuspidate internal edge; 1st and 2nd subequal and 3rd smaller. Dentition, i. $\frac{3}{3}$, c. $\frac{1}{1}$, p. $\frac{2}{2}$, m. $\frac{3}{3}$.

Neürotrichus gibbsii
Shrew-mole

See characters of the genus.

The shrew-mole occurs from sea level to 8000 feet elevation, preferring deep soft soil under a cover of deciduous trees, shrubs, or annuals. This species is both diurnal and nocturnal, and eats earthworms, isopods, adult and larval insects, and some vegetable matter, and has litters of 1 to 4 young in all months except December and January.

Neürotrichus gibbsii gibbsii (Baird)

1858. *Urotrichus gibbsii* Baird, Mammals, *in* Repts. Expl. Surv. . . . , 8(1):76, July 14, type from Naches Pass,

Fig. 32. *Neürotrichus gibbsii hyacinthinus*, 5 mi. NNE Point Reyes Lighthouse, Marin Co., California, No. 96374 M.V.Z., ♀, X 1.

4500 ft., Pierce Co., Washington (*fide* Dalquest and Burgner, 1941:12).

1880. *Neürotrichus* [*sic*] *gibbsi,* Günther, Proc. Zool. Soc. London, pl. 42, October.

1899. *Neurotrichus gibbsi major* Merriam, N. Amer. Fauna, 16:88, October 28, type from Carberry Ranch, 4100 ft., between Mt. Shasta and Mt. Lassen, Shasta Co., California.

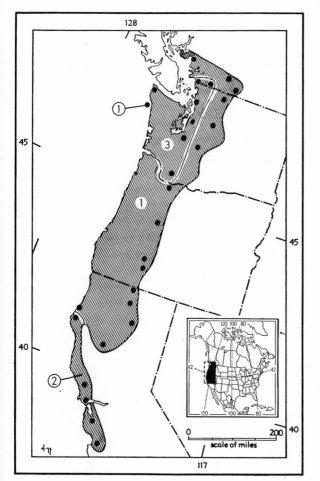

Map 37. *Neürotrichus gibbsii* and subspecies.

Guide to subspecies
1. *N. g. gibbsii*
2. *N. g. hyacinthinus*
3. *N. g. minor*

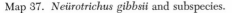

MARGINAL RECORDS (Jackson, 1915:97, unless otherwise noted).—British Columbia: Roberts Creek (Cowan and Guiguet, 1956:64); Hope (Dalquest and Burgner, 1941:13); Allison Pass (Cowan and Guiguet, 1956:64). Washington: Baker Lake (Dalquest, 1948:124); Stevens Pass (Dalquest and Burgner, 1941:12); type locality. Oregon: Multnomah Falls; McKenzie Bridge; Crater Lake (V. Bailey, 1936:355); Fort Klamath (*ibid.*). California: Beswick; Mt. Shasta; Carberry Ranch, Shasta Co.; South Yolla Bolly Mtn. (Anderson, 1947:13); Eureka. Washington: Destruction Island (Dalquest, 1942:334).

Neürotrichus gibbsii hyacinthinus Bangs

1897. *Neürotrichus gibbsi hyacinthinus* Bangs, Amer. Nat., 31:240, March, type from Nicasio, Marin Co., California.

MARGINAL RECORDS (Jackson, 1915:98).—California: Cuddeback; Guerneville; type locality; Palo Alto; Fremont Peak.

Neürotrichus gibbsii minor Dalquest and Burgner

1941. *Neürotrichus gibbsii minor* Dalquest and Burgner, Murrelet, 22:12, April 30, type from Univ. Washington Campus, Seattle, King Co., Washington.

MARGINAL RECORDS.—British Columbia: Vedder Crossing (Cowan and Guiguet, 1956:64); *Cultus Lake* (*ibid.*). Washington: Mt. Vernon (Dalquest, 1948:124); Cottage Lake (*ibid.*); Spanaway (Dalquest and Burgner, 1941:14); Yacolt (Dalquest, 1948:124); Neah Bay (Jackson, 1915:97). British Columbia: Crescent Beach (Cowan and Guiguet, 1956:64).

Genus **Scapanus** Pomel—Western Moles

Revised by Jackson, N. Amer. Fauna, 38:54–76, September 30, 1915.

1848. *Scapanus* Pomel, Arch. Sci. Phys. Nat. Genève, 9:247, November. Type, *Scalops townsendii* Bachman.

External measurements: 132–237; 21–51; 18–28. Greatest length of skull, 29.7–44.6. Body robust; tail short and thick, tapered toward tip, slightly constricted proximally, indistinctly annulated, bearing coarse hairs; snout shorter and less truncate than in *Scalopus,* naked anterior to nostrils; palms of forefeet as broad as long; soles of hind feet bearing 1–3 (usually 2) distinct tubercles; neither forefeet nor hind feet webbed; 4 pairs of mammae, 2 pectoral, 1 abdominal, 1 inguinal; skull conoidal, flattened; braincase relatively broad; interparietal large, somewhat rectangular; audital bullae complete, depressed; infraorbital foramen relatively small, but larger than in *Scalopus;* I1 long and broad; C simple and conical, approximately two-thirds as large as I1; M1 and M2 subequal, M3 much smaller than either of those teeth. Functional dentition, i. $\frac{3}{3}$, c. $\frac{1}{1}$, p. $\frac{4}{4}$ (in some specimens $\frac{2}{3}$ and in others $\frac{3}{3}$), m. $\frac{3}{3}$.

KEY TO SPECIES OF SCAPANUS

1. Unicuspid teeth evenly spaced and not crowded; rostrum long and narrow; color dark, almost black (except in some populations of the small *S. orarius*).
    2. Total length averaging more than 200; greatest length of skull more than 40; sublacrimal-maxillary ridge distinct.
                         S. townsendii, p. 68
    2′. Total length averaging less than 200; greatest length of skull less than 40; sublacrimal-maxillary ridge little developed.
                         S. orarius, p. 68
1′. Unicuspid teeth unevenly spaced and usually crowded; rostrum short and broad; color usually brown or gray, seldom almost black.
                         S. latimanus, p. 69

Scapanus townsendii (Bachman)
Townsend's Mole

1839. *Scalops Townsendii* Bachman, Jour. Acad. Nat. Sci., Philadelphia, 8:58, November, type from vicinity of Vancouver, Clark Co., Washington. (See True, Proc. U.S. Nat. Mus., 19:63, December 21, 1896.)
1848. *Scapanus Tow[n]sendii*, Pomel, Arch. Sci. Phys. Nat. Genève, 9:247, November.

External measurements: 195–237; 34–51; 24–28. Greatest length of skull, 41.2–44.6. Upper parts blackish brown to almost black; sublacrimal ridge well developed.

This large mole is predominantly nocturnal, eats terrestrial invertebrates and small amounts of vegetable matter, and has 3(2–4) young in late March.

MARGINAL RECORDS.—British Columbia: Huntingdon (Anderson, 1947:12). Washington: Sauk (Jackson, 1915:61); Skykomish (*ibid.*); Spray Park, Mt. Rainier National Park, 5500 ft. (Taylor and Shaw, 1927:28); Yacolt (Dalquest, 1948:126). Oregon (Jackson, 1915:61): Oregon City; Drain; Grants Pass. California (*ibid.*): Smith River; Ferndale. (See Map 39.)

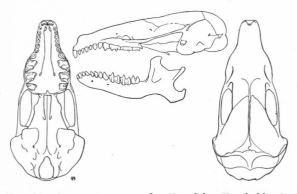

Fig. 33. *Scapanus townsendii*, Ferndale, Humboldt Co., California, No. 19115 M.V.Z., ♂, X 1.

Scapanus orarius
Coast Mole

External measurements: 162–175; 26–37; 21.5–23. Greatest length of skull, 32.8–39.0. Resembles *S. townsendii* but smaller; feet and claws relatively smaller; sublacrimal-maxillary ridge not much developed. Differs from *S. latimanus* in evenly spaced and uncrowded unicuspid teeth, narrower rostrum, undeveloped and indistinct sublacrymal-maxillary ridge, "weaker" mandible, and smaller incisors.

The coast mole occurs with the larger Townsend mole but seems to prefer better drained soil, lives in deeper burrows, enters dense deciduous woods (which the larger species avoids), and has 4 young in late March or early April.

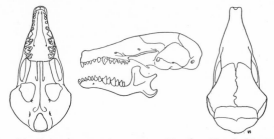

Fig. 34. *Scapanus orarius orarius*, Eureka, Humboldt Co., California, No. 19188 M.V.Z., ♂, X 1.

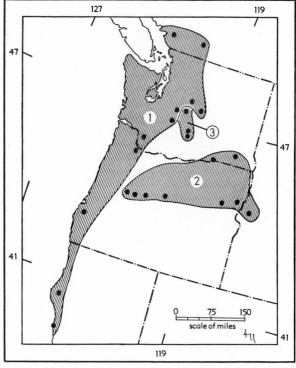

Map 38. *Scapanus orarius* and subspecies.

Guide to subspecies
1. S. o. orarius
2. S. o. schefferi
3. S. o. yakimensis

Scapanus orarius orarius True

1896. *Scapanus orarius* True, Proc. U.S. Nat. Mus., 19:52, December 21, type from Shoalwater Bay (= Willapa Bay), Pacific Co., Washington.

MARGINAL RECORDS.—British Columbia (Anderson, 1947:12): New Westminster; Hope. Washington: Wenatchee (Dalquest, 1948:130); Merritt (*ibid.*); Lester (*ibid.*); Owyhigh Lakes, 5100 ft., Mt. Rainier National Park (Taylor and Shaw, 1927:28); Yacolt (Dalquest, 1948:130). Oregon (Jackson, 1915:62): Portland; Myrtle Point. California (*ibid.*): Cuddeback; Mendocino.

Scapanus orarius schefferi Jackson

1915. *Scapanus orarius schefferi* Jackson, N. Amer. Fauna, 38:63, September 30, type from Walla Walla, Walla Walla Co., Washington.

MARGINAL RECORDS.—Washington: Dayton (Dalquest, 1948:130). Idaho: Cambridge (Caswell, 1953:9). Oregon: Halfway (V. Bailey, 1936:354); near Baker (*ibid.*); "Blue Mountains Country near Prineville" (*ibid.*); N base Three Sisters, 5000 and 5500 ft. (*ibid.*); McKenzie Bridge (Jackson, 1915:64); Vida (*ibid.*). Washington: Walla Walla (*ibid.*).

Scapanus orarius yakimensis Dalquest and Scheffer

1944. *Scapanus orarius yakimensis* Dalquest and Scheffer, Murrelet, 25:27, September 19, type from ¾ mi. N Union Gap, Yakima Co., Washington.

MARGINAL RECORDS (Dalquest and Scheffer, 1944:28).—Washington: Easton; Selah; type locality.

Scapanus latimanus
Broad-footed Mole

Revised by F. G. Palmer, Jour. Mamm., 18:280–314, August 14, 1937.

External measurements: 132–192; 21–45; 18–25. Greatest length of skull, 29.7–37.4. Smaller and less blackish than *S. townsendii*; differences from *S. orarius* are listed in the account of that species.

S. latimanus prefers moist soils with an abundance of invertebrate life; 4(2–5) young are born in March or April.

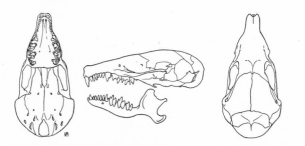

Fig. 35. *Scapanus latimanus monoensis*, East Walker River, 2 mi. NW Morgan's Ranch, Nevada, No. 63520 M.V.Z., ♂, X 1.

Scapanus latimanus anthonyi J. A. Allen

1893. *Scapanus anthonyi* J. A. Allen, Bull. Amer. Mus. Nat. Hist. 5:200, August 18, type from Sierra San Pedro Mártir, 7000 ft., Baja California.

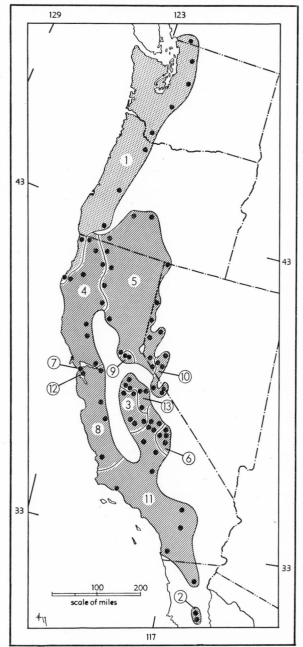

Map 39. *Scapanus latimanus* and *Scapanus townsendii*.

Guide to kinds
1. *S. townsendii*
2. *S. l. anthonyi*
3. *S. l. campi*
4. *S. l. caurinus*
5. *S. l. dilatus*
6. *S. l. grinnelli*
7. *S. l. insularis*
8. *S. l. latimanus*
9. *S. l. minusculus*
10. *S. l. monoensis*
11. *S. l. occultus*
12. *S. l. parvus*
13. *S. l. sericatus*

1937. *Scapanus latimanus anthonyi*, F. G. Palmer, Jour. Mamm. 18:312, August 14.

MARGINAL RECORDS (F. G. Palmer, 1937:313).—Baja California: Vallecitos, 7500 ft.; La Grulla, 7200 ft.

Scapanus latimanus campi Grinnell and Storer

1916. *Scapanus latimanus campi* Grinnell and Storer, Univ. California Publ. Zool., 17:1, August 23, type from Snelling, 250 ft., Merced Co., California.

MARGINAL RECORDS (F. G. Palmer, 1937:303).—California: El Portal, 2000 ft. (1937:303); Dunlap, 2000 ft.; Minkler, 200 ft.; 3 mi. N Sanger; type locality.

Scapanus latimanus caurinus F. G. Palmer

1937. *Scapanus latimanus caurinus* F. G. Palmer, Jour. Mamm., 18:290, August 14, type from Laytonville, Mendocino Co., California.

MARGINAL RECORDS (F. G. Palmer, 1937:291, unless otherwise noted).—California: E. Fork Illinois River, ¼ mi. S Oregon line; Poker Flat, 5800 ft., 12 mi. NW Happy Camp; Scott River, 6 mi. NW Callahan; Red Bluff; Snow Mtn. (Jackson, 1915:67); Long Valley; Lake Chabot; Cuddeback; Horse Mtn., 4700–5000 ft.

Scapanus latimanus dilatus True

1894. *Scapanus dilatus* True, Diagnoses of new North American mammals, p. 2, April 26 (preprint of Proc. U.S. Nat. Mus., 17:242, November 15, 1894), type from Fort Klamath, 4200 ft., Klamath Co., Oregon.
1913. *Scapanus latimanus dilatus*, Grinnell, Proc. California Acad. Sci., 3:269, August 28.
1897. *Scapanus truei* Merriam, Proc. Biol. Soc. Washington, 11:102, April 26, type from Lake City, Modoc Co., California.
1897. *Scapanus alpinus* Merriam, Proc. Biol. Soc. Washington, 11:102, April 26, type from Crater Lake, 7000 ft., Klamath Co., Oregon.

MARGINAL RECORDS (F. G. Palmer, 1937:297, unless otherwise noted).—Oregon: Fremont (Jackson, 1915:74). Nevada (Hall, 1946:111): Twelve Mile Creek, 1½ mi. E California boundary, 5300 ft.; 1 mi. W Hausen; N side State-line Peak; 3 mi. W Reno; 4 mi. W Nixon, S end Pyramid Lake; 5 mi. S, 3¾ mi. E Minden; Holbrook. California: Auburn (Jackson, 1915:74); Chico (*ibid.*); Tower House; Sisson; head of Doggett Creek [= Deer Camp], 5800 ft. Oregon: 6 mi. S Medford, 1600 ft.; Crater Lake (Merriam, 1897:102).

Scapanus latimanus grinnelli Jackson

1914. *Scapanus latimanus grinnelli* Jackson, Proc. Biol. Soc. Washington, 27:56, March 20, type from site of old Fort Independence (on ranch of Carl Walters), 2 mi. N Independence, 3900 ft., Inyo Co., California.

MARGINAL RECORDS.—California: type locality; Lone Pine (F. G. Palmer, 1937:309); Olancha, Owens Lake (True, 1896:57); Upper Funston Meadow, 6700 ft., Kern River (F. G. Palmer, 1937:309).

Scapanus latimanus insularis F. G. Palmer

1937. *Scapanus latimanus insularis* F. G. Palmer, Jour. Mamm., 18:297, August 14, type from Angel Island, San Francisco Bay, Marin Co., California. Known only from Angel Island.

Scapanus latimanus latimanus (Bachman)

1842. *Scalops latimanus* Bachman, Boston Jour. Nat. Hist., 4:34, type probably from Santa Clara, Santa Clara Co., California (*fide* Osgood, Proc. Biol. Soc. Washington, 20:52, 1907).
1856. *Scalops californicus* Ayres, Proc. California Acad. Sci., 1:54. Based on specimens from San Francisco, California.
1912. *Scapanus latimanus latimanus*, Grinnell and Swarth, Univ. California Publ. Zool., 10:131, April 13.

MARGINAL RECORDS.—California: Pinole (F. G. Palmer, 1937:300); Bells Station (Jackson, 1915:67); 1 mi. SE Summit San Benito Mtn., 4400 ft. (F. G. Palmer, 1937:300); Santa Margarita (*ibid.*).

Scapanus latimanus minusculus Bangs

1899. *Scapanus californicus minusculus* Bangs, Proc. New England Zool. Club, 1:70, July 31, type from Fyffe, 3500 ft., Eldorado Co., California.
1912. *Scapanus latimanus minusculus*, Grinnell and Swarth, Univ. California Publ. Zool., 10:133, April 13.

MARGINAL RECORDS.—California: Placerville (F. G. Palmer, 1937:302); type locality.

Scapanus latimanus monoensis Grinnell

1918. *Scapanus latimanus monoensis* Grinnell, Univ. California Publ. Zool., 17:423, April 25, type from Taylor Ranch, 5300 ft., 2 mi. S Benton Station, Mono Co., California.

MARGINAL RECORDS (F. G. Palmer, 1937:308–309, unless otherwise noted).—Nevada (Hall, 1946:113): in bend of Walker River, 4½ mi. E Wabuska; E. Walker River, 2 mi. NW Morgan's Ranch, 5050 ft. California: Pellisier Ranch, 5 mi. N Benton Station; type locality; Farrington's (near Williams Butte), 6800 ft., Mono Lake. Nevada: W. Walker River, 10½ mi. S Yerington, 4500 ft. (Hall, 1946:113).

Scapanus latimanus occultus Grinnell and Swarth

1912. *Scapanus latimanus occultus* Grinnell and Swarth, Univ. California Publ. Zool., 10:131, April 13, type from Santa Ana Canyon, 400 ft., 12 mi. NE Santa Ana, Orange Co., California.

MARGINAL RECORDS (F. G. Palmer, 1937:311–312, unless otherwise noted).—California: Kings River Canyon, 5000 ft.; Twin Lakes, 9800 ft., Sequoia National Park; Parker Meadow, 6400 ft.; Tehachapi (Jackson, 1915:69); San Bernardino Peak (*ibid.*); Strawberry Valley, 6000 ft., San Jacinto Mts. Baja California: Laguna Hanson, Sierra Juarez. California: Lakeside; Santa Barbara; 6 mi. WNW Porterville, 380 ft.; Big Meadow, 7660 ft.; Hume, 5300 ft.

Scapanus latimanus parvus F. G. Palmer

1937. *Scapanus latimanus parvus* F. G. Palmer, Jour. Mamm., 18:300, August 14, type from Alameda, Alameda Co., California. Known only from Alameda Island, Alameda Co., California.

Scapanus latimanus sericatus Jackson

1914. *Scapanus latimanus sericatus* Jackson, Proc. Biol. Soc. Washington, 27:55, March 20, type from Yosemite, Yosemite Valley, Mariposa Co., California.

MARGINAL RECORDS (F. G. Palmer, 1937:307).—California: Twain Harte P.O., 4000 ft.; Tuolumne Meadows, 8600 ft.; Shaver Ranger Station, 5300 ft.; type locality; Merced Grove Big Trees, 5400 ft.; 3 mi. NE Coulterville, 3200 ft.

Genus **Parascalops** True—Hairy-tailed Mole

Revised by Jackson, N. Amer. Fauna, 38:77–82, September 30, 1915.

1894. *Parascalops* True, Diagnoses of new North American mammals, p. 2, April 26 (preprint of Proc. U.S. Nat. Mus., 17:242, November 15, 1894). Type, *Scalops breweri* Bachman.

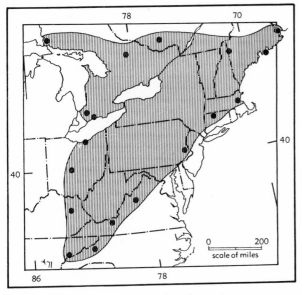

Map 40. *Parascalops breweri.*

External measurements: 139–153; 23–36; 18–20. Greatest length of skull, 31.0–33.8. Color blackish; tail thick, fleshy, constricted at base, annulated, and densely covered with long coarse hairs; snout shorter than in *Scalopus* or *Scapanus* and with median longitudinal groove on its anterior half; nostrils lateral, crescentic, with concavities directed upward; palms of forefeet as broad as long; toes not webbed; auditory bullae incomplete; M1 and M2 having trilobed internal basal shelf; corresponding part of M3 bilobed. Dentition, i. $\frac{3}{3}$, c. $\frac{1}{1}$, p. $\frac{4}{4}$, m. $\frac{3}{3}$.

Parascalops breweri (Bachman)
Hairy-tailed Mole

1842. *Scalops breweri* Bachman, Boston Jour. Nat. Hist., 4:32, type locality in eastern North America; type supposed by Bachman to have been taken on the island of Marthas Vineyard, Massachusetts, a locality where the animal probably does not occur.

1895. *Parascalops breweri*, True, Science, n. s., 1:101, January 25.

See characters of the genus. Only one species is known.

The hairy-tailed mole inhabits light, well-drained soils in forests and open areas, mates in March or April, and produces 4 or 5 young after a gestation period of 4 to 6 weeks. The young are sexually mature the following spring. The food is earthworms, insects, and other arthropods.

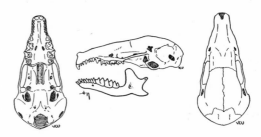

Fig. 36. *Parascalops breweri*, 2 mi. S Center Ossipee, Carroll Co., New Hampshire, No. 11335 K.U., sex ?, X 1.

MARGINAL RECORDS.—Ontario: Pancake Bay (Anderson, 1947:12); Rock Lake, Algonquin Park (Saunders, 1932:272). Quebec: Meaches Lake (Jackson, 1915:82). Maine: Lake Umbagog (*ibid.*). New Brunswick: Charlotte County (*ibid.*). Maine: Mount Desert Island (Manville, 1942:392). Massachusetts: Harvard (Jackson, 1915:82). Connecticut: West Winstead (*ibid.*). Pennsylvania: Brownsburg (*ibid.*). Virginia: Camp Todd, near Mt. Solon (Saylor, 1938:247); Mountain Lake (*ibid.*). North Carolina: Magnetic City, foot Roan Mountain (Jackson, 1915:82). Tennessee: Chapman Prong, 3200 ft. (Kellogg, 1939:247). Kentucky: Triplet Creek, near Clearfield (Welter and Sollberger, 1939:78). Ohio: Franklin Co. (Olive, 1950:459); Rocky River Metropolitan Park (Bole and Moulthrop, 1942:88). Ontario: Port Bruce on Lake Erie (Saunders, 1932:272); 15–20 mi. W London (*ibid.*).

Genus **Scalopus** É. Geoffroy St.-Hilaire
Eastern Mole

Revised by Jackson, N. Amer. Fauna, 38:27–54, September 30, 1915.

1803. *Scalopus* É. Geoffroy St.-Hilaire, Catalogue des mammifères du Muséum National d'Histoire Naturelle, Paris, p. 77. Type, *Sorex aquaticus* Linnaeus.

External measurements: 128–208; 18–38; 15–22. Greatest length of skull, 29.3–39.5. Tail less than a fourth of total length, terete, indistinctly annulated and nearly naked; nose a distinct snout, naked anterior to nostrils; palms of forefeet broader than long; toes webbed on hind feet and on forefeet; interparietal short and narrow; frontal sinuses swollen; anterior nares of skull directed forward; audital bullae complete; external pterygoid region much inflated posteriorly and slightly inflated anteriorly; I1 long and broad; C approximately two-thirds as large as first incisor and simple; M1 and M2 subequal; no persistent lower canine; lower premolars increasing in size posteriorly; lower molars successively decreasing in size posteriorly. Functional dentition, i. $\frac{3}{2}$, c. $\frac{1}{0}$, p. $\frac{3}{3}$, m. $\frac{3}{3}$.

S. *inflatus* and S. *montanus* from northern Mexico seem to be relict populations of the once more widespread S. *aquaticus*.

KEY TO SPECIES OF SCALOPUS

1. Known geographic range north of the United States-Mexican boundary. . S. *aquaticus*, p. 72
1'. Known geographic range south of the United States–Mexican boundary.
    2. Prelachrymal region much inflated; zygomata heavy; known geographic range confined to Tamaulipas, Mexico.
        S. *inflatus*, p. 75
    2'. Prelachrymal region not inflated; zygomata slender; known geographic range Sierra del Carmen, Coahuila, Mexico.
        S. *montanus*, p. 75

Scalopus aquaticus
Eastern Mole

For characters see account of the genus.

More than 99% of the eastern mole's life is spent below ground in tunnels of its own construction.

These tunnels are of two sorts. One is made only an inch or so below the surface of the ground by the mole's "swimming" through the relatively loose topsoil. In constructing this sort of runway, the mole leaves a ridge of earth on the ground. The other sort of tunnel is more permanent and is dug 6 to 10 inches below the surface of the ground. In constructing this latter sort of tunnel, no ridge of earth is left but mounds of earth are thrown up at intervals. Animal matter makes up nearly all of the food. This mole eats more earthworms than anything else; grubs, other soft-bodied insects, and even hard-shelled insects are eaten. The nest is constructed underground of fine grasses or leaves and is in a chamber that is 4 to 6 inches in diameter. Four young is the usual number and it seems that there is only one litter per year.

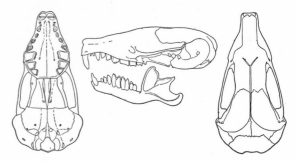

Fig. 37. *Scalopus aquaticus machrinoides*, Hamilton, Greenwood Co., Kansas, No. 95767 M.V.Z., ♂, X 1.

Scalopus aquaticus aereus (Bangs)

1896. *Scalops texanus aereus* Bangs, Proc. Biol. Soc. Washington, 10:138, December 28, type from Stilwell, Adair Co., Oklahoma.
1912. *Scalopus aquaticus aereus*, Miller, Bull. U.S. Nat. Mus., 79:8, December 31 (*fide* Hall and Kelson, Univ. Kansas Publ., Mus. Nat. Hist., 5:326, December 5, 1952).
1914. *Scalopus aquaticus pulcher* Jackson, Proc. Biol. Soc. Washington, 27:20, February 2, type from Delight, Pike Co., Arkansas.

MARGINAL RECORDS (Jackson, 1915:48–52, unless otherwise noted).—Oklahoma: Scraper (Blair, 1939:97); type locality. Arkansas: Fort Smith; Delight; Lake City; Wilmot. Louisiana: Oak Grove (Lowery, 1936:16); Tallulah (*ibid.*); Grand Coteau (Lowery, 1943:217); Avery Island (*ibid.*). Texas: 7 mi. NE Sour Lake; Denton (Davis, 1942:383); Denison (*ibid.*).

Scalopus aquaticus alleni Baker

1951. *Scalopus aquaticus alleni* Baker, Univ. Kansas Publ., Mus. Nat. Hist., 5:22, February 28, type from Rockport, Aransas Co., Texas.

MARGINAL RECORDS (Davis, 1942:386).—Texas: San Antonio; Kennedy; Aransas National Wildlife Refuge; Brownsville; *Benton*.

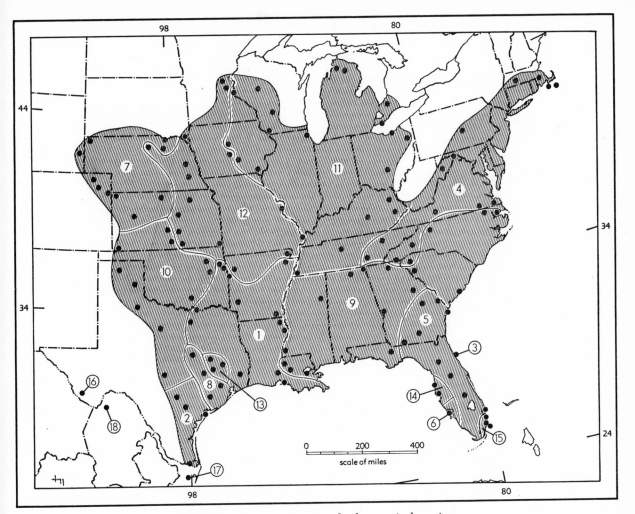

Map 41. *Scalopus aquaticus* and other nominal species.

1. *S. a. aereus*
2. *S. a. alleni*
3. *S. a. anastasae*
4. *S. a. aquaticus*
5. *S. a. australis*
6. *S. a. bassi*

7. *S. a. caryi*
8. *S. a. cryptus*
9. *S. a. howelli*
10. *S. a. intermedius*
11. *S. a. machrinus*
12. *S. a. machrinoides*

13. *S. a. nanus*
14. *S. a. parvus*
15. *S. a. porteri*
16. *S. a. texanus*
17. *S. inflatus*
18. *S. montanus*

Scalopus aquaticus anastasae (Bangs)

1898. *Scalops anastasae* Bangs, Proc. Boston Soc. Nat. Hist., 28:212, March, type from Point Romo, Anastasia Island, St. John Co., Florida. Known only from Anastasia Island, Florida.
1915. *Scalopus aquaticus anastasae*, Jackson, N. Amer. Fauna, 38:39, September 30.

Scalopus aquaticus aquaticus (Linnaeus)

1758. [*Sorex*] *aquaticus* Linnaeus, Syst. nat., ed. 10, 1:53. Type locality, eastern United States (Philadelphia, Pennsylvania; fixed by Jackson, N. Amer. Fauna, 38:33, September 30, 1915).

1905. *Scalopus aquaticus*, Oberholser, Mammals and summer birds of western North Carolina, Biltmore Forest School, Biltmore, North Carolina, p. 3, June 30.
1803. *Scalopus virginianus* É. Geoffroy St.-Hilaire, Catalogue des mammifères du Muséum National d'Histoire Naturelle, Paris, p. 78. Type locality, Virginia (?).
1814. *Talpa cupreata* Rafinesque, Précis des découvertes et travaux somiologiques . . . , p. 14. Type locality, "Atlantic States."
1825. *Scalops pennsylvanica* Harlan, Fauna Americana, p. 33, type from an unknown locality.

MARGINAL RECORDS (Jackson, 1915:36, unless otherwise noted).—Massachusetts: Holyoke; Middleboro; Nantucket; West Tisbury. Virginia: Dismal Swamp; Brunswick County (Handley and Patton, 1947:103); Montgomery

County (*ibid.*). North Carolina: Buncombe County. South Carolina: Greenville (Penney, 1950:83). North Carolina: Highlands (Odum, 1949:186). Tennessee: Briceville (Kellogg, 1939:248); Walden Ridge near Rathburn (Soddy P.O.) (*ibid.*). West Virginia: Moorefield (Wilson, 1944: 202); Berkeley Springs (Kellogg, 1937:445). Pennsylvania: Mifflintown.

Scalopus aquaticus australis (Chapman)

1893. *Scalops aquaticus australis* Chapman, Bull. Amer. Mus. Nat. Hist., 5:339, December 22, type from Gainesville, Alachua Co., Florida.
1905. *Scalopus aquaticus australis*, Elliot, Field Columb. Mus., Publ. 105, Zool. Ser., 6:470.

MARGINAL RECORDS (Jackson, 1915:39, unless otherwise noted).—Georgia: Pinetucky; Hursman's Lake; Montgomery. Florida: Hypoluxo (Schwartz, 1952:384); Orange Hammock (Sherman, 1937:104); Eustis (*ibid.*); Levy Lake (*ibid.*). Georgia: 10 mi. SSW Thomasville (Hall and Kelson, 1952:326); Nashville.

Scalopus aquaticus bassi Howell

1939. *Scalopus aquaticus bassi* Howell, Jour. Mamm., 20: 363, August 14, type from Englewood, Sarasota Co., Florida. Known only from the type locality.

Scalopus aquaticus caryi Jackson

1914. *Scalopus aquaticus caryi* Jackson, Proc. Biol. Soc. Washington, 27:20, February 2, type from Neligh, Antelope Co., Nebraska.

MARGINAL RECORDS (Jackson, 1915:49, unless otherwise noted).—Nebraska: Warbonnet Canyon; Niobrara River; type locality. Kansas (Cockrum, 1952:50): Smith Center; Logan County; 23 mi. (by road) NW St. Francis. Colorado: Wray (Warren, 1942:6); Akron (Burnett, 1924: 264); Merino (*ibid.*). Wyoming: Horse Creek, 3 mi. W Meriden (14772 KU).

Scalopus aquaticus cryptus Davis

1942. *Scalopus aquaticus cryptus* Davis, Amer. Midl. Nat., 27:384, March, type from College Station, Brazos Co., Texas.

MARGINAL RECORDS (Davis, 1942:385).—Texas: Waco; 3–5 mi. N Bryan; 2½ mi. N Hockley; 20 mi. S Eagle Lake.

Scalopus aquaticus howelli Jackson

1914. *Scalopus aquaticus howelli* Jackson, Proc. Biol. Soc. Washington, 27:19, February 2, type from Autaugaville, Autauga Co., Alabama.

MARGINAL RECORDS (Jackson, 1915:37–38, unless otherwise noted).—North Carolina: Jackson; Moran. South Carolina: Charleston. Georgia: Crawfordsville; Columbus. Florida: Rock Bluff (Sherman, 1937:104). Louisiana: New Orleans (Lowery, 1936:15); Baton Rouge (*ibid.*); St. Francisville (*ibid.*). Mississippi: Washington; Cedarbluff. Alabama: Huntsville; Sand Mtn., near Carpenter. Georgia: Young Harris. South Carolina: Abbeville. North Carolina: Wilkesboro.

Scalopus aquaticus intermedius (Elliot)

1899. *Scalops machrinus intermedius* Elliot, Field Columb. Mus., Publ. 37, Zool. Ser., 1:280, May 15, type from Alva, Woods Co., Oklahoma.
1905. *Scalopus aquaticus intermedius,* V. Bailey, N. Amer. Fauna, 25:207, October 24.

MARGINAL RECORDS.—Kansas (Cockrum, 1952:53): Little Salt Marsh; 4 mi. NE Harper. Oklahoma (Blair, 1939:97–98): Garnett; 3 mi. E Wainwright; Dougherty. Texas: Mason (Davis, 1942:385); Belknap (*ibid.*); Paducah (Blair, 1954b:242); 2½ mi. W and 6 mi. S Mobeetie (Stickel and Stickel, 1948:292); Stinnett (Blair, 1954b:242). Kansas: 9 mi. N and 3 mi. E Elkhart (Cockrum, 1952:53).

Scalopus aquaticus machrinus (Rafinesque)

1832. *Talpa machrina* Rafinesque, Atlantic Jour., 1:61. Type locality, near Lexington, Fayette Co., Kentucky.
1905. *Scalopus aquaticus machrinus,* Elliot, Field Columb. Mus., Publ. 105, Zool. Ser., 6:470.
1832. *Talpa sericea* Rafinesque, Atlantic Jour., 1:62, type locality near Nicholasville and Harrodsburg, Kentucky.
1842. *Scalops argentatus* Audubon and Bachman, Jour. Acad. Nat. Sci., Philadelphia, 8:292, type locality in southern Michigan.

MARGINAL RECORDS (Jackson, 1915:44, unless otherwise noted).—Michigan: Charlevoix Co. (Burt, 1946:86); Valentine Lake (Green, 1925:175). Ontario: Shathroy (Saunders, 1932:273); Point Pelee. Ohio: Cleveland; Salem; Fairfield Co. Kentucky: Rowan County (Welter and Sollberger, 1939:78); Quicksand (Hamilton, 1930:306); Eubanks. Tennessee: Nashville; Ellendale (Kellogg, 1939: 249). Iowa: Hillsboro; Knoxville; Jewell (Scott, 1937:52). Wisconsin: Prescott; Hewett Twp., Clark Co. (Schmidt, 1931:107); Camp Douglas; White City Resort, 1½ mi. N Dubuque, Iowa (Jackson, 1922:115). Illinois: Fremont.

Scalopus aquaticus machrinoides Jackson

1914. *Scalopus aquaticus machrinoides* Jackson, Proc. Biol. Soc. Washington, 27:19, February 2, type from Manhattan, Riley Co., Kansas.

MARGINAL RECORDS (Jackson, 1915:46, unless otherwise noted).—Minnesota: Elk River; Ramsey Co. (Swanson, 1945:56). Iowa: Ames (Scott, 1937:52). Missouri: St. Louis; Charleston. Arkansas: Greenway; Winslow. Kansas (Cockrum, 1952:52): Shole Creek; 6 mi. NE Wellington; Halstead; 6 mi. S Solomon; Blue Rapids. Nebraska: Lincoln; Everett; Perch. South Dakota: Vermillion.

Scalopus aquaticus nanus Davis

1942. *Scalopus aquaticus nanus* Davis, Amer. Midl. Nat., 27:383, March, type from 13 mi. E Centerville, Leon Co., Texas.

MARGINAL RECORDS.—Texas: type locality; 7 mi. E Trinity (Davis, 1942:384); 17 mi. WNW Huntsville (*ibid.*).

Scalopus aquaticus parvus (Rhoads)

1894. *Scalops parvus* Rhoads, Proc. Acad. Nat. Sci., Philadelphia, 46:157, type from Tarpon Springs, Pinellas Co., Florida.
1915. *Scalopus aquaticus parvus,* Jackson, N. Amer. Fauna, 38:41, September 30.

MARGINAL RECORDS (Jackson, 1915:42).—Florida: Port Richey; Port Tampa City.

Scalopus aquaticus porteri Schwartz

1952. *Scalopus aquaticus porteri* Schwartz, Jour. Mamm., 33:381, August 19, type from Uleta, Dade Co., Florida.

MARGINAL RECORDS (Schwartz, 1952:382–383).— Florida: type locality; Biscayne Gardens; Lemon City.

Scalopus aquaticus texanus (J. A. Allen)

1891. *Scalops argentatus texanus* J. A. Allen, Bull. Amer. Mus. Nat. Hist., 3:221, April 29, type from Presidio County, Texas. Known only from the type locality which, as Baker [see below] points out, might be in present day Brewster, Jeff Davis, or Presidio counties, Texas.

1951. *Scalopus aquaticus texanus* Baker, Univ. Kansas Publ., Mus. Nat. Hist., 5:21, February 28. Not of V. Bailey, 1905.

Scalopus inflatus Jackson
Tamaulipan Mole

1914. *Scalopus inflatus* Jackson, Proc. Biol. Soc. Washington, 27:21, February 2, type from Tamaulipas, 45 miles from Brownsville, Texas. Known only from the type locality.

External measurements: tail vertebrae, 18; hind foot, 16.5; skull high and arched; prelacrimal region much inflated; rostrum broad and truncate; zygomata heavy.

Scalopus montanus Baker
Coahuilan Mole

1951. *Scalopus montanus* Baker, Univ. Kansas Publ., Mus. Nat. Hist., 5:19, February 28, type from Club Sierra del Carmen, 2 mi. N, 6 mi. W Piedra Blanca, Coahuila. Known only from the type locality.

External measurements: 150; 27; 20. Greatest length of skull, 32.2. Upper parts Buffy Brown; underparts similar to upper parts; skull small, arched, slender across mastoid region, posterior part of cranium depressed; teeth small, especially M3.

SUBFAMILY **CONDYLURINAE**
Star-nosed Mole

Anterior nares of skull opening obliquely upward; snout provided with ring of fleshy appendages.

Genus **Condylura** Illiger—Star-nosed Mole

Revised by Jackson, N. Amer. Fauna, 38:82–91, September 30, 1915.

1811. *Condylura* Illiger, Prodromus systematis mammalium et avium . . . , p. 125. Type, *Sorex cristatus* Linnaeus.

External measurements: 183–211; 65–83.5; 26–30. Greatest length of skull, 33.9–35.2. Blackish brown to nearly black. Nose having ring of 22 fleshy appendages; tail approximately as long as body, constricted at base, scaled, annulated; palms of forefeet as broad as long; premaxillae much extended beyond nasals anteriorly; first upper incisors large, incurved, and projecting anteriorly.

Condylura cristata
Star-nosed Mole

Characters as for the genus.

The star-nosed mole prefers damp or muddy soil and this, rather than the type of plant cover, largely determines the local distribution. Tunnels are constructed and some of these lead directly into water; the animal is an expert swimmer. Food consists of aquatic insects, crustaceans, small fish, and annelids. A single litter of 3 to 7 young is born between mid-April and mid-June. The young are blind and naked at birth but are fully furred when they leave the nest at 3 weeks of age.

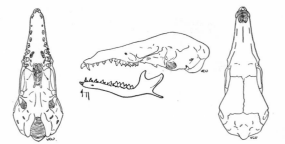

Fig. 38. *Condylura cristata cristata*, 2 mi. S Center Ossipee, Carroll Co., New Hampshire, No. 11336 K.U., ♂, X 1.

Condylura cristata cristata (Linnaeus)

1758. [*Sorex*] *cristatus* Linnaeus, Syst. nat., ed. 10, 1:53. Type locality, Pennsylvania.

1819. *Condylura cristata*, Desmarest, Jour. de Phys., Chim., Hist. Nat., et des Arts, 89:230, September.

MARGINAL RECORDS (Jackson, 1915:91, unless otherwise noted).—Labrador: Hamilton Inlet (C. F. Jackson, 1938:431). New Brunswick: Hampton. Virginia: Dismal Swamp; Richmond County (Handley and Patton, 1947: 102); Fairfax County (*ibid.*); Patrick County (*ibid.*).

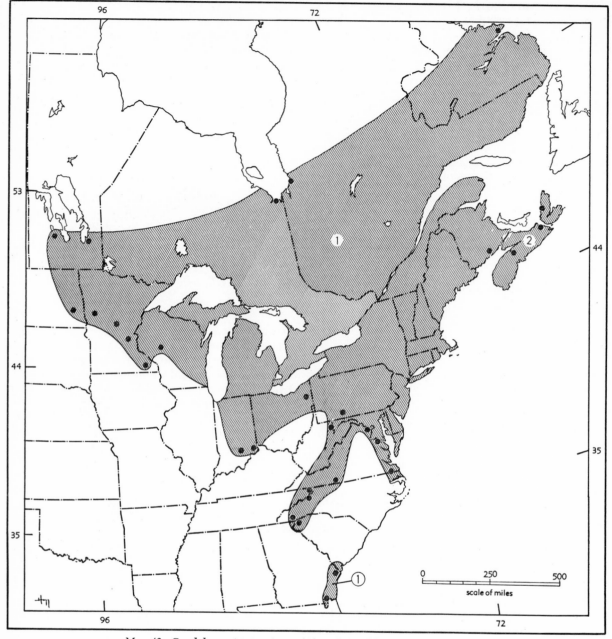

Map 42. *Condylura cristata cristata* (1) and *Condylura cristata nigra* (2).

South Carolina: "Upper South Carolina" (Penney, 1950: 83). North Carolina: Highlands (Odum, 1949:187); Weaverville. Tennessee: Shady Valley (Kellogg, 1939:249). West Virginia: Lake Terra Alta (Barbour, 1951:368). Pennsylvania: New Lexington. Ohio: Ellsworth. Indiana (Lyon, 1936:37): Dearborn County; Bartholomew County. Wisconsin: Worden Twp., Clark Co. (Schmidt, 1931:107). Minnesota: Olmstead County (Gunderson and Beer, 1953: 36); Elk River; Fort Ripley; Detroit Lakes (Swanson, 1945: 56). North Dakota: Tower (V. Bailey, 1927:200). Manitoba: Riding Mtn. (Anderson, 1947:13); Pine Falls (Soper, 1946:134). Ontario: Moose Factory. Quebec: East Main

River (Anderson, 1947:13). Also Georgia: Marlow; Mixon's Ferry, Okefinokee Swamp (Harper, 1927:269). For Illinois, Hoffmeister (1954:1) indicates that there are no authentic records.

Condylura cristata nigra Smith

1940. *Condylura cristata nigra* R. W. Smith, Amer. Midl. Nat. 24:218, July, type from Wolfville, Kings Co., Nova Scotia.

MARGINAL RECORDS (Smith, 1940:219).—Nova Scotia: Frizzleton; James River; Newport.

Family NESOPHONTIDAE
Nesophontid Insectivores

Greatest length of skull, 52. Lacking jugal bone and zygomatic arch; seemingly lacking auditory bulla; braincase low; rostrum elongate and tubular; sagittal and lambdoidal crests present, the latter especially prominent; occlusal outline of upper molars V-shaped; M3 no less than half as large as M2; incisors simple, smaller than canines; diastema between first upper incisors; canines daggerlike and two-rooted. Dentition, i. $\frac{3}{3}$, c. $\frac{1}{1}$, p. $\frac{3}{3}$, m. $\frac{3}{3}$. Only one genus, *Nesophontes*, is known.

Genus Nesophontes Anthony
Nesophontid Insectivores

1916. *Nesophontes* Anthony, Bull. Amer. Mus. Nat. Hist., 35:725, November 16. Type, *Nesophontes edithae* Anthony.

Generic characters are those of the family. The external appearance of these insectivores is unknown, since our knowledge of them is based on bones recovered from caves and kitchen middens in the Greater Antilles. The animals probably became extinct after the arrival of the Spaniards. Bones of *Nesophontes* and *Rattus* have been found together (Miller, 1929:3) and *Rattus* is thought not to have arrived before the Spaniards did. Miller (*loc. cit.*) says in relation to Haiti "it seems not improbable, however, that if any part of the island remains uninvaded by the roof rat, the native animal might now be found to exist there."

Key to Species of Nesophontes

1. Occurring in Puerto Rico. . . *N. edithae*, p. 77
1'. Occurring in Cuba or Haiti.
  2. Palatal length less than 10.7. *N. zamicrus*, p. 78
  2'. Palatal length more than 10.7.
    3. Occurring in Cuba.
      4. Upper premolars widely separated; first premolar widely separated from canine. *N. longirostris*, p. 77
      4'. Upper premolars not widely separated from each other; first premolar not widely separated from canine. . . . *N. micrus*, p. 77
    3'. Occurring in Haiti.
      5. Articular process to front of m1 more than 12.2; depths through coronoid process more than 7.3; combined length of m1 and m2 more than 4.2. . *N. paramicrus*, p. 77
      5'. Articular process to front of m1 less than 12.2; depth through coronoid process less than 7.3; combined length of m1 and m2 less than 4.2 . . . *N. hypomicrus*, p. 78

Nesophontes edithae Anthony
Puerto Rican Nesophontes

1916. *Nesophontes edithae* Anthony, Bull. Amer. Mus. Nat. Hist., 35:725, November 16, type from Cueva Catedral, near Morovis, Puerto Rico. Known only from skeletal remains from Puerto Rico.

Skulls of presumptive males are larger than those of presumptive females; the greatest length of skull is 52 in the former and 40.8 in the latter.

Nesophontes longirostris Anthony
Slender Cuban Nesophontes

1919. *Nesophontes longirostris* Anthony, Bull. Amer. Mus. Nat. Hist., 41:633, December 30, type from cave near the beach at Daiquiri, Cuba. Known only from skeletal remains from Cuba.

This species is distinguished from *N. micrus*, also of Cuba, by the longer and relatively more slender skull.

Nesophontes micrus G.M. Allen
Cuban Nesophontes

1917. *Nesophontes micrus* G. M. Allen, Bull. Mus. Comp. Zool., 61:5, January, type from Sierra de Hato-Nuevo, Province of Matanzas, Cuba. Known only from skeletal remains. Existed on Isle of Pines and throughout Cuba (see Koopman and Ruibal, 1955:2–3).

The difference between this species and *N. edithae* of Puerto Rico have been listed in detail by Anthony (1919:633) as well as by the describer of *N. micrus* in the original description. Some of the differences characterizing *N. micrus* are as follows: occipital region more constricted; premaxillary with a shallow concavity laterally instead of being flat; lacrimal foramen and first upper premolar larger.

Nesophontes paramicrus Miller
Large Haitian Nesophontes

1929. *Nesophontes paramicrus* Miller, Smiths. Miscl. Coll., 81(9):3, March 30, type from cave approximately 4 mi. E St. Michel, Haiti. Known only from skeletal remains from Haiti.

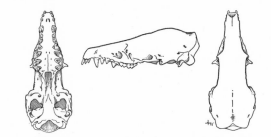

No. 39. *Nesophontes paramicrus*, composite drawing based on three specimens in U.S.N.M., without catalogue nos.; labels bear annotations "VIP" and "IIP". X 1.

Resembles *N. micrus* of Cuba but upper molars without well-defined sulcus which, in *N. micrus,* lies between base of metacone and posterior commisure of protocone; lower molars with entoconid and metaconid obviously less nearly terete than in the Cuban species.

Nesophontes hypomicrus Miller
Miller's Nesophontes

1929. *Nesophontes hypomicrus* Miller, Smiths. Miscl. Coll., 81(9):4, March 30, type from cave near Atalaye Plantation, approximately 4 mi. E St. Michel, Haiti. Known only from skeletal remains from Haiti.

Resembles *N. paramicrus* but smaller.

Nesophontes zamicrus Miller
Haitian Nesophontes

1929. *Nesophontes zamicrus* Miller, Smiths. Miscl. Coll., 81(9):7, March 30, type from cave approximately 4 mi. E St. Michel, Haiti. Known only from skeletal remains from Haiti.

Resembles *N. hypomicrus* but differs from it and all other known species of the genus in its lesser size. Palatal length, 10.6; 4 largest maxillary teeth, 5.0; 4 largest mandibular teeth, 5.6.

ORDER CHIROPTERA—Bats

Families and genera revised by Miller, Bull. U.S. Nat. Mus., 57:17 + 282, 13 pls., 49 figs. in text, June 29, 1907.

Placental mammals unique in being modified for flight; bones of fingers greatly lengthened and supporting wing-membrane made of relatively naked double layer of skin; membrane extends to and usually also between hind legs (interfemoral- or tail-membrane much reduced in some species) and enclosing tail; tail usually present, variable in length and sometimes extending beyond membrane; pectoral region much developed and sternum usually keeled; clavicle well developed; ulna much reduced; calcar present and often of extreme development; thumb free of wing membrane and clawed; knee joint directed outwards and posteriorly; ears well developed, often enormously so; eyes small; dentition tuberculosectorial, molars in some genera broadened and having reduced cusps, in some other genera (for example, *Leptonycteris*) much elongated.

The keys contained in this section are based mainly on those of Miller, 1907. Where other published sources have been employed, individual mention of the source is given. Length of upper tooth-row of bats is taken from the posteriormost point of the last tooth in the jaw to the anterior face of the canine on the same side.

SUBORDER MICROCHIROPTERA

All New World bats belong to this suborder. Second finger closely bound to third; humerus with trochiter and trochin large, the former usually articulating with the scapula; margin of external ear not forming complete ring.

KEY TO NORTH AMERICAN FAMILIES OF MICROCHIROPTERA

1. Premaxillaries usually free, always incomplete, their boundaries never obliterated. . Emballonuridae, p. 79
1'. Premaxillaries always fused with surrounding parts, complete or incomplete, their boundaries obliterated early in life.
  2. Ischia fused beneath posterior extremity of sacrum. . . . . Noctilionidae, p. 86
  2'. Ischia not fused beneath sacrum.
    3. Fibula robust, its diameter usually about half that of tibia and contributing much to strength of short, stout leg. . . . . Molossidae, p. 203
    3'. Fibula slender or rudimentary, not contributing much to strength of long, slender leg.
      4. Third phalanx of middle finger cartilaginous except at extreme base.
        5. Humerus with trochiter much longer than trochin, projecting conspicuously beyond head, and forming a complete secondary articulation with scapula. . . . Vespertilionidae, p. 157
        5'. Humerus with trochiter scarcely longer than trochin, not projecting conspicuously beyond head, and its articulation with scapula frequently slight or absent. . . . Natalidae, p. 152
      4'. Third phalanx of middle finger bony.
        6. Canine teeth shearlike; molars much reduced, without trace of crushing surface.
                    Desmodontidae, p. 150
        6'. Canine teeth not shearlike or specially modified; molars well developed with at least some trace of crushing surface.
          7. Toes, except hallux, with three phalanges each; thumb and foot without sucking disk.
                    Phyllostomidae, p. 88
          7'. Toes with two phalanges each; thumb and foot provided with sucking disk.
                    Thyropteridae, p. 156

FAMILY EMBALLONURIDAE
Sac-winged Bats

Skull having well-developed postorbital processes (partly obscured in *Diclidurus*); premaxillaries incomplete, possessing nasal portions only, never fused with maxillaries or with each other; auditory bullae emarginate on inner side. Humerus having well-developed trochiter; capitellum nearly in line with shaft; 2nd digit of manus having metacarpal but no phalanges; 7th cervical vertebra not fused to pectoral girdle; fibula complete, slender. Hind leg slender; tail perforating upper surface—not free edge —of interfemoral membrane; muzzle lacking leaflike excrescences.

The emballonurids, second only to the Old World Rhinopomidae, seem to combine the greatest number of primitive characters with the least degree of specialization according to Miller (1907: 84).

Key to North American Genera of Emballonuridae

1. Postorbital process broad, almost obliterated by markedly widened supraorbital ridge; clavicle greatly expanded. . . . . *Diclidurus*, p. 86
1'. Postorbital process slender, distinct; clavicle not expanded.
   2. Basisphenoidal pit divided by median septum.
      3. Anterior upper premolars tricuspidate.
         4. Sagittal crest pronounced, extending onto postorbital process of frontal. . . . *Cormura*, p. 82
         4'. Sagittal crest indistinct, not extending onto postorbital process of frontal. *Centronycteris*, p. 84
      3'. Anterior upper premolars simple spicules, not tricuspidate.
         5. Distal part of rostrum with dorsal inflations. . . . . *Balantiopteryx*, p. 84
         5'. Distal part of rostum without dorsal inflations. . . . . *Saccopteryx*, p. 81
   2'. Basisphenoidal pit not divided by median septum.
      6. Angle in profile between facial and cranial regions of skull less than 140°.
         7. Distal part of rostrum with dorsal inflations and with evident median depression between inflations. . . . . *Balantiopteryx*, p. 84
         7'. Distal part of rostrum without dorsal inflations. . . . . *Peropteryx*, p. 83
      6'. Angle in profile between facial and cranial regions of skull more than 160°.
         8. Sagittal crest pronounced. . . . . *Cormura*, p. 82
         8'. Sagittal crest absent. . . . . *Rhynchonycteris*, p. 80

Subfamily EMBALLONURINAE

Revised by Sanborn, Field. Mus. Nat. Hist., Zool. Ser., 20:321–354, December 28, 1937.

Postorbital processes long, curved, not obscured by supraorbital ridges, at least 4 times as long as wide; clavicle normal, about ⅙ as wide as long; tibia subterete or laterally flattened.

Genus Rhynchonycteris Peters—Long-nosed Bats

1867. *Rhynchonycteris* Peters, Monatsb. preuss. Akad. Wiss., Berlin, p. 477, July 25. Type, *Vespertilio naso* Wied-Neuwied.
1823. *Proboscidea* Spix, Simiarum et vespertilionum Brasiliensium . . . , p. 61. Type, *Proboscidea saxatilis* Spix [= *Vespertilio naso* Wied-Neuwied]. Not *Proboscidea* Brugière, 1791, a nematode.
1907. *Rhynchiscus* Miller, Proc. Biol. Soc. Washington, 20:65, June 12. Type, *Vespertilio naso* Wied-Neuwied, a renaming of *Rhynchonycteris* Peters, erroneously assumed

to be preoccupied by *Rhinchonycteris* Tschudi, 1844–1846 [= *Anoura* Gray, 1838].

No wing sacs; forearm dotted with tufts of fur; interfemoral membrane haired to exsertion of tail; muzzle greatly elongated; no angle between rostrum and forehead; first upper premolar large, triangular, possessing cingulum provided with a small anterior and a small posterior cusp (after Sanborn, 1937: 325). Dentition, i. $\frac{1}{3}$, c. $\frac{1}{1}$, p. $\frac{2}{2}$, m. $\frac{3}{3}$. The genus is monotypic.

Rhynchonycteris naso (Wied-Neuwied)
Brazilian Long-nosed Bat

1820. *Vespertilio naso* Wied-Neuwied, Reise nach Brasilien . . . , 1:251, footnote, type from bank of Rio Mucuri near Morro d'Arara, Minas Geraes, Brazil.
1867. *Rhynchonycteris naso*, Peters, Monatsb. preuss. Akad. Wiss., Berlin, p. 478, July 25.
1823. *Proboscidea rivalis et saxatilis* Spix, Simiarum et vespertilionum Brasiliensium . . . , p. 62. Types from Rio Amazon and Rio San Francisco, Brazil.
1835–1841. *Emballonura lineata* Temminck, Monographies de mammalogie . . . , 2:297, type from Dutch Guiana.
1855. *Proboscidea villosa* Gervais, Exped. Comte de Castelnau, Zool., Mamm., p. 68, pl. 11, type from Province Goyaz, Brazil.
1914. *Rhynchiscus naso priscus* G. M. Allen, Proc. Biol. Soc. Washington, 27:109, July 10, type from Xcopen, Quintana Roo. (Regarded as a synonym of *R. naso* by Sanborn, Field Mus. Nat. Hist. Publ. 399, Zool. Ser. 20: 325, 326, 328, December 28, 1937.)

Length of head and body approximately 40; length of forearm, 35.3–40.7; greatest length of skull, 11.2–12.6; interorbital breadth, 2.3–2.8; zygomatic breadth, 6.7–7.3; length of upper tooth-row, 4.3–4.7. Color of upper parts depending greatly on amount of wear; brownish hairs tipped with gray

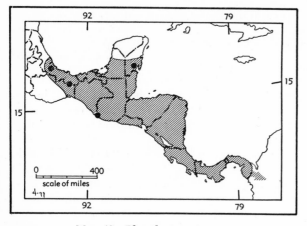

Map 43. *Rhynchonycteris naso.*

in fresh pelage, gray wanting in worn pelage; much the same below, but gray more pronounced; 2 curved, gray or white, lines usually apparent on lower back and rump. See also generic description.

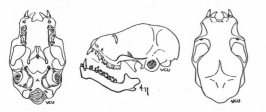

Fig. 40. *Rhynchonycteris naso,* 15 km. W Piedras Negras, 300 ft., Veracruz, No. 19096 K.U., ♀, X 2.

MARGINAL RECORDS.—Veracruz: 5 km. SW Boca del Río (19095 KU), thence across base of Peninsula of Yucatán to Quintana Roo: Chetumal (Hershkovitz, 1951: 553) and southward into South America; along Pacific Coast northward to Guatemala: Ocas (Sanborn, 1937:327). Veracruz: 22 km. SSE Jesús Carranza, 300 ft. (24570 KU); *15 km. W Piedras Negras* (19096 KU).

Genus **Saccopteryx** Illiger—White-lined Bats

1811. *Saccopteryx* Illiger, Prodromus systematis mammalium et avium . . . , p. 121. Type, *Vespertilio lepturus* Schreber.
1838–39. *Urocryptus* Temminck, Tijdschr. natuurl. Gesch. Phys., 5:31. Type, *Urocryptus bilineatus* Temminck.

Length of head and body approximately 49. Large glandular sac close to forearm near elbow and opening on upper surface of antebrachial membrane; wing-membrane from tarsus. Skull with slight angle between rostrum and forehead; premaxillae large, ending on upper surface of rostrum; postorbital processes long and relatively broad; sagittal crest on braincase; basisphenoidal pits large, separated by median septum; first upper premolar (P2) a small spicule (after Sanborn, 1937:328). Dentition, i. $\frac{1}{3}$, c. $\frac{1}{1}$, p. $\frac{2}{2}$, m. $\frac{3}{3}$.

These bats roost in secluded sites in small groups numbering 3 to rarely as many as 50 individuals.

KEY TO NORTH AMERICAN SPECIES OF SACCOPTERYX

1. Upper tooth-row more than 5.8. S. *bilineata,* p. 81
1'. Upper tooth-row less than 5.8. . S. *leptura,* p. 82

Saccopteryx bilineata (Temminck)
Greater White-lined Bat

1838–39. *Urocryptus bilineatus* Temminck, Tijdschr. natuurl. Gesch. Phys., 5:33, type from Surinam.
1867. *Saccopteryx bilineata,* Peters, Monatsb. preuss. Akad. Wiss., Berlin, p. 471, after July 29.
1855. *Saccopteryx insignis* Wagner, *in* Schreber, Die Säugthiere . . . Suppl., 5:695, type from Rio de Janeiro, Brazil.
1899. *Saccopteryx perspicillifer* Miller, Bull. Amer. Mus. Nat. Hist., 12:176, October 20, type from Caura, Trinidad.
1904. *Saccopteryx bilineata centralis* Thomas, Ann. Mag. Nat. Hist., ser. 7, 13:251, April, type from Teapa, Tabasco.

Length of forearm, 41.7–51.7; condylobasal length, 13.2–15.7; length of upper tooth-row, 5.8–7.4. Upper parts black in fresh pelage (deep brown

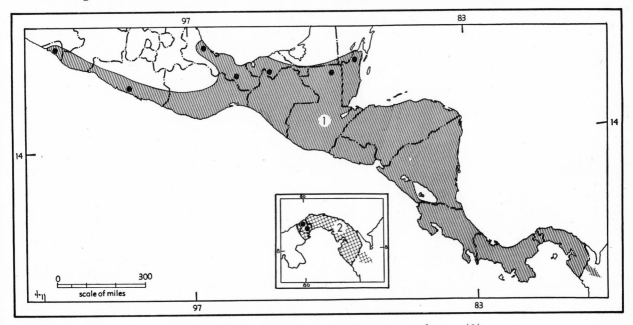

Map 44. *Saccopteryx bilineata* (1) and *Saccopteryx leptura* (2).

when worn), having 2 wavy lines of yellowish to whitish passing down back onto rump; underparts brownish or grayish in over-all tone. Interfemoral membrane thinly haired to exsertion of tail.

MARGINAL RECORDS.—Veracruz: Boca del Río (29578 KU). Tabasco: Teapa (Harris, 1943:7). Guatemala: Uaxactún (Murie, 1935:18). British Honduras: Kate's Lagoon (Hershkovitz, 1951:553) thence southward into South America and thence northward along Pacific Coast to Colima: Hda. Magdalena (Sanborn, 1937:330-331). Guerrero: Papayo (*ibid.*). Veracruz: Achotal (*ibid.*).

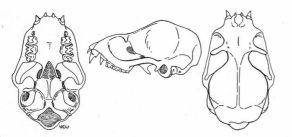

Fig. 41. *Saccopteryx bilineata*, 14 km. SW Coatzocoalcos, 100 ft., Veracruz, No. 19141 K.U., ♀, X 2.

Saccopteryx leptura (Schreber)
Lesser White-lined Bat

1774. *Vespertilio lepturus* Schreber, Die Säugthiere . . . , Theil 1, Heft 8, pl. 57, type from Dutch Guiana.
1811. *Saccopteryx lepturus*, Illiger, Prodromus systematus mammalium et avium . . . , p. 121.

Length of forearm, 37.4–42.3; greatest length of skull, 13.1–14.4; interorbital breadth, 3.2–3.8; zygomatic breadth, 8.4–9.1; length of upper tooth-row, 5.1–5.5. Upper parts uniform brown having 2 whitish longitudinal lines extending down back onto rump; underparts slightly paler shade of brown.

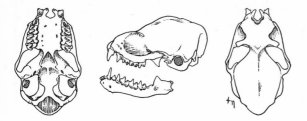

Fig. 42. *Saccopteryx leptura*, Porto Velho, Brazil, No. 21662 C.N.H.M., ♀, X 2.

MARGINAL RECORDS.—Panamá, Canal Zone (Sanborn, 1937:333): Fort Randolph; Barro Colorado Island, thence eastward into South America.

Genus Cormura Peters—Wagner's Sac-winged Bat

1867. *Cormura* Peters, Monatsb. preuss. Akad. Wiss., Berlin, p. 475, after July 29. Type *Emballonura brevirostris* Wagner.

Length of head and body approximately 60. Wing sac in center of antebrachial membrane, opening of sac directed distally and extending from anterior border almost to elbow; base of interfemoral membrane almost naked; wing-membrane from metatarsus. Rostrum short and broad; rim of orbit and zygoma broad; no angle between rostrum and forehead; first upper premolar provided with distinct anterior and posterior cusps (after Sanborn, 1937:349). Dentition, i. $\frac{3}{3}$, c. $\frac{1}{1}$, p. $\frac{2}{2}$, m. $\frac{3}{3}$. This little-known genus is monotypic.

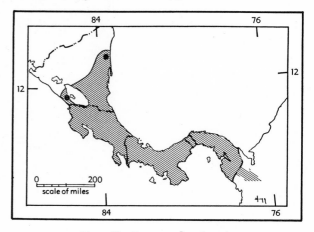

Map 45. *Cormura brevirostris*.

Cormura brevirostris (Wagner)
Wagner's Sac-winged Bat

1843. *Emballonura brevirostris* Wagner, Arch. Naturgesch., Jahrg. 9, 1:367, type from Marabitanas, Rio Negro, Amazonas, Brazil.
1867. *Cormura brevirostris*, Peters, Monastb. preuss. Akad. Wiss., Berlin, p. 475, after July 29.

Length of forearm, 43.3–49.8; greatest length of skull, 15–16.7; zygomatic breadth, 9.4–10.1; length of upper tooth-row, 6.1–6.8. Upper parts either deep blackish brown or reddish brown; underparts paler.

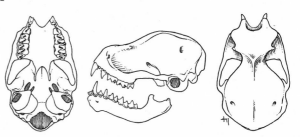

Fig. 43. *Cormura brevirostris*, Boca Curaray, Ecuador, No. 71637 A.M., ♀, X 2.

MARGINAL RECORDS (Sanborn, 1937:349).—Nicaragua: Prinzapolka; Peña Blanca, thence southeastward into South America.

Genus **Peropteryx** Peters—Doglike Bats

1867. *Peropteryx* Peters, Monatsb. preuss. Akad. Wiss., Berlin, p. 472, after July 29. Type, *Vespertilio caninus* Wied-Neuwied [= *Emballonura macrotis* Wagner].

Length of head and body approximately 46. Angle of approximately 115° between expanded rostrum and forehead; basisphenoidal pit not divided. Wing sac near upper edge of antebrachial membrane; opening of sac directed distally (after Sanborn, 1937:339); ears not joined at bases; dental formula as in *Saccopteryx*.

These bats, according to Sanborn (1937:344), frequent shallow caves and crevices between boulders where light can enter. Some hang from horizontal surfaces but others cling with outspread forearms and feet to vertical surfaces. Scanty information indicates that 1 or 2 young are born at a time.

Key to North American Species of Peropteryx

1. Greatest length of skull more than 16; forearm more than 45. . . . . . *P. kappleri*, p. 83
1'. Greatest length of skull less than 15.5; forearm less than 48.2. . . . . *P. macrotis*, p. 83

Peropteryx macrotis
Lesser Doglike Bat

Length of forearm, 38.3–48.2; greatest length of skull, 12–15; interorbital breadth, 2.3–3.3; zygomatic breadth, 7.6–8.9; length of upper tooth-row, 4.6–6.2. Upper parts varying much in color: buffy brown, reddish brown, grayish brown, blackish brown, or dull sepia; underparts somewhat paler; ears and membranes dark brown.

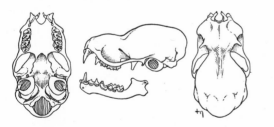

Fig. 44. *Peropteryx macrotis*, 35 km. SE Jesús Carranza, 500 ft., Veracruz, No. 23454 K.U., ♂, X 2.

Peropteryx macrotis macrotis (Wagner)

1821. *Vesp[ertilio]. caninus* Wied-Neuwied, *in* Schinz, Das Thierreich . . . , 1:179, type from east coast of Brazil. Not *Vespertilio caninus* Blumenbach, 1797.
1843. *Emballonura macrotis* Wagner, Arch. Naturgesch., Jahrg. 9, 1:367, type from Mato Grosso, Brazil.
1935. *Peropteryx macrotis macrotis*, G. M. Allen, Jour. Mamm., 16:227, August 12.

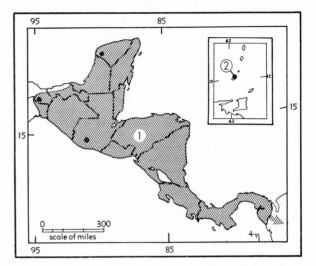

Map 46. *Peropteryx macrotis macrotis* (1) and *Peropteryx macrotis phaea* (2).

MARGINAL RECORDS.—Yucatán: Calcehtok (Hatt and Villa, 1950:227), thence southward along Caribbean Coast into South America; thence northward along Pacific Coast to Guatemala: Patalul (Sanborn, 1937:340). Veracruz: 35 km. SE Jesús Carranza, 5000 ft. (23441 KU).

Peropteryx macrotis phaea G. M. Allen

1911. *Peropteryx canina phaea* G. M. Allen, Bull. Mus. Comp. Zool., 54:222, July, type from Point Saline, Grenada, Lesser Antilles.
1937. *Peropteryx macrotis phaea*, Sanborn, Field Mus. Nat. Hist., Zool. Ser., 20:342, December 28.

MARGINAL RECORDS.—Grenada, Lesser Antilles (Sanborn, 1937:343): *Mt. Pleasant Estate*; type locality.

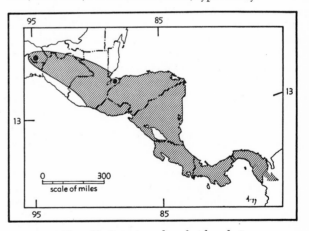

Map 47. *Peropteryx kappleri kappleri*.

Peropteryx kappleri
Greater Doglike Bat

Length of forearm, 45.0–53.6; greatest length of skull, 16–17.8; interorbital breadth, 2.6–3.5; zygomatic breadth, 9.5–10.9; length of upper tooth-row, 6.8–7.8. According to Sanborn (1937:343) there are two color phases, one close to Mummy Brown and the other slightly darker than Prouts Brown. In each phase the underparts are paler than the upper parts.

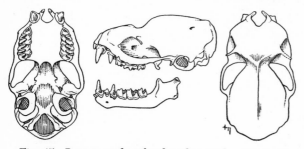

Fig. 45. *Peropteryx kappleri kappleri*, 38 km. SE Jesús Carranza, 500 ft., Veracruz, No. 23440 K.U. ♂, X 2.

Peropteryx kappleri kappleri Peters

1867. *Peropteryx kappleri* Peters, Monatsb. preuss. Akad. Wiss., Berlin, p. 473, after July 29, type from Surinam.

MARGINAL RECORDS.—Veracruz: 38 km. SE Jesús Carranza (Dalquest and Hall, 1949:424). Guatemala: Escobas (Sanborn, 1937:344), thence into South America.

Genus Centronycteris Gray

1838. *Centronycteris* Gray, Mag. Zool. Bot., 2:499, February. Type, *Vespertilio calcaratus* Wied-Neuwied [= V. *maximiliani* Fischer].

Angle wide (Fig. 46) between rostrum and forehead; lower edge of orbit so little expanded that edge of tooth-row can be seen from above; 1st upper premolar (P2) having one distinct anterior cusp and one distinct posterior cusp; basisphenoidal pit divided by median septum. No wing sac known; wing-membranes from metatarsus; fur long and soft; back without lines; dental formula as in *Saccopteryx* (after Sanborn, 1937:336).

Centronycteris maximiliani
Thomas' Bat

Selected measurements of the type, an adult male, are: length of head and body, 52; length of forearm, 45; greatest length of skull, 15; zygomatic breadth, 10; length of upper tooth-row, 6.1. Upper parts near raw umber; paler below; hairs on interfemoral membrane reddish.

Centronycteris maximiliani centralis Thomas

1912. *Centronycteris centralis* Thomas, Ann. Mag. Nat. Hist., ser. 8, 10:638, December, type from Bogava, Chiriquí, Panamá.

1936. *Centronycteris maximiliani centralis*, Sanborn, Field Mus. Nat. Hist., Zool. Ser., 20:94, August 15.

MARGINAL RECORDS.—Veracruz: 35 km. SE Jesús Carranza, 350 ft. (32088 KU). British Honduras: Double Falls (Hershkovitz, 1951:553). Guatemala: Escobas, near San Tomás (Sanborn, 1937:338), thence southeastward into South America.

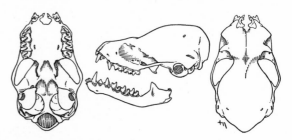

Fig. 46. *Centronycteris maximiliani centralis*, 35 km. SW Jesús Carranza, Veracruz, No. 32088 K.U., sex ?, X 2.

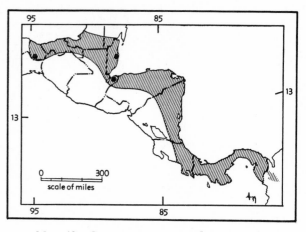

Map 48. *Centronycteris maximiliani centralis*.

Genus Balantiopteryx Peters

1867. *Balantiopteryx* Peters, Monatsb. preuss. Akad. Wiss., Berlin, p. 476, after July 29. Type, *Balantiopteryx plicata* Peters.

Wing sac near center of antebrachial membrane and with opening directed proximally; rostrum greatly inflated; basisphenoidal pit divided or not by median septum (after Sanborn, 1937:351). *Balantiopteryx* inhabits caves.

KEY TO NORTH AMERICAN SPECIES OF BALANTIOPTERYX

1. White line present on edge of alar membrane; interpterygoid fossa narrow, V-shaped; forearm more than 38.2. *B. plicata*, p. 85

1'. White line on edge of alar membrane wanting; interpterygoid fossa broadly U-shaped; forearm less than 38.9. . . . . . *B. io*, p. 85

Balantiopteryx plicata
Peters' Bat

Length of head and body approximately 48; length of forearm, 38.3–46.2; greatest length of skull, 11.5–14.8; zygomatic breadth, 8.3–9.3; length of upper tooth-row, 5–5.6. Interpterygoid fossa narrow. Upper parts dark gray to rich brown; underparts dark gray anteriorly, paler on lower abdomen.

Fig. 47. *Balantiopteryx plicata plicata*, Puente Nacionál, Veracruz, No. 19157 K.U., ♂, X 2.

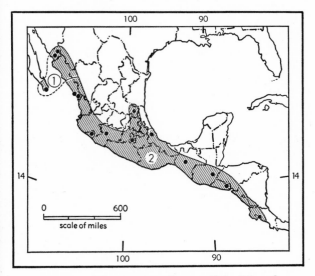

Map 49. *Balantiopteryx plicata pallida* (1) and *B. p. plicata* (2).

Balantiopteryx plicata pallida Burt

1948. *Balantiopteryx plicata pallida* Burt, Occas. Papers Mus. Zool., Univ. Michigan, 515:1, October 30, type from San Bernardo, Río Mayo, Sonora.

MARGINAL RECORDS.—Sonora: type locality; *Camoa, Río Mayo* (Sanborn, 1937:352). Baja California (Sanborn, 1937:352): *Santa Anita*; San José del Cabo. Sonora: Chinobampo (Burt, 1938:18). Note: Records cited are assigned to *B. p. pallida* on the basis of Burt's (1948:2) statement of the geographic range of that subspecies.

Balantiopteryx plicata plicata Peters

1867. *Balantiopteryx plicata* Peters, Monatsb. preuss. Akad. Wiss., Berlin, p. 476, after July 29, type from Puntarenas, Puntarenas, Costa Rica.

1938. *Balantiopteryx ochoterenai* Martínez and Villa, Anal. Inst. Biol., Univ. Nac. México, 9(3–4):339, November 14, type from Cuautla, Morelos. Regarded as identical with *plicata* by Burt and Hooper, Occas. Papers Mus. Zool., Univ. Michigan, 430:2, May 27, 1941.

MARGINAL RECORDS (Sanborn, 1937:352, unless otherwise noted).—Sinaloa: Mazatlán; Escuinapa (Burt, 1938:18). Nayarit: *San Blas*. Colima: Colima. Michoacán: Apatzingán (Hall and Villa, 1949:440). Morelos: Cuernavaca (Davis and Russell, 1952:234). San Luis Potosí: Cueva Sabinas near Valles (Koopman, 1957:547). Veracruz: Puente Nacionál (Davis, 1944:376). Chiapas: San Bartolomé. Guatemala: El Rancho, Zacapa. El Salvador: Río Goáscoran (Burt, 1948:2). Costa Rica: type locality, thence northward along Pacific Coast to point of beginning.

Balantiopteryx io Thomas
Thomas' Sac-winged Bat

1904. *Balantiopteryx io* Thomas, Ann. Mag. Nat. Hist., ser. 7, 13:252, April, type from Río Dolores, near Cobán, Alta Verapaz, Guatemala.

Length of head and body averaging 50; length of forearm, 35.6–38.8; greatest length of skull, 12.4–12.9; zygomatic breadth, 8.2–8.3; length of upper tooth-row, 4.5–4.8. Interpterygoid fossa broadly U-shaped. Upper parts dark brown; underparts paler.

Fig. 48. *Balantiopteryx io*, 38 km. SE Jesús Carranza, 500 ft., Veracruz, No. 23456 K.U., ♂, X 2.

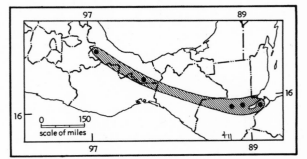

Map 50. *Balantiopteryx io*.

MARGINAL RECORDS.—Veracruz: 2 km. E Atoyac (Dalquest and Hall, 1949:424–425); 38 km. SE Jesús Carranza (*ibid.*). Guatemala: Escobas, near San Tomás (Sanborn, 1937:353); Chimoxan (Goodwin, 1934:8); type locality.

Subfamily DICLIDURINAE

Postorbital processes short, blunt, straight; clavicle markedly expanded, maximum width approximately ⅓ of length; tibia bearing a deep longitudinal groove.

Only one genus, *Diclidurus*, is included in the subfamily Diclidurinae; only one species, *D. virgo*, has been reported north of South America.

Genus **Diclidurus** Wied-Neuwied—White Bats

1820. *Diclidurus* Wied-Neuwied, Isis von Oken, 1819, p. 1629. Type, *Diclidurus albus* Wied-Neuwied.

Braincase large, flattened anteriorly and descending abruptly to rostrum; rostrum broad, bearing lateral ridges; wing sac absent; nose simple; tail shorter than and perforating interfemoral membrane. Dental formula as in *Saccopteryx*. For other characters see account of the subfamily.

Diclidurus virgo Thomas
White Bat

1903. *Diclidurus virgo* Thomas, Ann. Mag. Nat. Hist., ser. 7, 11:377, April, type from Escazú, San José, Costa Rica.

Selected measurements of the type, an adult female, are: length of forearm, 66; greatest length of skull, 18; length of upper tooth-row, 8.1. Color white. For additional characters see generic account.

MARGINAL RECORDS.—Oaxaca: Río Tonto, possibly neighborhood of Paso Real, 14 km. NNE Tuxtepec (Villa, 1951:435). Honduras: 3 mi. N Gracias on Río Grande (Goodwin, 1942:121). Costa Rica: La Palma (Villa, 1951: 436). Panamá: Pueblo Nuevo (Goldman, 1920:177), thence northward along coast to Guatemala: Champerico (Miller, 1907:95).

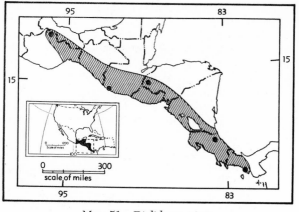

Map 51. *Diclidurus virgo.*

Family NOCTILIONIDAE—Bulldog Bats

Skull without distinct postorbital processes; premaxillae with both nasal and palatal branches, nasal branches markedly elongate; premaxillae, in adult, fused to each other and to maxillae; palate complete, closed anteriorly. Humerus having trochiter smaller than trochin, poorly articulated with scapula; capitellum slightly offset from axis of humeral shaft; 2nd digit of manus having metacarpal as long as that of 3rd; 7th cervical vertebra not fused with 1st thoracic; fibula threadlike, extending to head of tibia, but cartilaginous proximally; ischia fused together and to ventral side of sacrum. Muzzle and nose without excrescences; lips full and appearing swollen; internal cheek pouches present.

The family contains only one genus.

Genus **Noctilio** Linnaeus—Bulldog Bats

1766. *Noctilio* Linnaeus, Syst. Nat., ed. 12, 1:88. Type, *Noctilio americanus* Linnaeus [= *Vespertilio leporinus* Linnaeus].

1808. *Noctileo* Tiedemann, Zoologie . . . , 1:536. Type, [*Vespertilio*] *leporinus* Linnaeus; a *lapsus?*

1821. *Celaeno* Leach, Trans. Linn. Soc. London, 13:69. Type, *Celaeno brooksiana* Leach [= *V. leporinus*].

1906. *Dirias* Miller, Proc. Biol. Soc. Washington, 19:84, June 4. Type, *Noctilio albiventer* Spix. Regarded as synonymous with *Noctilio* by Osgood, Field Mus. Nat. Hist., Publ. 149, Zool. Ser., 10:31–32, October 20, 1910.

Length of head and body approximately 98. Braincase deep, oval in outline; mastoidal region conspicuously flaring, shelflike; sagittal crest distinct; rostrum strongly arched; nares opening anteriorly, somewhat tubular; palate concave transversely, almost flat anteroposteriorly, extending posteriorly beyond tooth-rows; auditory bullae small. Dentition: i. $\frac{2}{1}$, c. $\frac{1}{1}$, p. $\frac{1}{2}$, m. $\frac{3}{3}$. Ears separate, slender, pointed; tragus well-developed; muzzle pointed with pad strongly projecting; chin having well-developed transverse ridges; tail well-de-

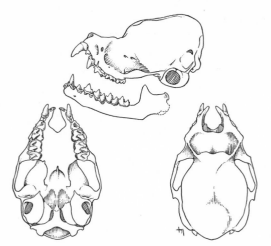

Fig. 49. *Diclidurus virgo,* Costa Rica, No. 7947 A.M., sex ?, × 2.

veloped, more than half as long as femur, extending approximately to middle of interfemoral membrane; tip of tail free on dorsal surface of interfemoral membrane. Hair short; feet robust; calcar greatly elongated.

Most bats have a musky smell but in *Noctilio* this odor is unusually strong and penetrating.

KEY TO NORTH AMERICAN SPECIES OF NOCTILIO

1. Length of tibia and foot approximately 60% of total length; length of forearm usually more than 70 . . . . . *N. leporinus*, p. 87
1'. Length of tibia and foot approximately 40% of total length; length of forearm usually less than 70 . . . . *N. labialis*, p. 88

Noctilio leporinus
Mexican Bulldog Bat

Measurements of an adult male, the type of *N. l. mexicanus*, are: length of forearm, 83.2; greatest length of skull, 28.5; interorbital breadth, 7.4; zygomatic breadth, 19.8; length of upper tooth-row, 10.7. Upper parts rich dark ochraceous-tawny in males, grayer in females, usually with a paler line middorsally; underparts paler in both sexes. Other characters as for the genus.

Bats of this species feed extensively on small fish, which are snatched from the surface of the water. The unusually long hind legs are adapted for this purpose. The diet is not confined to fish, however, some insect food being taken. The bats are often abroad in late afternoon and sometimes hunt fish where pelicans are feeding and are disturbing smaller marine vertebrates. Bull dog bats swim well with only the head above water, the wings being used as underwater oars. The daytime retreat often is a deep cleft or fissure overlooking water.

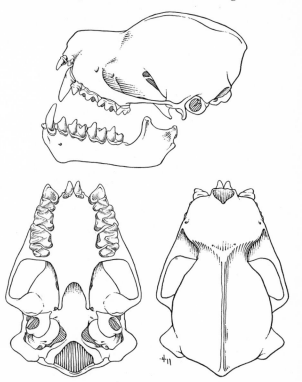

Fig. 50. *Noctilio leporinus mexicanus*, Papayo, Guerrero, No. 1681 K.U., ♀, X 2.

Noctilio leporinus leporinus (Linnaeus)

1758. [*Vespertilio*] *leporinus* Linnaeus, Syst. nat., ed. 10, 1:32. Type locality, Surinam (Thomas, Proc. Zool. Soc. London, p. 131, 1911).

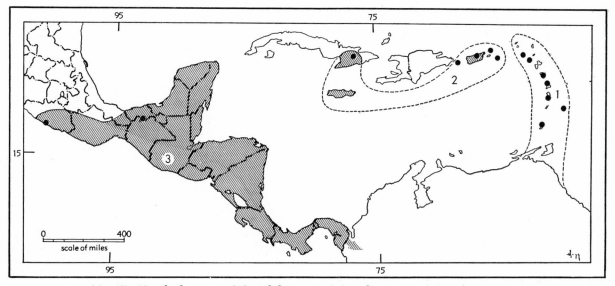

Map 52. *Noctilio leporinus*: (1) *N. l. leporinus*; (2) *N. l. mastivus*; (3) *N. l. mexicanus*.

1847. *Noctilio leporinus* D'Orbigny and Gervais, Voy. dans l'Amer. Merid., 4(2; Mamm.):12.

MARGINAL RECORDS (Jones, 1951:224, unless otherwise noted).—Antillean Islands: St. Kitts; Montserrat; Dominica; Sta. Lucia (G. M. Allen, 1937:514); St. Vincent; Barbados; Grenada. Note: The subspecific allocation of specimens from the northern localities here given is uncertain.

Noctilio leporinus mastivus (Dahl)

1797. *Vespertilio mastivus* Dahl, Skrivter af Naturh.-Selsk. Kjøbenhavn, 4:132, type from St. Croix, Virgin Islands, West Indies.
1884. *Noctilio leporinus mastivus,* True, Proc. U.S. Nat. Mus., 7(App. Circ. 29):603, November 29.

MARGINAL RECORDS.—Virgin Islands: Botany Bay, St. Thomas (Goodwin, 1928:111); type locality. Cuba: cave in eastern Cuba (Anthony, 1919:636). Mono [= Mona] Island (Goldman, 1915:137). Puerto Rico: *Vega Baja* (Goodwin, 1928:106); Old Leiza (Goodwin, 1928:111).

Noctilio leporinus mexicanus Goldman

1915. *Noctilio leporinus mexicanus* Goldman, Proc. Biol. Soc. Washington, 28:136, June 29, type from Papayo, Guerrero.

MARGINAL RECORDS.—Tabasco: 5 mi. SW Teapa (66299 KU); southward into South America; thence northward on Pacific Coast to Guerrero: type locality.

Noctilio labialis
Southern Bulldog Bat

Selected measurements of an adult female, the type of *N. labialis minor,* are: length of head and body, 67; length of forearm, 58.4; greatest length of skull, 17.2; zygomatic breadth, 14.6; length upper tooth-row, 7.5. Upper parts grayish brown to yellowish or bright rufous, with narrow whitish median stripe from shoulder region to rump; underparts paler. Many males are bright rufous and many females are dull brown to drab. Ear laid forward extending slightly beyond muzzle; chin with small plications.

This bat often is found in buildings, hollow trees, and caves. Usually there is only 1 young at a birth.

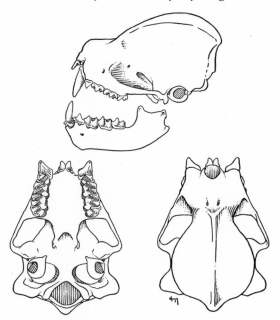

Fig. 51. *Noctilio labialis minor,* Summit, Panamá, No. 261402 U.S.N.M., ♂, X 2.

Noctilio labialis minor Osgood

1910. *Noctilio minor* Osgood, Field Mus. Nat. Hist., Publ. 149, Zool. Ser., 10:30, October 20, type from Encontrados, Zulia, Venezuela.
1949. *Noctilio labialis minor,* Hershkovitz, Proc. U.S. Nat. Mus., 99:433, May 10.

MARGINAL RECORDS.—Nicaragua: El Toro Rapids, Lake Nicaragua (Goodwin, 1946:297), thence southeastward into South America.

FAMILY PHYLLOSTOMIDAE
American Leaf-nosed Bats

Skull without postorbital processes; premaxillae complete, fused to each other and to maxillae, the palatal branches isolating two lateral palatal foramina; teeth variable according to genus. Tragus present, variable; nose leaf usually present. Humerus with well-developed trochiter, but smaller than trochin; capitellum distinctly offset from axis of shaft; 2nd digit of manus with well-developed metacarpal and small phalanx, 3rd finger with 3 complete bony phalanges; 7th cervical vertebra free from anterior thoracic vertebra; fibula present, cartilaginous proximally; pelvis normal; sacrum forming flattened, narrow urostyle posteriorly.

This family, the American leaf-nosed bats, comprises a diverse assemblage of genera a few of

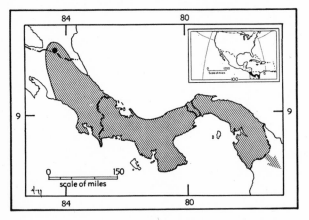

Map 53. *Noctilio labialis minor.*

which lack the nose-leaf. Except in *Lonchorina* and *Centurio*, the leaf is never so large or complex, respectively, as in Old World nose-leafed families. Phyllostomids are tropical in distribution.

KEY TO SUBFAMILIES OF PHYLLOSTOMIDAE

1. Trochiter not impinging upon scapula; nose-leaf absent (a trace in *Mormoops*).
           Chilonycterinae, p. 89
1'. Trochiter impinging upon scapula; nose-leaf present but sometimes small.
  2. Upper molars essentially normal, the configuration never obliterating the fundamental W-shaped pattern.
          Phyllostominae, p. 97
       and some Glossophaginae, p. 113
  2'. Upper molars modified so that fundamental W-shaped pattern is absent or much obscured.
    3. Upper molars with trace of commissures and styles; lower molars with 5 cusps. . . some Glossophaginae, p. 113
    3'. Upper molars without commissures and styles; cusps of lower molars (when present) strictly lateral.
      4. Crowns of both upper and lower molars trenchant. . Carollinae, p. 123
      4'. Crowns of both upper and lower molars grooved or flattened.
        5. Crowns of molars with well-developed cusps rising from a flattened crushing surface.
           Stenoderminae, p. 127
        5'. Crowns of molars with distinct longitudinal groove, cusps (when present) strictly lateral.
          6. Crowns of lower molars with distinct cusps on both margins of groove.
             Sturnirinae, p. 125
          6'. Crowns of lower molars without distinct cusps on both margins of groove.
           Phyllonycterinae, p. 146

SUBFAMILY CHILONYCTERINAE

Trochiter not impinging on scapula and much reduced relative to the trochiter in other members of the family; nose-leaf wanting.

KEY TO GENERA OF CHILONYCTERINAE

1. Basioccipital region markedly elevated (see Fig. 56). . . . . *Mormoops*, p. 95
1'. Basioccipital region not markedly elevated (see Figs. 52–55).
  2. Wing membranes attached to sides of body; fur on back evident. *Chilonycteris*, p. 89
  2'. Wing membranes attached to middle of back; concealing fur on back. *Pteronotus*, p. 93

Genus **Chilonycteris** Gray—Mustached Bats

Revised by Rehn, Proc. Acad. Nat. Sci. Philadelphia, 56:181–207, March 26, 1904.

1839. *Chilonycteris* Gray, Ann. Nat. Hist., 4:4, September. Type, *Chilonycteris macleayii* Gray.
1843. *Phyllodia* Gray, Proc. Zool. Soc. London, p. 50, October. Type, *Phyllodia parnellii* Gray.

Rostrum nearly as long as braincase, sides slightly inflated, and medially grooved; palate broader anteriorly than posteriorly; braincase roughly globose, having approximately equal length, breadth, and depth; floor of braincase elevated above level of dorsal lip of internal nares; auditory bullae small. Dentition, i. $\frac{2}{2}$, c. $\frac{1}{1}$, p. $\frac{2}{3}$, m. $\frac{3}{3}$ Upper medial incisors approximately twice as large as lateral pair; cheek-teeth normal with neither reduced cusps nor modified pattern. Wings arise from sides of body; back furred; dermal rugosites on chin weakly developed compared with those of *Mormoops*; dichromatic.

KEY TO NOMINAL NORTH AMERICAN SPECIES OF CHILONYCTERIS

1. In animals in the flesh and in those preserved in liquid, calcar not bound to tibia and projecting from 2 to 2.5 mm. beyond interfemoral membrane.
  2. Occurring in Cuba. . . . . *C. torrei*, p. 91
  2'. Occurring on mainland. . . *C. psilotus*, p. 91
1'. In animals in the flesh and in those preserved in liquid, calcar bound to tibia and not projecting free of interfemoral membrane.
  3. Occurring on mainland. . *C. parnellii*, p. 92
  3'. Occurring on Antillean islands.
    4. Conspicuous transverse fleshy ridge present on muzzle behind nose.
      5. Internal margin of ear thickened basally and bearing distinct angular notch (species does not occur on mainland). . *C. fuliginosa*, p. 89
      5'. Internal margin of ear not thickened basally and not bearing notch (species occurs also on mainland). . . . *C. parnellii*, p. 92
    4'. Transverse fleshy ridge on muzzle behind nose absent or almost so (species does not occur on mainland).
           C. macleayii, p. 90

Chilonycteris fuliginosa
Sooty Mustached Bat

Length of head and body approximately 40; total length, 56–70; length of forearm, 35–40; greatest length of skull, 14–15.1; interorbital breadth, 2.8–3.2; zygomatic breadth, 7.2–7.7. Size relatively

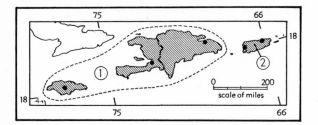

Map 54. *Chilonycteris fuliginosa.*

1. *C. f. fuliginosa*　　　2. *C. f. inflata*

small; ears high, narrow distally but broadening to a wide base; tragus seemingly notched owing to a plication on anterior edge; muzzle with transverse fleshy ridge behind nostrils; body furred everywhere; membranes naked; terminal fourth of tail free of membrane; calcar long, slender. Upper parts either rich, dark brown or paler grayish brown (dichromatic); underparts paler. Skull delicate; rostrum and braincase much swollen; basicranial region above, and at an angle to, axis of rostrum; zygomatic arches but little bowed laterally; sagittal crest low but distinct; mandibular condyle small and higher than coronoid process. Upper medial incisors bifid and larger than lateral pair; 1st premolar much smaller than 2nd; 1st 2 molars equal

and having prominent W-shaped pattern; 3rd molar much smaller.

These bats are partial to deep recesses and crevices for roosting. The flight is swift and they readily fly off when disturbed on the roost.

Chilonycteris fuliginosa fuliginosa Gray

1843. *Chilonycteris fuliginosus* Gray, Proc. Zool. Soc. London, p. 20, July, type from Port au Prince, Haiti.

MARGINAL RECORDS.—Dominican Republic: Caña Honda (J. A. Allen, 1908:581). Haiti: type locality. Jamaica (Koopman and Williams, 1951:19; recorded only to species).

Chilonycteris fuliginosa inflata Rehn

1904. *Chilonycteris macleayii inflata* Rehn, Proc. Acad. Nat. Sci. Philadelphia, 56:190, March 26, type from Cueva de Fari, near Pueblo Viejo, Puerto Rico.
1918. *Chilonycteris fuliginosa inflata*, Anthony, Mem. Amer. Mus. Nat. Hist., n.s., 2:344, October 12.

MARGINAL RECORDS.—Puerto Rico (Anthony, 1918:344): Cueva de Trujillo Alto; Mayaguez.

Chilonycteris macleayii
MacLeay's Mustached Bat

Length of head and body approximately 41; total length, 59–74; length of forearm, 37.5–44.5; greatest

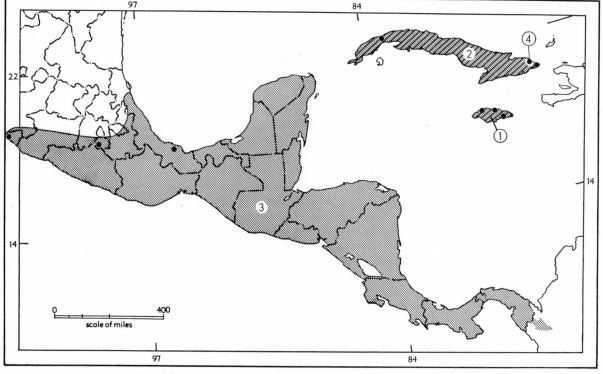

Map 55. *Chilonycteris macleayii, Chilonycteris psilotis,* and *Chilonycteris torrei.*

1. *C. m. grisea*　　　2. *C. m. macleayii*　　　3. *C. psilotis*　　　4. *C. torrei*

length of skull, 14–17; interorbital breadth, 3.0–3.5; zygomatic breadth, 7.5–8.1. Closely resembling *C. fuliginosa* but averaging larger and differing from other species of the genus in the absence—or almost so—of a transverse fleshy ridge extending across muzzle posterior to nose.

Chilonycteris macleayii grisea Gosse

1851. *Chilonycteris grisea* Gosse, A naturalist's sojourn in Jamaica, p. 326, type from Phoenix Park, St. Ann Parish, Jamaica.
1904. *Chilonycteris macleayii grisea*, Rehn, Proc. Acad. Nat. Sci. Philadelphia, 56:191, March 26.

MARGINAL RECORDS.—Jamaica (G. M. Allen, 1911: 225): Lucea; type locality; Kingston.

Chilonycteris macleayii macleayii Gray

1839. *Chilonycteris MacLeayii* Gray, Ann. Nat. Hist., 4:5, September, type from Cuba.
1840. [*Lobostoma*] *quadridens* Gundlach, Arch. Naturgesch., 4:357. Type locality, Cuba.

MARGINAL RECORDS.—Cuba (Rehn, 1904:188): Guanajay, Pinar del Río; 8 mi. E Baracoa, Santiago.

Chilonycteris psilotis Dobson
Dobson's Mustached Bat

1878. *Chilonycteris psilotis* Dobson, Catalogue of the Chiroptera in the . . . British Museum, p. 451. Type locality, unknown; fixed by de la Torre (Fieldiana-Zool., Chicago Nat. Hist. Mus., 37:696, June 19, 1955) as Tehuantepec, Oaxaca.
1938. *Chilonycteris torrei continentis* Sanborn, Occas. Papers Mus. Zool., Univ. Michigan, 373:1, May 26, type from Laguna de Zotz, Petén, Guatemala (arranged as a synonym of *psilotis* by de la Torre, Fieldiana-Zool., Chicago Nat. Hist. Mus., 37:696, June 19, 1955).

Chilonycteris personata Wagner, 1843, Wiegmann's Arch. Naturgesch., Jahrg. 9, 1:367, having the type locality in Mato Grosso, Brazil (probably at St. Vincent according to Goodwin, Bull. Amer. Mus. Nat. Hist., 87:297, December 31, 1946), is the name that has been used by most authors in the first half of the twentieth century but de la Torre (1955: 696–697) states that "Inasmuch as it has not been demonstrated that *C. psilotis* and the Brazilian *C. personata* are conspecific, the name *psilotis*, rather than *personata*, should be used for the small, mainland *Chilonycteris*."

Length of head and body, 46–49; length of forearm, 37–43; greatest length of skull, 14.5–15.1; interorbital breadth, 3.0–3.5; zygomatic breadth, 7.7–8.0; length of upper tooth-row, 5.6–7.0. Total length of a male from Morelos is 55. Size relatively small for the genus; dorsal rim of each nostril surmounted by transverse row of from 4 to 6 small,

roundish warts; transverse fleshy ridge present posterior to nose pad; interfemoral membrane and wings attached to underside of tarsal joint; calcaneum not bound to tibia; tip of calcaneum projecting free of interfemoral membrane for 2 to 2½ mm. In reddish color-phase: upper parts dull cinnamon-orange, brightest on shoulders; underparts dull cinnamon. In dark color-phase: upper parts dull wood brown; underparts brownish gray. Not differing significantly in cranial characters from *C. macleayii* except that rostrum of *C. psilotis* is shorter and more flattened above.

These bats emerge early in the evening and are difficult to identify in flight. They are not agile flyers for small bats but are surprisingly swift in their movements on the ground. They have been obtained in numbers from a hot, humid cave where they seemed to prefer to lie flat on horizontal or nearly horizontal surface of rock.

MARGINAL RECORDS.—Veracruz: *near Tuxpan* (Málaga Alba and Villa R., 1957:534); 3 km. E San Andrés Tuxtla, 1000 ft. (Dalquest and Hall, 1949:425), thence southward along Caribbean Coast into South America (de la Torre, 1955:697), thence northward along Pacific Coast to point of beginning. Colima: 7 mi. W and ½ mi. S Santiago, at sea level (Anderson, 1956:349). Morelos: Alpuyeca (Davis and Russell, 1952:234).

Fig. 52. *Chilonycteris psilotis*, 3 km. E San Andrés Tuxtla, 1000 ft., Veracruz, No. 23575, K.U., ♂, X 2.

Chilonycteris torrei G. M. Allen
Torrey's Mustached Bat

1916. *Chilonycteris torrei* G. M. Allen, Proc. New England Zool. Club, 6:4, February 8, type from La Cueva de la Majana, Baracoa, Cuba. Known only from type locality.

Selected measurements of the type, an adult female, are: length of head and body, 40; length of forearm, 37; greatest length of skull, 14.5; zygomatic breadth, 7.7; length of upper tooth-row, 7.0. Skull markedly less inflated than in *C. macleayii*, rostrum thus appearing more tapering. Dorsal rim of nostril bearing transverse row of 4 to 6 small excrescences; low transverse cutaneous ridge present on muzzle behind nose-pad; wings attached to underside of tarsal joint; calcaneum extending free of interfemoral membrane 2.0 to 2.5 mm.

Chilonycteris parnellii
Parnell's Mustached Bat

Length of head and body often 60–67; total length, 73.5–95.0; length of forearm, 49.6–63.0; greatest length of skull, 20.2–24.0; interorbital breadth, 4.0–5.0; zygomatic breadth, 11.0–12.7. Color of "reddish" phase: upper parts dark fulvous brown; underparts paler, approximately sepia or slightly darker. Brown phase: upper parts approximately walnut brown; underparts a little paler brown or grayish. External margin of ear notched near its middle; internal margin not thickened basally and without distinct angular notch; nose with excrescence varying from rounded and low to high and erect; tragus bearing accessory lobe. Rostrum slender, somewhat laterally compressed.

On the mainland this species roosts in large colonies principally in caves; some of the caves in which the bats have been found have temperatures exceeding 100° F. Where there are no caves the bats also are common. They are quick to take flight when disturbed. Some have been captured from closely packed colonies of *Myotis*. The animals on the mainland are larger than those on the islands.

De la Torre (1955:696) uses the specific name *rubiginosa* for this species "because it can not be established that *parnellii* Gray 1843 has priority over *rubiginosa* Wagner 1843."

Chilonycteris parnellii boothi Gundlach

1861. *Chilonycteris boothi* Gundlach, Monatsb. preuss. Akad. Wiss., Berlin, p. 154, type from Fundador, Matanzas, Cuba.
1904. *Chilonycteris parnellii boothi*, Rehn, Proc. Acad. Nat. Sci. Philadelphia, 56:197, March 26.

MARGINAL RECORDS.—Cuba: Güines, Havana (Rehn, 1904:197); Baracoa (G. M. Allen, 1911:225).

Chilonycteris parnellii fusca J. A. Allen

1911. *Chilonycteris rubiginosa fusca* J. A. Allen, Bull. Amer. Mus. Nat. Hist., 30:262, December 2, type from Las Quiguas, 650 ft., 5 mi. S Puerto Cabello, Venezuela.
1955. *Chilonycteris parnellii fusca*, Goodwin, Amer. Mus. Novit., 1744:1, August 12.

MARGINAL RECORDS.—British Honduras: Stann Creek Valley (Hershkovitz, 1951:554), thence southward along Caribbean Coast to South America, then northward along Pacific Coast to Guatemala: Dueñas (J. A. Allen, 1894: 247); 2 mi. S Flores (Goodwin, 1955d:1).

Chilonycteris parnellii gonavensis Koopman

1955. *Chilonycteris parnellii gonavensis* Koopman, Jour. Mamm., 36:110, February 25, type from cave near En Café, La Gonave Island, Republic of Haiti. Known only from La Gonave Island.

Chilonycteris parnellii mexicana Miller

1902. *Chilonycteris mexicana* Miller, Proc. Acad. Nat. Sci. Philadelphia, 54:401, September 12, type from San Blas, Nayarit.
1955. *C[hilonycteris]. p[arnellii]. mexicana*, Koopman, Jour. Mamm., 36:112, February 25.

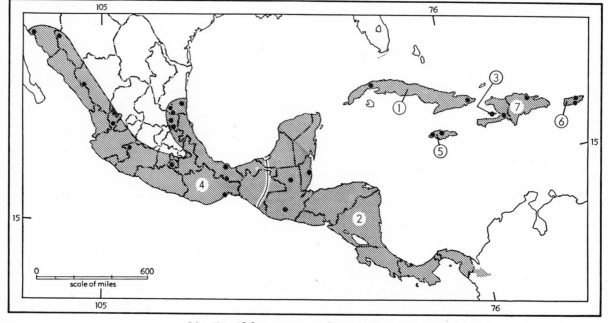

Map 56. *Chilonycteris parnellii* and subspecies.

Guide to subspecies	2. *C. p. fusca*	5. *C. p. parnellii*
1. *C. p. boothi*	3. *C. p. gonavensis*	6. *C. p. portoricensis*
	4. *C. p. mexicana*	7. *C. p. pusillus*

MARGINAL RECORDS.—Sonora: 15 mi. NW Guaymas (Burt, 1938:18). Chihuahua: cave near Carimechi (Burt and Hooper, 1941:2). Durango: Chacala (Burt, 1938:19). Jalisco: Bolaños (Rehn, 1904:204). Michoacán: S shore Lake Chapala (Hall and Villa, 1950:167). Morelos: Huajintlán (Davis and Russell, 1954:67). San Luis Potosí (Dalquest, 1953b:42): 1 km. W Huichihuayán; 3 km. N Taninul. Tamaulipas: El Pachón (Goodwin, 1954:4); Asseradero del Paraíso (*ibid.*); 10 mi. W and 2 mi. S Piedra, 1200 ft. (Anderson, 1956:349). Veracruz: 3 km. S San Andrés Tuxtla (Dalquest and Hall, 1949:425); 38 km. SE Jesús Carranza (*ibid.*). Oaxaca: near Tehuantepec (Rehn, 1904:204), thence northward along Pacific Coast to point of beginning.

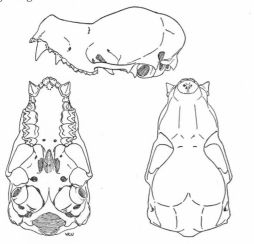

Fig. 53. *Chilonycteris parnellii mexicana,* 3 km. E San Andrés Tuxtla, 1000 ft., Veracruz, No. 23517 K.U., ♂, X 2.

Chilonycteris parnellii parnellii (Gray)

1843. *Phyllodia Parnellii* Gray, Proc. Zool. Soc. London, p. 50, October, type from Jamaica.
1855. *Ch[ilonycteris]. Parnellii,* Wagner, *in* Schreber, Die Säugthiere . . . , Suppl., 5:680.
1861. *Chilonycteris osburni* Tomes, Proc. Zool. Soc. London, p. 66, May, type from Sportsman's Hall Cave, Jamaica.

MARGINAL RECORDS.—Jamaica (G. M. Allen, 1911: 225): Lucea, Hanover Parish; Sportsman's Hall. Not found: Oxford Cave, Jamaica.

Chilonycteris parnellii portoricensis Miller

1902. *Chilonycteris portoricensis* Miller, Proc. Acad. Nat. Sci. Philadelphia, 54:400, September 12, type from Cueva de Fari, near Pueblo Viejo, Puerto Rico.
1904. *Chilonycteris parnellii portoricensis,* Rehn, Proc. Acad. Nat. Sci. Philadelphia, 56:199, March 26.

MARGINAL RECORDS.—Puerto Rico: type locality; Cayey (Anthony, 1918:343).

Chilonycteris parnellii pusillus G. M. Allen

1917. *Chilonycteris parnellii pusillus* G. M. Allen, Proc. Biol. Soc. Washington, 30:168, October 23, type from Arroyo Salado, Dominican Republic.

MARGINAL RECORDS.—Dominican Republic: type locality. Haiti: cave at Diquini (Miller, 1929a:8).

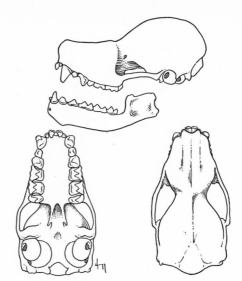

Fig. 54. *Chilonycteris parnellii portoricensis,* Trujillo Alto, Puerto Rico, from Anthony (1918:343), No. 39370 A.M., ♂, X 2.

Genus **Pteronotus** Gray—Naked-backed Bats

Revised under the name *Dermonotus* by Rehn, Proc. Acad. Nat. Sci. Philadelphia, 56:250–256, April 7, 1904.

1838. *Pteronotus* Gray, Mag. Zool. Bot., 2:500, February. Type, *Pteronotus davyi* Gray. Not *Pteronotus* Rafinesque, 1815, a *nomen nudum.*
1901. *Dermonotus* Gill, Proc. Biol. Soc. Washington, 14: 177, September 25. Type, *Pteronotus davyi* Gray. *Dermonotus* was a renaming of *Pteronotus,* which was thought to be preoccupied.

Skull not differing essentially from that of *Chilonycteris.* Volar membranes attached to median line of back, not sides, the hair of the back being thus concealed and only the naked membranes are immediately apparent.

KEY TO SPECIES OF PTERONOTUS

1. Length of forearm less than 49; greatest length of skull less than 17.0. . . *P. davyi,* p. 93
1'. Length of forearm more than 49; greatest length of skull more than 16.5. *P. suapurensis,* p. 94

Pteronotus davyi
Davy's Naked-backed Bat

Length of head and body approximately 50; total length, 59–75; length of forearm, 42–48; greatest length of skull, 15–17; interorbital breadth, 3.6–4.0; zygomatic breadth, 8.2–9.3; width of palatal constriction, 1.2–1.5. Reddish color phase: upper parts rich tawny or ochraceous; underparts golden ochraceous. Brown color phase: upper parts dark brown; underparts ecru-drab. This species differs

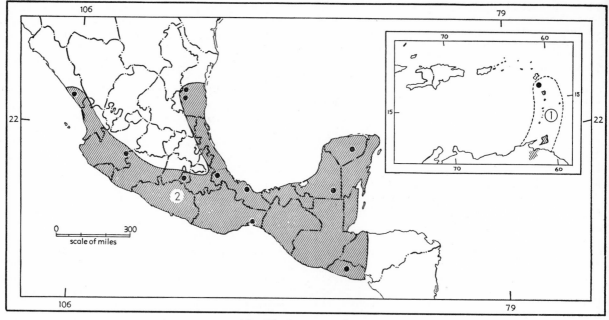

Map 57. *Pteronotus davyi.*

1. *P. d. davyi*   2. *P. d. fulvus*

from *P. suapurensis* chiefly in being smaller; size of skull averaging approximately ⅓ less than in *P. suapurensis.*

Fig. 55. *Pteronotus davyi fulvus,* 3 km. E San Andrés Tuxtla, 1000 ft., Veracruz, No. 23578 K.U., ♂, X 2.

Pteronotus davyi davyi Gray

1838. *Pteronotus davyi* Gray, Mag. Zool. Bot., 2:500, February, type from Island of Trinidad, British West Indies.
1843. *Chilonycteris gymnonotus* Wagner, Archiv Naturgeschichte, 9(Bd. 1):367, type from Cuyaba, Brazil.

MARGINAL RECORDS.—Lesser Antilles: Island of Dominica (Goodwin, 1946:299), thence southward into South America.

Pteronotus davyi fulvus (Thomas)

1892. *Chilonycteris davyi fulvus* Thomas, Ann. Mag. Nat. Hist., ser. 6, 10:410, November, type from Las Peñas, Jalisco.
1912. *Pteronotus davyi fulvus,* Miller, Bull. U.S. Nat. Mus., 79:33, December 31.

MARGINAL RECORDS (Davis and Russell, 1952:235, unless otherwise noted).—Tamaulipas: Rancho Santa Rosa,

25 km. N and 13 km. W Ciudad Victoria, 260 meters (Anderson, 1956:349). Veracruz: 3 km. E San Andrés Tuxtla (23578 KU). Yucatán: Chichén-Itzá. Campeche: La Tuxpena, Champoton. El Salvador: San Rafaeo Cedros (Felten, 1956:78). Oaxaca: Santa Efigenia, Tehuantepec, thence northward along Pacific Coast to Sinaloa: Escuinapa (J. A. Allen, 1906:236). Michoacán: Lake Chapala. Morelos: Temilpa (Davis and Russell, 1954:67). Veracruz: Mirador. Tamaulipas: Rancho Pano Ayuctle, 8 mi. N Gómez Fárias, 300 ft. (Anderson, 1956:350).

Pteronotus suapurensis (J. A. Allen)
Suapuré Naked-backed Bat

X ½

1904. *Dermonotus suapurensis* J. A. Allen, Bull. Amer. Mus. Nat. Hist, 20:229, June 29, type from Suapuré, north of Río Mato, Bolívar, Venezuela.
1932. *Pteronotus suapurensis*, Sanborn, Ann. Carnegie Mus., 21:173, September 15.
1942. *Pteronotus suapurensis centralis* Goodwin, Jour. Mamm., 23:88, February 16, type from Matagalpa, 3000 ft., Matagalpa, Nicaragua. Regarded as inseparable from *P. suapurensis* by Felten, Senkenbergiana Biol., 37:77, February 15, 1956.

Selected measurements of 59 adults (35 ♂ ♂ and 24 ♀ ♀) from El Salvador are: length of head and body, 58–67; length of forearm, 50–57; greatest length of skull, 16.8–17.6; interorbital breadth, 4.1–4.6; zygomatic breadth, 10.1–10.9; length of upper tooth-row, 7.3–7.7. To judge from published descriptions, this species differs in no significant particulars from *P. davyi* except in substantially greater size.

MARGINAL RECORDS.—Guatemala: Lanquin Cave, 1022 ft., (64797 KU). Southeastward into South America, thence up west coast at least to El Salvador: Suchitoto (Felten, 1956:75).

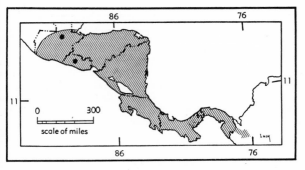

Map 58. *Pteronotus suapurensis.*

Genus **Mormoops** Leach—Leaf-chinned Bats

Revised by Rehn, Proc. Acad. Nat. Sci. Philadelphia, 54: 160–172, June 11, 1902.

1821. *Aëllo* Leach, Trans. Linn. Soc. London, 13:69. Type, *Aëllo cuvieri* Leach [= *Mormoops blainvillii cuvieri* (Leach)]. For use of *Mormoops*, in place of *Aëllo* that has eight pages of priority, see Opinion 462 (16[pt. 2]: 1–12, April 2, 1957) of the International Comm. on Zool. Nomenclature.
1821. *Mormoops* Leach, Trans. Linn. Soc. London, 13:76. Type, *Mormoops blainvillii* Leach [= *Aëllo cuvieri* Leach].
1829. *Mormops* Cuvier, Dict. Sci. Nat., 59:422, a *lapsus*.

"In general like *Chilonycteris,* but skull so greatly shortened that both rostrum and braincase are broader than long; braincase greatly deepened, its floor so elevated that lower rim of foramen magnum is above level of rostrum; teeth essentially as in *Chilonycteris,* except that lower incisors are of about equal size and uniform structure, the inner tooth

lacking all trace of backward extension of the crown; dermal outgrowths on chin very highly developed." (Miller, 1907:121.)

KEY TO SPECIES OF MORMOOPS
(adapted from Rehn, 1902:162)

1. Chin pad slightly divided; dermal flange connecting inner side of conch with supraocular region united to flange of opposite side.
   M. blainvillii, p. 95
1'. Chin pad considerably divided; dermal flange connecting inner side of conch with supraocular region not united to flange of opposite side except at extreme base. *M. megalophylla,* p. 96

Mormoops blainvillii
Blainville's Leaf-chinned Bat

Length of head and body approximately 51; total length, 80–86; length of forearm, 46–48; greatest length of skull, 13.8–14.4; interorbital breadth, 4.3–4.5; zygomatic breadth, 8.5–8.6; length of upper molar series, 6.0–6.4. According to Anthony (1918: 346) interfemoral membrane wide; face short; muzzle with small pad but no nose-leaf; ears large, exceedingly broad, joined across forehead; tragus large, complex; calcar long and well developed; tail long, enclosed except for tip; braincase globose; angle of almost 90° between dorsal face of rostrum and braincase; zygomatic arches scarcely flaring; palate long, narrow, shallowly concave posteriorly.

In pale phase: upper parts light brown; underparts buffy. In dark phase: upper parts dark brown; underparts ochraceous-tawny.

Mormoops blainvillii blainvillii Leach

1821. *Mormoops blainvillii* Leach, Trans. Linn. Soc. London, 13:77, type from Jamaica.

MARGINAL RECORDS.—Jamaica (G. M. Allen, 1911: 226): Sportsman's Cave; Kingston.

Mormoops blainvillii cuvieri (Leach)

1821. *Aëllo cuvieri* Leach, Trans. Linn. Soc. London, 13:71, type from unknown locality, here assumed to be Cuba, but possibly is Jamaica.
1840. *L[obostoma]. cinnamomeum* Gundlach, Arch. Naturgesch., Jahrg. 6, 1:357. Type locality, Cafetal St. [San] Antonio el Fundador, Matanzas, Cuba.

MARGINAL RECORDS.—Cuba: Casetal [= Cafetal] San Antonio el Fundador (Anthony, 1918:346); Baracoa (Miller, 1904:343). Haiti: La Gonave Island (Koopman, 1955:110); cave near St. Michel (Miller, 1929:8). Dominican Republic: Aquacate (G. M. Allen, 1911:227). Mona Island (Anthony, 1918:346). Puerto Rico: Cueva de Trujillo Alto (*ibid.*).

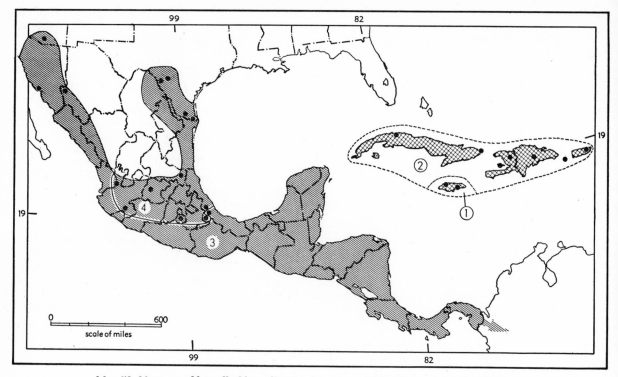

Map 59. *Mormoops blainvillii blainvillii* (1), *Mormoops blainvillii cuvieri* (2), *Mormoops megalophylla megalophylla* (3), and *Mormoops megalophylla senicula* (4).

Mormoops megalophylla
Peters' Leaf-chinned Bat

Length of head and body, 59–66; means of external measurements of 3 males from southern Veracruz are: 87, 23, 10, 14. Certain cranial measurements of a male and a female from Veracruz are, respectively: greatest length of skull, 15.1, 15.3; interorbital breadth, 5.1, 5.3; zygomatic breadth, 9.5, 9.4; length of upper tooth-row, 9.0, 8.9. Color much as in *M. blainvillii*. Differing structurally from *M. blainvillii* chiefly in the broadly and deeply divided chin lappet and in flange from inner margin of ear-conch which meets its opposite only at extreme base.

These bats usually roost in hot caverns in the jungle but in some areas have been taken from dwellings of man. Generally they do not tolerate much disturbance and take flight with little hesitation. A female obtained in southern Veracruz on April 23 contained one 22-mm. embryo.

Mormoops megalophylla megalophylla (Peters)

1864. *Mormops megalophylla* Peters, Monatsb. preuss. Akad. Wiss., Berlin, p. 381, type from southern México.

MARGINAL RECORDS.—Arizona: 5 mi. N, 2 mi. W Patagonia (Beatty, 1955:290). Chihuahua: near Carimechi (Burt and Hooper, 1941:2). Veracruz: Cañon of

Actopan (Ward, 1904:634), thence southward along Caribbean Coast to South America, then northward along Pacific Coast to Sonora: 15 mi. NW Guaymas (Burt, 1938: 19) and to opposite point of beginning.

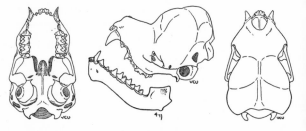

Fig. 56. *Mormoops megalophylla megalophylla*, 3 km. E San Andrés Tuxtla, 1000 ft., Veracruz, No. 23636 K.U., ♂, X 2.

Mormoops megalophylla senicula (Rehn)

1902. *Mormoops megalophylla senicula* Rehn, Proc. Acad. Nat. Sci. Philadelphia, 54:169, June 11, type from Fort Clark, Kinney Co., Texas.

MARGINAL RECORDS.—Texas: Concan (Blair, 1952: 95); *Haby Cave, Medina Co.* (Eads, Menzies and Wiseman, 1956:440); Edinburg (Blair, 1952:237); near Brownsville (Taylor and Davis, 1947:14). Veracruz: Mirador (Rehn, 1902:170); Orizaba (*ibid.*). Morelos: Cerro de Jojutla (Davis and Russell, 1954:67). Jalisco: Los Masos (J. A. Allen, 1906:261). Nayarit: Rancho Palo Amarillo, near Amatlan (*ibid.*). Guanajuato: Guanajuato (Rehn, 1902: 120). San Luis Potosí: 3 km. N Taninul (Dalquest, 1953:

44). Coahuila (Baker, 1956:172): *6 mi. S, 3 mi. W Hda. La Mariposa; Fortín.* Texas: type locality.

SUBFAMILY **PHYLLOSTOMINAE**

Teeth essentially normal, although in some genera mesostyle and commissures of M1 and M2, and paraconid and metaconid of m1 and m2 are reduced; humerus with definite secondary impingement (not articulation) with scapula; epitrochlea large, having slightly developed spinous process; nose-leaf present; lower lip without platelike outgrowths (after Miller, 1907:122).

KEY TO NORTH AMERICAN GENERA OF PHYLLOSTOMINAE

(adapted from Miller, 1907:122–123)

1. Lower incisors 1.
    2. Lower premolars 3. . . . . *Tonatia*, p. 105
    2'. Lower premolars 2.
        3. Crown of lateral upper incisor as wide as that of medial incisor; auditory bullae well developed.
                    Mimon, p. 106
        3'. Crown of lateral upper incisor much narrower than that of medial incisor; auditory bullae notably narrow. . . . . *Chrotopterus*, p. 111
1'. Lower incisors 2.
    4. Lower premolars 2. . . . . *Phyllostomus*, p. 107
    4'. Lower premolars 3.
        5. Rostrum as long as braincase; molars wider than palate, their W-shaped pattern much modified.
                    Vampyrum, p. 112
        5'. Rostrum shorter than braincase; molars narrower than palate, their W-shaped pattern essentially normal.
            6. Middle lower premolar about as large as third.
                7. Auditory bullae large, their greatest diameter much exceeding the distance between them. . . . . *Macrotus*, p. 101
                7'. Auditory bullae small, their greatest diameter approximately equal to the distance between them. . . . . *Micronycteris*, p. 97
            6'. Middle lower premolar much smaller than third.
                8. First lower premolar in contact or nearly so with 3rd, the 2nd displaced inward from tooth-row.
                    9. Length of rostrum much less than breadth of braincase. . . . . *Macrophyllum*, p. 104
                    9'. Length of rostrum approximately equal to breadth of braincase. . . . *Trachops*, p. 110
                8'. First lower premolar distant from 3rd, the 2nd being in normal position in tooth-row.
                    10. Dorsal profile of rostrum strongly convex; a deep depression present between orbits.
                        Lonchorhina, p. 104
                  10'. Dorsal profile of rostrum not convex; no depression between orbits. *Phylloderma*, p. 109

Genus **Micronycteris** Gray—Small-eared Bats

Revised by Andersen, Ann. Mag. Nat. Hist., ser. 7, 18: 50–58, July, 1906; and by Sanborn, Fieldiana-Zool., Chicago Nat. Hist. Mus., 31:215–233, April 29, 1949.

1866. *Micronycteris* Gray, Proc. Zool. Soc. London, p. 113, May. Type, *Phyllophora megalotis* Gray.

Skull slender, lightly constructed; rostrum narrow, tapering, more than half as long as, but shorter than, braincase; frontal region rising from axis of rostrum at angle of approximately 45° (but varying according to species); auditory bullae small, greatest diameter of one approximating interbullar space; middle lower premolar approximately as large as 3rd lower premolar. Dentition, i. $\frac{2}{2}$, c. $\frac{1}{1}$, p. $\frac{2}{3}$, m. $\frac{3}{2}$ Tail extending to middle of interfemoral membrane.

KEY TO NORTH AMERICAN SUBGENERA AND SPECIES OF MICRONYCTERIS

1. Ears connected by high, notched band; length of forearm 31–38; P3 of about same size as P4. . . . Subgenus *Micronycteris*, p. 98
    2. Interauricular band lightly notched medially. . . . . *M. megalotis*, p. 98
    2'. Interauricular band deeply notched.
                M. schmidtorum, p. 99
1'. Ears not connected by high, notched band; length of forearm more than 38.
    3. Interauricular band low, not notched; 3rd metacarpal shortest, 5th longest; greatest length of skull more than 22.
        Subgenus *Xenoctenes, M. hirsuta*, p. 99
    3'. Interauricular band absent; 3rd metacarpal not shortest; greatest length of skull less than 22.

4. Fifth metacarpal shortest, 3rd longest; P4 not recurved.
    Subgenus *Lampronycteris*,
        M. platyceps, p. 100
4'. Fourth metacarpal shortest, 5th longest; P4 slightly recurved.
    Subgenus *Glyphonycteris*,
        M. sylvestris, p. 100

Subgenus **Micronycteris** Gray

1866. *Micronycteris* Gray, Proc. Zool. Soc. London, p. 113, May. Type, *Phyllophora megalotis* Gray.
1856. *Schizostoma* Gervais, Mammifères *in* [Castelnau] Expéd. dans les partes centrales de l'Amer. du Sud . . . , pt. 7, p. 38. Type, *Schizostoma minuta*, Gervais. Not *Schizostoma* Bronn, 1835, a mollusk.
1862. *Schizastoma* Gray, Catalogue of the bones of Mammalia in the . . . British Museum, p. 38, a *lapsus*?

Ears connected by high, notched band; 3rd metacarpal shortest, 5th longest; forearm, 31–38; P3 large, about equal to P4; greatest length of skull, 17–20.

Micronycteris megalotis

Brazilian Small-eared Bat

Length of head and body approximately 48; interorbital breadth, 4.5–5.5; zygomatic breadth, 8.5–9.8; length upper tooth-row, 6.8–7.8. Upper parts medium darkish brown tinged with russet or dark brown without russet tinge; underparts paler brown; intermediate colors present on some specimens. Nose lancet approximately 1½ times higher than breadth of its base; calcar longer than foot and more than half as long as lower leg.

Bats of this species are widespread but not abundant. Seemingly they do not congregate in large groups; they roost singly or in small colonies in crevices and hollow trees.

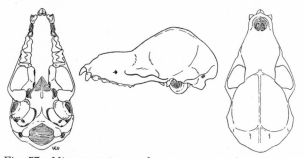

Fig. 57. *Micronycteris megalotis mexicana*, 4 km. W Peso de San Juan, 250 ft., Veracruz, No. 23639 K.U., ♂, X 2.

Micronycteris megalotis mexicana Miller

1898. *Micronycteris megalotis mexicanus* Miller, Proc. Acad. Nat. Sci. Philadelphia, 50:329, August 2, type from Platanar, Jalisco.
1904. *Macrotus pygmaeus* Rehn, Proc. Acad. Nat. Sci. Philadelphia, 56:444, June 30, type from Izamal, Yucatán. Goodwin (Bull. Amer. Mus. Nat. Hist., 102:246, August 31, 1953) regards *M. pygmaeus* as indistinguishable from *Micronycteris megalotis mexicana*.
MARGINAL RECORDS.—Tamaulipas: Pano Ayuctle (Goodwin, 1954:4). Veracruz: Cuesta de Don Lino, near Jalapa (Ward, 1904:653). Honduras: Sabana Grande, Tegucigalpa (Goodwin, 1942:124). Jalisco: type locality; *Ciudad Guzmán* (de la Torre, 1955:697). Morelos: Cuautla (Davis and Russell, 1954:67). San Luis Potosí: 8 mi. (by road) E Santa Barbarita (Dalquest, 1953b:23).

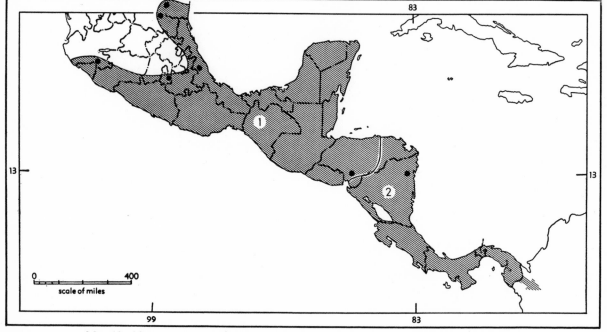

Map 60. *Micronycteris megalotis mexicana* (1) and *Micronycteris megalotis microtis* (2).

Micronycteris megalotis microtis Miller

1898. *Micronycteris microtis* Miller, Proc. Acad. Nat. Sci. Philadelphia, 50:328, July 12, type from Greytown [= San Juan del Norte], Comarca de San Juan del Norte, Nicaragua.
1949. *Micronycteris* (*Micronycteris*) *megalotis microtis*, Sanborn, Fieldiana-Zool., Chicago Nat. Hist. Mus., 31: 219, April 29.

MARGINAL RECORDS.—Nicaragua: Río Coco (J. A. Allen, 1910:110) thence southward to South America.

Micronycteris schmidtorum Sanborn
Schmidt's Small-eared Bat

1935. *Micronycteris schmidtorum* Sanborn, Field Mus. Nat. Hist., Publ. 340, Zool. Ser., 20:81, May 15, type from Bobos, Izabal, Guatemala.

Selected measurements of the type, an adult male, are: length of head and body, approximately 47; total length, 64; length of forearm, 35.3; greatest length of skull, 20.5; interorbital breadth, 4.3; zygomatic breadth, 9.1; length upper tooth-row, 7.9. Upper parts medium brown; underparts paler. Closely resembling *M. megalotis* (see key).

The type specimen was obtained from a hollow tree; a second specimen was obtained from the same place several months later.

MARGINAL RECORDS.—Yucatán: Oxkintok (Hatt and Villa, 1950:227). Honduras: Copán (Sanborn, 1949:220).

Subgenus Xenoctenes Miller

1907. *Xenoctenes* Miller, Bull. U.S. Nat. Mus., 57:124, June 29. Type, *Schizostoma hirsutum* Peters.

Ears connected by low band, not notched; 3rd metacarpal shortest, 5th metacarpal longest; forearm, 42.7–48.6; P3 large, about equal to P4; greatest length of skull, 22.6–24.0.

Micronycteris hirsuta (Peters)
Hairy Small-eared Bat

1869. *Schizostoma hirsutum* Peters, Monatsb. preuss. Akad. Wiss., Berlin, p. 396. Type from an unknown locality; tentatively fixed at Pozo Azul, San José, Costa Rica, by Goodwin, Bull. Amer. Mus. Nat. Hist., 87:302, December 31, 1946.
1906. *Micronycteris hirsuta*, Andersen, Ann. Mag. Nat. Hist., ser. 7, 18:57, July.

Selected measurements of an adult male and adult female from Palmar, Costa Rica, are, respectively (*fide* Goodwin, 1946:302): total length, 65, 70; length of forearm, 43.7, 48.6; interorbital breadth, 4.6, 5.0; zygomatic breadth, 11.7, 11.6; length upper tooth-row, 9.3, 9.3. Upper parts medium brown; underparts paler brown washed with buff. Braincase less elevated above facial region than in *M. megalotis*.

MARGINAL RECORDS.—Costa Rica: Pozo Azul, San José (Goodwin, 1946:302), thence southward into South America.

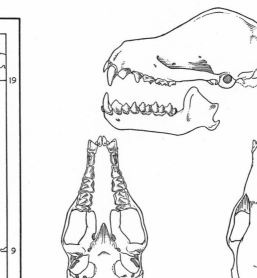

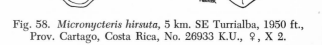

Map 61. *Micronycteris schmidtorum* (1) and *Micronycteris hirsuta* (2).

Fig. 58. *Micronycteris hirsuta*, 5 km. SE Turrialba, 1950 ft., Prov. Cartago, Costa Rica, No. 26933 K.U., ♀, X 2.

Subgenus **Lampronycteris** Sanborn

1949. *Lampronycteris* Sanborn, Fieldiana-Zool., Chicago Nat. Hist. Mus., 31:223, April 29. Type, *Micronycteris* (*Lampronycteris*) *platyceps* Sanborn.

Ears not connected by band; 5th metacarpal shortest, 3rd metacarpal longest; calcar shorter than foot with claws; braincase lower than in subgenera *Micronycteris* or *Xenoctenes*; teeth essentially as in *Micronycteris*, but P4 longer and narrower with its inner border more nearly straight and internal ledge more nearly horizontal.

Micronycteris platyceps Sanborn
Sanborn's Small-eared Bat

1949. *Micronycteris* (*Lampronycteris*) *platyceps* Sanborn, Fieldiana-Zool., Chicago Nat. Hist. Mus., 31:224, April 29, type from Guanapo, Trinidad.

Selected measurements of the type, an adult female, and 2 topotypes are, respectively: total length, 68, 70, 70; length of forearm, 39.8, 39.6, 40.0; greatest length of skull, 21.2, 21.3, 21.6; interorbital breadth, 4.9, 5.2, 5.2; zygomatic breadth, 10.3, 10.4, 10.6; length upper tooth-row, 8.0, 8.2, 8.2. Upper parts olive brown; chest and belly tawny-olive; throat yellowish.

MARGINAL RECORDS.—Nicaragua: Volcán de Chinandega (Sanborn, 1949:224), thence southward into South America.

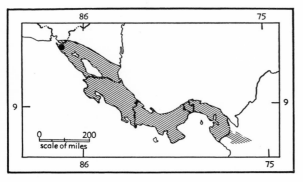

Map 62. *Micronycteris platyceps*.

Subgenus **Glyphonycteris** Thomas

1896. *Glyphonycteris* Thomas, Ann. Mag. Nat. Hist., 18(ser. 6):302, October. Type, *Glyphonycteris sylvestris* Thomas.

Ears not connected by a band; 4th metacarpal shortest, 5th metacarpal longest; P3 larger than P4; P4 slightly recurved; braincase expanded less than in *Micronycteris* but more than in *Lampronycteris*.

Micronycteris sylvestris (Thomas)
Brown Small-eared Bat

1896. *Glyphonycteris sylvestris* Thomas, Ann. Mag. Nat. Hist., ser. 6, 18:303, October, type from between 1400 and 2000 ft., near Hda. Miravalles, Guanacaste, Costa Rica.
1949. *Micronycteris* (*Glyphonycteris*) *sylvestris*, Sanborn, Fieldiana-Zool., Chicago Nat. Hist. Mus., 31:231, April 29.

Length of head and body approximately 52. Selected measurements of the type, an adult male, are: greatest length of skull, 19.8; interorbital breadth, 5.8; zygomatic breadth, 10.2; length of upper tooth-row, 8.2. "Hairs of upperside with four alternating rings of dark brown and whitish . . . ; narrow tips of hairs approaching clove brown. Fur of underside dark brown at base, greyish drab at tip." (Andersen, 1906:60.)

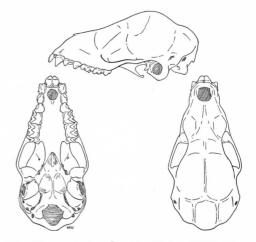

Fig. 59. *Micronycteris sylvestris*, 15 km. ENE Tlacotepec, 1500 ft., Veracruz, No. 23645 K.U., ♀, X 2.

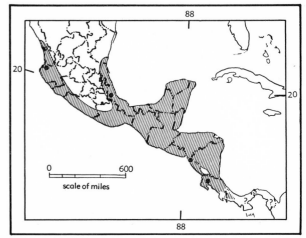

Map 63. *Micronycteris sylvestris*.

MARGINAL RECORDS.—Jalisco: 10 km. NW Soyatlán del Oro (Villa, 1956:544). Veracruz: 15 km. ENE Tlacotepec (Dalquest and Hall, 1949:427). Nicaragua: Volcán de Chinandega (Goodwin, 1946:302). Costa Rica: type locality.

Genus **Macrotus** Gray—Leaf-nosed Bats

Revised by Rehn, Proc. Acad. Nat. Sci. Philadelphia, 56: 427–446, June 27, 30, 1904.

1843. *Macrotus* Gray, Proc. Zool. Soc. London, p. 21, July. Type, *Macrotus waterhousii* Gray.

1891. *Otopterus* Lydekker, *in* Flower and Lydekker, An introduction to . . . mammals living and extinct, p. 673. Type, *Macrotus waterhousii*, a renaming of *Macrotus* Gray, erroneously assumed to be preoccupied by *Macrotis* Reid, 1837, a marsupial.

Rostrum moderately long, considerably lower than braincase; medial upper incisors chisel-shaped, long; lateral upper incisors weak. Head long; muzzle conical; nose-leaf simple, erect, lanceolate; nose-pad rounded; nostrils elongate, distinct; lower lip with triangular pad bearing longitudinal groove; ears large, united; tragus lanceolate; uropatagium large; tail long, projecting somewhat beyond posterior margin of uropatagium, which envelops tail except its free apex; calcanea short and stout (after Rehn, 1904:428). Dentition, i. $\frac{2}{2}$, c. $\frac{1}{1}$, p. $\frac{2}{3}$, m. $\frac{3}{3}$.

This bat is fairly common to abundant throughout its range. It seems to prefer man-made structures for roosting sites and is sometimes found hanging in open, light, airy places.

KEY TO SPECIES OF MACROTUS
(adapted from Rehn, 1904:429)

1. Ear medium or large, averaging 26 to 28 in length; skull with rostrum rather heavy; interorbital region broad.
    2. Foot robust, toes strong; occurring on Antillean islands. . . *M. waterhousii*, p. 101
    2′. Foot slender, toes weak; occurring on Mexican or Central American mainland.
        M. mexicanus, p. 102
1′. Ear large, averaging more than 30 in length; skull slender, rostrum and interorbital region narrow. . . . . . . *M. californicus*, p. 103

Macrotus waterhousii
Waterhouse's Leaf-nosed Bat

Length of head and body, 57–69; total length, 84.5–103.0; length of forearm, 49–55; greatest length of skull, 23.5–26.8; interorbital breadth, 3.5–4.9; zygomatic breadth, 10.6–12.3. Upper parts medium brown, approximately basal half of hairs whitish;

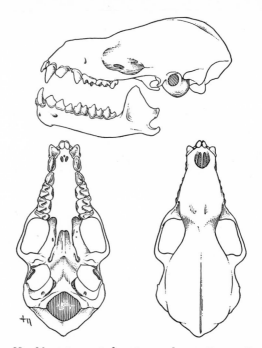

Fig. 60. *Macrotus waterhousii waterhousii*, Port-au-Prince, Haiti, No. 30764 C.N.H.M., ♂, X 2.

underparts brownish buff with silvery wash. Skull with rostrum as wide anteriorly as interorbital space; teeth robust, the first lower premolar thick, almost quadrate in basal outline; foot broad and robust.

Macrotus waterhousii compressus Rehn

1904. *Macrotus waterhousii compressus* Rehn, Proc. Acad. Nat. Sci. Philadelphia, 56:434, June 30, type from Eleuthera, Bahamas.

MARGINAL RECORDS.—Bahama Islands: 4 mi. S Georgetown, Eleuthera (Miller, 1905:381); Orange Creek, Cat Island (G. M. Allen and Sanborn, 1937:226); Hamilton, Long Island (*ibid.*); Salt Point, Jamaica Bay, Acklin Island (Shamel, 1931:251); Conch Sound, Andros (Elliot, 1905:509); Nassau, New Providence (G. M. Allen, 1911: 228).

Macrotus waterhousii heberfolium Shamel

1931. *Macrotus waterhousii heberfolium* Shamel, Jour. Washington Acad. Sci., 21:252, June 4, type from Kingston, Providenciale Island, Bahamas Islands. Known only from the type locality.

Macrotus waterhousii jamaicensis Rehn

1904. *Macrotus waterhousii jamaicensis* Rehn, Proc. Acad. Nat. Sci. Philadelphia, 56:432, June 27, type from Spanishtown, Jamaica.

MARGINAL RECORDS.—Jamaica: Bluefields (Dobson, 1878:467); Port Antonio (G. M. Allen, 1911, 227); Kingston (*ibid.*).

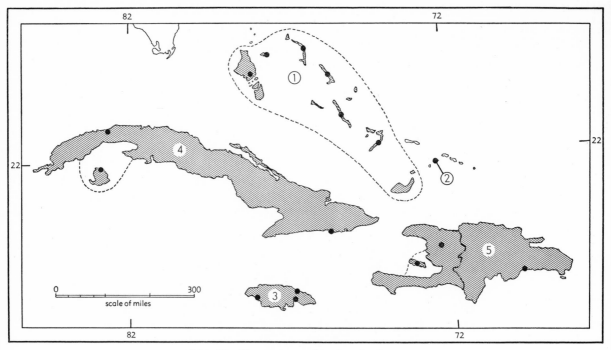

Map 64. *Macrotus waterhousii* and subspecies.

Guide to kinds	2. *M. w. heberfolium*	4. *M. w. minor*
1. *M. w. compressus*	3. *M. w. jamaicensis*	5. *M. w. waterhousii*

Macrotus waterhousii minor Gundlach

1864. *Macrotus minor* Gundlach, Monatsb. preuss. Akad. Wiss., Berlin, p. 382, type from western Cuba.
1904. *Macrotus waterhousii minor*, Rehn, Proc. Acad. Nat. Sci. Philadelphia, 56:435, June 30.

MARGINAL RECORDS.—Cuba: Guanajay, Pinar del Río (G. M. Allen, 1911:228); Daiquirí (Anthony, 1919: 637). Isle of Pines: Nueva Gerona (G. M. Allen, 1911:228).

Macrotus waterhousii waterhousii Gray

1843. *Macrotus waterhousii* Gray, Proc. Zool. Soc. London, p. 21, July, type from Haiti.

MARGINAL RECORDS.—Haiti: cave near St. Michel (Miller, 1929:8). Dominican Republic: San Domingo (G. M. Allen, 1911:227). Haiti: La Gonave Island (Koopman, 1955:110). Not found: Daiquini, Haiti (Hershkovitz, 1951:554).

Macrotus mexicanus
Mexican Leaf-nosed Bat

Length of head and body, 53–64; total length, 84.5–101; length of forearm, 47.5–53.5; greatest length of skull, 22.5–25.5; interorbital breadth, 3.9–4.5; zygomatic breadth, 10.5–12.5. Dark phase: upper parts dark brown with silvery wash; underparts brownish buff washed with white. Light phase: upper parts cinnamon; underparts drab washed with white. In both color phases hairs at base of ears whitish. Skull resembling that of *M. waterhousii* except for smaller size; interorbital region more depressed; rostrum slightly slenderer.

Macrotus mexicanus bulleri H. Allen

1890. *Macrotus bulleri* H. Allen, Proc. Amer. Philos. Soc., 28:73, May 10, type from Bolaños, Jalisco.
1904. *Macrotus mexicanus bulleri*, Rehn, Proc. Acad. Nat. Sci. Philadelphia, 56:439, June 30, 1904.

MARGINAL RECORDS (Rehn, 1904:441, unless otherwise noted).—Chihuahua: Barranca de Cobre (Knobloch, 1942:297). Durango: Chacala. Hidalgo: cave "acerca de Pinalito," Jacala (Málaga Alba and Villa R., 1957:538). Jalisco: type locality; San Pedro, near Guadalajara. Michoacán: S shore Lake Chapala (J. A. Allen, 1894:248). Jalisco: Ameca. Nayarit: María Madre Island. Chihuahua: near Batopilas.

Macrotus mexicanus mexicanus Saussure

1860. *Macrotus mexicanus* Saussure, Revue et Mag. Zool. Paris, ser. 2, 12:486, November, type from Yautepec, near Cuautla, Morelos.
1876. *Macrotus bocourtianus* Dobson, Ann. Mag. Nat. Hist., ser. 4, 18:436, type from Vera Paz, Guatemala.

MARGINAL RECORDS (Rehn, 1904:437, 439, unless otherwise noted).—Colima: Colima. Michoacán: La Salada. Morelos: Cuernavaca (Davis and Russell, 1952:235); *type locality*; Cuautla (Davis and Russell, 1954:67). Oaxaca: Reyes [= Papalo Santos Reyes]. Guatemala: Vera Paz. Oaxaca: Tehuantepec.

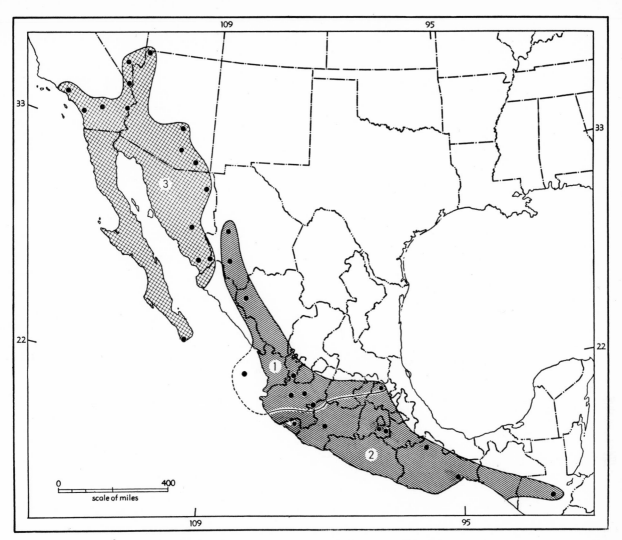

Map 65. *Macrotus mexicanus* and *Macrotus californicus*.

1. *M. m. bulleri*   2. *M. m. mexicanus*   3. *M. californicus*

Macrotus californicus Baird
California Leaf-nosed Bat

1858. *Macrotus californicus* Baird, Proc. Acad. Nat. Sci. Philadelphia, 10:116, type from Old Fort Yuma, Imperial Co., California, on right bank of Colorado River, opposite present town of Yuma, Arizona.

Length of head and body, 50–58; total length, 84.5–92.5 (5 topotypes in alcohol); length of forearm, 49.3–51.0; greatest length of skull, 23.0–24.1 (cranial measurements based on 6 specimens); interorbital breadth, 3.8–4.0; zygomatic breadth, 11–12. Upper parts varying from buffy gray to dark brown; underparts pale drab to buffy brown, usually with silvery wash. Ears large and subovate; skull,

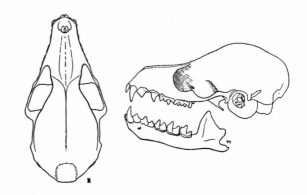

Fig. 61. *Macrotus californicus*, 14 mi. E Searchlight, Nevada, No. 61421 M.V.Z., ♂, X 2.

limbs and general form slender; teeth weak (see Rehn, 1904:441).

MARGINAL RECORDS.—Arizona: Virgin Narrows, NE of Littlefield (Hardy, 1949:434); Superior (G. M. Allen, 1922:156); 9 mi. N Tucson (Dice and Blossom, 1937:17); Tombstone (G. M. Allen, 1922:156). Sonora (Burt, 1938:19): near El Tigre; San Javier; Guirocoba; Chinobampo. Baja California: Cape San Lucas (Rehn, 1904:444). California: De Luz (*ibid.*); 2 mi. N Owensmouth (A. B. Howell, 1920:176); Indian Wells (Rehn, 1904:444); Riverside Mts. (Stager, 1939:226). Nevada: 14 mi. E Searchlight, Colorado River (Hall, 1946:130); Frenchmans Mine, 7 mi. E Las Vegas (*ibid.*). Not found: Cayetano Mts., Arizona (G. M. Allen, 1922:156).

Genus **Lonchorhina** Tomes
Tomes' Long-eared Bat

1863. *Lonchorhina* Tomes, Proc. Zool. Soc. London, p. 81, May. Type, *Lonchorhina aurita* Tomes.

Skull resembling that of *Chilonycteris*; a distinct concavity at base of rostrum between orbits; middle of braincase low, rising little above occiput; auditory bullae small; teeth much as in *Micronycteris*, but crowns of incisors wider (width approximately equal to height); 2nd lower premolar smaller than either of others. Dental formula as in *Macrotus*. Ears large, separate; nose-leaf large; tail longer than femur, extending to edge of membrane.

Only one species occurs within the geographic limits set for the present work.

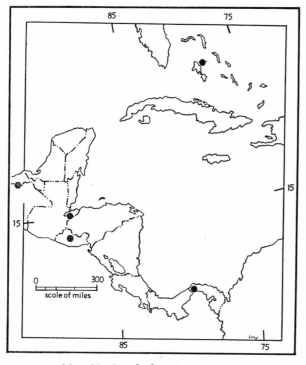

Map 66. *Lonchorhina aurita aurita.*

Lonchorhina aurita
Tomes' Long-eared Bat

Selected measurements of an adult male and female from Panamá are, respectively: length of head and body, 60, 62; tail, 57, 58; forearm, 49.6, 50; condylobasal length, 18.4, 19.2; interorbital breadth, 5, 5; zygomatic breadth, 11, 10.8; length upper tooth-row, 6.6, 6.6. This rare bat roosts in caves.

Lonchorhina aurita aurita Tomes

1863. *Lonchorhina aurita* Tomes, Proc. Zool. Soc. London, p. 83, May, type from "West Indies." [According to P. Hershkovitz, *in litt.* September 8, 1958, the type locality is Trinidad on basis of Thomas, Jour. Trinidad Field Nat. Club, 1:5, 1893 (not seen by us).]

MARGINAL RECORDS.—Bahama Islands: Nassau Harbor, New Providence (G. M. Allen, 1911:228). Panamá: Chilibrillo Cave, near Ahlajuela (Goldman, 1920:182). El Salvador (Felten, 1956:181): *Cueva Hedionda*; *Santa Ana*; Suchitoto. Guatemala: Las Quebradas, Izabal (Sanborn, 1936:95). Tabasco: 5 mi. W Teapa (Hall, 1955a:1).

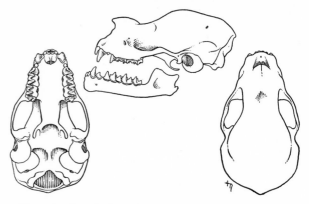

Fig. 62. *Lonchorhina aurita aurita*, Chilibrillo River, Panamá, No. 173849 U.S.N.M., sex ?, X 2.

Genus **Macophyllum** Gray—Long-legged Bat

1838. *Macrophyllum* Gray, Mag. Zool. Bot., 2:489, February. Type, *Macrophyllum nieuwiedii* Gray [= *Phyllostoma macrophyllum* Schinz].
1891. *Dolichophyllum* Lydekker, *in* Flower and Lydekker, An introduction to . . . mammals living and extinct, p. 673. Type, *Macrophyllum nieuwiedii* Gray, a renaming of *Macrophyllum* Gray, which Lydekker considered to be a homonym of *Macrophylla* Hope, 1837, a beetle.

Resembling *Micronycteris*, but: ears separate; tail longer than femur and continued to outer edge of broad interfemoral membrane. Skull with short rostrum, its length less than breadth of braincase; nares emarginate laterally and above, leaving noticeable flattened area over roots of incisors; basioccipital pits obsolete; auditory bullae small, not covering half of cochleae. Teeth essentially like those of *Micronycteris*, except that middle lower premolar, p3, minute and so crowded inward that 1st and 3rd are almost in contact, first upper premolar (P3) not much larger than outer incisor, middle upper incisors project more conspicuously, and crowns of lower incisors relatively wider (after Miller, 1907:128).

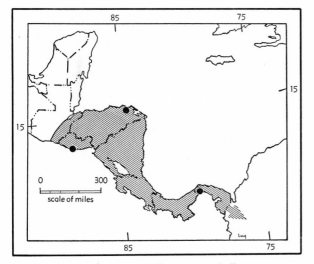

Map 67. *Macrophyllum macrophyllum.*

Macrophyllum macrophyllum (Schinz)
Long-legged Bat

1821. *Phyllost [oma]. macrophyllum* Schinz, Das Thierreich . . . , 1:163, type from Rio Mucurí, Minas Geraes, Brazil.
1912. *Macrophyllum macrophyllum,* Nelson, Proc. Biol. Soc. Washington, 25:93, May 4.
1838. *Macrophyllum nieuwiedii* [*sic*] Gray, Mag. Zool. and Bot., 2:489. Based on *Ph[yllostoma]. macrophyllum* Wied-Neuwied, Beiträge zur Naturgesch. Brasil., 2:188, 1826, type from Brazil.

Measurements of an adult male, in alcohol, from British Guiana are: length of head and body, 43; greatest length of skull, 15.7; zygomatic breadth, 9; length of upper tooth-row, 5.4. Dorsum medium brown (hairs paler basally); venter same or barely paler. Seemingly this is a solitary species.

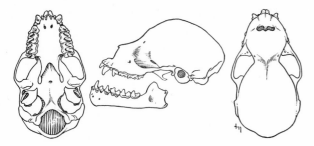

Fig. 63. *Macrophyllum macrophyllum,* Old Panamá, Panamá, No. 178236 U.S.N.M., ♂, X 2.

MARGINAL RECORDS.—Honduras: near Río Sicre (Handley, 1957:407). Panamá: Old Panamá City (Goodwin, 1946:304). El Salvador: Cueva Hedionda (Felten, 1956:183).

Genus Tonatia Gray—Round-eared Bats

Species reviewed by Goodwin, Jour. Mamm., 23:204–209, June 3, 1942.

1827. *Tonatia* Gray, *in* Griffith, The animal kingdom . . . Baron Cuvier . . . , 5:71. Type, *Vampyrus bidens* Spix.
1836. *Lophostoma* D'Orbigny and Gervais, Voy. dans l'Amer. Merid., 4(2; Mamm.):11. Type, *Lophostoma sylvicolum* D'Orbigny.

Length of head and body, 42.5–77. Skull resembling that of *Micronycteris* but more robust; zygoma abruptly expanded near anterior base; no basisphenoidal pits; auditory bullae small, covering less than half of cochleae; sagittal crest present, not divided anteriorly; ears large, rounded, separate or conjoined; tail shorter than femur, reaching approximately to middle of membrane; upper canines relatively large and nearly touching medial incisors, lateral incisors being displaced out of normal position in tooth-row; lower incisors reduced to 2; middle lower premolar much reduced. Dentition, i. $\frac{2}{1}$, c. $\frac{1}{1}$, p. $\frac{2}{3}$, m. $\frac{3}{3}$.

KEY TO NORTH AMERICAN SPECIES OF TONATIA

1. Length of forearm less than 40; greatest length of skull less than 20. *T. nicaraguae,* p. 106
1'. Length of forearm more than 40; greatest length of skull more than 20.
  2. Ear from notch less than 27. *T. bidens,* p. 105
  2'. Ear from notch more than 27.
                                               T. sylvicola, p. 106

Tonatia bidens (Spix)
Spix Round-eared Bat

1823. *Vampyrus bidens* Spix, Simiarum et vespertilionum Brasiliensium . . . , p. 65, type from bank of Rio São Francisco, Bahia, Brazil.
1840. [*Tonatia*] *bidens,* Gray, *in* Griffith, The animal kingdom . . . by the Baron Cuvier . . . , 5:69.
1838. *Phyllostoma childreni* Gray, Mag. Zool. and Bot., 2:488. Type from South America.

Selected measurements of an adult male and female from Palmar, Costa Rica, are, respectively: length of forearm, 58.5, 58.5; greatest length of skull, 28.6, 29.0; interorbital breadth, 5.6, 5.6; zygomatic breadth, 14.2, 14.8; length of upper tooth-row, 9.9, 10.2. Upper parts varying from approximately ochraceous to blackish brown; underparts paler, grayer, washed with buff. "Skull large and massive, rostrum broad, flat and not constricted in orbital region; superior outline evenly elevated from front of nasals and without depression in orbital region; palate narrow, toothrows only slightly converging anteriorly; saggital crest present in adult specimens but undeveloped." (Goodwin, 1946:304.)

MARGINAL RECORDS.—Costa Rica: Palmar, Puntarenas (Goodwin, 1946:304–305), thence southward into South America.

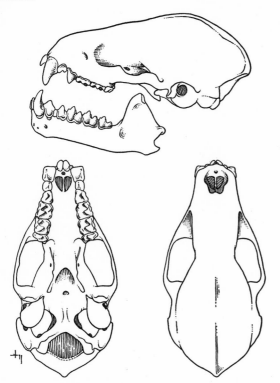

Fig. 64. *Tonatia bidens,* Palmar (Pacific), Costa Rica, No. 139439 A.M., ♂, X 2.

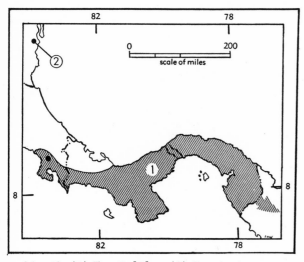

Map 68. (1) *Tonatia bidens;* (2) *Tonatia nicaraguae.*

Tonatia nicaraguae Goodwin
Pygmy Round-eared Bat

1942. *Tonatia nicaraguae* Goodwin, Jour. Mamm., 23:205, June 3, type from Kanawa Creek, 100 ft., near Cukra, Zelaya, Nicaragua. Known only from the type locality.

Selected measurements of the type, an adult female, are: length of forearm, 32; greatest length of skull, 17.9; interorbital breadth, 3.4; length of upper tooth-row, 6.5. Upper parts dark brown, almost black; underparts dull drab. "Skull small, evenly elevated behind nasals, rostrum parallel-sided, lower incisors small, faintly bifid; middle lower premolar minute." (Goodwin, 1946:305.)

Tonatia sylvicola
D'Orbigny's Round-eared Bat

Length of forearm, 50–55; ear from notch, 28–31; greatest length of skull, 25.1–28.0; zygomatic breadth, 12.2–14.2; length of upper tooth-row, 8.7–10.0. Upper parts medium to dark brown; underparts more grayish, sometimes white on throat. Skull narrow; superior outline elevated in interorbital region; rostrum long, constricted in postorbital region; posterior border of palate on a line across front of 3rd molars; sagittal crest moderately developed (after Goodwin, 1946:305).

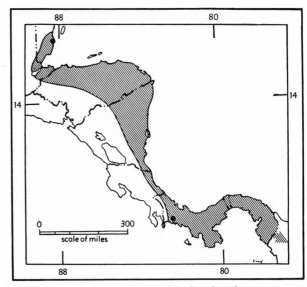

Map 69. *Tonatia sylvicola sylvicola.*

Tonatia sylvicola sylvicola (D'Orbigny)

1836. *Lophostoma sylvicolum* D'Orbigny, Voyage Amér. Merid., Atlas Zool., pl. 6, described in Vol. 4 (pt. 2):11, 1847, by D'Orbigny and Gervais. Type locality, Yungas de Bolivia between Río Securé and Río Isibara.
1843. *Phyllostoma amblyotis* Wagner, Arch. Naturgesch., Jahrg. 9, 1:365, type from Mato Grosso, Brazil.

MARGINAL RECORDS.—British Honduras: Freetown, Sittee River (Goodwin, 1942:209). Panamá: Bogava [= Bugaba] (*ibid.*), thence eastward into South America.

Genus **Mimon** Gray—Spear-nosed Bats

1847. *Mimon* Gray, Proc. Zool. Soc. London, p. 14, April 13. Type, *Phyllostoma bennettii* Gray.

1855. *Tylostoma* Gervais, Mammifères, *in* [Castelnau] Expéd. dans les parties centrales de l'Amér. du Sud . . . , p. 49. Type, *Phyllostoma crenulatum* É. Geoffroy St.-Hilaire. Not *Tylostoma* Sharpe, 1849.

1891. *Anthorhina* Lydekker, *in* Flower and Lydekker, An introduction to . . . mammals living and extinct, p. 674, a renaming of *Tylostoma* Gervais.

Skull slender; rostrum relatively broadly arched; zygoma without expansion either anteriorly or posteriorly; basisphenoidal pits broad and shallow, separated by a median septum; auditory bullae small, covering about half of cochleae, unusually narrow; ears large, not conjoined; tail approximately as long as femur, terminating in middle of membrane. Dentition, i. $\frac{2}{1}$, c. $\frac{1}{1}$, p. $\frac{2}{2}$, m. $\frac{3}{3}$.

Mimon bennettii, the type locality of which is in South America, has been recorded (Hershkovitz, 1951:555, for example) from the Peninsula of Yucatán. Hatt and Villa (1950:228–229), on geographic grounds, refer the material from Yucatán to *M. cozumelae*. We follow the latter arrangement also mainly on geographic grounds. We are strongly influenced in this by the lack of any authentic record of *M. bennettii* from the region between Yucatán and South America. Specimens from the state of Veracruz are indistinguishable from topotypes of *M. cozumelae* (see Dalquest, 1957:45–48).

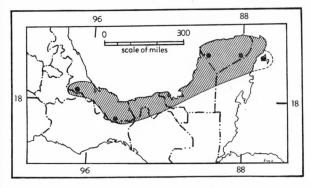

Map 70. *Mimon cozumelae.*

Mimon cozumelae Goldman
Cozumel Spear-nosed Bat

1914. *Mimon cozumelae* Goldman, Proc. Biol. Soc. Washington, 27:75, May 11, type from Cozumel Island, Quintana Roo.

Length of head and body approximately 67. Selected measurements of the type, an adult, are: length of forearm, 58; greatest length of skull, 26; zygomatic breadth, 14.3; length of upper tooth-row, 9.6. Upper parts light brown; underparts paler. Skull broader throughout than in *M. bennettii*; dentition closely resembling that of *M. bennettii* but individual teeth slightly larger.

MARGINAL RECORDS.—Yucatán: Calcehtok, Actun Tuz-ic (Hatt and Villa, 1950:227); Tekom (Hershkovitz, 1951:555). Quintana Roo: type locality. Veracruz: 38 km. SE Jesús Carranza, 500 ft. (23656 KU); 3 km. N Presidio, 1500 ft. (19169 KU).

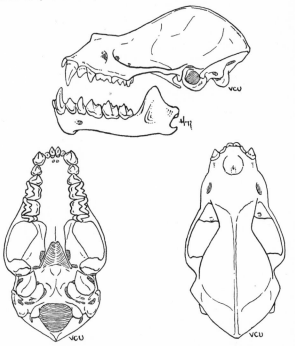

Fig. 65. *Mimon cozumelae,* 3 km. N Presidio, Veracruz, No. 19169 K.U., ♀, X 2.

Genus **Phyllostomus** Lacépède—Spear-nosed Bats

1799. *Phyllostomus* Lacépède, Tableau des divisions, sous-divisions, ordres et genres des mammifères, p. 16 (published as a supplement to Discours d'ouverture et de clôture du cours d'histoire naturelle. . . . Type, *Vespertilio hastatus* Pallas.

1866. *Alectops* Gray, Proc. Zool. Soc. London, p. 114, May. Type, *Alectops ater* Gray [= *P. elongatus* É Geoffroy-St.-Hilaire, 1810].

Skull robust; rostrum broad, low, flattened; sagittal crest high; paroccipital process shelflike; zygomata heavy, slightly expanded anteriorly and posteriorly; basisphenoidal pits present but faintly expressed; basicranial plane forming angle with roof of posterior nares; auditory bullae small, flattened; ears widely separated; nose-leaf well developed; tail less than half length of femur, projecting from base of membrane; teeth essentially as in *Micronycteris*. Dentition, i. $\frac{2}{2}$, c. $\frac{1}{1}$, p. $\frac{2}{2}$, m. $\frac{3}{3}$

KEY TO THE NORTH AMERICAN SPECIES OF PHYLLOSTOMUS

1. Length of forearm less than 75; zygomatic breadth less than 18. . . . *P. discolor,* p. 108
1'. Length of forearm more than 75; zygomatic breadth more than 18. . . . *P. hastatus,* p. 108

Phyllostomus hastatus
Spear-nosed Bat

Selected measurements of an adult male and female from Costa Rica are, respectively: length of head and body, 128, 109; ear, 30, 33; forearm, 92.5, 88; condylobasal length, 35.8, 34.2; zygomatic breadth, 23, 20.8; length of upper tooth-row, 14.5, 14. Upper parts seal brown, grayer on shoulders and sides of head; underparts paler, washed with gray; some individuals golden throughout. Skull robust; sagittal crest well developed.

In Central America this is one of the largest bats. It roosts in clusters in dimly lighted or totally dark caves. Colonies have been found numbering several thousand. According to Goodwin (1946:307), the food includes various kinds of fruit, such as bananas, but these bats kill and eat birds, small bats, mice, and insects.

Only one subspecies, *P. h. panamensis,* occurs within the geographic scope of this report.

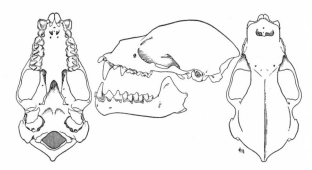

Fig. 66. *Phyllostomus hastatus panamensis,* Chilibrillo Cave, 10 mi. N Pedro Miguel, Panamá, No. 45063 K.U., ♀, X 1.

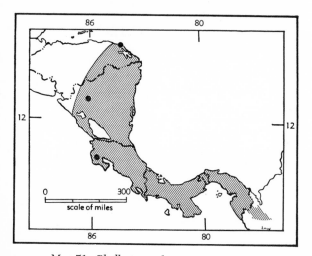

Map 71. *Phyllostomus hastatus panamensis.*

Phyllostomus hastatus panamensis J. A. Allen

1904. *Phyllostomus hastatus panamensis* J. A. Allen, Bull. Amer. Mus. Nat. Hist., 20:233, June 29, type from Boquerón, Chiriquí, Panamá.
1904. *Phyllostomus hastatus caurae* J. A. Allen, Bull. Amer. Mus. Nat. Hist., 20:234, June 29, type from Cali, upper Cauca Valley, Colombia.

MARGINAL RECORDS.—Honduras: Patuca (Goodwin, 1942:126), thence along Caribbean Coast to South America, then northward along Pacific Coast to Costa Rica: 27 de Abril (Goodwin, 1946:307). Nicaragua: Matagalpa (Goodwin, 1942:126).

Phyllostomus discolor
Pale Spear-nosed Bat

Selected measurements of two males from Honduras are: condylobasal length, 28, 28.1; zygomatic breadth, 15.7, 15.8; length of upper tooth-row, 10.2, 10.1. Certain measurements of the type are: total length, 105; forearm, 62.25. Upper parts dark brown posteriorly, becoming ochraceous tawny on head and shoulders; underparts cinnamon buff. Skull relatively slender; sagittal crest weakly developed.

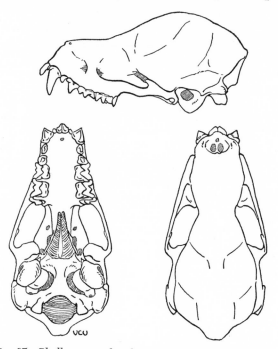

Fig. 67. *Phyllostomus discolor verrucosus,* 38 km. SE Jesús Carranza, 500 ft., Veracruz, No. 23660 K.U., ♀, X 2.

Phyllostomus discolor discolor Wagner

1843. *Phyllostoma discolor* Wagner, Arch., Naturgesch., Jahrg. 9, 1:366. Type locality, Cuyaba, Mato Grosso, Brazil.

MARGINAL RECORDS.—Panamá: Barro Colorado Island (Hall and Jackson, 1953:644), thence southward into South America.

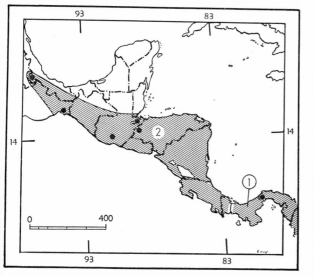

Map 72. *Phyllostomus discolor.*

1. *P. d. discolor*   2. *P. d. verrucosus*

Phyllostomus discolor verrucosus Elliot

1905. *Phyllostoma verrucossum* [*sic*] Elliot, Proc. Biol. Soc. Washington, 18:236, December 9, type from Niltepec, Oaxaca.
1936. *Phyllostomus discolor verrucosus*, Sanborn, Field Mus. Nat. Hist., Publ. 361, Zool. Ser., 20:97, August 15.

MARGINAL RECORDS.—Veracruz: Orizaba (Sanborn, 1936:97). Guatemala: Escobas, Izabal (*op. cit.*: 98). Honduras: Las Flores (Goodwin, 1942:126). Guatemala: Patulul (Sanborn, 1936:98). Oaxaca: type locality.

Genus **Phylloderma** Peters—Spear-nosed Bats

1865. *Phylloderma* Peters, Monatsb. preuss. Akad. Wiss., Berlin, p. 513. Type, *Phyllostoma stenops* Peters.

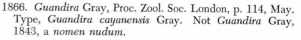

1866. *Guandira* Gray, Proc. Zool. Soc. London, p. 114, May. Type, *Guandira cayanensis* Gray. Not *Guandira* Gray, 1843, a *nomen nudum*.

Closely resembling *Phyllostomus* but differing in having bifid medial incisors, narrower-crowned molariform teeth, and a minute p3. Dentition, i. $\frac{2}{2}$, c. $\frac{1}{1}$, p. $\frac{2}{3}$, m. $\frac{3}{3}$.

Only one species, *P. septentrionalis,* occurs north of South America.

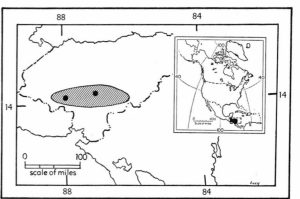

Map 73. *Phylloderma septentrionalis.*

Phylloderma septentrionalis Goodwin
Northern Spear-nosed Bat

1940. *Phylloderma septentrionalis* Goodwin, Amer. Mus. Novit., 1075:1, June 27, type from Las Pilas, about 4000 ft., 6 mi. N Marcala, La Paz, Honduras.

Selected measurements of the type, an adult female, are: length of head and body approximately 121; total length, 137 (dry); ear, 25 (dry); fore-

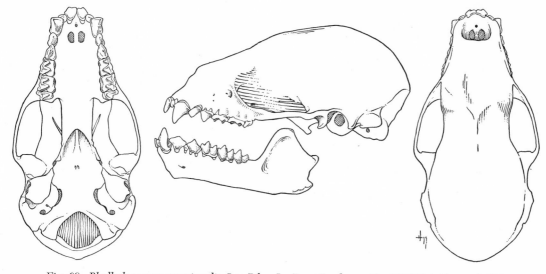

Fig. 68. *Phylloderma septentrionalis,* Las Pilas, La Paz, Honduras, No. 126867 A.M., sex ?, X 2.

arm, 80 (dry); greatest length of skull, 34.5; interorbital breadth, 10.5; zygomatic breadth, 18; length of upper tooth-row, 11. Upper parts dark brown, hairs buffy basally; underparts buffy.

The geographic occurrence of this species is noteworthy. It is described from Honduras and is not known from Nicaragua, Costa Rica, or Panamá, although another representative of the genus occurs in South America.

MARGINAL RECORDS.—Honduras: Las Flores, Tegucigalpa (Goodwin, 1942:127); type locality.

Genus Trachops Gray—Fringe-lipped Bats

1847. *Trachops* Gray, Proc. Zool. Soc. London, p. 14, April 13. Type, *Trachops fuliginosus* Gray [= *Vampyrus cirrhosus* Spix].
1825. *Istiophorus* Gray, Zool. Jour., 2:242. Type, *Vampyrus cirrhosus* Spix, or possibly *V. soricinus* Spix. Not *Istiophorus* Lacépède, 1802, a fish.
1846. *Histiophorus* Agassiz, Nomen. Zool., Index Univ., p. 183, an emendation of *Istiophorus* Gray.
1865. *Trachyops* Peters, Monatsb. preuss. Akad. Wiss., Berlin, p. 512, an emendation of *Trachops?*

Skull relatively elongated and rounded; interorbital region somewhat depressed; zygomata expanded anteriorly and posteriorly, the anterior expansion but faintly expressed; auditory bullae covering approximately half of cochleae and as high as wide; maxillary tooth-row resembling that of *Phyllostomus* but lateral incisor greatly reduced and cheek-teeth relatively larger; p3 present and lower molars relatively narrower; ear longer than head; tail much shorter than femur and projecting from upper surface of membrane; front and sides of lips and chin bearing numerous small warty excrescences. Dentition, i. $\frac{2}{2}$, c. $\frac{1}{1}$, p. $\frac{2}{3}$, m. $\frac{3}{3}$.

Trachops cirrhosus
Fringe-lipped Bat

Length of head and body, 76–77; length of forearm, 58.2–60.0; greatest length of skull, 27.5–28.2; interorbital breadth, 4.9–5.2; zygomatic breadth, 13.5–14.1; length of upper tooth-row, ——, 11.1. Upper parts approximately cinnamon brown or, in some specimens, a trifle darker; underparts dull brownish washed with gray.

Trachops cirrhosus cirrhosus (Spix)

1823. *Vampyrus cirrhosus* Spix, Simiarum et vespertilionum Brasiliensium : . . , p. 64, type from Brazil.
1878. *Trachyops* [sic] *cirrhosus*, Dobson, Catalogue of the Chiroptera in the . . . British Museum, p. 481.
1865. *Trachops fuliginosus* Gray, Proc. Zool. Soc. London, p. 14, June, type from Pernambuco, Brazil.

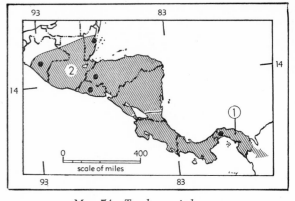

Map 74. *Trachops cirrhosus.*

1. *T. c. cirrhosus*   2. *T. c. coffini*

MARGINAL RECORDS.—Panamá: Chilibrillo Cave, near Alhajuela (Goldman, 1920:187), thence southward into South America. Not found: Tapia, Panamá (G. M. Allen, 1935:227).

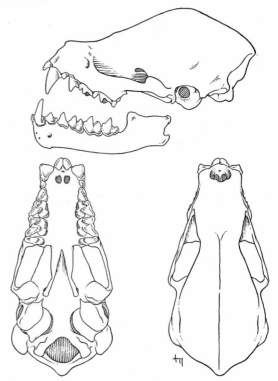

Fig. 69. *Trachops cirrhosus cirrhosus,* Chilibrillo Cave, Panamá, No. 174884 U.S.N.M., sex ?, X 2.

Trachops cirrhosus coffini Goldman

1925. *Trachops coffini* Goldman, Proc. Biol. Soc. Washington, 38:23, March 12, type from El Gallo, 8 mi. W Yaxha, on the Remate–El Cayo trail, Petén, Guatemala (see de la Torre, Proc. Biol. Soc. Washington, 69:189, December 31, 1956).
1956. *Trachops cirrhosus coffini,* Felten, Senckenbergiana Biol., 37:189, April 15.

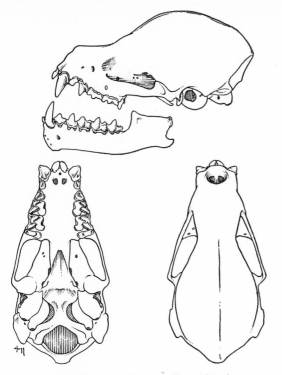

Fig. 70. *Trachops cirrhosus coffini*, Chinaltenango, Guatemala, No. 64634 C.N.H.M., ♂, X 2.

MARGINAL RECORDS.—British Honduras: Belize (Hershkovitz, 1951:555). Honduras: Las Flores, Gracias (Goodwin, 1942:127). El Salvador: Cueva Hedionda (Felten, 1956:189). Chiapas: Finca Esperanza (Villa, 1949: 499).

Genus **Chrotopterus** Peters—False Vampire Bats

1865. *Chrotopterus* Peters, Monatsb. preuss. Akad. Wiss., Berlin, p. 505. Type, *Vampyrus auritus* Peters.

Skull resembling that of *Phyllostomus* in general; rostrum and interorbital region subcylindrical; paroccipital expansion small but distinct; tympanic covering less than half cochlea; diameter of tympanic nearly twice its height at inner edge. Ears separate, simple and large (middle of conch, when laid forward, extending to nostril); tail barely perceptible in base of wide interfemoral membrane; lips and chin nearly smooth; fur unusually long and soft (after Miller, 1907:134). Dentition, i. $\frac{2}{1}$, c. $\frac{1}{1}$, p. $\frac{2}{3}$, m. $\frac{3}{3}$.

Chrotopterus auritus
Peters' False Vampire Bat

Length of head and body approximately 111. Selected measurements of an adult male and female from Veracruz are, respectively: greatest length of skull, 36.0, 36.8; interorbital breadth, 6.2, 5.9; zygomatic breadth, 18.2, 19.2; length of upper tooth-row, 13.7, 13.9. Length of forearm of an adult male from Brazil, 80. Upper parts dull dark brown; underparts slightly paler and washed with gray; ears and membranes dark brown but edged with whitish.

Specimens of this bat have been obtained near the mouth of a small cave. They did not take flight until greatly disturbed.

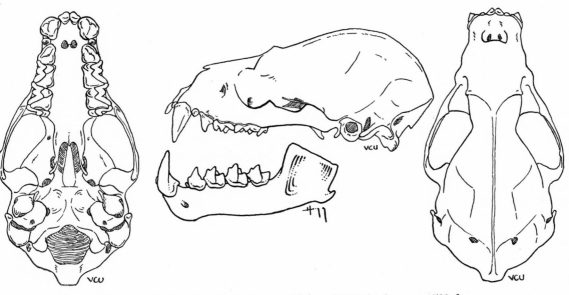

Fig. 71. *Chrotopterus auritus auritus*, 38 km. SE Jesús Carranza, 500 ft., Veracruz, No. 23661 K.U., ♀, X 2.

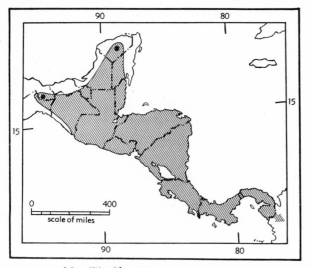

Map 75. *Chrotopterus auritus auritus.*

Chrotopterus auritus auritus (Peters)

1856. *Vampyrus auritus* Peters, Monatsb. preuss. Akad. Wiss., Berlin, p. 415, type from México.

1865. *Chrotopterus auritus* Peters, Monatsb. preuss. Akad. Wiss., Berlin, p. 505.

MARGINAL RECORDS.—Yucatán: Yaxcach (Gaumer, 1917:294). Veracruz: 38 km. SE Jesús Carranza (Dalquest and Hall, 1949:424), thence southeastward into South America.

Genus **Vampyrum** Rafinesque

1815. *Vampyrum* Rafinesque, Analyse de la nature, p. 54. Type, *Vespertilio spectrum* Linnaeus. (For use of this name in place of *Vampyrus* Leach, Trans. Linn. Soc. London, 13:79, 1822, and for selection of type see Andersen, Ann. Mag. Nat. Hist., ser. 8, 1:433, May, 1908.)

Skull elongated; breadth of braincase less than one-third greatest length; sagittal crest well developed, especially posteriorly; paroccipital expansions distinct; rostrum subcylindrical; zygomata slightly expanded anteriorly and posteriorly; tympanic small, covering less than half cochlear surface; height of inner edge of tympanic less than diameter. Externally resembles *Phyllostomus,* but chin smooth as in *Chrotopterus;* muzzle much elongated; tail absent; interfemoral membrane wide; ear extending to extremity of muzzle; fur normal (after Miller, 1907:135). Molars notably narrow and heightened, their basic W-shaped pattern discernible but much distorted; lower canines markedly enlarged, their bases nearly in contact posteromedially. Dentition, i. $\frac{2}{2}$, c. $\frac{1}{1}$, p. $\frac{2}{3}$, m. $\frac{3}{3}$.

Vampyrum spectrum
Linnaeus' False Vampire Bat

Length of head and body approximately 130. Selected measurements of the type of *V. s. nelsoni,*

an adult male, are: length of forearm, 106.9; greatest length of skull, 51; zygomatic breadth, 23.6; length of upper tooth-row, 20.2. Upper parts dark reddish brown; underparts slightly paler. See generic description for additional characters.

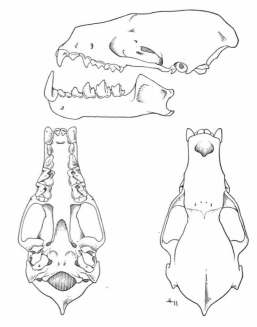

Fig. 72. *Vampyrum spectrum nelsoni,* Boquiron, Colombia, No. 18707 A.M., ♂, X 1.

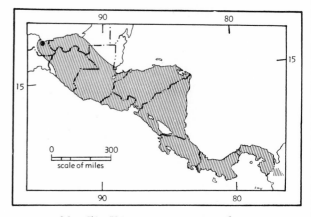

Map 76. *Vampyrum spectrum nelsoni.*

Vampyrum spectrum nelsoni (Goldman)

1917. *Vampyrus spectrum nelsoni* Goldman, Proc. Biol. Soc. Washington, 30:115, May 23, type from Coatzacoalcos, Veracruz.

MARGINAL RECORDS.—Veracruz: type locality, thence southward probably excluding the Peninsula of Yucatán to South America. The single specimen recorded from Jamaica (Koopman and Williams, 1951:19) should probably be regarded as an accidental occurrence.

Subfamily GLOSSOPHAGINAE
Long-tongued Bats

External characters summarized by Sanborn, Field Mus. Nat. Hist., Zool. Ser., 24:271–277, 1 fig., January 6, 1943.

Upper molars with styles reduced and closely approximated to paracone and metacone, this in connection with obsolescence of commissures nearly obliterating W-pattern. Lower molars having the five typical cusps, but reduced in height, especially paraconid; commissures rudimentary. All cheek-teeth elongated; rostrum much produced. Tongue long and highly extensible, its surface armed with conspicuous bristlelike papillae. Nose-leaf present, well developed, though never large (after Miller, 1907:136).

KEY TO NORTH AMERICAN GENERA OF GLOSSOPHAGINAE

1. Two upper and 2 lower molars on each side.
   2. Lower premolars 2–2. . . . . *Leptonycteris*, p. 121
   2'. Lower premolars 3–3. . . . . *Lichonycteris*, p. 122
1'. Three upper and 3 lower molars on each side.
   3. Upper premolars 3–3. . . . . *Anoura*, p. 119
   3'. Upper premolars 2–2.
      4. Lower incisors well developed in adult.
         5. Upper incisors showing no marked contrast in size; lower incisors with broad, flat crown; zygomatic arch complete. . . . . *Glossophaga*, p. 113
         5'. Upper incisors showing marked contrast in size; lower incisors with narrow trenchant crowns; zygomatic arch incomplete. . . . . *Lonchophylla*, p. 115
      4'. Lower incisors minute or absent in adult.
         6. Zygomatic arch complete; lower incisors usually present in adult, but minute. *Monophyllus*, p. 116
         6'. Zygomatic arch not complete; lower incisors absent in adult.
            7. Pterygoid processes convex on inner sides, the hamular processes not in contact with auditory bullae. . . . . *Hylonycteris*, p. 121
            7'. Pterygoids deeply concave on inner sides, the hamular processes in contact with auditory bullae.
               8. Rostrum greatly elongated; lower premolars with middle cusp longest.
                                       Choeronycteris, p. 119
               8'. Rostrum of normal proportions; cusps of lower premolars subequal. *Choeroniscus*, p. 120

Genus Glossophaga É. Geoffroy St.-Hilaire
Long-tongued Bats

Revised by Miller, Proc. U.S. Nat. Mus., 46:413–429, December 31, 1913.

1818. *Glossophaga* É. Geoffroy St.-Hilaire, Mem. Mus. Hist. Nat. Paris, 4:418. Type, *Vespertilio soricinus* Pallas.
1838. *Phyllophora* Gray, Mag. Zool. Bot., 2:489. Type, *Phyllophora amplexicaudata* Gray [= *Glossophaga amplexicaudata* Spix].
1847. *Nicon* Gray, Proc. Zool. Soc. London, p. 15, April 13. Type, *Nicon caudifer* Gray [= *Vespertilio soricinus* Pallas].

Skull with large, elongate, low, rounded, smooth braincase; rostrum shorter than braincase; basisphenoidal pits shallow; tympanic ring covering less than half surface of cochleae; tail shorter than tibia and not extending beyond middle of interfemoral membrane; zygoma complete; incisor series above and below unbroken; diastema between I1 and C less than width of outer incisor; crown of lower incisors about as broad as long and completely or nearly filling space between canines. Dentition, i. $\frac{2}{2}$, c. $\frac{1}{1}$, p. $\frac{2}{3}$, m. $\frac{3}{3}$.

In the two North American species, upper parts cinnamon mixed with varying amounts of black lending over-all tone of blackish brown to reddish brown; underparts slightly paler.

KEY TO NORTH AMERICAN SPECIES OF GLOSSOPHAGA
(adapted from Miller, 1913:415)

1. Outer upper incisor about equal to inner in bulk; upper premolars essentially alike in occlusal view. . . . . . *G. longirostris*, p. 115
1'. Outer upper incisor obviously less than inner in bulk; upper premolars usually unlike in occlusal view. . . . . *G. soricina*, p. 113

Glossophaga soricina
Pallas' Long-tongued Bat

Length of head and body, 48–64; length of forearm, 32.4–40; condylobasal length, 18.6–21.6; breadth of braincase, 8.4–9.0; length of upper toothrow, 6.8–8.0. Condylobasal length usually less than 21; rostrum small, appearing much shorter than braincase; outer upper incisor distinctly less than inner in bulk; P3 and P4 unlike in crown outline.

Bats of this species often roost in man-made structures as well as in caves. Normally these bats roost separated from each other by a few inches; in any one place there may be only one or two or

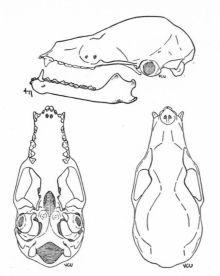

Fig. 73. *Glossophaga soricina leachii*, 4 km. WNW Fortín, 3200 ft., Veracruz, No. 17714 K.U., ♀, X 2.

several hundred. These bats take flight quickly when alarmed and are noisy in flight. Food consists of fruits and probably nectar. Colonies of *Glossophaga* usually contain both males and females. They breed, presumably, throughout most of the year, but most young are born in late spring or early autumn. One young at a time is the usual number.

There is some doubt as to the correct taxonomic arrangement of the central Mexican material. Villa (1953:325–329) places *G. s. alticola* Davis as a synonym of *G. s. morenoi* Martinez and Villa. Davis and Russell (1954:68) arrange *morenoi* as a synonym of *G. s. leachii* and retain *alticola* as valid.

Glossophaga soricina alticola Davis

1944. *Glossophaga soricina alticola* Davis, Jour. Mamm., 25:377, December 12, type from 13 km. NE Tlaxcala, 7800 ft., Tlaxcala. (Villa, Anal. del Instituto Biol., Univ. Nac. México, 23:325, May 20, 1953, arranges *G. s. alticola* Davis as a synonym of *Glossophaga soricina morenoi* Martínez and Villa.)

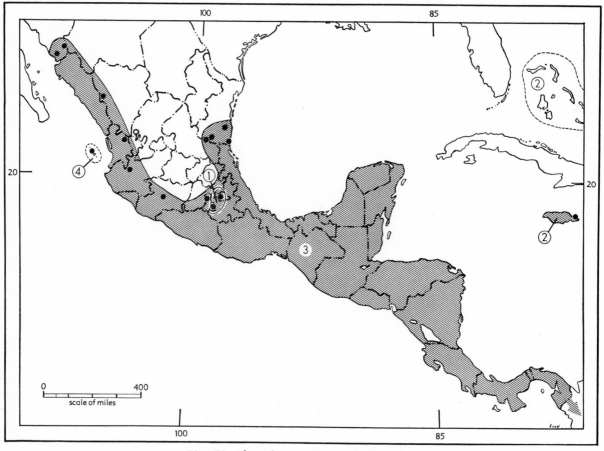

Map 77. *Glossophaga soricina* and subspecies.

1. *G. s. alticola*   3. *G. s. leachii*
2. *G. s. antillarum*   4. *G. s. mutica*

MARGINAL RECORDS.—Tlaxcala: type locality. Morelos: Santa Clara (Davis and Russell, 1954:68).

Glossophaga soricina antillarum Rehn

1902. *Glossophaga soricina antillarum* Rehn, Proc. Acad. Nat. Sci. Philadelphia, 54:37, April 23, type from Port Antonio, Jamaica.

MARGINAL RECORDS.—Bahama Islands (G. M. Allen, 1911:231). Jamaica: type locality.

Glossophaga soricina leachii (Gray)

1844. *Monophyllus leachii* Gray, *in* The zoology of the voyage of H.M.S. Sulphur . . . , 1(1, Mamm.):18, April, type from Realejo, Chinandega, Nicaragua.
1913. *Glossophaga soricina leachii*, Miller, Proc. U.S. Nat. Mus., 46:419, December 31.
1938. *Glossophaga morenoi* Martínez and Villa, Anal. del Instituto Biol., Univ. Nac. México, 9(3–4):347, November 14, type from Xiutepec, Morelos. According to Davis and Russell (Jour. Mamm., 35:68, February 10, 1954) indistinguishable from *G. s. leachii*, but Villa (Anal. del Instituto Biol., Univ. Nac. México, 23:325, May 20, 1953), recognizes *G. s. morenoi*.

MARGINAL RECORDS.—Sonora: cave near San Bernardo (Burt and Hooper, 1941:2). Durango: Chacala (Miller, 1913:420). Nayarit: Santiago (*ibid.*). Jalisco: Ameca (*ibid.*). Michoacán: Hda. El Sabino (Hall and Villa, 1949:441). Distrito Federal: Chicomostoc, Cerro Teutli, 2620 m. (Villa, 1953:325). Puebla: *Tuchitan* (Miller, 1913:420). San Luis Potosí: El Salto (Dalquest, 1953b:25). Tamaulipas: 5 mi. NE Antiguo Morelos, near El Pachón (de la Torre, 1954:114); 16 mi. W and 3 mi. S Piedra (Anderson, 1956:350); Altamira (Miller, 1913:420), thence southeastward into South America and thence northward along Pacific Coast to Sonora: Chinobampo (Burt, 1938:20).

Glossophaga soricina mutica Merriam

1898. *Glossophaga mutica* Merriam, Proc. Biol. Soc. Washington, 12:18, January 27, type from María Madre Island, Tres Marías Islands, Jalisco. Known only from Tres Marías Islands.
1913. *Glossophaga soricina mutica*, Miller, Proc. U.S. Nat. Mus., 46:420, December 31.

Glossophaga longirostris
Miller's Long-tongued Bat

Length of head and body, 56–65; length of forearm, 35.4–39.4; condylobasal length, 21.0–22.4; breadth of braincase, 8.8–9.4; length of upper toothrow, 7.8–8.8. Resembling *Glossophaga soricina*, but skull longer, its condylobasal length usually more than 21; rostrum so much more developed as to appear nearly as long as braincase; outer upper incisor about equal to inner in bulk; P3 and P4 not noticeably unlike in crown outline; braincase broad and high; usually an evident angle in interorbital region between forehead and rostrum. (After Miller, 1913:421.) Color essentially as in *soricina*.

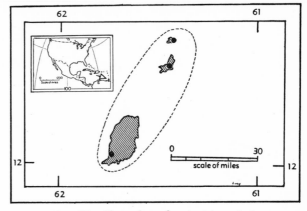

Map 78. *Glossophaga longirostris rostrata.*

Glossophaga longirostris rostrata Miller

1913. *Glossophaga rostrata* Miller, Proc. Biol. Soc. Washington, 26:32, February 8, type from Westerhall estate, Grenada, Lesser Antilles.
1913. *Glossophaga longirostris rostrata* Miller, Proc. U.S. Nat. Mus., 46:423, December 31.

MARGINAL RECORDS.—Lesser Antilles: Union Island (Miller, 1913:423); Carriacou (*ibid.*); Old Fort, St. Georges, Grenada (Jones, 1951:224). Two specimens from Dominica (Miller, 1913:423) may belong to this species, but are not positively identifiable.

Genus Lonchophylla Thomas—Long-tongued Bats

1903. *Lonchophylla* Thomas, Ann. Mag. Nat. Hist., ser. 7, 12:458, October. Type, *Lonchophylla mordax* Thomas.

"Like *Glossophaga*, but zygomatic arch incomplete; inner upper incisor higher than wide and more than double the bulk of outer tooth, which stands by itself near middle of space between large incisor and canine; lower incisors having narrow trifid cutting edges, the outer separated from canine by a space nearly equal to the length of its crown; and last upper molar nearly as large as either of the others, its parastyle short." (Miller, 1907:139.)
Dentition, i. $\frac{2}{2}$, c. $\frac{1}{1}$, p. $\frac{2}{3}$, m. $\frac{3}{3}$.

KEY TO NORTH AMERICAN SPECIES OF LONCHOPHYLLA

1. Length of forearm less than 40; inner lobe of second upper premolar reduced to inconspicuous swelling bearing a small cusp.
   L. concava, p. 115
1'. Length of forearm more than 40; inner lobe of second upper premolar conspicuous.
   L. robusta, p. 116

Lonchophylla concava Goldman
Goldman's Long-tongued Bat

1914. *Lonchophylla concava* Goldman, Smiths. Miscl. Coll., 63(5):2, March 14, type from Cana, 2000 ft., Darién, Panamá. Known only from the type locality.

Length of head and body approximately 58; selected measurements of the type, an adult male, are: total length, 68; length of forearm, 33.9; greatest length of skull, 23.4; interorbital breadth, 4.6; length of upper tooth-row, 8. Upper parts warm, dark brown; underparts slightly paler. Skull relatively broad and massive; braincase well inflated; 2nd upper premolar narrow, its inner lobe much reduced.

This species is known only from the type, which was obtained in a limestone cave.

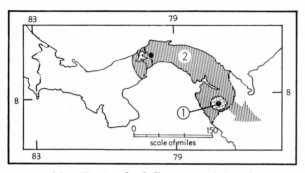

Map 79. *Lonchophylla concava* (1) and *Lonchophylla robusta* (2).

Lonchophylla robusta Miller
Panamá Long-tongued Bat

1912. *Lonchophylla robusta* Miller, Proc. U.S. Nat. Mus., 42:23, March 6, type from cave on Chilibrillo River, near Alhajuela, Panamá.

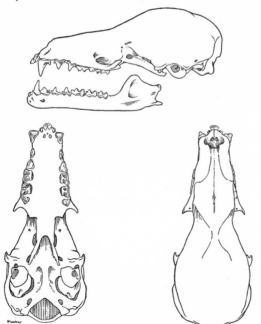

Fig. 74. *Lonchophylla robusta*, Chilibrillo Cave, 10 mi. N Pedro Miguel, Panamá, No. 45075 K.U., ♀, X 2.

Selected measurements of the type, an adult male, and a female topotype, are, respectively: length of head and body, 56, 60; length of forearm, 43.6, 43; condylobasal length, 25.2, 25.4; interorbital breadth, 5.2, 5.4; length of upper tooth-row, 9.8, 10. Upper parts dark brown; underparts slightly paler, having a still paler wash. Skull relatively broad and robust; braincase well inflated; 2nd upper premolar broad, its inner lobe conspicuously developed.

MARGINAL RECORDS.—Panamá: type locality, thence eastward into South America.

Genus **Monophyllus** Leach—Long-tongued Bats

Revised by Miller, Proc. Washington Acad. Sci., 2:31–38, March 30, 1900.

1821. *Monophyllus* Leach, Trans. Linn. Soc. London, 13:75. Type, *Monophyllus redmani* Leach.

"In general like *Glossophaga*; zygomatic arch complete; tail about half as long as femur, projecting beyond edge of . . . narrow interfemoral membrane. Teeth essentially as in *Glossophaga*, but upper incisors much smaller and of equal length, the outer sharp pointed, the inner with flat cutting edge, neither of the incisors in contact with the other or with canine; lower incisors . . . minute, with roundish flat crowns, the four teeth standing as two pairs, one pair on each side of a broad median space; upper and lower premolars with conspicuous styles; upper molars with inner margin obliquely truncate." (Miller, 1907:139.) Dentition, i. $\frac{2}{2}$, c. $\frac{1}{1}$, p. $\frac{2}{3}$, m. $\frac{3}{3}$.

Some of the species of *Monophyllus* are known from only one specimen and none is really well represented in collections. Therefore the extent and nature of individual variation is only poorly known. Further, the characters employed to distinguish each of several species from others are minor differences in proportion that are best appreciated only by direct comparison. It seems best, therefore, not to attempt to prepare a key based to an important degree on morphological characters at this time.

KEY TO NOMINAL SPECIES OF MONOPHYLLUS

1. Plane of basicranial region lying at angle of approximately 32° to plane of presphenoid; area of occurrence unknown.
   M. clinedaphus, p. 118
1'. Plane of basicranial region forming an angle of not more than 20° with plane of presphenoid.
   2. Occurring in Puerto Rico.
      3. Alveolar length of upper molar series exceeding 6.0. . . . . . *M. frater*, p. 118

3'. Alveolar length of upper molar series
less than 6.0. . . *M. portoricensis*, p. 117
2'. Not occurring in Puerto Rico.
4. Occurring in the Lesser Antilles.
5. Occurring on St. Lucia Island.
M. luciae, p. 118
5'. Occurring on Barbados.
M. plethodon, p. 118
4'. Occurring in the Greater Antilles.
6. Occurring on Jamaica.
M. redmani, p. 117
6'. Occurring in Cuba and Haiti.
M. cubanus, p. 117

Monophyllus redmani Leach
Jamaican Long-tongued Bat

1821. *Monophyllus redmani* Leach, Trans. Linn. Soc. London, 13:76, type from Jamaica.

Length of head and body approximately 60. Selected measurements of a male from Kingston, Jamaica, are: total length, 68; length of forearm, 40; greatest length of skull, 22.4; interorbital breadth, 4; zygomatic breadth, 10; length up upper tooth-row, 8.6. Upper parts dark brown; underparts paler and with grayish wash. Rostrum almost as long as braincase; zygomata slender, expanded vertically near anterior and posterior bases; frontal region rising above axis of rostrum at angle of about 20°; basicranial region lying at angle of about 16° to plane of presphenoid; 2nd upper premolar broader posteriorly than anteriorly and without postero-internal lobe; first premolar shorter than 2nd or 3rd, and relatively broader.

MARGINAL RECORDS.—Jamaica: Kingston (Miller, 1902:410). Not found: Oxford Cave, Jamaica (Dobson, 1878:505).

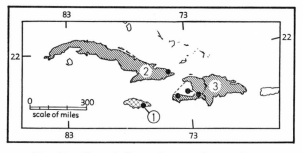

Map 80. *Monophyllus redmani* and *M. cubanus*.

Guide to kinds
1. *M. redmani*
2. *M. c. cubanus*
3. *M. c. ferreus*

Monophyllus cubanus
Cuban Long-tongued Bat

Length of head and body approximately 59. Selected measurements of the type of *M. cubanus*

cubanus, an adult male, are: total length, 67; length of forearm, 38.6; greatest length of skull, 21.4; interorbital breadth, 4; zygomatic breadth, 9.6; length of upper tooth-row, 8. Upper parts dark brown; underparts paler with dull brown wash. "The skull resembles that of *Monophyllus redmani* in general appearance, but the rostrum is much more slender, a character equally noticeable whether viewed from above or below." (Miller, 1902:410.)

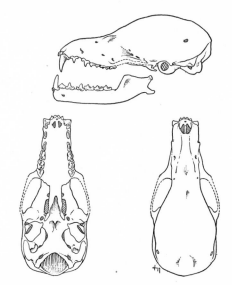

Fig. 75. *Monophyllus cubanus cubanus,* Baracoa, eastern Cuba, No. 113689 U.S.N.M., sex ?, X 2.

Monophyllus cubanus cubanus Miller

1902. *Monophyllus cubanus* Miller, Proc. Acad. Nat. Sci. Philadelphia, 54:410, September 12, type from Baracoa, Oriente, Cuba.

MARGINAL RECORDS.—Cuba: *Rangel* (G. M. Allen, 1911:231; locality not found), *Pinar del Río* (Koopman and Ruibal, 1955:3); type locality.

Monophyllus cubanus ferreus Miller

1918. *Monophyllus cubanus ferreus* Miller, Proc. Biol. Soc. Washington, 31:40, May 16, type from cave 8 mi. WSW Jérémie, Haiti.

MARGINAL RECORDS.—Haiti: La Gonave Island (Koopman, 1955:110); cave at Diquini (Miller, 1929:8); type locality.

Monophyllus portoricensis Miller
Puerto Rican Long-tongued Bat

1900. *Monophyllus portoricensis* Miller, Proc. Washington Acad. Sci., 2:34, March 30, type from cave near Bayamón, Puerto Rico.

Length of head and body, 52–64. Extremes of selected measurements of 5 specimens from Puerto

Rico are: total length, 60–67; length of forearm, 36–37. Certain cranial measurements of the type are: greatest length, 19.6; interorbital breadth, 4; zygomatic breadth, 8.8; length of upper tooth-row, 7. Color approximately as in the other species. Rostrum of skull much shorter than braincase; braincase rising at an angle of about 25° to axis of rostrum; gap in tooth-row anterior to posterior premolar much reduced as compared to that of *M. redmani*; 2nd upper premolar with well-developed posteriointernal lobe; 1st lower premolar slightly shorter than 2nd or 3rd, conspicuously broader.

MARGINAL RECORDS.—Puerto Rico: type locality; *Cueva de Fari* (Anthony, 1918:348); *Cueva de Trujillo Alto* (*ibid.*).

Monophyllus plethodon Miller
Barbados Long-tongued Bat

1900. *Monophyllus plethodon* Miller, Proc. Washington Acad. Sci., 2:35, March 30, type from St. Michael Parish, Barbados, Lesser Antilles. Known only from the type locality.

Length of head and body approximately 59. Selected measurements of the type, an adult male, are: total length, 68; length of forearm, 38; greatest length of skull, 21.6; interorbital breadth, 4.6; zygomatic breadth, 9.8; length of upper tooth-row, 7.2. "The teeth . . . differ conspicuously from those of other members of the genus in that they are so crowded that all trace of the characteristic space in front of posterior premolar of both jaws is obliterated. This tendency to crowding is also evident in the upper incisors, the innermost pair of which are almost in contact. . . ." (Miller, 1900:36.)

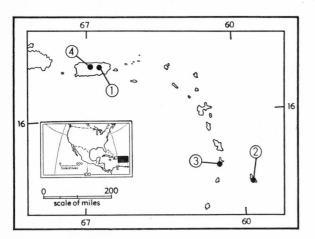

Map 81. Four species of *Monophyllus*.

1. *M. portoricensis*   3. *M. luciae*
2. *M. plethodon*   4. *M. frater*

Monophyllus luciae Miller
St. Lucia Long-tongued Bat

1902. *Monophyllus luciae* Miller, Proc. Acad. Nat. Sci. Philadelphia, 54:411, September 12, type from St. Lucia, Lesser Antilles. Known only from the type locality.

Selected measurements of the type, an adult male, are: length of head and body approximately 65; total length, 80; length of forearm, 42; greatest length of skull, 24; interorbital breadth, 4.4; zygomatic breadth, 10; length of upper tooth-row, 8. "In general form the skull agrees with that of *Monophyllus plethodon*, and differs from that of *M. redmani* and *M. cubanus* in the large, inflated braincase, broad interorbital region and short rostrum. The zygomatic arches are strong and well developed, more so, apparently, than in *M. plethodon*. Rostrum broader than in the Barbados species [*plethodon*]." (Miller, 1902:411.)

Monophyllus frater Anthony
Anthony's Long-tongued Bat

1917. *Monophyllus frater* Anthony, Bull. Amer. Mus. Nat. Hist., 37:565, September 7, type from cave near Morovis, Puerto Rico. Known only from the type locality.

Selected measurements of the type and 2 topotypes are, respectively: interorbital breadth, 4.6, 4.8, 4.9; alveolar length of upper molar series, 7.1, 6.8, ——. "Very similar to *Monophyllus portoricensis* but decidedly larger. Skull narrow and elongate; rostrum . . . long, tubular, with shallow nasal depression in region of terminal suture, . . . interorbital constriction scarcely noticeable; braincase incompletely known but of rounded type; zygomatic arch doubtless complete; palate long, narrow, shallowly concave posteriorly, incisive foramina large; . . . dentition normal for the genus." (Anthony, 1917:565.)

This species is known only from bone fragments.

Monophyllus clinedaphus Miller
Island Long-tongued Bat

1900. *Monophyllus clinedaphus* Miller, Proc. Washington Acad. Sci., 2:36, March 30, type from an unknown locality. Known only by the type.

Length of head and body approximately 53. Selected measurements of the type, an adult male, are: total length, 65; length of forearm, 39; greatest length of skull, 21.8; interorbital breadth, 4; zygomatic breadth, 9; length of upper cheek-teeth, 8. Skull resembling that of *M. redmani*, but slightly smaller; rostrum slightly narrower anteriorly; basicranial region lying at angle of about 32° to plane of presphenoid; palate narrow and conspicuously arched.

Genus **Anoura** Gray—Tailless Bats

Revised by Sanborn, Field Mus. Nat. Hist., Publ. 323, Zool. Ser., 20:23–27, December 11, 1933.

1838. *Anoura* Gray, Mag. Zool. Bot., 2:490, February. Type, *Anoura geoffroyi* Gray.
1844–46. *Rhinchonycteris* Tschudi, Untersuchungen über die fauna Peruana . . . , p. 71. Type, *Rhinchonycteris peruana* Tschudi [= *Anoura geoffroyi* Gray].
1846. *Anura* Agassiz, Nomen. Zool., Index Univ., p. 27, an emendation ?
1868. *Lonchoglossa* Peters, Monatsb. preuss. Akad. Wiss., Berlin, p. 364. Type, *Glossophaga caudifera* É. Geoffroy St.-Hilaire.
1868. *Glossonycteris* Peters, Monatsb. preuss. Akad. Wiss., Berlin, p. 365. Type, *Glossonycteris lasiopyga* Peters.

This American genus contains only *A. geoffroyi* and *A. caudifera*, the latter limited to South America. Tail absent or rudimentary; zygomatic arch rudimentary in 105 of 106 specimens; skull and teeth shown in Fig. 76. Dentition, i. $\frac{2}{0}$, c. $\frac{1}{1}$, p. $\frac{3}{3}$, m. $\frac{3}{3}$.

Anoura geoffroyi
Geoffroy's Tailless Bat

Length of head and body approximately 60. Selected measurements are: length of forearm, 40–47.3; greatest length of skull, 24.5–27.0. Additional measurements of a female from Texolo, Veracruz, are: total length, 64; interorbital breadth, 4.4; mastoidal breadth, 10.0. Upper parts dull brown usually becoming silvery gray over sides of neck and shoulders; underparts grayish brown.

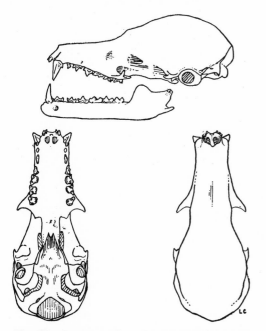

Fig. 76. *Anoura geoffroyi lasiopyga*, 2 mi. WSW Teopisca, Chiapas, No. 61037 K.U., ♂, X 2.

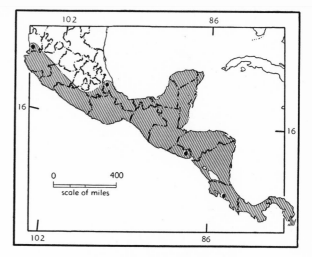

Map 82. *Anoura geoffroyi lasiopyga*.

Anoura geoffroyi lasiopyga (Peters)

1868. *Glossonycteris lasiopyga* Peters, Monatsb. preuss. Akad. Wiss., Berlin, p. 365, type from southern México.
1933. *Anoura geoffroyi lasiopyga*, Sanborn, Field Mus. Nat. Hist. Publ. 323, Zool. Ser., 20:27, December 11.

MARGINAL RECORDS.—Nayarit: 2 mi. SE Jalcocotán, 3000 ft. (Anderson, 1956:350). *Jalisco:* San Sebastian (Sanborn, 1933:27). Veracruz: Texolo [probably Teocelo] (*ibid.*). El Salvador: Mt. Cacaguatique (*ibid.*); *Volcán de San Vicente* (Felten, 1956:196). Costa Rica: San Rafael de Tarrazi, 30 km. S San José (39249 KU).

Genus **Choeronycteris** Tschudi
Long-tongued Bats

1844. *Choeronycteris* Tschudi, Untersuchungen über die fauna Peruana . . . , p. 70. Type, *Choeronycteris mexicana* Tschudi.

Rostrum elongated, comprising more than half length of skull; zygomata incomplete; pterygoid processes strongly concave on inner sides; hamulae in contact with auditory bullae; tail approximately half length of femur and not extending to mid-point of interfemoral membrane; calcar weakly developed; lower incisors absent in adults; W-shaped pattern of upper molars nearly obliterated. Dentition, i. $\frac{2}{0}$, c. $\frac{1}{1}$, p. $\frac{2}{3}$, m. $\frac{3}{3}$.

Specimens have been taken in Morelos in a shady retreat among the exposed roots of trees along the edge of a ravine; others were taken near the entrance of a cave.

Wille (1954) found the effective origin of the tongue in this and other glossophagine bats to be on the posteriormost end of the breastbone, making for exceptional extensibility of the tongue. Loss of the lower incisor teeth also is correlated with the habit of feeding, by means of the long tongue, on nectar from deep corollas of tropical flowers.

Choeronycteris mexicana Tschudi
Mexican Long-tongued Bat

1844. *Choeronycteris mexicana* Tschudi, Untersuchungen über die fauna Peruana . . . , p. 72, type from México.

Measurements of a male and female from Morelos are, respectively: head and body, 60, 68; total length, 76, 78; forearm, 44.4, 43.0; greatest length of skull, 30.5, 30.2; zygomatic breadth, 10.6, 10.3; length of upper tooth-row, 11.6, 11.3.

MARGINAL RECORDS.—California: Hermosa Way, San Diego (Olson, 1947:183). Arizona: *Patagonia* (Campbell, 1934:241); Miller Canyon, Huachuca Mts. (*ibid.*); 8 mi. W Paradise (Cahalane, 1939:421). Sonora: near El Tigre (Burt, 1938:20). Coahuila: 9 mi. W, 4 mi. S San Buenaventura, 1800 ft. (48234 KU); 1 mi. S, 4 mi. W Bella Unión, 7000 ft. (34549 KU). Tamaulipas: 4 km. N Joya Verde, 4000 ft. (Anderson, 1956:350). Hidalgo: Río Tasquillo, 26 km. E Zimapán (Davis, 1944:378). Tlaxcala: 13 km. NE Tlaxcala (*ibid.*). Guatemala: Dueñas (J. A. Allen, 1910:111); Hda. California (Goodwin, 1934:10). Michoacán: 2 mi. W Pátzcuaro (Hall and Villa, 1949:441). Jalisco: Los Masos (J. A. Allen, 1906:261). Nayarit: Tres Marías Islands (Elliot, 1905:517). Baja California: 8 mi. N Santa Catarina (Huey, 1954:437).

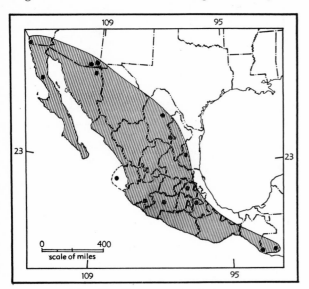

Map 83. *Choeronycteris mexicana.*

Genus Choeroniscus Thomas—Long-tailed Bats

1928. *Choeroniscus* Thomas, Ann. Mag. Nat. Hist., ser. 10, 1:122, January. Type, *Choeronycteris minor* Peters.

Resembling *Choeronycteris* in most features; rostrum much elongated and slender, but less than half length of skull; mandible long, slender; nose-leaf small, triangular; cusps of lower premolars subequal; upper incisors minute. Dentition, i. $\frac{2}{0}$, c. $\frac{1}{1}$, p. $\frac{2}{3}$, m. $\frac{3}{3}$.

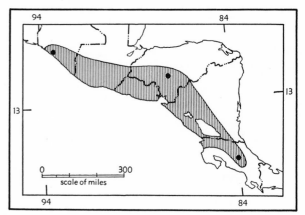

Map 84. *Choeroniscus godmani.*

Choeroniscus godmani (Thomas)
Godman's Bat

1903. *Choeronycteris Godmani* Thomas, Ann. Mag. Nat. Hist., ser. 7, 11:288, March, type from Guatemala.
1928. [*Choeroniscus*] *godmani* Thomas, Ann. Mag. Nat. Hist., ser. 10, 1:122, January.

Selected measurements of a male and female from San José, Costa Rica, are, respectively: length of head and body, 53, 53; length of forearm, 32.4, 33.5; greatest length of skull, 19.5, 21.0; interorbital breadth, 3.4, 3.4; length of upper tooth-row, 7.0, 7.1. Dorsum uniform dark brown; venter barely paler.

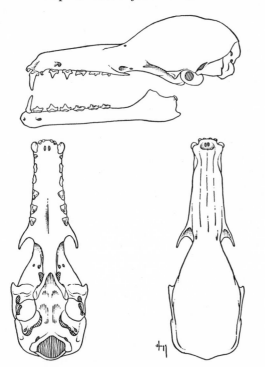

Fig. 77. *Choeronycteris mexicana*, 1 mi. S, 4 mi. W Bella Unión, 1000 ft., Coahuila, No. 34550 K.U., ♂, X 2.

MARGINAL RECORDS.—Chiapas: Pijijiapan (Hooper, 1947:43). Honduras: Cantoral, Tegucigalpa (Goodwin, 1942:129); *La Flor Archaga* (*ibid.*). Costa Rica: San José, San José (Goodwin, 1946:313), thence northward along Pacific Coast to point of beginning.

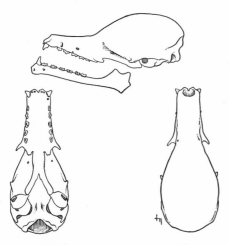

Fig. 78. *Choeroniscus godmani,* La Flor Archaga, Honduras, No. 127597 A.M., ♂, X 2.

Genus **Hylonycteris** Thomas

1903. *Hylonycteris* Thomas, Ann. Mag. Nat. Hist., ser. 7, 11:286, March. Type, *Hylonycteris underwoodi* Thomas.

Resembling *Choeroniscus* in all respects except that pterygoids are normal, convex medially rather than concave, not inflated, and not in contact with bullae. The genus is monotypic and poorly represented in collections.

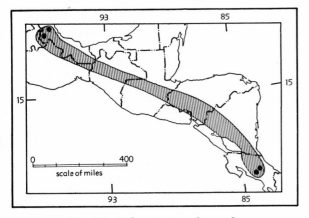

Map 85. *Hylonycteris underwoodi.*

Hylonycteris underwoodi Thomas
Underwood's Long-tongued Bat

1903. *Hylonycteris underwoodi* Thomas, Ann. Mag. Nat. Hist., ser. 7, 11:286, March, type from Rancho Redondo, San José, Costa Rica.

Length of head and body approximately 53. Selected measurements of the type are: length of forearm, 34.5; greatest length of skull, 23; interorbital breadth, 4.2; length of upper tooth-row, 8.5. Upper parts uniform dark brown; underparts slightly paler.

This bat is a nectar-feeder. It roosts in small groups in caves and tunnels.

MARGINAL RECORDS.—Veracruz: 15 km. ENE Tlacotepec (23709 KU). Costa Rica: type locality; Tarbaca, San José (Goodwin, 1946:314). Veracruz: Metlac (G. M. Allen, 1942b:97).

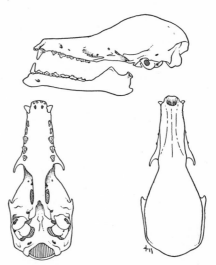

Fig. 79. *Hylonycteris underwoodi,* 15 km. ENE Tlacotepec, Veracruz, No. 23709 K.U., ♂, X 2.

Genus **Leptonycteris** Lydekker—Long-nosed Bat

1860. *Ischnoglossa* Saussure, Revue et Mag. Zool., Paris, ser. 2, 12:491, November. Type, *Ischnoglossa nivalis* Saussure. Not *Ischnoglossa* Kraatz, 1856, a beetle.
1891. *Leptonycteris* Lydekker, *in* Flower and Lydekker, An introduction to . . . mammals living and extinct, p. 674. Type, *Ischnoglossa nivalis* Saussure.

Skull of the usual glossophagine type; zygomata slender but complete; tail absent; interfemoral membrane much reduced; calcar small; lower incisors normally present but often lost presumably by traumatic means; molars elongated and W-shaped pattern nearly lost. Dentition, i. $\frac{2}{2}$, c. $\frac{1}{1}$, p. $\frac{2}{3}$, m. $\frac{2}{2}$.

The genera *Leptonycteris* and *Lichonycteris* are unique among bats in lacking the 3rd molars. Normally these two genera are easily separated on the basis of the presence of lower incisors in *Leptonycteris* and their absence in *Lichonycteris*. *Leptonycteris*, however, often lacks lower incisors in which case identification depends primarily on the upper incisors, which are evenly spaced in *Lichonycteris* and either continuously arranged or paired in *Leptonycteris*.

Leptonycteris nivalis
Long-nosed Bat

Selected measurements of a large series of adult males from Jalisco are: total length, 76–88; basilar length of skull, 22.1–23.7; interorbital breadth, 4.3–5.0; zygomatic breadth, 10.5–11.0; length of upper cheek-teeth, 8.2–9.2. Upper parts medium brown posteriorly, paler over shoulders; underparts paler than posterior part of back, approximately same as on shoulder region.

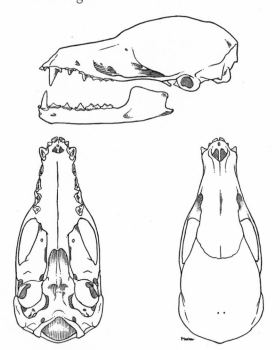

Fig. 80. *Leptonycteris nivalis longala*, 12 mi. S, 2 mi. E Arteago, 7500 ft., Coahuila, No. 33077 K.U., ♂, X 2.

Leptonycteris nivalis longala Stains

1957. *Leptonycteris nivalis longala* Stains, Univ. Kansas Publs., Mus. Nat. Hist., 9:355, January 21, type from 12 mi. S and 2 mi. E Arteaga, 7500 ft., Coahuila.
MARGINAL RECORDS (Stains, 1957:356).—Texas: cave W side Emory Peak, Chisos Mts., 7500 ft. Coahuila: type locality. Nuevo León: Cerro Potosí, Municipio de Galeana, 11,500 ft.

Leptonycteris nivalis nivalis (Saussure)

1860. M [= *Ischnoglossa*]. *nivalis* Saussure, Revue et Mag. Zool., Paris, ser. 2, 12:492, November, type from near snow line of Mt. Orizaba, Veracruz.
1900. *Leptonycteris nivalis*, Miller, Proc. Biol. Soc. Washington, 13:126, April 6.
1940. *Leptonycteris nivalis yerbabuenae* Martínez and Villa, Anal. Inst. Biol., Univ. Nac. México, 11:313, August, type from Yerba Buena, Guerrero. (Regarded by de la Torre, Fieldiana-Zool., Chicago Nat. Hist. Mus., 37:698, June 19, 1955, as indistinguishable from *L. n. nivalis*.)

MARGINAL RECORDS.—Arizona: Miller Canyon, Huachuca Mts. (Hoffmeister, 1954:54). Veracruz: 3 km. W Boca del Río (Park and Hall, 1951:64). Guatemala: Dueñas (Goodwin, 1942:130). *Nicaragua* (J. A. Allen, 1910:111), thence northward along Pacific Coast to Sonora: *Chinobampo* (Burt, 1938:21); ¼ mi. W Aduana (24837 KU).

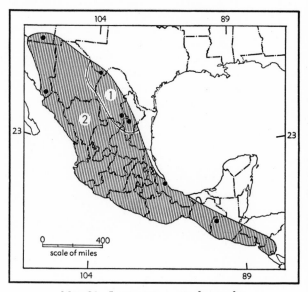

Map 86. *Leptonycteris nivalis nivalis.*

Genus Lichonycteris Thomas

1895. *Lichonycteris* Thomas, Ann. Mag. Nat. Hist., ser. 6, 16:55, July. Type, *Lichonycteris obscura* Thomas.

Closely resembling *Leptonycteris*; differing in having more or less evenly spaced upper incisors; no lower incisors; "upper incisors . . . [with] crowns narrow though scarcely trenchant, longer than high, that of inner tooth distinctly emarginate on cutting edge, so that it appears bilobed when viewed from in front, that of outer tooth with sharp, backward-directed cusp near inner edge, and a flattish outer projection" (Miller, 1907:143). The genus is monotypic.

Lichonycteris obscura Thomas
Brown Long-nosed Bat

1895. *Lichonycteris obscura* Thomas, Ann. Mag. Nat. Hist., ser. 6, 16:56, July, type from Managua, Managua, Nicaragua.

Selected measurements of 2 females from Costa Rica are: length of head and body, 51, 55; length of forearm, 32.5, 33.5; greatest length of skull, 18.5, 19.3; interorbital breadth, 3.9, 4.4; length of upper tooth-row, 5.8, 6.5. Upper parts uniform dark brown; underparts slightly darker.

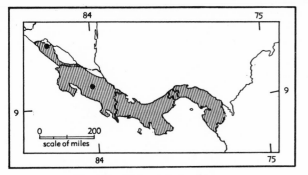

Map 87. *Lichonycteris obscura.*

MARGINAL RECORDS.—Nicaragua: type locality.
Costa Rica: San José, San José (Goodwin, 1946:315);
Fuentes, Montes de Oca, San José (*ibid.*), thence, presumably, to South America.

Subfamily CAROLLIINAE

Revised under the name *Hemiderma* by Hahn, Proc. U.S.
Nat. Mus., 32:103–118, February 8, 1907.

Trochiter impinging on scapula; nose-leaf present;
upper molars so modified that the W-shaped pattern is much altered or almost obliterated; upper
molars lacking commissures and styles; lower molars with cusps strictly lateral; crowns of upper and
lower molars trenchant.

One genus, *Carollia*, occurs in the area of our
study.

Genus Carollia Gray—Short-tailed Bats

1838. *Carollia* Gray, Mag. Zool. Bot., 2:488, February.
Type, *Carollia braziliensis* Gray [= *Vespertilio perspicillatus* Linnaeus]. *Carollia* is not a homonym of *Carolia*
Cantraine, 1837, and is available.
1855. *Hemiderma* Gervais, Mammifères, *in* [Castelnau]
Expéd. dans les parties centrales de l'Amér. du Sud . . . ,
p. 43. Type, *Phyllostoma brevicaudum* Wied-Neuwied
[= *Vespertilio perspicillatus* Linnaeus].
1866. *Rhinops* Gray, Proc. Zool. Soc. London, p. 115, May.
Type, *Rhinops minor* Gray [= *Vespertilio perspicillatus*
Linnaeus].

Skull relatively robust; rostrum approximately
two-thirds as long as braincase; braincase rising, but
not abruptly so, well above frontal region; zygomata incomplete; auditory bullae small, covering
less than half cochlear surface; ears small, separate;
tail about half as long as femur, extending to middle
of interfemoral membrane; lower molars distinctly
different in form from lower premolars. Dentition,
i. $\frac{2}{2}$, c. $\frac{1}{1}$, p. $\frac{2}{2}$, m. $\frac{3}{3}$.

Key Characters

C. castanea is smaller and *C. perspicillata* is larger.
It seems that at any one locality the two species can
be distinguished on the basis of size of the skull. For ex-

ample, in El Salvador, according to Felten (1956:199),
the two species can be separated by the following key:

1. Greatest length of skull more than 21.9;
condylobasal length more than 19.9; maxillary tooth-row more than 7.2.
$\qquad$ *C. perspicillata*, p. 123
1'. Greatest length of skull less than 21.9;
condylobasal length less than 19.9; maxillary
tooth-row less than 7.2. . . *C. castanea*, p. 124

Individuals of each species are larger in the northern
part of the geographic range than in the southern part.
Some individuals of *C. castanea* from the north are
larger than some individuals of *C. perspicillata* from the
south. In the present state of our knowledge we are
unable to make one key that distinguishes the two
species from each other at *all* of the places where they
occur together but it is our understanding that at any
one locality there is no overlap in size of each of several parts of the skull.

Carollia perspicillata
Seba's Short-tailed Bat

Length of head and body approximately 65;
length of forearm, 40.0–45.3; greatest length of
skull, 21.0–24.6; interorbital breadth, 5.8–6.0; length
of upper tooth-row, 7.0–8.8. Upper parts blackish
brown or reddish brown lightly washed with buff;
underparts slightly paler. Skull robust; braincase
rising above rostrum abruptly; interorbital constriction not well marked; rostrum relatively broad
and flat; 2nd upper premolar with posterior elongation; line of maxillary tooth-row not sharply curved.

Bats of this species roost in trees, buildings, caves,
tunnels, and among rocks, often in fairly well-lighted
places.

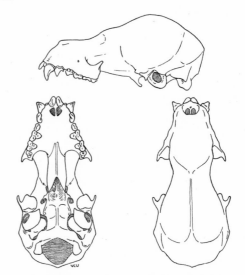

Fig. 81. *Carollia perspicillata azteca,* Mirador, 3500 ft.,
Veracruz, No. 23710 K.U., ♀, X 2.

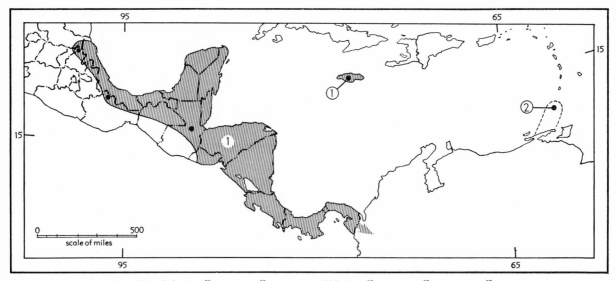

Map 88. (1) *Carollia perspicillata azteca*; (2) *Carollia perspicillata perspicillata*.

Carollia perspicillata azteca Saussure

1860. *Carollia azteca* Saussure, Revue et Mag. Zool., Paris, ser. 2, 12:480, November, type from southern México.
1924. *Carollia perspicillata azteca*, Miller, Bull. U.S. Nat. Mus., 128:54, April 29.

MARGINAL RECORDS.—San Luis Potosí: 1 km. W Huichihuayán (Dalquest, 1953:29); *10 km. N, 3 km. E Xilitla* (Dalquest, 1950:2). Oaxaca: Tuxtepec (Hahn, 1907: 112). Guatemala: Chipoc (Goodwin, 1934:11), thence southward into South America. Also recorded from Jamaica (G. M. Allen, 1911:232; Koopman and Williams, 1951:19), but subspecific identity uncertain.

Carollia perspicillata perspicillata (Linnaeus)

1758. [*Vespertilio*] *perspicillatus* Linnaeus, Syst. nat., ed. 10, 1:31, type from Surinam (Thomas, Proc. Zool. Soc. London, p. 130, March 22, 1911).
1924. *Carollia perspicillata perspicillata*, Miller, Bull. U.S. Nat. Mus., 128:53, April 29.
1821. *Phyllostoma brevicaudum* Wied-Neuwied, *in* Schinz, Das Thierreich . . . , 1:164. South America.
1823. *Vampyrus soricinus* Spix, Simiarum et vespertilionum Brasiliensium . . . , p. 66, pl. 36, figs. 2 and 6, type from Rio de Janeiro et ad fluvium St. Francisci, Brazil.
1826. *Phyllostoma brachyotum* Wied-Neuwied, Beiträge zur Naturgeschichte Brasiliens, 2:196, type from Brazil.
1839. *Phyllostoma grayi* Waterhouse, Mammals, *in* Darwin, Narrative of the . . . voyages of H.M.S. Adventure and Beagle . . . , p. 3. Based on specimens from Pernambuco, Brazil.
1840. *Phyllostoma bicolor* Wagner, Schreber's Säugthiere, Suppl. 1, p. 400, type from Brazil.
1843. *Phyllostoma lanceolatum* Gray, List of the . . . Mammalia in the . . . British Museum, p. 20. Based on "*Temm. Mss. P. Max. Abbild. t.*"
1843. *Phyllostoma calcaratum* Wagner, Arch. Naturgesch., 1:366, type from Brazil.
1844. *Carollia verrucata* Gray, *in* The zoology of voyage of H.M.S. Sulphur . . . , 1(1; Mamm.):20, type from South America.

1866. *Rhinops minor* Gray, Proc. Zool. Soc. London, p. 115, May, type from South America.

MARGINAL RECORDS.—Lesser Antilles: Grenada (G. M. Allen, 1911:232).

Carollia castanea
Allen's Short-tailed Bat

In 198 adults (99 of each sex) from El Salvador, selected external measurements are: length of head and body, 53–64; length of tail, 3–14; length of forearm, 36–42. Cranial measurements of a few specimens from elsewhere are: greatest length of skull, 20.0–20.8; interorbital breadth, 5.0–6.0; length of upper tooth-row, 6.5–7.8. Upper parts brown with a buffy or golden wash; underparts like back or faintly paler.

In 1946 and 1947 in the southern half of the Mexican state of Veracruz, Dr. Walter W. Dalquest observed bats of the genus *Carollia*. He did not distinguish between the species *C. perspicillata* and *C. castanea*—indeed he concluded that the two alleged species were one and the same. In his field notes on file in the Museum of Natural History at the University of Kansas it is recorded that "this bat" is one of the most abundant fruit-eating bats occurring in Veracruz, other species abundant there being *Glossophaga soricina* and *Artibeus jamaicensis*. *Carollia* inhabited principally caves but was found also in tubular culverts beneath roadbeds, and, in extreme southern Veracruz, in more than one hollow tree. On March 27 the 10 individuals saved from 50 or so in a cave all were females. In a cave only a few yards away, on April 1, the 10 individuals saved from approximately 100 there all were males.

Carollia castanea castanea H. Allen

1890. *Carollia castanea* H. Allen, Proc. Amer. Philos. Soc., 28:19, February 25, type from Costa Rica.

MARGINAL RECORDS.—Honduras: La Piedra de Jesús, Sabana Grande, Tegucigalpa (Goodwin, 1942:132). Costa Rica: Río Sixaola, Límon (Goodwin, 1946:316), thence southward into South America.

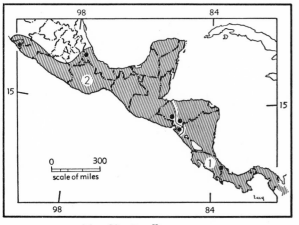

Map 89. *Carollia castanea.*

1. *C. c. castanea*   2. *C. c. subrufa*

Carollia castanea subrufa (Hahn)

1905. *Hemiderma subrufum* Hahn, Proc. Biol. Soc. Washington, 18:247, December 9, type from Santa Efigenia, 8 mi. NW Tapanatepec, Oaxaca.
1956. *Carollia castanea subrufa*, Felten, Senckenbergiana Biol., 37:211, April 15.

MARGINAL RECORDS.—Veracruz: Mirador (Hahn, 1907:115). Honduras: Muya, La Paz (Goodwin, 1942: 132); San Marcos, Sabana Grande (*ibid.*). Colima: Hidalgo Magdalena (Hahn, 1907:115).

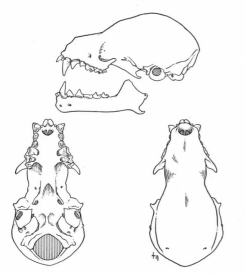

Fig. 82–83. *Carollia castanea subrufa,* Sololá, Moca, Guatemala, No. 41866 C.N.H.M., ♂, X 2.

SUBFAMILY STURNIRINAE

Trochiter impinging on scapula; nose-leaf present; upper molars so modified that W-shaped pattern is at least partly obliterated, cusps and commissures much reduced; crowns of molars with distinct longitudinal groove, the cusps being laterally placed; crowns of lower molars with distinct cusps on both margins of groove.

KEY TO GENERA OF STURNIRINAE

1. Length of upper tooth-row less than 27 per cent greatest length of skull; interorbital breadth less than 24 per cent greatest length of skull. . . . . *Sturnirops,* p. 127
1'. Length of upper tooth-row more than 27 per cent greatest length of skull; interorbital breadth more than 24 per cent greatest length of skull. . . . . *Sturnira,* p. 125

Genus Sturnira Gray

1842. *Sturnira* Gray, Ann. Mag. Nat. Hist., 10:257, December. Type, *Sturnira spectrum* Gray [= *Phyllostoma lilium* É. Geoffroy St.-Hilaire].
1849. *Nyctiplanus* Gray, Proc. Zool. Soc. London, p. 58, December 20. Type, *Nyctiplanus rotundatus* Gray [= *Phyllostoma lilium* É. Geoffroy St.-Hilaire].

Braincase moderately high with moderately developed sagittal crest; rostrum more than half as long as braincase; greatest interorbital breadth slightly more than depth in same region, and about equal to distance from incipient postorbital process to canine (after Miller, 1907:149); calcar small, tail absent. Dentition, i. $\frac{2}{2}$, c. $\frac{1}{1}$, p. $\frac{2}{2}$, m. $\frac{3}{3}$.

KEY TO SPECIES OF STURNIRA

1. Lower incisors trilobate; length of forearm less than 43 (in Central American specimens; up to 45 in some Mexican specimens). *S. lilium,* p. 125
1'. Lower incisors bilobate; length of forearm more than 43. . . . . . . *S. ludovici,* p. 126

Sturnira lilium
Yellow-shouldered Bat

Length of head and body approximately 62. Rostrum relatively short; forearm relatively short (averaging 40.4 in 12 topotypes from Paraguay); lower incisors trilobate; upper tooth-row evenly curved. Upper parts pinkish buff overlaid with brown, shoulders marked by reddish or straw-colored epaulettes; underparts like back but lacking dark overlay.

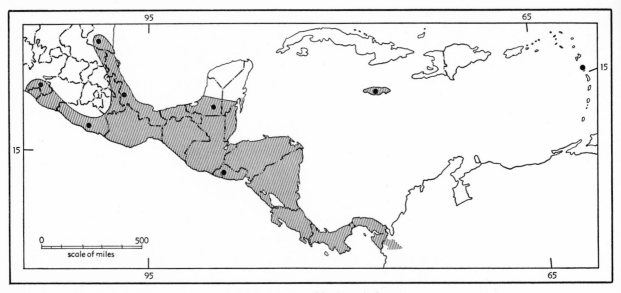

Map 90. *Sturnira lilium parvidens.*

Sturnira lilium parvidens Goldman

1917. *Sturnira lilium parvidens* Goldman, Proc. Biol. Soc. Washington, 30:116, May 23, type from Papayo, about 25 mi. NW Acapulco, Guerrero.

MARGINAL RECORDS.—Tamaulipas: Pano Ayuctle, near Gómez Farías (de la Torre, 1954:114). Veracruz: Mirador (Hershkovitz, 1949:442). Campeche: La Tuxpeña (Goldman, 1917:116), thence southward along Caribbean Coast to South America, then northward along Pacific Coast to El Salvador: San Salvador (Felten, 1956:341). Jalisco: *2 mi. N Ciudad Guzmán* (de la Torre, 1955:699, 700);

Sierra Nevada de Colima (J. A. Allen, 1890:181). Guerrero: type locality. The species has also been recorded as occurring on Jamaica (Koopman and Williams, 1951:19) and the island of Dominica (G. M. Allen, 1911:233); neither of these records was identified as to subspecies.

Sturnira ludovici Anthony
Anthony's Bat

1924. *Sturnira ludovici* Anthony, Amer. Mus. Novit., 139:8, October 20, type from near Gualea, about 4000 ft., north-western Ecuador.

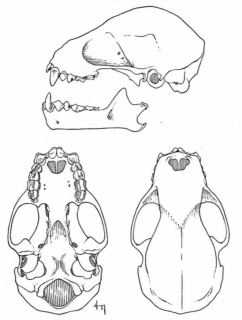

Fig. 84. *Sturnira lilium parvidens,* 2 mi. N Cuidad Guzmán, Jalisco, No. 31866 K.U., ♂, X 2.

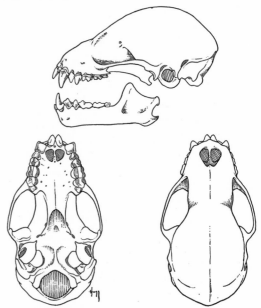

Fig. 85. *Sturnira ludovici,* 11 km. W Quira, Michoacán, No. 95704 Mich., ♀, X 2.

1927. *Sturnira lilium bogotensis* Shamel, Proc. Biol. Soc. Washington, 40:129, September 26, type from Bogotá, Colombia. Regarded as a synonym by Hershkovitz, Proc. U.S. Nat. Mus., 99:441, May 10, 1949.

1940. *Sturnira hondurensis* Goodwin, Amer. Mus. Novit., 1075:1, June 27, type from La Cruz Grande, near San José, about 3000 ft., La Paz, Honduras. Regarded as a synonym by Hershkovitz, Proc. U.S. Nat. Mus., 99:441, May 10, 1949.

Length of head and body, 65–70. Resembling S. *lilium* externally but averaging larger [forearm approximately 45]; rostrum seems longer; lower incisors deeply bilobate in young individuals but simple or weakly bilobate and often with a minute lobe in fully adult specimens; second upper molar turned inward and not in line with first molar. (After Hershkovitz, 1949:442.)

MARGINAL RECORDS.—San Luis Potosí: 3 km. W Xilitla (Dalquest, 1953:32). Veracruz: Mirador (de la Torre, 1952:1), thence southward into South America; in western México north to Michoacán: 11 km. W Quiroga (*ibid.*).

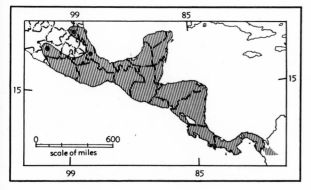

Map 91. *Sturnira ludovici.*

Genus **Sturnirops** Goodwin—Hairy-footed Bat

1938. *Sturnirops* Goodwin, Amer. Mus. Novit., 976:1, May 4. Type, *Sturnirops mordax* Goodwin.

Skull relatively long and narrow; rostrum and tooth-row short as compared with length of skull; canines large and massive; molars comparatively small; interorbital and postpalatal area elongated (after Goodwin, 1938:1).

The genus is known by only one specimen.

Sturnirops mordax Goodwin
Hairy-footed Bat

1938. *Sturnirops mordax* Goodwin, Amer. Mus. Novit., 976:1, May 4, type from El Sauce Peralta, Cartago, Costa Rica. Known only from the type locality.

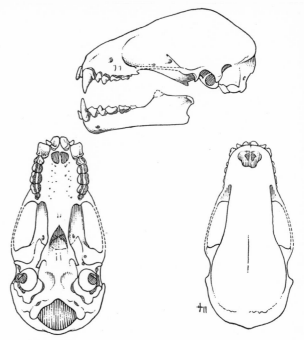

Fig. 86. *Sturnirops mordax*, from photo of holotype, El Sauce Peralta, Costa Rica, No. 250310 U.S.N.M., ♂, X 2.

Selected measurements of the holotype, a male, are: length of head and body, 60; greatest length of skull, 24.6; interorbital breadth, 5.2; length of upper molar series, 3.2. Upper parts dark brown, darkest on head and rump; underparts like back.

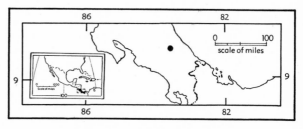

Map 92. *Sturnirops mordax.*

Subfamily **STENODERMINAE**

Trochiter impinging on scapula; nose-leaf usually present, but sometimes much reduced or absent; upper molars with cusps and commissures so reduced that the W-shaped pattern is obliterated; upper molars lacking styles; crowns of upper and lower molars much flattened and with well-developed cusps arising from crushing surface.

KEY TO NORTH AMERICAN GENERA OF STENODERMINAE

1. Rostrum less than half as long as braincase. . . . . *Centurio*, p. 146
1′. Rostrum more than half as long as braincase.
   2. Rostrum deep, parallel-sided, almost cuboid in form. . . . . *Pygoderma*, p. 145
   2′. Rostrum not cuboid.
      3. Nasal region occupied by a narrow emargination extending back from nares to orbital level.
                                                        Chiroderma, p. 134
      3′. Nasal region without emargination.
         4. Interpterygoid space extended forward as a deep palatal emargination.
            5. Rostrum strongly depressed between high supraorbital ridges; nares extending halfway from front of premaxillae to point of juncture of supraorbital ridges. . . *Stenoderma*, p. 145
            5′. Rostrum rising above level of low supraorbital ridges; nares extending much less than halfway from front of premaxillae to juncture of supraorbital ridges.
               6. Borders of palatal emargination strongly converging anteriorly; inner upper incisor with crown slender, noticeably higher than long. . . . . *Phyllops*, p. 143
               6′. Borders of palatal emargination not strongly converging anteriorly; inner upper incisor with crown short and thick, scarcely or not higher than long.
                  7. Upper molars 3–3. . . . . *Ardops*, p. 142
                  7′. Upper molars 2–2. . . . . *Ariteus*, p. 144
   4′. Interpterygoid space not extended forward as a deep palatal emargination.
        8. Inner upper incisor slightly higher than outer, but not twice as large, the two teeth usually not conspicuously different in form or size.
           9. Length of rostrum fully three-fourths that of braincase, depth of rostrum at front of 2nd premolar more than half depth of braincase. . . . . *Uroderma*, p. 130
           9′. Length of rostrum slightly more than half that of braincase; depth of rostrum at front of 2nd premolar less than half that of braincase.
              10. Inner upper incisor bifid, M3 and m3 present or absent, but when present so reduced that they have no effect on the form of surrounding bone. *Artibeus*, p. 135
              10′. Inner upper incisor entire, M3 and m3 well developed and affecting form of surrounding bone. . . . . *Enchisthenes*, p. 141
      8′. Inner upper incisor much higher than outer, usually at least twice as large, the two teeth conspicuously different in form and size.
        11. First lower molar with distinct posterointernal cusp, the crown notably different in form from that of last premolar.
           12. Crowns of molars both above and below heavily wrinkled; 2nd upper molar with large protoconule; upper canine with large secondary cusp.
                                      Brachyphylla, p. 128
           12′. Crowns of molars above and below nearly smooth; 2nd upper molar without protoconule; upper canine with no secondary cusp.
               13. Upper molars 3–3, the 2nd with large metacone. . . . *Platyrrhinus*, p. 131
               13′. Upper molars 2–2, the 2nd with metacone obsolete. . . *Vampyrodes*, p. 132
     11′. First lower molar without posterointernal cusp, the crown resembling that of last premolar.
        14. Inner cusps of 2nd lower molar large, their height about half width of crown.
                                      Vampyressa, p. 133
        14′. Inner cusps of 2nd lower molar obsolete or absent. . . . . *Ectophylla*, p. 135

Genus **Brachyphylla** Gray—Fruit-eating Bats

1834. *Brachyphylla* Gray, Proc. Zool. Soc. London, p. 122, March 12. Type, *Brachyphylla cavernarum* Gray.

Length of head and body (78–118) essentially equal to total length owing to vestigial tail. Skull relatively long, narrow; upper incisors markedly different in size and shape, inner one large, higher than long, recurved, outer one rounded, minute, flat-crowned; shaft of upper canine with large secondary cusp extending nearly to middle of posterior edge (unique for subfamily); anterior upper premolar minute; posterior upper premolar high and short; crowns of upper and lower molars heavily wrinkled; first lower molar with distinct posterointernal cusp, differing markedly from last premolar; interpterygoid space not extended forward as a palatal emargination; nasal region without emargination; ears small, separate; nose-leaf rudimentary; tail approximately a fourth length of femur, wholly enclosed by interfemoral membrane. Dentition, i. $\frac{2}{2}$, c. $\frac{1}{1}$, p. $\frac{2}{2}$, m. $\frac{3}{3}$.

Brachyphylla cavernarum Gray
St. Vincent Fruit-eating Bat

1834. *Brachyphylla cavernarum* Gray, Proc. Zool. Soc. London, p. 123, March 12, type from St. Vincent, Lesser Antilles.

Selected measurements of 10 specimens are: total length, 100–118; length of forearm, 63.0–66.4; greatest length of skull, 30.1–32.3; interorbital breadth, 6.0–6.8; zygomatic breadth, 16.3–17.8; length of maxillary teeth, 8.6–9.0. Upper parts ivory yellow, hairs tipped with sepia, patches on neck, shoulders, and sides appearing paler because dark wash is absent; underparts brown. Skull robust; rostrum little longer than broad, slightly flattened above; interorbital constriction slight; braincase broadest posteriorly, with well-developed sagittal crest; zygomatic arches widely and evenly bowed; interpterygoid notch not extending anteriorly to level of anterior root of zygoma; tympanic completely covering cochleae. First upper premolar small; 2nd upper premolar with greatly heightened cusp on cutting edge (much the highest cusp in molariform series); cusps progressively lower in posterior teeth.

No appreciable geographic variation occurs in this species.

MARGINAL RECORDS.—Puerto Rico: Corozal (Anthony, 1918:350). Lesser Antilles: Barbuda (*ibid.*); Barrouallie, St. Vincent (G. M. Allen, 1911:234).

Brachyphylla minor Miller
Barbados Fruit-eating Bat

1913. *Brachyphylla minor* Miller, Proc. Biol. Soc. Washington, 26:32, February 8, type from Coles Cave, St. Thomas Parish, Barbados, Lesser Antilles. Known only from Barbados.

Selected measurements of the type, an adult female, are: length of head and body, 78; length of forearm, 61.5; condylobasal length, 26.6; zygomatic breadth, 16.0; length of upper tooth-row, 10.4 (exclusive of incisors). "Like *Brachyphylla cavernarum* . . . but size at and below the minimum; area of cheek-teeth reduced." (Miller, 1913:32.)

Brachyphylla nana Miller
Cuban Fruit-eating Bat

1902. *Brachyphylla nana* Miller, Proc. Acad. Nat. Sci. Philadelphia, 54:409, September 12, type from El Guamá, Pinar del Río, Cuba.

Selected measurements of the type, sex indet., are: basal length, 22; interorbital breadth, 6; zygomatic breadth, 14.6; alveolar length of upper tooth-

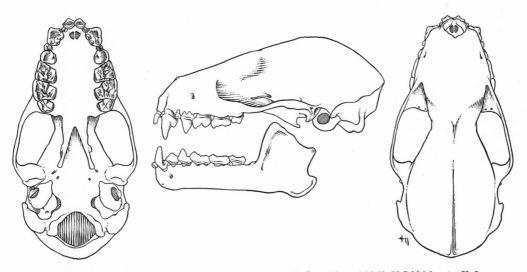

Fig. 87. *Brachyphylla cavernarum*, Antigua, West Indies, No. 123270 U.S.N.M., ♂, X 2.

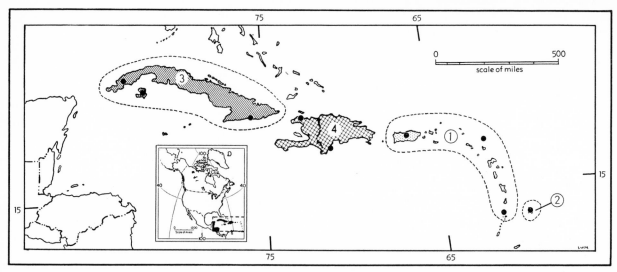

Map 93. Four species of *Brachyphylla*.

1. *B. cavernarum*   3. *B. nana*
2. *B. minor*   4. *B. pumila*

row, 9. Measurements of an adult female are: length of head and body, 83; length of forearm, 60. In general appearance resembles *Brachyphylla cavernarum* from St. Vincent more closely than peculiarities of skull would lead one to expect; *nana* smaller in general size and its nose-leaf broader and more nearly flat. (After Miller, 1902b:249.)

MARGINAL RECORDS.—Cuba: type locality; Santiago (Anthony, 1919:638). Isle of Pines (Anthony, 1918:350, assigned this material to *cavernarum*; assigned here to *nana* on geographic grounds; specimen not seen by us).

Brachyphylla pumila Miller
Haitian Fruit-eating Bat

1918. *Brachyphylla pumila* Miller, Proc. Biol. Soc. Washington, 31:39, May 16, type from cave near Port de Paix, Haiti.

Selected measurements of the type, sex indet., are: condylobasal length, 25.2; interorbital breadth, 6.3; zygomatic breadth, 14.8; length of upper tooth-row, 9.2. Like Cuban *Brachyphylla nana,* but first upper molar with inner portion of crown narrower; protocone rising abruptly from posterior margin to summit; base of protocone noticeably wider in proportion to length than in any other known member of genus (after Miller, 1918:39).

MARGINAL RECORDS.—Haiti: type locality. *Dominican Republic:* Los Patos (Goodwin, 1933:154).

Genus Uroderma Peters—Tent-making Bat

Revised by Andersen, Proc. Zool. Soc. London, pp. 212–221, September 7, 1908.

1865. *Uroderma* Peters, Monatsb. preuss. Akad. Wiss., Berlin, p. 588. Type, *Phyllostoma personatum* Peters [= *Uroderma bilobatum* Peters].

Rostrum at least three-fourths as long, and half as deep, as braincase; incisors resembling those of *Artibeus* but lateral upper one distinctly and evenly bilobed; incisors subequal in size; interpterygoid space not extended forward as a deep palatal emargination; nose-leaf well developed, lanceolate. Dentition, i. $\frac{2}{2}$, c. $\frac{1}{1}$, p. $\frac{2}{2}$, m. $\frac{3}{3}$.

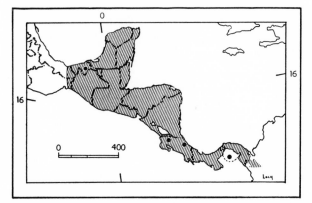

Map 94. *Uroderma bilobatum bilobatum.*

Uroderma bilobatum
Tent-making Bat

Selected measurements of two adult males from Costa Rica are: length of head and body, 61, 54; length of forearm, 43, 42.5; greatest length of skull, 23.5, 22.5; zygomatic breadth, 13.5, 12.5; length of upper tooth-row, 8, 8. Upper parts grayish brown; pair of whitish stripes extends from sides of nose-leaf to area between ears and another pair extends from corners of mouth to bases of ears; narrow whitish stripe over posterior back; color of underparts resembling that of upper parts.

By means of their teeth these bats cut the ribs of a palm frond in such a manner that its distal part droops and forms a tentlike frond, on the inside surface of which these bats roost.

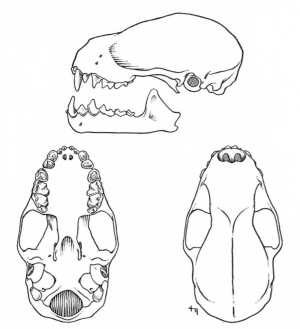

Fig. 88. *Uroderma bilobatum bilobatum,* San Geronimo, Costa Rica, No. 256485 U.S.N.M., ♂, X 2.

Uroderma bilobatum bilobatum Peters

1866. *Uroderma bilobatum* Peters, Monatsb. preuss. Akad. Wiss., Berlin, p. 394, type from São Paulo, Brazil.
1902. *Uroderma convexum* Lyon, Proc. Biol. Soc. Washington, 15:83, April 25, type from Colón, Panamá.

MARGINAL RECORDS.—Tabasco: 10 mi. E, 19 mi. N Macuspana (Hall, 1955a:1). Costa Rica: Miravalles (Andersen, 1908:220); Peralta (Goodwin, 1946:319), thence southeastward into South America and including Panamá: San José Island (Kellogg, 1946:2).

Genus Platyrrhinus Saussure—Broad-nosed Bats

1860. *Platyrrhinus* Saussure, Revue et Mag. Zool., Paris, ser. 2, 12:429, October. Type, *Phyllostoma lineatum* É. Geoffroy St.-Hilaire.
1865. *Vampyrops* Peters, Monatsb. preuss. Akad. Wiss., Berlin, p. 356. Type, *Phyllostoma lineatum* É. Geoffroy St.-Hilaire.

Resembling *Uroderma,* but incisors markedly unequal, inner pair being at least twice as high as outer pair; cutting edges entire; interfemoral membrane much narrower.

Following Alston (1879:48) many authors applied the name *Vampyrops lineatus* to Central American specimens on the now seemingly erroneous assumption that *Vampyrops helleri* Peters, 1865, of Mexico, was the same as *Phyllostoma lineatum* É. Geoffroy St.-Hilaire, 1810, from South America.

KEY TO NORTH AMERICAN SPECIES OF PLATYRRHINUS

1. Length of forearm less than 45; greatest length of skull less than 25. . *P. helleri,* p. 131
1'. Length of forearm more than 45; greatest length of skull more than 25. . *P. vittatus,* p. 132

Platyrrhinus helleri (Peters)
Heller's Broad-nosed Bat

1866. *Vampyrops helleri* Peters, Monatsb. preuss. Akad. Wiss., Berlin, p. 392, type from México.
1891. *Vampyrops zarhinus* H. Allen, Proc. Acad. Nat. Sci. Philadelphia, 43:400, type from "Brazil"; actually Bas Obispo, Canal Zone, Panamá; see Goldman, Smiths. Miscl. Coll., 69(5):200, April 26, 1920.

Measurements of an adult female from Costa Rica are: length of forearm, 39; greatest length of skull, 22; interorbital breadth, 5.7; zygomatic breadth, 12.3; length of upper tooth-row, 8. In general, in skull and color (including stripes), resembling *Uroderma bilobatum,* but differing as noted in generic account.

MARGINAL RECORDS.—Oaxaca: Fulta (Sanborn, 1955:412—locality not found by us) southward into South America. Not mapped.

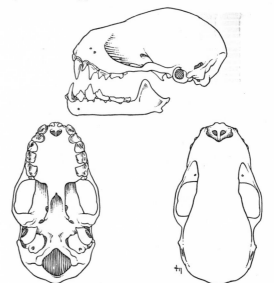

Fig. 89. *Platyrrhinus helleri,* Cabima, Panamá, No. 173833 U.S.N.M., sex ?, X 2.

Platyrrhinus vittatus (Peters)
Greater White-lined Bat

1859. *Artibeus vittatus* Peters, Monatsb. preuss. Akad. Wiss., Berlin, p. 225, type from Puerto Cabello, Carabobo, Venezuela.
1865. *V[ampyrops]. vittatus* Peters, Monatsb. preuss. Akad. Wiss., Berlin, p. 356.

Selected measurements of an adult from Valparaiso, Colombia, are: length of head and body, 95; length of forearm, 58; greatest length of skull, 31.8; interorbital breadth, 7.7; zygomatic breadth, 19.6; length of upper tooth-row, 12.7. Resembling *P. helleri* in general but differing in larger size, more anteriorly produced dorsal whitish stripe, dusky rather than whitish upper facial stripes, and obsolescence or lack of lower facial stripes.

MARGINAL RECORDS.—"Costa Rica" (Dobson, 1873: 525), presumably southeastward into South America. Sanborn (1955:406) questions the occurrence of this species in Costa Rica; other known occurrences are in South America. Not mapped.

Genus **Vampyrodes** Thomas

1900. *Vampyrodes* Thomas, Ann. Mag. Nat. Hist., ser. 7, 5:270, March. Type, *Vampyrops Caracciolæ* Thomas [= *Vampyrodes caraccioli* (Thomas)].

"Similar to . . . [*Platyrrhinus*], but with only 2–2 upper molars, and these conspicuously differing from each other in form, owing to the reduction of the metacone in the second to a mere trace." (Miller, 1907:156.)

Only one species, *V. major*, is recorded from our area.

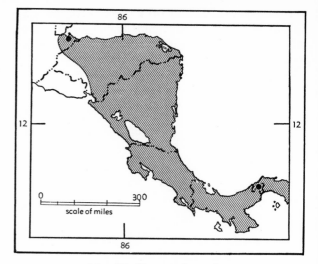

Map 95. *Vampyrodes major.*

Vampyrodes major G. M. Allen
San Pablo Bat

1908. *Vampyrodes major* G. M. Allen, Bull. Mus. Comp. Zool., 52:38, July, type from San Pablo, Panamá.

Length of head and body approximately 76. Selected cranial measurements of a male from Guatemala are: greatest length, 28.9; interorbital breadth, 6.8; zygomatic breadth, 17.5; length of upper tooth-row, 9.9. Pair of broad white facial stripes extending from nose backward, one on each side, over eye to above ear; white line extending from top of head down middle of back; another white mark extending from near corner of mouth to ear. These stripes are present in *Uroderma bilobatum, Platyrrhinus*

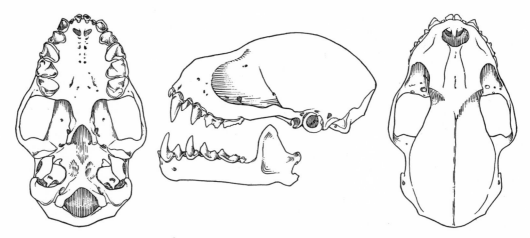

Fig. 90. *Vampyrodes major,* Barro Colorado Island, Canal Zone, Panamá, No. 45085 K.U., ♂, X 2.

helleri, and *P. vittatus*, but the longer forearm (approximately 55.5) in *Vampyrodes* is distinctive except from *P. vittatus* that has molars $\frac{3}{3}$ instead of $\frac{2}{2}$.

MARGINAL RECORDS.—Guatemala: Escobas, Izabal (Sanborn, 1936:101). Panamá: type locality.

Genus **Vampyressa** Thomas—Yellow-eared Bats

1900. *Vampyressa* Thomas, Ann. Mag. Nat. Hist., ser. 7, 5:270, March. Type, *Phyllostoma pusillum* Wagner.

In general like *Platyrrhinus* but molars only $\frac{2-2}{2-2}$ their surface sculpture much more distinct; middle upper incisor faintly bifid; metacone of M2 so reduced that tooth is irregularly pyriform in outline, the narrower portion (paracone) outward; m1 without cusps on inner side, and resembling last premolar. (After Miller, 1907:156.)

Two species, *V. nymphaea* and *V. thyone,* are known from Central America.

KEY TO NORTH AMERICAN SPECIES OF VAMPYRESSA

1. Upper parts smoke-gray, facial stripes conspicuous; greatest length of skull more than 20. . . . . *V. nymphaea,* p. 133
1'. Upper parts whitish brown anteriorly, uniform pale brown posteriorly, facial markings reduced and inconspicuous; greatest length of skull less than 20. . . . . *V. thyone,* p. 133

Vampyressa thyone Thomas
Little Yellow-eared Bat

1909. *Vampyressa thyone* Thomas, Ann. Mag. Nat. Hist., ser. 8, 4:231, type from Chimbo, 1000 ft., near Guayaquil, Bolívar Province, Ecuador.
1912. *Vampyressa minuta* Miller, Proc. U.S. Nat. Mus., 42:25, March 6, type from Cabima, Panamá, Panamá. (Arranged as a synonym of *thyone, fide* Hershkovitz, Proc. U.S. Nat. Mus., 99:444, May 10, 1949.)

Length of head and body approximately 49. Selected measurements of the type, an adult male, are: greatest length of skull, 19; zygomatic breadth, 11; length of upper tooth-row, 6.1. Upper parts whitish brown anteriorly, uniform pale brown posteriorly; facial stripes reduced. The smaller size and different color serves to distinguish *thyone* from *nymphaea*.

MARGINAL RECORDS.—Costa Rica: Agua Buena, Puntarenas (Goodwin, 1946:321), thence southeastward into South America.

Vampyressa nymphaea Thomas
Big Yellow-eared Bat

1909. *Vampyressa nymphaea* Thomas, Ann. Mag. Nat. Hist., ser. 8, 4:230, type from Novita, 150 ft., Río San Juan, Chocó, Colombia.

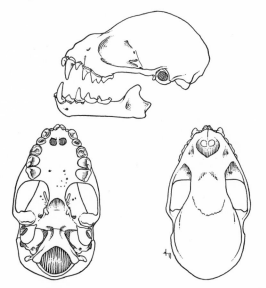

Fig. 91. *Vampyressa nymphaea*, Barro Colorado Island, Canal Zone, Panamá, No. 52455 K.U., ♀, X 2.

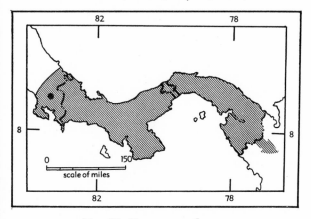

Map 96. *Vampyressa thyone.*

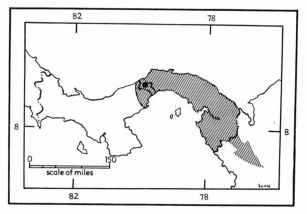

Map 97. *Vampyressa nymphaea.*

Length of head and body of a specimen from Panamá, 55. Selected measurements of the type, an adult male, are: length of forearm, 36; greatest length of skull, 21; zygomatic breadth, 12.2; length of upper tooth-row, 7.5. Upper parts smoke-gray; underparts a little paler; facial stripes conspicuous, the upper pair extending posteriorly beyond ears.

MARGINAL RECORD.—In North America, known only from Panamá: Barro Colorado Island (Hall and Jackson, 1953:645).

Genus **Chiroderma** Peters

1860. *Chiroderma* Peters, Monatsb. preuss. Akad. Wiss., Berlin, p. 747. Type, *Chiroderma villosum* Peters.
1866. *Mimetops* Gray, Proc. Zool. Soc. London, p. 117, May (cited in synonymy as manuscript name). Included two species: *Chiroderma villosum* Peters; *C. pictum* Gray.

Skull resembling that of *Platyrrhinus* but lacking nasal bones; cusps of molars much thickened and encroaching to considerable degree onto crushing surface of crown; externally much resembling *Platyrrhinus* but nose-leaf broader and forearm and uropatagium more heavily furred. Dentition, i. $\frac{2}{2}$, c. $\frac{1}{1}$, p. $\frac{2}{2}$, m. $\frac{2}{2}$.

KEY TO NORTH AMERICAN SPECIES OF CHIRODERMA

1. Facial markings absent or much reduced; length of forearm less than 48.
$\qquad$ *C. isthmicum,* p. 134
1′. Facial markings pronounced; length of forearm more than 48. . . . . . *C. salvini,* p. 134

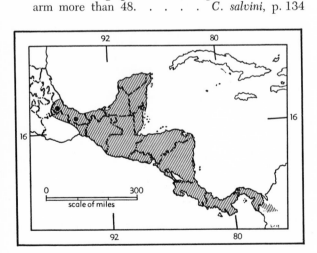

Map 98. *Chiroderma isthmicum.*

Chiroderma isthmicum Miller
Isthmian Bat

1912. *Chiroderma isthmicum* Miller, Proc. U.S. Nat. Mus., 42:25, March 6, type from Cabima, Panamá, Panamá.

Selected measurements of the type, an adult female, are: length of head and body, 65; length of forearm, 45; greatest length of skull, 24.6; interorbital breadth, 6.2; zygomatic breadth, 15.6; length of upper tooth-row, 8.8. Upper parts pale olivaceous brown (a whitish median line described in some individuals); underparts paler, somewhat buffy. Distinguishable readily from *salvini* by absence of, or only faint, facial markings and smaller size.

MARGINAL RECORDS.—Veracruz: Presidio (G. M. Allen, 1927:158); Achotal (Sanborn, 1936:103), thence southward into South America.

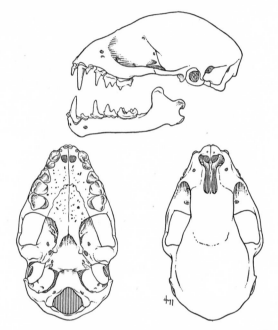

Fig. 92. *Chiroderma isthmicum,* Barro Colorado Island, Canal Zone, Panamá, No. 45096 K.U., ♂, X 2.

Chiroderma salvini Dobson
Salvin's White-lined Bat

1878. *Chiroderma salvini* Dobson, Catalogue of the Chiroptera in the . . . British Museum, p. 532, type from Costa Rica.

Selected measurements of an adult male from Costa Rica are: length of head and body, 77; length of forearm, 51.5; greatest length of skull, 27; interorbital breadth, 6.8; zygomatic breadth, 17.5; length of maxillary tooth-row, 10. Upper parts dark brown, white median stripe pronounced, extending from nape to uropatagium; facial markings distinct; underparts paler, more grayish, than upper parts. Skull robust; molariform teeth robust; inner pair of upper incisors high, slender; outer pair tiny; lower incisors small, subequal.

MARGINAL RECORDS.—Honduras: Tapasuna (Sanborn, 1941:378); San Marcos (Goodwin, 1942:134). Costa Rica: Angostura (Goodwin, 1946:322), thence southeastward into South America.

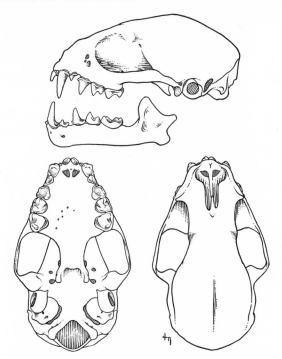

Fig. 93. *Chiroderma salvini*, Tapasuna, Honduras, No. 47640 C.N.H.M., ♂, X 2.

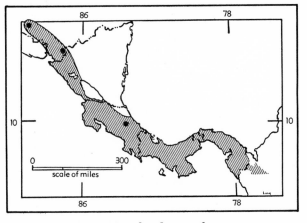

Map 99. *Chiroderma salvini*.

Genus Ectophylla H. Allen

1892. *Ectophylla* H. Allen, Proc. U.S. Nat. Mus., 15:441. Type, *Ectophylla alba* H. Allen.

Externally resembling a small whitish *Platyrrhinus*. In dental structure the most aberrant genus of the stenodermine bats. Basin-shaped crowns of 2nd upper and lower molars crossed by distinct longitudinal ridge; 1st upper molar with low protocone; 2nd lower molar with only one cusp, a well-developed paracone; 2nd lower molar markedly basined, broadly oval, wider than mandibular ramus; tail absent; tip of calcar free.

The genus is monotypic.

Ectophylla alba H. Allen
Honduran White Bat

1892. *Ectophylla alba* H. Allen, Proc. U.S. Nat. Mus., 15: 442, October 26, type from Segovia River, eastern Honduras [= Comarca de El Cabo, northern Nicaragua, according to Miller and Kellogg, Bull. U.S. Nat. Mus., 205:77, March 3, 1955].

Selected measurements of the type are: length of head and body "(from crown of head to base of tail)" (H. Allen, 1892:442), 36; length of forearm, 25. Upper parts dull whitish, paler over posterior parts; sides fawn colored; underparts dull white. Dentition, i. $\frac{2}{2}$, c. $\frac{1}{1}$, p. $\frac{2}{2}$, m. $\frac{2}{2}$.

MARGINAL RECORDS.—Nicaragua: type locality; San Emilio, Lake Nic Nac (Goodwin, 1946:323).

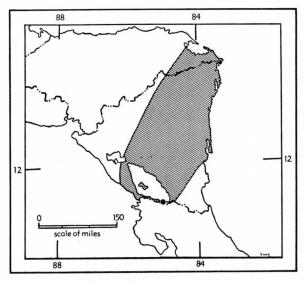

Map 100. *Ectophylla alba*.

Genus Artibeus Leach—Fruit-eating Bats

1821. *Artibeus* Leach, Trans. Linn. Soc. London, 13:75. Type, *Artibeus jamaicensis* Leach.
1821. *Madataeus* Leach, Trans. Linn. Soc. London, 13:81. Type, *Madataeus lewisii* Leach [= *Artibeus jamaicensis* Leach].
1827. *Medateus* Gray *in* Griffith, The animal kingdom . . . by the Baron Cuvier, 5:74, an emendation?
1838. *Arctibeus* Gray, Mag. Zool. Bot., 2:487, an emendation?

1843. *Medateus* Gray, List of the . . . Mammalia in the
. . . British Museum, p. xviii, an emendation?
1847. *Arctibius* Bonaparte, Proc. Zool. Soc. London, p. 115,
November 10, an emendation?
1855. *Pteroderma* Gervais, Mammifères, *in* [Castelnau]
Expéd. dans les partes centrales de l'Amer. du Sud . . . ,
pt. 7, p. 34. Type, "*perspicillatum.*"
1855. *Artibaeus* Gervais (*loc. cit.*), an emendation?
1855. *Dermanura* Gervais, *op. cit.* :36. Type, *Dermanura cinereum* Gervais.
1892. *Artobius* Winge, Jordf. og Nulevende Flagermus fra
Lagoa Santa, Minas Geraes, Brasilien, p. 10, an emendation?

Skull with moderately wide, slightly elevated braincase; zygomata widespreading and short; rostrum low and slightly more than half as long as braincase and about equal to lacrimal breadth; median depth in lacrimal region less than ½ lacrimal breadth; palate moderately wide, distance between 2nd upper premolars approximately equal to that from incisor to hypocone of 1st molar. Ears separate; nose-leaf well developed; no external tail; interfemoral membrane narrow; calcar short but distinct. (After Miller, 1907:161.) Upper incisors small, crowded, the inner distinctly bilobed, the outer much smaller and entire; lower incisors smaller than uppers, closely crowded and faintly bilobed; molars robust, crowns of crushing type and finely corrugated; molar teeth $\frac{2-2}{2-2}$, $\frac{2-2}{3-3}$ or $\frac{3-3}{3-3}$ sometimes according to species and sometimes individually. Usually paired facial stripes present but median dorsal stripe always absent.

The taxonomic conclusions reached by Andersen (1908) in his revision of the genus seem to be almost wholly untenable. We here employ the arrangement presented by Hershkovitz (1949:444–449) and Dalquest (1953a:61–65).

Key to North American Species of Artibeus

1. Length of forearm less than 50; greatest length of skull less than 24.
    2. Greatest length of skull 18.7 or more; length of upper tooth-row usually more than 6.0.
        3. Frontal region markedly bulging; rostrum inclined upward distally.
            A. turpis, p. 141
        3'. Frontal region not especially bulging; rostrum not inclined upward distally. . . . . . . *A. cinereus*, p. 139
    2'. Greatest length of skull 18.7 or less; length of upper tooth-row usually less than 6.0. . . . . *A. nanus*, p. 141
1'. Length of forearm more than 50; greatest length of skull more than 24.
    4. Greatest length of skull 29.7 or more; length of forearm 64 or more.
        A. lituratus, p. 138

4'. Greatest length of skull 29.7 or less; length of forearm 66 or less.
    5. Interfemoral membrane densely furred; color silvery gray.
        A. hirsutus, p. 136
    5'. Interfemoral membrane not densely furred; color either dark, medium, or light brown, but not silvery gray.
        A. jamaicensis, p. 136

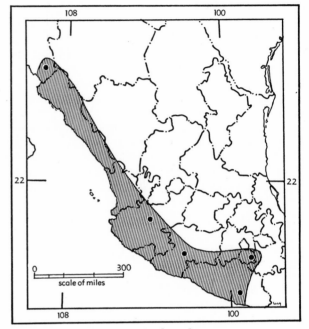

Map 101. *Artibeus hirsutus.*

Artibeus hirsutus Andersen
Hairy Fruit-eating Bat

1906. *Artibeus hirsutus* Andersen, Ann. Mag. Nat. Hist.,
ser. 7, 18:420, December, type from La Salada,
Michoacán.

Length of head and body, 79–86. Resembling *A. jamaicensis* but averaging smaller; tibia and interfemoral membrane densely haired; color of fur of upper side of body in adults drab with silvery tinge. Length of maxillary tooth-row, 9.5–10.4; forearm, 53.7–59.7. (After Andersen, 1906:420.)

MARGINAL RECORDS.—Sonora: ¼ mi. W Aduana (25053 KU). Jalisco: 8 mi. ENE Tala (36581 KU). Michoacán: type locality. Morelos: Jonacatepec (Davis and Russell, 1952:237). Guerrero: 4 mi. N Colotlipa, 3000 ft. (Lukens and Davis, 1957:7), thence up the coast to point of beginning.

Artibeus jamaicensis
Jamaican Fruit-eating Bat

Length of head and body approximately 75; length of forearm, 56.5–66.0; greatest length of skull, 27.0–29.7; zygomatic breadth, 16.2–18.5; length of upper tooth-row, 9.8–11.2. Upper parts variable individually, but usually of some shade of brown, sometimes smoky brown; facial markings present or absent, and when present of varying degrees of development; underparts often grayish and usually paler than upper parts. Skull short, broad, robust; braincase variable in degree of inflation both individually and geographically; sagittal crest moderately developed; rostrum short, low, wide; basisphenoidal pits absent. Number of molars variable.

The Jamaican fruit-eating bat is one of the commonest fruit bats throughout its geographic range. It lives in caves when possible but does not refuse crevices in trees when preferred sites are wanting. Usually these bats roost singly but under some circumstances a number may roost in a fairly compact mass. Food is mainly ripe fruits, the smaller kinds of which are plucked and carried to feeding sites. These bats are noisy fliers and feeders except during rainy weather when they pursue their activities in a strangely silent manner. Dalquest (MS) reports finding pregnant females in Veracruz in February and young bats in caves in March and April.

Artibeus jamaicensis jamaicensis Leach

1821. *Artibeus Jamaicensis* Leach, Trans. Linn. Soc. London, 13:75, type from Jamaica.
1821. *Madataeus Lewisii* Leach, Trans. Linn. Soc. London, 13:81, type from Jamaica.
1851. *Artibeus carpolegus* Gosse, A naturalist's sojourn in Jamaica, p. 271, type from Content, Jamaica.
1889. *Dermanura eva* Cope, Amer. Nat., 23:130, February, type from St. Martins, Lesser Antilles.
1890. *Artibeus coryi* J. A. Allen, Bull. Amer. Mus. Nat. Hist., 3:173, November 14, type from St. Andrews, Caribbean Sea.
1904. *Artibeus insularis* J. A. Allen, Bull. Amer. Mus. Nat. Hist., 20:231, June 29, type from St. Kitts, Lesser Antilles.
1908. *Artibeus jamaicensis richardsoni* J. A. Allen, Bull. Amer. Mus. Nat. Hist., 24:669, October 13, type from Matagalpa, Matagalpa, Nicaragua.

MARGINAL RECORDS.—Mainland segment: Tamaulipas: Aserradero del Paraíso (Goodwin, 1954:5), thence southward along coast to Campeche: Apazote (Andersen, 1908:266–267), southward along Caribbean Coast including Honduras: Ruatán Island (*ibid.*) to South America, thence northward along Pacific Coast to El Salvador: Hda. Nancuchiname (Felten, 1956:346). Guerrero: Papayo (Andersen, 1908:238). Michoacán: El Guayabo, 34 km. S Uruapan (Hall and Villa, 1949:442). Jalisco: 2 mi. N Ciudad Guzmán (de la Torre, 1955:698). Morelos: Las Estacas (Davis and Russell, 1952:237). Veracruz: Mirador (Andersen, 1908:267). San Luis Potosí: El Salto (Dalquest, 1953b:33). Tamaulipas: Pano Ayuctle (de la Torre, 1954:114). Insular segment: Haiti: cave near St. Michel (Miller, 1929a:9). Dominican Republic: San Gabriel Cave (Miller, 1929a:4).

Puerto Rico (Anthony, 1918:354): San German; Old Loiza. Lesser Antilles: Anegada Island (G. M. Allen, 1911:235); Anguilla Island (*ibid.*); Antigua Island (*ibid.*); Barbados (Sanborn, 1936:103); St. Kitts Island (Anthony, 1918:354). Old Providence Island (*ibid.*). St. Andrews Island (*ibid.*). Jamaica: Content (Andersen, 1908:267); Constant Springs (Hershkovitz, 1951:556). Haiti: La Gonave Island (Koopman, 1955:110); cave near Daiquini (Miller, 1929a:9).

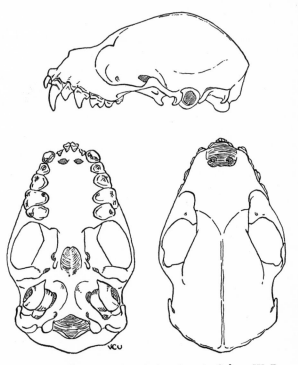

Fig. 94. *Artibeus jamaicensis jamaicensis*, 3 km. W Boca del Río, 10 ft., Veracruz, No. 23727 K.U., ♀, X 2.

Artibeus jamaicensis parvipes Rehn

1902. *Artibeus parvipes* Rehn, Proc. Acad. Nat. Sci. Philadelphia, 54:639, December 8, type from Santiago de Cuba, Oriente, Cuba.
1908. *Artibeus jamaicensis parvipes*, Andersen, Proc. Zool. Soc. London, 2:261, September 7.

MARGINAL RECORDS.—Bahama Islands (Shamel, 1931:251): Abrahams Hill, Mariguana Island; Great Inagua Island. Cuba: Baracoa (Andersen, 1908:262). Isle of Pines: Nueva Gerona (Miller, 1904:347). Cuba: Pinar del Río (*ibid.*). Note: G. M. Allen (1911:235) states that the supposed occurrence of this bat at Key West should be disregarded. In making this statement, G. M. Allen (*loc. cit.*) probably had in mind the account by Maynard (Quart. Jour. Boston Zool. Soc., 2(2):22, April, 1883).

Artibeus jamaicensis trinitatis Andersen

1906. *Artibeus planirostris trinitatis* Andersen, Ann. Mag. Nat. Hist., ser. 7, 18:420, December, type from St. Anns, Trinidad.
1949. *A[rtibeus]. j[amaicensis]. trinitatis*, Hershkovitz, Proc. U.S. Nat. Mus., 99:447, May 10.

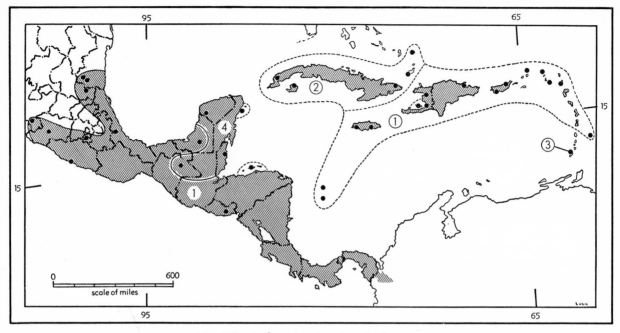

Map 102. *Artibeus jamaicensis* and subspecies.

1. *A. j. jamaicensis*   3. *A. j. trinitatis*
2. *A. j. parvipes*   4. *A. j. yucatanicus*

1906. *Artibeus planirostris grenadensis* Andersen, Ann. Mag. Nat. Hist., ser. 7, 18:420, December, type from Grenada.

MARGINAL RECORD.—Lesser Antilles: Grenada (Jones, 1951:224).

Artibeus jamaicensis yucatanicus J. A. Allen

1904. *Artibeus yucatanicus* J. A. Allen, Bull. Amer. Mus. Nat. Hist., 20:232, June 29, type from Chichén Itzá, Yucatán.
1908. *Artibeus jamaicensis yucatanicus*, Andersen, Proc. Zool. Soc. London, 2:263, September 7.

MARGINAL RECORDS.—Yucatán: Oxkintok Cave (Hatt, 1938:335). Quintana Roo: Cozumel Island (Andersen, 1908:263). British Honduras: Belize (*ibid.*). Chiapas: *Laguna Ocotal* (Burnett and Lyman, 1957:291); about 6 mi. SE Palenque (Kuns and Tashian, 1954:101).

Artibeus lituratus
Big Fruit-eating Bat

Length of head and body, 87–100; length of forearm, 64.0–75.8; greatest length of skull, 29.7–34.0; zygomatic breadth, 17.1–20.2; length of upper toothrow, 10.3–12.2. Color essentially as in *A. jamaicensis*. From that species, *A. lituratus* is distinguished mainly by larger size and the usually more heavily-furred membranes.

The species seemingly is uncommon and is difficult to collect because it is shy and quickly takes flight when disturbed.

Artibeus lituratus palmarum J. A. Allen and Chapman

1897. *Artibeus palmarum* J. A. Allen and Chapman, Bull. Amer. Mus. Nat. Hist., 9:16, February 26, type from Botanical Gardens at Port of Spain, Trinidad.
1949. *A[rtibeus]. l[ituratus]. palmarum*, Hershkovitz, Proc. U.S. Nat. Mus., 99:447, May 10.
1897. *Artibeus intermedius* J. A. Allen, Bull. Amer. Mus. Nat. Hist., 9:33, March 11, type from San José, Costa Rica.
1899. *Artibeus femurvillosum* Bangs, Proc. New England Zool. Club, 1:73, November 24, type from Santa Marta, Colombia.

MARGINAL RECORDS.—Tamaulipas: Pano Ayuctle, near Gómez Farías (de la Torre, 1954:114), thence southward along Caribbean Coast to South America, and then northward along Pacific Coast to El Salvador: Corinto (Felten, 1956:350). Jalisco: Las Peñas [= Puerto Vallarta] (J. A. Allen, 1897:48). Nayarit: Huajimic (Andersen, 1908:279). Morelos: Cuernavaca (28013 KU). San Luis Potosí (Dalquest, 1953b:35): 2 km. N Tamazunchale; El Salto. Lesser Antilles: St. Vincent Island (Andersen, 1908:279); Douglaston, Grenada (Jones, 1951:224).

Artibeus lituratus praeceps Andersen

1906. *Artibeus jamaicensis praeceps* Andersen, Ann. Mag. Nat. Hist., ser. 7, 18:421, December, type from Guadeloupe, Lesser Antilles.
1949. *A[rtibeus]. l[ituratus]. praeceps,* Hershkovitz, Proc. U.S. Nat. Mus., 99:447, May 10.
1908. *[Artibeus jamaicensis] dominicanus* Andersen, Proc. Zool. Soc. London, p. 249, September, A *nomen nudum.*

MARGINAL RECORDS (G. M. Allen, 1911:236).— Lesser Antilles: type locality; Dominica.

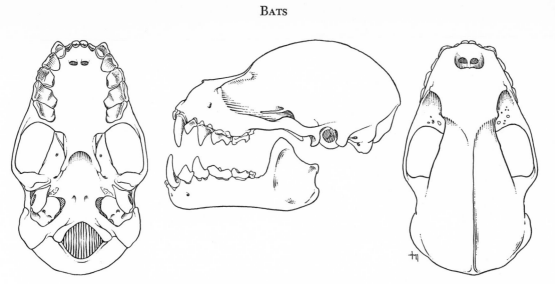

Fig. 95. *Artibeus lituratus palmarum*, Barro Colorado Island, Canal Zone, Panamá,
No 45086 K.U., ♀, X 2.

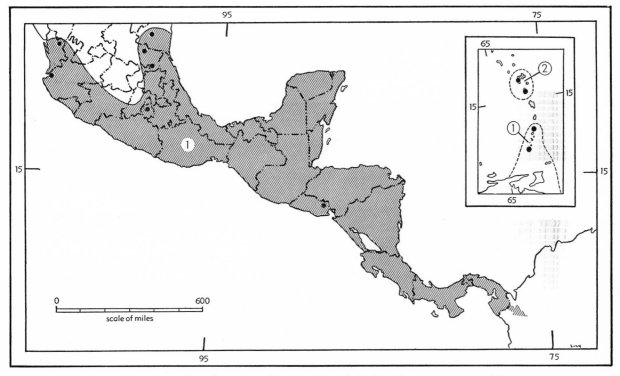

Map 103. *Artibeus lituratus palmarum* (1) and *Artibeus lituratus praeceps* (2).

Artibeus cinereus
Gervais' Fruit-eating Bat

Length of head and body approximately 58; length of forearm, 37.2–46.8; greatest length of skull, 18.7–21.2; zygomatic breadth, 11.2–13.0; length of upper tooth-row, 6.0–7.2. Resembling *A.*

jamaicensis but distinguishable mainly by smaller size.

The species as here recognized contains several subspecies that have usually been given full specific status (Andersen, 1908, *et auct.*). A revisionary study of this group is required properly to evaluate these forms and to characterize satisfactorily the species *A. cinereus.*

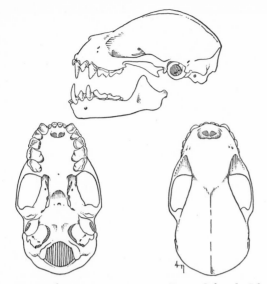

Fig. 96. *Artibeus cinereus watsoni,* Barro Colorado Island, Canal Zone, Panamá, No. 45087 K.U., ♂, X 2.

Artibeus cinereus aztecus Andersen

1906. *Artibeus aztecus* Andersen, Ann. Mag. Nat. Hist., ser. 7, 18:422, December, type from Tetela del Volcán, Morelos.

1953. *Artibeus cinereus aztecus,* Dalquest, Proc. Biol. Soc. Washington, 66:64, August 10.

MARGINAL RECORDS.—Tamaulipas: Rancho del Cielo (Goodwin, 1954:5). Morelos: type locality. Guerrero: 2 mi. W Omilteme (Lukens and Davis, 1957:11). San Luis Potosí: Cerro Campanario, 7800 ft. (Dalquest, 1953a:64).

Artibeus cinereus phaeotis (Miller)

1902. *Dermanura phaeotis* Miller, Proc. Acad. Nat. Sci. Philadelphia, 54:405, September 12, type from Chichén-Itzá, Yucatán.
1949. *Artibeus cinereus phaeotis,* Hershkovitz, Proc. U.S. Nat. Mus., 99:449, May 10.
1906. *Dermanura jucundum* Elliot, Proc. Biol. Soc. Washington, 19:50, May 1, type from Achotal, Veracruz.

MARGINAL RECORDS.—Yucatán: Calotmul (Gaumer, 1917:299). Guatemala: San Lucas (Goodwin, 1934:12). Veracruz: Río Solosuchil (Dalquest, 1953a:64); Achotal (*ibid.*).

Artibeus cinereus toltecus (Saussure)

1860. *Stenoderma tolteca* Saussure, Revue et Mag. Zool., Paris, ser. 2, 12:427, October, type from México; restricted to Mirador, Veracruz, by Hershkovitz, Proc. U.S. Nat. Mus., 99:449, May 10, 1949.
1949. *Artibeus cinereus toltecus,* Hershkovitz, Proc. U.S. Nat. Mus., 99:449, May 10.

MARGINAL RECORDS.—Sinaloa: Escuinapa (J. A. Allen, 1906:237; referred here to *toltecus,* not *phaeotis,* on

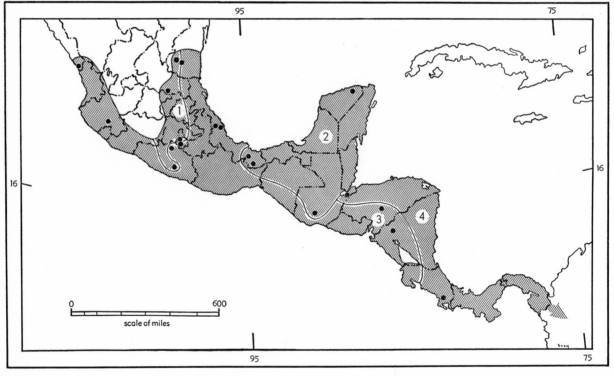

Map 104. *Artibeus cinereus* and subspecies.

1. *A. c. aztecus*   3. *A. c. toltecus*
2. *A. c. phaeotis*   4. *A. c. watsoni*

geographic grounds). Jalisco: Los Masos (J. A. Allen, 1906:261). Guerrero: 17 km. S Taxco (Lukens and Davis, 1957:10). Morelos: Cerro Frío, Hda. San Gabriel (Davis and Russell, 1954:69). Tamaulipas: Pano Ayuctle, near Gómez Farías (de la Torre, 1954:114). Veracruz: type locality; Plan del Río, 1000 ft. (Davis, 1944:378). Honduras: La Flor Archaga (Goodwin, 1942:136). Nicaragua: Jinotega (J. A. Allen, 1910:113). *Costa Rica* (Andersen, 1908:300).

Artibeus cinereus watsoni Thomas

1901. *Artibeus Watsoni* Thomas, Ann. Mag. Nat. Hist., ser. 7, 7:542, June, type from Bogava [= Bugaba], Chiriquí, Panamá.
1949. *Artibeus cinereus watsoni*, Hershkovitz, Proc. U.S. Nat. Mus., 99:449, May 10.

MARGINAL RECORDS.—Guatemala: Escobas, near San Tomas, Izabál (Sanborn, 1936:104). Costa Rica: Boruca, Puntarenas (Goodwin, 1946:325), thence southward to South America.

Artibeus nanus Andersen
Dwarf Fruit-eating Bat

1906. *Artibeus nanus* Andersen, Ann. Mag. Nat. Hist., ser. 7, 18:423, December, type from Tierra Colorada, Sierra Madre del Sur, Guerrero.

Length of head and body approximately 53. "Allied to *A. turpis*, with which species it shares all essential cranial and dental characters . . . , but readily distinguished by its conspicuously smaller size. Length of skull, inion to front of canines, 18.2–18.7; maxillary tooth-row, 5.8–6.1; forearm, 36.5–38; third metacarpal 32.2–35 mm." (Andersen, 1906:423.)

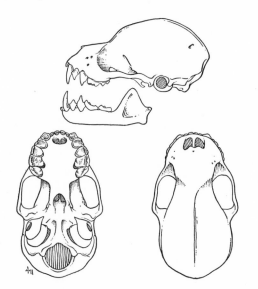

Fig. 97. *Artibeus nanus*, Uaxactún, Petén, Guatemala, No. 11381 K.U., ♂, X 2.

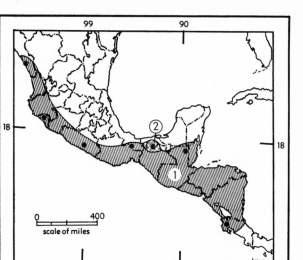

Map 105. *Artibeus nanus* (1) and *Artibeus turpis* (2).

MARGINAL RECORDS (Andersen, 1908:310, unless otherwise noted).—Sinaloa: Presidio. Colima: Hda. Magdalena. Guerrero: type locality. Veracruz: Buena Vista. Guatemala: Uaxactún (Murie, 1935:19). Costa Rica: 27 de Abril (Harris, 1943:8).

Artibeus turpis Andersen
Teapa Fruit-eating Bat

1906. *Artibeus turpis* Andersen, Ann. Mag. Nat. Hist., ser. 7, 18:422, December, type from Teapa, Tabasco. Known only from the type locality.

"Cranial rostrum unusually depressed and slightly, but distinctly, bent upwards; alveolar border of maxillary bone, therefore, more abruptly ascending than usual in the genus. Bony palate shortened: in *A.* [*cinereus*] *toltecus* (apparently the nearest relative of *A. turpis*) the length of the palate, from palation to posterior border of incisive foramina, is greater, in *A. turpis* less, than the length of the postpalatal portion of the skull, from palation to basion. Molars $\frac{2}{2}$. . . . Length of skull, inion to front of canines, 20; maxillary tooth-row 6.7; forearm 40.5; third metacarpal 37 mm." (Andersen, 1906:422.)

Genus Enchisthenes Andersen
Little Fruit-eating Bat

1906. *Enchisthenes* Andersen, Ann. Mag. Nat. Hist., ser. 7, 18:419, December. Type, *Artibeus hartii* Thomas.

Resembling *Artibeus*, but inner upper incisor not bifid, and 3rd molar both above and below well developed and affecting form of surrounding bone. (After Miller, 1907:162.)

The genus contains only one known species.

Enchisthenes hartii (Thomas)
Little Fruit-eating Bat

1892. *Artibeus hartii* Thomas, Ann. Mag. Nat. Hist., ser. 6, 10:409, November, type from Trinidad, Lesser Antilles.
1908. *Enchisthenes harti*, Andersen, Proc. Zool. Soc. London, 2:224, September 7.

Selected measurements of an adult male from Honduras are: length of head and body, 60; length of forearm, 37.6; greatest length of skull, 20.8; zygomatic breadth, 11.6; length of upper tooth-row, 7.2. Upper parts dark brown, almost blackish on head and shoulders; underparts paler than back, darkest anteriorly; facial stripes narrow, buffy.

This bat seems to be rare and is poorly represented in collections.

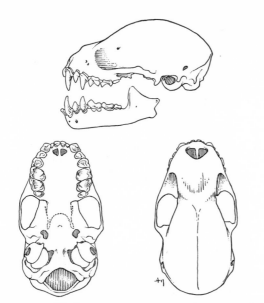

Fig. 98. *Enchisthenes hartii*, La Flor Archaga, Honduras, No. 26239 A.M., ♂, X 2.

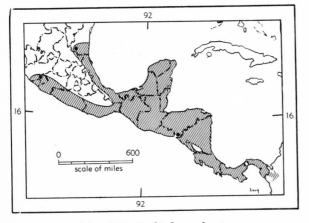

Map 106. *Enchisthenes hartii*.

MARGINAL RECORDS.—Tamaulipas: Aserradero [*sic*] del Infernillo (Goodwin, 1954:5). Honduras: La Flor Archaga, Tegucigalpa (Goodwin, 1942:137), thence southward into South America. On west coast known from Jalisco: 2 mi. N Ciudad Guzmán (de la Torre, 1955:700).

Genus **Ardops** Miller—Tree Bats

1906. *Ardops* Miller, Proc. Biol. Soc. Washington, 19:84, June 4. Type, *Stenoderma nichollsi* Thomas.

Skull resembling that of *Artibeus*, but relatively broader; rostrum moderately flattened; supra-orbital ridges thickened, rounded; interpterygoid space extending anteriorly to level of first molar; borders of palatal emargination almost parallel; inner upper incisors short, thick, barely if at all higher than long. Dentition, i. $\frac{2}{2}$, c. $\frac{1}{1}$, p. $\frac{2}{2}$, m. $\frac{3}{3}$.

The genus seems to be confined to the Lesser Antillean Islands. The currently recognized species are separated from each other seemingly on little more than slight differences in size and should possibly be regarded as actually constituting but one species.

KEY TO NOMINAL SPECIES OF ARDOPS

1. Forearm shorter than 46; greatest length of skull less than 21.5. . . . *A. nichollsi*, p. 143
1'. Forearm longer than 46; greatest length of skull more than 21.5.
   2. Forearm longer than 50; zygomatic breadth more than 15.8.
                    A. montserratensis, p. 142
   2'. Forearm shorter than 50; zygomatic breadth less than 15.8.
      3. Inner upper incisors conspicuously bifid; white spot present at junction of arm and body. . . . . *A. luciae*, p. 143
      3'. Inner upper incisors less conspicuously bifid; white markings absent.
                    A. annectens, p. 143

Ardops montserratensis (Thomas)
Montserrat Tree Bat

1894. *Stenoderma montserratense* Thomas, Proc. Zool. Soc. London, p. 133, June, type from Montserrat, Lesser Antilles. Known only from the type locality.
1906. *A[rdops]. montserratensis*, Miller, Proc. Biol. Soc. Washington, 19:84, June 4.

Selected measurements of the type, an adult male, are: length of head and body, 69; length of forearm, 51.5; greatest length of skull, 23.6; zygomatic breadth, 16. Lacks streaks or spots or other conspicuous markings.

"This Bat is said to hang all day under the branches of trees, and not to take refuge in holes and crannies as most species do" (Thomas, 1894:133).

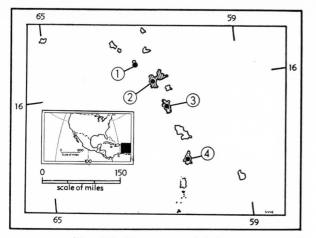

Map 107. Four species of *Ardops*.

1. *A. montserratensis* 3. *A. nichollsi*
2. *A. annectens* 4. *A. luciae*

Ardops annectens Miller
Guadeloupe Tree Bat

1913. *Ardops annectens* Miller, Proc. Biol. Soc. Washington, 26:33, February 8, type from Guadeloupe, Lesser Antilles. Known only from the type locality.

Selected measurements of the type, a female, and an adult male are, respectively: length of head and body, 68, 61; length of forearm, 48.6, 48.0; greatest length of skull, 23.6, 22.2; zygomatic breadth, 15.4, 14.8; length of upper tooth-row, 7.8, 7.0. Closely resembles *Ardops montserratensis* (Thomas) and *A. luciae* Miller, but intermediate in size, the length of forearm in each sex obviously more than in *luciae* and less than in *montserratensis* (after Miller, 1913:33).

Ardops nichollsi (Thomas)
Dominican Tree Bat

1891. *Stenoderma nichollsi* Thomas, Ann. Mag. Nat. Hist., ser. 6, 7:529, June, type from Dominica, Lesser Antilles. Known only from Dominica.
1906. *Ardops nichollsi*, Miller, Proc. Biol. Soc. Washington, 19:84, June 4.

Selected measurements of a male are: length of head and body, 53; length of forearm, 44; greatest length of skull, 20.4; zygomatic breadth, 13.6; length of upper tooth-row, 6.4.

Ardops luciae (Miller)
St. Lucia Tree Bat

1902. *Stenoderma luciae* Miller, Proc. Acad. Nat. Sci. Philadelphia, 54:407, September 12, type from St. Lucia, Lesser Antilles. Known only from the type locality.
1906. *A[rdops]. luciae*, Miller, Proc. Biol. Soc. Washington, 19:84, June 4.

Selected measurements of the type, an adult female, are: length of head and body, 65; length of forearm, 47; greatest length of skull, 23; zygomatic breadth, 15; length of upper tooth-row, 7.6. "Larger than . . . [*Ardops*] *nichollsi* of Dominica, its nearest geographical ally, and inner upper incisors more noticeably bifid. Much smaller than *S*. [= *A*.] *montserratense*, and with a distinct white shoulder spot." (Miller, 1902:407.)

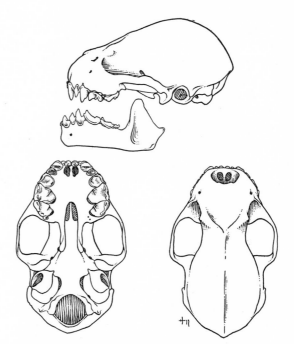

Fig. 99. *Ardops luciae*, St. Lucia, West Indies, No. 110918, U.S.N.M., sex ?, X 2.

Genus Phyllops Peters

1865. *Phyllops* Peters, Monatsb. preuss. Akad. Wiss., Berlin, p. 356. Type, *Phyllostoma albomaculatum* Gundlach [= *Arctibeus falcatus* Gray].

"Like *Ardops*, but inner upper incisor with crown higher than long, and without distinct secondary cusp, first and second upper molars with hypocone much lower than protocone, first lower molar with well-developed metaconid connected with ridge on inner side of protoconid, and palatal emargination with sides strongly converging, in continuation of the divergent pterygoids" (Miller, 1907:164–165).

Phyllops vetus, known only as a fossil, is not here included because Anthony (1917:336) states that "judging from the condition of the specimens [*P. vetus*] . . . has not been frequenting this region since the more recent animal remains, bats of the present day, were deposited."

KEY TO SPECIES OF PHYLLOPS

1. Palatal emargination U-shaped; length of forearm more than 40. . . . *P. falcatus*, p. 144
1'. Palatal emargination V-shaped; length of forearm less than 40. . . . *P. haitiensis*, p. 144

Phyllops falcatus (Gray)
Cuban Fig-eating Bat

1839. *Arctibeus falcatus* Gray, Ann. Nat. Hist., ser. 1, 4:1, September, type from Cuba.
1907. *Phyllops falcatus*, Miller, Bull. U.S. Nat. Mus., 57:165, June 29.

Length of head and body approximately 48; length of forearm of the type, an immature female, 41.9. Frontal area between supraorbital ridges flattened; palatal emargination U-shaped, extending anteriorly approximately to level of middle of 2nd upper molar.

MARGINAL RECORDS.—Cuba: Matanzas (G. M. Allen, 1911:238); Daiquirí (Anthony, 1919:640); near Cienfuegos (*ibid.*).

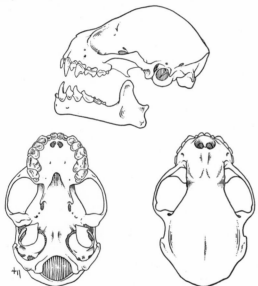

Fig. 100. *Phyllops falcatus*, Santiago, Cuba, No. 143844 U.S.N.M., ♀, X 2.

Phyllops haitiensis (J. A. Allen)
Dominican Fig-eating Bat

1908. *Ardops haitiensis* J. A. Allen, Bull. Amer. Mus. Nat. Hist., 24:581, September 11, type from Caña Honda, Dominican Republic.
1917. *Phyllops haitiensis*, Anthony, Bull. Amer. Mus. Nat. Hist., 37:337, May 28.

Differing from *P. falcatus* mainly in smaller size (forearm, 39), and V-shaped palatal emargination that extends anteriorly approximately to level of anterior edge of second upper molar.

MARGINAL RECORDS.—Haiti: cave near St. Michel (Miller, 1929a:9). Dominican Republic: type locality. Haiti: Port au Prince (Sanborn, 1941:379).

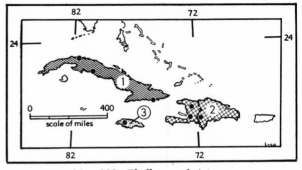

Map 108. *Phyllops* and *Ariteus.*

Guide to species
1. *Phyllops falcatus*
2. *Phyllops haitiensis*
3. *Ariteus flavescens*

Genus Ariteus Gray—Jamaican Fig-eating Bat

1838. *Ariteus* Gray, Mag. Zool. Bot., 2:491, February. Type, *Istiophorus flavescens* Gray.
1876. *Peltorhinus* Peters, Monatsb. preuss. Akad. Wiss., Berlin, p. 433. Type, *Artibeus achradophilus* Gosse.

Length of head and body approximately 51. "Like *Ardops*, but without the small upper molar; first lower molar with minute though evident metaconid." (Miller 1907:165.) Dentition, i. $\frac{2}{2}$, c. $\frac{1}{1}$, p. $\frac{2}{2}$, m. $\frac{2}{3}$.

The genus is monotypic.

Ariteus flavescens (Gray)
Jamaican Fig-eating Bat

1831. *Istiophorus flavescens* Gray, Zool. Misc., No. 1, p. 37, February, type from an unknown locality. Known definitely only from Jamaica.

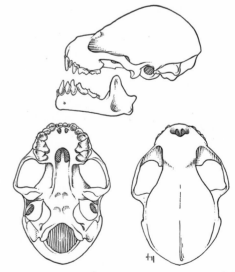

Fig. 101. *Ariteus flavescens*, Jamaica, No. 252771 U.S.N.M., ♀, X 2.

1838. *Ariteus flavescens* Gray, Mag. Zool. Bot., 2:491, February.
1851. *Artibeus achradophilus* Gosse, A naturalist's sojourn in Jamaica, p. 271, type from Content, Jamaica.

Characters as for the genus.

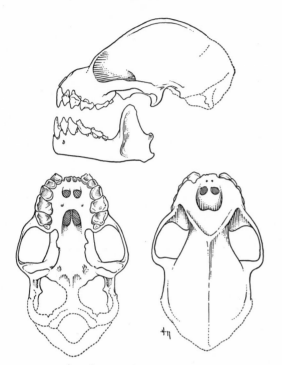

Fig. 102. *Stenoderma rufum*, Catedral Cave, Arecibo Province, Puerto Rico, No. 40951 A.M., sex ?, X 2.

Genus **Stenoderma** É. Geoffroy St.-Hilaire

1818. *Stenoderma* É. Geoffroy St.-Hilaire, Description de l'Egypte . . . , 2:114. Type, "le sténoderme roux" [= *Stenoderma rufa* Desmarest, 1820]. Not *Stenoderma* Oken, 1816; Oken's names are not available.
1869. *Histiops* Peters, Monatsb. preuss. Akad. Wiss., Berlin, p. 433. Type, *Artibaeus undatus* Gervais [= *Stenoderma rufa* Desmarest].

"In general like *Ardops*, but skull with nasal region much depressed between high supraorbital ridges; anterior nares directed chiefly upward and extending fully halfway from front of premaxillaries to point of juncture of supraorbital ridges which are not angulated at middle, but extend in a nearly straight line from front of orbit to sagittal crest; incisive foramina separated from roots of incisors by space equal to their greatest diameter; inner upper incisor with high slender crown, as in *Phyllops*; first and second upper molars with low but distinct metaconule on surface of crown between hypocone and metacone." (Miller, 1907:166.) Dentition, i. $\frac{2}{2}$, c. $\frac{1}{1}$, p. $\frac{2}{2}$, m. $\frac{3}{3}$.
The genus is monotypic.

Stenoderma rufum Desmarest
Red Fig-eating Bat

1820. *Stenoderma rufa* Desmarest, Mammalogie . . . , p. 117, type from an unknown locality. Not *St[enoderma]. rufus* Oken, 1816; Oken's names are unavailable.
1855. *Artibaeus undatus* Gervais, Mammifères, *in* [Castelnau] Expéd. dans les parties centrales de l'Amér. du Sud . . . , p. 35, pl. 9, fig. 3, type probably is the skull of the holotype of *Stenoderma rufum* (see Anthony, Mem. Amer. Mus. Nat. Hist., n. s., 2(2):354, October 12, 1918).

Characters as for the genus. Greatest length of skull, 23.1; zygomatic breadth, 15.2–15.8; length of upper tooth-row, approximately 6.5.
The only known material, other than the skin and skull on which the original description was based, is a group of fossil fragments from Cueva Catedral, Puerto Rico, recorded by Anthony (1918:352). Not mapped.

Genus **Pygoderma** Peters

1863. *Pygoderma* Peters, Monatsb. preuss. Akad. Wiss., Berlin, p. 83. Type, *Stenoderma (Pygoderma) microdon* Peters [= *Phyllostoma bilabiatum* Wagner].

Length of head and body approximately 61. Skull with deep, parallel-sided, almost cuboidal rostrum; palate short, almost circular; upper incisors grossly unequal in size, inner pair approximately half as high as canine, and outer pair minute.
The genus is monotypic.

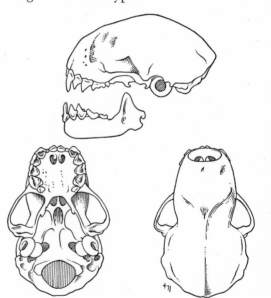

Fig. 103. *Pygoderma bilabiatum*, Sapucay, Paraguay, No. 105685 U.S.N.M., sex ?, X 2.

Pygoderma bilabiatum (Wagner)
Ipanema Bat

1843. *Phyllostoma bilabiatum* Wagner, Arch. Naturgesch., Jahrg. 9, 1:366, type from Ipanema, São Paulo, Brazil.

1865. *P[ygoderma]. bilabiatum,* Peters, Monatsb. preuss. Akad. Wiss., Berlin, p. 357.

Upper parts dark brown, almost blackish, each shoulder with white spot, underparts grayish brown. Other characters as for the genus.

The species occurs from "southern Mexico" (Goodwin, 1946:326) southward into South America. Not mapped.

Genus **Centurio** Gray—Wrinkle-faced Bat

Revised by Rehn, Proc. Acad. Nat. Sci. Philadelphia, 53: 295–302, June 8, 1901.

1842. *Centurio* Gray, Ann. Mag. Nat. Hist., ser. 1, 10:259, December. Type, *Centurio senex* Gray.
1861. *Trichocoryes* H. Allen, Proc. Acad. Nat. Sci. Philadelphia, p. 359. Type, *Centurio mcmurtrii* H. Allen [= *Centurio senex* Gray]. Proposed as a subgenus of *Centurio.*
1866. *Trichocorytes* Gray, Proc. Zool. Soc. London, p. 118, May, an emendation. (Raised to generic rank.)
1897. *Trichocoryctes* Trouessart, Catalogus Mammalium . . . , fasc. 1, p. 164, a *lapsus.*

Length of head and body approximately 61. Skull with high, rounded braincase and exceedingly short rostrum; palate short, approximately half as long as wide; upper canines having anterior basal cavity. No true nose-leaf but face completely covered with wrinkled growths.

The genus is probably monotypic.

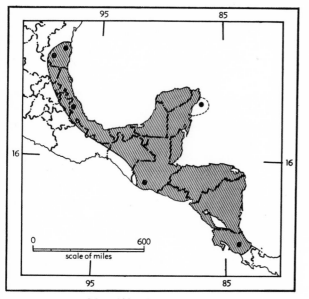

Map 109. *Centurio senex.*

Centurio senex Gray
Wrinkle-faced Bat

1842. *Centurio senex* Gray, Ann. Mag. Nat. Hist., ser. 10, 10:259, December, type locality erroneously given as Amboyna, East Indies; Realejo, Chinandega, Nicaragua,

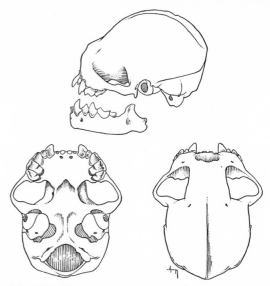

Fig. 104. *Centurio senex,* Mocá, Sololá, Guatemala, No. 41802 C.N.H.M., ♂, X 2.

subsequently suggested by Goodwin (Bull. Amer. Mus. Nat. Hist., 87:327, December 31, 1946).
1854. *Centurio flavogularis* Lichtenstein and Peters, Monatsb. preuss. Akad. Wiss., Berlin, p. 335, type from "Cuba."
1860. *Centurio mexicanus* Saussure, Revue et Mag. Zool., Paris, ser. 2, 12:381, type from "Les regions chaudes du México."
1861. *Centurio mcmurtrii* H. Allen, Proc. Acad. Nat. Sci. Philadelphia, 13:360, November 26, type from Mirador, Veracruz.
1891. *Centurio minor* Ward, Amer. Nat., 25:750, August, type from Cerro de los Pájaros, Las Vigas, Veracruz.

Selected measurements of Guatemalan specimens are: length of forearm, 41.0–43.6; greatest length of skull, 17.4–18.4; interorbital breadth, 4.8–5.4; zygomatic breadth, 14.6–15.3. Upper parts dark or medium brown; underparts appreciably paler.

MARGINAL RECORDS.—Tamaulipas: 14 mi. W and 3 mi. S Piedra (Anderson, 1956:350). Quintana Roo: Cozumel Island (1669 KU). Costa Rica: Cartago (Goodwin, 1946:327). Guatemala: Moca Sololá (Sanborn, 1936:104). Veracruz: Cerro de los Pájaros (Sanborn, 1949:198). Tamaulipas: *Aserradero del Infernillo* (Goodwin, 1954:5); Pano Ayuctle (de la Torre, 1954:114).

SUBFAMILY **PHYLLONYCTERINAE**
Flower Bats

Teeth unusual; upper molars with low, indistinct paracone and metacone at extreme outer edge of crown; protocone low or obsolete, situated at extreme inner margin; intermediate region occupied by wide, shallow groove, angled at middle; lower molars long and narrow, their cusps too indistinct to be identified positively; m1 and usually m2 with distinct median longitudinal groove, their structure almost exactly similar to that in Kiodontinae (a Subfamily of the Pteropidae, Old World fruit bats of the Suborder Megachiroptera); nose-leaf small or rudimentary; rostrum and tongue elongated; the tongue armed with lengthened, bristlelike papillae (after Miller, 1907:172).

KEY TO GENERA OF PHYLLONYCTERINAE

1. Second and 3rd lower molars distinctly cuspidate. . . . . *Erophylla*, p. 147
1'. Second and 3rd lower molars not distinctly cuspidate. . . . . . . *Phyllonycteris*, p. 148

Genus **Erophylla** Miller

1906. *Erophylla* Miller, Proc. Biol. Soc. Washington, 19: 84, June 4. Type, *Phyllonycteris bombifrons* Miller.

Length of head and body approximately 65. Calcar short but distinct; interfemoral membrane narrow; nose-leaf bifid distally; zygomatic arches usually complete; lower molars distinctly cuspidate and with trenchant edge.

The arrangement of species used here is that suggested by G. M. Allen (1917:166).

KEY TO SPECIES OF EROPHYLLA

1. Skull with high, rounded braincase rising from plane of rostrum at a distinct angle; rostrum relatively short, tapered; occurring west of Windward Channel, Greater Antilles.
. . . . *E. bombifrons*, p. 147
1'. Skull with low, flattened braincase not rising above rostral plane at a distinct angle; rostrum relatively long and less narrowed; occurring east of Windward Channel, Greater Antilles. . . . . *E. sezekorni*, p. 148

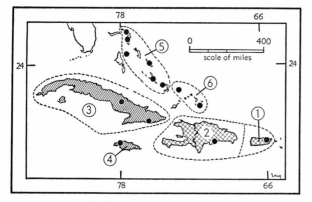

Map 110. *Erophylla bombifrons* and *Erophylla sezekorni*.

1. *E. b. bombifrons*
2. *E. b. santacristobalensis*
3. *E. s. sezekorni*
4. *E. s. syops*
5. *E. s. planifrons*
6. *E. s. mariguanensis*

Erophylla bombifrons
Brown Flower Bat

Selected measurements of the type of *E. b. bombifrons*, a male, are: length of forearm, 48.4; greatest length of skull, 24.4; interorbital breadth, 5; zygomatic breadth, 12; length of upper tooth-row, 8. Upper parts dark brown; slightly paler below. Braincase expanded, high and rounded, rising from rostral plane at definite angle; rostrum relatively short and narrow.

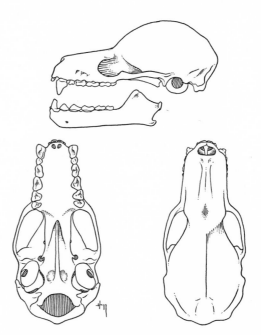

Fig. 105. *Erophylla bombifrons bombifrons*, Cueva Catedral, Puerto Rico, No. 39339 A.M., sex ?, X 2 from Anthony (1918:358).

Erophylla bombifrons bombifrons (Miller)

1899. *Phyllonycteris bombifrons* Miller, Proc. Biol. Soc. Washington, 13:36, May 29, type from cave near Bayamón, Puerto Rico.
1906. *Erophylla bombifrons*, Miller, Proc. Biol. Soc. Washington, 19:84, June 4.

MARGINAL RECORDS.—Puerto Rico: *Cueva de Fari, Pueblo Viejo* (Anthony, 1918:358); type locality.

Erophylla bombifrons santacristobalensis (Elliot)

1905. *Phyllonycteris santa-cristobalensis* Elliot, Proc. Biol. Soc. Washington, 18:236, December 9, type from San Cristóbal, Dominican Republic. Known only from the type locality.
1906. *E[rophylla]. santacristobalensis*, Miller, Proc. Biol. Soc. Washington, 19:84, June 4.

Erophylla sezekorni
Buffy Flower Bat

Selected measurements are: length of forearm, 47–49; greatest length of skull, 24.2–26.4; zygomatic breadth, 11–12; length of upper tooth-row, 7.6–8.0. Upper parts pale yellowish brown or buffy; underparts paler in varying degree. Braincase low, somewhat flattened, not rising above rostral plane at a distinct angle; rostrum relatively long, and broader than in *E. bombifrons*.

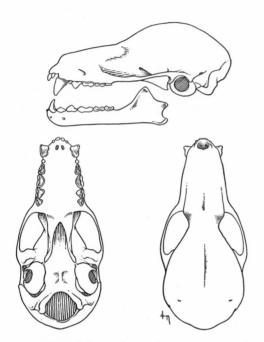

Fig. 106. *Erophylla sezekorni planifrons*, Great Abaco Island, Bahama Islands, No. 5179 K.U., ♀, X 2.

Erophylla sezekorni sezekorni (Gundlach)

1861. *Phyllonycteris sezekorni* Gundlach, Monatsb. preuss. Akad. Wiss., Berlin (for 1860), p. 818, type from Cuba.
1906. *E[rophylla]. sezekorni*, Miller, Proc. Biol. Soc. Washington, 19:84, June 4.

MARGINAL RECORDS (Koopman and Ruibal, 1955:4, unless otherwise noted).—Cuba: *Habana; Las Villas;* 7 km. W Banao; Siboney (Anthony, 1919:641).

Erophylla sezekorni syops G. M. Allen

1917. *Erophylla sezekorni syops* G. M. Allen, Proc. Biol. Soc. Washington, 30:167, October 23, type from Montego Bay, Jamaica. Known only from the type locality.

Erophylla sezekorni planifrons (Miller)

1899. *Phyllonycteris planifrons* Miller, Proc. Biol. Soc. Washington, 13:34, May 29, type from Nassau, New Providence Island, Bahama Islands.

1917. *E[rophylla]. s[ezekorni]. planifrons,* G. M. Allen, Proc. Biol. Soc. Washington, 30:167, October 23.

MARGINAL RECORDS (G. M. Allen, 1911:240, unless otherwise noted).—Bahama Islands: cave near Israel's Point, Great Abaco (G. M. Allen, 1905:70); Marsh Harbor, Great Abaco; Eleuthera Island; Long Island; Crooked Island (Koopman *et al.*, 1957:166); about 6 mi. from Nassau, New Providence (Miller, 1905:382).

Erophylla sezekorni mariguanensis Shamel

1931. *Erophylla planifrons mariguanensis* Shamel, Jour. Washington Acad. Sci., 21:252, June 4, type from Abrahams Hill, Mariguana [= Mayaguana] Island, Bahamas.

MARGINAL RECORDS.—Bahama Islands: type locality; Stubbs Guano Cave, East Caicos (Shamel, 1931:253).

Genus **Phyllonycteris** Gundlach

1861. *Phyllonycteris* Gundlach, Monatsb. preuss. Akad. Wiss., Berlin (for 1860), p. 817. Type, *Phyllonycteris poeyi* Gundlach.
1898. *Reithronycteris* Miller, Proc. Acad. Nat. Sci. Philadelphia, 50:333, August 2. Type, *Reithronycteris aphylla* Miller. Valid as a subgenus (see Koopman, Jour. Mamm., 33:255, May 14, 1952).
1904. *Rhithronycteris* Elliot, Field Columb. Mus., Publ. 95, Zool. Ser., 4:687, July, an invalid emendation.

Rostrum deep; zygomatic arches incomplete; auditory bullae covering more than half surface of cochleae; upper incisors small, inner pair twice size of lateral pair; first upper molar small, low; upper molars longer than broad, basin-shaped; ears moderately large, separate; nose-leaf rudimentary; calcar absent; interfemoral membrane narrow and extending to middle of tibia; tail approximately half length of femur. This genus is known principally from sub-fossil fragments. Dentition, i. $\frac{2}{2}$, c. $\frac{1}{1}$, p. $\frac{2}{2}$, m. $\frac{3}{3}$.

KEY TO SPECIES OF PHYLLONYCTERIS

1. Basicranial region anterior to basioccipital deeply grooved. . . . . . *P. aphylla*, p. 149
1'. Basicranial region normal, not deeply grooved.
   2. Greatest length of skull more than 26.0.
       P. major, p. 149
   2'. Greatest length of skull less than 26.0
      3. Distance from anterior edge of premaxilla to posterior lip of incisive foramen more than 70 per cent of palatal width taken immediately anterior to canine. . . . *P. poeyi*, p. 149
      3'. Distance from anterior edge of premaxilla to posterior lip of incisive foramen less than 70 per cent of palatal width taken immediately anterior to canine. . . . *P. obtusa*, p. 149

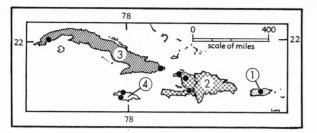

Map 111. Four species of *Phyllonycteris*.

1. *P. major*   3. *P. poeyi*
2. *P. obtusa*   4. *P. aphylla*

Phyllonycteris major Anthony
Puerto Rican Flower Bat

1917. *Phyllonycteris major* Anthony, Bull. Amer. Mus. Nat. Hist., 37:567, September 7, type from Cueva Catedral, near Morovis, Puerto Rico. Known only from the type locality.

Selected cranial measurements are: greatest length, 26.7–28.1; interorbital breadth, 5.5–5.9; length of upper molar series, 6.7–6.8. Skull with long, deep, somewhat tubular rostrum; interorbital constriction slight; braincase high, rounded, but not rising abruptly from rostral plane; palate long, narrowed anteriorly; interpterygoid notch V-shaped, not reaching plane of last molars. Known from skeletal remains only.

Phyllonycteris obtusa Miller
Haitian Flower Bat

1929. *Phyllonycteris obtusa* Miller, Smiths. Miscl. Coll. 81(9):10, March 30, type from Crooked Cave, near Atalaye Plantation, about 4 mi. E St. Michel, Haiti.

Selected measurements of the type and an additional specimen are: greatest length of skull, ——, 22.2; interorbital breadth, 5.6, 5.4; alveolar length of upper molar series, 7.0, 7.2. Resembling *P. major* but distinctive in the shorter relative length of that part of skull anterior to the palatine foramina. Known from skeletal remains only.

MARGINAL RECORDS (Miller, 1929a:11).—Haiti: cave near Port-de-Paix; type locality; cave at Diquini.

Phyllonycteris poeyi Gundlach
Cuban Flower Bat

1861. *Ph[yllonycteris]. poeyi* Gundlach, Monatsb. preuss. Akad. Wiss., Berlin, p. 817, type from Cuba.

Selected measurements of two specimens are: greatest length of skull, 25.7, 24.7; interorbital breadth, 7.3, 6.9; length of upper molar series, 6.1, 5.7. Similar to *P. major* but smaller, narrower brain-

case, relatively weaker dentition, especially 2nd upper premolar. Fur grayish white, hairs of crown and back distinctly washed with clay color at tip, fur of underparts washed with pale cream-buff apically; hairs of silky texture which produces silvery reflections in certain lights; membranes and ears light brown; outermost phalanges and adjacent part of membrane whitish (after Miller, 1904:345).

MARGINAL RECORDS (G. M. Allen, 1911:239).— Cuba: El Guama; Baracoa.

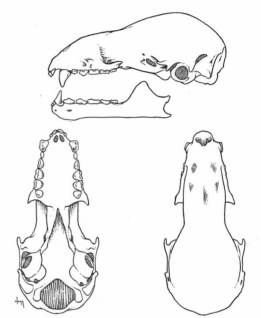

Fig. 107. *Phyllonycteris poeyi*, Guanajay, Cuba, No. 103555 U.S.N.M., ♀, X 2.

Phyllonycteris aphylla (Miller)
Jamaican Flower Bat

1898. *Reithronycteris aphylla* Miller, Proc. Acad. Nat. Sci. Philadelphia, 50:334, August 2, type from Jamaica.
1952. *Phyllonycteris (Reithronycteris) aphylla*, Koopman, Jour. Mamm., 33:257, May 14.

Selected measurements of the type, an adult male, are: length of head and body, approximately 76; total length, 88; length of forearm, 48; greatest length of skull, 26; interorbital breadth, 5.4; length of upper tooth-row, 8. Both upper and lower parts light yellowish brown (specimen in alcohol); fur short. Skull resembling those of other species of *Phyllonycteris* except that basisphenoidal-presphenoidal region is much elevated and that a deep, longitudinal dorsal groove proceeds posteriorly from the roof of the internal nares.

The holotype, now lost, was the only complete specimen known; all other materials are sub-fossil fragments.

MARGINAL RECORDS (Koopman and Williams, 1951: 15–16).—Jamaica: Dairy Cave, St. Ann Parish; Wallingford Cave, St. Elizabeth Parish.

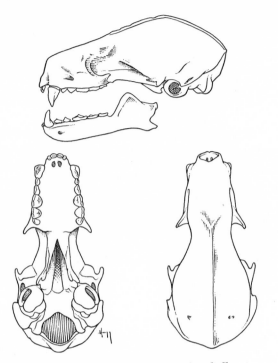

Fig. 108. *Phyllonycteris* (*Reithronycteris*) *aphylla*, ♂, type (after Miller 1907:174), X 2.

FAMILY DESMODONTIDAE
Vampire Bats

Like Phyllostomidae in respect to wing, pectoral girdle, and pelvis, except that tuberosities of humerus more nearly equal in size, and both more distinctly exceed head. Fibula large, extending to head of tibia. All long bones of leg and wing deeply grooved for accommodating muscles, this especially noticeable in tibia, fibula, and femur. Teeth highly specialized for cutting, all trace of crushing surface being absent, and cheek-teeth so reduced that length of entire upper row less than 1.7 times length of canine along alveolus. Stomach a slender caecumlike structure. Nostrils surrounded by dermal outgrowths forming rudimentary nose-leaf (after Miller, 1907:176).

Vampire bats are highly specialized in their feeding, and eat, so far as is known, nothing but fresh blood. The bat's sharp, sickle-shaped anterior teeth shave down, incise, or scoop out a basin in the skin so adroitly that a sleeping victim is seldom disturbed. The oozing or flowing blood is eaten and the wound may bleed for several hours. The bat sometimes consumes prodigious quantities of blood at a meal at which times its body becomes almost globose and the bat is barely capable of flight. When approaching a potential victim, vampires often alight nearby and "walk" to the place on which they feed. When "walking," the bat somewhat resembles a large spider and is, for a bat, surprisingly agile on all fours.

In some tropical areas depredations by vampires on domestic animals make stock raising uneconomical. For the most part such areas are local, however, and domestic animals sometimes live undisturbed in the vicinity of vampire roosting sites. Like most or all mammals, vampire bats contract rabies; these bats have been known to transmit rabies to other mammals by biting them.

KEY TO GENERA OF DESMODONTIDAE

1. Outer lower incisor seven-lobed; lower cheek-teeth 4. . . . . *Diphylla*, p. 151
1'. Outer lower incisors with no more than 2 lobes; lower cheek-teeth 3. . *Desmodus*, p. 150

Genus Desmodus Wied-Neuwied—Vampire Bat

1826. *Desmodus* Wied-Neuwied, Beiträge zur Naturgeschichte von Brasilien, 2:231. Type, *Desmodus rufus* Wied-Neuwied [= *Phyllostoma rotundum* É. Geoffroy St.-Hilaire].
1834–36. *Edostoma* D'Orbigny, Voy. dans l'Amer. Merid., p. viii. Type, *Edostoma cinerea* D'Orbigny.
1905. *Desmodon* Elliot, Field Columb. Mus., Publ. 105, Zool. Ser., 6:530, an invalid emendation.

Braincase broad posteriorly, markedly narrower anteriorly; rostrum extremely reduced, little more than a support for the large incisors and canines; palate deeply concave transversely; auditory bullae covering more than half cochlear surface; upper incisors greatly enlarged, with long, curved, sharp edge; lower incisors minute, bilobed; canines large, sharp-edged posteriorly; cheek-teeth minute, probably non-functional. Ears relatively small, separate, pointed; thumb long, having distinct basal pad; calcar reduced to a small nubbin; tail absent. Dentition, i. $\frac{1}{2}$, c. $\frac{1}{1}$, p. $\frac{1}{2}$, m. $\frac{1}{1}$. The genus is monotypic.

Desmodus rotundus—Vampire Bat

Selected measurements of a male and female from Costa Rica are, respectively: length of head and body, 86, 80; length of forearm, 59.5, 63.0; greatest length of skull, 25.8, 25.0; interorbital breadth, 6.0, 5.3; zygomatic breadth, 12.7, 11.5. Upper parts dark grayish brown, palest anteriorly; underparts paler, sometimes with faint buffy wash.

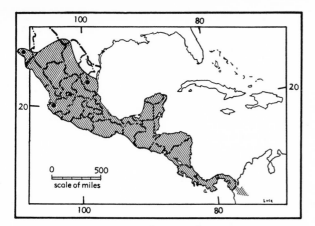

Map 112. *Desmodus rotundus murinus.*

The common vampire is normally a cave dweller but on occasion lives in hollow trees, old wells, and abandoned buildings. These bats often roost in great compact clusters; the acrid ammoniacal odor from the pool of liquid excreta below can be detected many yards away. At other places individual bats may be dispersed separately about the walls of a cave. Dalquest (MS) found no indication of a seasonal reproductive cycle in vampires in Veracruz.

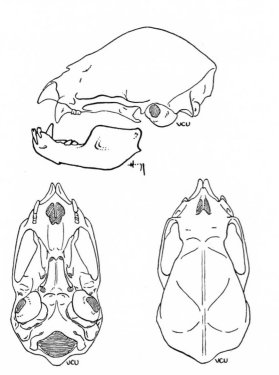

Fig. 109. *Desmodus rotundus,* 3 km. W Boca del Río, 10 ft., Veracruz, No. 23755 K.U., ♀, X 2.

Desmodus rotundus murinus Wagner

1840. *D[esmodus]. murinus* Wagner, *in* Schreber, Die Säugthiere . . . , Suppl., 1:377, type from México.
1912. *Desmodus rotundus murinus,* Osgood, Field Mus. Nat. Hist., Publ. 155, Zool. Ser., 10:63, January 10.

MARGINAL RECORDS.—Sonora: Pótam (Málaga Alba and Villa R., 1957:539). Tamaulipas: 12 km. W, 8 km. N C. Victoria, approximately 2500 ft. (36941 KU), thence along the Caribbean Coast to South America and then northward on Pacific Coast to Rancho Palo Amarillo [in Nayarit?], near Amatlán de Cañas (J. A. Allen, 1906:262).

Genus **Diphylla** Spix—Hairy-legged Vampire Bat

1823. *Diphylla* Spix, Simiarum et vespertilionum Brasiliensium . . . , p. 68. Type, *Diphylla ecaudata* Spix.
1896. *Haematonycteris* H. Allen, Proc. U.S. Nat. Mus., 18: 777. "Name based on a probably abnormal specimen of *Diphylla*" (Miller, Bull. U.S. Nat. Mus., 57:179, June 29, 1907).

Externally resembling *Desmodus* but usually smaller; ears shorter and rounded; thumb short and lacking basal pad; calcar well formed but small; interorbital region higher, broader; two pairs upper incisors, outer pair being minute; a second pair of molars present above, but much reduced; lower incisors relatively large, inner pair having 4 lobes, and outer pair 7. Dentition, i. $\frac{2}{2}$, c. $\frac{1}{1}$, p. $\frac{1}{2}$, m. $\frac{2}{2}$.

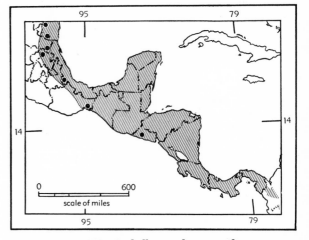

Map 113. *Diphylla ecaudata centralis.*

Diphylla ecaudata
Hairy-legged Vampire Bat

Selected measurements of the type, a male, of *D. e. centralis,* and another male from Honduras, are, respectively: length of head and body, 87, 84; length of forearm, 54.0, 55.4; greatest length of skull, 22.8, 23.1; zygomatic breadth, 12.6, 12.9. Dark brown, somewhat paler on shoulders, nape, and underparts. The genus contains only one species.

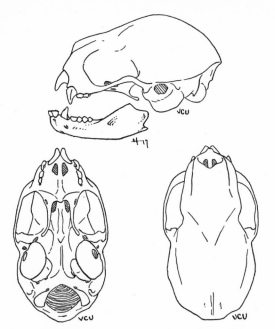

Fig. 110. *Diphylla ecaudata centralis*, 7 km. NW Potrero, 1700 ft., Veracruz, No. 32111 K.U., ♂, X 2.

Diphylla ecaudata centralis Thomas

1903. *Diphylla centralis* Thomas, Ann. Mag. Nat. Hist., ser. 7, 11:378, April, type from Boquete, 4500 ft., Chiriquí, Panamá.
1942. *Diphylla ecaudata centralis*, Goodwin, Bull. Amer. Mus. Nat. Hist., 79:138, May 29.

MARGINAL RECORDS (Málaga Alba and Villa, R., 1957:543, unless otherwise noted).—Tamaulipas: 7½ km. NNW Ciudad Victoria, thence along Caribbean Coast to South America, thence northward along Pacific Coast to El Salvador: Talnique (Felten, 1957:364). Oaxaca: Santa Efigenia. Veracruz: Orizaba. Hidalgo: Jacala. San Luis Potosí: 2 km. WSW Ahuactlán. Tamaulipas: Cueva el Pachón.

FAMILY NATALIDAE—Funnel-eared Bats

Summarized by Dalquest, Jour. Mamm., 31:436–443, November 21, 1950.

Total length usually less than 110; slender, even to wings, legs, tail, and skull. Gray, buffy, yellowish, reddish, or deep chestnut. Fur soft and long; tail inclosed in uropatagium; base of thumb bound to wing by membrane; ears large and funnel-like; large glandlike structure (natalid organ) on face of male. Dentition, i. $\frac{2}{3}$, c. $\frac{1}{1}$, p. $\frac{3}{3}$, m. $\frac{3}{3}$.

Only one genus is currently recognized; *Chilonatalus* and *Nyctiellus* are accorded subgeneric rank.

Genus Natalus Gray—Funnel-eared Bats

1838. *Natalus* Gray, Mag. Zool. Bot., 2:496, December. Type, *Natalus stramineus* Gray.

1855. *Spectrellum* Gervais, Mammifères, *in* [Castelnau] Expéd. dans les partes centrales de l'Amér. du Sud . . . , pt. 7, p. 51. Type, *Spectrellum macrourum* Gervais.
1855. *Nyctiellus* Gervais, Mammifères, *in* [Castelnau] Expéd. dans les partes centrales de l'Amér. du Sud . . . , pt. 7, p. 84. Type, *Vespertilio lepidus* Gervais. Valid as a subgenus.
1898. *Chilonatalus* Miller, Proc. Acad. Nat. Sci. Philadelphia, 50:326, July 12. Type, *Natalus micropus* Dobson. Valid as a subgenus.
1906. *Phodotes* Miller, Proc. Biol. Soc. Washington, 19:85, June 4. Type, *Natalus tumidirostris* Miller.

Characters as for the family.

KEY TO SUBGENERA OF NATALUS

1. Braincase rounded; lower lip grooved or cleft.
  2. Rostrum tipped downward; lower lip with shallow invagination; length of tibia approximately 59 per cent of length of forearm. . . . . *Natalus*, p. 152
  2'. Rostrum tipped upward; lower lip deeply grooved; length of tibia approximately 50 per cent of length of forearm.
             Chilonatalus, p. 154
1'. Braincase flattened; lower lip entire.
             Nyctiellus, p. 154

Subgenus Natalus Gray

Braincase rounded; rostrum tipped downward; dentition normal for the genus; duct area of pararhinal glands forming generally swollen area on muzzle; natalid organ large, bell-shaped, covering facial area; lower lip with shallow invagination; ears large, straight beyond median lobe; tibia approximately 59 per cent of length of forearm.

KEY TO NORTH AMERICAN SPECIES OF SUBGENUS NATALUS

1. Occurring on Antillean Islands; total length usually exceeding 107; greatest length of skull usually exceeding 17.
  2. Length of forearm exceeding 41.7; length of upper tooth-row exceeding 7.8.
    3. Length of mandible more than 14.
             N. primus, p. 154
    3'. Length of mandible less than 14.
             N. major, p. 153
  2'. Length of forearm less than 41.7; length of upper tooth-row less than 7.8.
             N. dominicensis, p. 154
1'. Not occurring on Antillean Islands; total length usually less than 107; greatest length of skull usually less than 17. *N. mexicanus*, p. 153

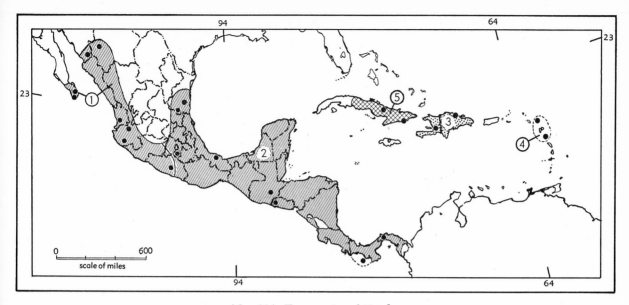

Map 114. Four species of *Natalus*.

| Guide to kinds | 2. *N. mexicanus saturatus* | 4. *N. dominicensis* |
| 1. *N. mexicanus mexicanus* | 3. *N. major* | 5. *N. primus* |

Natalus mexicanus
Mexican Funnel-eared Bat

Length of head and body approximately 50; total length, 93–105; length of forearm, 35.0–39.2; greatest length of skull, 16.0–16.6; interorbital breadth, 3.0–3.2; zygomatic breadth, 8.0–8.4; length of upper tooth-row, 6.7–7.0. Two color phases are known; in light phase upper parts buffy to pinkish-cinnamon, in dark phase rich yellowish- or reddish-brown; underparts paler. Skull long, narrow; braincase rounded, rising abruptly from rostrum.

These bats are insectivorous cave dwellers. Often they are associated with other species and are not shy; even the noise of shooting in caves does not induce these bats to take flight as soon as do most other species.

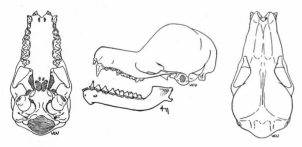

Fig. 111. *Natalus mexicanus saturatus*, 3 km. E San Andrés, Tuxtla, 1000 ft. Veracruz, No. 23815 K.U., ♂, X 2.

Natalus mexicanus mexicanus Miller

1902. *Natalus mexicanus* Miller, Proc. Acad. Nat. Sci. Philadelphia, 54:399, September 12, type from Santa Anita, Baja California.

MARGINAL RECORDS (Dalquest and Hall, 1949:153–154, except as noted).—Chihuahua: Mojaráchic. Jalisco: Itzatlán [= Etzatlán]. Guerrero: 4 mi. N Colotlipa, 3000 ft. (Lukens and Davis, 1957:12). Jalisco: 5 mi. S, 1 mi. E El Arado (31961 KU). Nayarit: 6 mi. SSE Las Varas (39620 KU). Sonora: 4 mi. N Alamos. Also Baja California: Las Cuebas; type locality.

Natalus mexicanus saturatus Dalquest and Hall

1949. *Natalus mexicanus saturatus* Dalquest and Hall, Proc. Biol. Soc. Washington, 62:153, August 23, type from 3 km. E San Andrés Tuxtla, 1000 ft., Veracruz.

MARGINAL RECORDS.—Tamaulipas: 14 mi. W and 3 mi. S Piedra (Anderson, 1956:350). Veracruz: type locality, thence southward along Caribbean Coast to Panamá: Chilibrillo Cave, 10 mi. N Pedro Miguel (Hall and Jackson, 1953:646), thence northward along Pacific Coast, including Coiba Island (G. M. Allen, 1935:228), to El Salvador (Felten, 1957:1): *Hda. Santa Rosa; Cueva Hedionda*; Laguna de Guija. Guatemala: Progresso (Goodwin, 1934:14). Morelos (Miller, 1907:184). Tamaulipas: El Pachón (Goodwin, 1954:5).

Natalus major Miller
Large Funnel-eared Bat

1902. *Natalus major* Miller, Proc. Acad. Nat. Sci. Philadelphia, 54:398, September 12, type from near Savaneta, Dominican Republic.

Selected measurements of the type, an adult male, are: length of head and body, 49; total length, 110; length of forearm, 42; greatest length of skull, 18; interorbital breadth, 3.6; zygomatic breadth, 9.6; length of upper tooth-row, 8. Upper parts reddish brown; underparts paler. *N. major* is distinguished from other natalids mainly by larger size.

MARGINAL RECORDS.—Dominican Republic: type locality. Haiti: Port au Prince (Sanborn, 1941:380).

Natalus dominicensis Shamel
Dominican Funnel-eared Bat

1928. *Natalus dominicensis* Shamel, Proc. Biol. Soc. Washington, 41:67, March 16, type from Dominica, Lesser Antilles.

Length of head and body of the type, 48. Selected measurements of 4 skulls are: condylobasal length, 15.4–16.0; width of braincase, 8.0–8.2; length of upper tooth-row, 7.2–7.5. Known specimens are in alcohol; their color is dark reddish brown above and paler below.

MARGINAL RECORDS.—Lesser Antilles: Antigua (G. M. Allen, 1942a:29); type locality.

Natalus primus Anthony
Cuban Funnel-eared Bat

1919. *Natalus primus* Anthony, Bull. Amer. Mus. Nat. Hist., 41:642, December 30, type from Cueva de los Indios, Daiquirí, Cuba.

Measurements of the type, a partly edentulous right mandibular ramus, are: greatest length, 14.4; depth at level of first molar, 1.5. This species is known only from skeletal material, and is thought to be extinct.

MARGINAL RECORDS (Koopman and Ruibal, 1955:4).—Cuba: *Las Villas*; 7 km. W Banao; type locality.

Subgenus Nyctiellus Gervais

1855. *Nyctiellus* Gervais, Mammifères, *in* [Castelnau] Expéd. dans les partes centrales de l'Amér. du Sud . . . , pt. 7, p. 84. Type, V*espertilio lepidus* Gervais.

Braincase flattened; rostrum tipped downward; first premolars and canines reduced in size; duct area of pararhinal glands forming broad, low swelling on muzzle distally; natalid organ small, rounded, on median part of muzzle; lower lip entire; ears relatively small, constricted beyond median lobe; tibia approximately 47 per cent of length of forearm.

The subgenus is monotypic.

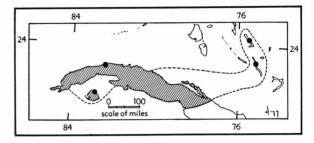

Map 115. *Natalus lepidus.*

Natalus lepidus (Gervais)
Gervais' Long-legged Bat

1837. *Vespertilio lepidus* Gervais, L'Institut, Paris, 5(218):253, August, type from Cuba.
1884. *Natalus lepidus*, True, Proc. U.S. Nat. Mus., 7(App. Circ. 29):603, November 29.

Selected measurements are: length of forearm, 27.3–30.4; greatest length of skull, 13.0–13.5; interorbital breadth, 2.5–2.8; zygomatic breadth, 6.2–6.5; length of upper tooth-row, 5.1–5.4. Pelage buffy or yellowish washed above with brown. Other characters as for the subgenus.

MARGINAL RECORDS (G. M. Allen and Sanborn, 1937:227, unless otherwise noted).—Bahama Islands: Sheep Hill Cave, Cat Island; Miller's Cave and Mortimer's, Long Island. Isle of Pines: Nueva Gerona (Miller, 1904:340). Cuba: *near Havana*; Almendarez, Havana.

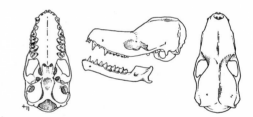

Fig. 112. *Natalus lepidus*, Long Island, Bahama Islands, No. 44535 C.N.H.M., ♂, X 2.

Subgenus Chilonatalus Miller

1898. *Chilonatalus* Miller, Proc. Acad. Nat. Sci. Philadelphia, 50:326, July 12. Type, *Natalus micropus* Dobson.

Length of head and body, approximately 42. Braincase rounded; rostrum tipped upward; dentition as in subgenus *Natalus*; duct area of pararhinal glands forming high swelling on muzzle distally; natalid organ of medium size, rounded, situated at base of muzzle; lower lip deeply grooved; ears large, truncated to 30° angle beyond median lobe; tibia approximately 50 per cent of length of forearm.

A study of the published descriptions of the nominal species of this subgenus leads us to suspect that they are all, at best, only subspecies of one species.

At any rate, the characters employed to distinguish between the named kinds are essentially of a minor quantitative nature and by no means trenchant. For the purposes of this report, it seems best to identify them only on the basis of their geographic occurrence.

GEOGRAPHIC OCCURRENCE OF NOMINAL SPECIES OF SUBGENUS CHILONATALUS

1. Old Providence Island, Caribbean Sea.
                                        N. brevimanus, p. 155
2. Cuba. . . . . *N. macer*, p. 155
3. Jamaica. . . . . *N. micropus*, p. 155
4. Watling Island, Bahamas. *N. tumidifrons*, p. 155

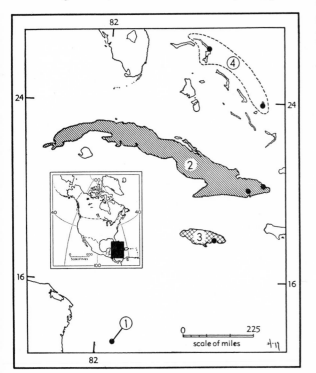

Map 116. Four species of *Natalus* (subgenus *Chilonatalus*).

    1. *N. brevimanus*   3. *N. micropus*
    2. *N. macer*   4. *N. tumidifrons*

Natalus brevimanus Miller
Providence Long-legged Bat

1898. *Natalus (Chilonatalus) brevimanus* Miller, Proc. Acad. Nat. Sci. Philadelphia, 50:328, July 12, type from Old Providence Island, off Caribbean Coast of Nicaragua. Known only from the type locality.

Selected measurements are: length of forearm, 31.0–33.4; length of tibia, 15–16. Miller (1898:328) states that this species is slightly smaller than *N. micropus* and has relatively longer ears and shorter fingers.

Natalus macer (Miller)
Cuban Long-legged Bat

1914. *Chilonatalus macer* Miller, Proc. Biol. Soc. Washington, 27:225, December 29, type from Baracoa, Oriente, Cuba.
1950. *Natalus macer*, Dalquest, Jour. Mamm., 31:443, November 21.

Selected measurements of the type, a female, and one topotype are, respectively: length of forearm, 32, 32; length of tibia, 18, 18; interorbital breadth, 2.8, 2.6; zygomatic breadth, 6.8, 6.8; length of upper tooth-row, 6.0, 6.0; breadth of braincase, 6.0, 6.0. Described as differing from *N. micropus* in longer tibia, and more elongate rostrum. Upper parts cinnamon-buff washed with brown; underparts approximately pinkish buff.

MARGINAL RECORDS.—Cuba: type locality; Guantanamo (Miller, 1914:226).

Natalus micropus Dobson
Jamaican Long-legged Bat

1880. *Natalus micropus* Dobson, Proc. Zool. Soc. London, p. 443, October, type from Kingston, Jamaica. Known only from the type locality.

Selected measurements are (numbers in parentheses are numbers of specimens measured): Length of forearm, 32–34 (3); length of tibia, 15.5–18.0 (4); breadth of braincase, 6.0 (2).

Natalus tumidifrons (Miller)
Bahaman Long-legged Bat

1903. *Chilonatalus tumidifrons* Miller, Proc. Biol. Soc. Washington, 16:119, September 30, type from Watling Island, Bahamas.
1950. *Natalus tumidifrons*, Dalquest, Jour. Mamm., 31:443, November 21.

Selected measurements of the type, an adult male, are: length of forearm, 32; length of tibia, 18; greatest length of skull, 15.8; zygomatic breadth, 7.4; length of upper tooth-row (alveoli), 18.0. Upper parts creamy buff washed with dark brown;

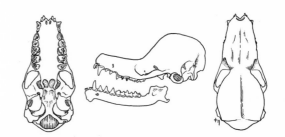

Fig. 113. *Natalus tumidifrons*, Watling Island, Bahama Islands, No. 122021 U.S.N.M., ♂, X 2.

underparts creamy buff. "Except for their greater size the skull and teeth do not differ appreciably from those of *Chilonatalus micropus*" (Miller, 1903: 120).

MARGINAL RECORDS.—Bahama Islands: Great Abaco Island (G. M. Allen, 1911:242); type locality.

FAMILY THYROPTERIDAE—Disk-winged Bats

"Shoulder joint and wing as in the Natalidae, except that trochiter is distinctly larger than trochin, second finger is reduced to a rudimentary metacarpal less than half as long as that of third finger, there are three bony phalanges in third digit, and first phalanx of thumb bears a large sucking disk, . . . foot abnormal, the toes with only two phalanges each, the third and fourth digits, together with their claws, anchylosed together from base to tip; fibula reduced to a minute osseous thread closely applied to the tibia and disappearing about midway between heel and knee; sole with well-developed sucking disk attached to metatarsals; pelvis not essentially abnormal, but with very small pectineal process, and with obturator foramen much reduced by bony outgrowth from its sides . . . , ischia wide apart posteriorly, a symphysis pubis in males, sacrum with the posterior two vertebrae distinct, the others fused; . . . skull without postorbital processes, much as in the Natalidae, the braincase large, smooth, and rounded, the rostrum slender and weak; premaxillaries complete, the very slender and easily broken palatal branches isolating two foramina; teeth normal, not essentially different from those of the Natalidae; ear, tragus, and muzzle as in *Natalus*" (Miller, 1907:191).

The family contains but a single genus.

Genus **Thyroptera** Spix—Disk-winged Bats

1823. *Thyroptera* Spix, Simiarum et vespertilionum Brasiliensium . . . , p. 61. Type, *Thyroptera tricolor* Spix.
1854. *Hyonycteris* Lichtenstein and Peters, Monatsb. preuss. Akad. Wiss., Berlin, p. 335. Type, *Hyonycteris discifera* Lichtenstein and Peters.

Braincase approximately 1½ times length of rostrum, rising at angle of about 50° from dorsal plane of rostrum; rostrum reduced; interorbital constriction pronounced; palate abruptly narrowed behind tooth-rows; auditory bullae small, covering less than half surface of cochleae; resembling *Natalus* externally but legs and tail not elongated, adhesive disks present on thumb and sole, and muzzle with small wartlike excrescence above nostrils. Dentition, i. $\frac{2}{3}$, c. $\frac{1}{1}$, p. $\frac{3}{3}$, m. $\frac{3}{3}$.

KEY TO SPECIES OF THYROPTERA

1. Underparts white or pale yellowish; ears blackish; calcar with two cartilaginous projections extending into posterolateral border of membrane. . . . . . . *T. tricolor*, p. 157
1'. Underparts brown; ears yellowish; calcar with one cartilaginous projection extending into posterolateral border of membrane.
T. discifera, p. 156

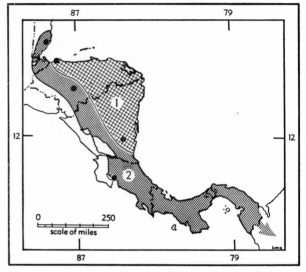

Map 117. *Thyroptera discifera discifera* (1) and *Thyroptera tricolor albigula* (2).

Thyroptera discifera
Honduran Disk-winged Bat

Selected measurements of a female from Nicaragua are: total length, 66; tail, 26; forearm, 31. Upper parts reddish brown; underparts slightly paler than back.

Only the nominate subspecies occurs within the geographic scope of this work.

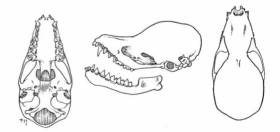

Fig. 114. *Thyroptera discifera* (*discifera?*) Loreto, Cumeria, Peru, No. 46160 C.N.H.M., ♂, X 2.

Thyroptera discifera discifera (Lichtenstein and Peters)

1854. *Hyonycteris discifera* Lichtenstein and Peters, Monatsb. preuss. Akad. Wiss., Berlin, p. 336, type from Puerto Caballos, Cortés, Honduras.

1865. *Th[yroptera]. discifera*, Peters, Monatsb. preuss. Akad. Wiss., Berlin, p. 581.

MARGINAL RECORDS.—Honduras: type locality. Nicaragua: Escondido River (Goodwin, 1946:330).

Thyroptera tricolor
Spix's Disk-winged Bat

Length of head and body, approximately 34–52; length of forearm, 32.0–38.0; greatest length of skull, 14.4–15.1; interorbital breadth, 2.6–2.9; zygomatic breadth, 7.1–7.6; length of upper tooth-row, 5.6–6.7. Upper parts reddish brown or somewhat darker; underparts white, but lateral extent of white area variable. Ears smaller than in *T. discifera*; calcar having two cartilaginous projections rather than one; braincase higher, more globose; teeth larger.

These bats are insectivorous and usually roost individually. The suctorial disks are used for clinging to smooth surfaces.

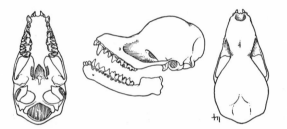

Fig. 115. *Thyroptera tricolor* (subsp. *albigula*), San José, Cauca, Colombia, No. 31678 A.M., ♀, X 2.

Thyroptera tricolor albigula G. M. Allen

1923. *Thyroptera tricolor albigula* G. M. Allen, Proc. New England Zool. Club, 9:1, December 10, type from Gutiérrez, in mountains about 25 mi. inland from Chiriquiscito, on trail from Chiriquí Lagoon to Boquete, Chiriquí, Panamá.
1931. *Thyroptera tricolor albiventer* Dunn, Jour. Mamm., 12:430, November 11, a *lapsus*.

MARGINAL RECORDS.—British Honduras: South Stann Creek, 15 mi. W All Pines (Sanborn, 1941:382). Honduras: San Marcos de Guaymaco (Goodwin, 1942:140). Costa Rica: Esparta, Puntarenas (Goodwin, 1946:331), thence southward to South America.

FAMILY VESPERTILIONIDAE
Vespertilionid Bats

American members of the genus revised by Miller, N. Amer. Fauna, 13:1–135, 3 pls., 40 figs. in text, October 16, 1897.

"Humerus with trochiter . . . noticeably larger than trochin and projecting distinctly beyond head, its surface of . . . [impingement] on scapula de-cidedly more than half as large as glenoid fossa, . . . capitellum scarcely out of line with shaft; ulna usually fused with radius at its head, the shaft reduced to a scarcely ossified fibrous strand; second finger with fully developed metacarpal and one small bony phalanx; . . . shoulder girdle strictly normal in its general structure, . . . foot normal; fibula thread-like, complete or with upper extremity cartilaginous, extending to head of tibia; . . . skull without postorbital processes; premaxillaries without palatal branches, the palate widely emarginate anteriorly; palate abruptly narrowed behind tooth-rows, the sides of its posterior extension parallel or nearly so; teeth usually normal, though in a few genera showing a tendency to reduction of the cusps; ears usually though not invariably separate, the anterior border with distinct basal lobe (except in Tomopeatinae); tragus usually well developed, simple; . . . tail well developed, extending to edge of wide interfemoral membrane" (Miller, 1907:195–196).

Most bats found north of Mexico are vespertilionids; hence the name "common bats." Vespertilionids are not, however, the most common bats of Mexico and Central America. This family, nevertheless, is almost world-wide in distribution, being absent only from Arctic and Antarctic regions and from certain oceanic islands.

Vespertilionids are insect-eaters. Locally they are at times as numerous as birds. Their nocturnal feeding complements the diurnal feeding of most birds.

KEY TO NORTH AMERICAN SUBFAMILIES OF VESPERTILIONIDAE

1. Nostrils opening forward beneath a conspicuous horseshoe-shaped ridge or low nose-leaf. . . . . Nyctophilinae, p. 201
1'. Nostrils opening laterally or vertically, the muzzle occasionally with warty elevations, but never with horseshoe-shaped ridge or low nose-leaf. . . . . Vespertilioninae, p. 157

SUBFAMILY VESPERTILIONINAE

Sternum slender, its entire length considerably more than twice greatest width of presternum; median lobe much smaller than body of presternum; 6 ribs connected with sternum; 7th cervical vertebra not fused with first dorsal; scapula with coracoid curved outward; nostrils simple, sometimes tubularly elongated, but never margined by special outgrowths; lower incisors in all known genera 3–3 (after Miller, 1907:197).

This subfamily contains the vast majority of kinds of vespertilionids.

Key to North American Genera of Vespertilioninae

1. Cheek-teeth $\frac{6-6}{9-9}$.
   2. Wing without glands; foot not markedly lengthened (approximately 60 per cent of length of tibia).
         Myotis, p. 158
   2'. Wing with large gland near elbow; foot greatly lengthened (approximately 95 per cent of length of tibia). . . . . *Pizonyx*, p. 178
1'. Cheek-teeth fewer than $\frac{6-6}{6-6}$.
   3. Upper premolars 2–2.
      4. Upper incisors 1–1; metacarpal of 3rd, 4th, and 5th fingers successively much shortened.
            Lasiurus, p. 188
      4'. Upper incisors 2–2; metacarpal of 3rd, 4th, and 5th fingers subequal in length.
         5. Lower premolars 3–3.
            6. Auditory bullae not especially enlarged; rostrum broad, concave on each side above; ear shorter than head. . . . . *Lasionycteris*, p. 179
            6'. Auditory bullae much enlarged; rostrum narrow, evenly convex above; ear much longer than head.
               7. Two distinct lappets or membranous leaves present near mid-line of band connecting bases of ears. . . . . *Idionycteris*, p. 201
               7'. Lappets absent from interauricular connecting band. . . . . . *Corynorhinus*, p. 198
        5'. Lower premolars 2–2.
            8. Lower canine small, its tip unequally bifid; diameter of auditory bulla equal to length of tooth-row exclusive of incisors; ear much longer than head. . . . . . *Euderma*, p. 197
            8'. Lower canine well developed, its tip not bifid; diameter of auditory bulla much less than length of tooth-row; ear not greatly enlarged.
               9. Upper outer incisor approximately equal in size to upper inner incisor; outer upper incisor having a flat or convex surface directed toward canine. . . *Pipistrellus*, p. 180
               9'. Upper outer incisor distinctly larger than upper inner incisor; outer upper incisor having a well-developed concave surface directed toward canine. . . . . *Myotis*, p. 158
  3'. Upper premolars 1–1.
     10. Upper incisors 2–2. . . . . *Eptesicus*, p. 183
     10'. Upper incisors 1–1.
        11. Skull short, deep, depth of braincase including bullae, approximately half greatest length; metacarpal of 3rd, 4th, and 5th fingers successively much shortened. . . *Dasypterus*, p. 193
        11'. Skull normal, depth of braincase including bullae much less than half greatest length; metacarpal of 3rd, 4th, and 5th fingers subequal in length.
           12. Third lower incisor noticeably smaller than 1st or 2nd.
               13. Crown of 3rd lower incisor in line with crowns of 1st and 2nd, the tooth functional. . . . . *Rhogeëssa*, p. 195
               13'. Crown of 3rd lower incisor barely visible under cingulum of canine, the tooth functionless. . . . . *Baeodon*, p. 197
           12'. Third lower incisor as large as 1st or 2nd. . . . . *Nycticeius*, p. 194

Genus **Myotis** Kaup—Mouse-eared Bats

North American species revised by Miller and G. M. Allen, Bull. U.S. Nat. Mus., 144:1–209, May 25, 1928.

1829. *Myotis* Kaup, Skizzirte Entwickelungs-Geschichte und natürliches System der Europäischen Thierwelt, 1:106. Type, *Vespertilio myotis* Borkhausen.
1829. *Nystactes* Kaup, Skizzirte Entwickelungs-Geschichte und natürliches System der Europäischen Thierwelt, 1:108. Type, *Vespertilio bechsteinii* Kuhl. Not *Nystactes* Gloger, 1827, an avian genus.
1830. *Leuconoë* Boie, Isis, p. 256. Type, *Vespertilio daubentonii* Kuhl. Valid as a subgenus.
1841. *Selysius* Bonaparte, Iconografia della fauna Italica . . . , 1:(introd.)3. Type, *Vespertilio mystacinus* Kuhl. Valid as a subgenus.
1841. *Capaccinius* Bonaparte, Iconografia della fauna Italica . . . , 1:1. Type, *Vespertilio capaccinii* Bonaparte.
1842. *Trilatitus* Gray, Ann. Mag. Nat. Hist., ser. 1, 10:258.

Included 3 species: *hasseltii* Temminck; *macellus* Temminck; *blepotis* Temminck [= *Miniopterus schreibersii blepotis*].
1849. *Tralatitus* Gervais, Dict. Univ. Hist. Nat., 13:213, a *lapsus* for *Trilatitus* Gray.
1856. *Brachyotis* Kolenati, Allgem. deutsch. Naturh. Zeit. Dresden, neue Folge, 2:131. Type, *Vespertilio mystacinus* Kuhl. Not *Brachyotis* Gould, 1837, an avian genus.
1856. *Isotus* Kolenati, Allgem. deutsch. Naturh. Zeit. Dresden, neue Folge, 2:131. Type, *Vespertilio nattereri* Kuhl. Valid as a subgenus.
1866. *Tralatitus* Gray, Ann. Mag. Nat. Hist., ser. 3, 17:90, a *lapsus* for *Trilatitus* Gray.
1867. *Pternopterus* Peters, Monatsb. preuss. Akad. Wiss., Berlin, p. 706. Type, *Vespertilio (Pternopterus) lobipes* Peters (?) [= *Vespertilio muricola* Gray].
1870. *Exochurus* Fitzinger, Sitzungsber. k. Akad. Wiss., Wien, 62:75. Included 3 species: *macrodactylus* Temminck; *horsfieldii* Temminck; *macrotarsus* Waterhouse.

1870. *Aeorestes* Fitzinger, Sitzungsber. k. Akad. Wiss., Wien, 62:427. Included 3 species: *villosissimus* É. Geoffroy St.-Hilaire; *albescens* É. Geoffroy St.-Hilaire; *nigricans* Wied-Neuwied.

1870. *Comastes* Fitzinger, Sitzungsber. k. Akad. Wiss., Wien, 62:565. Included 2 species: *Vespertilio capaccinii* Bonaparte; *Vespertilio dasycneme* Boie.

1899. *Euvespertilio* Acloque, Fauna France, Mamm., p. 38. Included *emarginatus* and *murinus* in a composite sense.

1910. *Chrysopteron* Jentink, Notes Leiden Mus., 32:74. Type, *Kerivoula weberi* Jentink. Valid as a subgenus.

1916. *Rickettia* Bianchi, Ann. Mus. Zool., Acad. St. Pétersbourg, 21:77. Type, *Vespertilio* (*Leuconoe*) *rickketti* Thomas. Valid as a subgenus.

1916. *Dichromyotis* Bianchi, Ann. Mus. Zool., Acad. St. Pétersbourg, 21:78. Type, *Vespertilio formosus* Hodgson.

1916. *Paramyotis* Bianchi, Ann. Mus. Zool., Acad. St. Petersburg, 21:79, a renaming of *Nystactes* Kaup, 1829.

Upper incisors well developed, closely crowded, outer distinctly larger than inner, and with crowns higher than long and subterete; inner incisor having distinct posterior secondary cusp; outer incisor, in many species, having well-developed concave surface directed toward canine; outer incisor separated from canine by space not quite equal to diameter of both incisors together. "Lower incisors with crowns about equal in length, forming a continuous, strongly convex row between canines. . . . Canines well developed, simple, with distinct though rather small cingulum. . . . Skull slender and lightly built, without special peculiarities of form, the rostrum nearly as long as braincase. . . . Ear well developed, slender, occasionally rather large; tragus slender and nearly or quite straight." (Miller, 1907: 201–202.) The number of upper premolars varies somewhat, both individually and in different species (notably in *M. occultus* and *M. fortidens*); consequently caution is advisable when identifying any given specimen that might be of this genus. The normal dentition, i. $\frac{2}{3}$, c. $\frac{1}{1}$, p. $\frac{3}{3}$, m. $\frac{3}{3}$

Myotis is almost cosmopolitan and possibly has the widest natural distribution of any genus of non-marine mammal. The various species as now understood present puzzling problems to specialists, some species being distinguishable from each other only by combinations of characters or by characters of degree that are best appreciated by direct comparisons. The drawings of skulls (Figs. 116–132) will be helpful in achieving correct identifications.

KEY TO NORTH AMERICAN SPECIES OF MYOTIS

(Adapted from Miller and G. M. Allen, 1928:34–37)

1. Maxillary cheek-teeth small relative to palatal area; rostrum of skull short (see Figs. 131, 132).
    2. Upper parts blackish washed with whitish. . . . . *M. argentatus*, p. 178
    2'. Upper parts light chocolate washed with pale buff. . . . . *M. albescens*, p. 177
1'. Maxillary cheek-teeth not small relative to palatal area; rostrum of skull not short (see Figs. 116–130).
    3. Combining blackish to dark brown dorsum, head and body less than 50, and occurrence only south from Isthmus of Tehuantepec and in lowlands of Veracruz and southern Tamaulipas.
            M. nigracans, p. 176
    3'. Not combining blackish to dark brown dorsum, head and body less than 50, and occurrence only south from Isthmus of Tehuantepec and in lowlands of Veracruz and southern Tamaulipas.
        4. Underside of wing furred to level of elbow; rostrum short; occipital region much elevated.
            M. volans, p. 171
        4'. Underside of wing not furred to level of elbow; rostrum not short; occiput not much elevated.
            5. Foot small, its length approximately 40 to 46 per cent of that of tibia.
                6. Forearm less than 28. . . . . *M. planiceps*, p. 174
                6'. Forearm more than 28.
                    7. Hairs of back with long shiny tips; 3rd metacarpal shorter than forearm; skull large, with flattened braincase and gradually rising profile. . . . . . *M. subulatus*, p. 175
                    7'. Hairs of back dull-tipped; 3rd metacarpal usually as long as forearm; skull small, with rounded braincase and abruptly rising profile. . . . . . *M. californicus*, p. 173
            5'. Foot normal, its length 48 to 60 per cent of that of tibia.
                8. Wing membrane attached to tarsus; fur of back without obviously darkened basal area; ratio of foot to tibia usually approximately 60. . . . . *M. grisescens*, p. 164
                8'. Wing membrane attached to side of foot; fur of back with obviously darkened basal area; ratio of foot to tibia usually less than 57.
                    9. Fur of back with obviously tricolored pattern; calcar usually with small but evident keel. . . . . *M. sodalis*, p. 171
                    9'. Fur of back not obviously tricolored; calcar usually lacking trace of keel.
                      10. Ear when laid forward extending noticeably beyond tip of muzzle.
                        11. Free border of uropatagium with inconspicuous, scattered, stiff hairs,
                          M. keenii, p. 167

11′. Free border of uropatagium with short but noticeable fringe of stiff hairs.
  12. Length of forearm usually 41–46; ear not exceptionally enlarged; fringe conspicuous.
                M. thysanodes, p. 170
  12′. Length of forearm usually 33–40; ear exceptionally enlarged; fringe not conspicuous.
    13. Braincase noticeably flattened; length of forearm 33–36. . . . . . . *M. milleri*, p. 170
    13′. Braincase not flattened; length of forearm 37–40. . . . . *M. evotis*, p. 168
10′. Ear when laid forward not extending noticeably beyond muzzle.
  14. Cheek-teeth robust, the breadth of upper molars great in comparison to palatal breadth (comparison usually necessary).
    15. Braincase flattened; pelage glossy. . . . . *M. occultus*, p. 167
    15′. Braincase highly arched; pelage dull. . . . . *M. velifer*, p. 165
  14′. Cheek-teeth not robust, the breadth of upper molars not great in comparison to palatal breadth (comparison usually necessary).
    16. Fur dense, wooly; sagittal crest low but always present in adults. . . *M. austroriparius*, p. 164
    16′. Fur long, silky, sagittal crest usually absent in adults.
      17. Length of forearm 32–37; greatest length of skull 13.2–14.2; hairs on back without conspicuously glossy tips. . . . . *M. yumanensis*, p. 162
      17′. Length of forearm 35–40; greatest length of skull 14.3–15.3; hairs of back with conspicuously glossy tips.
        18. Premolars $\frac{3-3}{3-3}$ . . . . *M. lucifugus*, p. 160
        18′. Premolars $\frac{2-2}{2-2}$ . . . . *M. fortidens*, p. 166

Myotis lucifugus
Little Brown Myotis

Length of head and body, 41–54; ear, 11.0–15.5; length of forearm, 34.5–41.0; greatest length of skull, 14.0–15.8; zygomatic breadth, 8.1–9.8; breadth of braincase, 7.0–7.8; length of upper tooth-row, 5.0–5.9. Upper parts cinnamon-buff to dark brown; underparts buffy to pale gray, often with lighter wash; buffy shoulder spot sometimes present; pelage long and silky, individual hairs being shiny (almost having metallic sheen) at tips. Braincase rises gradually from rostrum. Ear when laid forward reaching approximately to nostril; tragus approximately half as high as ear.

This bat is closely associated with, but not restricted to, timbered areas. It roosts singly or in clusters in caves, crevices in rock, holes in trees, behind shutters and in a variety of other situations. This myotis begins its evening flight at a fairly early hour and is sometimes abroad in late afternoon. In autumn these bats seek out caves in which to hibernate and in some regions travel several hundred miles in order to find suitable hibernation quarters.

The single young is born in early summer.

Myotis lucifugus alascensis Miller

1897. *Myotis lucifugus alascensis* Miller, N. Amer. Fauna, 13:63, October 16, type from Sitka, Alaska.

MARGINAL RECORDS (Miller and G. M. Allen, 1928: 49, unless otherwise noted).—Alaska: Mole Harbor, Admiralty Island. British Columbia: Fort St. James (Stanwell-Fletcher and Stanwell-Fletcher, 1943:79); Assiniboine (Anderson, 1947:25). Montana: Corvallis. Oregon: Cornucopia. Washington: Godman Springs. Idaho: Felton Mills (Davis, 1939:111). British Columbia: Okanagan. Washington: Whatcom Pass. Oregon: Bend (V. Bailey, 1936:368). California: Castle Lake; Chews Ridge, Santa Lucia Mts. (Benson, 1949:48), thence along coast and coastal islands to Alaska: type locality. (Cowan and Guiguet, 1956:85, have identified specimens from the Okanagan River Valley of south-central British Columbia as *M. l. carissima* and believe that *M. l. lucifugus* occurs in extreme southeastern British Columbia.)

Fig. 116. *Myotis lucifugus lucifugus*, 1½ mi. E, ¼ mi. N Blue Rapids, Kansas, No. 44694 K.U., ♂, X 2.

Myotis lucifugus carissima Thomas

1904. *Myotis (Leuconoë) carissima* Thomas, Ann. Mag. Nat. Hist., ser. 7, 13:383, May, type from Lake Hotel, Yellowstone National Park, Wyoming.
1917. *Myotis lucifugus carissima*, Cary, N. Amer. Fauna, 42:43, October 3.
1916. *Myotis yumanensis altipetens* H. W. Grinnell, Univ. California Publ. Zool., 17:9, August 23, type from 1 mi. E Merced Lake, 7500 ft., Yosemite National Park, California.
1919. *Myotis albicinctus* G. M. Allen, Jour. Mamm., 1:2, November 28, type from upper limit of timber, 11,000 ft., Mt. Whitney, Tulare Co., California.

Myotis lucifugus

× 1

(V. Bailey, 1936:369). Washington: Vantage (Dalquest, 1938:211). Not found (Miller and G. M. Allen, 1928:52): California: Bluff Lake; Gilmore Lake. Probably not Texas: Fort Hancock (Hall and Dalquest, 1950:585); the pertinent specimen, having an abnormal dentition, now is thought probably to be of the species *Myotis occultus*. Davis (1944: 379), under the name *Myotis lucifugus lucifugus* recorded a specimen (2916 Texas A. and M.) from 5 km. NW Texcoco, state of Mexico, that to one of us (Hall) is indistinguishable from *M. l. carissima*.

Myotis lucifugus lucifugus (Le Conte)

1831. V[*espertilio*]. *lucifugus* Le Conte, *in* McMurtrie, The animal kingdom . . . by the Baron Cuvier, 1:(App.)431, type from Georgia; probably the Le Conte Plantation, near Riceboro, Liberty Co.
1897. *Myotis lucifugus*, Miller, N. Amer. Fauna, 13:59, October 16.
1832. *Vespertilio gryphus* F. Cuvier, Nouv. Ann. Mus. d'Hist. Nat. Paris, 1:15, type from New York.
1832. ? *Vespertilio salarii* F. Cuvier, Nouv. Ann. Mus. d'Hist. Nat. Paris, 1:16, type from New York.
1832. ? *Vespertilio crassus* F. Cuvier, Nouv. Ann. Mus. d'Hist. Nat. Paris, 1:18, type from New York.
1832. *Vespertilio domesticus* Green *in* Doughty, Cabinet of natural history, 2:290, type from western Pennsylvania.
1839. ? *Vespertilio lanceolatus* Wied-Neuwied, Reise in das innere Nord-America . . . , 1:364, footnote, type from Bethlehem, Pennsylvania.
1840. *Vespertilio carolii* Temminck, Monographies de mammalogie . . . , 2:237, based on specimens from Philadelphia and New York.
1841. *Vespertilio Virginianus* Audubon and Bachman, Jour. Acad. Nat. Sci. Philadelphia, ser. 1, 1:93, type from mountains of Virginia.
1860. *Vespertilio brevirostris* Wied-Neuwied, Verzeichniss der, auf Seiner Reise in Nord-America beobachteten Säugethiere, p. 19, type from Freiburg, Pennsylvania.
1864. *Vespertilio affinis* H. Allen, Smiths. Miscl. Coll., 165: 53, figs. 48–50, June, type from Fort Smith, Arkansas.

MARGINAL RECORDS (Miller and G. M. Allen, 1928: 45–46, unless otherwise noted).—Alaska: Fort Yukon (Osgood, 1900b:45). Yukon: Mayo Landing (Rand, 1945b: 14). Mackenzie: Salt River. Quebec: Rupert House. Labrador: Makkovik. Newfoundland: Nicholsville; Bay St. George. Nova Scotia (Smith, 1940:224): Cape North; Halifax. Georgia: type locality (?). Arkansas: 12 mi. NW Hot Springs (Sealander and Young, 1955:24); Fort Smith. Kansas: Double Entrance S Cave (Cockrum, 1952:58). South Dakota: Fort Pierre. North Dakota: Devils Lake (V. Bailey, 1927:214). Alberta: Waterton Lakes National Park (Banfield, 1948:126). British Columbia: Tupper Creek (Cowan, 1939:71); Atlin (Swarth, 1936:400). Alaska: Kodiak Island; Bristol; Nulato (Osgood, 1900b:45). Not found (Miller and G. M. Allen, 1928:46): South Dakota: Cedar Island.

Myotis lucifugus pernox Hollister

1911. *Myotis pernox* Hollister, Smiths. Miscl. Coll., 56(26): 4, December 5, type from Henry House, Alberta.
1943. *Myotis lucifugus pernox*, Crowe, Bull. Amer. Mus. Nat. Hist., 80:395, February 4.

MARGINAL RECORDS (Miller and G. M. Allen, 1928: 52, unless otherwise noted).—Washington: Stehikin (Dalquest, 1938:211); Newport (*ibid.*). Oregon: Baker County. Montana: Corvallis; Cut Bank; Glasgow. North Dakota: 8 mi. N Towner (V. Bailey, 1927:215); Cannon Ball. Nebraska: Agate (Webb and Jones, 1952:274). New Mexico: Sierra Grande. Utah (Durrant, 1952:41): Donkey Lake, 10,000 ft., Boulder Mtn.; Provo. Nevada: W side Ruby Lake, 3 mi. N White Pine Co. line (Hall, 1946:132). California: Lone Pine; Bear Lake, San Bernardino Mts.; Yosemite National Park; Castle Lake. Oregon: Paulina Lake

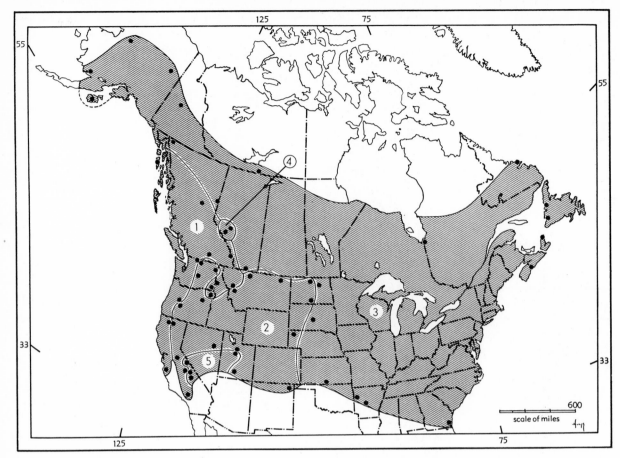

Map 118. *Myotis lucifugus* and subspecies.

Key to subspecies
1. *M. l. alascensis*
2. *M. l. carissima*
3. *M. l. lucifugus*
4. *M. l. pernox*
5. *M. l. phasma*

MARGINAL RECORDS.—Alberta: type locality; Entrance (Anderson, 1947:25).

Myotis lucifugus phasma Miller and G. M. Allen

1928. *Myotis lucifugus phasma* Miller and G. M. Allen, Bull. U.S. Nat. Mus., 144:53, May 25, type from Snake River, south of Sunny Peak, Routt Co., Colorado.

MARGINAL RECORDS.—Utah: Burriston (Durrant, 1952:42). California (von Bloeker, 1943:403): Shepherd Canyon, Argus Mts.; Keeler; Mammoth Lakes.

Myotis yumanensis
Yuma Myotis

Length of head and body, 37.8–49.0; ear, 11.0–14.5; length of forearm, 32.0–38.0; greatest length of skull, 13.0–14.2; zygomatic breadth, 7.8–8.8; breadth of braincase, 6.6–7.5; length of maxillary tooth-row, 4.6–5.2. Upper parts tawny, buffy, or even brown; darker subspecies often with buffy wash; underparts paler, buffy to yellowish white; membranes pale brownish; fur dull, lacking brassy sheen of *lucifugus* except in some specimens of *M. y. satura-tus.* Braincase rising abruptly from level of rostrum; sagittal crest usually absent; foot relatively large, robust; tail barely extending beyond membrane.

M. yumanensis is less restricted to forested areas than is *M. lucifugus* and is found in more open areas. Bats of the species *M. yumanensis* have a wide altitudinal range; they have been taken below sea level and at altitudes near 11,000 ft. They roost singly or in clusters in caves or little-used buildings. One young is usually born in late spring or early summer.

Fig. 117. *Myotis yumanensis yumanensis*, ½ mi. S Pyramid Lake, Nevada, No. 88052 M.V.Z., ♂, X 2.

Myotis yumanensis lambi Benson

1947. *Myotis yumanensis lambi* Benson, Proc. Biol. Soc. Washington, 60:45, May 19, type from San Ignacio, lat. 27° 17′ N, Baja California. Known only from the type locality.

Myotis yumanensis lutosus Miller and G. M. Allen

1928. *Myotis yumanensis lutosus* Miller and G. M. Allen, Bull. U.S. Nat. Mus., 144:72, May 25, type from Pátzcuaro, Michoacán.

MARGINAL RECORDS.—Zacatecas: San Juan Capistrano (Miller and G. M. Allen, 1928:72). San Luis Potosí: Ahualulco (*ibid.*). Hidalgo: Río Tasquillo (Davis, 1944:379). Michoacán: type locality; El Molino (Hall and Villa, 1949:443).

Myotis yumanensis oxalis Dalquest

1947. *Myotis yumanensis oxalis* Dalquest, Amer. Midl. Nat., 38:228, July, type from Oxalis, San Joaquin Valley, Fresno Co., California.

MARGINAL RECORDS (Dalquest, 1947:228).—California: Davis; type locality; Berkeley.

Myotis yumanensis saturatus Miller

1897. *Myotis yumanensis saturatus* Miller, N. Amer. Fauna, 13:68, October 16, type from Hamilton, Skagit Co., Washington.

MARGINAL RECORDS.—British Columbia (Anderson, 1947:26, unless otherwise noted): Princess Royal Island (Cowan and Guiguet, 1956:89); Kimsquit; Shuswap; Kamloops; Okanagan; *Skagit*; Chilliwack. Washington (Dalquest, 1948:151): Goldendale; Hamilton. Oregon: Crooked River (Miller and G. M. Allen, 1928:71). California: Baird (*ibid.*); ½ mi. S Oroville (Dalquest, 1947:229); Lake Alta (*ibid.*); Yosemite Valley (*ibid.*); San Simeon (*ibid.*) thence northward along coast and coastal islands to point of beginning.

Myotis yumanensis sociabilis H. W. Grinnell

1914. *Myotis yumanensis sociabilis* H. W. Grinnell, Univ. California Publ. Zool., 12:318, December 4, type from Old Fort Tejon, Tehachapi Mts., Kern Co., California.

MARGINAL RECORDS (Miller and G. M. Allen, 1928:69, unless otherwise noted).—British Columbia (Anderson, 1947:26): Kamloops; Sicamous; Creston. Montana: Belton; Powderville. Wyoming: Fremont Peak. Idaho: South Fork, Owyhee River (Davis, 1939:113). California: Alturus Lake. Nevada: Calneva (Hall, 1946:135). California: Weldon (Dalquest, 1947:227); San Bernardino Mts.; Lake Hodges, near Escondido (Dalquest, 1947:227); Fresno; *Tahoe City* (Dalquest, 1947:227); Nevada City; Dale's (Grinnell, *et al.*, 1930:455); Beswick. Oregon: Klamath Falls; Lone Rock. Washington (Dalquest, 1948:150): Selah; Stehekin. British Columbia (Anderson, 1947:26): Lehman; Okanagan Landing. Also in Sonora (Burt, 1938:21): Pilares; Guirocoba.

Myotis yumanensis yumanensis (H. Allen)

1864. *Vespertilio yumanensis* H. Allen, Smiths. Misc. Coll., 7(Publ. 165):58, June, type from Old Fort Yuma, Im-

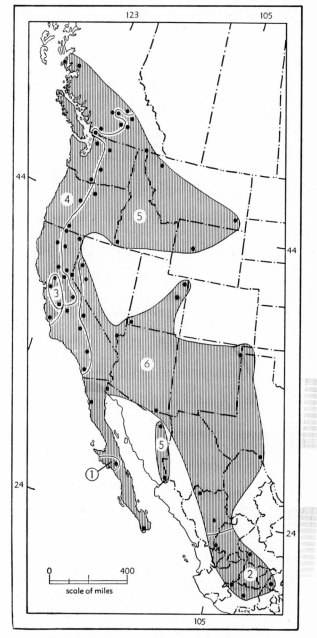

Map 119. *Myotis yumanensis* and subspecies.

1. *M. y. lambi*	3. *M. y. oxalis*	5. *M. y. sociabilis*
2. *M. y. lutosus*	4. *M. y. saturatus*	6. *M. y. yumanensis*

perial Co., California, on right bank of Colorado River, opposite present town of Yuma, Arizona.

1897. *Myotis yumanensis*, Miller, N. Amer. Fauna, 13:66, October 16.

1866. *Vespertilio obscurus* H. Allen, Proc. Acad. Nat. Sci. Philadelphia, p. 281, type from Baja California.

1866. *Vespertilio macropus* H. Allen, Proc. Acad. Nat. Sci. Philadelphia, p. 288, type from Fort Mohave, Colorado River, Arizona. Not *Myotis macropus* Gould, 1854, from Australia.

1903. *Myotis californicus durangae* J. A. Allen, Bull. Amer. Mus. Nat. Hist., 19:612, November 12, type from San Gabriel, Río Sestín, Durango.

MARGINAL RECORDS (Miller and G. M. Allen, 1928: 67–68, unless otherwise noted).—Nevada (Hall, 1946:136): 3 mi. W. Sutcliffe, Pyramid Lake; *E shore Pyramid Lake. 15 mi. N Nixon;* Fallon; Colorado River. Utah: 2 mi. SW Jensen (Krutzsch and Heppenstall, 1955:126); Apex Mine (Durrant, 1952:43); Willow Creek, 25 mi. S Ouray (Durrant, *et al.,* 1955:72). New Mexico: Apache Canyon, near Clayton (V. Bailey, 1932:392). Texas: Del Rio. Durango: San Gabriel; Arroyo de Bucy. Arizona: Huachuca Mts. Sonora: Colonia Lerdo (Burt, 1938:21). Baja California: Cape San Lucas (Benson, 1947:46); Rancho San Antonio (*ibid.*). California: Mt. Whitney.

Myotis austroriparius
Southeastern Myotis

Length of head and body, 45.5–53.0; ear, 12–14; length of forearm, 36.2–41.0; greatest length of skull, 13.9–15.0; zygomatic breadth, 8.4–9.4; breadth of braincase, 6.8–7.6; length of upper tooth-row, 5.0–5.6. Fur thick, wooly; overhairs sparse; upper parts medium orange-brown to light buff-brown, dull; underparts dull buff. Skull slender; low but having complete sagittal crest in adults; otherwise generally resembling that of *M. lucifugus.*

Fig. 118. *Myotis austroriparius austroriparius,* Alachua Co., Florida, No. 9523 K.U., ♀, × 2.

Myotis austroriparius austroriparius (Rhoads)

1897. *Vespertilio lucifugus austroriparius* Rhoads, Proc. Acad. Nat. Sci. Philadelphia, 49:227, May 22, type from Tarpon Springs, Pinellas Co., Florida.
1928. *Myotis austroriparius,* Miller and G. M. Allen, Bull. U.S. Nat. Mus., 144:76, May 25.

MARGINAL RECORDS.—Georgia: Spring Hill Plantation, about 10 mi. SSW Thomasville (Quay, 1949:66). Florida: Gainesville (Sherman, 1937:106); Key West (Hamilton, 1943:79); type locality; Marianna (Sherman, 1937:106).

Myotis austroriparius gatesi Lowery

1943. *Myotis austroriparius gatesi* Lowery, Occas. Pap. Mus. Zool., Louisiana State Univ., 13:219, November 22, type from University Campus, near Baton Rouge, Louisiana.

MARGINAL RECORDS.—Louisiana: Provencal (Lowery, 1943:221); type locality.

Myotis austroriparius mumfordi Rice

1955. *Myotis austroriparius mumfordi* Rice, Quart. Jour. Florida Acad. Sci., 18(1):67, May 17, type from Bronson's Cave, Spring Mill State Park, 3 mi. E Mitchell, Lawrence Co., Indiana.

MARGINAL RECORDS (D. W. Rice, 1955:68).—Indiana: Ray's Cave in Greene County; Bronson's Cave 3 mi. E Mitchell; Saltpeter Cave in Crawford Co. Arkansas: 12 mi. NW Hot Springs. Illinois: ½ mi. N Olive Branch; Cave Spring Cave 2½ mi. S Eichorn.

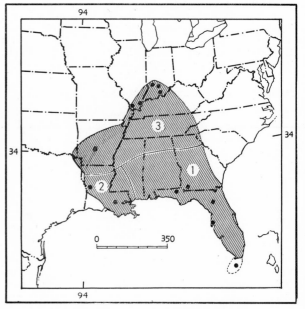

Map 120. *Myotis austroriparius.*

Guide to subspecies
1. *M. a. austroriparius*
2. *M. a. gatesi*
3. *M. a. mumfordi*

Myotis grisescens A. H. Howell
Gray Myotis

1909. *Myotis grisescens* A. H. Howell, Proc. Biol. Soc. Washington, 22:46, March 10, type from Nickajack Cave, near Shellmound, Marion Co., Tennessee.

Length of head and body, 45.4–53.0; ear, 13.0–16.5; length of forearm, 40.6–45.8; greatest length of skull, 15.5–16.4; zygomatic breadth, 9.4–10.2; breadth of braincase, 7.4–8.0; length of upper tooth-row, 5.8–6.2. Hairs of upper parts not markedly darkened basally; upper parts either dusky or russet, but underparts paler and washed with whitish or pale buffy. Skull large; sagittal and lambdoidal crests conspicuous. Wing inserts on tarsus instead of side of foot as in other North American species.

Colonies of gray myotis are found in the same caves in summer and winter, but breeding females seem to congregate apart from the males. A single young, approximately a third the weight of the mother, is born between early June and early July.

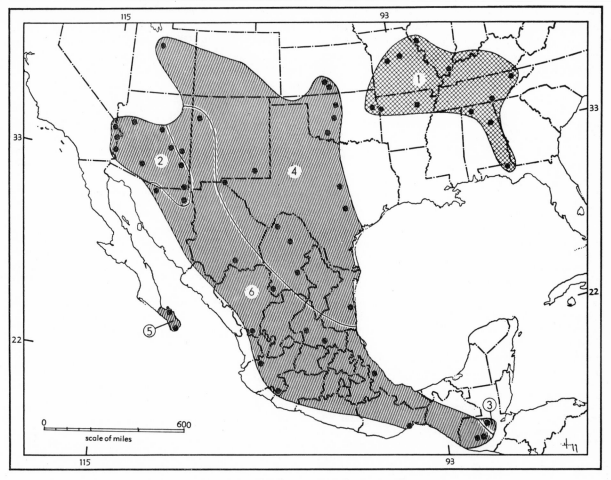

Map 121. *Myotis grisescens* and *Myotis velifer.*

1. *M. grisescens*   3. *M. v. cobanensis*   5. *M. v. peninsularis*
2. *M. v. brevis*   4. *M. v. incautus*   6. *M. v. velifer*

MARGINAL RECORDS.—Illinois: 4 mi. E Nebo (Smith and Parmalee, 1954:201); Cave Spring, 5½ mi. E and ½ mi. N Elizabethtown (Hoffmeister, 1954:2). Indiana: *southern Indiana* (Hamilton, 1943:72). Tennessee: Indian Cave (Bole, 1943:403); type locality. Alabama: Anniston (Miller and G. M. Allen, 1928:83). Florida: Marianna (Rice, 1955:289). Alabama: Saltpetre Cave (Mohr, 1932:272). Arkansas: near Marcella (Sealander and Young, 1955:24); 25 mi.

SW Fayetteville (*op. cit.*:23). Oklahoma: Scraper (Blair, 1939:100). Missouri: Columbus (Miller and G. M. Allen, 1928:83); Rocheport Cave (Guthrie, 1933:15).

Myotis velifer
Cave Myotis

Length of head and body, 44.2–55.0; ear, 13.0–16.6; length of forearm, 36.5–47.0; greatest length of skull, 14.2–17.6; zygomatic breadth, 9.0–11.6; breadth of braincase, 7.0–8.2; length of upper tooth-row, 6.0–7.0. Pelage of back dull, of moderate length; upper parts dull sepia to drab; underparts paler. Skull large, robust; rostrum broad, its area when viewed from above but little less than that of braincase; breadth of maxillary teeth exceeding that of all other North American species of *Myotis*, except *M. occultus*; calcar well developed, terminating in a minute lobule, but not keeled.

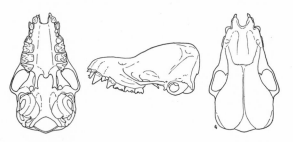

Fig. 119. *Myotis grisescens*, Hunter's Cave (= Kelly Cave), Boone Co., Missouri, No. 63095 M.V.Z., ♂, X 2.

Myotis velifer is typically a colonial cave dweller often congregating in great numbers. Where manmade structures are available for roosting sites, these bats often hang in small groups and are sometimes locally known as house bats.

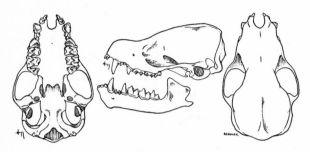

Fig. 120. *Myotis velifer incautus*, Harvard Cave, 4½ mi. SW Sun City, Barber Co., Kansas, No. 9713 K.U., ♂, X 2.

Myotis velifer brevis Vaughan

1954. *Myotis velifer brevis* Vaughan, Univ. Kansas Publ., Mus. Nat. Hist., 7:509, July 23, type from Madera Canyon, 5000 ft., Santa Rita Mts., Pima Co., Arizona.

MARGINAL RECORDS (Vaughan, 1954:512, unless otherwise noted).—Arizona: Big Sandy Creek; Camp Verde; 5 mi. SW Roosevelt; Snow Flat, Graham Mts.; San Bernardino Ranch. Sonora: Santa María Mine, El Tigre Mts. Arizona: Gila Bend; Ehrenburg (on geographic grounds; referred by Miller and G. M. Allen, 1928:91, to *M. v. velifer*). California: Riverside Mts., 35 mi. N Blythe; Needles (on geographic grounds; referred by Stager, 1939:225, to *M. v. velifer*).

Myotis velifer cobanensis Goodwin

1955. *Myotis velifer cobanensis* Goodwin, Amer. Mus. Nov., 1744:2, August 12, type from Cobán, 1305 m., Alta Verapaz, Guatemala. Known only from the type locality.

Myotis velifer incautus (J. A. Allen)

1896. *Vespertilio incautus* J. A. Allen, Bull. Amer. Mus. Nat. Hist., 8:239, November 21, type from San Antonio, Bexar Co., Texas.
1928. *Myotis velifer incautus*, Miller and G. M. Allen, Bull. U.S. Nat. Mus., 144:92, May 25.

MARGINAL RECORDS (Miller and G. M. Allen, 1928: 93, unless otherwise noted).—Utah: Thistle Valley (Durrant, 1952:43). Kansas (Cockrum, 1952:60): Pratt; Harper. Oklahoma (Blair, 1939:99): Enid; Fort Reno; Cache Creek. Texas: Lampasas; New Braunfels. Tamaulipas: Soto la Marina. Coahuila: San Lazaro, 4800 ft., 62 mi. N, 22 mi. W Saltillo (35672 KU); 8 mi. N, 4 mi. W Musquiz, 1800 ft. (44718 KU); 1 mi. N Boquillas, 700 ft. (44711 KU). Texas: El Paso (Taylor and Davis, 1947:14). New Mexico: Carlsbad.

Myotis velifer peninsularis Miller

1898. *Myotis peninsularis* Miller, Ann. Mag. Nat. Hist., ser. 7, 2:124, August, type from San José del Cabo, Baja California.

1928. *Myotis velifer peninsularis,* Miller and G. M. Allen, Bull. U.S. Nat. Mus., 144:93, May 25.

MARGINAL RECORDS.—Baja California: La Paz (Miller and G. M. Allen, 1928:94); type locality.

Myotis velifer velifer (J. A. Allen)

1890. *Vespertilio velifer* J. A. Allen, Bull. Amer. Mus. Nat. Hist., 3:177, December 10, type from Santa Cruz del Valle, Guadalajara, Jalisco.
1897. *Myotis velifer,* Miller, N. Amer. Fauna, 13:56, October 16.
1901. *Myotis californicus jaliscensis* Menegaux, Bull. Mus. Hist. Nat. Paris, 7:321, type from near Lake Zacoalco, Jalisco.

MARGINAL RECORDS (Miller and G. M. Allen, 1928: 91, unless otherwise noted).—New Mexico: Fort Wingate. Chihuahua: 5 mi. E Parral, 5700 ft. (40819 KU). Coahuila: Vallé de Río Aguanaval, La Flor, 4500 ft. (55002 KU). San Luis Potosí: Ahualulco; Río Verde (Dalquest, 1953b: 47). Veracruz: 5 km. N Jalapa (Davis, 1944:378). Guatemala: Ciudad Vieja; Panajachel, Lake Atitlán. Oaxaca: Tehuantepec. Jalisco: Tonila; San Marcos. Durango: Huasamota. Sonora: Saric (Burt, 1938:22). Arizona: Nantan Plateau.—Baker (1956:178) assigned the Coahuilan specimens to *incautus*.

Myotis fortidens Miller and G. M. Allen
Cinnamon Myotis

1928. *Myotis lucifugus fortidens* Miller and G. M. Allen, Bull. U.S. Nat. Mus., 144:54, May 25, type from Teapa, Tabasco.
1950. *Myotis fortidens,* Hall and Dalquest, Univ. Kansas Publ., Mus. Nat. Hist., 1:586, January 20.
1902. *Pipistrellus cinnamomeus* Miller, Proc. Acad. Nat. Sci. Philadelphia, 54:390, September 12, type from Montecristo, Tabasco. Not *Vespertilio cinnamomeus* Wagner, 1855, a renaming of *Vespertilio ruber* É. Geoffroy St.-Hilaire, 1806 [= *Myotis ruber* É. Geoffroy St.-Hilaire, from Paraguay].

Length of head and body, 46.0–53.6; length of forearm, 35.6–38.6; greatest length of skull, 14.8–15.5; zygomatic breadth, 9.4–9.7; breadth of braincase, 6.8–7.4; length of upper tooth-row, 5.4–5.8. Upper parts cinnamon-brown, the hairs black basally; underparts but little paler. In general closely resembling *M. lucifugus* but molariform teeth markedly larger, sagittal crest well developed, zygomatic breadth averaging greater, premolars $\frac{2-2}{2-2}$ ($\frac{3-3}{3-3}$ in *M. lucifugus*). Closely related to *M. occultus*.

Fig. 121. *Myotis fortidens*, 20 km. ENE Jesús Carranza, 200 ft., Veracruz, No. 32112 K.U., ♂, X 2.

MARGINAL RECORDS (Hall and Dalquest, 1950:588). —Sinaloa: Escuinapa. Guerrero: Papayo. Veracruz: 20 km. ENE Jesús Carranza; 20 km. WNW Piedras Negras, thence eastward along coast to Tabasco: Montecristo.

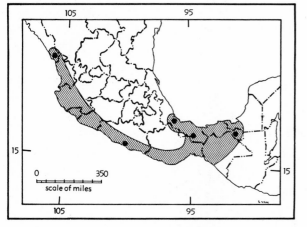

Map 122. *Myotis fortidens.*

Myotis occultus Hollister
Arizona Myotis

1909. *Myotis occultus* Hollister, Proc. Biol. Soc. Washington, 22:43, March 10, type from west side Colorado River, 10 mi. above Needles, San Bernardino Co., California.
1909. *Myotis baileyi* Hollister, Proc. Biol. Soc. Washington, 22:44, March 10, type from base of White Mts., 7500 ft., near Ruidosa, Lincoln Co., New Mexico.

Length of head and body, 43.8–50.4; ear, 11.2–15.0; length of forearm, 33.0–40.6; greatest length of skull, 15.0–16.0; zygomatic breadth, 9.3–10.5; breadth of braincase, 7.0–7.8; length of upper tooth-row, 5.6–6.6. Hairs with burnished tips, giving a glossy appearance; upper parts bright ochraceous tawny; underparts more buffy or sometimes grayish; occasionally olive-brown individuals occur which closely resemble *M. lucifugus* in color. Skull with large rostrum and low, flattened braincase; cheek-teeth enlarged and relatively crowded; premolars $\frac{3}{3}$, $\frac{2}{3}$, or $\frac{2}{2}$ depending on area of origin.

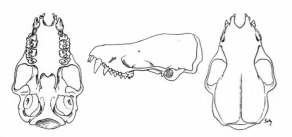

Fig. 122. *Myotis occultus,* 4 mi. S Potholes, Imperial Co., California, No. 10702 M.V.Z., ♀, X 2.

MARGINAL RECORDS (Miller and G. M. Allen, 1928: 100, unless otherwise noted).—Arizona: San Francisco Mts. New Mexico: Bear Ridge, Mt. Sedgwick, Luni Mts.; Ruidosa. Texas: Fort Hancock (recorded as *M. lucifugus carissima* by Hall and Dalquest, 1950:585; re-examination of this abnormal specimen by Hall indicates that it is best referred to *M. occultus*). Sonora: W side Alamos (24849 KU). California: 5 mi. NE Yuma; Riverside Mts. (Stager, 1943:197); type locality.

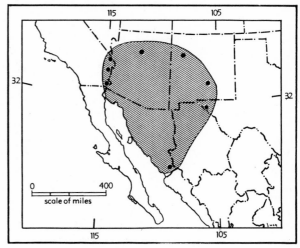

Map 123. *Myotis occultus.*

Myotis keenii
Keen's Myotis

Length of head and body, 40.4–55.0; ear, 14.2–18.6; length of forearm, 34.6–38.8; greatest length of skull, 14.6–15.6; zygomatic breadth, 8.2–9.2; breadth of braincase, 6.8–7.6; length of maxillary tooth-row, 5.4–6.0. Pelage long, silky, dull; color essentially as in *M. lucifugus.* Skull relatively lightly built, slender, sagittal crest sometimes present; length of upper tooth-row slightly exceeds greatest palatal breadth including molars. Metacarpals subequal (not of graded sizes as in *M. lucifugus*); ears relatively long (when laid forward surpassing muzzle by about 4 mm.) and slender.

Myotis keenii is probably more common than specimens in collections would indicate because it roosts singly or in small colonies in obscure places. It usually flies late at night and when roosting is easily awakened. The single young is probably born later than those of most other bats in the United States; Hamilton (1943:78) suggests that parturition takes place in July in the state of New York.

Myotis keenii keenii (Merriam)

1895. *Vespertilio subulatus keenii* Merriam, Amer. Nat., 29: 860, September, type from Massett, Graham Island, Queen Charlotte Islands, British Columbia.

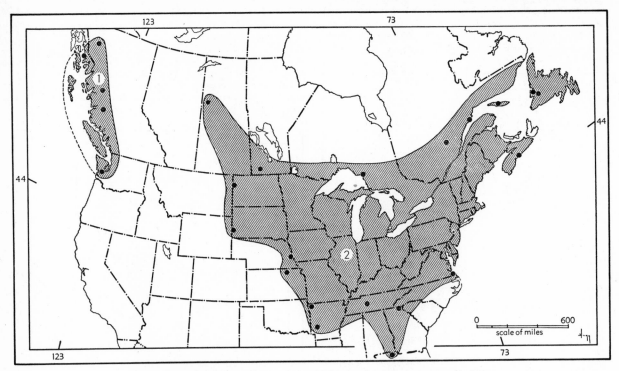

Map 124. *Myotis keenii keenii* (1) and *Myotis keenii septentrionalis* (2).

1928. *Myotis keenii keenii*, Miller and G. M. Allen, Bull. U.S. Nat. Mus., 144:104, May 25.

MARGINAL RECORDS.—British Columbia (Anderson, 1947:26): Telegraph Creek; Telkwa; Stuie. Washington: Lake Cushman (Dalquest, 1948:151), thence up the coast, including coastal islands, to Alaska: Wrangell (Anderson, 1947:26).

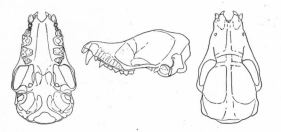

Fig. 123. *Myotis keenii septentrionalis*, Crystal Cave, 5 mi. N Bentonville, Benton Co., Arkansas, No. 83535 M.V.Z., ♀, X 2.

Myotis keenii septentrionalis (Trouessart)

1897. [*Vespertilio gryphus*] var. *septentrionalis* Trouessart, Catalogus mammalium . . . , fasc. 1, p. 131. Type locality, Halifax, Nova Scotia.
1928. *Myotis keenii septentrionalis*, Miller and G. M. Allen, Bull. U.S. Nat. Mus., 144:105, May 25.

MARGINAL RECORDS (Miller and G. M. Allen, 1928: 106–107, unless otherwise noted).—Saskatchewan: Buffalo Narrows, Churchill Lake (Novakowski, 1957:142). Manitoba: Souris (Soper, 1946:135). Ontario: Michipicoten. Quebec: Lake Edward; Godbout; Anticosti Island. Newfoundland: Lewis Hills; Spruce Brook. Nova Scotia: Halifax (Anderson, 1947:26), thence southward along Atlantic Coast to Virginia: Norfolk Co. (Handley and Patton, 1947:116). South Carolina: *northern South Carolina* (Penney, 1950:84). Georgia: Young Harris. Florida: 3 mi. N Marianna (Rice, 1955:567). Tennessee: Hickman County (Kellogg, 1939: 254). Arkansas (Dellinger and Black, 1940:188): Delight; Crystal Cave, 5 mi. N Bentonville. Kansas: 1½ mi. W, ½ mi. N Blue Rapids (Jones, *et al.*, 1952:312). Nebraska: ½ mi. W Meadow (Webb and Jones, 1952:273). South Dakota: Elk Mountain. North Dakota: Fort Buford. Not found: Newfoundland: Romain's Brook. Ontario: Malden.

Myotis evotis
Long-eared Myotis

Length of head and body, 41.6–56.0; ear, 18.0–22.4; length of forearm, 35.5–41.0; greatest length of skull, 15.0–16.4; zygomatic breadth, 8.6–10.1; breadth of braincase, 7.0–8.2; length of maxillary tooth-row, 6.0–6.8. Upper parts light to medium brown, ears conspicuously darker. Skull closely resembling that of *M. keenii*; upper profile curving gradually from rostrum to summit of braincase; sagittal crest often present but never large; braincase viewed from above oval and bulging posteriorly beyond lamboidal ridges. Ear and tragus large, when laid forward ear extends about 7 mm. beyond muzzle; tail membrane usually edged with sparse and inconspicuous fringe of hairs.

The long-eared myotis is an inhabitant of thinly forested to semi-desert areas. Nowhere does it seem to be common. It is not a cave bat and prefers to roost singly or in small clusters in secluded niches of buildings and probably in trees.

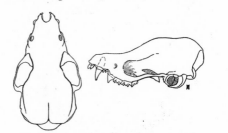

Fig. 124. *Myotis evotis evotis*, Burned Corral Canyon, Nevada, No. 57366 M.V.Z., ♂, X 2.

Myotis evotis auriculus Baker and Stains

1955. *Myotis evotis auriculus* Baker and Stains, Univ. Kansas Publ., Mus. Nat. Hist., 9:83, December 10, type from 10 mi. W and 2 mi. S Piedra, 1200 ft., Sierra de Tamaulipas, Tamaulipas.
1955. *Myotis evotis apache* Hoffmeister and Krutzsch, Nat. Hist. Miscl., Chicago Acad. Sci., 151:1, December 28, type from Snow Flat, 8750 ft., Graham Mts., Graham Co., Arizona. *M. e. apache* is here arranged as a synonym of *M. e. auriculus* because the geographic range ascribed to *apache* by its describers included the geographic range of *auriculus* that was described 18 days earlier. The describers of *auriculus*, however, excluded from its geographic range a specimen from northern Chihuahua and inferentially also all populations of *M. evotis* in Arizona, from which State *apache* was named (its type locality is there). Therefore, *apache* may not be a synonym of *auriculus*.

MARGINAL RECORDS (Hoffmeister and Krutzsch, 1955:3, unless otherwise noted).—Arizona: Cooley Ranch, T. 8½ N, R. 23 E; Chiricahua Mts. New Mexico: Vermejo River (V. Bailey, 1932:389, as *M. e. chrysonotus*). Chihuahua: E side San Luis Mts. Coahuila: 4 mi. W Hda. La Mariposa, 2300 ft. (Baker and Stains, 1955:84). Nuevo León: Iturbide, 5000 ft., (*ibid.*). Tamaulipas: type locality. Veracruz: Perote. Jalisco: Los Masos. Arizona: 30 mi. SE Tucson.

Myotis evotis evotis (H. Allen)

1864. *Vespertilio evotis* H. Allen, Smiths. Miscl. Coll., 7 (Publ. 165):48, June. Type locality, by subsequent restriction, Monterey, California (see Dalquest, Proc. Biol. Soc. Washington, 56:2, February 25, 1943).
1897. *Myotis evotis*, Miller, N. Amer. Fauna, 13:77, October 16.
1896. *Vespertilio chrysonotus* J. A. Allen, Bull. Amer. Mus. Nat. Hist., 8:240, November 21, type from Kinney Ranch, Bitter Creek, Sweetwater Co., Wyoming.
1909. *Myotis micronyx* Nelson and Goldman, Proc. Biol. Soc. Washington, 22:28, March 10, type from Comondú, Baja California.

MARGINAL RECORDS (Miller and G. M. Allen, 1928: 116–118, unless otherwise noted).—Alberta: Red Deer River

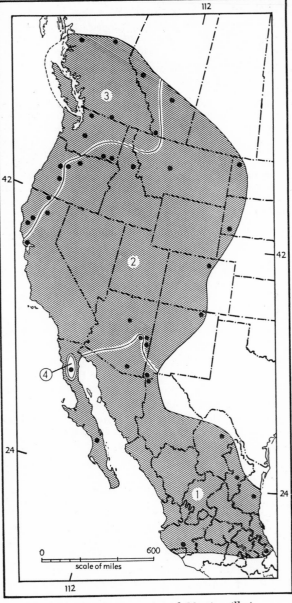

Map 125. *Myotis evotis* and *Myotis milleri*.

1. *M. e. auriculus*   3. *M. e. pacificus*
2. *M. e. evotis*   4. *M. milleri*

near Rumsey (Anderson, 1947:27). North Dakota: Beaver Creek, 4 mi. W Grinnell (V. Bailey, 1927:217). South Dakota: Corral Draw. Colorado: Loveland (Warren, 1942: 20). New Mexico: Vermejo River (V. Bailey, 1932:389). Arizona (Hoffmeister and Krutzsch, 1955:3): 4 mi. S Hannagan Meadow; 25 mi. NE White River; Sunset Crater. Baja California: Comondú, thence northward along Pacific Coast to California: San Rafael; Antelope Creek (Grinnell, *et al.*, 1930:455). Oregon (V. Bailey, 1936:374): Sisters; Fossil. Washington (Dalquest, 1948:153): South Touchet; Godman Springs. Idaho: Selway Falls (Rust, 1946:312). Montana: Big Belt Mts., 4 mi. S Fort Logan.

Myotis evotis pacificus Dalquest

1943. *Myotis evotis pacificus* Dalquest, Proc. Biol. Soc. Washington, 56:2, February 25, type from 3½ mi. E and 5 mi. N Yacolt, 500 ft., Clark Co., Washington.

MARGINAL RECORDS.—British Columbia (Cowan and Guiguet, 1956:80–82): Kimsquit; Summit Lake, near Prince George (as *M. e. evotis*). Alberta (Anderson, 1947: 27): Jasper; Waterton Lakes National Park. British Columbia: Rock Creek (Miller and G. M. Allen, 1928:116). Washington (Dalquest, 1948:153): Baker Lake; Easton. Oregon (V. Bailey, 1936:373): McKenzie Bridge; Fremont. California (Miller and G. M. Allen, 1928:116): Beswick; South Yolla Bolly Mtn.; Mt. Sanhedrin, thence northward along Pacific Coast, including coastal islands, to point of beginning. (Cowan and Guiguet, 1956:80, refer specimens from eastern British Columbia to the subspecies *E. e. evotis*.)

Myotis milleri Elliot
Miller's Myotis

1903. *Myotis milleri* Elliot, Field Columb. Mus., Publ. 74, Zool. Ser., 3:172, May 7, type from La Grulla, Sierra San Pedro Mártir, Baja California. Known definitely only from the type locality.

Length of head and body, 41.2–46.6; ear, 19–20; length of forearm, 34–37; greatest length of skull, 14.8–15.2; zygomatic breadth, 8.8–8.9; breadth of braincase, 7.0–7.2; length of upper tooth-row, 5.4–6.0. "Externally resembling *Myotis evotis* but smaller, . . . brain case less elevated, noticeably flat-topped, the sagittal crest absent in each of the six specimens examined. . . . Teeth small, the crown area of the upper molars equal to that of the upper molars of *M. keenii*. . . . The color does not differ appreciably from that of *Myotis evotis chrysonotus* [= *evotis*]" (Miller and G. M. Allen, 1928:119).

Myotis thysanodes
Fringed Myotis

Length of head and body, 43–52; ear, 16–19; length of forearm, 39.8–46.0; greatest length of skull, 16.2–17.2; zygomatic breadth, 9.2–10.8; breadth of braincase, 7.2–8.2; length of upper tooth-row, 6.0–6.6. Upper parts yellowish brown to darker olivaceous tones; underparts barely, if any, lighter. Skull resembling that of *M. evotis* but larger, more robust, broader; sagittal crest well developed; length of upper tooth-row exceeded by greatest breadth of palate including molars; fringe of short, stiff hairs along free edge of interfemoral membrane well developed; ear large, projecting 3–5 mm. beyond muzzle when laid forward.

This bat is probably a cave-dweller, but most of the known specimens seem to have been obtained from abandoned buildings. Nowhere does it seem to be common.

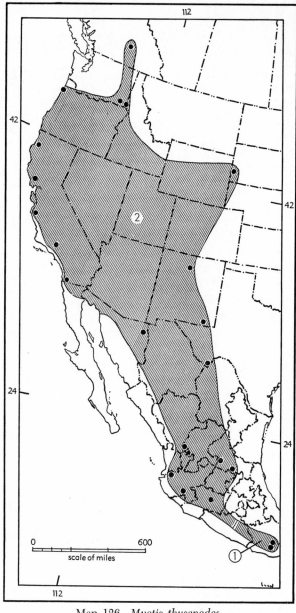

Map 126. *Myotis thysanodes*.

1. *M. t. aztecus*   2. *M. t. thysanodes*

Myotis thysanodes aztecus Miller and G. M. Allen

1928. *Myotis thysanodes aztecus* Miller and G. M. Allen, Bull. U.S. Nat. Mus., 144:128, May 25, type from San Antonio, Oaxaca.

MARGINAL RECORDS.—Oaxaca: type locality; Hda. de Cinco Señores (Miller and G. M. Allen, 1928:128).

Myotis thysanodes thysanodes Miller

1897. *Myotis thysanodes* Miller, N. Amer. Fauna, 13:80, October 16, type from Old Fort Tejon, Tehachapi Mts., Kern Co., California.

MARGINAL RECORDS (Miller and G. M. Allen, 1928: 127, unless otherwise noted).—British Columbia: Vernon (Anderson, 1927:27). Washington: Anatone (Jones and Webb, 1953:122). South Dakota: Jewel Cave (Bole, 1935: 148). New Mexico (V. Bailey, 1932:387): Espanola; Carlsbad. Texas: SE slope Mariscal Mtn. (Borell and Bryant, 1942:8). San Luis Potosí: Hda. La Parada; Hda. Capulín (Dalquest, 1953b:48). Michoacán: Pátzcuaro (Hall and Villa, 1949:444). Jalisco: Los Masos; La Laguna. Zacatecas: Hda. San Juan Capistrano. Sonora: near El Tigre (Burt, 1938:24). California: Dulzura (Grinnell, 1933:88); Lebec (Dalquest and Ramage, 1946:62); Stonewall Creek near Soledad (Grinnell, 1933:88); Howell Mtn. (Longhurst, 1940:246); Willow Creek (Orr, 1957:545). Oregon: Tillamook (Walker, 1942:62). Washington: Blue Mts. (Dalquest, 1938:212). Not found: Idaho: Karney Lake, Boise Co. (Jones and Webb, 1953:122).

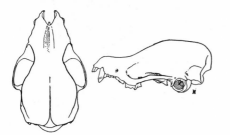

Fig. 125. *Myotis thysanodes thysanodes*, Horse Spring, 4750 ft., San Bernardino Co., California, No. 86119 M.V.Z., ♂, X 2.

Myotis sodalis Miller and G. M. Allen
Indiana Myotis

1928. *Myotis sodalis* Miller and G. M. Allen, Bull. U.S. Nat. Mus., 144:130, May 25, type from Wyandotte Cave, Crawford Co., Indiana.

Length of head and body, 41.4–49.0; ear, 10.4–14.8; length of forearm, 36.0–40.6; greatest length of skull, 14.2–15.0; zygomatic breadth, 8.3–9.3; breadth of braincase, 6.8–7.2; length of tooth-row, 5.2–5.6. Pelage unusually fine and fluffy; upper parts dull grayish chestnut, each hair slightly glossy at tip, basal two-thirds blackish; underparts having general effect of pinkish white; membranes and ears blackish brown. Skull resembling that of *M. lucifugus* but with smaller, narrower, and lower braincase; delicate but complete sagittal crest usually present in adults. Calcar obviously keeled.

This bat has been collected chiefly from hibernating colonies in caves; little is known of its habits.

MARGINAL RECORDS (Griffin, 1940:181, unless otherwise noted).—Vermont: Vershire. Massachusetts: Worcester (Parker, 1939:407). Connecticut: Roxbury. Virginia (Handley and Patton, 1947): Madden's Cave; Nellie's Hole. South Carolina: *upper western tip of state* (Penney, 1950:84). Alabama: Anniston (Miller and G. M. Allen, 1928:133). Florida: Old Indian Cave, 3 mi. N Marianna (Jennings and Layne, 1957:259). Arkansas: near Cushman (Sealander and Young, 1955:24); 25 mi. SW Fayetteville (Sealander and Young, 1955:23). Oklahoma: 5 mi. S Kansas (Glass, 1955:128). Missouri: Rocheport Cave (Folk, 1940:308). Illinois: 8 mi. SE Galena (Smith and Parmalee, 1954:202). Wisconsin: 2¼ mi. W Beetown (Davis, 1955: 567). Michigan: Grosse Isle (Burt, 1946:108). New York: Altamont. Vermont: Brandon (Osgood, 1938:436).

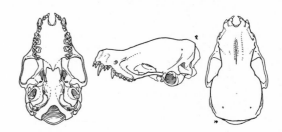

Fig. 126. *Myotis sodalis*, White Rock Camp, ½ mi. E fifty-six, Stone Co., Arkansas, No. 47581 M.V.Z., ♀, X 2.

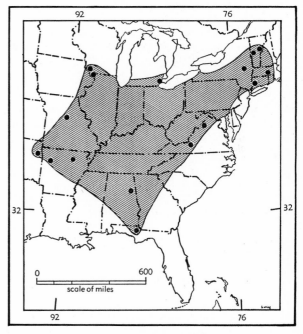

Map 127. *Myotis sodalis.*

Myotis volans
Long-legged Myotis

Length of head and body, 43–54; ear, 11–14; length of forearm, 35.2–41.2; greatest length of skull, 12.2–15.0; zygomatic breadth, 8–9; breadth of braincase, 6.7–7.6; length of upper tooth-row, 4.6–5.6. Pelage long, soft, extending distally on interfemoral membrane for a distance approximately equal to length of femur, extending onto wing below to a line joining elbow and knee; upper parts varying from ochraceous tawny to dark smoky brown; underparts smoky brown to dull yellowish white washed with buffy; tips of hairs above slightly burnished. Skull small, delicate; rostrum short; braincase abruptly elevated from rostral level; occipital region somewhat inflated; sagittal crest low, poorly defined; palatal region resembling that of *M. lucifugus*. Ears low, rounded, barely reaching rostrum when laid forward; foot small; calcar distinctly keeled.

Although the long-legged myotis is fairly common throughout its range, little is known of the habits of this bat. It is seemingly not social in roosting behavior and seems not to frequent caves.

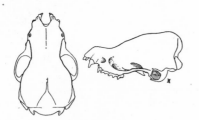

Fig. 127. *Myotis volans interior*, Smiths Creek, 5800 ft., Lander Co., Nevada, No. 63535 M.V.Z., ♂, X 2.

Myotis volans amotus Miller

1914. *Myotis longicrus amotus* Miller, Proc. Biol. Soc. Washington, 27:212, October 31, type from Cofre de Perote, 12,500 ft., Veracruz.
1928. *Myotis volans amotus*, Miller and G. M. Allen, Bull. U.S. Nat. Mus., 144:145, May 25.

MARGINAL RECORDS.—Jalisco: Los Masos (Miller and G. M. Allen, 1928:145). Veracruz: type locality.

Myotis volans interior Miller

1914. *Myotis longicrus interior* Miller, Proc. Biol. Soc. Washington, 27:211, October 31, type from 5 mi. S Twining, 11,300 ft., Taos Co., New Mexico.
1928. *Myotis volans interior*, Miller and G. M. Allen, Bull. U.S. Nat. Mus., 144:142, May 25.

MARGINAL RECORDS (Miller and G. M. Allen, 1928: 143–144, unless otherwise noted).—Idaho: Mission (Davis, 1939:115). Montana: Florence; Buffalo. South Dakota: Bull Springs (Moulthrop, 1936:413). Nebraska: Warbonnet Twp., 8 mi. N Harrison (Webb and Jones, 1952:275). New Mexico: Raton Range (V. Bailey, 1932:375). Texas: 5 mi. E Mt. Livermore (Blair, 1940:21). Coahuila: Club Sierra del Carmen, 4950 ft., 2 mi. N and 6 mi. W Piedra Blanca (35674 KU). Chihuahua: Colonia Garcia. Arizona: Santa Rita Mts. California: Dulzura; San Emigdio; Dudley; Nevada City; Mt. Shasta. Oregon: Fremont (V. Bailey, 1936:376). Washington: Walla Walla (Dalquest, 1948: 156).

Myotis volans longicrus (True)

1886. *Vespertilio longicrus* True, Science, 8:588, December 24, type from vicinity of Puget Sound, Washington.
1911. *Myotis altifrons* Hollister, Smiths. Miscl. Coll., 56(26):3, December 5, type from Henry House, Alberta.
1928. *Myotis volans longicrus*, Miller and G. M. Allen, Bull. U.S. Nat. Mus., 144:140, May 25.

1938. *Myotis ruddi* Silliman and von Bloeker, Proc. Biol. Soc. Washington, 51:167, August 23, type from Lime Kiln Creek, 250 ft., southwestern Santa Lucia Mts., Monterey Co., California.

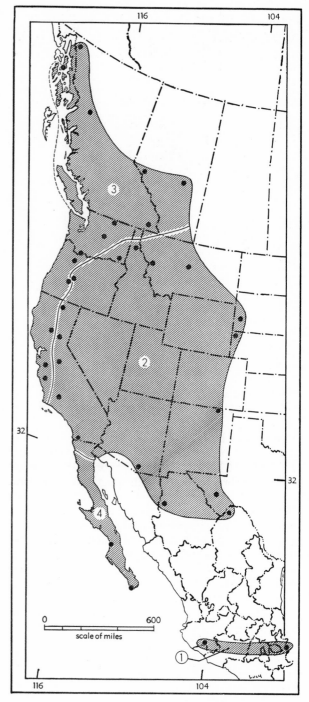

Map 128. *Myotis volans* and subspecies.

1. *M. v. amotus*   3. *M. v. longicrus*
2. *M. v. interior*   4. *M. v. volans*

MARGINAL RECORDS (Miller and G. M. Allen, 1928: 141–142, unless otherwise noted).—British Columbia: S end Atlin Lake (Anderson, 1947:28); Kispiox (Cowan and Guiguet, 1956:87); Hazelton (Swarth, 1924:373). Alberta (Soper, 1947:147): Henry House; Dried Meat Lake, near Camrose. British Columbia: Cranbrook. Washington (Dalquest, 1948:155): Oroville; Entiat; Carson. Oregon (V. Bailey, 1936:375): Estacada; E of Mt. Thielson. California: Hurleton; Pacheco Pass; Priest Valley (Benson, 1950:49), thence northward along coast, including coastal islands, to Alaska: Mole Harbor, Admiralty Island.

Myotis volans volans (H. Allen)

1866. V[espertilio]. volans H. Allen, Proc. Acad. Nat. Sci. Philadelphia, 18:282, type from Cabo San Lucas, Baja California.
1914. Myotis volans, Goldman, Proc. Biol. Soc. Washington, 27:102, May 11.
1909. Myotis capitaneus Nelson and Goldman, Proc. Biol. Soc. Washington, 22:28, March 10, type from San Jorge, 30 mi. SW Comondú, Baja California.

MARGINAL RECORDS.—Baja California: San Jorge (Miller and G. M. Allen, 1928:139); type locality.

Myotis californicus
California Myotis

Length of head and body, 35.0–44.8; ear, 11.2–14.6; length of forearm, 29.0–36.2; greatest length of skull, 12.6–14.2; zygomatic breadth, 7.4–8.6; breadth of braincase, 5.8–7.0; length of upper toothrow, 4.8–5.2. Upper parts brown to distinctly yellowish; underparts usually paler; hairs extending sparingly onto upper side of uropatagium to a line connecting knees, extending half as far on ventral side of membrane. Skull delicate and slender; rostrum relatively long and tapering; braincase rising abruptly from rostral level, flat-topped; sagittal crest obsolete or absent. Ear extending beyond muzzle when laid forward; calcar keeled.

Bats of this species hibernate in caves and old mines. They are principally dwellers of open semi-arid to arid regions. The flight is highly erratic; abrupt changes of direction are both vertical and lateral. The single young is born in late June or July.

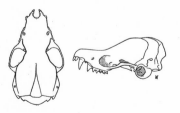

Fig. 128. Myotis californicus stephensi, Cave Spring, Esmeralda Co., Nevada, No. 40519 M.V.Z., ♂, X 2.

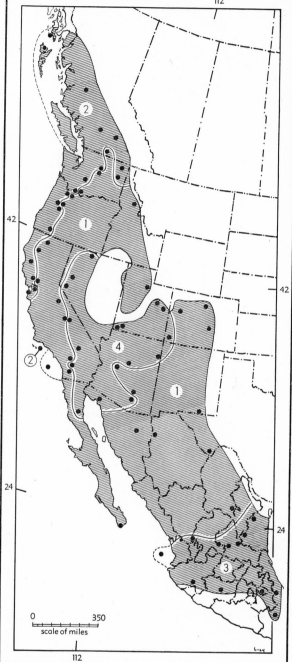

Map 129. Myotis californicus and subspecies.
1. M. c. californicus
2. M. c. caurinus
3. M. c. mexicanus
4. M. c. stephensi

Myotis californicus californicus (Aud. and Bach.)

1842. Vespertilio californicus Audubon and Bachman, Jour. Acad. Nat. Sci. Philadelphia, ser. 1, pt. 2, 8:285, type from "California"; subsequently restricted to Monterey,

Monterey Co., California (see Miller and G. M. Allen, Bull. U.S. Nat. Mus., 144:153, May 25, 1928).

1897. *Myotis californicus,* Miller, N. Amer. Fauna, 13:69, October 16.

1862. *Vespertilio nitidus,* H. Allen, Proc. Acad. Nat. Sci. Philadelphia, p. 247, type from Monterey, California.

1864. *Vespertilio oregonensis* H. Allen, Smiths. Miscl. Coll., 165:61, June, based on specimens from Old Fort Yuma, California, and Cabo San Lucas, Baja California.

1866. *Vespertilio exilis* H. Allen, Proc. Acad. Nat. Sci. Philadelphia, 18:283, type from Cabo San Lucas, Baja California.

1866. *Vespertilio tenuidorsalis* H. Allen, Proc. Acad. Nat. Sci. Philadelphia, 18:283, type from Cabo San Lucas, Baja California.

1914. *Myotis californicus quercinus* H. W. Grinnell, Univ. California Publ. Zool., 12:317, December 4, type from Seven Oaks, 5000 ft., San Bernardino Co., California.

MARGINAL RECORDS (Miller and G. M. Allen, 1928: 154–155, unless otherwise noted).—Western segment: British Columbia: Hedley (Anderson, 1947:28). Idaho: Selway Falls (Rust, 1946:312). Utah: Aspen Grove, Mt. Timpanogos (Durrant, 1952:47). California: Yosemite Valley; Mt. Whitney; Kenworthy; Julian, thence southward in Baja California west of Sierra San Pedro Mártir to Cape St. Lucas, thence northward along Pacific Coast, including San Clemente Island, to California: *Pacheco Pass*; Vacaville; Trinity Mts. E of Hoopa; Mt. Shasta. Oregon (V. Bailey, 1936: 376): Blue River; Mt. Hood. Washington (Dalquest, 1948: 158): Lyle; Orondo. Eastern segment: Colorado (Warren, 1942:21): Marchioness Tunnel, Boulder Canyon; Van Andert's Spring. New Mexico: Carlsbad Cave (V. Bailey, 1932:390). Texas: E base Burro Mesa (Borell and Bryant, 1942:8). Coahuila (Baker, 1956:176): *10 mi. S, 5 mi. E Boquillas; El Río Alamos, Rancho Las Margaritas; La Gacha;* Guadalupe. Chihuahua: Pacheco. Sonora: Providencia Mines (Burt, 1938:23). Arizona: Oracle; Yarnell (Hatfield, 1942: 146). Colorado: Rifle (Warren, 1942:21).

Myotis californicus caurinus Miller

1897. *Myotis californicus caurinus* Miller, N. Amer. Fauna, 13:72, October 16, type from Massett, Graham Island, Queen Charlotte Islands, British Columbia.

MARGINAL RECORDS (Miller and G. M. Allen, 1928: 156, unless otherwise noted).—Alaska: Howkan, Long Island. British Columbia (Cowan and Guiguet, 1956:79): Stuie; Lillooet; Okanagan Landing. Washington: Colville (Dalquest, 1948:158); Blue Creek (*ibid.*); Chelan (*ibid.*); Mt. Rainier (*ibid.*); White Salmon. Oregon (V. Bailey, 1936:378): Marmot; Holly; McKenzie Bridge; Fish Lake. California: Mt. Sanhedrin; Howell Mtn. (Longhurst, 1940: 247); Walnut Creek; Menlo Park, thence northward along coast, including coastal islands and type locality, to point of beginning. Also California: Prisoners Harbor, Santa Cruz Island (Pearson, 1951:366).

Myotis californicus mexicanus (Saussure)

1860. V[*espertilio*]. *mexicanus* Saussure, Revue et Mag. Zool., Paris, ser. 2, 12:282, July, type from an unknown locality. (Dalquest, Louisiana State Univ. Studies, Biol. Ser., 1:49, December 28, 1953, gives the type locality as "The desert (warmer part) of the state of México, México.")

1897. *Myotis californicus mexicanus,* Miller, N. Amer. Fauna, 13:73, October 16.

1866. *Vespertilio agilis* H. Allen, Proc. Acad. Nat. Sci. Philadelphia, 18:282, type from Mirador, Veracruz.

MARGINAL RECORDS (Miller and G. M. Allen, 1928: 160, unless otherwise noted).—Tamaulipas: San José (Dice, 1937:249). Veracruz: Mirador. Oaxaca: Cuicatlán. Tlaxcala: 13 km. NE Tlaxcala (Davis, 1944:379). Michoacán: Pátzcuaro (Hall and Villa, 1949:444). Jalisco: Los Masos. Nayarit: Tres Mariás Islands. Zacatecas: San Juan Capistrano. San Luis Potosí: Cerro Peñon Blanco (Dalquest, 1953b:50); Hda. La Parada; 10 km. NW Villar (Dalquest, 1953:50). Tamaulipas: Miquihuana.

Myotis californicus stephensi Dalquest

1900. *Myotis californicus pallidus* Stephens, Proc. Biol. Soc. Washington, 13:153, June 13, type from Vallecito, San Diego Co., California. Not K[*erivoula*]. *pallida* Blyth, 1863 [= *Myotis pallidus* = *Myotis formosus formosus* Hodgson, 1835, from Nepal], from Chaibassa, Orissa, India.

1946. *Myotis californicus stephensi* Dalquest, Proc. Biol. Soc. Washington, 59:67, March 11, type (not the same as the type of *pallidus* Stephens) from Vallecito, San Diego Co., California.

MARGINAL RECORDS (Miller and G. M. Allen, 1928: 158, unless otherwise noted).—Nevada: Cottonwood Range (Hall, 1946:142). Utah (Durrant, 1952:47): St. George; campground Zion National Park; Sunnyside; 4 mi. N Thompson (Krutzsch and Heppenstall, 1955:127). Colorado: Ashbaugh's Ranch (Warren, 1942:22). Arizona: Fort Defiance; Fort Verde; Santa Catalina Mills. Sonora: Sierra del Pinacate (Johnson, *et al.,* 1948:341). Baja California: Sierra San Pedro Mártir. California: La Puerta Valley; Lavic; Lone Pine Creek. Nevada (Hall, 1946:142): 9 mi. E, 2 mi. S Yerington; Fallon.

Myotis planiceps Baker
Flat-headed Myotis

1955. *Myotis planiceps* Baker, Proc. Biol. Soc. Washington, 68:165, December 31, type from 7 mi. S and 4 mi. E Bella Unión, 7200 ft., Coahuila. Known only from the type locality.

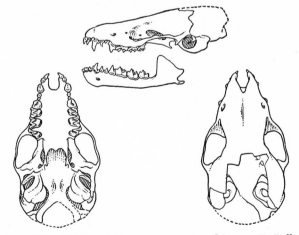

Fig. 129. *Myotis planiceps,* 7 mi. S and 4 mi. E Bella Unión, 7200 ft., Coahuila, No. 48242 K.U., ♂, X 3.

Selected measurements of the type, an adult male, are: length of head and body, 51; length of forearm, 26.5; condylobasal length of skull, 13.3; zygomatic breadth, 8.1; length of maxillary tooth-row, 4.9. Size small for the genus; forearm distinctively short; ears and membranes dark; pelage long (8.2 mm. on middle of back), on upper parts tipped with Cinnamon-Brown, on underparts tipped with buffy; skull much flattened (see Fig. 129); occlusal surface of 2nd premolar only slightly smaller than that of 1st premolar, both in upper jaw and in lower jaw.

Myotis subulatus
Small-footed Myotis

Length of head and body, 34.4–48.0; ear, 12.2–15.0; length of forearm, 30.8–36.0; greatest length of skull, 13.2–14.7; zygomatic breadth, 8–9; breadth of braincase, 6.2–7.1; length of upper tooth-row, 4.9–5.5. Pelage long, silky, the tips frequently glossy; ears and face black; upper parts light buff to golden brown; underparts buffy to almost white. Skull small, delicate, resembling that of *M. californicus*; braincase not rising abruptly from rostral level but instead sloping upward gradually; low sagittal crest sometimes present; braincase conspicuously flattened. Ear, when laid forward, barely exceeding muzzle; fur extending slightly onto membranes below; foot small, delicate; calcar long, slender, terminating in a minute lobule, keeled.

In much of the earlier literature (prior to 1928), the name *M. subulatus* was applied to the bat now known as *M. keenii septentrionalis*. The small-footed myotis is relatively common in the western United States. It is not a colonial form and is to be found hanging singly in caves, old mines, and occasionally in abandoned buildings. Seldom is it found above the Transition Life-zone. The single young is born in late June or July.

Fig. 130. *Myotis subulatus subulatus*, 5 mi. W Elkader, Logan Co., Kansas, No. 5561 K.U., ♂, X 2.

Myotis subulatus leibii (Audubon and Bachman)

1842. *Vespertilio leibii* Audubon and Bachman, Jour. Acad. Nat. Sci. Philadelphia, ser. 1, 8:284, type from Erie County, Ohio.

1928. *Myotis subulatus leibii,* Miller and G. M. Allen, Bull. U.S. Nat. Mus., 144:171, May 25.
1913. *Myotis winnemana* Nelson, Proc. Biol. Soc. Washington, 26:183, August 8, type from Plummers Island, Montgomery Co., Maryland.

MARGINAL RECORDS.—Quebec: La Fliche Cave, near Wakefield (Anderson, 1947:29). Vermont: Vershire (Griffin, 1940:181). Maine: Otter Point, Mt. Desert Island (Manville, 1942:393), thence southward along coast to Maryland: Plummers Island (Goldman and Jackson, 1939:132). Virginia: Millboro Cave (Johnson, 1950:197). North Carolina: Bat Cave (Adams, 1950:97). Kentucky: Harlan County (Barbour, 1951:103). Missouri: 3 mi. S Graniteville (Davis and Lidicker, 1955:289). Ohio: type locality. Ontario: Mt. Brydges (Anderson, 1947:29); cave near Latta (*ibid.*); Fourth Chute (Hitchcock, 1949:48).

Myotis subulatus melanorhinus (Merriam)

1890. *Vespertilio melanorhinus* Merriam, N. Amer. Fauna, 3:46, September 11, type from Little Spring, 8250 ft., N base San Francisco Mtn., Coconino Co., Arizona.
1928. *Myotis subulatus melanorhinus,* Miller and G. M. Allen, Bull. U.S. Nat. Mus., 144:169, May 25.
1894. *V[espertilio]. nitidus henshawii* H. Allen, Bull. U.S. Nat. Mus., 43:103, March 14, type from near Wingate, McKinley Co., New Mexico.
1903. *Myotis orinomus* Elliot, Field Columbian Mus., Publ. 79, Zool. Ser., 3:228, August 15, type from La Grulla, 8000 ft., Sierra San Pedro Mártir, Baja California.

MARGINAL RECORDS (Miller and G. M. Allen, 1928:170–171, unless otherwise noted).—British Columbia: Oyama (Cowan and Guiguet, 1956:86). Washington (Dalquest, 1948:158): 5 mi. S Grand Coulee Dam; Bly. Idaho (Davis, 1939:117): Double Springs; ½ mi. E Portneuf. Utah: 15 mi. N Logan (Durrant, 1955b:72); *Salt Lake City (ibid.)*; Ferron (Durrant, 1952:49); 25 mi. E Vernal (Krutzsch and Heppenstall, 1955:127). Colorado (Warren, 1942:23): Snake River; Antonito. Oklahoma (Glass, 1949:26): 3 mi. N Kenton. New Mexico (V. Bailey, 1932:391): Guadalupe Canyon; Hot Springs. Chihuahua: San Luis Mts. Arizona: Huachuca Mts. Baja California: Laguna Hanson; Santa Eulalia. California: Santa Ysabel; 1 mi. SW Cholame (Koford and Koford, 1948:417); 7½ mi. ESE Panoche (Dalquest, 1946:88); Petes Valley (Grinnell, *et al.*, 1930:456). Oregon (V. Bailey, 1936:379): Warner Valley; Twelve Mile Creek. Washington (Dalquest, 1948:158–159): Lyle; Selah; Wenatchee.

Myotis subulatus subulatus (Say)

1823. *V[espertilio]. subulatus* Say, *in* Long, Account of an exped. . . . to the Rocky Mts. . . . , 2:65 (footnote), type from the Arkansas River near present town of La Junta, Otero Co., Colorado.
1897. *Myotis subulatus,* Miller, N. Amer. Fauna, 13:75, October 16. Note: Although the referred specimens in Miller, p. 76, are *M. keenii septentrionalis,* his name combination *Myotis subulatus* was intended to apply to *V. subulatus* (Say).
1886. *Vespertilio ciliolabrum* Merriam, Proc. Biol. Soc. Washington, 4:2, December 17, type from a bluff on Hackberry Creek, about 1 mi. from Castle Rock, near Banner, Trego Co., Kansas.

MARGINAL RECORDS (Miller and G. M. Allen, 1928:169, unless otherwise noted).—Alberta: Red Deer River

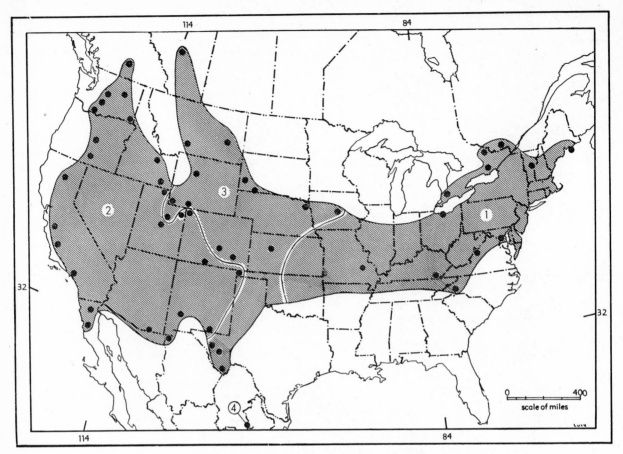

Map 130. *Myotis subulatus* and *Myotis planiceps*.

1. *M. s. leibii* 3. *M. s. subulatus*
2. *M. s. melanorhinus* 4. *M. planiceps*

near Rumsey (Anderson, 1947:28). Montana: Miles City. South Dakota: Hermosa; Pine Ridge. Nebraska: Crystal Lake (Webb and Jones, 1952:274). Iowa: Ames (Scott, 1939:240). Kansas: Banner (Cockrum, 1952:63). Texas: Fort Davis (Davis, 1944:201); Terlingua Creek (*ibid.*); 16 mi. SE Van Horn (Davis and Robertson, 1944:262). Colorado: type locality; Colorado Springs (Warren, 1942:23). Wyoming: Kinney Ranch. Utah: Soldier Canyon (Durrant, 1952:48). Wyoming: Fort Bridger; Bull Lake. Montana: Big Timber.

Myotis nigricans
Black Myotis

Length of head and body, 37.6–49.0; ear, 10.2–13.2; length of forearm, 31.8–39.0; greatest length of skull, 12.8–14.8; zygomatic breadth, 7.3–9.1; breadth of braincase, 5.8–7.4; length of upper tooth-row, 4.7–5.5. Pelage varying from short and wooly to long and silky, each hair glossy-tipped, but pelage as a whole seldom glossy; upper parts dark brown to blackish, color of tip of hair being but

little different from that of base; underparts paler, often washed with yellowish; a tawny phase seems to be rare. Skull small, delicate; braincase globular, rising abruptly from rostral level; low sagittal crest sometimes present; rostrum, in proportion to its length, relatively broad. Tip of tail rarely free of membrane; foot small, delicate; calcar sometimes keeled; tail relatively short; ear when laid forward extending approximately to nostril.

Myotis nigricans dominicensis Miller

1902. *Myotis dominicensis* Miller, Proc. Biol. Soc., Washington, 15:243, December 16, type from Dominica, Lesser Antilles. Known only from the type locality.
1928. *Myotis nigricans dominicensis*, Miller and G. M. Allen, Bull. U.S. Nat. Mus., 144:183, May 25.

Myotis nigricans extremus Miller and G. M. Allen

1928. *Myotis nigricans extremus* Miller and G. M. Allen, Bull. U.S. Nat. Mus., 144:181, May 25, type from Huehuetán, 300 ft., Chiapas.

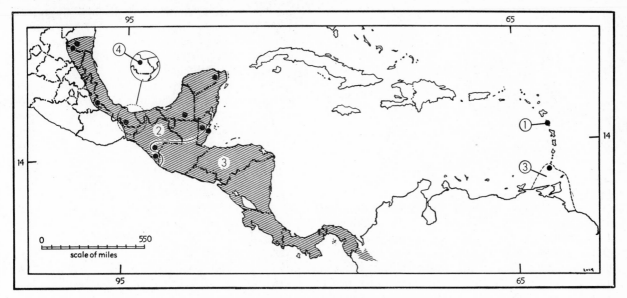

Map 131. *Myotis nigricans* and *Myotis argentatus*.

1. *M. n. dominicensis*   2. *M. n. extremus*   3. *M. n. nigricans*   4. *M. argentatus*

MARGINAL RECORDS.—Tamaulipas: 8 km. SW Chamal (Goodwin, 1954:6), thence southward along coast to Yucatán: Chem Donot (Gaumer, 1917:270). Campeche: La Tuxpeña (Miller and G. M. Allen, 1928:182). British Honduras: Augustine (9670 KU). Chiapas: type locality. Veracruz: 38 km. SE Jesús Carranza (Dalquest and Hall, 1949:425); 4 km. WNW Fortín, 3200 ft. (17840 KU). San Luis Potosí: El Salto (Dalquest, 1953b:51).

Myotis nigricans nigricans (Schinz)

1821. *Vesp[ertilio]. nigricans* Schinz, Das Thierreich . . . , 1:179, type from Fazenda de Aga, near Rio Iritiba, Espírito Santo, Brazil.
1924. *Myotis nigricans nigricans*, Miller, Bull. U.S. Nat. Mus., 128:72, April 29.
1823. *Vesp[ertilio]. brasiliensis* Spix, Simiarum et vespertilionum Brasiliensium . . . , p. 63, type from an unknown locality. Not *Vespertilio brasiliensis* Desmarest, 1822 [= an *Eptesicus*].
1829. *Vespertilio spixii* Fischer, Synopsis Mammalium, p. 111, a renaming of *V. brasiliensis* Spix.
1840. *Vespertilio parvulus* Temminck, Monographies de mammalogie, . . . 2:246, type from Brazil.
1847. *Vespertilio hypothrix* D'Orbigny and Gervais, Voy. dans l'Amér. merid., 4(pt. 2; Mamm.):14, footnote, type from eastern Bolivia.
1849. *Vespertilio osculati* Cornalia, Vert. Syn. Mus. Medialan., p. 11. Maybe a synonym here: original not seen.
1854. *Vespertilio quixensis* Cornalia, *in* Osculati, Gaetano, Esplorazione delle regioni equatoriali . . . d'Amazzoni, p. 312, type from South America.
1866. *Vespertilio concinnus* H. Allen, Proc. Acad. Nat. Sci. Philadelphia, 18:280, type from El Salvador.
1866. *Vespertilio exiguus* H. Allen, Proc. Acad. Nat. Sci. Philadelphia, 18:281, type from Aspinwall [= Colón Panamá].
1904. *Myotis chiriquensis* J. A. Allen, Bull. Amer. Mus. Nat. Hist., 20:77, February 29, type from Boquerón, Panamá.

1914. *Myotis ruber keaysi* J. A. Allen, Bull. Amer. Mus. Nat. Hist., 33:383, July 9, type from Inca Mines, lat. 13° 30′ S, long. 70° W, 6000 ft., Perú.
1914. *Myotis punensis* J. A. Allen, Bull. Amer. Mus. Nat. Hist., 33:383, July 9, type from Puna Island, Ecuador.
1914. *Myotis bondae* J. A. Allen, Bull. Amer. Mus. Nat. Hist., 33:384, July 9, type from Bonda, Colombia.
1914. *Myotis maripensis* J. A. Allen, Bull. Amer. Mus. Nat. Hist., 33:385, July 9, type from Maripa, Venezuela.
1914. *Myotis esmeraldae* J. A. Allen, Bull. Amer. Mus. Nat. Hist., 33:385, July 9, type from Esmeraldas, Ecuador.
1914. *Myotis caucensis* J. A. Allen, Bull. Amer. Mus. Nat. Hist., 33:386, July 9, type from Río Frío, 3500 ft., Cauca River, Colombia.

MARGINAL RECORDS.—British Honduras: Stann Creek Valley (Hershkovitz, 1951:558). Chiapas: Prusia (Hooper, 1947:43), thence southward throughout mainland into South America. Also occurring in Lesser Antilles: Grenada (Miller and G. M. Allen, 1928:180).

Myotis albescens (É. Geoffroy St.-Hilaire)
Paraguay Myotis

1806. *Vesp[ertilio]. albescens* É. Geoffroy St.-Hilaire, Ann. Mus., Hist. Nat., Paris, 8:204, type from Paraguay.
1900. *Myotis albescens*, Thomas, Ann. Mus. Civ. Storia Nat. Genova, 40:546, July 4.
1826. *Vespertilio leucogaster* Wied-Neuwied, Beiträge zur Naturgeschichte Brazil, 2:271, type from Moucouri River, Brazil.
1840. *Vespertilio aenobarbus* Temminck, Monographies de mammalogie . . . , 2:247, type from South America.
1840. *Vespertilio arsinoë* Temminck, Monographies de mammalogie . . . , 2:247, type from Surinam.
1847. *Vespertilio isidori* D'Orbigny and Gervais, Voy. dans l'Amér. merid., 4(pt. 2; Mamm.):16, type from Corrientes, Argentina.
1866. *Vespertilio mundus* H. Allen, Proc. Acad. Nat. Sci. Philadelphia, 18:280, type from Maracaibo, Venezuela.

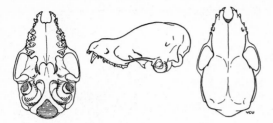

Fig. 131. *Myotis albescens*, Tacuaral, Paraguay,
No. 105664 U.S.N.M., ♀, X 2.

Length of head and body, 44.2–50.0; ear, 11.2–
14.6; length of forearm, 34.6–37.4; greatest length
of skull, 13.0–14.4; zygomatic breadth, 8–9; breadth
of braincase, 6.7–7.6; length of upper tooth-row,
4.7–5.2. Pelage thin; hairs of upper parts light
chocolate on basal three-fourths, glistening pale
buff terminally; below, tips paler lending appearance distinctly contrasted to that of upper parts.
Skull with distinctively large, smooth, rounded
braincase, short and weak rostrum; cheek-teeth
small in occlusal area.

MARGINAL RECORDS (Dalquest and Hall, 1947:239,
unless otherwise noted).—Nicaragua: Prinzapolca River;
Escondido River; Río San Juan (Miller and G. M. Allen,
1928:203). Costa Rica: Bebedero (Goodwin, 1946:332),
thence southward into South America.

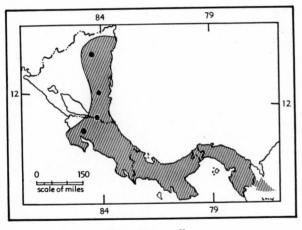

Map 132. *Myotis albescens*.

Myotis argentatus Dalquest and Hall
Silver-haired Myotis

1947. *Myotis argentatus* Dalquest and Hall, Univ. Kansas
Publ., Mus. Nat. Hist., 1:239, December 10, type from
14 km. SW Coatzocoalcos, 100 ft., Veracruz. Known only
from the type locality.

Selected measurements of the type, an adult male,
are: length of head and body, 55; length of fore-

arm, 33; greatest length of skull, 14.5; zygomatic
breadth, 9.1; breadth of braincase, 7.5; length of
upper tooth-row, 5.3. Size medium for the genus;
tail short; foot long; ears and membranes black;
pelage long and black; overhairs on upper parts
tipped with whitish especially on rump; underparts
from posterior part of thorax posteriorly having all
hairs tipped with this same whitish color; skull with
preorbital part small in relation to braincase; teeth
small in relation to total area of palate; braincase
much inflated; ventral margin of foramen magnum
evenly rounded (after Dalquest and Hall, 1947:
239).

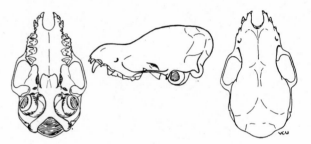

Fig. 132. *Myotis argentatus*, 14 km. SW Coatzacoalcos,
100 ft. Veracruz, No. 19228 K.U., sex ?, X 2.

Genus **Pizonyx** Miller—Fish-eating Bat

Revised by Miller and G. M. Allen, Bull. U.S. Nat. Mus.,
144:209–214, May 25, 1928.

1906. *Pizonyx* Miller, Proc. Biol. Soc. Washington, 19:85,
June 4. Type, *Myotis vivesi* Menegaux.

Superficially resembling *Myotis* except for larger
size and enormously elongated feet; teeth *Myotis*-
like but with strong tendency toward higher, slenderer cusps; claws much enlarged and laterally
compressed; glandular mass present near middle of
forearm. Dentition, i. $\frac{2}{3}$, c. $\frac{1}{1}$, p. $\frac{3}{3}$, m. $\frac{3}{3}$. Only one
species, *P. vivesi*, is known.

Pizonyx vivesi (Menegaux)
Fish-eating Bat

1901. *Myotis vivesi* Menegaux, Bull. Mus. Hist. Nat. Paris,
7:323, type from islet of Cardonal or Islo, Archipelago of
Salsipuedes, off San Rafael Bay, Baja California (probably
Isla Partida, 28° 53′ N lat., 113° 04′ W long.; see Reeder
and Norris, 1954:83–85).
1906. *Pizonyx vivesi*, Miller, Proc. Biol. Soc. Washington,
19:85, June 4.

Selected measurements of the two female cotypes
are: total length, 145, 140; tibia, 24.0, 24.6; foot,
23.0, 23.8. Additional selected measurements of
these and other specimens are: length of head and
body, 71–76.2; length of forearm, 59–62.2; greatest

length of skull, 21.0–22.0; zygomatic breadth, 14.0–14.6; breadth of braincase, 10.0–10.8; length of upper tooth-row, 8.8–9.4. Upper parts dark buff or pale tan; underparts whitish. Other characters as for the genus.

This curious species of bat seems to feed almost exclusively on small fish, which it catches on the surface of the ocean. Presumably the characteristic long feet with their long, compressed claws assist in the capture of the prey. By day the bats secrete themselves in crevices among rocks or under rocks.

MARGINAL RECORDS (Reeder and Norris, 1954:82).—Sonora: Isla San Jorge; Bahía de San Carlos. Baja California: Puerto San Bartolomé; Punta Malarrimo; Isla Encantada.

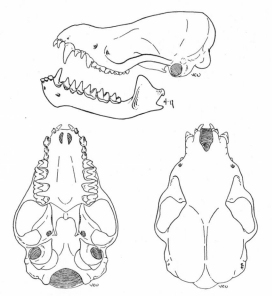

Fig. 133. *Pizonyx vivesi*, Isla Partida, 28° 53′ N, 113° 04′ W, Gulf of California, Baja California, No. 9254 K.U., ♂, X 2.

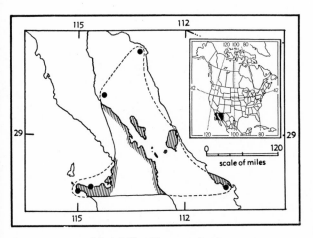

Map 133. *Pizonyx vivesi*.

Genus **Lasionycteris** Peters—Silver-haired Bat

1866. *Lasionycteris* Peters, Monatsb. preuss. Akad. Wiss., Berlin, p. 648. Type, *Vespertilio noctivagans* Le Conte.
1875. *Vesperides* Coues, *in* Coues and Yarrow, Report . . . mammals . . . Nevada, Utah, California, New Mexico, and Arizona . . . , Repts. . . . Expl. Surv. West of . . . Hundredth meridian . . . , 5:83. Proposed as a subgenus. Type, *Vespertilio* (*Vesperides*) *noctivagans* Le Conte.

Length of head and body approximately 60. Structure of teeth as in *Myotis*; inner incisor strongly bicuspidate and outer one simple; P3 absent; hypocone distinctly indicated in M1 and M2; M3 with more than half the crown area of M1; in M3 metacone nearly as large as paracone, and its three commissures well developed. Skull flattened; rostrum broad; depth of braincase including auditory bullae approximately three-fourths of mastoid breadth; sagittal crest obsolete; interorbital region wide, flattish; upper edge of orbit with low "bead"; central part of bead forming angle suggesting incipient postorbital process; upper surface of rostrum distinctly concave on each side between lacrimal region and nares; other features of skull essentially as in *Myotis*, except for general tendency toward broadening and shortening. Ear short, nearly as broad as long; interfemoral membrane furred on basal half above (after Miller, 1907:203–204). Dentition, i. $\frac{2}{3}$, c. $\frac{1}{1}$, p. $\frac{2}{3}$, m. $\frac{3}{3}$.

This genus is monotypic.

Lasionycteris noctivagans (Le Conte)
Silver-haired Bat

1831. V[*espertilio*]. *noctivagans* Le Conte, *in* McMurtrie, The animal kingdom . . . by the Baron Cuvier . . . , 1:(app.)431, type from eastern United States.
1894. *Lasionycteris noctivagans*, H. Allen, Bull. U.S. Nat. Mus., 43:105, March 14.

Upper parts dark brownish black, strongly washed with silver; underparts slightly lighter, silvery wash less pronounced. Other characters as for the genus.

These bats are usually relatively abundant throughout their geographic range. They begin flying in early evening or late afternoon. The flight is slow and erratic. They hunt most commonly along streams and, where water is scarce, along the edges of stands of trees. Silver-haired bats are gregarious and often congregate in great numbers but males, at least seasonally, may be solitary. One or two young are born in June or July.

MARGINAL RECORDS.—British Columbia: Charlie Lake (Cowan, 1939:72). *Saskatchen:* [*near?*] *Frobisher Lake* (Nero, 1957:41). Alberta: Henry House (Miller, 1897b:86). Ontario: Northern Light Lake (Cahn, 1937:22). Quebec: Ottawa (Rand, 1945c:115). New Brunswick: St.

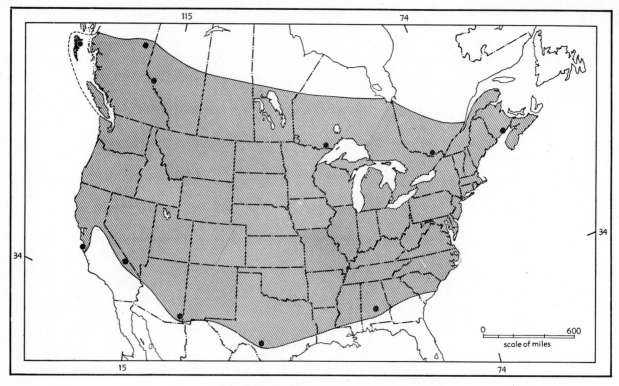

Map 134. *Lasionycteris noctivagans.*

John County (Morris, 1948:168), thence southward along Atlantic Coast to South Carolina: *most of state* (Penney, 1950:84). Alabama: Autaugaville (A. H. Howell, 1921:24). Texas: about 18 mi. W Medina (Blair, 1952:95). Arizona: Fly Park, Chiricahua Mts. (Cahalane, 1939:422). California: Death Valley (Grinnell, 1937:127); Pacific Grove (Grinnell, 1918:302), thence northward along Pacific Coast and larger coastal islands to British Columbia: Skidegate, Moresby Island (Osgood, 1901:36).

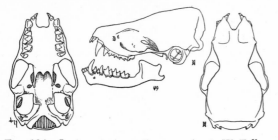

Fig. 134. *Lasionycteris noctivagans,* 4 mi. W Fallon, Nevada, No. 88058 M.V.Z., ♂, X 2.

Genus **Pipistrellus** Kaup—Pipistrelles

American representatives revised by Hall and Dalquest, Univ. Kansas Publ., Mus. Nat. Hist., 1:591–602, January 20, 1950.

1829. *Pipistrellus* Kaup, Skizzirte Enwickelungs-Geschichte und natürliches System der Europäischen Thierwelt, 1:98. Type, *Vespertilio pipistrellus* Schreber.

1838. *Romicia* Gray, Mag. Zool. Bot., 2:495, February. Type, *Romicia calcarata* Gray [= *Vespertilio kuhlii* Kuhl].

1856. *Hypsugo* Kolenati, Allgem. deutsch. Naturh. Zeit. Dresden, neue Folge, 2:131. Included two species: *Vesperugo maurus* Blasius; *Vesperugo krascheninikowii* Eversmann.

1856. *Nannugo* Kolenati, Allgem. deutsch. Naturh. Zeit. Dresden, neue Folge, 2:131. Included three species: *Vesperugo nathusii* Keyserling and Blasius; *Vespertilio pipistrellus* Daubenton; *Vespertilio kuhlii* Kuhl.

Length of head and body approximately 41. Teeth essentially as in *Myotis* and *Lasionycteris* except for fewer premolar teeth; upper incisors subequal, outer one extending considerably beyond its cingulum; inner upper incisor simple, or more often with well-developed secondary cusp; anterior upper premolar barely or not in tooth-row; other teeth with no special peculiarities; skull essentially as in *Myotis*, though with tendency to greater breadth. External characters not essentially different from those of *Myotis*, but ear usually shorter and broader, and tragus less acutely pointed; in one species, tragus bent forward at tip. Dentition, i. $\frac{2}{3}$, c. $\frac{1}{1}$, p. $\frac{2}{2}$, m. $\frac{3}{3}$.

The genus is widely distributed in the Eastern Hemisphere, and in the Western Hemisphere occurs southward to Honduras.

Key to North American Species of Pipistrellus

1. Foot less than half as long as tibia; skull nearly straight in dorsal profile; palate extending far behind molars. . *P. hesperus*, p. 181

1'. Foot more than half as long as tibia; skull concave in dorsal profile; palate extending little behind molars. . . . *P. subflavus*, p. 182

Pipistrellus hesperus
Western Pipistrelle

Subspecies revised by Hatfield, Jour. Mamm., 17:257–262, August 17, 1936.

"Smoke Gray to Buff Brown . . . dorsally; total length, 60 to 86; foot less than half as long as tibia; tragus blunt with terminal part bent forward; skull nearly straight in dorsal profile; inner upper incisors unicuspidate; outer upper incisor with accessory cusp on anterointernal face; P1, viewed from occlusal face, less than a seventh of area of canine, and from labial aspect concealed by canine and fourth premolar; lower, third premolar lower than anterior cusp of canine; lower premolars crowded, distance between canine and first molar less than length of second lower molar" (Hall and Dalquest, 1950:595).

The western pipistrelle, in the United States, is one of the smallest bats. It takes flight early in the evening and is sometimes abroad in the afternoon. The bat is easily recognized in flight by the contrast between the grayish back and blackish membranes and by erratic flight pattern.

Fig. 135. *Pipistrellus hesperus hesperus*, Crystal Spring, Lincoln Co., Nevada, No. 52203 M.V.Z., ♂, X 2.

Pipistrellus hesperus australis Miller

1897. *Pipistrellus hesperus australis* Miller, N. Amer. Fauna, 13:90, October 16, type from Barranca Ibarra, Jalisco.
1904. *Pipistrellus hesperus apus* Elliot, Field Columb. Mus., Publ. 90, Zool. Ser., 3:269, March 7, type from Providencia Mines, Sonora.

MARGINAL RECORDS (Hall and Dalquest, 1950:597, unless otherwise noted).—Arizona: Camp Verde; near Portal (Cahalane, 1939:422; referred to *P. h. merriami*, here referred to *australis* on geographic grounds); Guadalupe Canyon (*ibid.*). Chihuahua: 4 mi. NW Chihuahua (38268 KU); 1 mi. NW Camargo, 4000 ft. (34293 KU). Coahuila: 4 mi. N Acatita (40828 KU); 9 mi. W, 4 mi. S San Buena-

ventura, 1800 ft. (48279 KU); San Lazaro, 4800 ft., 62 mi. N and 22 mi. W Saltillo (35676 KU); 11 mi. N, 8 mi. W Saltillo (35690 KU); El Chiflon, 21.7 mi. W Saltillo (39211 KU). Nuevo Léon: Iturbide, 5000 ft. (55136 KU). Hidalgo: Río Tasquillo, 26 km. E Zimapán (Davis, 1944: 379). Jalisco: 27 mi. S, 12 mi. W Guadalajara (38284 KU). Baja California: Miraflores; San Ignaeio. Arizona: Bates Well.—Baker (1956:181) refers the Coahuilan specimens to *maximus*.

Pipistrellus hesperus hesperus (H. Allen)

1864. *Scotophilus hesperus* H. Allen, Smiths. Miscl. Coll., 7(Publ. 165):43, June, type from Old Fort Yuma, Imperial Co., California, on right bank of Colorado River, opposite present town of Yuma, Arizona.
1897. *Pipistrellus hesperus*, Miller, N. Amer. Fauna, 13:88, October 16.

MARGINAL RECORDS (Hall and Dalquest, 1950:596–597, unless otherwise noted).—Washington: Vantage; Almota. Oregon: Watson. Idaho: 8 mi. W Rogerson. Nevada: 4 mi. W Mountain Well (Hall, 1946:151); Middle Stormy Spring. Utah (Durrant, 1952:53, unless otherwise noted); Old Lincoln Highway, 18 mi. SW Orr's Ranch in Skull Valley; [3 mi.] E of Ogden, Weber Co. (Durrant, 1955b:72); 7 mi. N Greenriver, 4100 ft.; *mouth Florence Creek Canyon, 4300 ft., 35 mi. N [of the town of] Green River* (Krutzsch and Heppenstall, 1955:127); near Green River, 15 mi. SW Ouray, 4700 ft. (*ibid.*); Desert Springs, 10 mi. SW Ouray (*ibid.*); *4 mi. N Thompson (ibid.)*; Colorado River, 5 mi. E Moab Bridge; Riverview. Arizona: 5 mi. N Wickenburg (Hatfield, 1942:146); Tinajas Altas. Baja California: Cataviña; San José; Laguna Hanson. California: type locality; Banning; 12 mi. below Bodfish; Little Lake; 2 mi. S Benton Station. Nevada: 9 mi. W Mason City (Alcorn, 1944:309); Deephole. Oregon: Princeton. Washington: Maryhill.

Pipistrellus hesperus maximus Hatfield

1936. *Pipistrellus hesperus maximus* Hatfield, Jour. Mamm., 17:261, August 17, type from Dog Spring, Hidalgo Co., New Mexico.

MARGINAL RECORDS (Hall and Dalquest, 1950:598, unless otherwise noted).—New Mexico: Malpais Spring, 15 mi. W Three Rivers (Blair, 1941:219); Carlsbad Cave. Texas: mouth of Pecos River. Coahuila: 1 mi. N Boquillas, 700 ft. (44731 KU). Texas: Glen Spring. New Mexico: Animas Valley. Arizona: mouth Grant Canyon, 5250 ft., 1 mi. NE Fort Grant (Van Gelder and Goodpaster, 1952: 491).—Baker (1956:181) includes all Coahuila in the range of *maximus*.

Pipistrellus hesperus merriami (Dobson)

1866. *Vesperugo merriami* Dobson, Ann. Mag. Nat. Hist., ser. 5, 18:124, August, type from Red Bluff, Tehama Co., California.
1913. *Pipistrellus hesperus merriami*, Grinnell, Proc. California Acad. Sci., ser. 4, 3:279, August 28.

MARGINAL RECORDS (Hall and Dalquest, 1950:597, unless otherwise noted).—California: Dale's, on Paines Creek; Fyffe; Yosemite Valley; Springville; Fort Tejon; Jacumba (P. H. Krutzsch, *in litt.*), thence northward along coast to Rumsey; type locality.

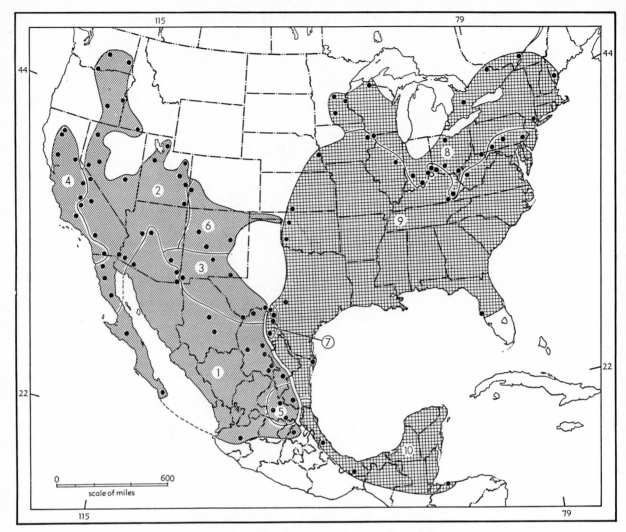

Map 135. *Pipistrellus hesperus* and *Pipistrellus subflavus*.

Guide to	3. *P. h. maximus*	7. *P. s. clarus*
kinds	4. *P. h. merriami*	8. *P. s. obscurus*
1. *P. h. australis*	5. *P. h. potosinus*	9. *P. s. subflavus*
2. *P. h. hesperus*	6. *P. h. santarosae*	10. *P. s. veraecrucis*

Pipistrellus hesperus potosinus Dalquest

1951. *Pipistrellus hesperus potosinus* Dalquest, Proc. Biol. Soc. Washington, 64:105, August 24, type from Presa de Guadalupe, San Luis Potosí.

MARGINAL RECORDS (Dalquest, 1953b:53, unless otherwise noted).—Tamaulipas: Joya Verde, 35 km. SW Victoria (60209 KU). San Luis Potosí: type locality; Hda. Capulín; San Luis Potosí.

Pipistrellus hesperus santarosae Hatfield

1936. *Pipistrellus hesperus santarosae* Hatfield, Jour. Mamm., 17:261, August 17, type from Santa Rosa, Guadalupe Co., New Mexico.

MARGINAL RECORDS (Hall and Dalquest, 1950:598). —Colorado: Bedrock. New Mexico: type locality; Socorro; Laguna.

Pipistrellus subflavus

Eastern Pipistrelle

Silvery gray to darker than Mummy Brown, dorsally; "total length, 73–89; foot more than half as long as tibia; tragus tapering and straight; dorsal profile of skull convex in interorbital region; inner upper incisor bicuspidate; outer upper incisor unicuspidate (lacking accessory cusp on anterointernal face); P1 viewed from occlusal face more than a seventh of area of canine and visible from labial aspect; lower, third premolar as high as anterior cusp of canine; lower premolars less crowded than in *P. hesperus* and distance between canine and first molar less than length of second lower molar. . . .

"In winter this species hibernates in caves in clusters of fewer than fifty individuals, but in summer fewer of the bats live there and at this season some have been captured as far as thirty miles from any such retreat, suggesting that the bats inhabit other types of shelter." (Hall and Dalquest, 1950: 598–599.)

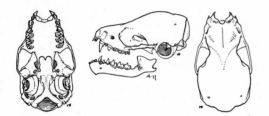

Fig. 136. *Pipistrellus subflavus subflavus*, Bat Cave, 2 mi. N War Eagle, Benton Co., Arkansas, No. 81387 M.V.Z., ♀, X 2, but lower jaw from cave along Missouri River 1 mi. SE Leavenworth Co., Kansas, ♂, X 2, No. 38797 K.U.

Pipistrellus subflavus clarus Baker

1954. *Pipistrellus subflavus clarus* Baker, Univ. Kansas Publ., Mus. Nat. Hist., 7:585, November 15, type from 2 mi. W Jiménez, 850 ft., Coahuila.

MARGINAL RECORDS (Baker, 1954:585–586).—Texas: Comstock; *Devils River*; Del Rio. Coahuila: type locality; 2 mi. S, 3 mi. E San Juan de Sabinas, 1160 ft.

Pipistrellus subflavus obscurus Miller

1897. *Pipistrellus subflavus obscurus* Miller, N. Amer. Fauna, 13:93, October 16, type from Lake George, Warren Co., New York.

MARGINAL RECORDS (Hall and Dalquest, 1950:600, unless otherwise noted).—Wisconsin: Hurley. Ohio: Fremont (Bole and Moulthrop, 1942:116). Ontario: Rockwood, near Guelph (Anderson, 1941:28); Renfrew County (Anderson, 1947:30). Quebec: Joliet. Maine: Windham (Norton, 1930:17). New York: Hastings-on-Hudson. West Virginia: Cornwall's Cave. Kentucky: Lynch (Barbour, 1951: 103). Ohio: Symmes Creek; Dry Cave. Indiana (Kirkpatrick and Conaway, 1948:130): Dearborn County; Langton's Cave; Sullivan's Cave. Illinois: bank of Mississippi River, SW of Galena (Beer and Greeley, 1948:1). Minnesota: St. Peter; St. Cloud (Goehring, 1954:435); Marine.

Pipistrellus subflavus subflavus (F. Cuvier)

1832. *V[espertilio]. subflavus* F. Cuvier, Nouv. Ann. Mus. Hist. Nat. Paris, 1:17, type from eastern United States, probably Georgia.

1897. *Pipistrellus subflavus*, Miller, N. Amer. Fauna, 13:90, October 16.

1835–1841. *Vespertilio erythrodactylus* Temminck, Monographies de mammalogie, . . . , 2:238. Type locality, vicinity of Philadelphia, Pennsylvania.

1841. (?) *Vespertilio monticola* Audubon and Bachman, Jour. Acad. Nat. Sci. Philadelphia, 1(7):92, October, based on specimens from Grey Sulphur Springs, Virginia.

1864. *Scotophilus georgianus* H. Allen, Smiths. Miscl. Coll., 7(Publ. 165):35, June. Allen attributed the name *georgianus* to Cuvier 1832 but Cuvier's name may apply to some other species.

1894. *Vesperugo carolinensis* H. Allen, Bull. U.S. Nat. Mus., 43:121, March 14. Allen attributed the name *carolinensis* to É. Geoffroy St.-Hilaire, 1806 [= *Eptesicus fuscus*], type locality, "Carolina."

MARGINAL RECORDS (Hall and Dalquest, 1950:599, unless otherwise noted).—Iowa: Dubuque (Scott, 1939: 239). Illinois: Urbana. Indiana: Franklin Co. Ohio: Smoky Creek. Kentucky: 4 mi. E Harlan (Barbour, 1951:103). West Virginia: Charleston. Pennsylvania: Sideling Hill, E. tunnel, Pennsylvania Turnpike (Mohr, 1942:376); Carlisle; Germantown, thence southward along Atlantic Coast to Florida: Tarpon Springs, thence west along Gulf Coast to Tamaulipas: Matamoros (H. Allen, 1894:128). Texas: Rocksprings (Blair, 1952:96). Oklahoma (Glass, 1955: 128): 3 mi. W & 1 mi. S Reed; *3 mi. N Jester*; Alabaster Cavern, Woodward County. Kansas: 4½ mi. SW Sun City (Cockrum, 1952:68). Nebraska: ½ mi. W Meadow (Webb and Jones, 1952:276).

Pipistrellus subflavus veraecrucis (Ward)

1891. *Vesperugo veraecrucis* Ward, Amer. Nat., 25:745, August, type from Las Vigas, Canton of Jalapa, Veracruz.

1950. *Pipistrellus subflavus veracrucis* [*sic*], Hall and Dalquest, Univ. Kansas Publ., Mus. Nat. Hist., 1:601, January 20.

MARGINAL RECORDS (Hall and Dalquest, 1950:601). Veracruz: type locality. Honduras: Jilamo Farm, Tela District. Veracruz: 30 km. SSE Jesús Carranza.

Genus Eptesicus Rafinesque—Big Brown Bats

North American species revised under the name *Vespertilio* by Miller, N. Amer. Fauna, 13:95–104, October 16, 1897.

1820. *Eptesicus* Rafinesque, Annals of nature . . . , p. 2. Type, *Eptesicus melanops* Rafinesque [= *Vespertilio fuscus* Palisot de Beauvois].

1829. *Cnephaeus* Kaup, Skizzirte Entwickelungs-Geschichte und natürliches System der Europäischen Thierwelt, 1:103. Type, *Vespertilio serotinus* Schreber.

1837. *Noctula* Bonaparte, Iconografia della fauna Italica . . . , fasc. 21, vol. 1. Type, *Noctula serotina* Bonaparte.

1856. *Cateorus* Kolenati, Allgem. deutsch. Naturh. Zeit. Dresden, neue Folge, 2:131. Type, *Vespertilio serotinus* Schreber.

1858. *Amblyotis* Kolenati, Sitzungsber. k. Akad. Wiss., Wien, 29:252. Type, *Amblyotis atratus* Kolenati [= *Vespertilio nilssonii* Keyserling and Blasius].

1866. *Pachyomus* Gray, Ann. Mag. Nat. Hist., ser. 3, 17:90. Type, *Scotophilus pachyomus* Tomes.

1870. *Nyctiptennis* Fitzinger, Sitzungsber. k. Akad. Wiss., Wien, 62:424. Type, *Vespertilio smithii* Wagner.

1891. *Adelonycteris* H. Allen, Proc. Acad. Nat. Sci. Philadelphia, p. 466, a renaming of *Vesperus* Keyserling and Blasius, 1839, which included parts of both *Vespertilio* and *Eptesicus* and which is a homonym of *Vesperus* Latreille, 1829, an insect.

1916. *Pareptesicus* Bianchi, Ann. Mus. Zool., Acad. St. Petersburg, 21:76. Type, *Vesperugo pachyotis* Dobson.

1916. *Rhyneptesicus* Bianchi, Ann. Mus. Zool., Acad. St. Petersburg, 21:76. Type, *Vesperugo nasutus* Dobson.

1926. *Neoromicia* Roberts, Ann. Transvaal Mus., 11:245. Type, *Eptesicus zuluensis* Roberts.

1934. *Vespadelus* Iredale and Troughton, Mem. Australian Mus., 6:95.

Upper incisors well developed, inner larger than the outer and usually having distinct secondary cusp; outer incisor separated from canine by space equal to greatest diameter of incisor; lower incisors subequal, trifid, closely crowded and distinctly imbricated, forming a strongly convex row between canines; with crown on 3rd wider than on first or second; M1 and M2 with hypocone always indicated and in some species well developed; distinct concavity between hypocone and protocone; M3 variable in form, usually with well-developed metacone and three commissures in smaller species, but having metacone and third commissure obsolete in larger forms; skull not essentially different from that of *Pipistrellus*; rostrum flattish or more usually rounded off above; palatal emargination at least as deep as wide (after Miller, 1907:208–209). Ears small; tragus short, straight; interfemoral membrane bearing sprinkling of hairs above on basal fourth.

KEY TO NORTH AMERICAN SPECIES OF EPTESICUS

1. Greatest length of skull more than 17.4; length of forearm 46 or more. . *E. fuscus*, p. 184
1'. Greatest length of skull less than 17.4; length of forearm 48.5 or less.
  2. Underparts strongly washed with pale buffy white; not occurring in Antillean islands. . . . . . *E. albigularis*, p. 187
  2'. Underparts usually without whitish wash but when present, occurring in Antilles.
    3. Occurring in Antilles. . . *E. lynni*, p. 187
    3'. Occurring on mainland.
      4. Length of forearm more than 44; length of upper tooth-row more than 6.1. . . . *E. chiriquinus*, p. 188
      4'. Length of forearm less than 44; length of upper tooth-row less than 6.1. . . . *E. brasiliensis*, p. 188

Eptesicus fuscus
Big Brown Bat

Subspecies revised by G. M. Allen, Canadian Field-Nat., 47:31–32, February, 1932; western subspecies revised by Engels, Amer. Midl. Nat., 17:653–660, May, 1936.

Length of head and body approximately 70; total length, 108–122; length of forearm, 42–52. Apex of second triangle of M3 less than half height of anterior side of first triangle. Upper parts brown, usually dark, and sometimes reddish brown; underparts paler than upper parts, sometimes cinnamon or even buffy.

The *fuscus* group of big brown bats is the dominant group in North America and in the Antillean islands. *Eptesicus fuscus* resembles, except for its conspicuously larger size, the bats of the genus *Myotis*. The big brown bats are wholly insectivorous. They tolerate man well and often roost in occupied dwellings. In northern parts of their range they hibernate in caves where they are sometimes found singly and sometimes in clusters. Two young are usual but as many as four are known to be litter mates.

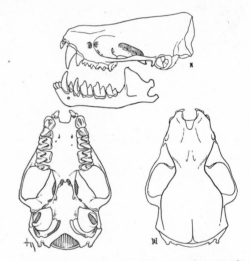

Fig. 137. *Eptesicus fuscus pallidus*, E slope Irish Mtn., 6900 ft., Lincoln Co., Nevada, No. 47851 M.V.Z., ♂, X 2.

Eptesicus fuscus bahamensis (Miller)

1897. *Vespertilio fuscus bahamensis* Miller, N. Amer. Fauna, 13:101, October 16, type from Nassau, New Providence, Bahamas. Known only from the type locality.

1945. *Eptesicus fuscus bahamensis*, Shamel, Proc. Biol. Soc. Washington, 58:108, July 18.

Eptesicus fuscus bernardinus Rhoads

1902. *Eptesicus fuscus bernardinus* Rhoads, Proc. Acad. Nat. Sci. Philadelphia, 53:619, February 6, type from near San Bernardino, San Bernardino Co., California.

1904. *Eptesicus fuscus melanopterus* Rehn, Proc. Acad. Nat. Sci. Philadelphia, 46:590, October 18, type from Mt. Tallac, Eldorado Co., California. Not *Vesperus melanopterus* Jentink, July 15, 1904 [= *Eptesicus melanopterus* from Dutch Guiana].

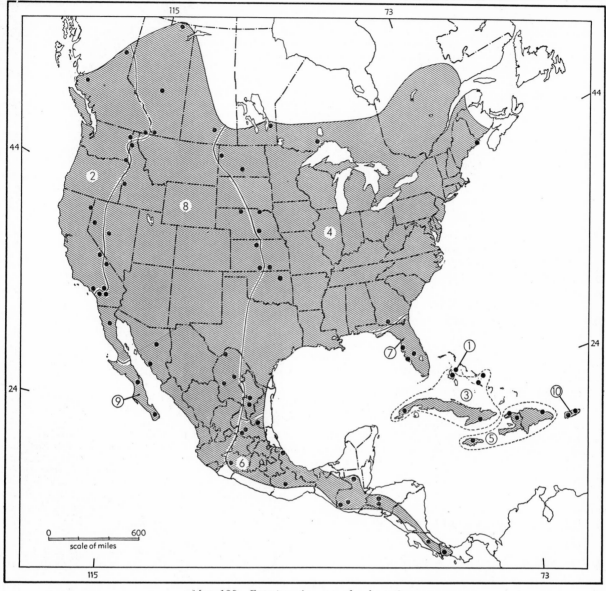

Map 136. *Eptesicus fuscus* and subspecies.

Guide to
subspecies
1. *E. f. bahamensis*
2. *E. f. bernardinus*
3. *E. f. dutertreus*
4. *E. f. fuscus*
5. *E. f. hispaniolae*
6. *E. f. miradorensis*
7. *E. f. osceola*
8. *E. f. pallidus*
9. *E. f. peninsulae*
10. *E. f. wetmorei*

MARGINAL RECORDS.—British Columbia: Charlie Lake (referred by Cowan, 1939:72, to *E. f. fuscus*; here referred to *E. f. bernardinus* on the basis of Anderson, 1947:30); Newgate (Anderson, 1947:30). Washington (Dalquest, 1948:165): Newport; Grand Ronde River. California: 8 mi. SW Ravendale (Hall, 1946:154). Nevada: Wadsworth (*ibid.*). California (Engels, 1936:655–656): Robert's Ranch, Weyman Creek, White Mts.; Kenworthy; Trabuco Canyon, thence northward along Pacific Coast, including larger coastal islands, to British Columbia: Stuie (Anderson, 1947: 30). (After the above account was prepared, Cowan and Guiguet, 1956:72, identified *Eptesicus fuscus* from most of the Province of British Columbia as subspecies *pallidus* and in that province applied the subspecific name *bernardinus* to specimens from only a small area in the southwest.)

Eptesicus fuscus dutertreus (P. Gervais)

1837. *Vespertilio dutertreus* P. Gervais, Ann. Sci. Nat., Paris, ser. 2; Zool. 8:61, July, type from Cuba.
1955. *Eptesicus fuscus dutertreus,* Miller and Kellogg, Bull. U.S. Nat. Mus., 205:103, March 3.
1839. *Scotophilus cubensis* Gray, Ann. Nat. Hist., 4:7, September, type from Cuba.

MARGINAL RECORDS.—Andros Island (Koopman, et al., 1957:167). Watling Island, Cockburntown (G. M. Allen and Sanborn, 1937:227). Cuba (Miller, 1904:337): El Cobre; Pinar del Río. Long Island: Clarencetown (G. M. Allen and Sanborn, 1937:227). Not found: McKinnon's Cave and Mortimer's, Long Island (ibid.).

Eptesicus fuscus fuscus (Palisot de Beauvois)

1796. Vespertilio fuscus Palisot de Beauvois, Catalogue raisonné du muséum de Mr. C. W. Peale, Philadelphia, p. 18 (p. 14 of English edition by Peale and Beauvois), type from Philadelphia, Pennsylvania.
1900. Eptesicus fuscus Méhely, Magyarország denevéreinek monographiája (Monographia Chiropterorum Hungariae), pp. 206, 338.
1806. Vespertilio carolinensis É. Geoffroy St.-Hilaire, Ann. Mus. Hist. Nat., Paris, 8:193. Type locality, "Carolina."
1818. Vespertilio phaiops Rafinesque, Amer. Month. Mag., 3:445. Type locality, Kentucky.
1820. Vespertilio melanops Rafinesque, Annals of nature . . . , p. 2, a renaming of phaiops Rafinesque.
1823. Vespertilio arquatus Say, in Long, Account of an exped. . . . to the Rocky Mts. . . . , 1:167, type from Engineer Cantonment, about 12 mi. SE Blair, Washington Co., Nebraska.
1835–1841. Vespertilio ursinus Temminck, Monographies de mammalogie, . . . , 2:235.
1843. Scotophilus greenii Gray, List of the . . . Mammalia in the . . . British Museum, p. 30, a nomen nudum (fide Miller, N. Amer. Fauna, 13:27, 96, October 16, 1897).

MARGINAL RECORDS.—Quebec: central Quebec (Anderson, 1947:30). Maine: Eastport (Morris, 1948:168), thence southward along Atlantic Coast to Georgia: about 10 mi. SSW Thomasville (Quay, 1949:67), thence westward along Gulf Coast and inland to Nuevo León: La Placeta (Koestner, 1941:10); Río Ramos, 20 km. NW Montemorelos (Davis, 1944:379). Oklahoma: Tulsa (Blair, 1939:101). Kansas: Winfield (Cockrum, 1952:71). Nebraska: Hastings (Webb and Jones, 1952:276); 1 mi. W Niobrara (Jones, 1954:482). North Dakota (V. Bailey, 1927:210): Cannon Ball; Buford. Manitoba: Lake Winnipeg (Soper, 1946:135). Ontario: Cavern Lake, 30 mi. NE Port Arthur (Allin, 1942:91).

Eptesicus fuscus hispaniolae Miller

1918. Eptesicus hispaniolae Miller, Proc. Biol. Soc. Washington, 31:39, May 16, type from Constanza, Dominican Republic.
1945. Eptesicus fuscus hispanolae [sic], Shamel, Proc. Biol. Soc. Washington, 58:108, July 18.

MARGINAL RECORDS.—Haiti: Port de Paix (Miller, 1918:40). Dominican Republic: San Gabriel Cave (Miller, 1929c:4). Haiti: near St. Michel (Miller, 1929a:11). Jamaica: Sherwood Forest (Sanborn, 1941:383; the three specimens concerned should be re-examined to ascertain if they are E. lynni named four years later from Jamaica by Shamel, Proc. Biol. Soc. Washington, 58:107, July 18, 1945).

Eptesicus fuscus miradorensis (H. Allen)

1866. S[cotophilus]. miradorensis H. Allen, Proc. Acad. Nat. Sci. Philadelphia, 18:287, type from Mirador, Veracruz.
1912. Eptesicus fuscus miradorensis, Miller, Bull. U.S. Nat. Mus., 79:62, December 31.

MARGINAL RECORDS.—Tamaulipas: Aserradero del Paraíso (Goodwin, 1954:6). Veracruz: 3 km. E Las Vigas (19230 KU); 5 km. N Jalapa (Davis, 1944:380). Guatemala: Flores (Goodwin, 1955d:4). Honduras: El Manteado (Goodwin, 1942:141). Costa Rica: San José (Goodwin, 1946:333). Panamá: Boquete (Goldman, 1920:216; the specimens concerned should be re-examined to ascertain if they are Eptesicus chiriquinus named in the same month from the same place by Thomas, 1920:362). Honduras: El Pedrero (Goodwin, 1942:141). Guatemala: Chichivac (Goodwin, 1934:15); Zunil (Miller, 1897b:100). Oaxaca: Oaxaca (ibid.). Michoacán: Rancho Escondido, 1 mi. N Apo (Hall and Villa, 1949:444). San Luis Potosí: Villa de Reyes (Dalquest, 1953b:54); 3 km. SW San Isidro (ibid.). Thomas (1920:361) named E. f. pelliceus from Venezuela, and shading on Map 136 should extend into S. America.

Eptesicus fuscus osceola Rhoads

1902. Eptesicus fuscus osceola Rhoads, Proc. Acad. Nat. Sci. Philadelphia, 53:618, February 6, type from Tarpon Springs, Pinellas Co., Florida.

MARGINAL RECORDS (Sherman, 1945:201).—Florida: type locality; southern Highlands Co.; Englewood.

Eptesicus fuscus pallidus Young

1908. Eptesicus pallidus Young, Proc. Acad. Nat. Sci. Phila., 60:408, Oct. 14, type from Boulder, Colorado.
1912. Eptesicus fuscus pallidus, Miller, Bull. U.S. Nat. Mus., 79:62, December 31.

MARGINAL RECORDS.—Alberta: Pine Lake, 24 mi. S Great Slave Lake, Wood Buffalo Park (Soper, 1942:125). Saskatchewan: Regina (Anderson, 1947:31). Nebraska: Ft. Niobrara Wildlife Refuge, 4 mi. E Valentine (Jones, 1954:482). Kansas: Court House, Osborne Co. (Cockrum, 1952:71); Medicine Lodge (ibid.). Coahuila: 1 mi. N Boquillas, 700 ft. (44744 KU); 9 mi. W, 4 mi. S San Buenaventura, 2000 ft. (48282 KU); Acatita, 3600 ft. (40864 KU). Sonora (Burt, 1938:26): Providencia Mines; Guaymas. Baja California: La Grulla (Engels, 1936:657). California (ibid.): Escondido; Julian; Hanapah Canyon, Panamint Mts. Nevada: Peterson Creek, Shoshone Mts. (Hall, 1946:154). Idaho (Davis, 1939:122): Payette Valley; Fort Sherman. Alberta (Anderson, 1947:31); Waterton Lakes; Edmonton.

Eptesicus fuscus peninsulae (Thomas)

1898. Vespertilio fuscus peninsulae Thomas, Ann. Mag. Nat. Hist., ser. 7, 1:43, January, type from Sierra Laguna, Baja California.
1912. Eptesicus fuscus peninsulae, Miller, Bull. U.S. Nat. Mus., 79:63, December 31.

MARGINAL RECORDS (Engels, 1936:658).—Baja California: Comondú; Agua Caliente.

Eptesicus fuscus wetmorei Jackson

1916. Eptesicus wetmorei Jackson, Proc. Biol. Soc. Washington, 29:37, Feb. 24, type from Maricao, Puerto Rico.
1945. Eptesicus fuscus wetmorei, Shamel, Proc. Biol. Soc. Washington, 58:108, July 18.

MARGINAL RECORDS (Anthony, 1918:359).—Puerto Rico: Cueva de Farid (Pueblo Viejo); San German; type locality.

Eptesicus lynni Shamel
Lynn's Brown Bat

1945. *Eptesicus lynni* Shamel, Proc. Biol. Soc. Washington, 58:107, July 18, type from cave 3 mi. E Montego Bay, Jamaica. Known only from the type locality.

Selected measurements of the type, an adult female, are: length of head and body, 55.0; length of forearm, 44.5; greatest length of skull, 16.8; breadth of braincase, 8.0; length of upper tooth-row, 6.0. Dichromatic; "typical" phase reddish-brown; alternate phase paler sometimes almost white (only alcoholic specimens described); underparts paler than back in each phase.

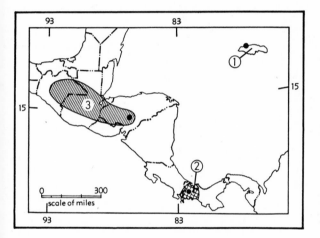

Map 137. Three species of *Eptesicus*.

1. *E. lynni* 2. *E. chiriquinus*
3. *E. albigularis*

Eptesicus brasiliensis
Brazilian Brown Bat

Eptesicus brasiliensis propinquus, the only subspecies occurring in the region here considered, may be characterized as follows: Selected measurements of specimens from Costa Rica are: total length, 96–105; length of forearm, 39–42; greatest length of skull, 15.8–16.0; zygomatic breadth, 10.8–11.0; breadth of braincase, 7.5–8.0; length of upper tooth-row, 5.8–6.0. Upper parts blackish brown or sometimes a little paler, often frosted with buff; underparts dark brown, strongly washed with some shade of buff. Skull resembling that of *E. fuscus*, but smaller, shorter, smoother; rostrum short, wide, somewhat flattened above. Specimens from the northern part of the range of the subspecies average smaller and slightly paler.

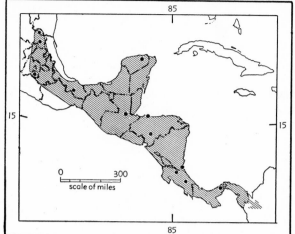

Map 138. *Eptesicus brasiliensis propinquus.*

Eptesicus brasiliensis propinquus (Peters)

1872. *Vesperus propinquus* Peters, Monatsb. preuss. Akad. Wiss., Berlin, p. 262, type from Santa Isabel, Petén, Guatemala.
1953. *Eptesicus brasiliensis propinquus*, Dalquest, Louisiana State Univ., Biol. Sci. Ser., 1:55, December 28.
1897. *Adelonycteris gaumeri* J. A. Allen, Bull. Amer. Mus. Nat. Hist., 9:231, September 28, type from Izamal, Yucatán.

MARGINAL RECORDS (Goodwin, 1942:141, unless otherwise noted).—San Luis Potosí (Dalquest, 1953b:55): El Salto; 1 km. W Huichihuayán. Veracruz: Achotal. Yucatán: Izamal. Guatemala: type locality. Honduras: near Tela (Test, 1934:316). Nicaragua: Greytown. Panamá: San Pablo (Goldman, 1920:215). Costa Rica (Goodwin, 1946:334): Santa Teresa Perálta; Vijagual San Carlos. Honduras: Camayaguela. Morelos: Cueva del Salitre (Málaga Alba and Villa R., 1957:552).

Eptesicus albigularis (Peters)
Peters' Brown Bat

1872. *Vesperus (Marsipolaemus) albigularis* Peters, Monatsb. preuss. Akad. Wiss., Berlin, p. 260, type from "Mexico."
1942. *Eptesicus albigularis*, Goodwin, Amer. Mus. Novit., 1199:1, October 9.

Selected measurements of an adult male from Honduras are: total length, 88; length of forearm, 40.0; greatest length of skull, 15.8; zygomatic breadth, 10.3; breadth of braincase, 7.5; length of upper tooth-row, 5.6. Upper parts dark brown washed with buff; underparts pale buffy, almost white. Skull small; braincase rounded; rostrum narrow and not conspicuously flattened; posterior border of palate relatively straight.

This bat is known by only two specimens.

MARGINAL RECORDS.—*"Mexico"* (= type locality). Honduras: Camayaguela (Goodwin, 1946:334).

Eptesicus chiriquinus Thomas
Chiriquí Brown Bat

1920. *Eptesicus chiriquinus* Thomas, Ann. Mag. Nat. Hist., ser. 9, 5:362, April, type from Boquete, Chiriquí, Panamá. Known only from the type locality.

Selected measurements of the type, an adult male, are: length of head and body, 70; greatest length of skull, 16.2; zygomatic breadth, 11.1; breadth of braincase, 7.8; length of upper tooth-row, 6.3. Fur long, soft; upper parts blackish brown; paler ends on hairs of posterior back short and inconspicuous; underparts almost as dark as upper parts (after Thomas, 1920:362).

Genus **Lasiurus** Gray—Hairy-tailed Bats

North American species revised by Miller, N. Amer. Fauna, 13:105–115, October 16, 1897.

1797. *Nycteris* B[orkhause]n, Der Zoologe (Compendiose Bibliothek gemeinnützigsten Kenntnisse für alle Stände, pt. 21), Heft 4–7, p. 66. Type, *Vespertilio borealis* Müller [= *Lasiurus borealis*]. *Nycteris* Borkhausen is a homonym of *Nycteris* G. Cuvier and É. G. St.-Hilaire, 1795, type *Vespertilio hispidus* Schreber, 1774 [= *Nycteris hispida*], from Senegal. Although *Nycteris* Cuvier and Geoffroy St.-Hilaire is a *nomen nudum*, Opinion 111 of the International Commission of Zoological Nomenclature establishes the name as available for a genus of Old World bats. Thus *Nycteris* Borkhausen is not available for the New World genus. *Nycteris* É. Geoffroy St.-Hilaire, 1803, is a synonym of *Nycteris* Cuvier and Geoffroy St.-Hilaire, 1795, as given status by the Commission.

1831. *Lasiurus* Gray, Zool. Miscl., No. 1, p. 38. Type, *Vespertilio borealis* Müller.

Skull short, broad; braincase high, rounded; upper surface of rostrum nearly in line with that of braincase; width of palatal emargination greater than depth; floor of braincase and palate not parallel; diameter of auditory bullae approximately equal to space between bullae. Ear short, rounded; uropatagium well furred above; 3rd, 4th, and 5th fingers progressively shortened. Dentition, i. $\frac{1}{3}$, c. $\frac{1}{1}$, p. $\frac{2}{2}$, m. $\frac{3}{3}$. The anterior upper premolar is minute, peg-like, and displaced inwardly out of the normal tooth-row; occasionally this tooth is lacking.

KEY TO NORTH AMERICAN SPECIES OF LASIURUS

1. Occurring on Antillean islands.
    2. Length of upper tooth-row less than 4.5.
        L. minor, p. 191
    2'. Length of upper tooth-row more than 4.5
        3. Greatest length of skull 13.9 or less.
            L. pfeifferi, p. 191
        3'. Greatest length of skull 13.9 or more.
            L. degelidus, p. 191

1'. Occurring on mainland and coastal islands.
    4. Total length more than 120; forearm more than 45. . . . . *L. cinereus*, p. 191
    4'. Total length less than 120; forearm less than 45.
        5. Upper parts brick red to rusty red washed with white. . . *L. borealis*, p. 188
        5'. Upper parts mahogany brown washed with white. . . . . *L. seminolus*, p. 190

Lasiurus borealis
Red Bat

x ½

Length of head and body, approximately 55; total length, 91–112; length of forearm, 37–43. Upper parts brick red to rusty red washed with white (males usually more brightly colored than females); underparts usually slightly paler; anterior part of shoulder with buffy white patch. Ears low, broad, rounded, naked inside, densely furred outside on basal two-thirds; tragus triangular. Uropatagium densely furred above, sparsely furred below.

The red bat of Canada and the United States ordinarily winters farther south. In summer, at least, it is solitary, roosts mostly in trees or shrubs, often near or even on the ground, begins flying early in the evening, usually hunts along watercourses or about trees, mates in August, bears 2–4 young in May or June, and has several subspecies endemic to South America.

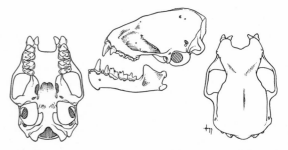

Fig. 138. *Lasiurus borealis borealis*, 1½ mi. S Galena, Cherokee Co., Kansas, No. 38813 K.U., ♀, X 2.

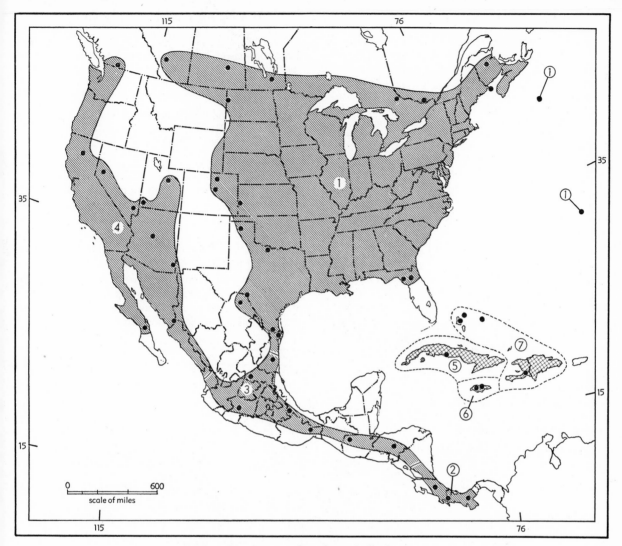

Map 139. *Lasiurus borealis* and allied species.

Guide to kinds	2. *L. b. frantzii*	5. *L. pfeifferi*
	3. *L. b. ornatus*	6. *L. degelidus*
1. *L. b. borealis*	4. *L. b. teliotis*	7. *L. minor*

Lasiurus borealis borealis (Müller)

1776. *Vespertilio borealis* Müller, Des Ritters Carl von Linné . . . vollständiges Natursystem . . . , Suppl., p. 20, type from New York.

1897. *Lasiurus borealis*, Miller, N. Amer. Fauna, 13:105, October 16.

1777. [*Vespertilio*] *noveboracensis* Erxleben, Systema regni animalis . . . , 1:155. Based on "the New York bat of Pennant (Synop. Quad., p. 367), 'Die nordamerikanische Fledermaus' of Schreber (Säugthiere, I, p. 176), and 'Der Neujorker' of Müller" (*antea*) (Miller, N. Amer. Fauna, 13:32, October 16, 1897).

1781. *Vespertilio lasiurus* Schreber, Die Säugthiere . . . , Abth. 1, pl. 62. Type locality, North America.

1796. *Vespertilio rubellus* Palisot de Beauvois, Catalogue raissoné du muséum de Mr. C. W. Peale, Philadelphia, p. 204. Type locality unknown.

1815. *Vespertilio rubra* Ord, *in* Guthrie, A new geogr., hist., coml. grammar . . . , Philadelphia, Amer. ed. 2, 2:291. Based on the red bat of Wilson, Amer. Ornith., 6:60.

1818. *Vespertilio tesselatus* Rafinesque, Amer. Monthly Mag., 3:445. Type locality unknown.

1818. *Vespertilio monachus* Rafinesque, Amer. Monthly Mag., 3:445. Type locality unknown.

1820. *Vespertilio rufus* Warden, Desc. États-Unis de l'Amer. Septentrionale, 5:606. Based on the red bat of Wilson, Amer. Ornith., 6:60.

1870. *Lasiurus funebris* Fitzinger, Sitzungsber. k. Akad. Wiss., Wien, 62:46. Based on *Nycticejus noveboracensis* Temminck, 1840, type locality Tennessee.

1930. *Myotis quebecensis* Yourans, Naturaliste Canadien, ser. 3, 57(vol. 1):65, March, type from Anse-à-Wolfe, Quebec. For status see "La Direction" [= Georges Maheux], Naturaliste Canadien, ser. 3, 57(vol. 1):185–186, October, 1930.

MARGINAL RECORDS.—Saskatchewan: Touchwood Hills (Hall, 1938:108). Manitoba: Winnipeg (Soper, 1946:135). Ontario: North Bay (Miller, 1897b:108). Quebec: Ottawa (Rand, 1945c:116). New Brunswick: vicinity Long Lake, Tobique Valley (Hagmeier, 1957:35); Grand Manan Island (Anderson, 1947:31), thence southward along Atlantic Coast to Florida (Sherman, 1937:107): Gainesville; Old Town, thence westward along Gulf Coast to Tamaulipas: Matamoros (Miller, 1897b:108). Texas: Edinburg (Blair, 1952:238). Coahuila: Fortín (44745 KU). Texas: Devils River (Blair, 1952:96); Wichita Falls (Miller, 1897b:108); Stinnett (Blair, 1954b:242). Kansas (Cockrum, 1952:77): 1 mi. E Coolidge. Colorado (Warren, 1942:28): NW of Littleton; Greeley. North Dakota: Yellowstone River, probably Buford (V. Bailey, 1927:209). Alberta: Calgary (Anderson, 1947:31). Also, 42° 42' N, 62° 58' W (Brown, 1953:139), and Bermuda (G. M. Allen, 1923:61).

Lasiurus borealis frantzii (Peters)

1871. *Atalapha frantzii* Peters, Monatsb. preuss. Akad. Wiss., Berlin, p. 908, type from Costa Rica.
1932. *Lasiurus borealis frantzii*, Goldman, Proc. Biol. Soc. Washington, 45:148, September 9.

MARGINAL RECORDS.—Costa Rica: San José (Goodwin, 1946:335). Panamá (Goldman, 1932e:148): Colobre [= Calobre]; Boquete.

Lasiurus borealis ornatus Hall

1951. *Lasiurus borealis ornatus* Hall, Univ. Kansas Publ., Mus. Nat. Hist., 5:226, December 15, type from Penuela, Veracruz. Equals *Lasiurus borealis mexicanus* (Saussure), Auct., but *mexicanus* Saussure is properly assignable to *Lasiurus cinereus*.

MARGINAL RECORDS.—Tamaulipas: 10 mi. W, 2 mi. S Piedra (Anderson, 1956:351). Veracruz: type locality. Honduras: La Flor Archaga (Goodwin, 1942:142). Guatemala: Barrillos (Goodwin, 1934:15). Oaxaca: Guichicovi (Miller, 1897b:112). Michoacán: Nuevo San Juan, 5 mi. SW Uruapan (Hall and Villa, 1949:444). *Jalisco* (Miller, 1897b:112). San Luis Potosí: Bledos (Dalquest, 1953b:61). Tamaulipas: *14 mi. W and 3 mi. S Piedra* (Anderson, 1956:351).

Lasiurus borealis teliotis (H. Allen)

1891. *Atalapha teliotis* H. Allen, Proc. Amer. Philos. Soc., 29:5, April 10, type from an unknown locality, probably some part of California.
1897. *Lasiurus borealis teliotis*, Miller, N. Amer. Fauna, 13:110, October 16.

MARGINAL RECORDS.—British Columbia: Skagit (Anderson, 1947:31). California: Dale's (Grinnell, *et al.*, 1930:457). Nevada (Hall, 1946:155): 5 mi. SW Fallon; Overton. Utah (Durrant, 1952:56): St. George; *La Verkin Cave*; Kenilworth Mine. Arizona: Montezuma Well (Davis, 1945:194); Cave Creek, near Portal (Cahalane, 1939:422). Sonora: Guirocoba (Burt, 1938:26). Baja California: Comondú (Anthony, 1928:61), thence northward along Pacific Coast to point of beginning.

Lasiurus seminolus (Rhoads)
Seminole Bat

1895. *Atalapha borealis seminola* Rhoads, Proc. Acad. Nat. Sci. Philadelphia, 47:32, March 19, type from Tarpon Springs, Pinellas Co., Florida.
1932. *Lasiurus seminolus*, Poole, Jour. Mamm., 13:162, May 11.
1896. *Atalapha borealis peninsularis* [Coues], The Nation, 62:404, May 21. Type locality, Florida. Described by Cory, Hunting and Fishing in Florida . . . , pp. 115–116, 1896.

Resembling *L. borealis* and differing mainly in color. Upper parts rich mahogany brown lightly frosted with grayish white; posterior part of underparts slightly paler than back; throat and chest whitish.

This bat has long been considered to be a subspecies of *Lasiurus borealis*. There is ample evidence, however, that the two kinds occupy the same habitat simultaneously without evidence of intergradation and *seminolus* therefore is accorded specific rank. But, see Koopman, *et al.* (1957:168).

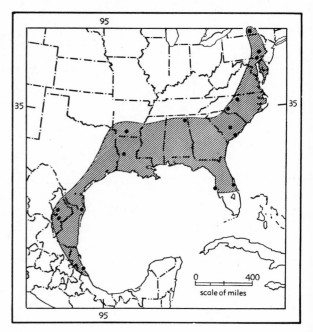

Map 140. *Lasiurus seminolus*.

MARGINAL RECORDS.—New York: Ithaca (Layne, 1955:453). Pennsylvania (Poole, 1949:80): Hopewell; shore of Susquehanna River near mouth Fishing Creek. South Carolina: Charleston (Penney, 1950:84), thence southward along coast to Florida (Sherman, 1937:107–108): Micco; Seven Oaks, thence westward along Gulf Coast to Texas: Brownsville (Strecker, 1926:10). Veracruz: Tecolutla (Villa, 1955:238). Nuevo León (Villa, 1955:237–238): Galeana; Monterrey. Louisiana: Vowell's Mill (Lowery, 1943:223). Arkansas: Newport Landing (Sealander and Hoiberg, 1954:584). Alabama: Fort Payne (A. H. Howell, 1921:27). South Carolina: 9 mi. N Orangeburg (Coleman, 1950:190). North Carolina: Camp Steere (Barkalow and Adams, 1955:453); Raleigh (*ibid.*).

Lasiurus pfeifferi (Gundlach)
Pfeiffer's Hairy-tailed Bat

1861. *Atalapha pfeifferi* Gundlach, Monatsb. preuss. Akad. Wiss., Berlin, p. 152, type from Cuba. Known only from Cuba, specifically, Trinidad (Miller, 1931:410).
1931. *Lasiurus pfeifferi,* Miller, Jour. Mamm., 12:409, November 11.

Head and body, approximately 55. "Differs from the red bat of eastern United States in larger size (forearm 42 mm. or more instead of 42 mm. or less; tibia about 21 mm. instead of 18.6–20 mm.), and in the marked reduction of the pale hair tips on both upper and lower surfaces of body. Skull equal in size to that of the largest individuals of *L. borealis borealis*" (Miller, 1931:409–410).

Lasiurus degelidus Miller
Jamaican Hairy-tailed Bat

1931. *Lasiurus degelidus* Miller, Jour. Mamm., 12:410, November 11, type from Sutton's, District of Vere, Jamaica.

Head and body, approximately 55. "Skull in two females larger than in two males of *Lasiurus pfeifferi,* and cheek-teeth (in crown view) conspicuously larger. Color of females about as in brightest males of *Lasiurus borealis borealis* but with no trace of grayish 'frosting' on upper parts; underparts darker than in the mainland animal, and, in two of four specimens, with no whitish tips on the hairs of the chest, the white shoulder spots thus thrown into very strong relief" (Miller, 1931:410).

MARGINAL RECORDS.—Jamaica: type locality; Spanishtown (Miller, 1931:410).

Lasiurus minor Miller
Small Hairy-tailed Bat

1931. *Lasiurus minor* Miller, Jour. Mamm., 12:410, November 11, type from "Voute l'Église," 1350 ft., a cave near the Jacmel road a few kilometers N Trouin, Haiti. (Regarded as a subspecies of *L. borealis* by Koopman, *et al.,* Jour. Mamm., 38:168, May 27, 1957.)

Skull noticeably smaller than in Cuban or Jamaican species (greatest length of skull of two specimens, 13 and 12), and about the same as in *L. b. borealis* from Virginia; braincase, as compared with that of the mainland animal, more rounded when viewed from above, and more nearly flat-topped when viewed from behind; lacrimal ridge and tubercle poorly developed; upper cheek-teeth essen-

tially like those of *L. borealis borealis* except that P4 smaller (after Miller, 1931:410).

MARGINAL RECORDS.—Bahama Islands: New Providence Island (Koopman, *et al.,* 1957:168); Orange Creek, Cat Island (G. M. Allen and Sanborn, 1937:228; identification stated to be uncertain). Haiti: type locality. Bahama Islands: Andros Island (Koopman, *et al.,* 1957:168).

Lasiurus cinereus
Hoary Bat

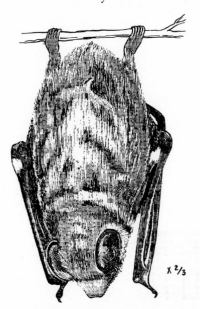

Length of head and body, approximately 85; total length, 134–140; length of forearm, 46–55. Upper parts varying considerably in color but not geographically, yellowish brown to mahogany brown strongly frosted with silver; underparts whitish on

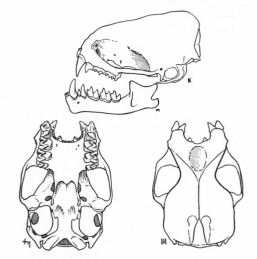

Fig. 139. *Lasiurus cinereus,* Camp Verde, Yavapai Co., Arizona, No. 71588 M.V.Z., ♀, X 2.

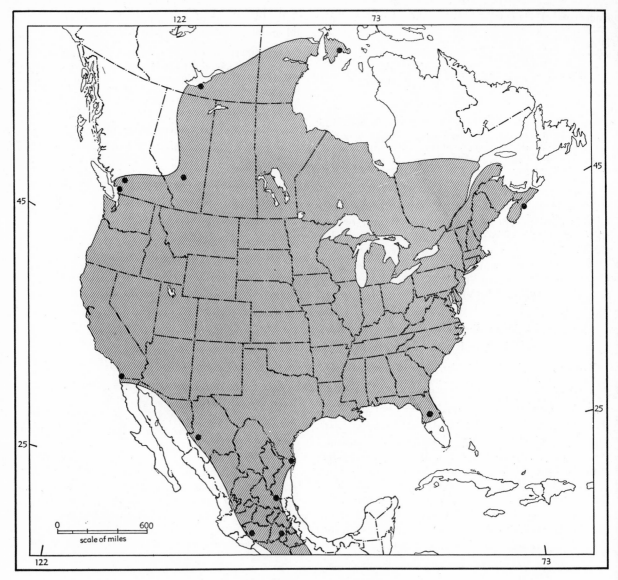

Map 141. *Lasiurus cinereus cinereus.*

belly, pale brown on chest, yellowish on throat; ears rimmed with black. Skull robust; rostrum broad, short; zygomatic arches widespread.

This bat is migratory and usually moves to warm climates in winter. The adult males arrive in the summering areas later than females. Young are born in June; two is the usual number but as many as four are known. Like *L. borealis,* the hoary bat is solitary and roosts in trees and shrubs rather than in caves. It occurs also in South America.

Lasiurus cinereus cinereus (Palisot de Beauvois)

1796. *Vespertilio cinereus* (misspelled *linereus*) Palisot de Beauvois, Catalogue raisonné du muséum de Mr. C. W.

Peale, Philadelphia, p. 18, type from Philadelphia, Pennsylvania.
1864. *Lasiurus cinereus* H. Allen, Smiths. Miscl. Coll., 7(publ. 165):21, June.
1823. *Vespertilio pruinosus* Say, *in* Long, Account of an exped. . . . to the Rocky Mts. . . . , 1:167, type from Engineer Cantonment, Washington Co., Nebraska.
1861. *A[talapha]. mexicana* Saussure, Revue et Mag. Zool., Paris, ser. 2, 13:97, March, type from an unknown locality, probably from Veracruz, Puebla or Oaxaca.

MARGINAL RECORDS.—Keewatin: Bear Island, Southampton Island (Anderson, 1947:32). Nova Scotia: Halifax (Morris, 1948:168), thence southward along Atlantic Coast to Florida: between Tavares and Apopka (Sherman, 1956: 282), thence westward along Gulf Coast to Tamaulipas: Matamoros (Miller, 1897b:114). San Luis Potosí: El Salto (Dalquest, 1953b:60). Distrito Federal (Villa, 1953:338):

El Peñón; Tacubaya. Michoacán: Barrancá Seca (Hall and Villa, 1949:445). Chihuahua: Mojarachic (Knobloch, 1942: 297). California: Chula Vista (P. H. Krutzsch, *in litt.*), thence northward along Pacific Coast to British Columbia: Vancouver (Anderson, 1947:32); Alta Lake (Cowan and Guiguet, 1956:76). Alberta: 8 mi. NW Red Deer (Miller, 1897b:114). Mackenzie: Resolution (Anderson, 1947:32).

Genus **Dasypterus** Peters—Yellow Bats

Revised by Miller, N. Amer. Fauna, 13:115–118, October 16, 1897.

1871. *Dasypterus* Peters, Monatsb. preuss. Akad. Wiss., Berlin, p. 912. Type, *Lasiurus intermedius* H. Allen.

Closely resembling *Lasiurus;* differs principally in absence of minute, peglike P2. Dalquest (1953b: 61) seemingly considers the two genera to be synonymous; he applies the name *Lasiurus ega xanthinus* to bats from San Luis Potosí.

KEY TO SPECIES OF DASYPTERUS

1. Total length more than 119; length of upper tooth-row more than 6.2.
   D. floridanus, p. 193, and *D. intermedius,* p. 193
1'. Total length less than 119; length of upper tooth-row less than 6.2. . . . . *D. ega,* p. 194

Dasypterus intermedius (H. Allen)
Yellow Bat

1862. *Lasiurus intermedius* H. Allen, Proc. Acad. Nat. Sci., Philadelphia, 14:246, type from Matamoros, Tamaulipas.
1894. *Dasypterus intermedius* H. Allen, Bull. U.S. Nat. Mus., 43:137, March 14.

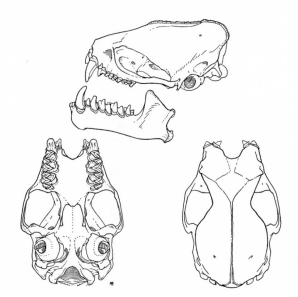

Fig. 140. *Dasypterus intermedius,* Houston, Harris Co., Texas, No. 84218 M.V.Z., ♀, X 2.

Length of head and body, approximately 75. Average measurements of 10 near-topotypes are: total length, 145; length of forearm, 55. Cranial measurements of a topotype are: greatest length, 19.8; zygomatic breadth, 14; length of upper tooth-row, 7. Upper parts light yellowish brown faintly washed with black; underparts like upper parts but usually lacking wash. Skull short, deep, and broad.

MARGINAL RECORDS.—Texas: Houston (84218 MVZ); Padre Island (Strecker, 1926:10). Cuba: cave at San Blas (De Beaufort, 1934:316). *Chiapas* (Miller, 1924:80). Texas: Mission (Taylor and Davis, 1947:18).

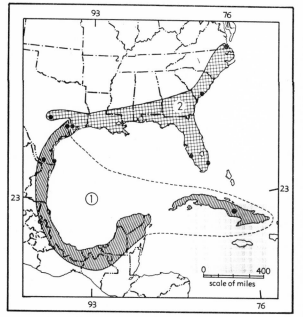

Map 142. *Dasypterus intermedius* (1) and *Dasypterus floridanus* (2).

Dasypterus floridanus Miller
Florida Yellow Bat

1902. *Dasypterus floridanus* Miller, Proc. Acad. Nat. Sci., Philadelphia, 54:392, September 12, type from Lake Kissimmee, Osceola Co., Florida.

Selected measurements of the type, an adult female, are: length of head and body, approximately 77; total length, 129; length of forearm, 49; greatest length of skull, 18; zygomatic breadth, 13; length of upper tooth-row, 6.8. This species closely resembles *D. intermedius* from which it differs mainly in smaller size.

MARGINAL RECORDS.—Virginia: Willoughby Beach (Rageot, 1955:456). South Carolina: Charleston (Penney, 1950:84), thence southward along coast to Florida (Moore, 1949:50): Miami; Punta Gorda, thence westward along Gulf Coast to Texas: Harris County (Taylor and Davis, 1947:19); Austin (Eads, Menzies and Wiseman, 1956: 440), thence to point of beginning.

Dasypterus ega
Southern Yellow Bat

Size small; two males from Costa Rica measure: length of head and body, approximately 65, 61; total length, 115, 109; length of forearm, 44.0, 45.8. Cranial measurements of one of these are: greatest length, 14.5; zygomatic breadth, 10.4; breadth of braincase, 8.1; length of upper tooth-row, 5.5. Color highly variable, ranging from dark brownish washed with black to buffy white. Differing osteologically from *D. intermedius* mainly in smaller size.

Two subspecies, *D. e. panamensis* and *D. e. xanthinus*, occur within the geographic scope of this report. Dalquest (1953b:62) seems to consider the two subspecies as indistinguishable since he employs the name *Lasiurus ega xanthinus* for specimens from San Luis Potosí and states that the subspecies ranges northward from Panamá. Because no reason is given for his taxonomic arrangement we have not employed it. The species occurs also in South America.

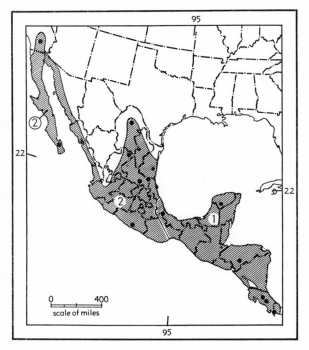

Map 143. *Dasypterus ega.*

1. *D. e. panamensis*   2. *D. e. xanthinus*

Dasypterus ega panamensis Thomas

1901. *Dasypterus ega panamensis* Thomas, Ann. Mag. Nat. Hist., ser. 7, 8:246, September, type from Bogava [= Bugaba], Chiriquí, Panamá.

MARGINAL RECORDS.—Yucatán: Ebizt Cave, Oxkutzcab (Pearse and Kellogg, 1938:303). Honduras: Teguci-galpa (Goodwin, 1942:142). Costa Rica (Goodwin, 1946:336): San José; Lajas Villa Quesada. Panamá: type locality. Veracruz: Achotal (Elliot, 1907:514).

Dasypterus ega xanthinus Thomas

1897. *Dasypterus ega xanthinus* Thomas, Ann. Mag. Nat. Hist., ser. 6, 20:544, December, type from Sierra Laguna, Baja California.

MARGINAL RECORDS.—California: Palm Springs (Constantine, 1946:107). Sinaloa: 1 mi. S Pericos (61173 KU). Zacatecas: Concepción del Oro, 7680 ft. (Baker, 1956:186). Coahuila: 4 mi. W Hacienda La Mariposa, 2300 ft. (*op. cit.*: 185). Tamaulipas: 10 mi. W, 3 mi. S Piedra (55321 KU). San Luis Potosí (Dalquest, 1953b:62): 4 mi. SSW Ajinche; 1½ mi. E Río Verde. Guerrero: El Papayo (Lukens and Davis, 1957:12). Baja California: type locality.

Genus Nycticeius Rafinesque—Evening Bats

Revised by Miller, N. Amer. Fauna, 13:118–121, October 16, 1897.

1819. *Nycticeius* Rafinesque, Jour. Phys. Chim. Hist. Nat. et Arts, Paris, 88:417, June. Type, *Vespertilio humeralis* Rafinesque.
1827. *Nycticeus* Lesson, Manuel de mammalogie . . . , p. 98, a variant spelling of *Nycticeius* Rafinesque.
1827. *Nyctejus* Temminck, Monographies de mammalogie . . . , 1:xvii, a variant spelling of *Nycticeius* Rafinesque.
1830. *Nycticeyx* Wagler, Naturliches system der amphibien . . . , p. 13, a variant spelling of *Nycticeius* Rafinesque.
1831. *Nycticea* Le Conte, *in* McMurtrie, The animal kingdom . . . by the Baron Cuvier . . . , 1(App.):432, a variant spelling of *Nycticeius* Rafinesque.

Lower teeth as in *Eptesicus*; I1 simple, unicuspid, nearly half as high as C and in contact with C or nearly so; upper premolar without cusp on inner side; M3 with area of crown more than half that of M1 or M2; mesostyle, metacone, and three commissures well developed on M3. Dentition, i. $\frac{1}{3}$, c. $\frac{1}{1}$, p. $\frac{1}{2}$, m. $\frac{3}{3}$.

KEY TO SPECIES OF NYCTICEIUS

1. Total length less than 85; occurring in Cuba. . . . . *N. cubanus*, p. 195
1'. Total length usually more than 85; occurring on mainland. . . . . . *N. humeralis*, p. 194

Nycticeius humeralis
Evening Bat

Length of head and body, approximately 56; total length, 85–99; length of forearm, 33.6–39; greatest length of skull, 14.0–14.7. Skull short, low, broad, and robust; dorsal profile from nares to occiput almost straight; teeth small for size of skull. Pelage short, sparse; upper parts medium to dark brown, hairs plumbeous basally; underparts paler, sometimes as pale as tawny; membranes naked.

Evening bats roost in trees, crevices, and houses. The flight is slow and deliberate and only in late evening do these bats fly near the ground. Two young are born in May but, unlike those of many other bats, probably are left at the roost while the mother forages.

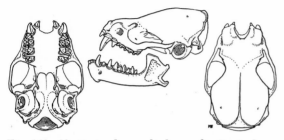

Fig. 141. *Nycticeius humeralis humeralis*, St. Andrews Parish, Charleston Co., South Carolina, No. 97176 M.V.Z., ♂, X 2.

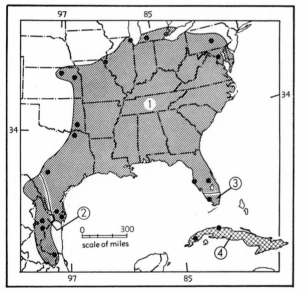

Map 144. *Nycticeius humeralis* and *N. cubanus*.

1. *N. h. humeralis*
2. *N. h. mexicanus*
3. *N. h. subtropicalis*
4. *N. cubanus*

Nycticeius humeralis humeralis (Rafinesque)

1818. *Vespertilio humeralis* Rafinesque, Amer. Monthly Mag., 3(6):445, October, type from Kentucky.
1819. *N[ycticeius]. humeralis* Rafinesque, Jour. Phys. Chim. Hist. Nat. et Arts, Paris, 88:417, June.
1831. *Nycticea crepuscularis* Le Conte, *in* McMurtrie, The animal kingdom . . . by the Baron Cuvier . . . , 1(App.):432. Type locality not stated.

MARGINAL RECORDS.—Ontario: Point Pelee (Anderson, 1947:32). Pennsylvania: Carlisle (Gifford and Whitebread, 1951:54). District of Columbia: Washington (Miller, 1897b:120), thence southward along Atlantic Coast to Florida (Sherman, 1937:108): Kenansville; Indian Key, Tampa Bay, thence westward along Gulf Coast to Tamau-

lipas: Matamoras (Miller, 1897b:120). Texas: Hidalgo (*ibid.*); 20 mi. SW Hunt (Blair, 1952:96); Paris (Taylor and Davis, 1947:19). Oklahoma: 4 mi. NE Tuskahoma (Blair, 1939:102). Kansas (Cockrum, 1952:73): 7½ mi. SSW Lawrence; 6 mi. SW Clay Center. Illinois (Necker and Hatfield, 1941:46): Warsaw; Sugar Mound. Michigan: Climax (Burt, 1946:115).

Nycticeius humeralis mexicanus Davis

1944. *Nycticeius humeralis mexicanus* Davis, Jour. Mamm., 25:380, December 12, type from Río Ramos, 1000 ft., 20 km. NW Montemorelos, Nuevo León.

MARGINAL RECORDS.—Coahuila (Baker, 1956:186): *2 mi. W. Jiménez, 850 ft.* Nuevo León: type locality; Linares (17842 KU). San Luis Potosí: 19 km. SW Ebano (Dalquest: 1953b:57). Coahuila (Baker, 1956:186): *8 mi. N and 4 mi. W Musquiz; 10 mi. E Hda. La Mariposa.*

Nycticeius humeralis subtropicalis Schwartz

1951. *Nycticeius humeralis subtropicalis* Schwartz, Jour. Mamm., 32:233, May 21, type from 2½ mi. W Monroe Station, Collier Co., Florida. Known only from between ½ mi. and 2⁹⁄₁₀ mi. W Monroe Station, Florida.

Nycticeius cubanus (Gundlach)
Cuban Evening Bat

1861. *Vesperus cubanus* Gundlach, Monatsb. preuss. Akad. Wiss., Berlin, p. 150, type from near Cárdenas, Matanzas, Cuba.
1904. *Nycticeius cubanus*, Miller, Proc. U.S. Nat. Mus., 27:338, January 23.

Length of head and body, approximately 52. Closely resembling *N. humeralis*; differs mainly in smaller size (total length, 73–83; length of forearm, 28.6–32.4).

MARGINAL RECORDS.—Cuba: type locality; Pinar del Río (Miller, 1904:338).

Genus Rhogeëssa H. Allen—Little Yellow Bats

Revised by Miller, N. Amer. Fauna, 13:122–129, October 16, 1897; see also Hall, Univ. Kansas Publ., Mus. Nat. Hist., 5:227–232, April 10, 1952.

1866. *Rhogeëssa* H. Allen, Proc. Acad. Nat. Sci. Philadelphia, 18:285. Type, *Rhogeëssa tumida* H. Allen.
1873. *Rhogoessa* Marschall, Nomenclator Zool., Mamm., p. 11, a variant spelling.

Length of head and body, approximately 41. Skull small, light, papery, narrow, and deep; outer lobe of all three lower incisors obsolete, inner lobe almost absent from outer incisor and that tooth therefore much reduced in bulk. Dentition, i. $\frac{1}{3}$, c. $\frac{1}{1}$, p. $\frac{1}{2}$, m. $\frac{3}{3}$

KEY TO NORTH AMERICAN SPECIES OF RHOGEËSSA

1. Ear more than 15. . . . . *R. gracilis*, p. 197
1'. Ear less than 15. . . . . . *R. parvula*, p. 196

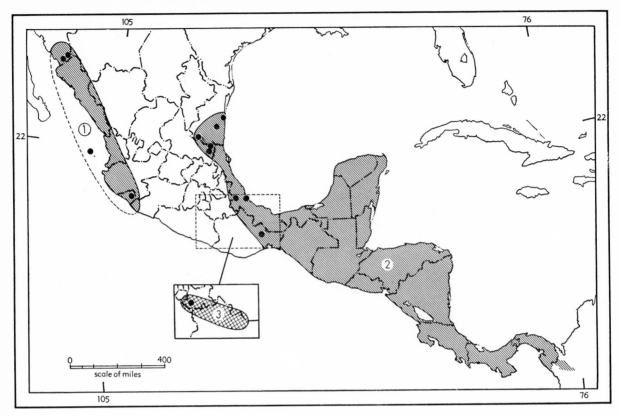

Map 145. *Rhogeëssa parvula* and *R. gracilis*.

Guide to kinds   2. *R. p. tumida*
1. *R. p. parvula*   3. *R. gracilis*

Rhogeëssa parvula
Little Yellow Bat

Selected cranial measurements are: greatest length, 11.25–13.5; zygomatic breadth, 7.4–8.5; length of upper tooth-row, 4.1–5.0. Length of forearm, 26.0–32.6. Upper parts light brown; underparts slightly paler. Skull resembling that of *Nycticeius* but occiput higher, rostrum relatively narrower, and dorsal profile concave in preorbital region.

Fig. 142. *Rhogeëssa parvula parvula*, W side Alamos, Sonora, No. 24854 K.U., ♀, X 2.

Rhogeëssa parvula parvula H. Allen

1866. *R[hogeëssa]. parvula* H. Allen, Proc. Acad. Nat. Sci. Philadelphia, 18:285, type from Tres Marías Islands, Nayarit.

MARGINAL RECORDS (following general statement of geographic range by Hall, 1952:231).—Sonora: San Rafael (Burt, 1938:26). Colima: Colima (*ibid.*), thence northward along Pacific Coast, including type locality, to Sonora: Alamos (Hall, 1952:232).

Rhogeëssa parvula tumida H. Allen

1866. *R[hogeëssa]. tumida* H. Allen, Proc. Acad. Nat. Sci. Philadelphia, 18:286, type from Mirador, Veracruz.
1952. *Rhogeëssa parvula tumida*, Hall, Univ. Kansas Publ., Mus. Nat. Hist., 5:231, April 10.

MARGINAL RECORDS (following general statement of geographic range by Hall, 1952:231).—Tamaulipas: 4 mi. N La Pesca (Anderson, 1956:350). San Luis Potosí: 10 km. WSW Ebano (Dalquest, 1953b:58). Veracruz: Boca del Río, 10 ft. (Hall, 1952:232), thence southward along Atlantic Coast to South America, thence northward along Pacific Coast to Oaxaca: Santo Domingo (Miller, 1897b: 129). Veracruz: type locality. San Luis Potosí: 3 km. N

Taninul (Dalquest, 1953b:58). Tamaulipas: Santa María (Goodwin, 1954:6); 10 mi. W and 2 mi. S Piedra, 1200 ft. (Anderson, 1956:350).

Rhogeëssa gracilis Miller
Slender Yellow Bat

1897. *Rhogeëssa gracilis* Miller, N. Amer. Fauna, 13:126, October 16, type from Piaxtla, Puebla.

External measurements of the type, an adult female, are: total length, 82; length of forearm, 33. Described as differing markedly from *R. parvula* in more slender form and larger ear (height of ear more than 15, and less in *R. parvula*).

This is an exceedingly rare bat and as yet its morphological characters are inadequately known.

MARGINAL RECORDS.—Puebla: type locality. Also known from *Isthmus of Tehuantepec* (Hall, 1952:231).

Genus **Baeodon** Miller

1906. *Baeodon* Miller, Proc. Biol. Soc. Washington, 19:85, June 4. Type, *Rhogeëssa alleni* Thomas.

Length of head and body of the type, an adult female, 47. Resembles *Rhogeëssa* but outer lower incisor so reduced that tooth is mere functionless spicule less than one-twentieth as large as 1st or 2nd incisor and nearly concealed beneath cingulum of canine. Only one species is known.

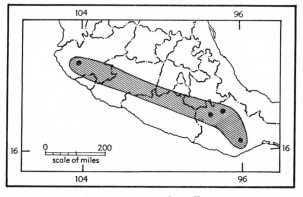

Map 146. *Baeodon alleni*.

Baeodon alleni (Thomas)
Allen's Baeodon

1892. *Rhogeëssa alleni* Thomas, Ann. Mag. Nat. Hist., ser. 6, 10:477, December, type from Santa Rosalía, near Autlán, Jalisco.
1906. *Baeodon alleni*, Miller, Proc. Biol. Soc. Washington, 19:85, June 4.

Characters as for the genus.

MARGINAL RECORDS.—Jalisco: type locality. Oaxaca: Cuicatlan, 590 m (Hall, 1955a:2); 6 mi. W and 2 mi. N Nejapa (Anderson, 1956:350); 2 mi. NNW Tamazulapan (Hall, 1955a:2).

Genus **Euderma** H. Allen—Spotted Bat

1892. *Euderma* H. Allen, Proc. Acad. Nat. Sci. Philadelphia, 43:467, January 19. Type, *Histiotus maculatus* J. A. Allen.

Skull with low, rounded, and large braincase; rostrum markedly reduced; zygomata abruptly expanded at middle; auditory bullae much enlarged, their greatest diameter approximately equalling length of upper tooth-row exclusive of incisors; lower canine relatively smallest in subfamily, and when viewed from slightly anterior to a lateral view, appears unequally bilobed. Dentition, i. $\frac{2}{3}$, c. $\frac{1}{1}$, p. $\frac{2}{2}$, m. $\frac{3}{3}$.

Only one species is known.

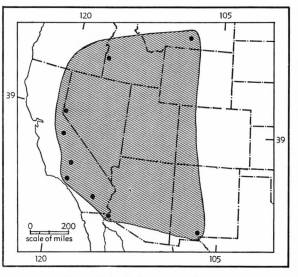

Map 147. *Euderma maculatum*.

Euderma maculatum (J. A. Allen)
Spotted Bat

1891. *Histiotus maculatus* J. A. Allen, Bull. Amer. Mus. Nat. Hist., 3:195, February 20, type from near Piru, Ventura Co., California; probably at mouth Castac Creek, Santa Clara Valley, Los Angeles Co., 8 mi. E Piru.
1894. *Euderma maculata*, H. Allen, Bull. U.S. Nat. Mus., 43:61, March 14.

Measurements of an adult female from Utah are: length of head and body, approximately 65; total length, 115; length of ear, 47; length of forearm, 51; condylobasal length, 16.2; breadth of braincase, 10.0; length of upper tooth-row, 6.1 (unworn). Upper parts black or nearly so with two "saddle marks" and spot at base of tail white; underparts white. Ears exceedingly large. Other characters as for the genus.

MARGINAL RECORDS (Nicholson, 1950:197, unless otherwise noted).—Montana: Billings. New Mexico: Mesilla Park. Arizona: Yuma. California: Mecca; type locality; Red Rock Canyon (Hall, 1939:103); Yosemite Valley. Nevada: Reno. Idaho: 15 mi. SW Caldwell (Tucker, 1957: 406).

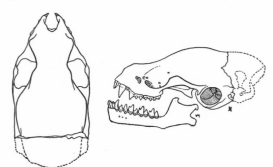

Fig. 143. *Euderma maculatum*, Reno, Nevada, No. 65171 M.V.Z., sex ?, X 2.

Genus Corynorhinus H. Allen—Big-eared Bats

Revised by Miller, N. Amer. Fauna, 13:49–54, October 16, 1897; and G. M. Allen, Bull. Mus. Comp. Zool., 60:333–356, April, 1916. Application of names changed by Handley, Jour. Washington Acad. Sci., 45:147, May 23, 1955.

1865. *Corynorhinus* H. Allen, Proc. Acad. Nat. Sci. Philadelphia, 17:173. Type, *Plecotus macrotis* Le Conte.
1865. *Corynorhynchus* Peters, Monatsb. preuss. Akad. Wiss., Berlin, p. 524, October, a *lapsus*?

Length of head and body, approximately 64. Skull slender, highly arched; rostrum relatively greatly reduced; lacrimal region smoothly rounded. Ears much enlarged, joined basally across forehead. Muzzle bearing conspicuous glandular mass on either side between eye and nostril. Dentition, i. $\frac{2}{3}$, c. $\frac{1}{1}$, p. $\frac{2}{3}$, m. $\frac{3}{3}$.

This genus closely resembles the Old World genus *Plecotus*, and some modern authors (Simpson, 1945: 59; Blair and Miller, 1949:76; Dalquest, 1953b: 63) regard the two as synonymous and employ the name *Plecotus* for the New World species.

KEY TO SPECIES OF CORYNORHINUS

1. Underparts washed with white; hairs of dorsum sharply bicolored. . . *C. rafinesquii*, p. 200
1'. Underparts washed with tan to pale buff; hairs of dorsum grading from brown at tip to slate at base. . . . . *C. townsendii*, p. 198

Corynorhinus townsendii
Townsend's Big-eared Bat

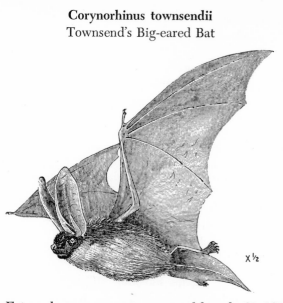

External measurements are: total length, 89–109; length of forearm, 39–44. Cranial measurements are: greatest length, 15.6–17.4; zygomatic breadth, 8–9; breadth of braincase, 7.6–8.6; length of upper tooth-row, 6.0–6.5. Upper parts pinkish buff to blackish; underparts buffy to brownish.

Townsend's bat is primarily a cave-dweller but is often found in attics and barns. Usually it roosts in small groups in semi-light areas. Bats of this species are easily disturbed and take flight readily. They emerge from roosting sites in late dusk and at that time fly at considerable elevations. Only after dark do they descend near the ground. Usually only one young is born and that in early summer.

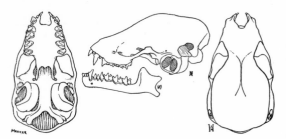

Fig. 144. *Corynorhinus townsendii pallescens*, 7 mi. S Cleveland Ranch, White Pine Co., Nevada, No. 45899 M.V.Z., ♂, X 2.

Corynorhinus townsendii australis Handley

1955. *Corynorhinus townsendii australis* Handley, Jour. Washington Acad. Sci., 45:147, May 23, type from 2 mi. W Jacala, Hidalgo.

MARGINAL RECORDS (Handley, 1955:148, unless otherwise noted).—Coahuila: 4 mi. W Hacienda La Mariposa; 9 mi. N, 4 mi. W San Buenaventura; ½ mi. N Muralla;

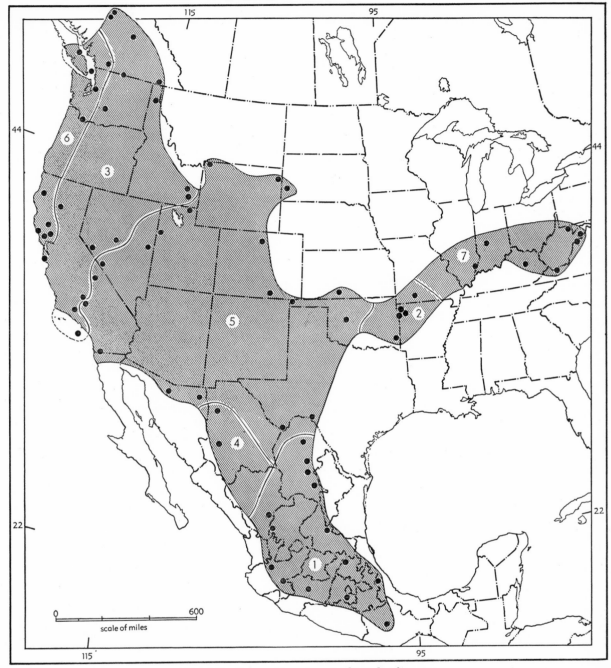

Map 148. *Corynorhinus townsendii* and subspecies.

Guide to	2. *C. t. ingens*	5. *C. t. pallescens*
subspecies	3. *C. t. intermedius*	6. *C. t. townsendii*
1. *C. t. australis*	4. *C. t. mexicanus*	7. *C. t. virginianus*

1 mi. S, 4 mi. W Bella Unión. San Luis Potosí: Presa de Guadalupe. Hidalgo: type locality. Veracruz: Jico (G. M. Allen, 1916:349). Oaxaca: Oaxaca. Morelos: Cuernavaca. Michoacán: Pátzcuaro (Hall and Villa, 1949:445). Jalisco: San Pedro, Guadalajara; San Andrés, 10 mi. W Magdalena. Zacatecas: Sierra de Valparaíso. Durango: San Juan, 12 mi. W Lerdo.

Corynorhinus townsendii ingens Handley

1955. *Corynorhinus townsendii ingens* Handley, Jour. Washington Acad. Sci., 45:148, May 23, type from Hewlitt Cave, 12 mi. W Fayetteville, Washington Co., Arkansas.

MARGINAL RECORDS.—Missouri: Stone County (Handley, 1955:148). Arkansas: Basset Cave near Hicks (Handley, 1955:148). Oklahoma (Blair, 1939:102): 2 mi. W Smithville; *Houston*. Arkansas (Handley, 1955:148): Devils Icebox, 25 mi. SW Fayetteville; type locality.

Corynorhinus townsendii intermedius H. W. Grinnell

1914. *Corynorhinus macrotis intermedius* H. W. Grinnell, Univ. California Publ. Zool., 12:320, December 4, type from Auburn, 1300 ft., Placer Co., California.

MARGINAL RECORDS.—British Columbia (Cowan and Guiguet, 1956:67): Williams Lake; Adams River; Creston. Idaho: Derr Island, mouth Clark Fork River (Jones, 1949:48); Blackfoot (Davis, 1939:124); Schutt's mine (*ibid.*). Nevada (Hall, 1946:162): ¼ mi. WNW Austin; Stanmoore Mine, Lapon Canyon, Mt. Grant. California (Dalquest, 1947:20): Weldon; Lebec; Johnson's Harbor, Santa Catalina Island, thence northward along Pacific Coast and including coastal islands to 2 mi. E Pescadero; mouth Battle Creek. Washington: Boulder Cave (Dalquest, 1948:164). British Columbia: Keremeos (Cowan and Guiguet, 1956:67); Riske Creek (*ibid.*).

Corynorhinus townsendii mexicanus G. M. Allen

1916. *Corynorhinus megalotis mexicanus* G. M. Allen, Bull. Mus. Comp. Zool., 60:347, April, type from near Pacheco, Chihuahua.

MARGINAL RECORDS.—Chihuahua: type locality; Mojarachic (Knobloch, 1942:297).

Corynorhinus townsendii pallescens Miller

1897. *Corynorhinus macrotis pallescens* Miller, N. Amer. Fauna, 13:52, October 16, type from Keam Canyon, Navajo Co., Arizona.
1955. *C[orynorhinus]. t[ownsendii]. pallescens*, Handley, Jour. Washington Acad. Sci., 45:147, May 23.

MARGINAL RECORDS.—Wyoming (G. M. Allen, 1916:343–344): Mammoth Hot Springs, Yellowstone National Park; Sand Cr., 10 mi. E Sundance. South Dakota: Custer (*ibid.*). Colorado (Warren, 1942:29): Ft. Collins; Trinidad. Oklahoma: Tesequite Canyon (Glass, 1949:26). Kansas (Cockrum, 1952:78–79): 4½ mi. SW Sun City; *Sinkhole, ⅛ mi. NE Dancer's Cave*. Oklahoma: 3 mi. SE Southard (Blair, 1939:102). Texas: Val Verde County (Taylor and Davis, 1947:19); SE slope Mariscal Mtn. (Borell and Bryant, 1942:10). Sonora (Burt, 1938:26): near El Tigre; Saric. California: Otay Mtn. (P. H. Krutzsch, *in verbis*); Red Rock Canyon (Dalquest, 1947:19): 4½ mi. SW Bishop (*ibid.*). Nevada (Hall, 1946:162): Chiatovich Ranch (= Arlemont); Spring Valley, 7 mi. S Cleveland Ranch. Utah (Durrant, 1955b:72–73): Goldhill; Logan Canyon.

Corynorhinus townsendii townsendii (Cooper)

1837. *Plecotus townsendii* Cooper, Ann. Lyc. Nat. Hist. New York, 4:73, November, paratypes from Columbia River, Oregon.
1955. *C[orynorhinus]. t[ownsendii]. townsendii*, Handley, Jour. Washington Acad. Sci., 45:147, May 23.

MARGINAL RECORDS.—British Columbia: Comox, Vancouver Island (Anderson, 1947:33); Hope (Cowan and Guiguet, 1956:69). Washington (Dalquest, 1948:163): Blakeley Island; Seattle; Fort Vancouver. California (Dalquest, 1947:20): Carlotta; 4 mi. E Upper Lake; Pope Cr.,

about 8 mi. NW Monticello; 4 mi. S Calistoga; 10 mi. E Stewart's Point, thence northward along coast to point of beginning.

Corynorhinus townsendii virginianus Handley

1955. *Corynorhinus townsendii virginianus* Handley, Jour. Washington Acad. Sci., 45:148, May 23, type from Schoolhouse Cave, 4⅖ mi. NE Riverton, 2205 ft., Pendleton Co., West Virginia.

MARGINAL RECORDS.—West Virginia: Preston Co. (Wilson, 1946:86); Baker's Cave, near Durgon (*ibid.*); Hoffman School Cave, 4⁹⁄₁₀ mi. SSW Franklin (Handley, 1955:49). Virginia: Burkes Garden (*ibid.*). Kentucky: Natural Bridge State Park (Barbour, 1957:141). Illinois: Mt. Carmel (Necker and Hatfield, 1941:46). Indiana: Greencastle (G. M. Allen, 1916:341).

Corynorhinus rafinesquii (Lesson)
Rafinesque's Big-eared Bat

1818. *Vespertilio megalotis* Rafinesque. Amer. Monthly Mag., 3(6):446, October. Type locality, the lower parts of the Ohio River, probably in southern Indiana and Illinois or western Kentucky in the area between the Wabash and Green rivers. Not *Vespertilio megalotis* Bechstein, 1800.
1827. *Plecotus rafinesquii* Lesson, Manuel de mammalogie . . . , p. 96, a renaming of *Vespertilio megalotis* Rafinesque.
1916. *Corynorhinus rafinesquii* Thomas, Proc. Biol. Soc. Washington, 29:127, June 6.
1831. *Plec[otus]. macrotis* Le Conte, *in* McMurtrie, The animal kingdom . . . by the Baron Cuvier . . . , 1:431. Type locality, Georgia, probably the Le Conte Plantation, near Riceboro, Liberty Co.
1837. *Plecotus lecontii* Cooper, Ann. Lyc. Nat. Hist. New York, 4:72, a renaming of *macrotis* Le Conte which Cooper considered as "nowise distinctive of the species" (*loc. cit.*).

"Distinguished from . . . [*C. townsendii*] and its subspecies by the clear white tips to the belly hairs, and the contrasted brown tips and blackish bases of

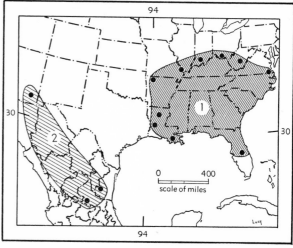

Map 149. *Corynorhinus* (part) and *Idionycteris*.

1. *Corynorhinus rafinesquii*   2. *Idionycteris phyllotis*

the hair of the back; inner upper incisor bicuspidate" (G. M. Allen, 1916:350).

MARGINAL RECORDS.—Ohio: Waggoner Ripple Cave (Goslin, 1954:431). West Virginia: Collison Cave (Frum, 1948:418). Virginia: Dismal Swamp (Handley and Patton, 1947:125), thence southward along Atlantic Coast to Florida: Zellwood (Moore, 1949:50), thence westward along Gulf Coast to Louisiana ·(Lowery, 1943:224): Houma; Kisatchie; Ruston. Arkansas: Osage River (Black, 1936:30). Illinois: ½ mi. N Olive Branch (Smith and Parmalee, 1954: 204). Indiana: Mitchell (Goodpaster and Hoffmeister, 1952:366).

Genus **Idionycteris** Anthony—Allen's Big-eared Bat

1923. *Idionycteris* Anthony, Amer. Mus. Novit., 54:1, January 17. Type, *Idionycteris mexicanus* Anthony [= *Corynorhinus phyllotis* G. M. Allen].

Resembles *Corynorhinus* and *Plecotus* but differs in: nostril unspecialized; accessory basal lobe of auricle developed into projecting lappet; calcar having well-developed keel; breadth of braincase amounting to more than half of greatest length of skull.

Idionycteris phyllotis (G. M. Allen)
Allen's Big-eared Bat

1916. *Corynorhinus phyllotis* G. M. Allen, Bull. Mus. Comp. Zool., 60:352, April, type from San Luis Potosí, probably near city of same name.
1956. *Idionycteris phyllotis*, Handley, Proc. Biol. Soc. Washington, 69:53, May 21.
1923. *Idionycteris mexicanus* Anthony, Amer. Mus. Novit., 54:1, January 17, type from Miquihuana, Tamaulipas. Regarded as inseparable from *Corynorhinus phyllotis* by Handley, Proc. Biol. Soc. Washington, 69:53, May 21, 1956.

Selected measurements of the holotype of *Idionycteris mexicanus,* an adult female, are: length of head and body, approximately 60; total length, 110; greatest length of skull, 17.2; length of upper toothrow, 6.3. Upper parts tawny olive, hairs blackish brown basally; underparts slightly paler.

MARGINAL RECORDS.—Arizona: Southwestern Research Station, Chiricahua Mts. (Cockrum, 1957:546). Tamaulipas: Miquihuana (Anthony, 1923:1). San Luis Potosí: type locality.

Subfamily NYCTOPHILINAE

Differs from Vespertilioninae in abruptly truncate muzzle, on anterior face of which nostrils open forward beneath distinct horseshoe-shaped ridge or small nose-leaf (after Miller, 1907:234).

Only one genus of the subfamily occurs in the New World.

Genus **Antrozous** H. Allen—Pale Bats

Revised by Miller, N. Amer. Fauna, 13:42–46, October 16, 1897.

1862. *Antrozous* H. Allen, Proc. Acad. Nat. Sci. Philadelphia, 14:248. Type, *Vespertilio pallidus* Le Conte.

Length of head and body, approximately 60. Skull with high, smooth braincase; rostrum relatively large, more than half as long as braincase; basisphenoidal pits absent; auditory bullae normally shaped and large, almost covering cochleae. Ears separate, large, extending well beyond muzzle when laid forward. Other characters as for subfamily. Dentition, i. $\frac{1}{2}$, c. $\frac{1}{1}$, p. $\frac{1}{2}$, m. $\frac{3}{3}$.

Antrozous, limited in occurrence to the western part of North America, has only a low horseshoe-shaped ridge on the muzzle instead of an evident nose-leaf that characterizes the one other genus, *Nyctophilus*, of the subfamily. *Nyctophilus* does not occur in the Americas.

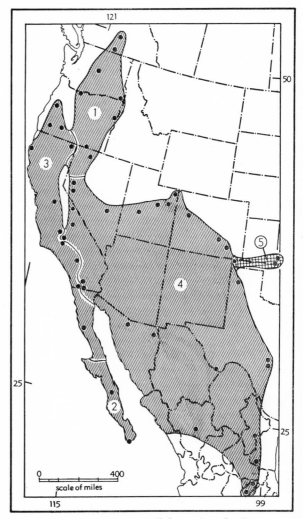

Map 150. *Antrozous pallidus* and *A. bunkeri.*

Guide to kinds
1. *A. p. cantwelli*
2. *A. p. minor*
3. *A. p. pacificus*
4. *A. p. pallidus*
5. *A. bunkeri*

Antrozous pallidus
Pallid Bat

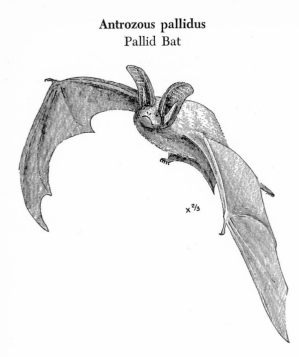

x²/₃

External measurements: total length, 92–135; ear, 23–37; length of forearm, 48.0–60.2. Upper parts creamy, yellowish, even light brown; underparts paler, sometimes almost whitish. Other characters as for the genus.

Orr (1954) recently has reported on the natural history of the pallid bat. The species is migratory, at least in the northern parts of its range. The roosting colonies are small; the daytime roosts are in natural crevices or in houses, barns, and other man-made structures. Both sexes occur together. There is but one annual molt; it takes place any time between May and August (California-taken specimens). The flight is relatively slow (10–11 wing strokes per second) and the bats often fly near the ground. In desert regions they are especially prone to hawk back and forth in an arroyo below the level of the surrounding desert floor. Occasionally they alight and feed on ground-dwelling insects and under such conditions have actually been taken by collectors' mouse traps.

One or two young are born in early summer and are on the wing in about 6 or 7 weeks.

Pallid bats are often heavily parasitized by various arthropods, especially wingless flies of the family Nycteribiidae.

Antrozous pallidus cantwelli V. Bailey

1936. *Antrozous pallidus cantwelli* V. Bailey, N. Amer. Fauna, 55:391, August 29, type from Rogersburg, Asotin Co., Washington.

MARGINAL RECORDS.—British Columbia: Okanagan Landing (Anderson, 1947:33). Washington: type locality. Oregon: Home (V. Bailey, 1936:392). Nevada: Quinn River Crossing (Hall, 1946:166). Oregon: Catlow Cave, 110 mi. S Burns (Cressman and Reed, 1938:248); The Dalles (V. Bailey, 1936:392). Washington: Wenatchee (Dalquest, 1948:169). British Columbia: between Oliver and Okanagan Falls (Anderson, 1947:33).

Antrozous pallidus minor Miller

1902. *Antrozous minor* Miller, Proc. Acad. Nat. Sci. Philadelphia, 54:389, September 3, type from Comondú, Baja California.
1951. *Antrozous pallidus minor*, Goldman, Smiths. Miscl. Coll., 115:356, July 31.

MARGINAL RECORDS (according to statements, on distribution, of Goldman, 1951:412–413, and Orr, 1954:173).—Baja California: type locality southward to Cape St. Lucas (Miller, 1897b:45).

Antrozous pallidus pacificus Merriam

1897. *Antrozous pallidus pacificus* Merriam, Proc. Biol. Soc. Washington, 11:180, July 1, type from Old Fort Tejon, 3200 ft., Tehachapi Mts., Kern Co., California.

MARGINAL RECORDS.—Oregon (V. Bailey, 1936:390): Eugene; Fort Klamath. California: Goose Lake (Grinnell, 1933:94); Snelling (Grinnell, 1918:355); White River (*ibid.*); Kelso Valley (*ibid.*); Bear Valley, San Bernardino Mts. (V. Bailey, 1936:390); Campo (P. H. Krutzsch, *in verbis*). Baja California: San Fernando (Miller, 1897b:45), thence northward along Pacific Coast, including coastal islands, to California: Ferndale (Grinnell, 1933:94). Oregon: ridge between Salt and Evans creeks, about 40 mi. N Rogue River P. O. (V. Bailey, 1936:390).

Antrozous pallidus pallidus (Le Conte)

1856. V[*espertilio*]. *pallidus* Le Conte, Proc. Acad. Nat. Sci. Philadelphia, 7:437, type from El Paso, El Paso Co., Texas.
1864. *Antrozous pallidus*, H. Allen, Smiths. Miscl. Coll., 7(Publ. 165):68, June.

MARGINAL RECORDS.—Utah: 6 mi. N Jensen (Krutzsch and Heppenstall, 1955:127). Colorado: 7 mi. W Rifle (Warren, 1942:31); Pueblo (Finley, 1954:110–111; 3 mi. NW Higbee (*ibid.*). Oklahoma: 6½ mi. N Kenton (Glass, 1949:26, recorded only to species). Texas: Tascosa (V. Bailey, 1905:214); Kerrville (Blair, 1952:96); 16 mi. S Kerrville (*ibid.*). Nuevo León: Maguayes, Río Pilon [= Rosalía] (Davis, 1944:380). Tamaulipas: Aserradero del Paraíso (Goodwin, 1954:6). Querétaro (Málaga Alba and Villa R., 1957:557, map 9): Jalpan; Cadereyta, 2100 meters. Durango: 1 mi. N Chorro, 6450 ft. (48379 KU). Texas: E base Burro Mesa (Borell and Bryant, 1942:11). Sonora (Burt, 1938:27): Pilares; Saric. California: Jacumba (P. H. Krutzsch, *in verbis*); Vallecitos (Grinnell, 1933:93); Walker Basin (Miller, 1897b:44); Independence (Grinnell, 1933:94); 5 mi. N Benton Station (Huey, 1936:285). Nevada (Hall, 1946:166): 9 mi. E, 2 mi. N Yerington; 3 mi. WSW Lahontan Dam; Burned Corral Canyon, Quinn Canyon Mts., 6700 ft. Utah (Durrant, 1952:62): volcanic caves, 10 mi. W Meadow; Price; Willow Cr., 25 mi. S Ouray, 5250 ft.

Antrozous bunkeri Hibbard
Bunker's Bat

1934. *Antrozous bunkeri* Hibbard, Jour. Mamm., 15:227, August 10, type from 7 mi. S Sun City, Barber Co., Kansas, in the tunnel by the natural bridge on the south fork of Bear Creek.

External measurements: total length, 115–130; ear, 26–28; length of forearm, 51–58.

This nominal species, upon careful study, will almost surely be found to be at most a subspecies of *A. pallidus*.

MARGINAL RECORDS.—Kansas (Cockrum, 1952:81): 5½ mi. S Sun City; 1 mi. SW Aetna. Oklahoma: 3 mi. N Kenton (Burt, 1945:309).

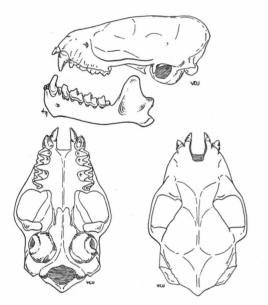

Fig. 145. *Antrozous bunkeri*, Natural Bridge, Barber Co., Kansas, No. 9302 K.U., ♀, X 2.

FAMILY **MOLOSSIDAE**—Free-tailed Bats

"Humerus with trochiter much larger than trochin, the discrepancy in size usually more noticeable than in the Vespertilionidae, trochin articulating with scapula by a surface nearly as large as glenoid fossa, . . . capitellum almost directly in line with nearly straight shaft; ulna less reduced than in the Vespertilionidae, the very slender shaft usually about half as long as radius; second finger with well-developed metacarpal and one rudimentary phalanx; . . . shoulder girdle normal . . . , except that seventh cervical vertebra is fused with first dorsal; foot short and broad, but of normal structure; fibula complete, bowed outward from tibia . . . ; skull without postorbital processes; pre-maxillaries with nasal branches present or absent, when present forming two palatal foramina, when absent allowing the formation of one; . . . teeth normal; ears variable in size and form, sometimes joined across forehead, the tragus much reduced, the antitragus usually very large . . . ; muzzle obliquely truncate, usually sprinkled with short, modified hairs with spoon-shaped tips, the nostrils usually opening on a special pad . . . ; membranes thick and leathery, the tail projecting conspicuously beyond its free edge" (Miller, 1907:242–243).

This family is widely distributed through the warmer parts of the Old and New worlds.

KEY TO NORTH AMERICAN GENERA OF MOLOSSIDAE

1. Bony palate with conspicuous median emargination extending back of roots of incisors.
  2. Upper premolars 1–1. . *Mormopterus*, p. 209
  2'. Upper premolars 2–2. . . *Tadarida*, p. 204
1'. Bony palate without conspicuous median emargination, but a small notch may be present which never extends back of roots of incisors.
  3. Upper incisor with length along cingulum equal to or greater than height of shaft. . . . . *Molossus*, p. 214
  3'. Upper incisor with length along cingulum decidedly less than height of shaft.
    4. Palate conspicuously dome-shaped.
      Promops, p. 214
    4'. Palate arched transversely but little, if any, longitudinally.
      5. Rostrum noticeably flattened, its length about equal to lacrimal breadth. . . . . *Cynomops*, p. 203
      5'. Rostrum subcylindrical, its length considerably greater than lacrimal breadth. . . . . . *Eumops*, p. 210

Genus **Cynomops** Thomas—Dog-faced Bats

1920. *Cynomops* Thomas, Ann. Mag. Nat. Hist., ser. 9, 5:189, February. Type, *Molossus cerastes* Thomas.

Closely resembling *Molossops* (of South America) except that M3 is simplified, with no 3rd commissure, transversely oblong, and scarcely broader externally than internally; m3 equally simplified, posterior lobe linear, with one cusp only (after Thomas, 1920:189).

KEY TO SPECIES OF CYNOMOPS

1. Greatest length of head and body less than 62; underparts whitish yellow.
  C. planirostris, p. 204
1'. Greatest length of head and body more than 62; underparts blackish slate. . *C. malagai*, p. 204

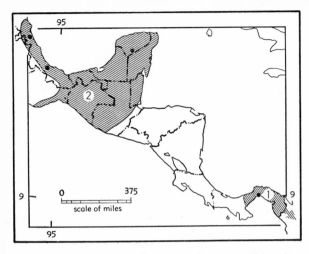

Map 151. *Cynomops planirostris planirostris* (1) and *Cynomops malagai* (2).

Cynomops planirostris
Dog-faced Bat

Length of head and body, approximately 60. Skull with high, broad, flattened rostrum with conspicuous laterally projecting lacrimal ridges. Other characters as for the genus.

Only one specimen of this primarily South American bat has been reported from north of South America.

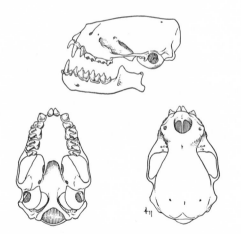

Fig. 146. *Cynomops planirostris* (subsp. *planirostris*), Maripa, Colombia, No. 17096 A.M., ♀, X 2.

Cynomops planirostris planirostris (Peters)

1865. *M[olossus]. planirostris* Peters, Monatsb. preuss. Akad. Wiss., Berlin, p. 575, type from British Guiana.
1920. *C[ynomops]. planirostris,* Thomas, Ann. Mag. Nat. Hist., ser. 9, 5:189, February.

MARGINAL RECORDS.—Known, within the geographic scope of the present work, only from Panamá: near Panamá City (Goldman, 1920:219).

Cynomops malagai Villa
Mexican Dog-faced Bat

1955. *Cynomops malagai* Villa, Acta Zoologica Mexicana, 1(4):2, September 15, type from Tuxpan de Rodríguez Cano, 20° 57', 97° 24', four meters, Veracruz.

Length of head and body, 64–80; forearm, 49–51; greatest length of skull, 20.8–21.0; zygomatic breadth, 12.9–13.3. Upper parts slate-black and underparts blackish slate.

MARGINAL RECORDS (Villa, 1955:1–2).—Veracruz: type locality; Veracruz. Yucatán: Peto.

Genus Tadarida Rafinesque—Free-tailed Bats

Revised by Shamel, Proc. U.S. Nat. Mus., 78:1–27, May 6, 1931.

1814. *Tadarida* Rafinesque, Précis des découvertes et travaux somiologiques . . . , p. 55. Type, *Cephalotes teniotis* Rafinesque.
1902. *Nyctinomops* Miller, Proc. Acad. Nat. Sci. Philadelphia, 54:393, September 12. Type, *Nyctinomus femorosaccus* Merriam.

Differs from other North American molossids, except *Mormopterus*, in deep vertical grooves or wrinkles on upper lip. Z-shaped structure of M3, and separation of premaxillae between upper incisors.

KEY TO NORTH AMERICAN SPECIES OF TADARIDA

1. Second phalanx of 4th digit more than 5.0; ears not extending appreciably beyond muzzle when laid forward, inner bases not conjoined; breadth of anterior part of rostrum markedly greater than interorbital breadth.
T. brasiliensis, p. 205
1'. Second phalanx of 4th digit less than 5.0; ears extending appreciably beyond muzzle when laid forward, inner bases conjoined; breadth of anterior part of rostrum barely greater than interorbital breadth.
  2. Length of forearm more than 55.0.
T. molossa, p. 208
  2'. Length of forearm less than 55.0.
    3. Greatest length of skull 18.4 or more.
      4. M1, viewed from crown surface, nearly square. . *T. femorosacca,* p. 207
      4'. M1, viewed from crown surface, with hypocone expanded posteromedially into a broad heel making tooth broader posteriorly than anteriorly. . . *T. laticaudata,* p. 207
    3'. Greatest length of skull 18.3 or less.
T. yucatanica, p. 208

Tadarida brasiliensis
Brazilian Free-tailed Bat

Subspecies reviewed by Schwartz, Jour. Mamm., 36:106–109, February 28, 1955.

Length of head and body, 46.6–65.2; length of forearm, 36.6–46.4; greatest length of skull, 14.6–18.0; zygomatic breadth, 8.4–10.4; length of upper tooth-row, 5.0–6.6. Upper parts dark brown, bases of hairs whitish; underparts slightly paler. For other characters see key to the species.

This species congregates, often in vast numbers, in caves and suitable places in and on buildings. It is this species that occurs in tremendous numbers at Carlsbad Cavern, New Mexico. The Brazilian free-tailed bat leaves its roosting place usually in late evening. The diet consists exclusively of insects; the bat is a voracious feeder and an evening's meal may be as much as half the animal's weight. Seemingly, contrary to a commonly held belief, relatively few mosquitoes are taken, the bulk of the insects being moths. One young born in the spring is usual.

Tadarida brasiliensis antillularum (Miller)

1902. *Nyctinomus antillularum* Miller, Proc. Acad. Nat. Sci. Philadelphia, 54:398, September 12, type from Roseau, Dominica, West Indies.
1955. *Tadarida brasiliensis antillularum,* Schwartz, Jour. Mamm., 36:108, February 28.

MARGINAL RECORDS (Shamel, 1931:11).—*Puerto Rico.* Lesser Antilles: Barbuda; St. Lucia.

Tadarida brasiliensis bahamensis (Rehn)

1902. *Nyctinomus bahamensis* Rehn, Proc. Acad. Nat. Sci. Philadelphia, 54:641, December 12, type from Governors Harbor, Eleuthera, Bahama Islands.
1955. *Tadarida brasiliensis bahamensis,* Schwartz, Jour. Mamm., 36:108, February 28.

MARGINAL RECORDS.—Bahama Islands: Little Abaco Island (Shamel, 1931:9); Marsh Harbour, Great Abaco Island (G. M. Allen, 1911:245); type locality; Long Island (G. M. Allen and Sanborn, 1937:228).

Tadarida brasiliensis brasiliensis (I. Geof. St.-Hilaire)

1824. *Nyctinomus brasiliensis* I. Geoffroy St.-Hilaire, Ann. Sci. Nat., 1:343, type from Brazil, by subsequent restriction (Shamel, Proc. U.S. Nat. Mus., 78:4, May 6, 1931), Curityba, Paraná.
1920. *Tadarida brasiliensis,* Thomas, Proc. U.S. Nat. Mus., 58:222, November 10.
1827. *Dysopes nasutus* Temminck, Monographies de mammalogie . . . , 1:233. Type locality, Brazil.
1840. *Dysopes naso* Wagner, in Schreber, Die Säugthiere . . . , Suppl., 1:475. Type locality, Brazil.

MARGINAL RECORDS.—Costa Rica: San José (Goodwin, 1946:338), thence eastward into South America.

Tadarida brasiliensis constanzae Shamel

1931. *Tadarida constanzae* Shamel, Proc. U.S. Nat. Mus., 78:10, May 6, type from Constanza, Dominican Republic.
1955. *Tadarida brasiliensis constanzae,* Schwartz, Jour. Mamm., 36:108, February 28.

MARGINAL RECORDS.—Haiti (Shamel, 1931:10): Bombardopolis; St. Michel. Dominican Republic: type locality.

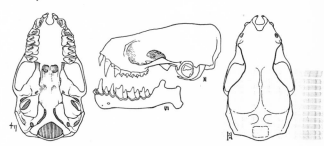

Fig. 147. *Tadarida brasiliensis mexicana,* Greenmonster Canyon, Monitor Range, Nye Co., Nevada, No. 57472 M.V.Z., ♂, X 2.

Tadarida brasiliensis cynocephala (Le Conte)

1831. *Nyct[icea]. cynocephala* Le Conte, in McMurtrie, The animal kingdom . . . by the Baron Cuvier . . . , 1:432, type from Georgia, probably in the neighborhood of the Le Conte Plantation, Liberty Co.
1955. *Tadarida brasiliensis cynocephala,* Schwartz, Jour. Mamm., 36:108, February 28.
1837. *Molossus fuliginosus* Cooper, Ann. Lyc. Nat. Hist. New York, 4:67, November, type from Milledgeville, Georgia.

MARGINAL RECORDS.—Alabama: Sauta Cave, near Scottsboro (Engle, 1957:40). South Carolina: Columbia (Shamel, 1931:8). Georgia: Savannah (*ibid.*), thence southward along Atlantic Coast to Florida (Sherman, 1937:109): Enterprise; Kissimmee; Marco Island (Schwartz, 1955:109), thence westward along Gulf Coast to Louisiana (Lowery, 1943:224, unless otherwise noted): Houma (Shamel, 1931:8); Baton Rouge; Robeline; Ruston; Monroe. Alabama (Barkalow, 1939:370): Greensboro.

Tadarida brasiliensis intermedia Shamel

1931. *Tadarida intermedia* Shamel, Proc. U.S. Nat. Mus., 78:7, May 6, type from Valley of Comitán, Chiapas.

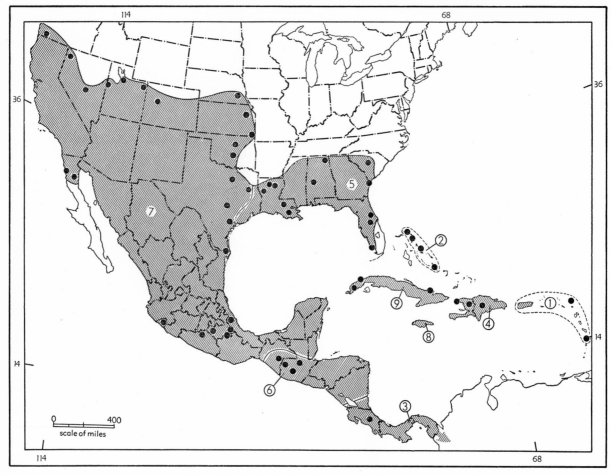

Map 152. *Tadarida brasiliensis* and subspecies.

1. *T. b. antillularum*	4. *T. b. constanzae*	7. *T. b. mexicana*
2. *T. b. bahamensis*	5. *T. b. cynocephala*	8. *T. b. murina*
3. *T. b. brasiliensis*	6. *T. b. intermedia*	9. *T. b. muscula*

1955. *Tadarida brasiliensis intermedia,* Schwartz, Jour. Mamm., 36:108, February 28.

MARGINAL RECORDS.—Chiapas: type locality. Guatemala: Cobán (Schwartz, 1955:108); Chimaltenango (*ibid.*); Jacatlenango (Shamel, 1931:7).

Tadarida brasiliensis mexicana (Saussure)

1860. *Molossus mexicanus* Saussure, Revue et Mag. Zool., Paris, ser. 2, 12:283, July, type from Cofre de Perote, 13,000 ft., México.

1955. *Tadarida brasiliensis mexicana,* Schwartz, Jour. Mamm., 36:108, February 28.

1889. *Nyctinomus mohavensis* Merriam, N. Amer. Fauna, 2:25, October 30, type from Fort Mojave, Arizona.

1894. *Nyctinomus brasiliensis californicus* H. Allen, Bull. U.S. Nat. Mus., 43:166, March 14, type from California.

1942. *Tadarida texana* Stager, Bull. Southern California Acad. Sci., 41(pt. 1):49, May 31, type from Ney Cave,

20 mi. N Hondo, Medina Co., Texas (*fide* Blair, Texas Jour. Sci., 4:96, March 30, 1952).

MARGINAL RECORDS.—Oregon: Medford (Stager, 1945:196). Nevada (Hall, 1946:168): mouth Little High Rock Canyon; Greenmonster Canyon, Monitor Range. Utah (Durrant, 1952:63): cave at Salt Springs, near Utah–Nevada boundary; Salt Lake City, 4250 ft.; Jensen. Colorado: Newcastle (Warren, 1942:32). Nebraska: Lincoln (Webb and Jones, 1952:278). Kansas (Cockrum, 1952:84): Lawrence; Galena. Oklahoma (Blair, 1939:103): Stillwater; Norman. Texas: 3 mi. E Roanoke (Miller, 1948:418); Nacogdoches (McCarley and Bradshaw, 1953:516); Austin (Shamel, 1931:6); Victoria (*ibid.*); Brownsville (Blair, 1952:238), thence southward along Gulf Coast to Veracruz: 5 km. N Jalapa (Davis, 1944:380); Maltrata (Shamel, 1931:18). Puebla: Tehuacán (*ibid.*). Morelos: Santa Clara (Davis and Russell, 1954:70). Guerrero: Teloloapan (Martínez and Villa, 1940:300; originally referred to *T. brasiliensis* but here referred to *T. b. mexicana* on geographic grounds; see Davis and Russell, 1954:70). Colima: Colima (Shamel, 1931:5), thence along coast to

Baja California (Shamel, 1931:6): San Pedro Mártir; San Telmo, thence northward along Pacific Coast to point of beginning.

Tadarida brasiliensis murina (Gray)

1827. *Nyctinomus murinus* Gray, *in* Griffith, The animal kingdom . . . by the Baron Cuvier . . . , 5:66, type from Jamaica. Known only from Jamaica.
1955. *Tadarida brasiliensis murina*, Schwartz, Jour. Mamm., 36:108, February 28.

Tadarida brasiliensis muscula (Gundlach)

1861. *Nyctinomus musculus* Gundlach, Monatsb. preuss. Akad. Wiss., Berlin, p. 149, paratypes from Cuba.
1955. *Tadarida brasiliensis muscula*, Schwartz, Jour. Mamm., 36:108, February 28.

MARGINAL RECORDS.—Cuba, Cabañas (Miller, 1904: 339): Cueva de los Americanos, ½ mi. S Gibara (Schwartz, 1955:109); Pinar del Río (Miller, 1904:339). Not found: El Guama.

Tadarida femorosacca (Merriam)
Pocketed Free-tailed Bat

1889. *Nyctinomus femorosaccus* Merriam, N. Amer. Fauna, 2:23, October 30, type from Agua Caliente [= Palm Springs], Riverside Co., California.
1924. *Tadarida femorosacca*, Miller, Bull. U.S. Nat. Mus., 128:86, April 29.

Length of head and body, 54.4–65.2; length of forearm, 45.5–49.2; greatest length of skull, 18.4–19.4; zygomatic breadth, 9.6–10.4; length of upper tooth-row, 7.0–7.5. Upper parts Vandyke Brown, sometimes distinctly reddish; underparts slightly paler, sometimes with buffy wash. Other characters as for the species-group (see artificial key).

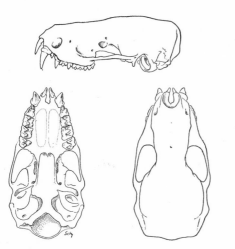

Fig. 148. *Tadarida femorosacca*, Palm Canyon, Borego Valley, San Diego Co., California, No. 94702 M.V.Z., sex ♂, X 2.

MARGINAL RECORDS (Cockrum, 1956:282–283, unless otherwise noted).—California: type locality. Arizona: Coyote Mts.; *Tucson*; 7 mi. E and 2 mi. N Tucson; Fort Huachuca. Sonora: 1 mi. NW Alamos. Tamaulipas: Sierra de Tamaulipas, 1200 ft., 10 mi. W and 2 mi. S Piedra (55393 KU); 10 km. NNE Antiguo Morelos. Jalisco: Zacoalco. Baja California: Santa Anita. California: 2 mi. SE Suncrest Store.

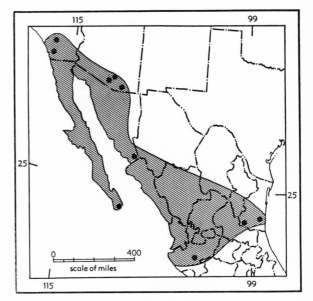

Map 153. *Tadarida femorosacca*.

Tadarida laticaudata
Broad-tailed Bat

Selected measurements of the type of *T. l. ferruginea*, an adult male, are: total length, 96.7; tail, 35.5; length of forearm, 42.2 dry (43.3–44.8 in 7 topotypes in spirits); greatest length of skull, 18.5; zygomatic breadth, 10.1; length of maxillary tooth-row, 6.8. Upper parts Vandyke Brown, hairs extensively white at base; underparts bister (white at base except on abdomen where also basal part of hair is bister) but hairs tipped with pinkish buff. From *T. femorosacca*, *laticaudata* differs in shape of M1 (see key); from *T. yucatanica*, *laticaudata* differs in wash of pinkish buff instead of wood brown and in larger skull. This species occurs also in South America.

Tadarida laticaudata ferruginea Goodwin

1954. *Tadarida laticaudata ferruginea* Goodwin, Amer. Mus. Novit., 1670:2, June 28, type from 8 mi. N Antiguo Morelos, Tamaulipas. Known only from the type locality and from *Antiguo Morelos* (Goodwin, 1954:6).

Map 154. Three species of *Tadarida*.

1. *T. molossa*   2. *T. laticaudata ferruginea*   3. *T. yucatanica*

Tadarida yucatanica (Miller)
Yucatán Free-tailed Bat

1902. *Nyctinomops yucatanicus* Miller, Proc. Acad. Nat. Sci. Philadelphia, 54:393, September 12, type from Chichén-Itzá, Yucatán.
1924. *Tadarida yucatanica*, Miller, Bull. U.S. Nat. Mus., 128:87, April 29.

Length of head and body, 54.0–63.5; length of forearm, 41.8–44.6; greatest length of skull, 17.6–18.2; zygomatic breadth, 9.2–9.8; length of upper tooth-row, 6.4–6.8. Color essentially as in *T. femorosacca*.

MARGINAL RECORDS.—Yucatán: type locality. British Honduras: El Cayo (Murie, 1935:19). El Salvador: San Salvador (Felten, 1957:8). Guatemala (Goodwin, 1955d: 4): Cobán; La Libertad. *Campeche: San José Carpizo* (Málaga Alba and Villa R., 1957:563).

Tadarida molossa (Pallas)
Big Free-tailed Bat

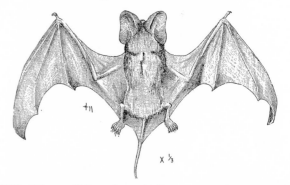

1766. *V[espertilio]. molossus* Pallas, . . . Miscl. Zool. . . . ; Spicilegia Zool. . . . , fasc. 3, p. 8, 1767. Type from "America," probably Surinam.

1949. *Tadarida molossa,* Hershkovitz, Proc. U.S. Nat. Mus., 99:452.
1830. *Molossus caecus* Rengger, Saëugethiere [*sic*] Paraguay, p. 88. Type locality, Asunción, Paraguay.
1839. *Nyctinomus macrotis* Gray, Ann. Nat. Hist., 4:5, September, type from Cuba.
1843. *Dysopes auritus* Wagner, Arch. Naturgesch., Jahrg. 9, 1:368, type from Cuyaba, Brazil.
1876. *Nyctinomus megalotis* Dobson, Proc. Zool. Soc. London, p. 728, November 7, type from Surinam.
1891. *Nyctinomus depressus* Ward, Amer. Nat., 25:747, August, type from Tacubaya, Distrito Federal, México.
1894. *Nyctinomus macrotis nevadensis* H. Allen, Bull. U.S. Nat. Mus., 43:171, March 17, type from California.
1900. *Promops affinis* J. A. Allen, Bull. Amer. Mus. Nat. Hist., 13:91, December, type from Taguaga [= Taganga], Colombia.
1914. *Nyctinomus aequatorialis* J. A. Allen, Bull. Amer. Mus. Nat. Hist., 33:386, July 9, type from Ecuador.

Length of head and body, 66.6–79.0; length of forearm, 58.0–63.8; greatest length of skull, 22.2–24.0; zygomatic breadth, 10.2–13.0; length of upper tooth-row, 8.2–9.5. Upper parts dark (mummy) brown; underparts slightly paler. Skull large, robust, and with relatively long rostrum.

MARGINAL RECORDS.—British Columbia: Essondale, near Westminster (Anderson, 1947:34). Utah: Pine Valley, Desert Range Exp. Sta., U.S. Forest Service, Sec. 33, T. 25S, R. 17W, Salt Lake Meridian (Durrant, 1952:64). Colorado: Grand Junction (Snead, 1938:104). Iowa (Scott, 1937:58): Marshalltown; Cedar Rapids. Kansas: 9 mi. N Elkhart (38926 KU). Oklahoma: 4 mi. S Elkhart, Kansas (Cockrum, 1952:492). Texas: Chisos Mts. (Taylor and Davis, 1947:21), thence, presumably, southward along Caribbean Coast to South America, and then northward along Pacific Coast to California: San Diego (Anderson,

1947:34). Also known from Cuba: 7 km. W Banao (Koopman and Ruibal, 1955:4). *Dominican Republic* (Shamel, 1931:16). *Jamaica* (*ibid.*).

Genus **Mormopterus** Peters—Goblin Bats

1865. *Mormopterus* Peters, Monatsb. preuss. Akad. Wiss., Berlin, p. 258. Type, *Nyctinomus jugularis* Peters.

Closely resembling *Tadarida*; differing from *Tadarida* primarily in possessing only one upper premolar and in slightly smaller ears that are joined basally. Dentition, i. $\frac{1}{3 \text{ or } 2}$, c. $\frac{1}{1}$, p. $\frac{1}{2}$, m. $\frac{3}{3}$.

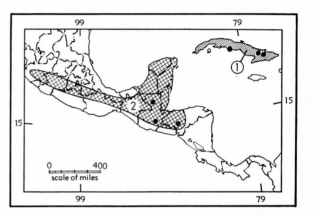

Map 155. *Mormopterus minutus* (1) and *Promops centralis* (2).

Mormopterus minutus (Miller)
Little Goblin Bat

1899. *Nyctinomus minutus* Miller, Bull. Amer. Mus. Nat. Hist., 12:173, October 20, type from Trinidad, Santa Clara, Cuba.
1907. *M[ormopterus]. minutus* Miller, Bull. U.S. Nat. Mus., 57:254, June 29.

Measurements of the type, an adult male, are: length of head and body, approximately 46; total length, 74; length of forearm, 29. Cranial measurements of a female topotype are: greatest length, 13.4; zygomatic breadth, 8.6; breadth of braincase,

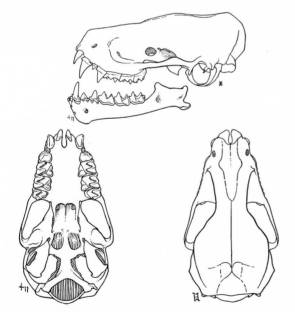

Fig. 149. *Tadarida molossa,* Pine Canyon, Chisos Mts., 6000 ft., Brewster Co., Texas, No. 81683 M.V.Z., ♀, X 2.

Fig. 150. *Mormopterus minutus,* Oriente, Omaja, Cuba. Skull is of No. 72994 C.N.H.M., ♀. Mandible is of No. 72977 C.N.H.M., ♂. X 2.

7; length of upper tooth-row, 5. Skull flattened and lightly constructed; dorsal profile nearly straight; rostrum short and broad. Other characters as for the genus.

MARGINAL RECORDS (Sanborn, 1953:383).—Cuba: type locality; Omaja; a few mi. S Guaro, near Preston.

Genus **Eumops** Miller—Mastiff Bats

Revised by Sanborn, Jour. Mamm., 13:347–357, November 2, 1932.

1906. *Eumops* Miller, Proc. Biol. Soc. Washington, 19:85, June 4. Type, *Molossus californicus* Merriam.

Skull slender but robust; rostrum well developed; dorsal profile of skull almost straight; premaxillaries wholly lacking palatal branches; 1st upper premolar small but usually well formed (absent, so far as known, in *E. maurus*), and usually crowded from normal position in dental arcade. External form slender; ears large, rounded or angular, usually conjoined basally, and extending slightly beyond nostril when laid forward. Dentition, i. $\frac{1}{2}$, c. $\frac{1}{1}$, p. $\frac{2}{2 \text{ or } 1}$, m. $\frac{3}{3}$.

KEY TO NORTH AMERICAN SPECIES OF EUMOPS
(Adapted from Sanborn, 1932:348–349)

1. Length of forearm more than 52.
  2. Length of forearm more than 73.
                                E. perotis, p. 210
  2'. Length of forearm less than 73.
    3. Length of forearm more than 64; length of upper tooth-row more than 11. . . . . . . *E. underwoodi*, p. 212
    3'. Length of forearm less than 64; length of upper tooth-row less than 11.
      4. Lacrimal ridge slight; tragus small (3.5 from posterior notch), pointed.
        5. Premolars $\frac{2}{2}$. . *E. abrasus*, p. 211
        5'. Premolars $\frac{1}{2}$. . *E. maurus*, p. 212
      4'. Lacrimal ridge absent; tragus large (4–5 from posterior notch), quadrate. . . . *E. glaucinus*, p. 213
1'. Length of forearm less than 52.
                                E. bonariensis, p. 213

Eumops perotis
Greater Mastiff Bat

Length of head and body, approximately 105; length of forearm, 73–80; greatest length of skull, 30.3–32.9; zygomatic breadth, 17.2–19.8; length of upper tooth-row, 11.9–13.6. Upper parts sooty brown; slightly paler below.

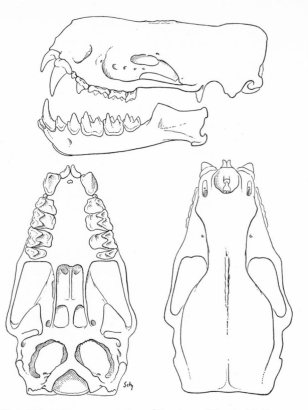

Fig. 151. *Eumops perotis californicus*, 1½ mi. N Barrett Junction, San Diego Co., California, No. 94706 M.V.Z., ♀, X 2.

These bats seem to be uncommon wherever they occur. They roost in small colonies in cracks and small holes and seem to prefer man-made structures. They leave the roost only when darkness has fallen and are only rarely seen on the wing. Possibly they hawk at considerable elevation.

Eumops perotis californicus (Merriam)

1890. *Molossus californicus* Merriam, N. Amer. Fauna, 4:31, October 8, type from Alhambra, Los Angeles Co., California.
1932. *Eumops perotis californicus*, Sanborn, Jour. Mamm., 13:351, November 2.

MARGINAL RECORDS.—California: Haywards (Sanborn, 1932:351); Fresno (Dalquest, 1946:86); Traver (H. W. Grinnell, 1918:373); near Colton (A. B. Howell, 1920:113). Arizona (Sanborn, 1932:351): Parker; Tempe. Texas: Langtry (Taylor and Davis, 1947:21). Coahuila: cave near Cuatro Ciénegas (Gilmore, 1947:154). Sonora: Pilares (Burt, 1938:28). California: Otay (H. W. Grinnell, 1918:372).

Eumops perotis perotis (Schinz)

1821. *Molossus perotis* Schinz, Das Thierreich . . . , 1:870. Type locality, Villa São Salvador, Campos dos Goaytocassas [= Goitzcazes], Rio Parahyba [= Paraiba], Brazil.

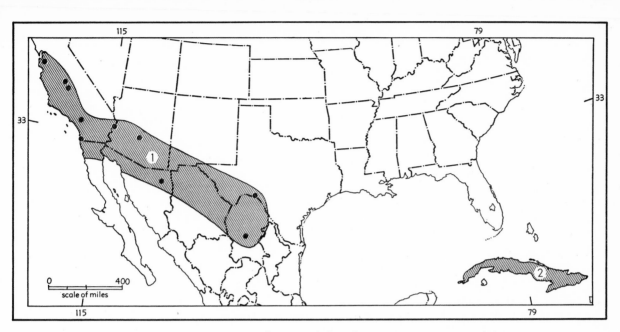

Map 156. *Eumops perotis californicus* (1) and *Eumops perotis perotis* (2).

1906. *E[umops]. perotis*, Miller, Proc. Biol. Soc. Washington, 19:85, June 4.
1864. *Dysopes (Molossus) gigas* Peters, Monatsb. preuss. Akad. Wiss., Berlin, p. 381, type from Cuba.

MARGINAL RECORDS.—Within the geographic scope of this work known only from Cuba (Sanborn, 1932:349).

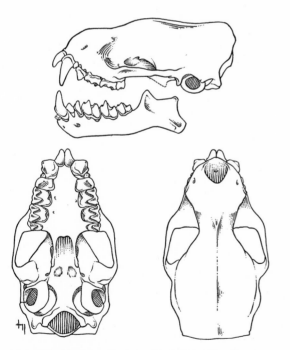

Fig. 152. *Eumops abrasus milleri*, Turrialba, Province Cartago, Costa Rica, No. 26952 K.U., ♂, X 2.

Eumops abrasus
Temminck's Mastiff Bat

Length of head and body, approximately 81; length of forearm, 56–63; greatest length of skull, 23.0–25.7; zygomatic breadth, 14.9–15.3; length of upper tooth-row, 9.4–10.6. Upper parts dark reddish brown, hairs buffy white basally; underparts slightly paler. Lacrimal ridge slight; lambdoidal crest well developed and extending posteriorly beyond occipital area; 3rd commissure on M3 less developed than in other kinds of *Eumops*; posterior half of outer edge of M3 shorter than in *E. glaucinus*.

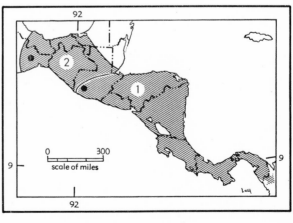

Map 157. *Eumops abrasus.*

1. *E. a. milleri*   2. *E. a. oaxacensis*

Eumops abrasus milleri (J. A. Allen)

1900. *Promops milleri* J. A. Allen, Bull. Amer. Mus. Nat. Hist., 13:92, May 12, type from Guayabamba, Perú.

1932. *Eumops abrasus milleri,* Sanborn, Jour. Mamm., 13: 352, November 2.

MARGINAL RECORDS.—Guatemala: Finca Cipres (Goodwin, 1934:16), thence southward into South America.

Eumops abrasus oaxacensis Goodwin

1956. *Eumops abrasus oaxacensis* Goodwin, Amer. Mus. Novit., 1757:2, March 8, type from Mazatlán, about 3000 ft., Oaxaca. Known only from the type locality.

Eumops maurus (Thomas)
Guianan Mastiff Bat

1901. *Molossus maurus* Thomas, Ann. Mag. Nat. Hist., ser. 7, 8:141, August, type from Kamuku Mts., British Guiana, South America. Known in North America from a single specimen from Quintana Roo: 10 km. from the boundary of Yucatán in the Territory of Quintana Roo in the vicinity of the city of Valladolid (Villa, Anales del Inst. Biol., Univ. Nac. México, 26:543, June 20, 1956).

1906. *E*[*umops*]. *maurus,* Miller, Proc. Biol. Soc. Washington, 19:85, June 4.

Length of head and body, 64–90; length of tail, 41–51; length of forearm, 53.0–53.2. Resembles *Eumops abrasus* but differs in absence of the minute (in *abrasus*) upper premolar leaving one instead of two premolars in each upper tooth-row. The palate is described as extending 1 mm. behind the level of the last upper molars. The species is known from only two specimens, the holotype and the specimen from Quintana Roo.

Map 158. *Eumops maurus.*

Eumops underwoodi
Underwood's Mastiff Bat

Length of head and body, approximately 130; length of forearm, 65.3–71.5; zygomatic breadth, 16.7–18.8; length of upper tooth-row, 11.1–12.3. Upper parts rich ochraceous brown to dark brown, hairs whitish basally. Skull short, wide, and unusually strongly ridged; interorbital region hourglass-shaped.

Eumops underwoodi sonoriensis Benson

1947. *Eumops sonoriensis* Benson, Proc. Biol. Soc. Washington, 60:133, December 31, type from Rancho de Costa Rica 270 ft., Río Sonora, Sonora.

1949. *Eumops underwoodi sonoriensis,* Hall and Villa, Univ. Kansas Publ., Mus. Nat. Hist., 1:446, December 27.

MARGINAL RECORDS.—Arizona: 2 mi. E Sasabe (59092 KU). Sonora: type locality; 10 mi. NW Noche Buena (Benson, 1947:134).

Eumops underwoodi underwoodi Goodwin

1940. *Eumops underwoodi* Goodwin, Amer. Mus. Novit., 1075:2, June 27, type from El Pedrero, 6 km. N Chinaela [= Chinacla], La Paz, Honduras.

MARGINAL RECORDS.—Michoacán: Rancho Escondido, 2 mi. N Apo, Tancítaro Mtn. (Hall and Villa, 1949:445). Honduras: type locality.

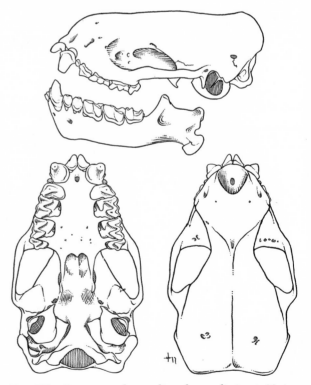

Fig. 153. *Eumops underwoodi underwoodi,* 2 mi. N Apo, Tancítaro Mt., Michoacán, No. 89461 Mich., ♀, X 2.

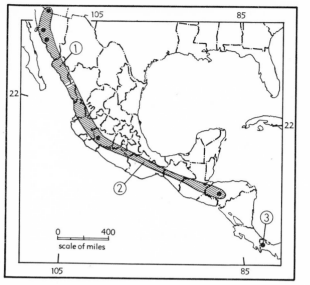

Map 159. *Eumops underwoodi* and *E. bonariensis.*

Guide to kinds
1. *E. u. sonoriensis*
2. *E. u. underwoodi*
3. *E. bonariensis nanus*

Eumops glaucinus (Wagner)
Wagner's Mastiff Bat

1843. *Dysopes glaucinus* Wagner, Arch. Naturgesch., Jahrg. 9, 1:368, type purportedly from Cuyaba, Mato Grosso, Brazil.
1906. *E[umops]. glaucinus,* Miller, Proc. Biol. Soc. Washington, 19:85, June 4.
1861. *Molossus ferox* Gundlach, Monatsb. preuss. Akad., Wiss., Berlin, p. 149, type from Cuba.

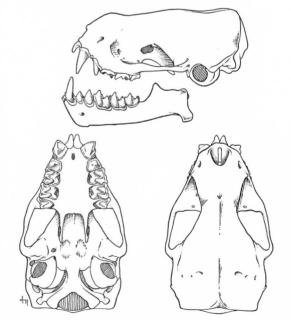

Fig. 154. *Eumops glaucinus,* Jesús Carranza, Veracruz, No. 19234 K.U., ♀, X 2.

1889. *Nyctinomus orthotis* H. Allen, Proc. Amer. Philo. Soc., 26:561, December 18, type from Spanishtown, Jamaica.

Length of head and body, approximately 80; length of forearm, 58–61; greatest length of skull, 22.4–24.3; zygomatic breadth, 13.9–15.4; length of upper tooth-row, 9.5–10.3. Upper parts dark cinnamon brown, slightly paler below. Supraoccipital region extending posteriorly beyond lambdoidal crest; lacrimal ridges lacking. Tragus broad and truncate distally.

MARGINAL RECORDS.—Florida: Miami (Sherman, 1937:109). Cuba: Guantanamo (Sanborn, 1932:353). Jamaica: St. Andrews (*ibid.*); *Spanishtown* (*ibid.*), thence southward into South America; northward to Morelos (Davis and Russell, 1954:70). Cuba: Pinar del Río (Sanborn, 1932:353).

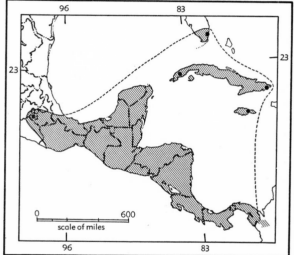

Map 160. *Eumops glaucinus.*

Eumops bonariensis
Peters' Mastiff Bat

Length of head and body, approximately 42; length of forearm, 39–49; greatest length of skull, 16.4–20.1; zygomatic breadth, 10.4–12.4; length of upper tooth-row, 6.6–8.1. Upper parts reddish brown to blackish brown; underparts drab to gray. Skull resembling that of *E. glaucinus* but smaller, relatively broader across rostrum, and with crests less developed. See map 159.

Eumops bonariensis nanus (Miller)

1900. *Promops nanus* Miller, Ann. Mag. Nat. Hist., ser. 7, 6:470, November, type from Bogava [= Bugaba], 800 ft., Chiriquí, Panamá.
1932. *Eumops bonariensis nanus,* Sanborn, Jour. Mamm., 13:356, November 11.

MARGINAL RECORDS.—Panamá: Boquerón (Sanborn, 1932:356); *type locality*.

Genus **Promops** Gervais

1855. *Promops* Gervais, Mammifères, *in* [Castelnau, Expéd. dans les partes centrales de l'Amer. du Sud . . .] pt. 7, p. 58. Type, *Promops ursinus* Gervais [= *Molossus nasutus* Spix].

Skull short, broad (somewhat rounded when viewed from above), robust; sagittal crest pronounced; rostrum markedly short and deep; palate strongly dome-shaped. Ears short and rounded, extending barely to nostril when laid forward; pad of muzzle small but distinct and without processes.

Promops centralis Thomas
Thomas' Mastiff Bat

1915. *Promops centralis* Thomas, Ann. Mag. Nat. Hist., ser. 8, 16:62, July, type from northern Yucatán.

Selected measurements of the type, an adult female, are: length of forearm, 54; greatest length of skull (occiput to base of incisors), 20.2; length of upper tooth-row, 8.3. Upper parts dark brown to glossy black, the hairs whitish basally; underparts slightly paler. Other characters as for the genus.

MARGINAL RECORDS.—Yucatán: *type locality*. Honduras: El Pedrero (Goodwin, 1942:143). Guatemala: Salamá (Sanborn, 1936:105). *Jalisco* (Goodwin, 1946:338). Guatemala: Libertad (Sanborn, 1938:5). See Map 155.

Genus **Molossus** É. Geoffroy St.-Hilaire
Mastiff Bats

"Notes" on the genus *Molossus*, as nearly monographic in character as the material would permit, were published by Miller, Proc. U.S. Nat. Mus., 46:85–92, August 23, 1913.

1805. *Molossus* É. Geoffroy St.-Hilaire, Ann. Mus. Hist. Nat. Paris, 6:151. Type, *Vespertilio molossus major* Kerr [= *Vespertilio molossus* (part) of authors other than Pallas].
1811. *Dysopes* Illiger, Prodromus systematis mammalium et avium . . . , p. 76, a renaming of *Molossus* É. Geoffroy St.-Hilaire.

Skull resembling that of *Promops* but crests even better developed and palate arched anteroposteriorly but not strongly domed; auditory bullae well developed for the family; basisphenoidal pits distinct; upper incisor peculiar, its shaft so reduced that height is less than width of crown through heel. Dentition, i. $\frac{1}{1}$, c. $\frac{1}{1}$, p. $\frac{1}{2}$, m. $\frac{3}{3}$. Tragus minute and subterete.

The taxonomy of this group of bats is not yet agreed upon, even in broad outline. It is not possible, therefore, to construct an adequate key, even a completely artificial one, to separate the several species. In fact, several of the named kinds are so poorly diagnosed that much of the literature pertaining to the taxonomy of the species of *Molossus* is virtually unusable. One fact, seemingly often overlooked, is that many—perhaps all—of the species are dichromatic.

Molossus rufus
Red Mastiff Bat

Selected measurements of the type of *M. r. nigricans* are: length of head and body, approximately 92; total length, 145; length of forearm, 52.6; great-

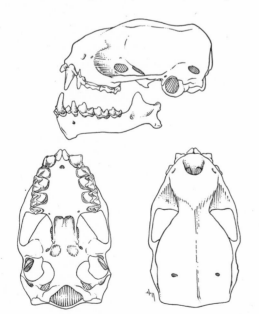

Fig. 155. *Promops centralis*, Baja Verapaz, Guatemala, No. 42088 C.N.H.M., ♀, X 2.

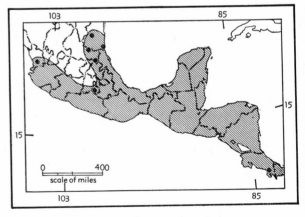

Map 161. *Molossus rufus nigricans*.

est length of skull, 23.6; zygomatic breadth, 15.2; length of upper tooth-row, 8.8. Upper parts rich russet or blackish; underparts slightly paler. Skull robust; saggital crest and lambdoidal crest well developed.

Molossus rufus nigricans Miller

1902. *Molossus nigricans* Miller, Proc. Acad. Nat. Sci. Philadelphia, 54:395, September 12, type from Acaponeta, Nayarit.
1955. *M[olossus]. r[ufus]. nigricans,* de la Torre, Fieldiana-Zool., Chicago Nat. Hist. Mus., 37:701, June 19.

MARGINAL RECORDS.—Tamaulipas: 2 mi. S Ciudad Victoria (Davis, 1951:219); Altamira (*ibid.*), thence southward along Caribbean Coast to Costa Rica: Boruca (Goodwin, 1946:341), and presumably into South America; thence northward along Pacific Coast to Nayarit: type locality. Morelos: Hda. Cocoyotla (Davis and Russell, 1954:70). San Luis Potosí (Dalquest, 1953b:67): Río Moctezuma at Tamazunchale; El Salto.

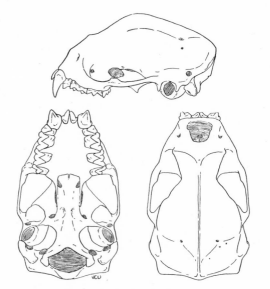

Fig. 156. *Molossus rufus nigricans,* Río Atoyac, 8 km. NW Potrero, Veracruz, No. 17857 K.U., ♀, X 2.

Molossus pretiosus
Miller's Mastiff Bat

Selected measurements of the type of *M. p. macdougalli* are: length of head and body, 70; total length, 113; length of forearm, 48.7; greatest length of skull, exclusive of incisors, 20.0; zygomatic breadth, 12.7; maxillary tooth-row exclusive of incisors, 7.8. Uniformly blackish pelage. Skull massive but having relatively low and weak sagittal- and lambdoidal-crest.

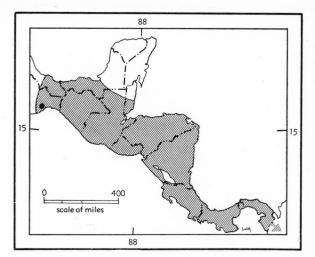

Map 162. *Molossus pretiosus macdougalli.*

Molossus pretiosus macdougalli Goodwin

1956. *Molossus pretiosus macdougalli* Goodwin, Amer. Mus. Novit., 1757:3, March 8, type from San Blas, 3 km. SE Tehuantepec, approximately 100 ft., Oaxaca. Known only from the type locality.

Molossus sinaloae J. A. Allen
Allen's Mastiff Bat

1906. *Molossus sinaloae* J. A. Allen, Bull. Amer. Mus. Nat. Hist., 22:236, July 25, type from Escuinapa, Sinaloa.

Selected measurements of the type, an adult female, are: length of head and body, 69.5; length of forearm, 45.6; greatest length of skull, 19.5; zygomatic breadth, 12.2; length of upper tooth-row, 7.2. Upper parts dark brownish drab; underparts paler, grayer. Braincase relatively narrow and high.

MARGINAL RECORDS.—Sinaloa: type locality, thence southeastward to Yucatán: Calcehtok (Hatt and Villa, 1950:

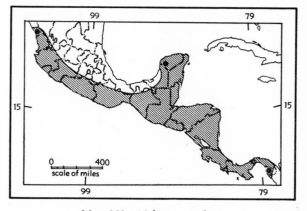

Map 163. *Molossus sinaloae.*

232), thence southward along Caribbean Coast to Panamá: El Real (G. M. Allen, 1935:228), thence northward along Pacific Coast to point of beginning.

Molossus bondae J. A. Allen
Bonda Mastiff Bat

1904. *Molossus bondae* J. A. Allen, Bull. Amer. Mus. Nat. Hist., 20:228, June 29, type from Bonda, Santa Marta, Colombia.

Selected measurements of the type, an adult female, are: length of forearm, 39; greatest length of skull, 18; zygomatic breadth, 13; length of upper tooth-row, 6.5. Upper parts either dark brown or approximately rich russet; underparts paler than back. Purportedly resembling *Molossus sinaloae* but smaller.

MARGINAL RECORDS.—Honduras (Goodwin, 1942: 145): Los Encuentros; El Manteado, thence southward into South America.

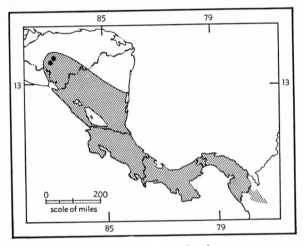

Map 164. *Molossus bondae.*

Molossus fortis Miller
Large Mastiff Bat

1913. *Molossus fortis* Miller, Proc. U.S. Nat. Mus., 46:89, August 23, type from Luquillo, Puerto Rico.

Selected measurements of the type, an adult male, are: length of head and body, 66; length of forearm, 40; greatest length of skull, 17.5; length of upper tooth-row, 7.2. Described as differing from closely related species in size.

MARGINAL RECORDS (Anthony, 1918:363).—Puerto Rico: type locality; San German.

Molossus milleri Johnson
Jamaican Mastiff Bat

1952. *Molossus milleri* Johnson, Proc. Biol. Soc. Washington, 65:197, November 5.

1838. *Molossus fuliginosus* Gray, Mag. Zool. Bot., 2:501, February, based on material from an unknown locality; lectotype from Jamaica. Not *Molossus fuliginosus* Cooper, 1837. [= *Tadarida cynocephala* (Le Conte)]. Known precisely only from Jamaica.

"Like *Molossus fortis* . . . but rostral portion of skull obviously shortened . . ." (Miller, 1913:90).

Molossus major
Kerr's Mastiff Bat

Length of head and body, approximately 58. *M. major* comprises a group of poorly diagnosed subspecies each of which was originally described and named as a separate species. Information necessary to frame an adequate diagnosis of the species as here recognized is not available in the literature and is to be obtained only by study of original materials and probably additional specimens. The current assemblage is made up of large to small bats of various shades of reddish brown to blackish. The currently recognized nominal species *debilis*, *fortis*, and *milleri* may be only subspecies of *M. major*. Also, some named kinds now considered to be subspecies of *M. major* (for example, *M. m. coibensis*—see Felten, 1957:14) may not belong in the species *M. major*.

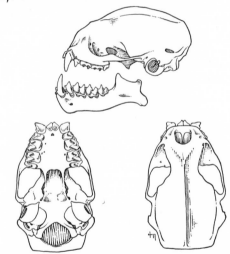

Fig. 157. *Molossus major coibensis*, Barro Colorado Island, Canal Zone, Panamá, No. 45092 K.U., ♂, X 2.

Molossus major aztecus Saussure

1860. *M[olossus]. aztecus* Saussure, Revue et Mag. Zool., Paris, ser. 2, 12:285, July, type from Amecameca, México. Considered as a subspecies of *M. major* by Hershkovitz, Proc. U.S. Nat. Mus., 99:454, May 10, 1949.

MARGINAL RECORDS.—San Luis Potosí: Río Verde (Dalquest, 1953b:69). British Honduras: Mountain Pine Ridge (Murie, 1935:20). El Salvador: San Salvador (Felten, 1957:13). Chiapas: Huehuetan (Miller, 1913:91). México: type locality.

Molossus major coibensis J. A. Allen

1904. *Molossus coibensis* J. A. Allen, Bull. Amer. Mus. Nat. Hist., 20:227, June 29, type from Coiba Island, Panamá. Considered as a subspecies of *M. major* by Hershkovitz, Proc. U.S. Nat. Mus., 99:454, May 10, 1949, but arranged as a subspecies of *M. tropidorhynchus* by Felten, Senckenbergiana Biologica, 38:14, January 15, 1957.

MARGINAL RECORDS.—El Salvador: San Salvador (Felten, 1957:14). Panamá (Goldman, 1920:222): Bohio; Panamá City; type locality; Chorrera.

Molossus major major (Kerr)

1792. *V[espertilio]. mol[ossus]. major* Kerr, The animal kingdom . . . , p. 97. Type locality, Martinique.
1792. *V[espertilio]. mol[ossus]. minor* Kerr (*loc. cit.*). Type locality, Martinique, Lesser Antilles.
1913. *Molossus major,* Miller, Proc. U.S. Nat. Mus., 46:90, August 23.

MARGINAL RECORDS.—Lesser Antilles: Dominica (Miller, 1924:89); type locality.

Molossus major obscurus É. Geoffroy St.-Hilaire

1805. *Molossus obscurus* É. Geoffroy St.-Hilaire, Ann. Mus. Hist. Nat., Paris, 6:155, type from Surinam. Considered as a subspecies of *M. major* by Hershkovitz, Proc. U.S. Nat. Mus., 99:454, May 10, 1949.
1805. *Molossus longicaudatus* É. Geoffroy St.-Hilaire (*loc. cit.*). No type or type locality designated.
1805. *Molossus fusciventer* É. Geoffroy St.-Hilaire (*loc. cit.*). No type or type locality designated.

MARGINAL RECORDS.—Lesser Antilles: St. Lucia (Miller, 1924:89); Barbardos (*ibid.*); St. Georges on Grenada (Jones, 1951:224).

Molossus major verrilli J. A. Allen

1908. *Mollossus [sic] verrilli* J. A. Allen, Bull. Amer. Mus. Nat. Hist., 24:581, September 11, type from Samaná, Dominican Republic.
1951. *Molossus major verrilli,* Hershkovitz, Fieldiana-Zool., Chicago Nat. Hist. Mus., 31:558, July 10.

MARGINAL RECORDS.—Dominican Republic: type locality. Haiti: Petionville (Hershkovitz, 1951:558).

Molossus debilis Miller
St. Kitts Mastiff Bat

1913. *Molossus debilis* Miller, Proc. U.S. Nat. Mus., 46:90, August 23, type from St. Kitts, Lesser Antilles.

Like *M. major major* but crown area of molars less. In type, ad. ♀ : head and body, 56.6; tail, 36; forearm, 38; greatest length of skull, 15.4; maxillary tooth-row, 5.4 (after Miller, 1913:90).

MARGINAL RECORDS (Miller, 1924:89).—Lesser Antilles: type locality; Nevis; Antigua; Montserrat.

Molossus tropidorhynchus Gray
Cuban Mastiff Bat

1839. *Molossus tropidorhynchus* Gray, Ann. Nat. Hist., 4:6, September, type from Cuba.

Head and body *circa* 55. Like *M. major pygmaeus* and *M. m. coibensis* but paler (usually between Raw Umber and Wood Brown), and without evident trace of drab.

MARGINAL RECORDS (Miller, 1904:339).—Cuba: Pinar del Río; El Cobre.

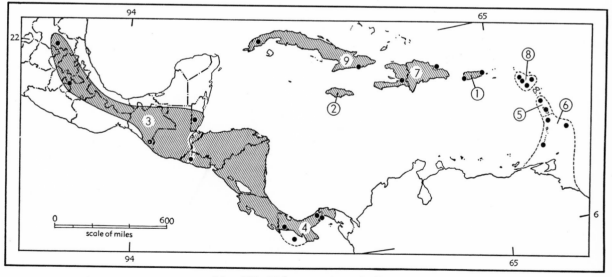

Map 165. *Molossus major* and allies.

1. *M. fortis*	4. *M. major coibensis*	7. *M. major verrilli*
2. *M. milleri*	5. *M. major major*	8. *M. debilis*
3. *M. major aztecus*	6. *M. major obscurus*	9. *M. tropidorhynchus*

ORDER **PRIMATES**—Man, Monkeys, Lemurs, and Allies

The Recent (living) members may be characterized as follows: plantigrade; pentadactyl; ethmoturbinals 4–3; clavicle present, well developed; teeth tuberculosectorial; 3rd incisor and 1st premolar absent above and below; orbit directed more or less anteriorly and separated from temporal fossa by bony bar or partition.

SUBORDER **ANTHROPOIDEA**—Man, Monkeys, and Allies

Incisors chisel-shaped; lower canine pointed (caniniform); molars bunodont; auditory bullae little inflated; ethmoturbinals 3; tibia and fibula always separate; penis pendulous, with or without baculum.

The suborder Anthropoidea as used here excludes primates belonging to the suborder Prosimii.

Key to Families and Genera of North American Primates

1. Premolars $\frac{2-2}{2-2}$.
2. Tail absent (externally); forelimbs not modified for walking; C less than twice as long as I2.
  family Hominidae, p. 233
  Homo, p. 234
  2′. Tail present (approximately as long as head and body); forelimbs modified for walking; C more than twice as long as I2 (introduced from Africa). . . . . family Cercopithecidae, p. 233
  Cercopithecus, p. 233
1′. Premolars $\frac{3-3}{3-3}$.
  3. Nape chestnut; top of head between ears white; claws (true nails absent) projecting beyond fleshy ends of digits for a distance more than width of base of claw; molars $\frac{2-2}{2-2}$ (32 teeth) in adults.
  family Callithricidae, p. 230
  Saguinus, p. 230
  3′. Nape not chestnut; top of head between ears not white; nails (true claws absent) not projecting beyond fleshy ends of digits for a distance as much as width of base of nail; molars $\frac{3-3}{3-3}$ (36 teeth) in adults. . . . . family Cebidae, p. 219
    4. Back uniformly gray; hair of face with 3 narrow black lines (one from outer corner of each eye to nape and a 3rd on center of face and head; these lines border whitish areas, one above each eye); greatest breadth of skull is across orbits. . . . . *Aotus*, p. 219
    4′. Back reddish or black; hair of face lacking 3 black lines; greatest breadth of skull not across orbits.
      5. Forearms distinctly reddish or yellow; over-all length of upper dental arcade less than 25.
      Saimiri, p. 226
      5′. Forearms black; over-all length of upper dental arcade more than 25.
        6. Topknot absent and face black; less than 34 per cent of length of skull (gnathion to inion) lies behind glenoid fossa; less than one-fifth of skull projects behind lower jaw (when skull, with lower mandible in place, rests on horizontal surface on inferior margin of lower jaw); height of vertical ramus of lower jaw (as measured from notch between coronoid and articular processes) more than distance between external auditory meatus and infraorbital foramen. . . . . *Alouatta*, p. 221
        6′. Topknot (tuft of hair directed upward and forward) present (*Ateles*) or face, chest, and shoulders white (*Cebus*); more than 34 per cent of skull lies behind glenoid fossa; more than one-fifth of skull lies behind lower jaw; height of vertical ramus of lower jaw less than distance between external auditory meatus and infraorbital canal.
          7. Pelage black or reddish (without white face, chest, and shoulders); topknot present; tail averaging more than 1½ times as long as head and body; distal 4th or more of underside of tail bare; thumbs normally absent; occlusal area of M3 not smaller than that of P2; occlusal area of m3 larger than that of p3; inferior margin of lower mandible approximately straight. . . . . *Ateles*, p. 227
          7′. Pelage black except for white face, chest, and shoulders; topknot absent; tail averaging less than 1½ times as long as head and body; underside of tail haired for entire length; occlusal area of M3 less than that of P2; occlusal area of m3 smaller than that of p3; inferior margin of lower mandible with angular part produced downward.
          Cebus, p. 223

SUPERFAMILY **CEBOIDEA**—New World Monkeys

Premolars $\frac{3-3}{3-3}$; nose broad in most (not all) species. This superfamily includes all of the New World monkeys. All Old World monkeys have premolars $\frac{2-2}{2-2}$ and are narrow-nosed.

FAMILY **CEBIDAE**—Capuchins, Howlers, Spider Monkeys, and Allies

Dentition, i. $\frac{2}{2}$, c. $\frac{1}{1}$, p. $\frac{3}{3}$, m. $\frac{3}{3}$; nose usually broad and nostrils opening laterally; tail present and well developed; bare ischial callosities and cheek pouches absent; no bony external auditory meatal tube. Arboreal in habit.

Genus **Aotus** Illiger—Douroucouli Monkeys

1811. *Aotus* Illiger, Prodromus systematis mammalium et avium, p. 71. Type, *Simia trivirgata* Humboldt, 1809.
1823. *Nyctipithecus* Spix, Simiarum et vespertilionum Brasiliensium . . . , p. 24. Included *Nyctipithecus felinus* Spix and *N. vociferans* Spix.
1824. *Nocthora*, F. Cuvier, Hist. Nat. Mamm., 5, livr. XLIII, pl., August. Type, *Simia trivirgata* Humboldt.

Size small (see measurements of species); muzzle conical and truncated; tail not prehensile; eyes enormously enlarged; laryngeal pouch absent; thoracolumbar vertebrae 22; brain small, the external surface of cerebral hemispheres relatively smooth and almost devoid of convolutions; occipital region of braincase not produced posteriorly; premaxillaries small and distinctly separated from each other; nails small and slightly compressed laterally.

There seems to be more individual variation in color in specimens of this genus than there is in some other genera of Central American primates. The differences in color have been used in several instances to separate some of the nominal species. Possibly there is only one species having several subspecies.

KEY TO NORTH AMERICAN SPECIES OF AOTUS

1. Occurring on Azuero Peninsula, Panamá.
   A. bipunctatus, p. 219
1'. Occurring in Canal Zone, Panamá, and eastward into South America. . *A. trivirgatus*, p. 219

Aotus bipunctatus Bole
Bole's Douroucouli

1937. *Aotus bipunctatus* Bole, Sci. Publ. Cleveland Mus. Nat. Hist., 7:152, August 31, type from Paracoté, 3 mi. E Montijo Bay, and 1½ mi. S mouth Río Angulo, Veraguas, Panamá. Known only from the type locality.

External measurements of a male and a female (the type) are, respectively: 839, 806; 430, 413; 101, 95. Greatest length of skull, ––, 61.5. Back and sides pale wood brown lightly washed with ochraceous-tawny along mid-dorsal region; underparts light ochraceous-buff to slightly paler, slightly darker in axillary and inguinal regions; tail suffused with russet basally, becoming darker (blackish) distally, the distal half black; supraorbital spots white. Cranially this nominal species differs from *A. trivirgatus* mainly in larger size. *A. bipunctatus* almost surely is no more than a subspecies of *A. trivirgatus*.

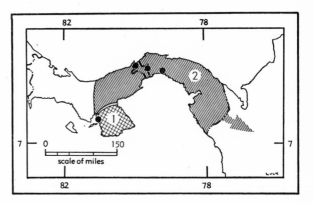

Map 166. *Aotus.*

1. *Aotus bipunctatus*
2. *Aotus trivirgatus griseimembra*

Aotus trivirgatus
Three-banded Douroucouli

Total length of the type of *A. t. griseimembra*, 1047; occipitonasal length, 58.2. Average external measurements of five adults (Boca de Cupe, 2; Gatún, 1; Cana, 1; Río Indio, 1; all in Panamá): 657 (620–685); 360 (325–390); 88 (83–90). Occipitonasal length, 57.2 (56.5–59.8). Pelage short (25), semi-wooly, brownish gray, changing to black on distal two-thirds of tail and backs of hands and feet; underparts of body ochraceous white; face bare; top of head blackish but with triangular white area above each eye, the 2 white areas separated by a narrow (3 mm. wide) anterior extension of median line from black area on top of head (description based on specimens from Panamá).

These monkeys are nocturnal, and several together have been found in hollow trees. The species has a wide geographic range in South America.

A specimen of *Aotus vociferans* (Spix) is said to have been taken in the forest of Quindín, Costa Rica (Sclater, Proc. Zool. Soc. London, 1872, p. 3),

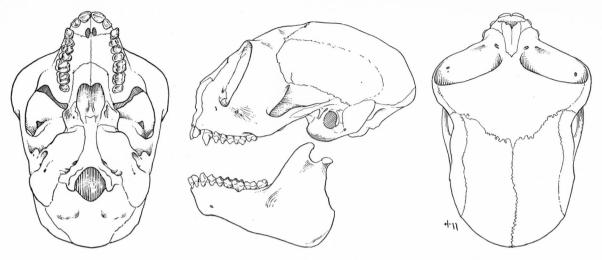

Fig. 158. *Aotus trivirgatus griseimembra*, ½ mi. from Juan Mina, Panamá.
No. 284776 U.S.N.M., ♀, X 1.

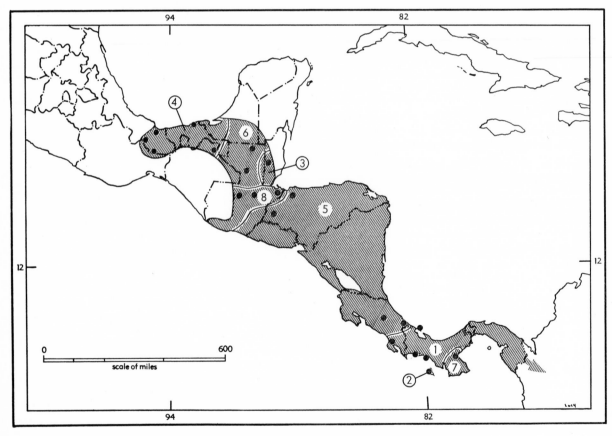

Map 167. *Alouatta villosa*.

| 1. *A. v. aequatorialis* | 3. *A. v. luctuosa* | 5. *A. v. palliata* | 7. *A. v. trabeata* |
| 2. *A. v. coibensis* | 4. *A. v. mexicana* | 6. *A. v. pigra* | 8. *A. v. villosa* |

but this record is almost certainly erroneous (Elliot, Rev. Primates, vol. 2, pp. 14–15 (1912), June, 1913). Hershkovitz (Proc. U.S. Nat. Mus., 98:408, May 10, 1949) regards the specimen as *Aotus trivirgatus lemurinus* (I. Geoffroy St.-Hilaire) that occurs naturally only in Colombia, South America.

A specimen of the genus *Aotus* was received alive by the Zoological Society of London from San Juan del Norte, Nicaragua. This specimen was named by Sclater (*loc. cit.*) as a new species, *Nyctipithecus rufipes*. As pointed out by Hershkovitz (1949:405), the "original description and color plate indicate that the type most probably originated in Brazil and was transported as a pet to Nicaragua. The monkey cannot be identified with *griseimembra*. . . . So far, there is not one authenticated record of occurrence of the genus in Central America outside of Panamá."

Aotus trivirgatus griseimembra Elliot

1912. *Aotus griseimembra* Elliot, Bull. Amer. Mus. Nat. Hist., 31:33, March 4, type from Hda. Cincinnati, Santa Marta, Colombia.
1949. *Aotus trivirgatus griseimembra*, Hershkovitz, Proc. U.S. Nat. Mus., 98:402, May 10.
1914. *Aotus zonalis* Goldman, Smiths. Miscl. Coll., 63(5):6, March 14, type from Gatún, 100 ft., Canal Zone, Panamá. Regarded as a synonym of *A. t. griseimembra* by Hershkovitz (*supra cit.*).

MARGINAL RECORDS (Hershkovitz, 1949:405).— Panamá: Gatún, Canal Zone; Alajuela, Canal Zone; Pacora, thence eastward into South America.

Genus **Alouatta** Lacépède—Howler Monkeys

1799. *Alouatta* Lacépède, Tableau des divisions, sous-divisions, ordres et genres des mammifères, p. 4. (Published as supplement to Discours d'ouverture et de clôture du cours d'histoire naturelle. . . .) Type, *Simia belzebub* Linnaeus.
1811. *Mycetes* Illiger, Prodromus systematis mammalium et avium . . . , p. 70. Type species not designated; species included were *Simia belzebub* Linnaeus and *S. seniculus* Linnaeus.
1812. *Stentor* É. Geoffroy St.-Hilaire, Ann. Mus. Hist. Nat. Paris, 19:107, October 12. Type species not designated; species included were *Stentor seniculus* (Linnaeus), *S. ursinus* Humboldt, *S. stramineus* É. Geoffroy St.-Hilaire, *S. fuscus* É. Geoffroy St.-Hilaire, *S. flavicaudatus* É. Geoffroy St.-Hilaire, and *S. niger* É. Geoffroy St.-Hilaire.

Total length, 1000–1500. Muzzle short, somewhat flattened; tail prehensile and naked on under surface distally; thumb well developed; hyoid bone enlarged into large capsule, forming resonance chamber; angular region of mandible greatly enlarged; much enlarged laryngeal pouch present; face bare and black; beard present on males; M3 smaller than M2 or M1; premolars smaller than M1 or M2; p2 larger than p3.

Alouatta villosa
Howler Monkey

X ⅛

Subspecies revised by Lawrence, Bull. Mus. Comp. Zool., 75:315–354, November, 1933, under the name *Alouatta palliata*. Lawrence employed *palliata* Gray, 1849, as the specific name for Central American howlers because the strict application of the earlier name *Mycetes villosus* Gray, 1845, is "indeterminable due to the absence of a [positively known] type locality and the imperfect condition of the type" (*op. cit.*:336). Nevertheless, Sclater (Proc. Zool. Soc. London, p. 5, 1872) considered Guatemalan specimens to be identical with Gray's type specimen of *Mycetes villosus*. So did Schlegel (Mus. Hist. Nat. Pays-Bas, Leiden, 7 (pt. 12; Monogr. 40: Simiae):151–152, 1876). Alston (Mammalia, in Salvin and Godman, Biologia Centrali-Americana, pp. 3, 5, 1879) took the same view. Handley (Special Scientific Rept.: Wildlife No. 5, U.S. Fish and Wildlife Service, p. 150, June, 1950) uses the name *villosa* in a subspecific sense for Guatemalan populations. It seems to us that on the basis of priority, and also on the basis of choice of first reviser, *Alouatta villosa* is the name of the species.

Average external measurements of 4 males and 6 females from Veracruz, México, are, respectively: 1145, 1104; 621, 605; 144, 140. Occipitonasal length, 99–107 (males); 92–95 (females). Pelage black or black and reddish; underparts thinly haired. Occipital region of skull vertical and truncated; temporal ridges on braincase almost uniting in some old males, and forming a sagittal ridge, but not a crest.

Howler monkeys live in bands of 6 to 50 individuals. The loud, resounding roar of the male carries long distances, and in early morning the cries of different individuals from different places in the jungle produces a constant roar. Howlers can walk on the ground but seldom do so; they spend almost all of their lives in trees. When one member of a band is shot, others sometimes throw small missiles with remarkably poor aim at the hunter. So far as we know, however, they never actually physically attack humans.

Alouatta villosa aequatorialis Festa

1903. *Alouata* [*sic*] *aequatorialis* Festa, Bull. Mus. Zool. Anat. Comp., Univ. Torino, 18(435):3, February 11, type from Vinces, Ecuador.

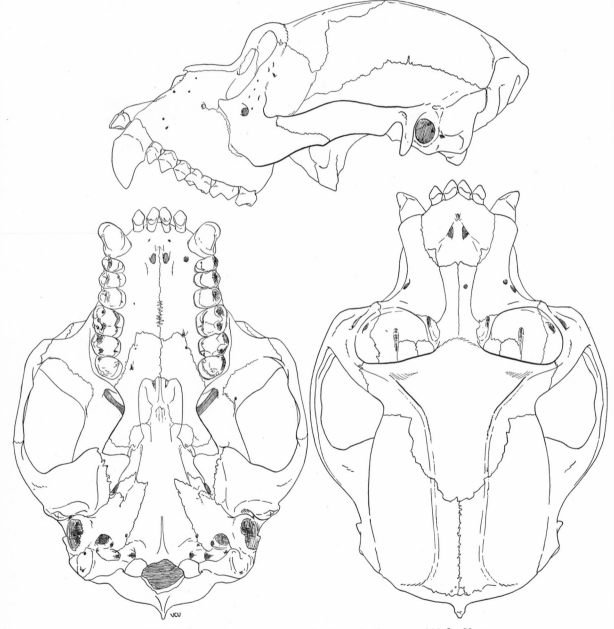

Fig. 159. *Alouatta villosa mexicana*, 20 km. E Jesús Carranza, 300 ft., Veracruz, No. 23932 K.U., ♂, X 1.

1913. *Alouatta palliata inconsonans* Goldman, Smiths. Miscl. Coll., 60(22):17, February 28, type from Cerro Azul, 2500 ft., near headwaters Chagres River, Panamá.

MARGINAL RECORDS.—Panamá: Bocas del Toro (Lawrence, 1933:327), thence eastward along Caribbean Coast to South America, thence westward along Pacific Coast but north of the range of *A. v. trabeata*, but including Insoleta Island (Goldman, 1920:229); Sevilla Island (*ibid.*). Costa Rica: Puerto Cortez (Goodwin, 1946:348).

Alouatta villosa coibensis Thomas

1902. *Alouatta palliata coibensis* Thomas, Nov. Zool., 9:135, April 10, type from Coiba Island, Panamá. Known only from Coiba Island.

Alouatta villosa luctuosa Lawrence

1933. *Alouatta palliata luctuosa* Lawrence, Bull. Mus. Comp. Zool., 75:337, November, type from Mountain Cow, British Honduras. Known only from the type locality.

Alouatta villosa mexicana Merriam

1902. *Alouatta palliata mexicana* Merriam, Proc. Biol. Soc. Washington, 15:67, March 22, type from Minatitlán, Veracruz.

MARGINAL RECORDS.—Tabasco: 15 km. NW Alvara Obregon, 10 ft. (19284 KU). Chiapas: 6 mi. SE Palenque (Kuns and Tashian, 1954:101). Veracruz: 35 km. SE Jesús Carranza, 400 ft. (23941 KU); Achotal (Lawrence, 1933: 341); 10 km. NW Minatitlán, 100 ft. (19282 KU).

Alouatta villosa palliata (Gray)

1849. *Mycetes palliatus* Gray, Proc. Zool. Soc. London, p. 138, June 1, type from Lake Nicaragua, not Caracas, Venezuela; see Sclater, Proc. Zool. Soc. London, pp. 7–8, June, 1872.
1908. *Alouatta palliata matagalpae* J. A. Allen, Bull. Amer. Mus. Nat. Hist., 24:670, October 13, type from Lavala, Matagalpa, Nicaragua. For status see J. A. Allen, Bull. Amer. Mus. Nat. Hist., 28:114, April 30, 1910.

MARGINAL RECORDS.—Honduras: Chamelecón (Lawrence, 1933:322), thence along Caribbean Coast to Costa Rica (Goodwin, 1946:347): Cuabré; Guayábo, thence northwestward along shores of Lake Nicaragua (Lawrence, 1933:318) to Guatemala: *along Pacific Coast* (Handley, 1950:150). Honduras: Copan (Goodwin, 1942:148).

Alouatta villosa pigra Lawrence

1933. *Alouatta palliata pigra* Lawrence, Bull. Mus. Comp. Zool., 75:333, November, type from Uaxactún, Petén, Guatemala.

MARGINAL RECORDS.—Guatemala: type locality; 9 mi. S La Libertad (Goodwin, 1955d:4). *Chiapas: Laguna Ocotal* (Burnett and Lyman, 1957:292).

Alouatta villosa trabeata Lawrence

1933. *Alouatta palliata trabeata* Lawrence, Bull. Mus. Comp. Zool., 75:328, November, type from Capina,

Herrera, Panamá. (According to Barbara Lawrence, *in litt.*, Jan. 7, 1957, Capina is approximately 10 mi. SW Chitre and between the Río de la Villa and the Río Parita.)

MARGINAL RECORDS.—Panamá: *type locality*; Parita (Lawrence, 1933:330).

Alouatta villosa villosa (Gray)

1845. *Mycetes villosus* Gray, Ann. Mag. Nat. Hist., 16:220, October, type from Guatemala.
1950. [*Alouatta palliata*] *villosa*, Handley, *in* A fish and wildlife survey of Guatemala, Specl. Sci. Rept.: Wildlife No. 5, U.S. Dept. Int., p. 150, June.

MARGINAL RECORDS (Goodwin, 1934:59).—Guatemala: altos W of Cobán; Río Polochic; lower Motagua.

Genus **Cebus** Erxleben—Capuchin Monkeys

1777. *Cebus* Erxleben, Systeme regni animalis . . . , 1:44. Type, *Simia capucina* Linnaeus.
1792. *Sapajus* Kerr, The animal kingdom . . . , 1(Mamm.): 74–79. Type not designated.
1862. *Calyptrocebus* Reichenbach, Die vollständigste Naturgeschichte der Affen, p. 55. Type not designated.
1862. *Pseudocebus* Reichenbach, Die vollständigste Naturgeschichte der Affen, p. 55. Type not designated.
1862. *Otocebus* Reichenbach, Die vollständigste Naturgeschichte der Affen, pp. 55–56. Type not designated.
1862. *Eucebus* Reichenbach, Die vollständigste Naturgeschichte der Affen, p. 56. Type not designated.

Size small (see measurements under species); pelage black except that face, chest, and shoulders white or pale; head crested or non-crested; ectopterygoid fossa present; thumb well developed; mandible not modified; laryngeal pouch absent; brain large, elongated hemispheres overlaying cerebellum, braincase produced posteriorly; tail prehensile in some degree but not naked on under surface; facial part of skull short.

Because capuchins are so frequently kept as pets, it is pertinent to give in part the account of them published by Cruz Lima (1945:134).

"They live in any type of terrain but seem to prefer the inundated forests, avoiding the tops of the highest trees to live, by preference, on the medium level where in general the woods are denser. They are very quick and restless, using their tails a lot for their acrobatics through the branches, but only as a support, this member not serving as a supplementary hand as is the case in *Ateles* and *Lagothrix*. Their food is mixed, including not only fruits and shoots, but also eggs, grubs and insects; they possess a special faculty for catching flies. They are easily domesticated, especially when they are captured young, and therefore are often found as pets. Their vivacity, intelligence, mobility of expression, at times singularly human attitudes, their marked bodily resistance to the fatal consequences

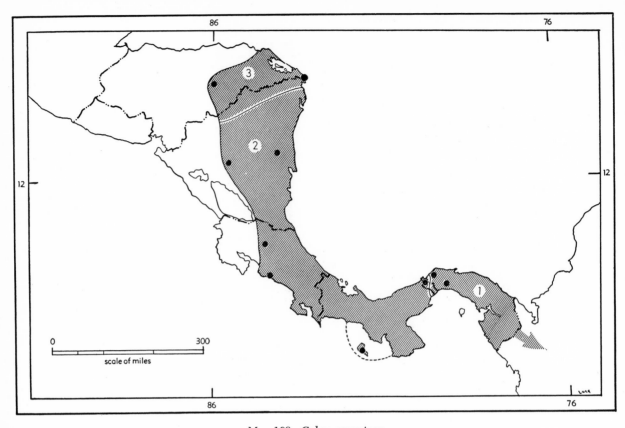

Map 168. *Cebus capucinus.*

1. *C. capucinus capucinus*   2. *C. capucinus imitator*   3. *C. capucinus limitaneus*

of loss of liberty are factors which contribute to their long life under such conditions, without equal among the neotropical monkeys. They adapt themselves to climatic changes as no other platyrrhine monkey, a fact which explains why they have been known alive in Europe and North America for such a long period. This side of the medal has its reverse, however. Even when domesticated for a long time monkeys of the genus *Cebus* keep a native trait of violence and cruelty which occasionally crops up unexpectedly and which as a rule is more accentuated with age. Furthermore their personal habits shock even the less refined, as may also the unfolding of instincts which conventionally are considered low, heightened by their unnatural life in captivity."

Cebus capucinus
Capuchin

Average external measurements of 3 adults from Panamá are: 947; 503; 135. Occipitonasal length, 86. Pelage black except for face, shoulders and sides of neck, which are white; head not crested; hind foot less than 150; tail averaging less than one and one-half times length of head and body. Angular part of mandible produced downward below inferior margin of horizontal ramus; approximately 39 per cent of length of skull (gnathion to inion) behind glenoid fossa when skull, with lower jaw in place, rests on inferior points of lower mandible on horizontal surface; upper cheek-teeth decreasing in size posteriorly (P2 to M3); occlusal area of last lower molar less than that of second lower cheek-tooth (p3).

Cebus capucinus capucinus (Linnaeus)

1758. [*Simia*] *capucina* Linnaeus, Syst. nat., ed. 10, 1:29. Type locality unknown; subsequently fixed as northern Colombia by Goldman, Proc. Biol. Soc. Washington, 27: 99, May 11, 1914.
1909. *C[ebus]. capucinus*, Elliot, Bull. Amer. Mus. Nat. Hist., 26:229, April 17.

MARGINAL RECORDS.—Panamá (Goldman, 1920:231): Cerro Bruja; Cerro Azul, thence southward into South America.

Cebus capucinus imitator Thomas

1903. *Cebus imitator* Thomas, Ann. Mag. Nat. Hist., ser. 7, 11:376, April, type from Boquete, Chiriquí, Panamá.

1914. *Cebus capucinus imitator,* Goldman, Proc. Biol. Soc. Washington, 27:99, May 11.

MARGINAL RECORDS.—Nicaragua: Ocotal (J. A. Allen, 1910:115), thence down the Caribbean Coast to Panamá

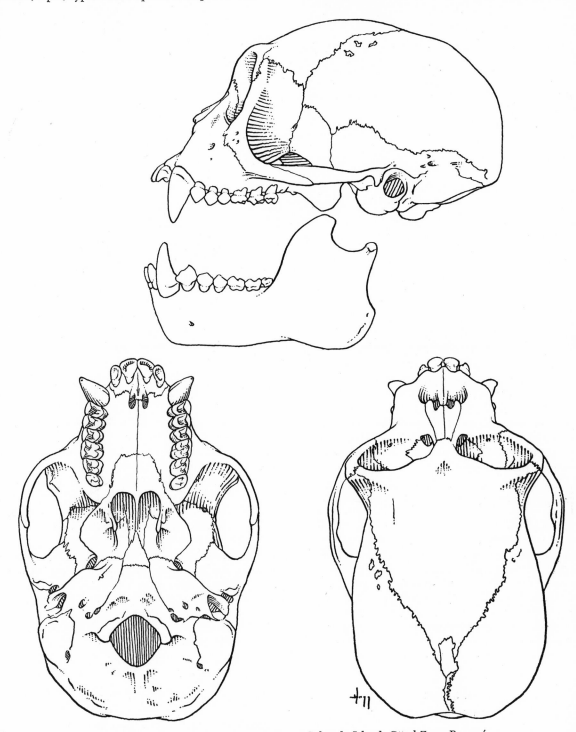

Fig. 160. *Cebus capucinus imitator,* Barro Colorado Island, Canal Zone, Panamá, No. 45098 K.U., ♂, X 1.

(Goldman, 1920:233); Gatún; *Barro Colorado Island* (Ingles 1953:267—recorded only to species); Coiba Island, thence up Pacific Coast to Costa Rica (Goodwin, 1946:343): Pozo Azul; Cataratos, San Carlos. Nicaragua: Muy Muy (J. A. Allen, 1910:115).

Cebus capucinus limitaneus Hollister

1914. *Cebus capucinus limitaneus* Hollister, Proc. Biol. Soc. Washington, 27:105, May 11, type from Río Segovia, eastern Honduras, subsequently restricted to Cabo Gracias a Dios at the mouth of the Río Segovia, eastern border between Honduras and Nicaragua by Hershkovitz, Proc. U.S. Nat. Mus., 98:347, May 10, 1949.

MARGINAL RECORDS.—Honduras: type locality; Catacamas (Goodwin, 1942:146).

Genus **Saimiri** Voigt—Squirrel Marmosets

1831. *Saimiri* Voigt, *in* G. Leopold v. Cuvier, Das Thierreich . . . , 1:95. Type, *Simia sciurea* Linnaeus. For use of this name in place of *Chrysothrix* Kaup see Palmer, Proc. Biol. Soc. Washington, 11:174, June 9, 1897.
1835. *Chrysothrix* Kaup, Das Thierreich . . . , 1:50. Type, *Simia sciurea* Linnaeus.
1840. *Pithesciurus* Lesson, Nouveau tableau du règne animal . . . mammifères, p. 7. Type, *Pithesciurus saimiri* Lesson.

Size small (see measurements under species); pelage short, thick, soft, and brilliantly colored; eyes large and placed close together; ears large and shaped approximately as in man; thumbs short; tail non-prehensile, long, covered with short hair, and slightly tufted at tip; ectopterygoid fossa present; thumb well developed; mandible not modified; laryngeal pouch absent; brain large, the elongated hemispheres overlaying the cerebellum, the braincase produced posteriorly; facial part of skull small in proportion to cranial part; foramen magnum in horizontal plane.

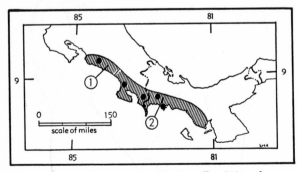

Map 169. *Saimiri örstedii citrinellus* (1) and *Saimiri örstedii örstedii* (2).

Saimiri örstedii
Titi Monkey

External measurements: 612–695; 350–415; 80–90. Occipitonasal length, 54–56. Skin of lips including

area around nostrils black and nearly devoid of hair; hair around eyes, ears, on throat and sides of neck white; top of head black to grayish (depending on subspecies); back, hind feet, forefeet, and forearms reddish or yellow; shoulders and hind feet suffused with gray; underparts whitish or light ochraceous; tail bicolored like body except that distal fourth is black.

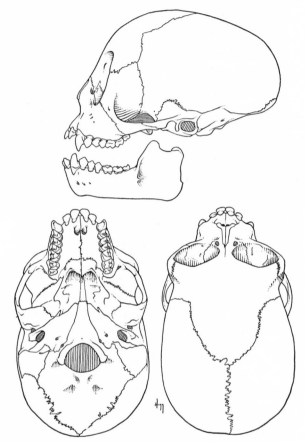

Fig. 161. *Saimiri örstedii örstedii*, Burica Peninsula, Panamá, No. 291050 U.S.N.M., ♀, X 1.

Saimiri örstedii citrinellus Thomas

1904. *Saimiri oerstedi citrinellus* Thomas, Ann. Mag. Nat. Hist., ser. 7, 13:250, April, type from Pozo Azul, 9 mi. upstream from mouth Río Pirris, San José, Costa Rica. Known only from the type locality.

Saimiri örstedii örstedii (Reinhardt)

1872. *Chrysothrix örstedii* Reinhardt, Vidensk. Meddel. nat. For. Kjöbenhavn, ser. 3, 4(nos. 6–9):157, type from vicinity of David, Chiriquí, Panamá.
1901. *Saimiri oerstedii*, Miller and Rehn, Proc. Boston Soc. Nat. Hist., 30:297, December 27.

MARGINAL RECORDS.—Costa Rica (Goodwin, 1946: 349): Palmar; Coto. Panamá (Goldman, 1920:223–224): Boquerón; *Veragua*; Sevilla Island.

Genus **Ateles** É. Geoffroy St.-Hilaire
Spider Monkeys

Revised by Kellogg and Goldman, Proc. U.S. Nat. Mus., 96:1–45, November 2, 1944.

1799. *Sapajou* Lacépède, Tab-des divisions . . . mammifères, p. 4. Type, *Sapajou paniscus* Lacépède [= *Simia paniscus* Linnaeus]. For use of *Ateles*, in place of *Sapajou* that has 6 years priority, see Opinion 91 of the International Commission on Zoological Nomenclature.

1806. *Ateles* É. Geoffroy St.-Hilaire, Ann. Mus. d'Hist. Nat., Paris, 7:262. Type, *Simia paniscus* Linnaeus.

1806. *Atelocheirus* É. Geoffroy St.-Hilaire, Ann. Mus. d'Hist. Nat., Paris, 7:272. Type, *Ateles belzebuth* É. Geoffroy St.-Hilaire.

1815. *Paniscus* Rafinesque, Anal. de la Nature, p. 53. Type *Simia paniscus* Linnaeus. Not *Paniscus* Schrank, 1802, an insect.

1911. *Montaneia* Ameghino, Anal. Mus. Nac. Hist. Nat. Buenos Aires, ser. 3, 13:317. Type, *Montaneia anthro-*

pomorpha Ameghino, from an Indian grave in a cave near Sancti Spiritus, Cuba [= an *Ateles* probably brought from South America; see Miller, Smiths. Miscl. Coll., 66(13), December 8, 1916].

Ectopterygoid fossa absent; tail prehensile; thumb absent or poorly developed and appressed to 2nd digit; mandible not modified; laryngeal pouch absent; brain and braincase essentially as in *Cebus*; legs and tail exceptionally long relative to length of body; head small; muzzle prominent; molars small, each with 4 pronounced cusps; inferior margin of lower mandible approximately straight.

KEY TO NORTH AMERICAN SPECIES OF ATELES

1. General coloration of entire back chiefly black. . . . . *A. fusciceps*, p. 228
1'. General coloration of entire back not chiefly (jet) black. . . . . . . *A. geoffroyi*, p. 228

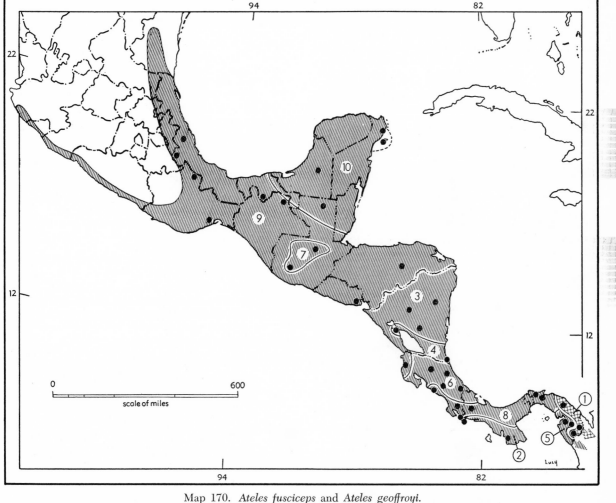

Map 170. *Ateles fusciceps* and *Ateles geoffroyi*.

Guide to kinds	2. A. g. azuerensis	5. A. g. grisescens	8. A. g. panamensis
1. A. f. robustus	3. A. g. frontatus	6. A. g. ornatus	9. A. g. vellerosus
	4. A. g. geoffroyi	7. A. g. pan	10. A. g. yucatanensis

Ateles fusciceps
Brown-headed Spider Monkey

Differs from *A. geoffroyi* only in nearly uniform black coloration. Additional collecting in geographically critical areas is required to show certainly that this monkey is specifically distinct from *A. geoffroyi*.

Only one subspecies, *A. f. robustus*, is pertinent to the present work.

Ateles fusciceps robustus J. A. Allen

1914. *Ateles robustus* J. A. Allen, Bull. Amer. Mus. Nat. Hist., 33:652, December 14, type from Gallera, Department of Cauca, 5000 ft., Colombia.
1944. *Ateles fusciceps robustus*, Kellogg and Goldman, Proc. U.S. Nat. Mus., 96:29, November 2.
1915. *Ateles dariensis* Goldman, Proc. Biol. Soc. Washington, 28:101, April 13, type from near head Río Limón, 5200 ft., Mt. Pirre, Panamá.

MARGINAL RECORDS (Kellogg and Goldman, 1944: 29–30).—Panamá: Río Bayano; Cituro; near head Río Limón, 5200 ft.; thence into South America.

Ateles geoffroyi
Geoffroy's Spider Monkey

x ¹/₁₀

External measurements: 1129–1280; 698–840; 159–194. Occipitonasal length, 85–100. Pelage of back with some buff or rufescent; hair of head

directed upward and backward forming more or less of a topknot; tail more than 1½ times length of head and body and distal fourth (usually more) of under surface bare; upper cheek-teeth of relatively uniform width except the 1st premolar and last molar, which are narrower (and shorter).

These monkeys are social and occur in pairs or in bands of as many as 25 individuals; in southern Veracruz as many as 50 were seen in a single band. An outstanding trait of this species is its curiosity; a passing animal of any considerable size will be investigated by spider monkeys. They live in the taller jungle. Their ability to hang by the tail alone, or a foot, or a hand, is an indication of their exceptional arboreal ability; they are extreme in the direction of specialization for arboreal life among all of the New World primates and are equalled, perhaps, only by the gibbons of the Old World.

Ateles geoffroyi azuerensis Bole

1937. *Ateles azuerensis* Bole, Sci. Publ. Cleveland Mus. Nat. Hist., 7:149, August 31, type from Altos Negritos, 1500 ft., 10 mi. E Montijo Bay, Mariato Suay Lands, Azuero Peninsula, Veraguas, Panamá.
1944. *Ateles geoffroyi azuerensis* Kellogg and Goldman, Proc. U.S. Nat. Mus., 96:41, November 2.

MARGINAL RECORDS.—Panamá: Río La Vaca, near Puerto Armuelles, Burica Peninsula (Kellogg and Goldman, 1944:42); type locality.

Ateles geoffroyi frontatus (Gray)

1842. *Eriodes frontatus* Gray, Ann. Mag. Nat. Hist., ser. 1, 10:256, December, type from "South America"; actually from harbor of Culebra, Bahía de Culebra, Guanacaste, Costa Rica (see Kellogg and Goldman, Proc. U.S. Nat. Mus., 96:37, November 2, 1944).
1944. *Ateles geoffroyi frontatus*, Kellogg and Goldman, Proc. U.S. Nat. Mus., 96:37, November 2.

MARGINAL RECORDS.—Nicaragua: Río Yoya, tributary of Río Princapolca (Kellogg and Goldman, 1944:38); Peña Blanca (Goodwin, 1946:343). Costa Rica: type locality. Nicaragua: Tuma (Goodwin, 1946:343).

Ateles geoffroyi geoffroyi Kuhl

1820. *Atele[s] geoffroyi* Kuhl, Beiträge zur Zoologie und vergleichenden Anatomie, 1:26, type from an unknown locality; fixed at San Juan del Norte, Nicaragua, by Kellogg and Goldman, Proc. U.S. Nat. Mus., 96:31, November 2.
1820. *Ateles melanochir* Desmarest, Mammalogie, . . . , pt. 1, p. 76, *in* Encyclopédie méthodique . . . , type from an unknown locality.

MARGINAL RECORDS.—Nicaragua: Managua (Kellogg and Goldman, 1944:32); type locality.

Ateles geoffroyi grisescens Gray

1866. *Ateles grisescens* Gray, Proc. Zool. Soc. London, p. 732 (for 1865), April, type from an unknown locality, presumably the valley of Río Tuyra, Darién, Panamá

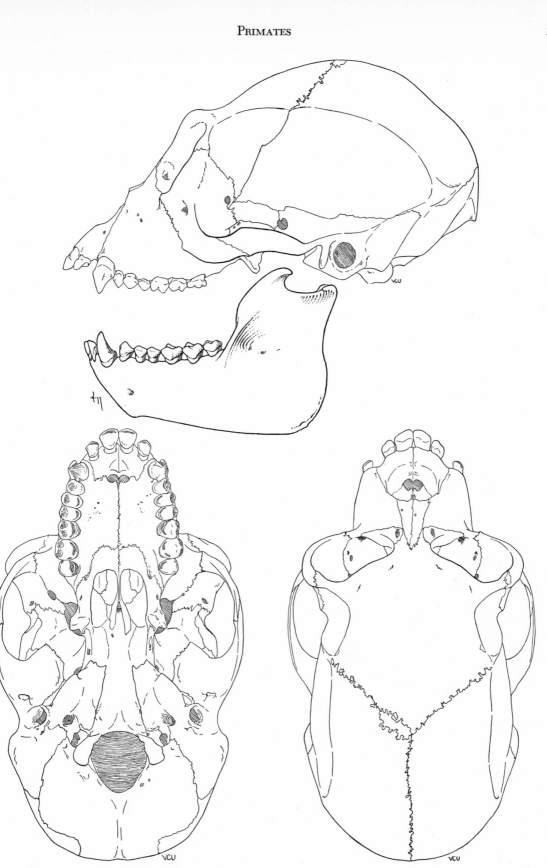

Fig. 162. *Ateles geoffroyi vellerosus*, 20 km. E Jesús Carranza, 300 ft., Veracruz, No. 23916 K.U., ♀, X 1.

(see Kellogg and Goldman, Proc. U.S. Nat. Mus., 96:43, November 2).

1944. *Ateles geoffroyi grisescens* Kellogg and Goldman, Proc. U.S. Nat. Mus., 96:43, November 2.

1866. *Ateles cucullatus* Gray, Proc. Zool. Soc. London, p. 733 (for 1865), April, type from an unknown locality.

1872. *Ateles rufiventris* Sclater, Proc. Zool. Soc. London, p. 688, November, type from Río Atrato, Darién, Colombia. Regarded as a synonym of *Ateles geoffroyi grisescens* by Hershkovitz (Proc. U.S. Nat. Mus., 98:381, May 10, 1949), who states: "Type an immature; head, tail, upperparts of trunk and limbs black, chest, belly, inner sides of upper arms and thighs rufous (*ex* type, British Museum)."

MARGINAL RECORDS.—Panamá: Chepigana (Kellogg and Goldman, 1944:44); type locality.

Ateles geoffroyi ornatus Gray

1870. *Ateles ornatus* Gray, Catalogue of monkeys, lemurs, and fruit-eating bats in the . . . British Museum, p. 44, type from an unknown locality; fixed at Cuabre, Limón, Costa Rica, by Kellogg and Goldman, Proc. U.S. Nat. Mus., 96:39, November 2.

1944. *Ateles geoffroyi ornatus*, Kellogg and Goldman, Proc. U.S. Nat. Mus., 96:39, November 2.

MARGINAL RECORDS.—Costa Rica (Goodwin, 1946: 344): Cataratos, San Carlos; Guápiles; type locality; Santa María.

Ateles geoffroyi pan Schlegel

1876. *Ateles pan* Schlegel, Mus. Hist. Nat. Pays-Bas, Leiden, 7(pt. 12; Monogr. 40 Simiae):180, cotypes from Cobán, Alta Vera Paz, Guatemala.

1944. *Ateles geoffroyi pan*, Kellogg and Goldman, Proc. U.S. Nat. Mus., 96:36, November 2.

MARGINAL RECORDS (Kellogg and Goldman, 1944: 14).—Guatemala: type locality; Volcán Atitlán.

Ateles geoffroyi panamensis Kellogg and Goldman

1944. *Ateles geoffroyi panamensis* Kellogg and Goldman, Proc. U.S. Nat. Mus., 96:40, November 2, type from Cerro Bruja, about 15 mi. SE Portobello, Colón, Panamá.

1862. *Ateles Beelzebuth* Geoff., Varietas *triangulifera* Weinland, Zool. Gart., a M., Jahrg. 3(No. 3):206–207, fig. Type locality, unknown. This name may apply here; if so, it will replace *Ateles geoffroyi panamensis* because of eighty-two years priority. According to Hershkovitz (Proc. U.S. Nat. Mus., 98:380, footnote, May 10, 1949), "The name is based on a menagerie individual of unknown origin. Judged by the description, the type is most probably a representative of one of the Central American races of *Ateles geoffroyi*. For the present, there is no good reason for giving priority to *triangulifera* over any of the later named forms recognized by Kellogg and Goldman."

MARGINAL RECORDS.—Costa Rica (Goodwin, 1946: 345): Pozo Azul; Agua Buena. Panamá: Chiriquí (*ibid.*); type locality; Cerro Azul, near head Chagres River (Kellogg and Goldman, 1944:41). Costa Rica (formerly in Panamá): Coto (*ibid.*).

Ateles geoffroyi vellerosus Gray

1866. *Ateles vellerosus* Gray, Proc. Zool. Soc. London, p. 773 (for 1865), April, type from "Brazil?"; fixed at

Mirador, 2000 ft., about 15 mi. NE Huatusco, Veracruz, by Kellogg and Goldman, Proc. U.S. Nat. Mus., 96:33, November 2, 1944.

1944. *Ateles geoffroyi vellerosus*, Kellogg and Goldman, Proc. U.S. Nat. Mus., 96:32, November 2.

1873. *Ateles neglectus* Reinhardt, Vidensk. Meddel. nat. For. Kjöbenhavn, ser. 3, 4(6–9):150, type from Mirador, Veracruz.

1914. *Ateles tricolor* Hollister, Proc. Biol. Soc. Washington, 27:141, July 10, type from Hda. Santa Efigenia, 8 mi. N Tapanatepec, Oaxaca.

MARGINAL RECORDS (Kellogg and Goldman, 1944: 35, unless otherwise noted).—Veracruz: Barranca de Boca, Canton de Jalapa. Tabasco: Teapa. Chiapas: 6 mi. SE Palenque (Kuns and Tashian, 1954:101). Guatemala: *lowland forests of . . . [Caribbean Coast]* (Handley, 1950: 150). Honduras: Catacamas. El Salvador: Laguna Lomego, San Miguel. Guatemala: *lowland forests of . . . [Pacific Coast]* (Handley, 1950:150). Oaxaca: Tehuantepec; Tuxtepec. Veracruz: Volcán de Orizaba (Elliot, 1905:535).

Ateles geoffroyi yucatanensis Kellogg and Goldman

1944. *Ateles geoffroyi yucatanensis* Kellogg and Goldman, Proc. U.S. Nat. Mus., 96:35, November 2, type from Puerto Morelos, 100 ft., Quintana Roo.

MARGINAL RECORDS.—Quintana Roo: type locality; Cozumel Island (885 KU). Guatemala: Uaxactún (Kellogg and Goldman, 1944:36). Campeche: Apazote (*ibid.*).

FAMILY CALLITHRICIDAE—Marmosets

Reviewed by Hershkovitz, Proc. U.S. Nat. Mus., 98:409–424, May 10, 1949.

Total length not exceeding 750; molars $\frac{2-2}{2-2}$ (dentition, i. $\frac{2}{2}$, c. $\frac{1}{1}$, p. $\frac{3}{3}$, m. $\frac{2}{2}$; the total number of teeth is 32, therefore agreeing with that in man and Old World monkeys, both of which, however, have only 2 premolars and 3 molars); face naked in adults; ears large; hind limbs longer than forelimbs; claws (not nails) on all digits except hallux, which has a flattened nail; thumb elongated, parallel to other digits and not opposable; ischial callosities and cheek pouches absent.

Genus Saguinus Hoffmannsegg—Tamarins

1807. *Saguinus* Hoffmannsegg, Mag. Gesell. Naturforsch. Freunde, Berlin, 1:102. Type, *Saguinus ursula* Hoffmannsegg [= *Saguinus tamarin* Link].

1840. *Marikina* Lesson, Species des mammifères, bimanes et quadrumanes; . . . , p. 199 (listed under synonymy of *Oedipus titi* Lesson [= *Simia oedipus* Linnaeus] in an erroneous combination with [*Midas*] *bicolor* Spix and the bibliographic references thereto). Type, *Marikina bicolor* Lesson.

1763. *Cercopithecus* Gronov, Zoophylacium Gronovianum, fasc, 1, p. 5. Type, *Simia midas* Linnaeus, designated by Elliot, Bull. Amer. Mus. Nat. Hist., 30:341, December 21, 1911; eliminated from availability by Opinion 89 of the International Commission on Zoological Nomenclature.

"Hands normal; palm broad, digits not markedly elongated; first phalanges of middle digits usually free, webbing, if present, extremely narrow; length of longest finger (with claw) less than twice width of palm; sides of crown and sides of face completely covered with hair or nearly bare; ears entirely or partially exposed [instead of completely covered by mane]. Sphenoidal pits or vacuities obsolete or absent" (Hershkovitz, 1949:410).

Subgenus **Oedipomidas** Reichenbach
Crested Bare-faced Tamarins

1840. *Oedipus* Lesson, Species des mammifères, bimanes et quadrumanes; . . . , p. 184. Type, *Oedipus titi*. Not *Oedipus* Tschudi, 1838, an amphibian.
1862. *Oedipomidas* Reichenbach, Die vollständigste Naturgeschichte der Affen, p. 5. Type, *Simia oedipus* Linnaeus, a renaming of *Oedipus* Lesson.

Conspicuous median crest of long white hairs on forehead and crown; ears small, lamina of lower posterior margin of pinna deeply emarginate or obsolete (after Hershkovitz, 1949:411).

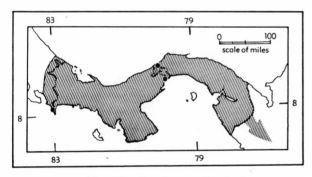

Map 171. *Saguinus geoffroyi.*

Saguinus geoffroyi (Pucheran)
Geoffroy's Tamarin

1823. *Midas Oedipus* (varietas) Spix, Simiarum et vespertilionum Brasiliensium . . . , p. 30, pl. 23, "habitat, ut opinor, in provincia Guiana. Not *Simia oedipus* Linnaeus.
1845. *Hapale Geoffroyi* Pucheran, Revue et Mag. Zool., Paris, 8(ar. 2):336, September, type from Panamá, subsequently restricted to Canal Zone by Hershkovitz, Proc. U.S. Nat. Mus., 98:417, May 10, 1949.
1862. *J[acchus]. spixii* Reichenbach, Die vollständigste Naturgeschichte der Affen, p. 1, pl. 1, fig. 2. (Copied, with slight modification, from Spix, pl. 23.)

External measurements (7 adults from Panamá): 620–685; 325–390; 83–90. Occipitonasal length, 56.5–59.8. Face so sparsely haired as to appear bare except for narrow wedge of white pelage extend-

ing from between eyes onto crown, and narrow (1 mm. wide) line of white hairs extending from posterior angle of ear to below ear; upper parts black marbled with light ochraceous (marbling a result of an ochraceous subapical band on otherwise black hairs); nape hazel, individual hairs as long as 29 mm. and forming a partial mane and mantle; underparts, postorbital area, medial sides of legs and arms, lateral side of forearms, hands, and feet yellowish white; basal fourth of under surface of tail hazel, remainder of tail black.

In specimens from Panamá, and perhaps in all species of *Saguinus*, the long curved claws, obviously adapted for a scansorial habit, are much compressed laterally, the bases of the claws being narrower than the distance to which the claws project beyond the fleshy ends of the digits.

Goldman (1920:226) records this species as the most common primate in the parts of eastern Panamá visited by him. Usually 4 or 5 were seen together, but at sight of him they would scatter like squirrels and scurry along branches, leaping several feet in passing from tree to tree.

MARGINAL RECORDS.—Panamá: Río Indio, near Gatún (Hershkovitz, 1949:418). Thence southward into South America and on west coast of Panamá: La Chorrera (*ibid.*); Coto region (Carpenter, 1935:170).

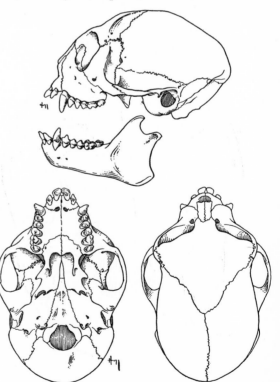

Fig. 163. *Saguinus geoffroyi*, La Cascades, Panamá, No. 257313 U.S.N.M., ♀, X 1.

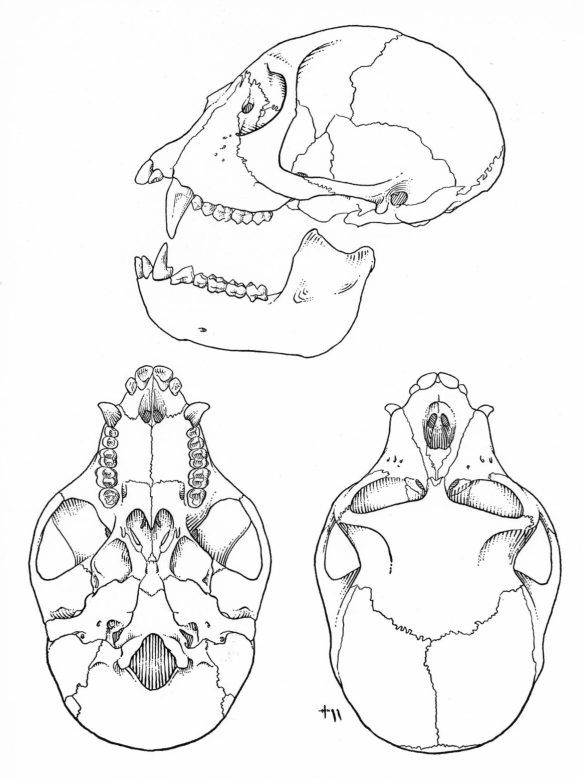

Fig. 164. *Cercopithecus mona mona*, Mpivia, French Congo, Africa,
No. 220358 U.S.N.M., ♂, X 1.

SUPERFAMILY CERCOPITHECOIDEA
Macaquelike Primates

Premolars, $\frac{2-2}{2-2}$; nose narrow. Two species have been introduced in the Lesser Antilles from the Old World.

FAMILY CERCOPITHECIDAE—Guenons, Guerzas, and allies

Dentition, i. $\frac{2}{2}$, c. $\frac{1}{1}$, p. $\frac{2}{2}$, m. $\frac{3}{3}$; tail present and well developed; bare ischial callosities present and often brightly colored; face more or less naked. Arboreal in habitat.

SUBFAMILY CERCOPITHECINAE—Guenons

Arms and legs of approximately equal length; tail relatively long; skull usually with supraorbital ridges; muzzle somewhat extended; thumb normal; stomach simple.

Genus Cercopithecus Linnaeus—Guenons

1758. *Cercopithecus* Linnaeus, Syst. nat., ed. 10, 1:26. Type, *Simia diana* Linnaeus. For use of *Cercopithecus* rather than *Lasiopyga* Illiger, 1811, see Opinion 104, International Commission of Zoological Nomenclature.

Head rounded; muzzle truncate; cheek pouches large; tail long; ischial callosities small; m3 quadrituberculate.

The following key and descriptions are based only on the particular subspecies that have been introduced into the New World. The accounts do not necessarily apply to other subspecies of the 2 pertinent species, *C. aethiops* and *C. mona*.

KEY TO INTRODUCED SPECIES OF CERCOPITHECUS

1. Muzzle much reduced (facial angle approximately 70°); upper parts speckled reddish and black. . . . . *C. mona*, p. 233
1'. Muzzle more pronounced (facial angle approximately 50°); upper parts yellowish with strong greenish cast. . . . *C. aethiops*, p. 233

Cercopithecus aethiops
Green Guenon

External measurements: 1308; 762; 152. Occipitonasal length, 92. Upper parts bright gold-green; face black; forearms and forelegs gray; underparts, cheeks, sides of neck white; tail grayish green on basal two-thirds, yellowish distally. Facial part of skull prolonged, the facial angle being approximately 50°; supraorbital ridges pronounced.

Ceropithecus aethiops sabaeus (Linnaeus)

1766. [*Simia*] *Sabaea* Linnaeus, Syst. nat., ed. 12, 1:38. Type locality, Cape Verde Islands; probably from Senegal (see J. A. Allen, Bull. Amer. Mus. Nat. Hist., 47:352, February 6, 1925).
1926. *Cercopithecus aethiops sabaeus*, Schwarz, Zeitschr. Säugeth., Berlin, 1:34, August 31.
1851. *Cercopithecus callitrichus* I. Geoffroy St.-Hilaire, Catalogue méthodique de la collection des mammifères . . . du muséum . . . Paris, p. 23, type from an unknown locality [West Africa].

MARGINAL RECORDS.—Introduced and established in the New World on Lesser Antillean islands of St. Kitts (Hollister, 1912b:93); Barbados (*ibid.*). Not mapped.

Cercopithecus mona
Mona Monkey

External measurements: 1295; 785; 145. Occipitonasal length, 77.9. Upper parts speckled reddish and black, darkest toward rump; lateral surfaces of hands and arms black; lateral surfaces of legs black speckled with small red spots; underparts and medial surfaces of limbs grayish white; patch beneath tail to hip white; upper and lower surfaces of tail colored like respective surfaces of body on basal third, black distally. Facial part of skull truncate, facial angle being approximately 70°; supraorbital ridges reduced.

Cercopithecus mona mona (Shreber)

1774. *Simia mona* Schreber, Die Säugthiere . . . , 2(pt. 1):pl. 15(7:97 contains the vernacular name and description). Type locality, "Barbary."
1777. *Cercopithecus mona*, Erxleben, Systema regni animalis . . . , 1:30.

MARGINAL RECORDS.—Introduced and established in the New World on Lesser Antillean islands of St. Kitts (Hollister, 1912b:93); Grenada (*ibid.*). Not mapped.

SUPERFAMILY HOMINOIDEA
Manlike Primates

Radius and ulna capable of complete rotation; thumb opposable and articular face of trapezium rounded; cheek pouches absent; dentaries firmly fused at mental symphysis; tail absent (represented by coccyx). Dentition, i. $\frac{2}{2}$, c. $\frac{1}{1}$, p. $\frac{2}{2}$, m. $\frac{3}{3}$.

FAMILY HOMINIDAE—Men, Apes, and Gibbons

Characters as for the superfamily. Some authors have accorded separate family rank to man (genus *Homo*) because of an assumed wide gap in intelligence between man and the next most intelligent anthropoid. To follow this reasoning one would have to exclude from the family Hominidae (in such a restricted sense) certain fossil ancestors of man. Nor am I convinced that the gap in intelligence between some microgeographic races of man and some races of apes is very wide—no wider than that between genera in some other families, for example, that between the two genera *Canis* and *Dusicyon* of the family Canidae. The morphological features of the several living and fossil anthropoids, viewed objectively, give basis for including gibbons, apes, and men in one family.—E. R. H.

Genus **Homo** Linnaeus—Man

1758. *Homo* Linnaeus, Syst. nat., ed. 10, 1:20. Type, *Homo sapiens* Linnaeus.

Hind limbs longer than forelimbs and modified for upright stance; femur longer than humerus; foramen magnum situated near center of ventral face of skull; diastema absent between i2 and c; tendencies present toward (1) formation of pronounced chin; (2) loss of supraorbital prominences; (3) reduction in prognathism; (4) reduction of height of canine so that, in all but earliest representatives of genus, canine not notably higher than other teeth; (5) increase in absolute and relative size of brain (approximately 1400 grams in adult males); and (6) decrease in thickness of cranial bones.

Homo sapiens
Modern Man

Characterized by having achieved the greatest degree of development of the generic characters. The species *H. sapiens* is the only species still existing.

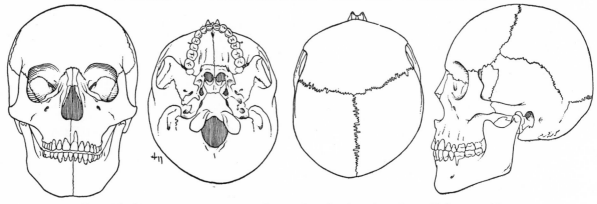

Fig. 165. *Homo sapiens americanus,* Prairie Dog Creek at State Line, Phillips Co., Kansas, No. 14PH4–1436 U.S.N.M., ♂, X ¼.

Homo sapiens afer Linnaeus

1758. [*Homo sapiens*] *afer* Linnaeus, Syst. nat., ed. 10, 1:22. Type locality, Africa. Introduced and widely established in North America.

Homo sapiens americanus Linnaeus

1758. [*Homo sapiens*] *americanus* Linnaeus, Syst. nat., ed. 10, 1:20. Type locality, eastern North America. Known from North, Central, and South America.

Homo sapiens asiaticus Linnaeus

1758. [*Homo sapiens*] *asiaticus* Linnaeus, Syst. nat., ed. 10, 1:21. Type locality, Asia. Introduced and now widely established in North America.

Homo sapiens sapiens Linnaeus

1758. [*Homo*] *sapiens* Linnaeus, Syst. nat., ed. 10, 1:20. Type locality, Upsala, Sweden. Cosmopolitan.

Order EDENTATA
Sloths, Anteaters, and Armadillos

Teeth incomplete in one sense or another; teeth lacking enamel in many Recent members of order, and absent in Myrmecophagidae; deciduous dentition absent except in armadillos; teeth single-rooted and absent from anteriormost parts of jaws; processes on basicranial region absent or much reduced; ilium everted and strongly crested.

Suborder XENARTHRA

Differs from suborder Palaeanodonta (extinct) in (1) xenarthrous vertebrae (secondary articulations between vertebrae of the lumbar series), (2) ischiocaudal symphysis present (incipient in some palaeanodonts), and (3) canines, when present, lacking enamel and never sectorial.

The systematic positions of both xenarthrans and palaeanodonts have been long debated. It seems to be agreed now that the 2 groups are closely related and that the palaeanodonts were ancestral to the xenarthrans.

Key to Superfamilies and Families of Xenarthra

1. Teeth absent; mouth tubular with small terminal opening.
   Superfamily Myrmecophagoidea, p. 236
   Family Myrmecophagidae, p. 236
1'. Teeth present; mouth neither tubular nor with small terminal opening.
   2. Top and sides of body covered with horny scutes; teeth more than $\frac{6}{6}$.
      Superfamily Dasypodoidea, p. 242
      Family Dasypodidae, p. 242
   2'. Top and sides of body covered with hair, horny scutes absent; teeth fewer than $\frac{6}{6}$.
      3. Fewer than 4 claws on each foot; diameter of largest upper cheek-tooth (excepting anteriormost, caniniform) less than 8.
         Superfamily Bradypodoidea, p. 240
         Family Bradypodidae, p. 240
      3'. Four or more claws on some or all feet; diameter of largest upper cheek-tooth (excepting anteriormost, caniniform) more than 8.
         Superfamily Megalonychoidea, p. 235
         Family Megalonychidae, p. 235

Infraorder PILOSA

Exoskeleton absent or present as irregular separate plaques embedded in skin; teeth $\frac{5}{4}$ or fewer, prismatic, lacking enamel and with roots open; all vertebrae separate; intermaxillary usually small to rudimentary; lacrimal large or small, with facial lacrimal-foramen; zygomatic arch more or less incomplete; coracoid process forming coracoscapular foramen.

Superfamily MEGALONYCHOIDEA

Teeth not more than $\frac{5}{4}$; skull elongate or short; zygomatic arch complete; jugal with upward-directed process; lacrimal nipple-shaped and with large lacrimal-foramen; dentaries fused and mental region prolonged as a distinct projection; thoracolumbar vertebrae, 19–25; manus pentadactyl with 5th digit somewhat reduced.

Family MEGALONYCHIDAE—Ground Sloths

Cheek-teeth prismatic, quadrangular to transversely elliptical with 2 transverse ridges; anterior cheek-tooth caniniform and separated from others by diastema; last molar smallest; alveolar canal opening either anterior to base of ascending tubercle or on lateral side (seldom on medial side) near tubercle.

Key to North American Genera of Megalonychidae

1. Lesser trochanter absent from femur; humerus approximately 200 long. . *Parocnus*, p. 236
1'. Lesser trochanter present on femur; humerus approximately 135 long. . . *Acratocnus*, p. 235

Genus **Acratocnus** Anthony—Ground Sloths

1916. *Acratocnus* Anthony, Ann. New York Acad. Sci., 27:195, August 9. Type, *Acratocnus odontrigonus* Anthony.

Canines trigonal; sagittal crest present; preorbital fossa large; limbs slender; humerus approximately 135 mm. long; spines low on dorsal vertebrae; caudal vertebrae wide; lesser trochanter present on femur; entepicondylar foramen present; teeth $\frac{5}{4}$

This genus is included in the present work because of Miller's (1929c:11) statement that there seems to be no "doubt that a ground sloth was a member of the recently man-exterminated fauna of Hispaniola."

KEY TO SPECIES OF ACRATOCNUS

1. Occurring in Puerto Rico.
   2. Postorbital process of frontal peglike; distance from mental foramen to anterior end of lower jaw more than 50. A. *major*, p. 236
   2'. Postorbital process of frontal sharp but not peglike; distance from mental foramen to anterior end of lower jaw less than 50. . . . . . A. *odontrigonus*, p. 236
1'. Occurring in Hispaniola. . . . A. *comes*, p. 236

Acratocnus odontrigonus Anthony
Small Cuban Ground Sloth

1916. *Acratocnus odontrigonus* Anthony, Ann. New York Acad. Sci., 27:195, August 9, type from Cueva de la Ceiba, Hda. Jobo, near Utuado, Puerto Rico. Known only from skeletal remains from Puerto Rico.

Distinct sagittal crest; greatest length of skull approximately 135; mastoidal breadth approximately 53; postorbital process on frontal distinct but not peglike. Not mapped.

Acratocnus comes Miller
Haitian Ground Sloth

1929. *Acratocnus* (?) *comes* Miller, Smiths. Miscl. Coll., 81(9):26, March 30, type from large cave near St. Michel, Haiti. Known only from skeletal remains from Haiti (see Miller, *antea*, and Smiths. Miscl. Coll., 82(5):11, December 11, 1929) and La Gonave Island (see Miller, Smiths. Miscl. Coll., 82(15):5, December 24, 1930).

Resembles A. *odontrigonus* from Puerto Rico but having conspicuous tubercle at middle of shaft of femur, and neck of femur shorter and less bowed outward. Weight of animal in life probably 50 pounds. Not mapped.

Acratocnus major Anthony
Big Cuban Ground Sloth

1918. *Acratocnus major* Anthony, Mem. Amer. Mus. Nat. Hist., n.s., 2:412, October 12, type from cave on property of Don Gervacio Torano, near Utuado, Puerto Rico. Known only from skeletal remains from the type locality.

Resembles A. *odontrigonus* but larger (tip of lower mandible to mental foramen approximately 53 as opposed to 48); frontals with peglike postorbital processes (not peglike in A. *odontrigonus*); basioccipital elevated noticeably above plane of basisphenoid. Not mapped.

Genus Parocnus Miller—Big Haitian Ground Sloth

1929. *Parocnus* Miller, Smiths. Miscl. Coll., 81(9):28, March 30. Type, *Parocnus serus* Miller.

Femur with lesser trochanter absent and upper half of shaft wide and flattened. These are differences from *Acratocnus* and the latter is a point of resemblance to the extinct genus *Nothrotherium*. The genus is monotypic.

Parocnus serus Miller
Big Haitian Ground Sloth

1929. *Parocnus serus* Miller, Smiths. Miscl. Coll., 81(9):29, March 30, type from large cave near St. Michel, Haiti. Known only from skeletal remains from Haiti.

Femur approximately 145; humerus approximately 200. Weight of animal in life probably 150 pounds. Not mapped.

SUPERFAMILY MYRMECOPHAGOIDEA
Anteaters

Clothed with hair (not scutes); teeth absent; head elongated; mouth tubular; clavicle rudimentary; 3rd digit of manus large and provided with strong claw; other toes of manus suppressed or smaller; pes with 4 or 5 subequal digits.

FAMILY MYRMECOPHAGIDAE—Anteaters

Characters as for the superfamily. The mouth cavity is tubular with a small terminal aperture through which the long, slender tongue, covered with a sticky secretion of the enormously enlarged submaxillary glands, is rapidly protruded in feeding and withdrawn with the adhering particles of food. Each of the 3 living genera occurs in South America and Central America.

KEY TO GENERA OF MYRMECOPHAGIDAE

1. Combined length of head and body less than 300; 2 claws on forefoot; pterygoids not meeting below posterior nares. . *Cyclopes*, p. 239
1'. Combined length of head and body more than 300; 4 claws on forefoot; pterygoids meeting below posterior nares.
   2. Length of head and body less than 900; tail naked distally; longest hair on tail less than one-third as long as hind foot; prelacrimal region of skull shorter than postlacrimal region. . . . *Tamandua*, p. 237
   2'. Length of head and body more than 900; all of tail clothed with hair; longest hair on tail more than twice length of hind foot; prelacrimal region of skull more than twice as long as postlacrimal region.
   Myrmecophaga, p. 237

Genus **Myrmecophaga** Linnaeus
Giant Anteaters

1758. *Myrmecophaga* Linnaeus, Syst. nat., ed. 10, 1:35. Type, by subsequent selection (Fleming, The philosophy of zoology . . . , 2:194, May or June, 1822), *Myrmecophaga jubata* Linnaeus [= *M. tridactyla* Linnaeus].
1900. *Falcifer* Rehn, Amer. Nat., 34:576, July. Type, *Myrmecophaga jubata* Linnaeus [= *M. tridactyla* L.].

External measurements (after Goodwin, 1946: 356): 1860; 650; 135. Greatest length of skull, 365. Four claws on forefoot, 5 on hind foot; 3rd digit much the largest on forefoot; hair (285 mm. in a Costa Rican specimen) on tail more than twice as long as hind foot; pterygoids joined below narial passage and prolonging it for almost entire length of skull; prelacrimal region of skull more than twice as long as postlacrimal region; zygoma incomplete and jugal attached to maxilla; one bulla on each side of base of skull (tympanic and alisphenoidal parts not separate as in *Tamandua*); alisphenoidal part twice as large as tympanic part.

Myrmecophaga tridactyla
Giant Anteater

In a Costa Rican specimen: upper parts grizzled, hairs being banded alternately with black and light buff; black stripe 2.5 to 6.3 mm. wide extending from throat over shoulder and ending on lower back, forming with its opposite a collar; forelimbs yellowish white; head yellowish white but hairs sparse and bristly; small area above toes and band above ankles black; hind limbs, tail, and most of underparts blackish.

Myrmecophaga tridactyla centralis Lyon

1906. *Myrmecophaga centralis* Lyon, Proc. U.S. Nat. Mus., 31:570, November 14, type from Pacuare, Costa Rica.
1920. *Myrmecophaga tridactyla centralis*, Goldman, Smiths. Misc. Coll., 69(5):64-65, April 26.

MARGINAL RECORDS.—British Honduras: near Punta Gorda (J. A. Allen, 1910:94), thence southward along Caribbean Coast to South America and thence up Pacific Coast to Guatemala: *Pacific Coast region between San José and the border of El Salvador* (Handley, 1950:158).

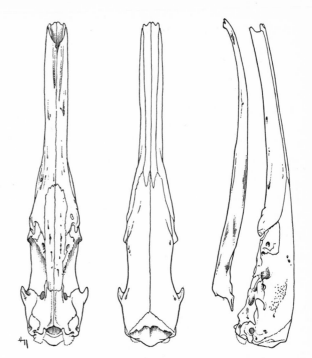

Fig. 166. *Myrmecophaga tridactyla centralis*, Talamanca, Costa Rica, No. 14107 U.S.N.M., sex ?, X ¼.

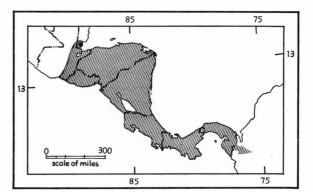

Map 172. *Myrmecophaga tridactyla centralis*.

Genus **Tamandua** Gray—Tamandua

Revised by J. A. Allen, Bull. Amer. Mus. Nat. Hist., 20: 385-398, October 29, 1904. See also Reeve, Proc. Zool. Soc. London, 111:279-302, February 17, 1942.

1825. *Tamandua* Gray, Ann. Philos., 10(n.s.):343, November. Type, *Myrmecophaga tamandua* Cuvier [= *M. tetradactyla* Linnaeus]; see Gray, London Med. Repos., 15 (88):305, April 1, 1821. Tamandua Gray (*ibid.*) is a vernacular name and therefore is not available. Not *Tamandua* Frisch, 1775; Frisch names are non-Linnaean and unavailable. Not *Tamandua* Rafinesque, 1815, which was not differentiated from *Myrmecophaga* and included no species.

1830. *Uroleptes* Wagler, Natürliches System der Amphibien
. . . , p. 36. Type, *Myrmecophaga tetradactyla* Linnaeus.
1841. *Dryoryx* Gloger, Gemeinnütziges Hand- und Hilfs-
buch der Naturgeschichte, 1:xxxi, 112. Type, the tamandua.
1882. *Uropeltes* Alston, Biologia Centrali-Americana, p.
191 (misprint for *Uroleptes* Wagler).

Total length approximately 1200. Three large
claws and one small claw on forefoot, 5 claws on
hind foot; pelage short and coarse; hair on tail less
than one-third as long as hind foot; tail naked at
tip and on all of underside; tail prehensile; pterygoids united below narial passage and prolonging
passage for almost entire length of skull; prelacrimal region of skull shorter than postlacrimal region;
zygomatic arch incomplete, jugal attached to maxilla; 3 bullae (2 sphenoidal and 1 tympanic) on
each side of basicranial region.

Tamandua tetradactyla
Tamandua

X ¹/₁₂

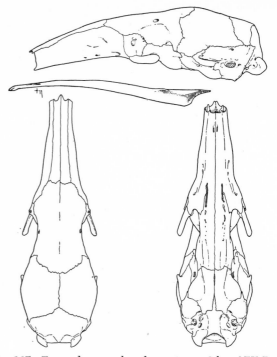

Fig. 167. *Tamandua tetradactyla mexicana*, 6 km. NW Paso
Nuevo, 100 ft., Veracruz, No. 19906 K.U., ♀, X ½.

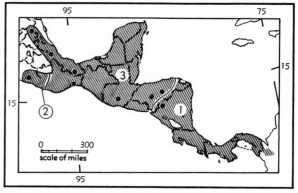

Map 173. *Tamandua tetradactyla.*

Guide to subspecies   2. *T. t. hesperia*
1. *T. t. chiriquensis*   3. *T. t. mexicana*

Average external measurements of 3 females from
the state of Veracruz: 1132; 553; 97. Height of
ear from notch, 41; greatest length of skull of other
specimens, 123–128. In specimens from Veracruz:
body black from immediately anterior to hind limbs
to immediately behind forelimbs, a black stripe continuing over shoulder to axilla; otherwise tan
colored, and tan vertebral stripe extends almost to
end of black area; naked, scaly, distal part (two-
thirds in specimens from Veracruz) of tail tan with
irregular black markings.

Tamandua tetradactyla chiriquensis J. A. Allen

1904. *Tamandua tetradactyla chiriquensis* J. A. Allen, Bull.
Amer. Mus. Nat. Hist., 20:395, October 29, type from
Boquerón, Chiriquí, Panamá.

MARGINAL RECORDS.—Nicaragua: Ocotal (J. A. Allen,
1910:94), thence southward into South America.

Tamandua tetradactyla hesperia Davis

1955. *Tamandua tetradactyla hesperia* Davis, Jour. Mamm.,
36:588, December 14, type from near Acahuizotla, 2800
ft., Guerrero.

MARGINAL RECORDS.—Guerrero: type locality; *Chapalapa* (Davis, 1955:558).

Tamandua tetradactyla mexicana (Saussure)

1860. *"Myrmecophaga tamandua* (?), Desm. (Var. *mexicana* Sauss.)" Saussure, Revue et Mag. Zool., Paris, ser. 2, 12:9, January, type from Tabasco.

1906. *Tamandua tetradactyla mexicana,* J. A. Allen, Proc. Biol. Soc. Washington, 19:200, December 31.

1889. *Myrmecophaga sellata* Cope, Amer. Nat. 23:133, February, type from Honduras. Regarded as tenable by Lönnberg, Archiv för Zool., 29A(19):27, August 9, 1937, and probably synonymous with *T. t. mexicana* by Reeve, Proc. Zool. Soc. London, 111(ser. A; pts. 3–4):301, February 17, 1942.

1904. *Tamandua tetradactyla tenuirostris* J. A. Allen, Bull. Amer. Mus. Nat. Hist., 20:394, October 29, type from Pasa Nueva, Veracruz.

MARGINAL RECORDS.—San Luis Potosí: 5 km. S Tamazunchale (Dalquest, 1953b:72), thence southward along Caribbean Coast to Honduras (Goodwin, 1942:149): Catacamas; La Cueva Archaga, thence westward along Pacific Coast to Guatemala: Dueñas (Gaumer, 1917:18). Oaxaca: Huilotepec (Davis, 1955:559); Las Cuevas [= 15 km. NW Tehuantepec] (*ibid.*). Veracruz: Arroyo Saoso, 37 km. E, 7 km. S Jesús Carranza (39428 KU); Mirador (Dalquest, *in Litt.*).

Genus Cyclopes Gray—Two-toed Anteaters

1821. *Cyclopes* Gray, London Med. Repos., 15:305. Type, *Myrmecophaga didactyla* Linnaeus. For use of *Cyclopes* rather than *Cyclothurus* Lesson, 1842, see Thomas, Ann. Mag. Nat. Hist., ser. 6, 15:191, February, 1895, and Palmer, Proc. Biol. Soc. Washington, 13:72, September 28, 1899.

1830. *Myrmedon* Wagler, Natürliches system der amphibien, . . . , p. 36. Type, *Myrmecophaga didactyla* Linnaeus.

1836. *Myrmecolichnus* Reichenbach, K. Sächische Naturh. Mus., Dresden, Ein Leitfaden, p. 51. Type, *Myrmecophaga didactyla* Linnaeus.

Size small (head and body approximately 200); forefoot with 2 digits (II and III), lateral being

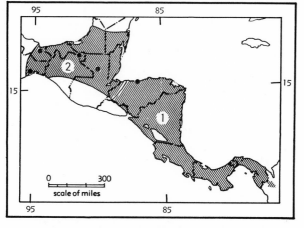

Map 174. *Cyclopes didactylus dorsalis* (1) and *Cyclopes didactylus mexicanus* (2).

much the larger; dorsal profile of skull strongly convex; pterygoids and posterior part of palatines not meeting below posterior nares and thus forming channel rather than tube; ribs unusually broad and flattened; zygomatic arch absent and jugal absent in specimens seen by us.

This small, nocturnal, arboreal anteater moves slowly and deliberately.

Cyclopes didactylus
Two-toed Anteater

External measurements: 398–422; - - - –227; 30–36. Greatest length of skull, 50.2. Color golden brown marbled with silvery and in some specimens with dark brownish or blackish middorsal and midventral areas. Pelage long (15 mm.) and semiwooly.

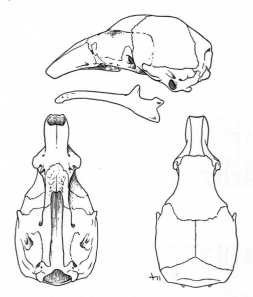

Fig. 168. *Cyclopes didactylus dorsalis*, Panamá, No. 283876 U.S.N.M., ♀, X 1.

Cyclopes didactylus dorsalis (Gray)

1865. *Cyclothurus dorsalis* Gray, Proc. Zool. Soc. London, p. 385, pl. 19, October, type from Costa Rica, subsequently restricted to Orosi, near Cartago, Costa Rica (Goodwin, Bull. Amer. Mus. Nat. Hist., 87:354, December 31, 1946).

1900. *C[yclopes]. d[idactylus]. dorsalis,* Thomas, Ann. Mag. Nat. Hist., ser. 7, 6:302, September.

MARGINAL RECORDS.—Honduras: Ceiba (Goodwin, 1942:149), thence southward into South America.

Cyclopes didactylus mexicanus Hollister

1914. *Cyclopes mexicanus* Hollister, Proc. Biol. Soc. Washington, 27:210, October 31, type from Tehuantepec, Oaxaca.

1952. *Cyclopes didactylus mexicanus,* Hall and Kelson, Univ. Kansas Publ., Mus. Nat. Hist., 5:316, November 21.

MARGINAL RECORDS (Hall and Kelson, 1952:317).— Veracruz: Minatitlán. Tabasco: Montecristo. Guatemala: Libertad. Oaxaca: type locality.

Superfamily BRADYPODOIDEA—Sloths

Pelage long, crisp, and strawlike usually supporting growth of algae that imparts greenish tinge in wet seasons; teeth $\frac{5}{4-5}$, subcylindrical, persistently growing; clavicle present; forelimbs longer than hind limbs; 2 or 3 claws on foot; tail rudimentary or less than third of total length; stomach complex; caecum absent; uterus simple and globular.

Family BRADYPODIDAE—Sloths

Characters as for the superfamily.

Key to Genera of Bradypodidae

1. Tail present; 3 claws on forefoot; anterior tooth in upper jaw smaller than succeeding tooth and space between them less than length of crown of 2nd tooth. . *Bradypus,* p. 240
1'. Tail absent; 2 claws on forefoot; anterior tooth in upper jaw larger than succeeding tooth and space between them several times longer than length of crown of 2nd tooth.
                               Choloepus, p. 241

Genus Bradypus Linnaeus—Three-toed Sloth

1758. *Bradypus* Linnaeus, Syst. nat., ed. 10, 1:34. Type, *Bradypus tridactylus* Linnaeus.
1779. *Ignavus* Blumenbach, Handbuch der Naturgeschichte, 1:70. Type, *Ignavus tridactylus* [= *Bradypus tridactylus* Linnaeus].
1850. *Arctopithecus* Gray, Proc. Zool. Soc. London, for 1849, p. 65, Jan.–June. Based on *Bradypus gularis* Rüppell, *Arctopithecus marmoratus* Gray, *A. blainvillii* Gray, *A. flaccidus* Gray, and *A. problematicus* Gray. Not *Arctopithecus* Virey, 1819, a primate.
1864. *Scaeopus* Peters, Monatsber. preuss. Akad. Wiss., Berlin, p. 678. Type, *Bradypus torquatus* Illiger.
1906. *Hemibradypus* R. Anthony, Compt. Rend. Acad. Sci., Paris, 142 (fasc. 5):292. Type, *Bradypus torquatus* Illiger.
1942. *Eubradypus* Lönnberg, Arkiv Zool., 34A(9):5. Type, *Bradypus (Eubradypus) tocantinus* Lönnberg [= *Arctopithecus marmoratus* Gray].
1942. *Neobradypus* Lönnberg, loc. cit.:15. Type, *Arctopithecus marmoratus* Gray.

Forefoot with 3 claws; tail comprising approximately one-eighth of total length; anterior tooth in upper jaw smaller than succeeding teeth; anterior tooth in lower jaw broader than succeeding teeth but compressed anteroposteriorly; space between 1st and 2nd tooth, both above and below, shorter than length of crown of 2nd; tympanic bullae present.

Bradypus griseus
Gray Three-toed Sloth

External measurements: 570–660; 66–70; 120–130. Greatest length of skull, 70–80. Pelage of 2 distinct types: long (as long as 110) overhairs of large diameter, and short (as long as 35) underfur of fine texture; arms to shoulders, top of head, neck, and chin drab; face white having brown stripe on each side, enclosing eye; white extending to throat; forehead having ruff of brownish hair; chest, top of neck, and shoulders slightly paler brown than ruff; remainder of body soiled yellowish white; females having median dorsal stripe; males having dorsal speculum where hair is short and yellow, with narrow (10–20) black or brownish black middorsal stripe. When the genus is revised, the specific name *tridactylus* may replace *griseus*.

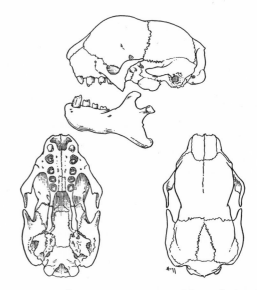

Fig. 169. *Bradypus griseus griseus,* Monte Lirio, Canal Zone, Panamá, No. 256178 U.S.N.M., ♀, X ½.

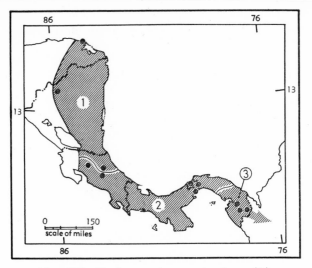

Map 175. *Bradypus griseus castaneiceps* (1),
Bradypus griseus griseus (2), and
Bradypus griseus ignavus (3).

Bradypus griseus castaneiceps (Gray)

1871. *Arctopithecus castaneiceps* Gray, Proc. Zool. Soc.
London, p. 444, August, type from woods surrounding
Javali gold mine, 2000 ft., Chontales District, Nicaragua.
1920. *Bradypus griseus castaneiceps,* Goldman, Smiths.
Miscl. Coll., 69(5):57, April 24.

MARGINAL RECORDS.—Honduras: Patuca (Goodwin,
1946:352). Costa Rica: Jiménez (*ibid.*). Nicaragua: *type
locality*; Río Coco (J. A. Allen, 1910:93).

Bradypus griseus griseus (Gray)

1871. *Arctopithecus griseus* Gray, Ann. Mag. Nat. Hist.,
ser. 4, 7:302, April, type from Cordillera de Chucu, Veraguas, Panamá (see Alston, Mamm., pp. 183–184, December, 1880, *in* Godman and Salvin, Biologia Centrali-
Americana; . . .).
1891. *Bradypus griseus,* J. A. Allen, Bull. Amer. Mus. Nat.
Hist., 3:216, April 17.

MARGINAL RECORDS (Hall and Kelson, 1952:315,
unless otherwise noted).—Costa Rica: Vijagual; Juan Viñas.
Panamá: Gatún (Goldman, 1920:57); vicinity of Frijoles
(Enders, 1930:283); La Chorrera, thence westward along
Pacific Coast to point of beginning.

Bradypus griseus ignavus Goldman

1913. *Bradypus ignavus* Goldman, Smiths. Miscl. Coll.
60(22):1, February 28, type from Marraganti, about 2
mi. above Real de Santa María, near head of tidewater on
the Río Tuyra, Darién, Panamá.
1952. *Bradypus griseus ignavus,* Hall and Kelson, Univ.
Kansas Publ., Mus. Nat. Hist., 5:315, November 21.

MARGINAL RECORDS.—Panamá (Hall and Kelson,
1952:315): Real de Santa María; Tapalisa; Cituro, thence
into South America.

Genus Choloepus Illiger—Two-toed Sloth

1811. *Choloepus* Illiger, Prodromus systematis mammalium
et avium . . . , p. 108. Type, *Bradypus didactylus*
Linnaeus.

Forefoot with 3 claws; tail absent or vestigial;
anterior tooth, above and below, caniniform, wear-
ing to sharp beveled edge against opposing tooth,
upper tooth anterior to lower tooth when mouth
closed; anterior tooth, above and below, much
larger than any succeeding tooth, and separated
from succeeding tooth by diastema several times
longer than crown of succeeding tooth; tympanic
annulus present; pterygoid and alisphenoid inflated
to form large bulla with openings in posterior nares;
dorsal profile of skull convex with highest point
approximately at middle of skull; only part of
occipital condyle posterior to paroccipital process.

Choloepus hoffmanni
Two-toed Sloth

External measurements, 600–640; no tail; 110–
120. Greatest length of skull, 106–109. Pelage including fur and long guard hairs but with hairs of
intermediate type so that the two types are not
sharply distinct; longest hairs up to 170.

In a considerable series of specimens from Costa
Rica, Goodwin (1946:354) noted great differences
in pallor and darkness among different individuals
and described the average coloration as follows:
Hair on brow and saddle white or buffy white to
roots; forelimbs, shoulders, hind limbs and rump
Mummy Brown or Cinnamon-Brown, the hair more
or less broadly tipped with buffy white; throat
brownish white; underparts Mummy Brown,
washed with brownish white; neck and shoulders,
and in some individuals entire pelage, tinged with
bright green. Very young specimens are uniform
pale Cinnamon-Brown.

Choloepus hoffmanni hoffmanni Peters

1858. *Choloepus hoffmanni* Peters, Monatsb. preuss. Akad. Wiss., Berlin, p. 128, type from Costa Rica, subsequently restricted to Escazú by Goodwin, Bull. Amer. Mus. Nat. Hist., 87:353, December 31, 1946.

MARGINAL RECORDS.—Nicaragua: Matagalpa (J. A. Allen, 1910:93), thence southward into South America.

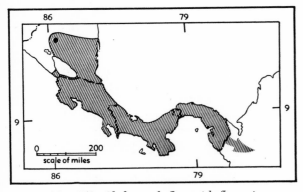

Map 176. *Choloepus hoffmanni hoffmanni.*

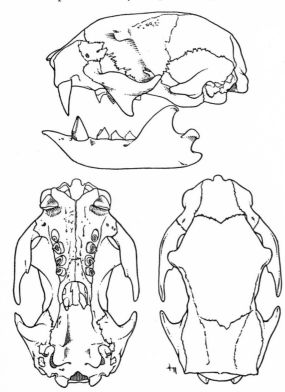

Fig. 170. *Choloepus hoffmanni hoffmanni*, La Palma, Costa Rica, No. 15954 U.S.N.M., ♀, X ½.

INFRAORDER **CINGULATA**

Major part of skin ossified; ossified part consisting of regularly arranged bony scutes forming an armor; scutes covered by horny epidermal plates; teeth 7 or more, simple, single-rooted; in some species 1 or 2 teeth in premaxilla, in other species all teeth in maxilla; at least 2nd and 3rd cervical vertebrae fused; zygomatic arch complete; tibia and fibula fused proximally and distally.

SUPERFAMILY **DASYPODOIDEA**—Armadillos

The Dasypodoidea differ from the Glyptodontoidea, the other recognized superfamily, in lacking ventrally projecting process on zygoma; dentary longer than high, ascending ramus extending obliquely, rather than steeply, upward; clavicle present; skull shallow rather than deep.

FAMILY **DASYPODIDAE**—Armadillos

Horns absent from head-shield; symphyseal part of mandible V-shaped; mandibular condyle flat or concave.

SUBFAMILY **DASYPODINAE**

Differs from Stegotheriinae in much broader and more flattened skull, occipital condyles placed relatively higher, and less reduced jaws and dentition; differs from Chlamytheriinae in lacking anteroposteriorly lengthened teeth, which are partially dissected into prisms by vertical grooves; differs from Chlamyphorinae in having skull elongated, tapering rather than short, pointed.

KEY TO TRIBES OF DASYPODINAE

1. Eleven to 13 bands on back; scales on tail not segmentally arranged; 3rd digit unusually enlarged. . . . . . Tribe Priodontini, p. 242
1'. Seven to 11 bands on back; scales on tail segmentally arranged (in rings); 3rd digit not unusually enlarged. Tribe Dasypodini, p. 243

TRIBE **PRIODONTINI**

Anterior and posterior shields present; bands on back, 11–13; bands on neck, 3–4; scales on tail not segmentally arranged; forefoot with 5 digits, each bearing claw; 3rd digit and its claw much enlarged.

Genus **Cabassous** McMurtrie—Eleven-banded Armadillos

1831. *Cabassous* McMurtrie, The animal kingdom . . . by the Baron Cuvier . . . , 1:164. Type, *Dasypus unicinctus* Linnaeus.
1830. *Xenurus* Wagler, Natürliches system der amphibien . . . , p. 36, August. Type, *Dasypus gymnurus* Wied-Neuwied [= *Dasypus unicinctus* Linnaeus]. Not *Xenurus* Boie, 1826, a genus of birds.

1841. *Arizostus* Gloger, Gemeinnütziges Hand- und Hilfs-buch der Naturgeschichte, 1:xxxii, 114. Type, *Dasypus gymnurus* [= *Dasypus unicinctus* Linnaeus].
1865. *Tatoua* Gray, Proc. Zool. Soc. London, p. 378, Octo-ber. Type, *Dasypus unicinctus* Linnaeus.
1873. *Ziphila* Gray, Hand-list of the edentate, thick-skinned and ruminant mammals in the British Museum, p. 22. Type, *Ziphila lugubris* [= *Dasypus tatouay* Desmarest].
1891. *Lysiurus* Ameghino, Revista Argentina Hist. Nat., 1(entr. 4a):254, renaming of *Xenurus* Wagler, 1830.

Teeth $\frac{8}{7}$ or $\frac{10}{8}$; teeth absent from premaxilla; scales on tail small; claws 3 and 4 largest.

Cabassous centralis (Miller)
Central American Five-toed Armadillo

1899. *Tatoua* (*Ziphila*) *centralis* Miller, Proc. Biol. Soc. Washington, 13:4, January 31, type from Chamelicón [= Chamelecón], Honduras.
1899. *C[abassous]. centralis* Palmer, Proc. Biol. Soc. Wash-ington, 13:72, September 28.

External measurements of holotype (from dried specimen): 450; 150; 58. Greatest length of skull, 80.0. Crown shields, 37–39, pentagonal or hexag-onal, arranged in bilaterally symmetrical pattern; less than 12 irregularly arranged scales on cheek; distance between bases of ears approximately 1½ times length of ear from notch; scapular shield of 7 or 8 rows of plates of which longest row contains approximately 28 plates; 2 or 3 rows of scales on neck in front of scapular shield; dorsal rings, 10; pelvic shield with 10 rows of plates; rostrum short; anterior opening of infraorbital canal approx-imately midway between anterior tip of nasals and posterior tip of pterygoid; mastoidal breadth more than 40 (47 in holotype) per cent of length of skull.

The tremendously enlarged, flattened and ven-trally concave claws are indicative of the excep-tional fossorial powers of this species. In the holo-type the claw of the third digit is 38 mm. long and 13 mm. wide and, although rounded at the tip, is nearly uniform in width.

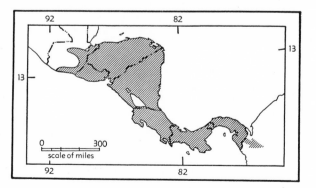

Map 177. *Cabassous centralis*.

MARGINAL RECORDS (Handley, 1950:159).—Guate-mala: *mts. of Quiché* and *Pacific coastal plain*, thence south-ward into South America.

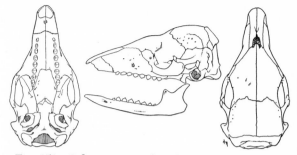

Fig. 171. *Cabassous centralis*, El Muñeco, Costa Rica, No. 67548 Mich., ♂, X ½.

TRIBE DASYPODINI

Teeth $\frac{7-9}{7-9}$, small, subcylindrical, allegedly lacking enamel, 1st 2 laterally compressed and last half or less (in occlusal area) as large as others; tooth-row short, terminating anterior to root of zygoma; snout long; pterygoids meeting below posterior nares; ears close together on occiput; 7–11 movable bands in carapace between anterior and posterior bucklers; pattern of sculpture on scutes V-shaped; tail scutes arranged in rings, 3rd digit not unusually enlarged; polyembryonic young.

Genus Dasypus Linnaeus—Nine-banded Armadillo

1758. *Dasypus* Linnaeus, Syst. nat., ed. 10, 1:50. Type by tautonomy, *Dasypus novemcinctus* Linnaeus.
1762. *Cataphractus* Storr, Prodromus methodi mamm., p. 40, Tab. B. Based on *Armadillo, Armadillo orientalis, A. in-dicus, A. mexicanus, A. brasilianus, A. guianensis,* and *A. africanus.*
1765. *Tatus* Fermin, Histoire naturelle de la Hollande Equinoxiale . . . , Amsterdam, p. 3. Type, *Tatus cucur-bitalis.*
1779. *Tatu* Blumenbach, Handbuch der Naturgeschichte, 1:74. Type, *Dasypus novemcinctus* Linnaeus.
1804. *Loricatus* Desmarest, Nouv. Dict. Hist. Nat., 24(pr. 6; Tabl. method mamm.):28. No type designated; in-cluded *Dasypus giganteus* É. Geoffroy St.-Hilaire, *Lorica-tus flavimanus* Desmarest, *L. tatouay* Desmarest, *L. villosus* Desmarest, *L. niger* Desmarest, *L. hybridus* Desmarest, *L. pichiy* Desmarest, and *L. matacus* Desmarest.
1827. *Tatusia* Lesson [F. Cuvier *in* Lesson of *Aucts.*], Manuel de mammalogie, . . . , p. 309. No type designated; in-cluded *Tatusia apar* Desmarest, *T. quadricincta* Lesson, *T. peba* Desmarest, *T. hybridus* Desmarest, *T. tatouay* Desmarest, and *T. villosa* Desmarest, and *T. minuta* Desmarest.
1831. *Cachicamus* McMurtrie, The animal kingdom . . . by the Baron Cuvier . . . , 1:163. Included *Dasypus novemcinctus* Linnaeus and *D. septemcinctus* Schreber.
1835. *Cachicama* I. Geoffroy St.-Hilaire, Résumé leçons mamm., 1:53, an invalid emendation of *Cachicamus* McMurtrie.
1841. *Zonoplites* Gloger, Gemeinnütziges Hand- und Hilfs-buch der Naturgeschichte, 1:114. Based on the arma-dillos having 4 toes on the forefoot, the two middle being larger than the others.

1854. *Praopus* Burmeister, Systematische Uebersicht der Thiere Brasiliens . . . , pt. 1, p. 295. Type, *Dasypus longicaudus* Wied-Neuwied.

1856. *Cryptophractus* Fitzinger, Versamml. Deutsch. Naturf. Aertz., p. 123. Type, *Cryptophractus pilosus* Fitzinger.

1864. *Hyperoambon* Peters, Monatsbr. preuss. Akad. Wiss., Berlin, p. 179. Included *Dasypus pentadactylus* Peters [= *Dasypus kappleri* Krauss] and *D. peba* Desmarest [= *Dasypus novemcinctus* Linnaeus].

1874. *Muletia* Gray, Proc. Zool. Soc. London, p. 244, August. Type, *Dasypus septemcinctus* Linnaeus.

On anterior and posterior shields, hairs arise from pits occurring at intersection of furrow surrounding large plaques with radial furrows that separate secondary (peripheral) plaques, which in turn surround each large plaque. Other characters as for the tribe.

Dasypus novemcinctus
Nine-banded Armadillo

External measurements: 615–800; 245–370; 75–100. Greatest length of skull, 85.5–100. Weight of adults in Texas up to 17 pounds. Ordinarily approximately two-thirds that weight. Four toes on forefoot and 5 on hind foot; all digits clawed; scapular shield and pelvic shield each of 18 to 20 rows of ossified scutes; bases of ears touching, at least in dried skins; rostrum long; anterior opening of infraorbital canal nearer posterior ends of pterygoids than anterior ends of nasals; mastoidal width less than 40 (usually less than 30) per cent of greatest length of skull.

Information on the natural history of this species has been summarized by Kalmbach (1943). After fertilization of the ovum, implantation is delayed for 14 weeks, and the ovum gives rise to identical quadruplets. Burrows are dug by the armadillo which serves importantly as a builder of homes and refuge sites for many other kinds of animals. A nervous response of the armadillo to danger is to jump upward and this works to its disadvantage with automobiles which strike and kill many individuals that otherwise might be passed over unhurt. The bony skin of the armadillo causes it to be heavier than most other mammals of the same size and it has the ability to ingest air in the digestive tract to increase its buoyancy when swimming. The armadillo is thought to have extended its geographic range northward and eastward in the United States since 1880 in spite of the hand of man having been

turned against it. Adverse climate (cold on the north and aridity on the west) are the real factors that have stopped the spread in those directions. In 281 stomachs from Texas, more than 93 per cent of the food, by volume, was animal matter—92 per cent was insects and other invertebrates. Because it destroys noxious insects, because of its value as food for man, and because it is an important den-maker for other animals, the damage that it occasionally does is thought to be counterbalanced and the armadillo is a natural and desirable part of the native fauna.

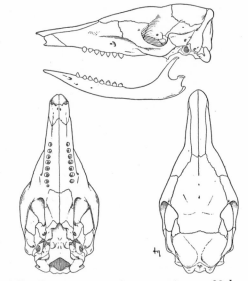

Fig. 172. *Dasypus novemcinctus mexicanus*, 20 km. ENE Jesús Carranza, 200 ft., Veracruz, No. 32118 K.U., ♂, X ½.

Dasypus novemcinctus davisi Russell

1953. *Dasypus novemcinctus davisi* Russell, Proc. Biol. Soc. Washington, 66:21, March 30, type from Huitzilac, 8500 ft., Morelos.

MARGINAL RECORDS.—Morelos (Russell, 1953:25): 5 km. N Tres Cumbres; Tlacotepec; type locality.

Dasypus novemcinctus fenestratus Peters

1864. *Dasypus fenestratus* Peters, Monatsb. preuss. Akad. Wiss., Berlin, p. 180, type from Costa Rica.

1911. *Dasypus novemcinctus fenestratus*, G. M. Allen, Bull. Mus. Comp. Zool., 54:199, July.

MARGINAL RECORDS.—Nicaragua: Río Coco (J. A. Allen, 1910:94), thence southward into South America.

Dasypus novemcinctus hoplites G. M. Allen

1911. *Dasypus novemcinctus hoplites* G. M. Allen, Bull. Mus. Comp. Zool., 54:195, July, type from hills back of Gouyave, Grenada, Lesser Antilles. Known only from the type locality.

Dasypus novemcinctus mexicanus Peters

1864. *Dasypus novemcinctus* var. *mexicanus* Peters, Monatsb. preuss. Akad. Wiss., Berlin, p. 180, type from Matamoros,

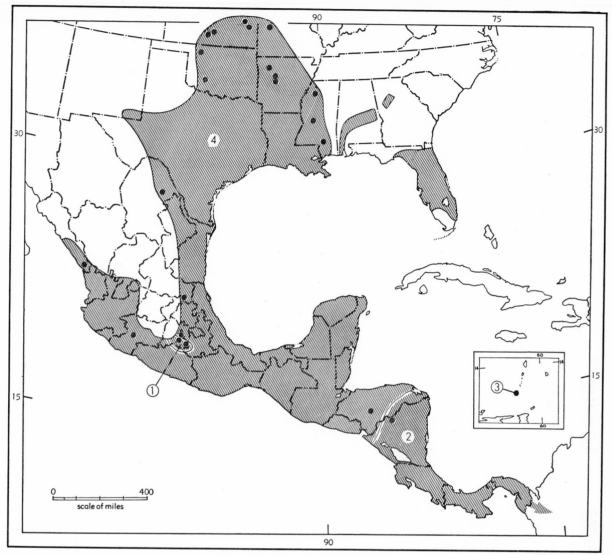

Map 178. *Dasypus novemcinctus.*

1. *D. n. davisi*   2. *D. n. fenestratus*   3. *D. n. hoplites*   4. *D. n. mexicanus*

Tamaulipas (see Hollister, Jour. Mamm., 6:60, February 9, 1925).

1920. *D[asypus]. novemcinctus mexicanus,* Goldman, Smiths. Miscl. Coll., 69(5):66, April 24.

1905. *Tatu novemcinctum texanum* V. Bailey, N. Amer. Fauna, 25:52, October 24, type from Brownsville, Cameron Co., Texas. Regarded as a synonym of *D. n. mexicanus* by Hollister (*antea*).

1917. *Dasypus cucurbitinus* Gaumer, Monographia de los mamíferos de Yucatán, p. 21. (In synonymy of *Dasypus novemcinctus*.)

MARGINAL RECORDS.—Kansas: Osage County (Cockrum, 1952:89); 1 mi. N, 4½ mi. W Harris (Hall, 1955b:60). Missouri: Brownington (Anonymous, 1947:12). Arkansas (Dellinger and Black, 1940:191): 2 mi. E Durham; Altus; Paris. Mississippi (Fitch, *et al.*, 1952:23): Tallahatchie County; Hinds County; Forrest County, thence along Gulf Coast to Honduras: La Cueva Archaga (Goodwin, 1942:149), thence northward along Pacific Coast to Sinaloa: Escuinapa (Russell, 1953:23). *Guanajuato* (Russell, 1953:23). Michoacán: Tancítaro (Hall and Villa, 1949:470). Distrito Federal: Cerro Zacayuca, 2 mi. N Tlalpam (Villa, 1953:350). San Luis Potosí: Xilitla (Dalquest, 1953b:73). Coahuila: Sabinas (Elliot, 1907:27). New Mexico: *southeastern corner* (V. Bailey, 1932:8). Oklahoma: Wichita Mts. Wildlife Refuge (Gardner, 1948:76); 8 mi. NW Freedom (Fitch, *et al.*, 1952:24). Kansas: Iuka (Cockrum, 1952:90); 5½ mi. N, 1¾ mi. W Abbyville (Hall, 1955b:60); *near Strong* (Cockrum, 1952:90). The species has been introduced in Florida and is now established over most of the peninsular part of that state (see Fitch, *et al.*, 1952:24, 26). The species has been found (probably was introduced) in Georgia at *Decatur* (*ibid.*) and in Alabama (Talmage and Buchanan, 1954:23).—Cockrum (1952:90) records *mexicanus* from *Stevens County*, Kansas, which is W of shaded area on Map 178.

Order LAGOMORPHA—Hares, Rabbits, and Pikas

Families and genera revised by Lyon, Smithsonian Miscl. Coll., 45:321–447, June 15, 1904. For taxonomic status of group see Gidley, Science, n.s., 36:285–286, August 30, 1912.

The order Lagomorpha is old in the geological sense; fossilized bones and teeth of both pikas and rabbits are known from deposits of Oligocene age, and even at that early time the structural features distinguishing these animals from other orders were well developed.

A noteworthy character of the order is the presence of 4 upper incisor teeth (instead of only 2 as in the Rodentia); also, the fibula is ankylosed to the tibia and articulates with the calcaneum. Each of the 1st upper incisors has a longitudinal groove on its anterior face.

All lagomorphs are herbivorous. They eat principally leaves and non-woody stems, although the bark of sprouts and bushes is taken as second choice by rabbits and hares.

Correlation of structure with function is well illustrated among the lagomorphs by the means employed by the different species to detect and escape from their enemies. A gradient series is evident in which the pikas and jack rabbits are the extremes. The black-tailed jack rabbit, for example, has the longest ears and longest hind legs in relation to size of the entire animal. This kind of lagomorph takes alarm when an enemy, for example a coyote, is yet a long way off. The jack rabbit seeks safety in running; even when being overtaken by a pursuer that is close behind, the jack rabbit still relies on its running ability instead of entering thick brush or a hole in the ground where its larger-sized pursuer would be unable to follow. A cottontail has shorter ears and shorter hind legs. It allows the enemy to approach more closely than the jack rabbit does before running, and then, although relying in some measure on its running ability for escape, flees to a burrow or thicket for safety from its pursuer. The brush rabbit, with ears and hind legs shorter than those of the cottontail, seldom if ever ventures farther than 45 feet away from the edge of dense cover. After an enemy is near, the brush rabbit has merely to scamper back into the brush. Still shorter of ear and hind leg is the pygmy rabbit; it ventures outside its burrow to feed only among the tall and closely-spaced bushes of sagebrush among which its burrow is dug. Detection of the slightest movement of an enemy on the opposite side of the bush sends the pygmy rabbit, in one or a few jumps, into the mouth of its burrow and, if need be, below ground. The pika, with the shortest ears and legs of all, lives in the rock slides and has to do little more than drop off the top of a rock into a space between the broken rocks when an enemy is detected near enough to the pika to have a chance of seizing it.

The number of molts in a year, depending on the kind of lagomorph, varies in adults from 1 (according to Nelson, 1909:31) in the cottontails (genus *Sylvilagus*) to as many as 3 (according to Lyman, 1943, and Severaid, 1945) in the varying hare (*Lepus americanus*). Difficulties that we have experienced in accounting for the variations in color and wear of the pelage of the pika, *Ochotona princeps*, on the basis of 2 molts per year, make us wonder if it, too, has 3 molts. *Lepus townsendii* certainly has at least 2 molts per year.

Key to North American Families and Genera of Lagomorpha

1. Hind legs scarcely larger than forelegs; hind foot less than 40; nasals widest anteriorly; no supraorbital process on frontal; 5 cheek-teeth on each side above. . Family Ochotonidae, p. 246
        Ochotona, p. 247
1′. Hind legs notably larger than forelegs; hind foot more than 40; nasals widest posteriorly; supraorbital process on frontal; 6 cheek-teeth on each side above. . Family Leporidae, p. 251
    2. Interparietal fused with parietals (see Figs. 185–191); hind foot usually more than 105. . . . . *Lepus*, p. 271
    2′. Interparietal not fused with parietals (see Figs. 175–184); hind foot usually less than 105. . . . . *Romerolagus*, p. 253
        Sylvilagus, p. 253

Family OCHOTONIDAE—Pikas

Certain characters in which this family differs from the Leporidae (hares and rabbits) are: hind legs scarcely longer than forelegs; ears short, approximately as wide as high; no postorbital process on frontal; rostrum slender; nasals widest anteriorly; maxilla having a single, large fenestra; jugal long and projecting far posteriorly to zygomatic arm of squamosal; no pubic symphysis; one less cheek-tooth above, the dental formula being i. $\frac{2}{1}$, c. $\frac{0}{0}$, p. $\frac{3}{2}$, m. $\frac{2}{3}$; second upper maxillary tooth unlike third in form; last lower molar simple (not double) or absent (in the extinct genus *Oreolagus*); cutting edge of first upper incisor V-shaped; mental foramen situated under last lower molar.

Genus **Ochotona** Link—Pikas

North American species revised by A. H. Howell, N. Amer. Fauna, 47:1–57, August 21, 1924. For a synopsis see Hall, Univ. Kansas Publ., Mus. Nat. Hist., 5:125–133, December 15, 1951.

1795. *Ochotona* Link, Beytrage zur Naturgeschichte, 1 (pt. 2):74. Type, *Lepus ogotona* Pallas.

Five cheek-teeth in lower jaw; 1st cheek-tooth (p3) with more than one re-entrant angle; columns of lower molars angular internally; transverse width of any one column of a lower molariform tooth more than double the width of the neck connecting it to the other column.

Subgenus **Pika** Lacépède

1799. *Pika* Lacépède, Tableau des divisions, sous-divisions, ordres et genres des mammifères, p. 9. Type, *Lepus alpinus* Pallas.

Skull flattened; interorbital region wide; maxillary orifice roundly triangular; palatal foramina separate from anterior palatine foramina.

All of the living members of the family Ochotonidae belong to this genus. American pikas all belong to the subgenus *Pika*, which occurs also in Eurasia.

The pikas are of boreal distribution and the animals live in talus. This broken rock at the foot of a cliff provides interstices in which the animals live and store grass and herbs. These plant materials are cut for food and stacked in piles to dry in the sun, often beneath slabs of rock, which protect the hay-piles from rain. Pikas are diurnal, active throughout the year, and have a characteristic call, "chickck-chickck." Young number two to five per litter.

KEY TO NOMINAL AMERICAN SPECIES OF OCHOTONA

1. Occurring north of 58° N latitude; underparts creamy white, without buffy wash; an indistinct grayish "collar" on shoulders.
   O. collaris, p. 248
1'. Occurring south of 58° N latitude; underparts washed with buff; no grayish "collar" on shoulders. . . . . . . *O. princeps*, p. 248

Ochotona collaris (Nelson)
Collared Pika

1893. *Lagomys collaris* Nelson, Proc. Biol. Soc. Washington, 8:117, December 21, type from near head of Tanana River, Alaska.
1897. [*Ochotona*] *collaris*, Trouessart, Catalogus mammalium . . . , p. 648.

Total length, 189; hind foot, 30. Upper parts drab to light drab; underparts creamy white; grayish patch on nape and shoulders; skull broad; tympanic bullae large.

MARGINAL RECORDS (Hall, 1951c:126–127).—Alaska: Mt. McKinley. Yukon: head of Coal Creek, Ogilvie Mts. Mackenzie: mile 63E on Little Keel River, Canol Road. Yukon: *Macmillan Pass, mile 282, Canol Road*; Ross River, mile 96, Canol Road; vicinity Teslin Lake. British Columbia: Tagish Lake; Stonehouse Creek, 5½ mi. W junction Stonehouse Creek and Kelsall River. Alaska: Tanana River.

Ochotona princeps
Pika

Total length, 162–216; hind foot, 25–35; weight of *O. p. tutelata*: average of 6 males, 121 (108–128); 2 females, 121 and 129 grams. Upper parts varying from grayish to Cinnamon-Buff depending on the subspecies; underparts with wash of buff. Eight Nevadan females had an average of 3.1 (2–4) embryos. The mode was 3.

Ochotona princeps albata Grinnell

1912. *Ochotona albatus* Grinnell, Univ. California Publ. Zool., 10:125, January 31, type from 11,000 ft., near Cottonwood Lakes, Sierra Nevada, Inyo Co., California.
1951. *Ochotona princeps albata*, Hall, Univ. Kansas Publ., Mus. Nat. Hist., 5:127, December 15.

MARGINAL RECORDS (Hall, 1951c:127).—California: Bullfrog Lake; 10,000 ft., Independence Creek; type locality; Mineral King, E Fork Kaweah River.

Ochotona princeps barnesi Durrant and Lee

1955. *Ochotona princeps barnesi* Durrant and Lee, Proc. Biol. Soc. Washington, 68:6, May 20, type from Johnson's Reservoir, 8800 ft., 15 mi. by road N Loa (Fishlake Plateau), Sevier Co., Utah.

MARGINAL RECORDS (Durrant and Lee, 1955:8).—Utah: *1 mi. NW Mt. Marvine (Seven Mile Valley)*, 9200 ft.; type locality; *Seven Mile Canyon, 4 mi. N Johnson's Res.*, 8800 ft.

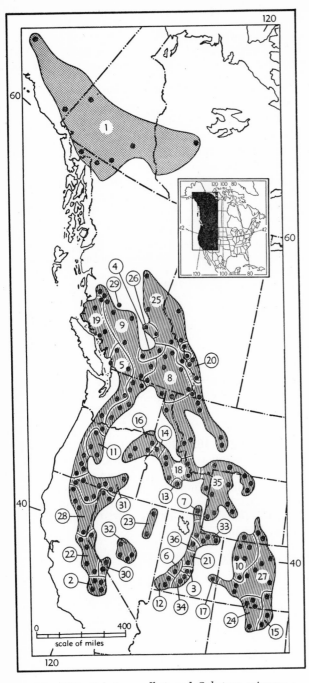

Map 179. *Ochotona collaris* and *Ochotona princeps*.

1. *O. collaris*	13. *O. p. goldmani*	25. *O. p. princeps*
2. *O. p. albata*	14. *O. p. howelli*	26. *O. p. saturata*
3. *O. p. barnesi*	15. *O. p. incana*	27. *O. p. saxatilis*
4. *O. p. brooksi*	16. *O. p. jewetti*	28. *O. p. schisticeps*
5. *O. p. brunnescens*	17. *O. p. lasalensis*	29. *O. p. septentrionalis*
6. *O. p. cinnamomea*	18. *O. p. lemhi*	30. *O. p. sheltoni*
7. *O. p. clamosa*	19. *O. p. littoralis*	31. *O. p. taylori*
8. *O. p. cuppes*	20. *O. p. lutescens*	32. *O. p. tutelata*
9. *O. p. fenisex*	21. *O. p. moorei*	33. *O. p. uinta*
10. *O. p. figginsi*	22. *O. p. muiri*	34. *O. p. utahensis*
11. *O. p. fumosa*	23. *O. p. nevadensis*	35. *O. p. ventorum*
12. *O. p. fuscipes*	24. *O. p. nigrescens*	36. *O. p. wasatchensis*

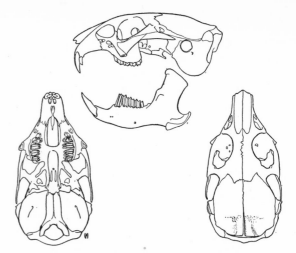

Fig. 173. *Ochotona princeps tutelata*, Greenmonster Canyon, 8150 ft., Nevada, No. 38519 M.V.Z., ♂, X 1.

Ochotona princeps brooksi A. H. Howell

1924. *Ochotona princeps brooksi* A. H. Howell, N. Amer. Fauna, 47:30, September 23, type from Sicamous, British Columbia.

MARGINAL RECORDS.—British Columbia (Cowan and Guiguet, 1956:95): [mts. E of] Shuswap [Lake]; *type locality*; Robbins Range, 20 mi. SE Kamloops.

Ochotona princeps brunnescens A. H. Howell

1919. *Ochotona fenisex brunnescens* A. H. Howell, Proc. Biol. Soc. Washington, 32:108, May 20, type from Keechelus, Kittitas Co., Washington.
1924. *Ochotona princeps brunnescens* A. H. Howell, N. Amer. Fauna, 47:31, September 23.

MARGINAL RECORDS (Hall, 1951c:127).—British Columbia: Alta Lake; Hope, Lake House. Washington: *Whatcom Pass*; Stevens Pass; *Cowlitz Pass*. Oregon: Mt. Hood; ½ mi. W Salt Creek Falls, 4000 ft. (Roest, 1953:133); Crater Lake; Mt. McLoughlin; Diamond Lake. Washington: Tumtum Mtn.; Mt. Index. British Columbia: Chilliwack; North Vancouver.

Ochotona princeps cinnamomea J. A. Allen

1905. *Ochotona cinnamomea* J. A. Allen, Mus. Brooklyn Inst. Arts and Sci., Sci. Bull., 1:121, March 31, type from 11,000 ft., Briggs [= Britts] Meadows, Beaver Range, Beaver Co., Utah (5 mi. by road W Puffer Lake, according to Hardy, Jour. Mamm., 26:432, February 12, 1946). Known from type locality only.
1934. *Ochotona princeps cinnamomea*, Hall, Proc. Biol. Soc. Washington, 47:103, June 13.

Ochotona princeps clamosa Hall and Bowlus

1938. *Ochotona princeps clamosa* Hall and Bowlus, Univ. California Publ. Zool., 42:335, October 12, type from 8400 ft., north rim Copenhagen Basin, Bear Lake Co., Idaho.

MARGINAL RECORDS (Hall, 1951c:129).—Idaho: type locality; *Deep Lake, Bear River Mts. 2 mi. E Strawberry Creek Ranger Station, Wasatch Mts.*

Ochotona princeps cuppes Bangs

1899. *Ochotona cuppes* Bangs, Proc. New England Zool. Club, 1:40, June 5, type from 4000 ft., Monashee Divide, Gold Range, British Columbia.
1924. *Ochotona princeps cuppes,* A. H. Howell, N. Amer. Fauna, 47:27, September 23.

MARGINAL RECORDS (Cowan, 1955:23, unless otherwise noted).—British Columbia: Glacier (Hall, 1951c:129); Toby Creek, 18 mi. W Invermere; Morrissey. Idaho: Cabinet Mts. (Hall, 1951c:129). Washington: Sullivan Lake (*ibid.*). British Columbia: Kettle Valley; type locality; Mt. Revelstoke.

Ochotona princeps fenisex Osgood

1863. *Lagomys minimus* Lord, Proc. Zool. Soc. London, p. 98, lectotype from 7000 ft., Ptarmigan Hill, near head of Ashnola River, Cascade Range, British Columbia. *Nec* Schinz, 1821.
1924. *Ochotona princeps fenisex,* A. H. Howell, N. Amer. Fauna, 47:28, September 23.
1913. *Ochotona fenisex* Osgood, Proc. Biol. Soc. Washington, 26:80, March 22, renaming of *L. minimus* Lord.

MARGINAL RECORDS (Cowan, 1955:23, unless otherwise noted).—British Columbia: Kimsquist [= ? Kimsquit]; Rainbow Mts.; *Caribou Mtn.* [52° 20', 125° 35']; 24 mi. W Williams Lake; Okanagan (Hall, 1951c:129). Washington (Hall, 1951c:129): Horseshoe Basin, near Mt. Chopaka; mts. near Wenatchee; Steamboat Mtn.; Easton; Lyman Lake; Barron. British Columbia: Ashnola River; *Cathedral Lake;* McGillivray Creek; Kleena Kleene; Stuie. Not found: Blackwater River in British Columbia (Cowan and Guiguet, 1956:96).

Ochotona princeps figginsi J. A. Allen

1912. *Ochotona figginsi* J. A. Allen, Bull. Amer. Mus. Nat. Hist., 31:103, May 28, type from Pagoda Peak, Rio Blanco Co., Colorado.
1924. *Ochotona princeps figginsi,* A. H. Howell, N. Amer. Fauna, 47:21, September 23.

MARGINAL RECORDS (Hall, 1951c:129).—Wyoming: Bridger Peak, Sierra Madre. Colorado: Mt. Zirkel; Trappers Lake; *Crested Butte;* Irwin; type locality; Sand Mtn., 9 mi. SW Hahns Peak P.O.

Ochotona princeps fumosa A. H. Howell

1919. *Ochotona fenisex fumosa* A. H. Howell, Proc. Biol. Soc. Washington, 32:109, May 20, type from Permilia [= Pamelia?] Lake, W base Mt. Jefferson [Linn Co. ?], Oregon.
1924. *Ochotona princeps fumosa* A. H. Howell, N. Amer. Fauna, 47:33, September 23.

MARGINAL RECORDS (Hall, 1951:130, unless otherwise noted).—Oregon: About 900 ft., 15 mi. above Estacada; Lost Lake in Newberry Crater (Roest, 1953:133); *Paulina Lake; Three Sisters; Lava Butte* (Roest, 1953:133); Lost Creek Ranger Station, 10 mi. SE McKenzie Bridge.

Ochotona princeps fuscipes A. H. Howell

1919. *Ochotona schisticeps fuscipes* A. H. Howell, Proc. Biol. Soc. Washington, 32:110, May 20, type from Brian Head, Parowan Mts., Iron Co., Utah.
1941. *O[chotona]. p[rinceps]. fuscipes,* Hall and Hayward, The Great Basin Naturalist, 2:108, July 20.

MARGINAL RECORDS (Hall, 1951c:130).—Utah: type locality; 9000 ft., Duck Creek.

Ochotona princeps goldmani A. H. Howell

1924. *Ochotona schisticeps goldmani* A. H. Howell, N. Amer. Fauna, 47:40, September 23, type from Echo Crater, Snake River Desert, 20 mi. SW Arco, Butte Co., Idaho.
1938. *Ochotona princeps goldmani,* Hall and Bowlus, Univ. California Publ. Zool., 42:337, October 12.

MARGINAL RECORDS (Hall, 1951c:130).—Idaho: S *base Grassy Cone;* type locality; *Fissure Crater; Great Owl Cavern.*

Ochotona princeps howelli Borell

1931. *Ochotona princeps howelli* Borell, Jour. Mamm., 12:306, August 24, type from 7500 ft., near head of Bear Creek, summit of Smith Mtn., S end Seven Devils Mts., Adams Co., Idaho.

MARGINAL RECORDS (Hall, 1951c:130).—Idaho: ½ *mi. E Black Lake;* type locality.

Ochotona princeps incana A. H. Howell

1919. *Ochotona saxatilis incana* A. H. Howell, Proc. Biol. Soc. Washington, 32:107, May 20, type from 12,000 ft., Pecos Baldy, Santa Fe Co., New Mexico.
1924. *Ochotona princeps incana* A. H. Howell, N. Amer. Fauna, 47:25, September 23.

MARGINAL RECORDS (Hall, 1951c:130).—Colorado: Medano Creek. New Mexico: Wheeler Peak; type locality.

Ochotona princeps jewetti A. H. Howell

1919. *Ochotona schisticeps jewetti* A. H. Howell, Proc. Biol. Soc. Washington, 32:109, May 20, type from head of Pine Creek, near Cornucopia, S slope Wallowa Mts., Baker Co., Oregon.
1951. *Ochotona princeps jewetti,* Hall, Univ. Kansas Publ., Mus. Nat. Hist., 5:130, December 15.

MARGINAL RECORDS (Hall, 1951c:130).—Oregon: Wallowa Lake; Cornucopia, near head East Pine Creek; *Anthony;* Strawberry Butte; Austin.

Ochotona princeps lasalensis Durrant and Lee

1955. *Ochotona princeps lasalensis* Durrant and Lee, Proc. Biol. Soc. Washington, 68:4, May 20, type from Warner Ranger Station, 9750 ft., La Sal Mts., Grand Co., Utah.

MARGINAL RECORDS (Durrant and Lee, 1955:6).—Utah: ½ mi. N Warner R.S., 9000 ft., La Sal Mts.; *Geyser Pass; Mt. Mellithin* [= *Mellenthin*], *12,280 ft.;* ½ mi. S *Warner R.S., 9700 ft.*

Ochotona princeps lemhi A. H. Howell

1919. *Ochotona uinta lemhi* A. H. Howell, Proc. Biol. Soc. Washington, 32:106, May 20, type from Lemhi Mountains, 10 mi. W Junction, Lemhi Co., Idaho.
1924. *Ochotona princeps lemhi* A. H. Howell, N. Amer. Fauna, 47:16, September 23.

MARGINAL RECORDS (Hall, 1951c:131).—Idaho: Elk Summit, about 15 mi. SE Warren; mts. E of Leadore; mts. E of Birch Creek; Ketchum; *Stanley Lake*; 5 mi. W Cape Horn.

Ochotona princeps littoralis Cowan

1955. *Ochotona princeps littoralis* Cowan, Murrelet, 35:22, August 27, type from Hagensborg, British Columbia.

MARGINAL RECORDS.—British Columbia (Cowan, 1955:23): type locality; Purcell Point; Fawn Bluff; Arran Rapids; head Rivers Inlet.

Ochotona princeps lutescens A. H. Howell

1919. *Ochotona princeps lutescens* A. H. Howell, Proc. Biol. Soc. Washington, 32:105, May 20, type from approximately 8000 ft., Mt. Inglesmaldie, near Banff, Alberta.

MARGINAL RECORDS.—Alberta (Cowan, 1955:23, unless otherwise noted): Mistaya Creek [= River], Banff-Jasper Highway (Hall, 1951c:131); *head of Dorimer River*; type locality; *Canmore* (Hall, 1951c:131); Mt. Forget-me-not (*ibid.*); head Brewster Creek.

Ochotona princeps moorei Gardner

1950. *Ochotona princeps moorei* Gardner, Jour. Washington Acad. Sci., 40:344, October 23, 1950, type from 10,000 ft., 1 mi. NE Baldy Ranger Station, Manti National Forest, Sanpete Co., Utah. Known from type locality only.

Ochotona princeps muiri Grinnell and Storer

1916. *Ochotona schisticeps muiri* Grinnell and Storer, Univ. California Publ. Zool., 17:6, August 23, type from 9300 ft., near Ten Lakes, Yosemite National Park, Tuolumne Co., California.
1934. *Ochotona princeps muiri*, Hall, Proc. Biol. Soc. Washington, 47:103, June 13.

MARGINAL RECORDS (Hall, 1951c:131).—Nevada: 8500 ft., 3 mi. S Mt. Rose. California: Markleeville; mts. W Bishop Creek; Washburn Lake; lat. 39° N, summit of Sierra.

Ochotona princeps nevadensis A. H. Howell

1919. *Ochotona uinta nevadensis* A. H. Howell, Proc. Biol. Soc. Washington, 32:107, May 20, type from 10,500 ft., Ruby Mts., SW Ruby Valley P. O., Elko Co., Nevada.
1924. *Ochotona princeps nevadensis* A. H. Howell, N. Amer. Fauna, 47:21, September 23.

MARGINAL RECORDS (Hall, 1951c:131).—Nevada: 7830 ft., Long Creek; type locality.

Ochotona princeps nigrescens V. Bailey

1913. *Ochotona nigrescens* V. Bailey, Proc. Biol. Soc. Washington, 26:133, May 21, type from Goat Peak, head of

Santa Clara Creek, 10,000 ft., Jemez Mountains, Sandoval Co., New Mexico.
1924. *Ochotona princeps nigrescens,* A. H. Howell, N. Amer. Fauna, 47:26, September 23.

MARGINAL RECORDS (Hall, 1951c:132).—Colorado: Upper Navajo River; Osier. New Mexico: type locality. Colorado: Navajo Peaks.

Ochotona princeps princeps (Richardson)

1828. *Lepus (Lagomys) princeps* Richardson, Zool. Jour., 3:520, type from headwaters of Athabaska River, near Athabaska Pass, Alberta.
1897. [*Ochotona*] *princeps,* Trouessart, Catalogus mammalium . . . , p. 648.
1912. *Ochotona levis* Hollister, Proc. Biol. Soc. Washington, 25:57, April 13, type from Chief Mountain [= Waterton] Lake, Glacier Co., Montana. (Regarded as subspecifically inseparable from *O. p. princeps* by Cowan, Murrelet, 35:20, August 27, 1955.)

MARGINAL RECORDS (Hall, 1951c:132, unless otherwise noted).—British Columbia: headwaters South Pine River. Alberta: Muskeg Creek "about" 60 mi. N Jasper House; Medicine Lake (Cowan, 1955:24); Sunwapta Pass (*ibid.*); *Pipestone River* (*ibid.*); Baker Lake (*ibid.*); Waterton Lake (*ibid.*). Montana: Chief Mountain Lake; Little Belt Mts.; Belt Mts.; mts. near St. Marys Lake; mts. 15 mi. E Corvallis; Lake Como, Bitterroot Mts. Idaho: Coeur d'Alene National Forest. British Columbia: Mt. Rowe (Cowan, 1955:24); Spillamacheen River; Kinbasket Lake (Cowan, 1955:24); Indianpoint Lake (*ibid.*).

Ochotona princeps saturatus Cowan

1955. *Ochotona princeps saturatus* Cowan, Murrelet, 35:23, August 27, type from Mount Huntley in Wells Gray National Park, British Columbia.

MARGINAL RECORDS.—British Columbia (Cowan, 1955:24): *Myrtle Lake*; type locality.

Ochotona princeps saxatilis Bangs

1899. *Ochotona saxatilis* Bangs, Proc. New England Zool. Club, 1:41, June 5, type from Montgomery, "near" Mt. Lincoln, Park Co., Colorado.
1924. *Ochotona princeps saxatilis,* A. H. Howell, N. Amer. Fauna, 47:23, September 23.

MARGINAL RECORDS (Hall, 1951c:132).—Wyoming: Medicine Bow Mts.; just above Centennial in mts. Colorado: Estes Park; Pikes Peak; Silverton; Crystal Lake, 5 mi. W Lake City; Middle Brush Creek; Ten Mile Creek; Berthoud Pass; *Irwin Lakes* not found.

Ochotona princeps schisticeps (Merriam)

1889. *Lagomys schisticeps* Merriam, N. Amer. Fauna, 2:11, October 30, type from Donner [= Summit], Placer Co., California.
1936. *Ochotona princeps schisticeps,* A. H. Miller, Jour. Mamm., 17:175, May 18 (*princeps* and *schisticeps* regarded as conspecific by Borell, Jour. Mamm., 12:307-308, August 24, 1931).

MARGINAL RECORDS (Hall, 1951c:132).—Nevada: 12 mi. E and 3 mi. N Fort Bidwell, 5700 ft.; 8400-8600 ft., Duffer Peak, Pine Forest Mts. California: Tahoe; *Donner Pass*; 12 mi. NE Prattville; Lassen Peak; Mt. Shasta.

Ochotona princeps septentrionalis Cowan and Racey

1947. *Ochotona princeps septentrionalis* Cowan and Racey, Canadian Field-Nat., 60:102, April 22, type from 6500 ft., Itcha Mountains, lat. 52° 45′ N, long. 125° W, British Columbia. Known from type locality only.

Ochotona princeps sheltoni Grinnell

1918. *Ochotona schisticeps sheltoni* Grinnell, Univ. California Publ. Zool., 17:429, April 25, type from 11,000 ft., "near" Big Prospector Meadow, White Mountains, Mono Co., California.
1946. *Ochotona princeps sheltoni,* Hall, Mammals of Nevada, p. 592, July 1.

MARGINAL RECORDS (Hall, 1951c:132–133).—Nevada: 8700 ft., Pinchot Creek. California: type locality.

Ochotona princeps taylori Grinnell

1912. *Ochotona taylori* Grinnell, Proc. Biol. Soc. Washington, 25:129, July 31, type from 9000 ft., Warren Peak, Warner Mts., Modoc Co., California.
1951. *Ochotona princeps taylori,* Hall, Univ. Kansas Publ., Mus. Nat. Hist., 5:133, December 15.

MARGINAL RECORDS (Hall, 1951c:133).—Oregon: N end Steens Mts.; Guano Valley; Jack Lake, 20 mi. NE Adel; Adel. California: type locality; 5400 ft., near Termo, Madeline Plains; near head Little Shasta River. Oregon: Lower Klamath Lake.

Ochotona princeps tutelata Hall

1934. *Ochotona princeps tutelata* Hall, Proc. Biol. Soc. Washington 47:103, June 13, type from 8150 ft., Greenmonster Canyon, Monitor Mts., Nye Co., Nevada.

MARGINAL RECORDS (Hall, 1951c:133).—Nevada: 7500 ft., Smiths Creek, Desatoya Mts.; 8600 ft., type locality; 8700–11,000 ft., SW and W slopes Mt. Jefferson, Toquima Range; South Twin River; *Arc Dome.*

Ochotona princeps uinta Hollister

1912. *Ochotona uinta* Hollister, Proc. Biol. Soc. Washington, 25:58, April 13, type from near head E. Fork Bear River, Uinta Mts., Summit Co., Utah.
1924. *Ochotona princeps uinta,* A. H. Howell, N. Amer. Fauna, 47:19, September 23.

MARGINAL RECORDS (Hall, 1951c:133).—Utah: type locality; Elk Park; *11,000 to 11,500 ft., The Nipple;* 10,500 ft., SW slope Bald Mtn.; 8500 ft., Morehouse Canyon, 5 mi. above Weber River; *Spirit Lake* not found.

Ochotona princeps utahensis Hall and Hayward

1941. *Ochotona princeps utahensis* Hall and Hayward, Great Basin Nat., 2:107, July 20, type from 2 mi. W Deer Lake, Garfield Co., Utah.

MARGINAL RECORDS (Hall, 1951c:133).—Utah: 9000 ft., Donkey Lake, Boulder Mtn.; type locality.

Ochotona princeps ventorum A. H. Howell

1919. *Ochotona uinta ventorum* A. H. Howell, Proc. Biol. Soc. Washington, 32:106, May 20, type from Fremont Peak, 11,500 ft., Wind River Mts., Fremont Co., Wyoming.

1924. *Ochotona princeps ventorum* A. H. Howell, N. Amer. Fauna, 47:18, September 23.

MARGINAL RECORDS (Hall, 1951c:133).—Montana: Emigrant Peak; Beartooth Mts. Wyoming: 9600 ft., 19½ mi. E and 4½ mi. S Shell; head of Trappers Creek; Medicine Wheel Ranch, 28 mi. E Lovell; Needle Mtn.; Lake Fork; 8450 ft., 17½ mi. S and 6½ mi. W Lander; Middle Piney Lake, near Stanley; Salt River, 16 mi. S Afton; Teton Pass. Idaho: Teton Canyon.

Ochotona princeps wasatchensis Durrant and Lee

1955. *Ochotona princeps wasatchensis* Durrant and Lee, Proc. Biol. Soc. Washington, 68:2, May 20, type from 10 mi. above lower powerhouse, road to Cardiff Mine, Big Cottonwood Canyon, Salt Lake Co., Utah.

MARGINAL RECORDS.—Utah (Durrant and Lee, 1955: 4); type locality; *near Lake Solitude, 9000 ft., Silver Lake P.O. (Brighton); Mt. Timpanogos; Big Willow Canyon, 7000 ft.; Little Cottonwood Canyon, 6 mi. above Wasatch Blvd.*

FAMILY LEPORIDAE—Rabbits and Hares

Hind legs longer than forelegs; ears longer than wide; frontal bone carrying supraorbital process consisting always of posterior arm and often also of anterior arm; rostrum wide; nasals not wider anteriorly than posteriorly; maxillae having numerous fenestrae; jugal projecting less than halfway from zygomatic root of squamosal to external auditory meatus (except in *Romerolagus*); pubic symphysis well marked; dental formula, i. $\frac{2}{1}$, c. $\frac{0}{0}$, p. $\frac{3}{2}$, m. $\frac{3}{3}$ (but m. $\frac{2}{3}$ in *Pentalagus* of Liu Kiu Islands south of Japan); 2nd upper maxillary tooth like 3rd in form; last lower molar double; cutting edge of 1st upper incisor straight; mental foramen of mandible situated under 1st lower cheek-tooth. Females average larger than males in all members of this family. (See Orr, 1940:20.) The reverse is true in most other families of mammals.

Hare is a name applied to any lagomorph whose young are born fully haired, with the eyes open, and able to run about a few minutes after birth. The young are born in the open, not in a nest. All of the species of the genus *Lepus* are hares. The species of leporids of all genera other than *Lepus*, in North America at least, are rabbits. Their young are born naked, blind, and helpless, in a nest especially built for them and lined with fur. Considering the degree of development of the young at birth, the gestation periods are about what would be expected: 26 to 30 days in *Sylvilagus* and 36 to 47 days in *Lepus* (see Severaid, 1950:356–357). Vernacular names are misleading because the names jack rabbit and snowshoe rabbit are applied to hares; also, Belgian hare is a name applied to a rabbit (genus *Oryctolagus*) that is commonly bred in captivity.

Rabbits and hares are crepuscular and possibly more nocturnal than diurnal. So far as we know they do not store food as do their diurnal relatives, the pikas. Some leporids, however, have an unusual, and possibly unique, method of processing food: two types of vegetable pellets are expelled from the anal opening of the digestive tract; the dark brownish pellets, from which the nutriments have been extracted, are feces, but the greenish pellets seem to be only slightly predigested foods which are re-eaten. Southern (1942:553) and Kirkpatrick (1956:300), among others, have written about this. This system functionally resembles that in the ruminants where a cud of vegetation is returned to the mouth, from one part of the stomach, to be re-chewed and finally swallowed.

KEY TO SPECIES OF SYLVILAGUS AND ROMEROLAGUS

1. Antorbital extension of supraorbital process more than ½ length of posterior extension; 1st upper cheek-tooth with only 1 re-entrant angle on anterior face; re-entrant angle of 2nd upper cheek-tooth not crenate. . . . . *Sylvilagus idahoensis*, p. 254
1′. Antorbital extension of supraorbital process less than ½ of posterior extension or entirely absent; 1st upper cheek-tooth with more than 1 (usually 3) re-entrant angles on anterior face; re-entrant angle of 2nd upper cheek-tooth crenate.
2. Anterior extension of supraorbital process absent (or if a point is barely indicated, then five-sixths or all of posterior process fused to braincase).
3. Tympanic bulla smaller than foramen magnum; hind foot more than 74; geographic range wholly in United States.
4. Ear more than 58 from notch in dried skin; basilar length of skull more than 63.
   Sylvilagus aquaticus, p. 268
4′. Ear less than 58 from notch in dried skin; basilar length of skull less than 63.
5. Underside of tail white; posterior extension of supraorbital process tapering to a slender point, this point free of braincase or barely touching it and leaving a slit or long foramen. . . . . *Sylvilagus transitionalis*, p. 263
5′. Underside of tail brown or gray; posterior extension of supraorbital process always fused to skull, usually for entire length but in occasional specimens there is small foramen at middle of posterior extension of supraorbital process. . . . . . *Sylvilagus palustris*, p. 258
3′. Tympanic bulla as large as foramen magnum; hind foot less than 74; geographic range limited to southern edge of Mexican tableland at high elevations. . . . . . *Romerolagus diazi*, p. 253
2′. Anterior extension of supraorbital process present, and posterior extension free of braincase or leaving a slit between the process and braincase.
6. Tympanic bullae large (see Fig. 182). . . . . *Sylvilagus audubonii*, p. 265
6′. Tympanic bullae small (see Figs. 177, 179 and 181).
7. Restricted to Pacific coastal strip from Columbia River south to tip of Baja California, west of Sierra Nevada-Cascade Mountain Chain; hind foot less than 81.
   Sylvilagus bachmani and *S. mansuetus*, pp. 256, 258
7′. East of Pacific coastal strip mentioned in 7; hind foot usually more than 81.
8. North of United States–Mexican boundary.
9. In Arizona, New Mexico, and southern Colorado posterior extension of supraorbital process free of braincase, and supraoccipital shield posteriorly pointed; from central Colorado north into Canada, diameter of external auditory meatus more than crown length of last 3 cheek-teeth. . . . . *Sylvilagus nuttallii*, p. 264
9′. In Arizona, New Mexico, and southeastern Colorado posterior extension of supraorbital process of frontal with its tip against, or fused to, braincase, and supraoccipital shield posteriorly truncate or notched; from central Colorado north into Canada, diameter of external auditory meatus less than crown length of last 3 cheek-teeth.
   Sylvilagus floridanus, p. 259
8′. South of United States–Mexican boundary.
10. Geographic range restricted to Tres Marias Islands. . . . *Sylvilagus graysoni*, p. 271
10′. Geographic range not including Tres Marias Islands.
11. Underside of tail dingy gray or buffy (not white).
12. Tail short (less than 30) and brown like rump; ear from notch (dry) less than 53; interorbital breadth less than 16. . . *Sylvilagus brasiliensis*, p. 255
12′. Tail of moderate length (more than 30) and dingy gray; ear from notch (dry) more than 53; interorbital breadth more than 16.
   Sylvilagus insonus, p. 270

11′. Underside of tail distinctly white.
  13. Total length more than 476; ear from notch (dry) more than 64; interorbital breadth usually more than 19.3; geographic range, southwestern México north of the Isthmus of Tehuantepec.
  Sylvilagus cunicularius, p. 270
  13′. Total length less than 476; ear from notch (dry) less than 64; interorbital breadth usually less than 19.3; geographic range, Canada to Panamá. . . . . *Sylvilagus floridanus*, p. 259

Genus **Romerolagus** Merriam—Volcano Rabbit

1896. *Romerolagus* Merriam, Proc. Biol. Soc. Washington, 10:173, December 29. Type, *Romerolagus nelsoni* Merriam [=*Lepus diazi* Diaz].

Total length, 300–311; tail rudimentary; hind foot, 52; ear from notch (dry), 36; upper parts grizzled buffy brown or dull cinnamon brown; underparts dingy gray; anterior projection of supraorbital process absent; jugal projecting posteriorly past squamosal root of zygomatic arch more than halfway to external auditory meatus. The two cranial characters mentioned are resemblances to pikas although the skull otherwise resembles that of the true rabbits. The genus contains only the one living species.

Living in well-defined runways in the dense sacoton grass, these small rabbits are mainly nocturnal and crepuscular, but sometimes are active by day, especially in cloudy weather in the period of mating.

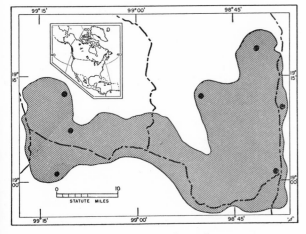

Map 180. *Romerolagus diazi.*

Romerolagus diazi (Diaz)
Volcano Rabbit

1893. *Lepus diazi* Diaz, Catálogo, Comisión Geográfico-Exploradora de la República Méxicana Exposición Internacional Colombina de Chicago . . . , pl. 42, March, type from eastern slope of Mount Ixtaccíhuatl, Puebla. (Villa, An. Inst. Biol. Méx., 23:353, May 20, 1953, cites the name *Lepus diazi* from Ferrari-Pérez *in* Diaz.)
1911. *Romerolagus diazi* Miller, Proc. Biol. Soc. Washington, 24:228, October 31.

1896. *Romerolagus nelsoni* Merriam, Proc. Biol. Soc. Washington, 10:173, December 29, type from west slope Mount Popocatépetl, 11,000 ft., México.

MARGINAL RECORDS (Hall, 1951c:138, unless otherwise noted).—México: Monte Río Frío, 45 km. ESE Mexico City. Puebla: type locality. México: Mt. Popocatépetl. Morelos: 37 km. S, 5 km. W México, 3220 m. (Villa, 1953:354). Distrito Federal: Ajusco (Goodwin, 1954:7); 31 km. S Mexico City. México: Llano Grande, 3 km. W Tlalmanalco.

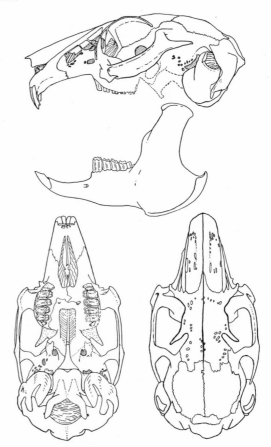

Fig. 174. *Romerolagus diazi*, 31 km. S Mexico City, Distrito Federal, No. 30815 K.U., ♀, × 1.

Genus **Sylvilagus** Gray—Cottontails and Allies

Revised by Nelson, N. Amer. Fauna, 29:159–278, August 31, 1909. For a synopsis see Hall, Univ. Kansas Publ., Mus. Nat. Hist., 5:138–170, December 15, 1951.

1867. *Sylvilagus* Gray, Ann. Mag. Nat. Hist., ser. 3, 20:221, September. Type, *Lepus sylvaticus* Bachman [= *Lepus nuttalli mallurus* Thomas].

Total length, 291–538; tail, 18–73; hind foot, 71–111; ear from notch (dry), 41–74. Grayish to dark brownish above and lighter below; sutures of interparietal bone distinct throughout life; second to fourth cervical vertebrae broader than long with dorsal surface flattened and without carination.

The delectable flesh of members of this genus, the large numbers that occur on a small area, even in thickly settled rural areas, and the wariness that rabbits soon develop when much hunted, give them top ranking among small game mammals. Tens of thousands of cottontails in Kansas and Missouri (*Sylvilagus floridanus* and some *S. audubonii*) have been captured alive, transported to the eastern United States, and released there in the vain hope that they would multiply and increase the population of rabbits (see Langenbach and Beule, 1942: 14, 15, and 30).

The genus *Sylvilagus* is restricted to the New World; the two species *Sylvilagus brasiliensis* and *S. floridanus* are the only two which occur in South America and they occur also in North America.

Subgenus **Brachylagus** Miller—Pygmy Rabbit

1900. *Brachylagus* Miller, Proc. Biol. Soc. Washington, 13:157, June 13. Type, *Lepus idahoensis* Merriam.

For characters see subgenus *Sylvilagus*.

Sylvilagus idahoensis (Merriam)
Pygmy Rabbit

1891. *Lepus idahoensis* Merriam, N. Amer. Fauna, 5:76, July 30, type from head of Pahsimeroi Valley, near Goldburg, Custer Co., Idaho (Davis, The Recent mammals of Idaho, p. 363, April 5, 1939).
1930. *Sylvilagus idahoensis*, Grinnell, Dixon, and Linsdale, Univ. California Publ. Zool., 35:553, October 10.

Total length, 250–290; tail, 20–30; hind foot, 65–72; ear from notch (dry), 36–48; weight, average of 6 males, 409(375–435), average of 9 females, 398(246–458) grams. Upper parts pinkish to blackish or dark grayish depending on amount of wear. The pygmy rabbit lives in burrows, mostly dug by itself, preferably where tall sagebrush grows densely. This species feeds extensively on sagebrush, at least in winter. Six young seem to be the rule and they are born any time from late in May until early in August.

MARGINAL RECORDS (Hall, 1951c:139, unless otherwise noted).—In southeastern Washington: about 5 mi. W Lower Coulee (Johnson, Cheney and Scheffer, 1950:41); Ritzville; Lind; Warden. In remainder of range: Montana: Bannack. Idaho: Trail Creek near Pocatello. Utah: 3 mi. NE Clarkson; W side Utah Lake; 20 mi. W Parowan; 10 mi. SW Cedar City. Nevada: 8½ mi. NE Sharp; Fallon. Cali-

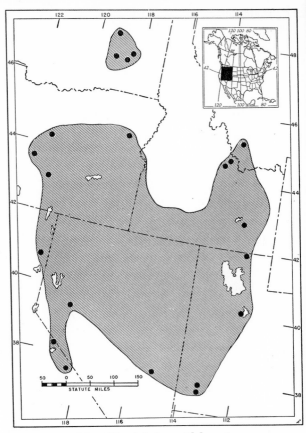

Map 181. *Sylvilagus idahoensis*.

fornia: Bodie; Crowley Lake area, 60 mi. SE Bodie (Jones, 1957:274); 3 mi. S Ravendale, 5000 ft. Oregon: Silver Lake; Fremont; Redmond; 10 mi. N Baker. Idaho: type locality; Junction.

Subgenus **Sylvilagus** Gray—Cottontails and Allies

1867. *Sylvilagus* Gray, Ann. Mag. Nat. Hist., ser. 3, 20:221, September. Type, *Lepus sylvaticus* Bachman [= *Lepus nuttalli mallurus* Thomas].
1867. *Tapeti* Gray, Ann. Mag. Nat. Hist., ser. 3, 20:224, September. Type, *Lepus brasiliensis* Linnaeus.
1897. *Microlagus* Trouessart, Catalogus mammalium . . . , p. 660. Type, *Lepus cinerascens* J. A. Allen.
1897. *Limnolagus* Mearns, Science, n.s., 5:393, March 5. Type, *Lepus aquaticus* Bachman.
1950. *Paludilagus* Hershkovitz, Proc. U.S. Nat. Mus., 100:333, May 26. Type, *Lepus palustris* Bachman.

Characters of subgeneric worth, in contrast to those of the subgenus *Brachylagus*, are: 1st premolar, in upper jaw and in lower jaw, with more than 1 fold in the enamel; infolded enamel, which divides each molar tooth into 2 parts, crenate.

Differences between some of the species are of lesser magnitude than was supposed to be the case when the 5 names for genera or subgenera listed immediately above were proposed. Some species

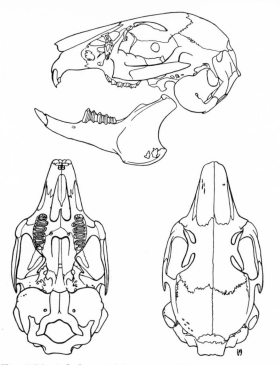

Fig. 175. *Sylvilagus idahoensis*, Millett P.O., Nevada, No. 37275 M.V.Z., ♂, X 1.

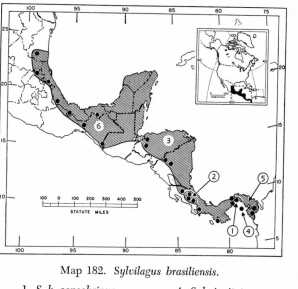

Map 182. *Sylvilagus brasiliensis*.

1. *S. b. consobrinus*
2. *S. b. dicei*
3. *S. b. gabbi*

4. *S. b. incitatus*
5. *S. b. messorius*
6. *S. b. truei*

can be placed in each of 2 subgenera with almost equal propriety. If used, 4 of the 5 subgeneric names mentioned above would contain only 1 species each. It seems that no useful purpose is served by attempting to fit the several species of the genus *Sylvilagus* into more than the 2 subgenera *Brachylagus* and *Sylvilagus*; the other names, *Tapeti* Gray, *Microlagus* Trouessart, *Limnolagus* Mearns, and *Paludilagus* Hershkovitz, are here arranged as synonyms of the subgeneric name *Sylvilagus* Gray.

Sylvilagus brasiliensis
Forest Rabbit

Total length, 380–420; tail, 20–21; hind foot, 77–80; ear from notch (dry), 39–46. The principal characters of this species are small size, dark color, short tail, and dingy buffy (not white) undersurface of tail. These rabbits rest in forests or other thick vegetal cover and do not venture far from such cover to feed.

Sylvilagus brasiliensis consobrinus Anthony

1917. *Sylvilagus gabbi consobrinus* Anthony, Bull. Amer. Mus. Nat. Hist., 37:335, May 28, type from Old Panamá, Panamá. Known from type locality only.
1950. *Sylvilagus brasiliensis consobrinus*, Hershkovitz, Proc. U.S. Nat. Mus., 100:353, May 26.

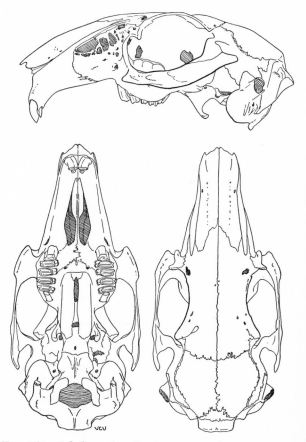

Fig. 176. *Sylvilagus brasiliensis truei*, 30 km. SSE Jesús Carranza, Veracruz, No. 32128 K.U., ♂, X 1.

Sylvilagus brasiliensis dicei Harris

1932. *Sylvilagus dicei* Harris, Occas. Papers Mus. Zool.
Univ. Michigan, 248:1, August 4, type from 6000 ft., El
Copey de Dota, in the Cordillera de Talamanca, Costa
Rica.
1950. *Sylvilagus brasiliensis dicei*, Hershkovitz, Proc. U.S.
Nat. Mus., 100:352, May 26.

MARGINAL RECORDS (Hall, 1951c:142).—Costa Rica:
Rancho de Río Jimenez; Juan Viñas; type locality; *San
José.*

Sylvilagus brasiliensis gabbi (J. A. Allen)

1877. *Lepus brasiliensis* var. *gabbi* J. A. Allen, *in* Coues and
Allen, Monogr. N. Amer. Rodentia, p. 349, August. Type
locality, Costa Rica and Chiriquí; restricted by Nelson (N.
Amer. Fauna, 29:259, August 31, 1909), by designation
of type specimen, to Talamanca [= Sipurio, Río Sixaola,
near Caribbean Coast], Costa Rica.
1950. *Sylvilagus brasiliensis gabbi*, Hershkovitz, Proc. U.S.
Nat. Mus., 100:351, May 26.
1908. *Lepus gabbi tumacus* J. A. Allen, Bull. Amer. Mus.
Nat. Hist., 24:649, October 13, type from Tuma, Nicaragua.

MARGINAL RECORDS (Hall, 1951c:142).—Honduras:
San Pedro Sula; to Gulf Coast and southward along coast
to Panamá Canal, Panamá: Gatún; Corozal; Gobernador
Island; Divala; *Chiriquí.* Northward east of the range of
S. b. dicei, thence westward in Costa Rica: Vijagual, San
Carlos. Nicaragua: Matagalpa; Ocotal. Honduras: San José,
Santa Barbara.

Sylvilagus brasiliensis incitatus (Bangs)

1901. *Lepus (Tapeti) incitatus* Bangs, Amer. Nat., 35:633,
August, type from San Miguel Island, Bay of Panamá.
Known from type locality only.
1950. *Sylvilagus brasiliensis incitatus*, Hershkovitz, Proc.
U.S. Nat. Mus., 100:352, May 26.

Sylvilagus brasiliensis messorius Goldman

1912. *Sylvilagus gabbi messorius* Goldman, Smiths. Miscl.
Coll., 60(2):13, September 20, type from Cana, 1800 ft.,
mts. of eastern Panamá.
1950. *Sylvilagus brasiliensis messorius*, Hershkovitz, Proc.
U.S. Nat. Mus., 100:352, May 26.

MARGINAL RECORDS (Hall, 1951c:143).—Panamá:
Boca de Cupe; *Tacarcuna; Tapalisa;* type locality.

Sylvilagus brasiliensis truei (J. A. Allen)

1890. *Lepus truei* J. A. Allen, Bull. Amer. Mus. Nat. Hist.,
3:192, December 10, type from Mirador, Veracruz.
1950. *Sylvilagus brasiliensis truei*, Hershkovitz, Proc. U.S.
Nat. Mus., 100:351, May 26.

MARGINAL RECORDS (Hall, 1951c:143, unless otherwise noted).—Tamaulipas: Rancho del Cielo (Goodwin,
1954:7). San Luis Potosí: Rancho Apetsco, Xilitla, thence
down coast to Tabasco: Teapa. Chiapas: Huehuetan.
Oaxaca: Santo Domingo. Veracruz: Buena Vista, Motzorongo. Puebla: Metlaltoyuca.

Sylvilagus bachmani
Brush Rabbit

Size small. Total length, 300–375; tail, 20–43;
hind foot, 64–81; ear from notch (dry), 50–64;
weight (topotypes of *S. b. macrorhinus*) average of
16 males, 679(561–832), average of 22 females, 707
(517–843) grams. Body uniformly dark brown or
brownish gray, but tail whitish beneath; hair on
midventral part of body gray at base; only a slight
crenulation on the ridge of enamel that separates
an individual molariform tooth into anterior and
posterior sections. From *Sylvilagus audubonii,* the
only other species of *Sylvilagus* in the same geographic area, *S. bachmani* differs in smaller size,
less white on underparts (the hairs on the midventral part of the body being gray instead of white
at base), shorter ears and legs, and a less crenulated
ridge of enamel separating the anterior and posterior parts of a molariform tooth.

The brush rabbit is a Pacific Coastal species; as
may be seen from Map 183, this species occurs from
the Columbia River on the north to the tip of Baja
California on the south. Nowhere, so far as we can
learn, does it occur as far east as the crest of the
Cascade–Sierra Nevada Mountain Chain. Throughout its range the brush rabbit lives in chaparral that
is dense enough to afford protection from raptorial
birds and the larger carnivorous mammals.

Brush rabbits use simple "forms" in the brush for
resting. Only one observer (Orr, 1940:173) has reported an individual entering a hole. In patches of
chaparral in which the rabbits live they make runways that are especially well defined at the edges
of the brush. The outer entrance to a runway is
tunnellike and 1 to 2 feet from the outer entrance
there is a special form that serves as a lookout post.
A brush rabbit that is about to venture into the
open ordinarily pauses in such a form for several
minutes, presumably to satisfy itself that no enemy
is in the open area whither the rabbit is bound.

The breeding season is from January to June, at
least in California. There are 2 to 5 young, averaging 3.5 per litter. They are born in a nest.

Sylvilagus bachmani bachmani (Waterhouse)

1839. *Lepus bachmani* Waterhouse, Proc. Zool. Soc. London, p. 103 (for 1838), February 7, type from California,
probably between Monterey and Santa Barbara.
1904. *Sylvilagus (Microlagus) bachmani,* Lyon, Smiths.
Miscl. Coll., 45:336, June 15.
1855. *Lepus trowbridgii* Baird, Proc. Acad. Nat. Sci. Philadelphia, 7:333, April, type from Monterey Co., California.

MARGINAL RECORDS (Hall, 1951c:145).—California:
2 mi. S mouth Salinas River; near Morro.

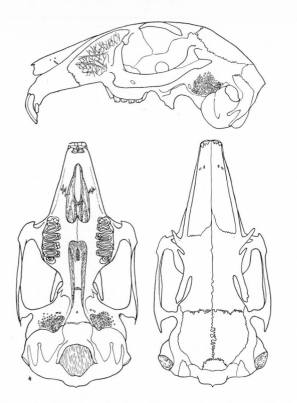

Fig. 177. *Sylvilagus bachmani macrorhinus*, Alpine Creek Ranch, 1700 ft., San Mateo Co., California, No. 53382 M.V.Z., ♀, X 1.

Sylvilagus bachmani cerrosensis (J. A. Allen)

1898. *Lepus cerrosensis* J. A. Allen, Bull. Amer. Mus. Nat. Hist., 10:145, April 12, type from Cerros [= Cedros] Island, Baja California. Known from Cerros Island only.
1909. *Sylvilagus bachmani cerrosensis*, Nelson, N. Amer. Fauna, 29:255, August 31.

Sylvilagus bachmani cinerascens (J. A. Allen)

1890. *Lepus cinerascens* J. A. Allen, Bull. Amer. Mus. Nat. Hist., 3:159, October 8, type from San Fernando, Los Angeles Co., California.
1907. *Sylvilagus bachmani cinerascens*, Nelson, Proc. Biol. Soc. Washington, 20:84, July 22.

MARGINAL RECORDS (Hall, 1951c:145).—California: 5700 ft., San Emigdio Canyon; Reche Canyon; 3500 ft., Dos Palmas Springs, Santa Rosa Mts. Baja California: La Huerta, thence northward up coast to point of beginning.

Sylvilagus bachmani exiguus Nelson

1907. *Sylvilagus bachmani exiguus* Nelson, Proc. Biol. Soc. Washington, 20:84, July 22, type from Yubay, central Baja California.

MARGINAL RECORDS (Hall, 1951c:145).—Baja California: Agua Dulce; Santana.

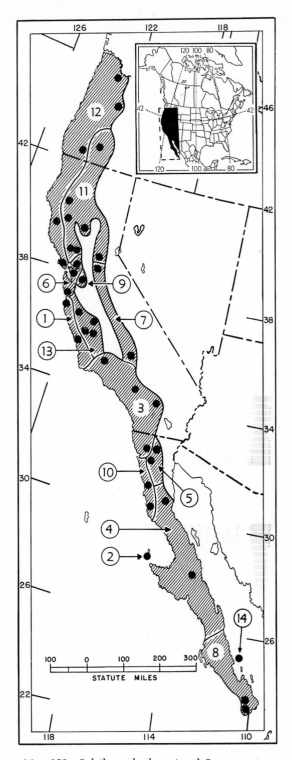

Map 183. *Sylvilagus bachmani* and *S. mansuetus*.

Guide to kinds
1. *S. b. bachmani*
2. *S. b. cerrosensis*
3. *S. b. cinerascens*
4. *S. b. exiguus*
5. *S. b. howelli*
6. *S. b. macrorhinus*
7. *S. b. mariposae*
8. *S. b. peninsularis*
9. *S. b. riparius*
10. *S. b. rosaphagus*
11. *S. b. tehamae*
12. *S. b. ubericolor*
13. *S. b. virgulti*
14. *S. mansuetus*

Sylvilagus bachmani howelli Huey

1927. *Sylvilagus bachmani howelli* Huey, Trans. San Diego Soc. Nat. Hist., 5:67, July 6, type from 10 mi. SE Alamo, Baja California, lat. 31° 35′ N, long. 116° 03′ W.

MARGINAL RECORDS.—Baja California (Hall, 1951c: 145, unless otherwise noted): Laguna Hanson, Sierra Juarez; Valle de la Trinidad (Huey, 1940:145); *Ojos Negros* (*ibid.*).

Sylvilagus bachmani macrorhinus Orr

1935. *Sylvilagus bachmani macrorhinus* Orr, Proc. Biol. Soc. Washington, 48:28, February 6, type from Alpine Creek Ranch, 3½ mi. S and 2⅔ mi. E Portola, 1700 ft., San Mateo Co., California.

MARGINAL RECORDS (Hall, 1951c:145).—California: 10 mi. SW Suisun; W side Mt. Diablo; Summit Station, Santa Cruz Mts., thence north along coast to Golden Gate.

Sylvilagus bachmani mariposae Grinnell and Storer

1916. *Sylvilagus bachmani mariposae* Grinnell and Storer, Univ. California Publ. Zool., 17:7, August 23, type from McCauley Trail, 4000 ft., near El Portal, Mariposa Co., California.

MARGINAL RECORDS (Hall, 1951c:145–146).—California: Carbondale; French Gulch, 6700 ft., Piute Mtn.

Sylvilagus bachmani peninsularis (J. A. Allen)

1898. *Lepus peninsularis* J. A. Allen, Bull. Amer. Mus. Nat. Hist., 10:144, April 12, type from Santa Anita, Baja California.
1909. *Sylvilagus bachmani peninsularis*, Nelson, N. Amer. Fauna, 29:255, August 31.

MARGINAL RECORDS (Hall, 1951c:146).—Baja California: type locality; Cape San Lucas.

Sylvilagus bachmani riparius Orr

1935. *Sylvilagus bachmani riparius* Orr, Proc. Biol. Soc. Washington, 48:29, February 6, type from west side San Joaquin River, 2 mi. NE Vernalis, in Stanislaus Co., California. Known from type locality only.

Sylvilagus bachmani rosaphagus Huey

1940. *Sylvilagus bachmani rosaphagus* Huey, Trans. San Diego Soc. Nat. Hist., 9:221, July 31, type from 2 mi. W Santo Domingo Mission, Baja California, México, lat. 30° 45′ N, long. 115° 58′ W, near the huge red cliff that marks the entrance of the Santo Domingo River Cañon from the coastal plain.

MARGINAL RECORDS (Hall, 1951c:146).—Baja California: San Quintín; El Rosario.

Sylvilagus bachmani tehamae Orr

1935. *Sylvilagus bachmani tehamae* Orr, Proc. Biol. Soc. Washington, 48:27, February 6, type from Dale's, on Paine Creek, 600 ft., Tehama Co., California.

MARGINAL RECORDS (Hall, 1951c:146).—Oregon: Prospect. California: Auburn; 7 mi. W and 14 mi. S Chico; Rumsey; Castle Springs; 3 mi. S Covelo; Mad River Bridge, S Fork Mtn.

Sylvilagus bachmani ubericolor (Miller)

1899. *Lepus bachmani ubericolor* Miller, Proc. Acad. Nat. Sci. Philadelphia, 51:383, September 29, type from Beaverton, Washington Co., Oregon.
1904. *Sylvilagus* (*Microlagus*) *bachmani ubericolor*, Lyon, Smiths. Miscl. Coll., 45:337, June 15.

MARGINAL RECORDS (Hall, 1951c:146).—Oregon: Portland; Mackenzie Bridge; above Grants Pass. California: Laytonville; Maillard [= 4 mi. E Lagunitas]; from *San Francisco Bay* up coast to *mouth* of *Columbia River* in *Oregon* and up *south bank* of that River to point of beginning.

Sylvilagus bachmani virgulti Dice

1926. *Sylvilagus bachmani virgulti* Dice, Occas. Papers Mus. Zool. Univ. Michigan, 166:24, February 11, type from Soledad, Monterey Co., California.

MARGINAL RECORDS (Hall, 1951c:146).—California: The Pinnacles; Waltham Creek, 4½ mi. SE Priest Valley; 2 mi. S San Miguel; Bryson.

Sylvilagus mansuetus Nelson
Brush Rabbit

1907. *Sylvilagus mansuetus* Nelson, Proc. Biol. Soc. Washington, 20:83, July 22, type from San José Island, Gulf of California, Baja California. Known from San José Island only.

This insular species is closely related to *Sylvilagus bachmani* and is distinguished by paleness, proportionately longer and narrower skull, fusion to skull of anterior arm of supraorbital process, and larger jugal.

Sylvilagus palustris
Marsh Rabbit

Total length, 425–440; tail, 33–39; hind foot, 88–91; ear from notch (dry), 45–52. Upper parts blackish brown or reddish brown; underside of tail brownish or dingy gray (not white); ears, tail, and hind feet short; posterior and anterior extensions of supraorbital processes joined to skull along most (or all) of their extent. The lack of white on the underside of the tail is a ready means of distinguishing this species from the other species of the genus that occur within its geographic range. The species occurs in the lowlands, possibly not above 500 feet altitude, of the Lower Austral and Tropical life-zones. In Florida, Blair (1936) found that the marsh rabbit ate 29 per cent of its bodily weight in green food each day and that the number of embryos in 3 females was 4, 4, and 3.

Sylvilagus palustris paludicola (Miller and Bangs)

1894. *Lepus paludicola* Miller and Bangs, Proc. Biol. Soc. Washington, 9:105, June 9, type from Fort Island, near Crystal River, Citrus Co., Florida.
1909. *Sylvilagus palustris paludicola*, Nelson, N. Amer. Fauna, 29:269, August 31.

MARGINAL RECORDS (Hall, 1951c:147).—Florida: Hibernia [= Green Cove Springs]; San Mateo; along Atlantic Coast at least to Micco; Kissimmee River; Cape Sable; northward along Gulf Coast and on coastal islands at least to Suwanee River.

Sylvilagus palustris palustris (Bachman)

1837. *Lepus palustris* Bachman, Jour. Acad. Nat. Sci. Philadelphia, 7:194. Type locality, eastern South Carolina.
1909. *Sylvilagus palustris*, Nelson, N. Amer. Fauna, 29:266, August 31.

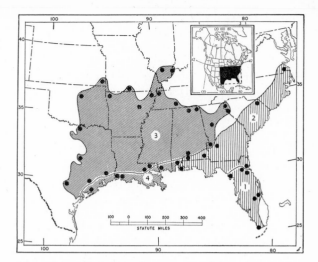

Map 184. *Sylvilagus palustris* and *Sylvilagus aquaticus*.

1. S. *palustris paludicola*   3. S. *aquaticus aquaticus*
2. S. *palustris palustris*   4. S. *aquaticus littoralis*

MARGINAL RECORDS (Hall, 1951c:147).—Virginia: Nansemond County, southward along Atlantic Coast to northern Florida: Anastasia Island. West to Gulf Coast and along coast to Alabama: Bon Secour; Flomaton; Dothan. Georgia: Americus. South Carolina: Society Hill.

Sylvilagus floridanus
Eastern Cottontail

Total length, 375–463; tail, 39–65; hind foot, 87–104; ear from notch (dry), 49–68; upper parts brownish or grayish; underside of tail white; skull with transversely thick posterior extension of supraorbital process of frontal. The geographic range is larger than that of any other North American species of the genus *Sylvilagus*; from Canada the species occurs south at least to Costa Rica and it may occur in Panamá for the species is recorded also from South America.

In the western part of the Great Plains this species is confined to the riparian growth along streams and *Sylvilagus audubonii* occupies the remainder of the terrain. In New Mexico and southwestern Texas S. *floridanus* is confined to the boreal life-zones where timber provides denser cover than is found in the lower life-zones. The zonal range is from the Canadian Life-zone into the Tropical Life-zone. It is not surprising, therefore, that there is much geographic variation in the shape and size of the skull. There is so much geographic variation in the form of the skull that it is impossible, at this writing at least, to frame a description that will enable the reader to distinguish the skull from those of all other species of the genus. In any given area, however, it is possible, easily and certainly, to dis-

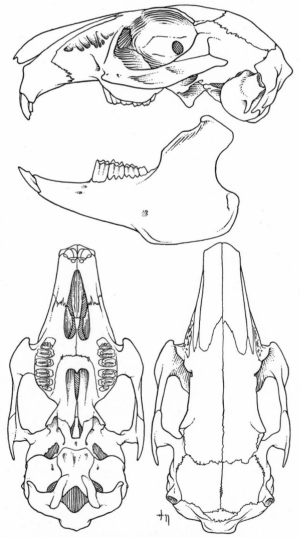

Fig. 178. *Sylvilagus palustris palustris*, Riceboro, Georgia, No. 45502 U.S.N.M., ♀, X 1.

tinguish the skulls of S. *floridanus* from those of the other species that occur in that area.

This species has been introduced and has become established in Washington (see Dalquest, 1948: 389). Also we have identified wild-taken specimens from Huntingdon, British Columbia (No. 2317 ♀ ad., taken on August 12, 1952) and Langley Prairie, British Columbia (No. 2300 ♂ ad., taken on March 20, 1952), both in the collection of Kenneth Racey. An adult was taken on February 1, 1951, at Mt. Scott, Oregon (51652 KU).

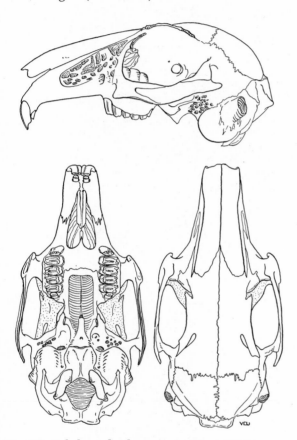

Fig. 179. *Sylvilagus floridanus mearnsi*, 4 mi. NE Lawrence, Douglas Co., Kansas, No. 3774 K.U., ♂, X 1.

Sylvilagus floridanus alacer (Bangs)

1896. *Lepus sylvaticus alacer* Bangs, Proc. Biol. Soc. Washington, 10:136, December 28, type from Stilwell, Boston Mountains, Adair Co., Oklahoma.
1904. *Sylvilagus (Sylvilagus) floridanus alacer*, Lyon, Smiths. Miscl. Coll., 45:336, June 15.

MARGINAL RECORDS (Hall, 1951c:154).—Missouri: Columbia; St. Louis. Illinois: Ozark. Tennessee: Samburg; Raleigh. Mississippi: Michigan City; Bay St. Louis. Texas: Port Lavaca; Brazos; Henrietta. Oklahoma: Norman. Kansas: *8 mi. NE Harper*; Rago; Halstead; *4 mi. S and 14 mi. W Hamilton*; 3 mi. N Chanute.

Sylvilagus floridanus ammophilus A. H. Howell

1939. *Sylvilagus floridanus ammophilus* A. H. Howell, Jour. Mamm., 20:365, August 14, type from "Oak Lodge," E of Micco, Florida. Known from type locality only.

Sylvilagus floridanus aztecus (J. A. Allen)

1890. *Lepus sylvaticus aztecus* J. A. Allen, Bull. Amer. Mus. Nat. Hist., 3:188, December 10, type from Tehuantepec [City], Oaxaca.
1904. *Sylvilagus (Sylvilagus) floridanus aztecus*, Lyon, Smiths. Miscl. Coll., 45:336, June 15.

MARGINAL RECORDS (Hall, 1951c:156).—Oaxaca: Santa Maria Petapa; Santa Efigenia. Chiapas: Tonala, 50 m. Oaxaca: Salina Cruz; *type locality*.

Sylvilagus floridanus chapmani (J. A. Allen)

1899. *Lepus floridanus chapmani* J. A. Allen, Bull. Amer. Mus. Nat. Hist., 12:12, March 4, type from Corpus Christi, Nueces Co., Texas.
1904. *Sylvilagus (Sylvilagus) floridanus chapmani*, Lyon, Smiths. Miscl. Coll., 45:336, June 15.
1899. *Lepus floridanus caniclunis* Miller, Proc. Acad. Nat. Sci. Philadelphia, 51:388, October 5, type from Fort Clark, Kinney Co., Texas.
1902. *Lepus simplicicanus* Miller, Proc. Biol. Soc. Washington, 15:81, April 25, type from Brownsville, Texas.

MARGINAL RECORDS (Hall, 1951c:156, unless otherwise noted).—Texas: Clyde; Victoria County; *Rockport*. Tamaulipas: Soto la Marina; Chamal (Goodwin, 1954:7); Juamave. Coahuila (Baker, 1956:200): Monclova; *Nadadores*; Sabinas; *1 mi. W Hda. La Mariposa; 12 mi. S Hda. Las Margaritas; Rancho Las Margaritas; 1 mi. S, 9 mi. W Villa Acuña*. Texas: Comstock; Stanton.

Sylvilagus floridanus chiapensis (Nelson)

1904. *Lepus floridanus chiapensis* Nelson, Proc. Biol. Soc. Washington: 17:106, May 18, type from San Cristóbal, Chiapas.
1909. *Sylvilagus floridanus chiapensis*, Lyon and Osgood, Bull. U.S. Nat. Mus., 62:32, January 28.

MARGINAL RECORDS (Hall, 1951c:156, unless otherwise noted).—Chiapas: type locality; Comitán. Guatemala: Hda. Chabcol near Zacopa (Handley, 1950:155); Panajachel. Chiapas: Tuxtla.

Sylvilagus floridanus cognatus Nelson

1907. *Sylvilagus cognatus* Nelson, Proc. Biol. Soc. Washington, 20:82, July 22, type from Tajique near summit of Manzano Mountains, Torrance Co., New Mexico.
1951. *Sylvilagus floridanus cognatus*, Hall and Kelson, Univ. Kansas Publ., Mus. Nat. Hist., 5:55, October 1.

MARGINAL RECORDS (Hall, 1951c:156).—New Mexico: Santa Rosa, 35 mi. N on Conchas River; Capitan Mts.; Datil Mts.; type locality.

Sylvilagus floridanus connectens (Nelson)

1904. *Lepus floridanus connectens* Nelson, Proc. Biol. Soc. Washington, 17:105, May 18, type from Chichicaxtle, central Veracruz.

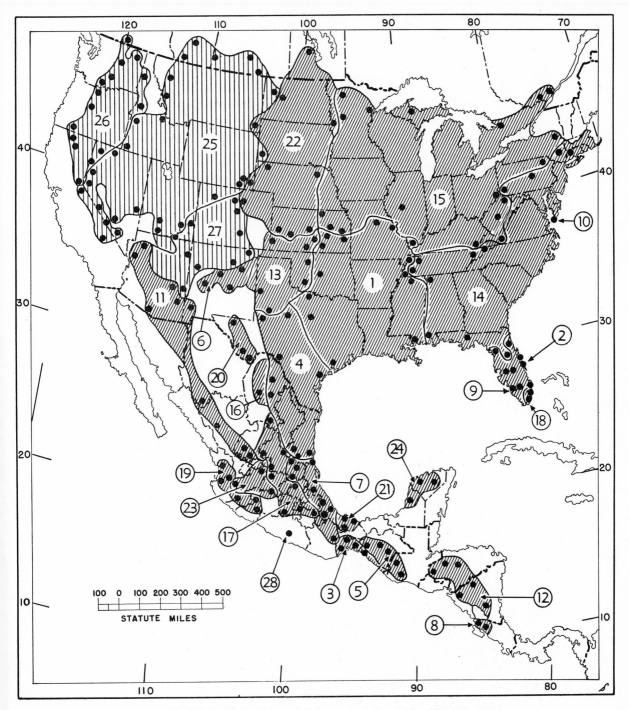

Map 185. *Sylvilagus floridanus, Sylvilagus nuttallii,* and *Sylvilagus insonus.*

1. S. *floridanus alacer*
2. S. *floridanus ammophilus*
3. S. *floridanus aztecus*
4. S. *floridanus chapmani*
5. S. *floridanus chiapensis*
6. S. *floridanus cognatus*
7. S. *floridanus connectens*

8. S. *floridanus costaricensis*
9. S. *floridanus floridanus*
10. S. *floridanus hitchensi*
11. S. *floridanus holzneri*
12. S. *floridanus hondurensis*
13. S. *floridanus llanensis*
14. S. *floridanus mallurus*

15. S. *floridanus mearnsii*
16. S. *floridanus nelsoni*
17. S. *floridanus orizabae*
18. S. *floridanus paulsoni*
19. S. *floridanus restrictus*
20. S. *floridanus robustus*
21. S. *floridanus russatus*

22. S. *floridanus similis*
23. S. *floridanus subcinctus*
24. S. *floridanus yucatanicus*
25. S. *nuttallii grangeri*
26. S. *nuttallii nuttallii*
27. S. *nuttallii pinetis*
28. S. *insonus*

1909. *Sylvilagus floridanus connectens,* Lyon and Osgood, Bull. U.S. Nat. Mus., 62:32, January 28.

MARGINAL RECORDS (Hall, 1951c:156, unless otherwise noted).—San Luis Potosí: 6½ mi. E Sabanito, at El Salto Junction (Dalquest, 1953b:78). Tamaulipas: Altamira. Veracruz: type locality. Oaxaca: Mt. Zempoaltepec. Veracruz: Orizaba (city of); Jico. Puebla: Metlaltoyuca. Querétaro: Pinal de Amoles. San Luis Potosí: Valles.

Sylvilagus floridanus costaricensis Harris

1933. *Sylvilagus floridanus costaricensis* Harris, Occas. Papers Mus. Zool., Univ. Michigan, 266:3, June 28, type from Hacienda Santa María, 22 mi. NE Liberia, Province of Guanacaste, 3200 ft., Costa Rica.

MARGINAL RECORDS (Hall, 1951c:156).—Costa Rica: El Pelón; *type locality;* Tenorio.

Sylvilagus floridanus floridanus (J. A. Allen)

1890. *Lepus sylvaticus floridanus* J. A. Allen, Bull. Amer. Mus. Nat. Hist., 3:160, October 8, type from Sebastian River, Brevard Co., Florida.
1904. *Sylvilagus floridanus,* Lyon, Smiths. Miscl. Coll., 45:322, June 15.

MARGINAL RECORDS (Schwartz, 1956:150, unless otherwise noted).—Florida: San Mateo (Hall, 1951c:157); *Enterprise (ibid.);* [S end of] Merritt Island; Lantana Road and Military Trail; Immokalee; Naples; Blitches Ferry; Miakka Lake (Hall, 1951c:157); Camp Hammock; *Welaka.*

Sylvilagus floridanus hitchensi Mearns

1911. *Sylvilagus floridanus hitchensi* Mearns, Proc. U.S. Nat. Mus., 39:227, January 9, type from Smiths Island, Northampton Co., Virginia.

MARGINAL RECORDS (Hall, 1951c:157).—Virginia: type locality; *Fishermans Island.*

Sylvilagus floridanus holzneri (Mearns)

1896. *Lepus sylvaticus holzneri* Mearns, Proc. U.S. Nat. Mus., 18:554, June 24, type from Douglas spruce zone, near summit of Huachuca Mountains, Cochise Co., Arizona.
1904. *Sylvilagus (Sylvilagus) floridanus holzneri,* Lyon, Smiths. Miscl. Coll., 45:336, June 15.
1896. [*Lepus sylvaticus*] subspecies *rigidus* Mearns, Proc. U.S. Nat. Mus., 18:555, June 24, type from Carrizalillo Mts., near Mon. 31, Mexican boundary, New Mexico.
1903. *Lepus (Sylvilagus) durangae* J. A. Allen, Bull. Amer. Mus. Nat. Hist., 19:609, November 12, type from Rancho Bailón, northwestern Durango.

MARGINAL RECORDS (Hall, 1951c:157, unless otherwise noted).—Arizona: Pine Springs, 15 mi. S of Canyon of Colorado; Reynolds Creek R. S., Sierra Ancha Mts.; W base Mt. Turnbull, 4500 ft. New Mexico: Silver City; *Animas Mts.* Zacatecas: Valparaiso; Plateado. Durango: Laguna del Progreso (Goodwin, 1954:7). Chihuahua: Guadalupe y Calvo. Arizona: Thomas Cañon, 2 mi. E Baboquivari Mts.; Hualpi Mts.—Anderson and Ogilvie (1957:35) list, to species, a fragment from 3½ *mi. ESE Los Lamentos, Chihuahua.*

Sylvilagus floridanus hondurensis Goldman

1932. *Sylvilagus floridanus hondurensis* Goldman, Proc. Biol. Soc. Washington, 45:122, July 30, type from Monte Redondo, 5100 ft., Honduras.

MARGINAL RECORDS (Hall, 1951c:157).—Honduras: Santa Barbara; Cedros. Nicaragua: Jinotega; Chontales ["District" of]; León. Honduras: Ocotepeque.

Sylvilagus floridanus llanensis Blair

1938. *Sylvilagus floridanus llanensis* Blair, Occas. Papers Mus. Zool., Univ. Michigan, 380:1, June 21, type from Old "F" Ranch headquarters, Quitaque, Texas.

MARGINAL RECORDS (Hall, 1951c:157).—Kansas: 15 mi. N and 3 mi. E Stafford; 1 mi. NE Aetna. Oklahoma: 3 mi. SE Southard; *Fort Cobb*; Mt. Scott. Texas: 6 mi. E Coahoma; 6 mi. SW Muleshoe. Kansas: Coolidge.

Sylvilagus floridanus mallurus (Thomas)

1898. *L*[*epus*]. *n*[*uttalli*]. *mallurus* Thomas, Ann. Mag. Nat. Hist., ser. 7, 2:320, October, type from Raleigh, Wake Co., North Carolina.
1904. *Sylvilagus floridanus mallurus,* Lyon, Smiths. Miscl. Coll., 45:323, June 15.
1837. *Lepus sylvaticus* Bachman, Jour. Acad. Nat. Sci. Philadelphia, 7:403, no type or type locality. Name given to "common gray rabbit" of eastern U.S., probably of South Carolina. Not *Lepus borealis sylvaticus* Nilsson, 1832.

MARGINAL RECORDS (Hall, 1951c:158, unless otherwise noted).—Connecticut: Bear Mountain, south along coast to Florida: Lake Julian; *Leesburg* (Schwartz, 1956:150); *Gulf Hammock (ibid.);* Rock Bluff. Alabama: Bayou Labatre; Leighton. Tennessee: Arlington; Hornbeak; Highcliff; Watauga Valley. West Virginia: *Ernshaw.* Pennsylvania: Waynesburg; Potts Grove. New York: Palenville.

Sylvilagus floridanus mearnsii (J. A. Allen)

1894. *Lepus sylvaticus mearnsii* J. A. Allen, Bull. Amer. Mus. Nat. Hist., 6:171, May 31, type from Fort Snelling, Hennepin Co., Minnesota.
1904. *Sylvilagus (Sylvilagus) floridanus mearnsi,* Lyon, Smiths. Miscl. Coll., 45:336, June 15.

MARGINAL RECORDS (Hall, 1951c:158, unless otherwise noted).—Minnesota: Fertile; Duluth. Michigan: Marquette County. Ontario: Lake Simcoe. Quebec: Montreal; Quebec side Ottawa River in Laurentian Hills. New York: "eastern New York." Pennsylvania: Lopez. Ohio: Oglebay (Barbour, 1951:371). West Virginia: 7 mi. E Phillipi; Gilboa. Virginia: Smith County (Handley and Patton, 1947:187). Kentucky: Big Black Mtn. (Barbour, 1951:109). Illinois: Sangamon. Kansas: Neosho Falls; 1 mi. N and ½ mi. E Lincolnville; *6 mi. SW Clay Center*; Strawberry. Minnesota: Otter Tail County.

Sylvilagus floridanus nelsoni Baker

1955. *Sylvilagus floridanus nelsoni* Baker, Univ. Kansas Publ., Mus. Nat. Hist., 7:611, April 8, type from 22 mi. S, 5 mi. W Ocampo, 5925 ft., Coahuila.

MARGINAL RECORDS (Baker, 1955:612).—Coahuila: *20 mi. S, 4 mi. W Ocampo, 5300 ft.; 21 mi. S, 4 mi. W Ocampo, 5700 ft.;* type locality.

Sylvilagus floridanus orizabae (Merriam)

1893. *Lepus orizabae* Merriam, Proc. Biol. Soc. Washington, 8:143, December 29, type from Mt. Orizaba, 9500 ft., Puebla.
1909. *Sylvilagus floridanus orizabae*, Nelson, N. Amer. Fauna, 29:183, August 31.
1903. *Lepus floridanus persultator* Elliott, Field Columb. Mus., Publ. 71, Zool. Ser., 3:147, March 20, type from Puebla, Puebla.

MARGINAL RECORDS (Hall, 1951c:158, unless otherwise noted).—Coahuila: Sierra Encarnación. San Luis Potosí (Dalquest, 1953b:79): Presa de Guadalupe; *Hacienda Capulín.* Hidalgo: Encarnación. Veracruz: *Las Vigas*; Mt. Orizaba. *Puebla: Chalchicomula.* México: Mt. Popocatépetl; Volcano of Toluca. Guanajuato: Santa Rosa. San Luis Potosí (Dalquest, 1953b:79): Bledos; Cerro Peñon Blanco. —Baker (1956:201) lists specimens in Coahuila from as far east as *13 mi. E San Antonio de las Alazanas*, thus modifying Map 185.

Sylvilagus floridanus paulsoni Schwartz

1956. *Sylvilagus floridanus paulsoni* Schwartz, Proc. Biol. Soc. Washington, 69:147, September 12, type from 6 mi. N Homestead, Dade Co., Florida.

MARGINAL RECORDS.—Florida (Schwartz, 1956:150): Ft. Lauderdale; type locality.

Sylvilagus floridanus restrictus Nelson

1907. *Sylvilagus floridanus restrictus* Nelson, Proc. Biol. Soc. Washington, 20:82, July 22, type from Zapotlán, Jalisco.

MARGINAL RECORDS (Hall, 1951c:159).—Nayarit: Tepic; Ojo de Agua. Jalisco: *La Cienega; Atenfuillo.* Michoacán: Mt. Tancítaro; Pátzcuaro. Jalisco: *type locality*; Las Canoas; La Laguna.

Sylvilagus floridanus robustus (V. Bailey)

1905. *Lepus pinetis robustus* V. Bailey, N. Amer. Fauna, 25:159, October 24, type from 6000 ft., Davis Mts., Jeff Davis Co., Texas.
1951. *Sylvilagus floridanus robustus*, Hall and Kelson, Univ. Kansas Publ., Mus. Nat. Hist., 5:56, October 1.

MARGINAL RECORDS (Hall, 1951c:159).—Texas: The Bowl, Guadalupe Mts.; Chisos Mts.; 35 mi. S Marfa.

Sylvilagus floridanus russatus (J. A. Allen)

1904. *Lepus (Sylvilagus) russatus* J. A. Allen, Bull. Amer. Mus. Nat. Hist., 20:31, February 29, type from Pasa Nueva, southern Veracruz.
1909. *Sylvilagus floridanus russatus*, Nelson, N. Amer. Fauna, 29:186, August 31.

MARGINAL RECORDS (Hall, 1951c:159).—Veracruz: Catemaco; Coatzacoalcos; *Minatitlán*; type locality; *Jimba.*

Sylvilagus floridanus similis Nelson

1907. *Sylvilagus floridanus similis* Nelson, Proc. Biol. Soc. Washington, 20:82, July 22, type from Valentine, Cherry Co., Nebraska.

MARGINAL RECORDS (Hall, 1951c:159).—Manitoba: Dauphin. Minnesota: Ten Mile Lake. Nebraska: Neligh. Kansas: *Long Island*; 3 mi. N and 2 mi. W Hoisington; Lane Co.; Elkader. Colorado: Arvada. Wyoming: 6400 ft., 3 mi. E Horse Creek P. O. Nebraska: 8 mi. E Chadron. Montana: *Little Missouri River, 7 mi. NE Albion*; Box Elder Creek, 25 mi. SW Sykes. North Dakota: Oakdale.

Sylvilagus floridanus subcinctus (Miller)

1899. *Lepus floridanus subcinctus* Miller, Proc. Acad. Nat. Sci. Philadelphia, 51:386, October 5, type from Hacienda El Molino, near Negrete, Michoacán.
1904. *Sylvilagus (Sylvilagus) floridanus subcinctus*, Lyon, Smiths. Misc. Coll., 45:336, June 15.

MARGINAL RECORDS (Hall, 1951c:159).—Jalisco: Lagos. Guanajuato: Acámbaro. Michoacán: *Querendaro.* Jalisco: *Ameca*; Etzatlán.

Sylvilagus floridanus yucatanicus (Miller)

1899. *Lepus floridanus yucatanicus* Miller, Proc. Acad. Nat. Sci. Philadelphia, 51:384, September 29, type from Mérida, Yucatán.
1904. *Sylvilagus (Sylvilagus) floridanus yucatanicus*, Lyon, Smiths. Misc. Coll., 45:336, June 15.

MARGINAL RECORDS (Hall, 1951c:159, unless otherwise noted).—Yucatán: *Progreso*; type locality; Chichén-Itzá (Laurie, 1953:382). Campeche: Campeche.

Sylvilagus transitionalis (Bangs)
New England Cottontail

1895. *Lepus sylvaticus transitionalis* Bangs, Proc. Boston Soc. Nat. Hist., 26:405, January 31, type from Liberty Hill, New London Co., Connecticut.
1909. *Sylvilagus transitionalis*, Nelson, N. Amer. Fauna, 29:195, August 31.

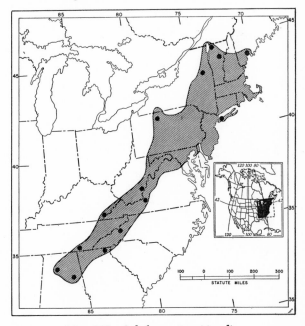

Map 186. *Sylvilagus transitionalis.*

Total length, 388; tail, 39; hind foot, 95; ear from notch (dry), 52. Upper parts almost pinkish buff, varying to almost ochraceous buff; back overlaid by a distinct black wash giving a penciled effect; anterior extension of supraorbital process obsolete or short and closely appressed to orbital rim; tympanic bullae small, smaller than in any subspecies of S. *floridanus* in the United States. S. *transitionalis* is a forest-inhabiting species—more so than is S. *floridanus*.

MARGINAL RECORDS (Hall, 1951c:160, unless otherwise noted).—Vermont: west side at Canadian boundary; Montpelier. Maine: Sagadahoc County; *Androscoggin County*. New York: Miller Place. Virginia: Roanoke County. North Carolina: Roan Mtn. Georgia: Brasstown Bald Mtn. Alabama: Erin; Ardell. Tennessee: Walden Ridge, near Soddy. Kentucky: Big Black Mtn. (Barbour, 1951:108). West Virginia: Ronceverte. Pennsylvania: Renovo. New York: Lake George.

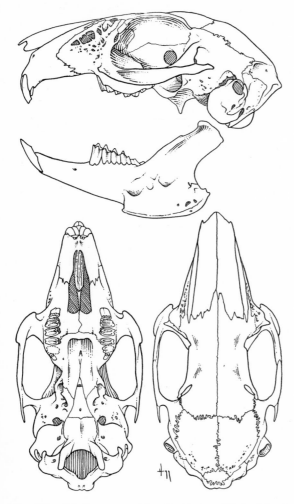

Fig. 180. *Sylvilagus transitionalis*, Exeter, Rhode Island, No. 125529 U.S.N.M., ♀, X 1.

Sylvilagus nuttallii
Nuttall's Cottontail

Total length, 350–390; tail, 44–50; hind foot, 88–100; ear from notch (dry), 55–56; weight in Nevada, male, 678, 3 females, 928(868–1032) grams. Hind feet densely covered with long hair; ear short; tympanic bulla of moderate size. In the northern part of its range S. *nuttallii* occurs principally in the areas of sagebrush but occurs also in timbered areas of the Transition Life-zone and almost exclusively in timbered areas in the southern part of its range. From S. *floridanus*, S. *nuttallii* along the eastern margin of its range differs in more slender rostrum, and larger external auditory meatus. In New Mexico and Arizona, S. *nuttallii* differs from S. *floridanus* in the posteriorly pointed and un-notched supra-occipital shield and in the posterior extension of the supraorbital process, the tip of which projects free from the braincase or merely lies against the braincase instead of being firmly welded to the side of the skull. From S. *audubonii*, S. *nuttallii* differs in shorter ears, smaller tympanic bullae and smaller hind legs. S. *nuttallii* usually occurs at higher elevations, or where the two occur at approximately the same elevation S. *nuttallii* occurs in wooded or brushy areas and S. *audubonii* lives on the plains or in relatively open country. Eight females contained an average of 6.1 (4–8) embryos. (See Map 185.)

Sylvilagus nuttallii grangeri (J. A. Allen)

1895. *Lepus sylvaticus grangeri* J. A. Allen, Bull. Amer. Mus. Nat. Hist., 7:264, August 21, type from Hill City, Black Hills, Pennington Co., South Dakota.
1909. *Sylvilagus nuttalli grangeri*, Nelson, N. Amer. Fauna, 29:204, August 31.
1904. *Lepus l[aticinctus]. perplicatus* Elliott, Field Columb. Mus., Publ. 87, Zool. Ser., 3:255, January 7, type from Hannopee [= Hannaupah] Canyon, Panamint Mts., Inyo Co., California.

MARGINAL RECORDS (Hall, 1951c:161–162).—Alberta: Steveville. Saskatchewan: Cypress Hills; Johnston Lake; Big Muddy Lake. North Dakota: Goodall. South Dakota: Custer. Wyoming: 2 mi. W Horse Creek P. O.; Sherman. Colorado: Meeker. Utah: Mt. Ellen; "Upper Kanab"; Panguitch. Nevada: ¼ mi. W Utah–Nevada boundary, 38° 17′ N, 7300 ft.; S end Belted Range, 5 mi. NW Whiterock Spring, 7200 ft.; Chiatovich Creek, 7000 ft.; 2½ mi. E and 1 mi. S Grapevine Peak, 6700 ft.; Charleston Park, Kyle Cañon, 8000 ft. California: Johnson Canyon, 6500 ft.; near Woodfords, 5500 ft. Nevada: Calvada; Hardscrabble Canyon; Paradise Valley. Idaho: S. Fork Owyhee River, 12 mi. N Nevada line; Crane Creek, 15 mi. E Midvale; Lemhi. Montana: 4 mi. W Hamilton; 2 mi. N Moise Lake. Alberta: Cardston.

Sylvilagus nuttallii nuttallii (Bachman)

1837. *Lepus nuttallii* Bachman, Jour. Acad. Nat. Sci. Philadelphia, 7:345. Type locality, probably eastern Oregon near mouth of Malheur River.

Sylvilagus audubonii
Desert Cottontail

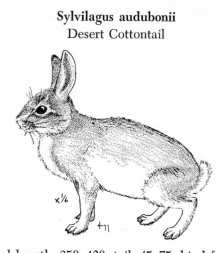

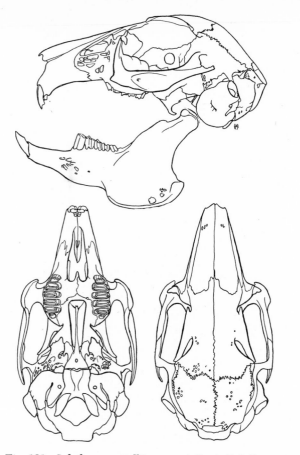

Fig. 181. *Sylvilagus nuttallii grangeri*, ½ mi. E Jefferson, Nevada, No. 58527 M.V.Z., ♀, X 1.

1904. *Sylvilagus nuttallii*, Lyon, Smiths. Miscl. Coll., 45: 323, June 15.

MARGINAL RECORDS (Hall, 1951c:162, unless otherwise noted).—British Columbia: Penticton (Cowan and Guiguet, 1956:108). Washington: Kettle Falls. Idaho: Couer d'Alene; *Lewiston*; Fiddle Creek. Nevada: 5800 ft., Quinn River Crossing; ½ mi. S *Granite Creek, Granite Mts.*; *Smoke Creek, 9 mi. E California line*; 4½ mi. S Flanigan. California: Truckee; *Beckwith*; Weed; Yreka. Oregon: near Ashland; Bend; The Dalles. Washington: Grand Dalles; Yakima Valley; Douglas.

Sylvilagus nuttallii pinetis (J. A. Allen)

1894. *Lepus sylvaticus pinetis* J. A. Allen, Bull. Amer. Mus. Nat. Hist., 6:348, December 7, type from White Mts., south of Mt. Ord, Apache Co., Arizona, according to Warren (Mammals of Colorado, p. 270, 1942).
1909. *Sylvilagus nuttalli pinetis*, Nelson, N. Amer. Fauna, 29:207, August 31.

MARGINAL RECORDS (Hall, 1951c:162).—Colorado: Arkins; Golden; Greenhorn Mts. New Mexico: Sierra Grande; Willis; Zuni Mts. Arizona: type locality; Spruce Creek, N slope Tunitcha Mts., 8000 ft. (227616 USBS). Utah: Navajo Mtn.; Block Canyon, 19 mi. SE Moab, 5400 ft.; *5 mi. NE La Sal P. O., 8000 ft*.

Total length, 350–420; tail, 45–75; hind foot, 75–100; ear from notch (dry), 55–70; weight of *S. a. vallicola*, average of 7 males, 912(835–988), 2 females 1096 and 1191 grams. Long hind legs, long ears, sparseness of hair on the ears, shortness of hair on the feet, prominent (upturned) supraorbital process of the skull and much inflated tympanic bullae are characters of this wide-spread species. Embryos in 19 Californian females averaged 3.6 (2–6) per female.

Sylvilagus audubonii arizonae (J. A. Allen)

1877. [*Lepus sylvaticus*] var. *arizonae* J. A. Allen, *in* Coues and Allen, Monogr. N. Amer. Rodentia, p. 332, August, type from Beals Spring, Yavapai Co. [= Beales Spring, Mohave Co.; see also Grinnell, Univ. California Publ. Zool., 40:203, September 26, 1933], Arizona.
1909. *Sylvilagus auduboni arizonae*, Nelson, N. Amer. Fauna, 29:222, August 31.
1896. *Lepus arizonae major* Mearns, Proc. U.S. Nat. Mus., 18:557, June 24, type from Calabasas, Santa Cruz Co., Arizona.
1904. *Lepus laticinctus* Elliot, Field Columb. Mus., Publ. 87, Zool. Ser., 3:254, January 7, type from Oro Grande, Mohave Desert, San Bernardino Co., California.
1904. *Lepus l[aticinctus]. rufipes* Elliot, Field Columb. Mus., Publ. 87, Zool. Ser., 3:254, January 7, type from Furnace Creek, Inyo Co., California.

MARGINAL RECORDS (Hall, 1951c:164, unless otherwise noted).—Utah: 2 mi. SW Fish Springs; Holden; 7 mi. SW Tropic. Arizona: Seligman; Ft. Verde; Superior (Hatfield, 1942:156); Dos Cabezos. Sonora: Tecoripa; La Libertad Ranch. Baja California: San Matias Pass. California: Vallecito; Fairmont, Antelope Valley; Little Lake, 3300 ft.; near Benton, 5300–5639 ft. Nevada: Arlemont; 4 mi. E Smith Creek Cave.

Sylvilagus audubonii audubonii (Baird)

1858. *Lepus audubonii* Baird, Mammals, *in* Repts. Expl. Surv. . . . , 8(1):608, July 14, type from San Francisco, San Francisco Co., California.
1909. *Sylvilagus auduboni*, Nelson, N. Amer. Fauna, 29: 214, August 31.

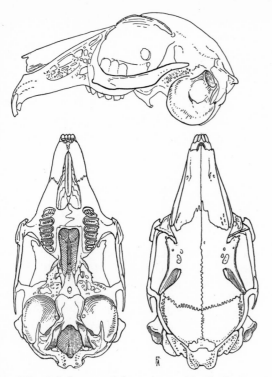

Fig. 182. *Sylvilagus audubonii minor,* Neville Spring, 3290 ft., Grapevine Mts., Big Bend, Brewster Co., Texas, No. 80519 M.V.Z., ♂, X 1.

MARGINAL RECORDS (Hall, 1951c:164).—California: 600 ft., Paines Creek; Rackerby; Pleasant Valley; Snelling; 2 mi. S mouth Salinas River, northward not reaching coast again except at San Francisco, thence around shores of San Francisco Bay to mouth of Carquinez Straits and northward along western side of Sacramento Valley to Winslow, 5 mi. W Fruto.

Sylvilagus audubonii baileyi (Merriam)

1897. *Lepus baileyi* Merriam, Proc. Biol. Soc. Washington, 11:148, June 9, type from Spring Creek, E side Big-horn Basin, Bighorn Co., Wyoming.
1908. *Sylvilagus auduboni baileyi,* Lantz, Trans. Kansas Acad. Sci., 22:336.

MARGINAL RECORDS (Hall, 1951c:164).—Montana: Great Falls of the Missouri. North Dakota: Wade on Can-nonball River. South Dakota: Corral Draw. Nebraska: Glen. Kansas: 12½ mi. S and 4 mi. W Oberlin; Wakeeney. Colorado: Monon; The Cedars; Quenda [= Querida]; Salida. Wyoming: ½ mi. W Horse Creek P. O. Colorado: White Rock [2 mi. above Meeker, 6400 ft.]; 20 mi. SW Rangely. Utah: 8 mi. S Myton; 6 mi. NW Duchesne; 10 mi. E Mountain Home. Wyoming: Ft. Bridger; Big Piney; Circle. Montana: Stillwater. Not found: Philips Creek in Montana.

Sylvilagus audubonii cedrophilus Nelson

1907. *Sylvilagus auduboni cedrophilus* Nelson, Proc. Biol. Soc. Washington, 20:83, July 22, type from Cactus Flat, 20 mi. N Cliff, Grant Co., New Mexico.

MARGINAL RECORDS (Hall, 1951c:164–165).—Arizona: San Francisco Mts. New Mexico: Gallup; Santa Rosa; Capitan; Ancho; Isleta; Burro Mts. Arizona: Springerville.

Sylvilagus audubonii confinis (J. A. Allen)

1898. *Lepus arizonae confinis* J. A. Allen, Bull. Amer. Mus. Nat. Hist., 10:146, April 12, type from Playa María, Baja California.
1909. *Sylvilagus auduboni confinis,* Nelson, N. Amer. Fauna, 29:220, August 31.

MARGINAL RECORDS (Hall, 1951c:165).—Baja California: type locality; San Bruno, thence southerly over peninsula to tip.

Sylvilagus audubonii goldmani (Nelson)

1904. *Lepus arizonae goldmani* Nelson, Proc. Biol. Soc. Washington, 17:107, May 18, type from Culiacán, Sinaloa.
1909. *Sylvilagus auduboni goldmani* Nelson, N. Amer. Fauna, 29:225, August 31.

MARGINAL RECORDS (Hall, 1951c:165).—Sonora: Ortiz; Camoa. Sinaloa: Bacubirito; type locality.

Sylvilagus audubonii minor (Mearns)

1896. *Lepus arizonae minor* Mearns, Proc. U.S. Nat. Mus., 18:557, June 24, type from El Paso, El Paso Co., Texas.
1907. S[ylvilagus]. a[uduboni]. minor, Nelson, Proc. Biol. Soc. Washington, 20:83, July 22.

MARGINAL RECORDS (Hall, 1951c:165).—New Mexico: [12 mi. N] Tularosa. Texas: Kent; Haymond; Langtry. Coahuila (Baker, 1956:198): *1 mi. S San Lázaro; 2 mi. E, 2 mi. N San Antonio de las Alazanas; La Ventura.* Durango: Inde; Rancho Bailón; Río Campo. Arizona: San Bernardino Ranch. New Mexico: Red Rock; *Lordsburg.*

Sylvilagus audubonii neomexicanus Nelson

1907. *Sylvilagus auduboni neomexicanus* Nelson, Proc. Biol. Soc. Washington, 20:83, July 22, type from Fort Sumner, De Baca Co., New Mexico.

MARGINAL RECORDS (Hall, 1951c:165).—Kansas: 1 mi. E Coolidge; Rezeau Ranch, 5 mi. N Belvidere. Texas: Wichita Falls; San Angelo; Adam [= 15 mi. E Adams]; 28 mi. S Alpine; *15 mi. S Alpine;* 7 mi. NE Marfa; Toyah-vale [= 10 mi. S of]; McKittrick Canyon. New Mexico: Roswell; Emory Peak.

Sylvilagus audubonii parvulus (J. A. Allen)

1904. *Lepus (Sylvilagus) parvulus* J. A. Allen, Bull. Amer. Mus. Nat. Hist., 20:34, February 29, type from Apam, Hidalgo.
1909. *Sylvilagus auduboni parvulus,* Nelson, N. Amer. Fauna, 29:236, August 31.

MARGINAL RECORDS (Hall, 1951c:165, unless otherwise noted).—Texas: Llano; San Diego; Kleberg County (Hightower, *et al.,* 1953:270); Rio Grande City (Blair, 1952:239). Tamaulipas: El Mulato; Miquihuana. San Luis Potosí: Río Verde. Veracruz: Perote. Puebla: Chalchico-mula. Guanajuato: Silao. Durango: Durango City. Coa-huila: Monclova. Texas: Comstock (Blair, 1952:239).

Sylvilagus audubonii sanctidiegi (Miller)

1899. *Lepus floridanus sanctidiegi* Miller, Proc. Acad. Nat. Sci. Phila., 51:389, October 5, type from Mexican Bound-ary Mon. No. 258, shore of Pacific Ocean, California.
1909. *Sylvilagus auduboni sanctidiegi,* Nelson, N. Amer. Fauna, 29:218, August 31.

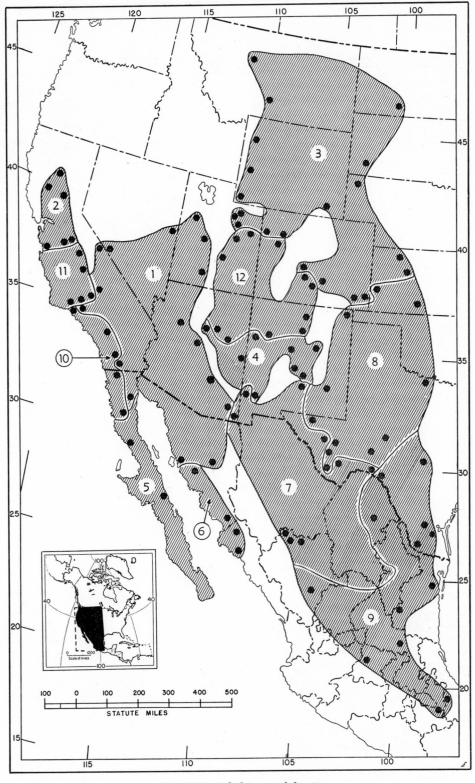

Map 187. *Sylvilagus audubonii.*

1. *S. a. arizonae*
2. *S. a. audubonii*
3. *S. a. baileyi*
4. *S. a. cedrophilus*
5. *S. a. confinis*
6. *S. a. goldmani*
7. *S. a. minor*
8. *S. a. neomexicanus*
9. *S. a. parvulus*
10. *S. a. sanctidiegi*
11. *S. a. vallicola*
12. *S. a. warreni*

MARGINAL RECORDS (Hall, 1951c:166).—California: Sespe; Reche Canyon near Colton; San Felipe Canyon. Baja California: Nachogüero Valley; Santo Tomás, thence northerly along coast.

Sylvilagus audubonii vallicola Nelson

1907. *Sylvilagus auduboni vallicola* Nelson, Proc. Biol. Soc. Washington, 20:82, July 22, type from San Emigdio Ranch, Kern Co., California.

MARGINAL RECORDS (Hall, 1951c:166).—California: Fresno Flat; Badger; 2750 ft., Onyx; Tehachapi; Mt. Pinos, northwesterly, seldom actually reaching coast, to central Monterey County, thence easterly to point of beginning.

Sylvilagus audubonii warreni Nelson

1907. *Sylvilagus auduboni warreni* Nelson, Proc. Biol. Soc. Washington, 20:83, July 22, type from Coventry, Montrose Co., Colorado.

MARGINAL RECORDS (Hall, 1951c:166).—Utah: 5250 ft., Willow Creek. Colorado: Rifle; Villa Grove; Medano Ranch. New Mexico: Hondo Canyon; Cieneguilla; Juan Tafoya. Arizona: Holbrook; Winslow. Utah: Canesville (*sic*); Wellington.

Sylvilagus aquaticus
Swamp Rabbit

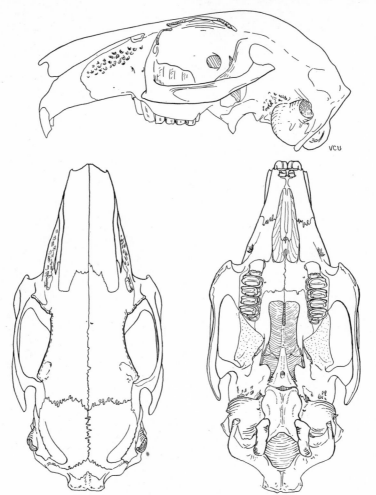

Total length, 530–540; tail, 67–71; hind foot, 105–110; length of ear from notch (dry), 63–67. Upper parts blackish brown or reddish brown; underparts

Fig. 183. *Sylvilagus aquaticus aquaticus,* Crawford Co., Kansas, No. 8544 K.U., ♂, X 1.

with some white; under side of tail white; skull robust; posterior extensions of supraorbital processes joined for their entire length with side of braincase or, in some specimens, with a small foramen between the braincase and the base of the posterior extension of the supraorbital process. This big rabbit is a stronger runner than the smaller marsh rabbit and is white instead of brownish or grayish on the under side of tail. (See Map 184, p. 259.)

Sylvilagus aquaticus aquaticus (Bachman)

1837. *Lepus aquaticus* Bachman, Jour. Acad. Nat. Sci. Philadelphia, 7:319. Type locality, western Alabama.
1909. *Sylvilagus aquaticus,* Nelson, N. Amer. Fauna, 29:270, August 31.
1895. *Lepus aquaticus attwateri* J. A. Allen, Bull. Amer. Mus. Nat. Hist., 7:327, November 8, type from Medina River, 18 mi. S San Antonio, Bexar Co., Texas.
1899. *Lepus telmalemonus* Elliot, Field Columb. Mus., Publ. 38, Zool. Ser., 1:285, May 25, type from Washita River, near Dougherty, Murray Co., Oklahoma.

MARGINAL RECORDS (Hall, 1951c:167, unless otherwise noted).—Illinois: 6 mi. N Sesser. Indiana: Point Township. Tennessee: 5 mi. W Hornbeak; Henryville. Alabama: Huntsville; Big Crow Creek near Stevenson. South Carolina: "about" 3 mi. SE Westminster; "about" 5 mi. W Iva. Georgia: Fulton Co.; Lumpkin. Alabama: Castleberry. Louisiana: Covington; Kleinpeter. Texas: Sourlake; Richmond; Medina River, 18 mi. SW San Antonio; Gurley; Cooke County (Nelson, 1909:273). Oklahoma: 7 mi. NW Stillwater. Kansas: Crawford Co. Arkansas: along White River near Springdale. Missouri: 3 mi. SW Udall. Arkansas: White River near Augusta. Missouri: St. Francis River, W of Senath.

Sylvilagus aquaticus littoralis Nelson

1909. *Sylvilagus aquaticus littoralis* Nelson, N. Amer. Fauna, 29:273, August 31, type from Houma, Terrebonne Parish, Louisiana.

MARGINAL RECORDS (Hall, 1951c:167–168).—Alabama: Blakely Island opposite Mobile. Mississippi: Bay St. Louis. Louisiana: Rayne; Hackberry. Texas: Matagorda.

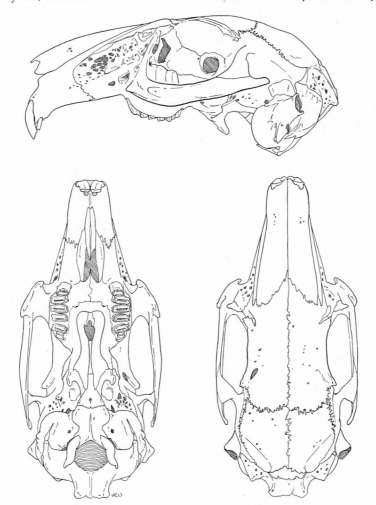

Fig. 184. *Sylvilagus cunicularius cunicularius,* 3 km. W Acultzingo, Veracruz, No. 30749 K.U., ♂, X 1.

Sylvilagus insonus (Nelson)
Omilteme Cottontail

1904. *Lepus insonus* Nelson, Proc. Biol. Soc. Washington, 17:103, May 18, type from Omilteme, Guerrero. Known from type locality only.
1909. *Sylvilagus insonus*, Lyon and Osgood, Bull. U.S. Nat. Mus., 62:34, January 28 (see Hershkovitz, Proc. U.S. Nat. Mus., 100:335, May 26, 1950, for allocation of *S. insonus* to subgenus *Sylvilagus* instead of to subgenus *Tapeti*).

Total length, 435; tail, 42.5; hind foot, 95; ear from notch (dry), 61. Color grayish brown above and dingy (not white) below; tail dingy buffy below and dull rusty brown above. The collectors

thought that the species was restricted to the forested parts of the Sierra Madre del Sur between 7000 and 10,000 feet altitude in the Mexican state of Guerrero. (See Map 185, p. 261.)

Sylvilagus cunicularius
Mexican Cottontail

Total length, 485–515; tail, 54–68; hind foot, 108–111; ear from notch (dry), 60–63. Pelage coarse; upper parts brownish gray; skull massive; posterior extensions of supraorbital processes varying from those that project free to those that have the tips, or

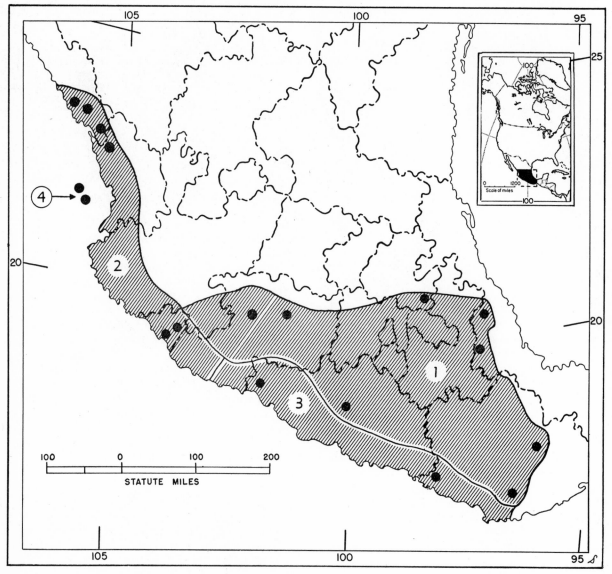

Map 188. *Sylvilagus cunicularius* and *Sylvilagus graysoni*.

1. *S. c. cunicularius*   2. *S. c. insolitus*   3. *S. c. pacificus*   4. *S. graysoni*

tips and a considerable part of the processes, attached to the braincase.

Sylvilagus cunicularius cunicularius (Waterhouse)

1848. *Lepus cunicularius* Waterhouse, A natural history of the Mammalia, 2:132, type from Zacualpan (probably in state of México).
1909. *Sylvilagus cunicularius*, Nelson, N. Amer. Fauna, 29:239, August 31.
1890. *Lepus verae-crucis* Thomas, Proc. Zool. Soc. London, p. 74, June, type from Las Vigas, Veracruz.

MARGINAL RECORDS (Hall, 1951c:169).—Hidalgo: Tulancingo, Veracruz: Las Vigas; Orizaba. Oaxaca: Mt. Zempoaltepec; Suchixtepec. Guerrero: Chilpancingo. Michoacán: Pátzcuaro; Tancítaro.

Sylvilagus cunicularius insolitus (J. A. Allen)

1890. *Lepus insolitus* J. A. Allen, Bull. Amer. Mus. Nat. Hist., 3:189, December 10, type from plains of Colima, Jalisco.
1909. *Sylvilagus cunicularius insolitus*, Nelson, N. Amer. Fauna, 29:243, August 31.

MARGINAL RECORDS (Hall, 1951c:169).—Sinaloa: Mazatlán; Rosario; Esquinapa. Nayarit: Acaponeta. Colima: Colima; Armeria, thence northward along Pacific Coast.

Sylvilagus cunicularius pacificus (Nelson)

1904. *Lepus veraecrucis pacificus* Nelson, Proc. Biol. Soc. Washington, 17:104, May 18, type from Acapulco, Guerrero.
1909. *Sylvilagus cunicularius pacificus*, Lyon and Osgood, Bull. U.S. Nat. Mus., 62:35, January 28.

MARGINAL RECORDS (Hall, 1951c:169).—Guerrero: El Limón. Oaxaca: Llano Grande, thence westward along Pacific Coast.

Sylvilagus graysoni (J. A. Allen)
Tres Marías Cottontail

1877. *Lepus graysoni* J. A. Allen, *in* Coues and Allen, Monogr. N. Amer. Rodentia, p. 347, August, type from Tres Marías Islands, Nayarit; probably María Madre Island. (See Nelson, N. Amer. Fauna, 14:16, April 29, 1899.)
1904. *Sylvilagus (Sylvilagus) graysoni*, Lyon, Smiths. Miscl. Coll., 45:336, June 15.

Total length, 480; tail, 51; hind foot, 99; ear from notch (dry), 57. This insular species is closely related to *Sylvilagus cunicularius* of the adjacent mainland but has notably shorter ears and is more reddish on the upper parts, sides, and legs; the skull is slenderer, especially in the rostral region. The posterior extensions of the supraorbital process are united to the braincase throughout most of their length as in *Sylvilagus palustris*. The species seems to have a narrow vertical range, occurring from sea level up to only 200 feet.

MARGINAL RECORDS (Hall, 1951c:169).—María Madre Island; María Magdalena Island.

Genus Lepus Linnaeus—Hares and Jack Rabbits

American species revised by Nelson, N. Amer. Fauna, 29:59–158, August 31, 1909. Concerning Shamel's (Proc. Biol. Soc. Washington, 55:25, May 12, 1942) proposed changes of names for several species, see Hall, Univ. Kansas Publ., Mus. Nat. Hist., 5:45, October 1, 1951. For synopsis see Hall, Univ. Kansas Publ., Mus. Nat. Hist., 5:170–195, December 15, 1951.

1758. *Lepus* Linnaeus, Syst. nat., ed. 10, 1:57. Type, *Lepus timidus* Linnaeus.
1895. *Macrotolagus* Mearns, Science, n. s., 1:698, June 21. Type, *Lepus alleni* Mearns. (See Mearns, Proc. U.S. Nat. Mus., 18:552, June 24, 1896.)
1904. *Poecilolagus* Lyon, Smiths. Miscl Coll., 45:395, June 15. Type, *Lepus americanus* Erxleben.
1904. *Lagos* Palmer, N. Amer. Fauna, 23:361, January 23. Type, *Lepus arcticus* Ross. *Lagos* J. Brooks, A catalogue of the anatomical and zoological museum, pt. 1, p. 54, July, 1828, appears to be a *nomen nudum*.
1911. *Boreolepus* Barrett-Hamilton, History of the British Mammalia, pt. 9, p. 160, November 17. Type, *Lepus groenlandicus* Rhoads. (For status see Sutton and Hamilton, Mem. Carnegie Mus., 12(pt. 2, sec. 1):78, August 4, 1932; also A. H. Howell, Jour. Mamm., 17:331, November 16, 1936.)

Total length, 363–664; tail, 25–112; hind foot, 112–189; ear from notch (dry), 62–144. Upper parts grayish, brownish, or black; interparietal bone fused to surrounding bones; cervical vertebrae long, 2nd and 3rd being longer than wide; transverse processes of lumbar vertebrae long, the longest one equal to the length of the centrum, to which it is attached, plus half of the length of the preceding centrum; free extremity of transverse process of lumbar vertebra considerably expanded; distance from anterior edge of acetabulum to extreme anterior point of ilium less than distance from former point to most distant point of ischium; ulna reduced in size along middle part of shaft, and, excepting the lower extremity, placed almost entirely behind radius.

All members of the genus *Lepus* are technically hares, according to the definition in the preceding account of the family Leporidae. The largest members of the order Lagomorpha are members of the genus *Lepus*. No domestic strains have been developed but effort in this direction might be profitable, inasmuch as the so-called Belgian hares of the related genus, *Oryctolagus*, have done well in captivity.

In the past it has been customary to recognize two or more subgenera of the genus *Lepus*. The species are a less diverse lot than those in some other genera, however, and it seems that no useful purpose is served by recognizing subgenera. Accordingly, the several names proposed for this purpose are arranged here as synonyms of the generic name *Lepus* Linnaeus.

The introduction of the European Hare (*Lepus europaeus*) into the eastern part of the North American Continent has been successful in the sense that the animal is multiplying. If it continues to increase, the increase almost certainly will be at the expense of some native species of leporid. This circumstance and the unfortunate consequences of the introduction of the European rabbit (*Oryctolagus cuniculus*) in New Zealand (see Wodzicki, 1950:107–141) and Australia (see Stead, 1925:355–358) give basis for effort to exterminate the alien species before it spreads more widely.

KEY TO NORTH AMERICAN SPECIES OF LEPUS

1. North of 34° N latitude.
  2. All white pelage (tips of ears sometimes black).
    3. North of line from Port Simpson, British Columbia, to Halifax, Nova Scotia.
      4. Basilar length of skull more than 67; ear from notch usually more than 73 dry (77 fresh); first upper incisors inscribing an arc of a circle the radius of which is more than 9.6 mm.
        5. Geographic range east of Mackenzie River. . . . . *Lepus arcticus*, p. 277
        5'. Geographic range west of Mackenzie River. . . . . *Lepus othus*, p. 275
      4'. Basilar length of skull less than 67; ear from notch usually less than 73 dry (77 fresh); first upper incisors inscribing an arc of a circle the radius of which is less than 9.6 mm.
                                           Lepus americanus, p. 272
    3'. South of a line from Port Simpson, British Columbia, to Halifax, Nova Scotia.
      5. Ear from notch more than 82 dry (87 fresh); least interorbital breadth more than 26.
                                      Lepus townsendii, p. 279
      5'. Ear from notch less than 82 dry (87 fresh); least interorbital breadth less than 26.
                                      Lepus americanus, p. 272
  2'. Brownish or grayish pelage.
    6. Tail blackish or brownish all around (in specimens not having completed molt on tail, white winter pelage may be present); basilar length less than 67 mm. . . . *Lepus americanus*, p. 272
    6'. Tail partly or wholly white.
      7. Tail black on upper surface.
        8. Upper sides of hind feet without a trace of white; upper parts tawny. *Lepus europaeus*, p. 288
        8'. Upper sides of hind feet with more or less white or whitish; upper parts grayish or brownish. . . . . *Lepus californicus*, p. 281
      7'. Tail all white or (in some *Lepus townsendii*) with faint buffy or dusky median line on top but this line not extending on to rump (as in *L. californicus*).
        9. Geographic range north of a line from Port Simpson, British Columbia, to Halifax, Nova Scotia.
          10. Geographic range east of Mackenzie River. . . . . *Lepus arcticus*, p. 277
          10'. Geographic range west of Mackenzie River. . . . . *Lepus othus*, p. 275
        9'. Geographic range south of a line from Port Simpson, British Columbia, to Halifax, Nova Scotia. . . . . *Lepus townsendii*, p. 279
1'. South of 34° N latitude.
  11. In state of Tamaulipas, México. . . . . *Lepus californicus*, p. 281
  11'. Range outside Tamaulipas, México.
    12. Ears with terminal black patch (on outside). *Lepus californicus* and *Lepus insularis*, pp. 281, 285
    12'. Ears without terminal black patch.
      13. Ear from notch, dry more than 130 (137 fresh). . . . . *Lepus alleni*, p. 286
      13'. Ear from notch, dry less than 130 (137 fresh).
        14. Nape more or less black.
          15. Ears yellow; range Pacific Coastal region of Isthmus of Tehuantepec in southern Oaxaca and Chiapas. . . . . *Lepus flavigularis*, p. 285
          15'. Ears dark buff, grayish, white and black; range north of Isthmus of Tehuantepec. . . . . *Lepus mexicanus*, p. 285
        14'. Nape gray or grayish buff. . . . . *Lepus gaillardi*, p. 285

Lepus americanus
Snowshoe Rabbit

Total length, 363–520; tail, 25–55; hind foot, 112–150; ear from notch (dry), 62–70. Upper parts brownish or dusky grayish; hind feet brownish or white depending on subspecies; winter pelage white except in certain populations along Pacific Coast; basilar length less than 67; first upper incisors inscribing an arc of a circle the radius of which is less than 9.6 mm. There are two to six young in a litter according to Orr (1940:59).

Lepus americanus americanus Erxleben

1777. [Lepus] americanus Erxleben, Systema regni animalis . . . , 1:330. Type locality, Hudson Bay, Canada. Restricted to Fort Severn, Ontario, by V. Bailey, N. Amer. Fauna, 49:138, January 8, 1927.

1778. Lepus hudsonius Pallas, Novae species quadrupedum e glirium . . . , p. 30, type locality not stated.

1790. Lepus nanus Schreber, Die Säugthiere . . . , 4:880–885, pl. 234B, a composite of Lepus americanus and Sylvilagus floridanus. No type or type locality designated. Range given as from Hudson Bay to Florida.

1899. Lepus bishopi J. A. Allen, Bull. Amer. Mus. Nat. Hist., 12:11, March 4, type from Mill Lake, Turtle Mts., North Dakota (inseparable from L. a. americanus according to V. Bailey, N. Amer. Fauna, 49:138, January 8, 1927 [not December, 1926]).

MARGINAL RECORDS (Hall, 1951c:174).—Keewatin: Hudson Bay. Ontario: Fort Severn; around shore of Hudson Bay to approximately 56° N, thence to Ungava: Fort Chimo. Labrador: Hamilton Inlet. Ontario: North Bay of Lake Nipissing; Michipicoten Island. Michigan: Isle Royale. Manitoba: Dog Lake. Saskatchewan: Indian Head. North Dakota: Mill Lake, Turtle Mts.; Grafton; near Fargo; Elbowoods; Buford. Saskatchewan: Battle Creek. Alberta: Red Deer; 50 mi. N Edmonton; Fort Chipewyan; Govt. Hay Camp, Slave River.

Lepus americanus bairdii Hayden

1869. Lepus bairdii Hayden, Amer. Nat., 3:115, May. Type locality, Columbia Valley, Wind River Mts., Fremont Co., Wyoming.

1875. [Lepus americanus] var. Bairdii, J. A. Allen, Proc. Boston Soc. Nat. Hist., 17:431, February 17.

MARGINAL RECORDS (Hall, 1951c:174, unless otherwise noted).—British Columbia: Elko. Alberta: Waterton Lakes Nat. Park. Montana: Ft. Benton; Big Snowy Mts. Wyoming: 5 mi. E and 9 mi. N Pinedale; 3 mi. ESE Browns Peak. Colorado: Boulder County. New Mexico: 10,500 ft., Agua Fria Mtn.; Pecos Baldy; Chasma. Utah: 18 mi. SE Manila; 30 mi. N Fort Duchesne; 28 mi. N Fruitland; 21 mi. N Escalante; 10 mi. E Marysvale; City Creek Canyon, Salt Lake City. Idaho: Pocatello; Payette; Cuddy Mtn.; Weippe; Bitterroot Valley. British Columbia: Newgate.

Lepus americanus cascadensis Nelson

1907. Lepus bairdi cascadensis Nelson, Proc. Biol. Soc. Washington, 20:87, December 11, type from Roabs Ranch, near Hope, British Columbia.

1936. Lepus americanus cascadensis, Racey and Cowan, Rep't Prov. Mus. British Columbia, 1936:H18.

MARGINAL RECORDS.—British Columbia (Cowan and Guiguet, 1956:104): Lillooet; Fairview-Keremeos Summit. Washington (Hall, 1951c:174): Lake Chelan; Trout Lake; Vance; Mt. Rainier; Entiat River, 20 mi. from mouth. British Columbia (Cowan and Guiguet, 1956:104): Chilliwack Lake; type locality; Whytecliffe; Sechelt Inlet; Brackendale; Alta Lake.

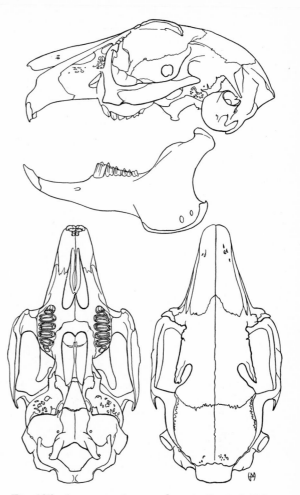

Fig. 185. Lepus americanus tahoensis, ½ mi. S Tahoe Tavern, Lake Tahoe, Placer Co., California, No. 37522 M.V.Z., ♂, X 1.

Lepus americanus columbiensis Rhoads

1895. Lepus americanus columbiensis Rhoads, Proc. Acad. Nat. Sci. Philadelphia, 47:242, July 2, type from Vernon, British Columbia.

MARGINAL RECORDS (Hall, 1951c:175, unless otherwise noted).—Alberta: Jasper National Park; Banff National Park. British Columbia: Creston; Rosalind (Cowan and Guiguet, 1956:104). Washington: Republic; Moulson. British Columbia: Indianpoint Lake.

Lepus americanus dalli Merriam

1900. Lepus americanus dalli Merriam, Proc. Washington Acad. Sci., 2:29, March 14, type from Nulato, Alaska.

MARGINAL RECORDS (Hall, 1951c:175, unless otherwise noted).—Alaska: Arctic Village (Rausch, 1953:116); Koyukuk; Anvik; Yukon Delta; Noatak River; Upper John River.

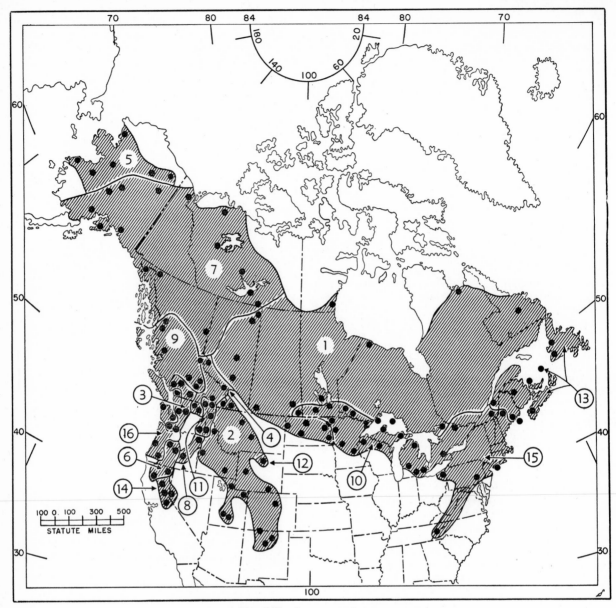

Map 189. *Lepus americanus.*

1. *L. a. americanus*	5. *L. a. dalli*	9. *L. a. pallidus*	13. *L. a. struthopus*
2. *L. a. bairdii*	6. *L. a. klamathensis*	10. *L. a. phaeonotus*	14. *L. a. tahoensis*
3. *L. a. cascadensis*	7. *L. a. macfarlani*	11. *L. a. pineus*	15. *L. a. virginianus*
4. *L. a. columbiensis*	8. *L. a. oregonus*	12. *L. a. seclusus*	16. *L. a. washingtonii*

Lepus americanus klamathensis Merriam

1899. *Lepus klamathensis* Merriam, N. Amer. Fauna, 16:
100, October 28, type from head of Wood River, near Fort
Klamath, Klamath Co., Oregon.

1936. *Lepus americanus klamathensis*, V. Bailey, N. Amer.
Fauna, 55:95, August 29.

MARGINAL RECORDS (Hall, 1951c:175).—Oregon:
Mt. Hood; mouth Davis Creek. California: vicinity Fort
Bidwell; 3000 ft., Rush Creek, 12 mi. N Weaverville. Ore-
gon: *Estacada.*

Lepus americanus macfarlani Merriam

1900. *Lepus americanus macfarlani* Merriam, Proc. Washington Acad. Sci., 2:30, March 14, type from Fort Anderson, near mouth of Anderson River, Mackenzie.

1900. *Lepus saliens* Osgood, N. Amer. Fauna, 19:39,
October 6, type from Caribou Crossing, between Lake
Bennett and Lake Tagish, Yukon.

1907. ? *Lepus niediecki* Matschie, Niedieck's Kreuzfahrten
im Beringmeer, p. 240, type locality Kasilof Lake, Kenai
Peninsula, Alaska.

MARGINAL RECORDS (Hall, 1951c:175, unless otherwise noted).—Mackenzie: type locality; Fort Franklin; Fort Rae; Fort Resolution; Fort Smith. British Columbia: Peace River and Alaska Highway; Bennett; Stonehouse Creek near junction with Kelsall River (Cowan and Guiguet, 1956:105). Alaska: Cordova; Mills Creek; *Naknek Lake* (Shiller and Rausch, 1957:196), on geographic grounds; Lake Clark; E. Fork Kuskokwim River; head N. Fork Kuskokwim; Fort Yukon. Yukon: Russell Mts.

Lepus americanus oregonus Orr

1934. *Lepus bairdii oregonus* Orr, Jour. Mamm., 15:152, May 15, type from 12 mi. S Canyon City, Oregon.
1942. *Lepus americanus oregonus,* Dalquest, Jour. Mamm., 23:179, June 3.

MARGINAL RECORDS (Hall, 1951c:175).—Oregon: 22 mi. N Enterprise; *Wallowa Lake; summit of Blue Mts.;* Ochoco National Forest, Harney Co.

Lepus americanus pallidus Cowan

1938. *Lepus americanus pallidus* Cowan, Jour. Mamm., 19:242, May 12, type from Chezacut Lake, Chilcotin River, British Columbia.

MARGINAL RECORDS (Cowan and Guiguet, 1956:106, unless otherwise noted).—British Columbia: 23 mi. N Hazelton (Hall, 1951c:176); Indianpoint Lake; Sicamous; Falkland; Bonaparte River, 5 days N Ashcroft (Hall, 1951c:176); *Hagensborg*; Kimsquit; Hazelton (Hall, 1951c:176).

Lepus americanus phaeonotus J. A. Allen

1899. *Lepus americanus phaeonotus* J. A. Allen, Bull. Amer. Mus. Nat. Hist., 12:11, March 4, type from Hallock, Kittson Co., Minnesota.

MARGINAL RECORDS (Hall, 1951c:176).—Manitoba: Selkirk Settlement. Ontario: Lake of the Woods; Rainy Lake. Michigan: Houghton; Chippewa County; Presque Isle County; Wayne County; Jackson County; Allegan County. Wisconsin: Rhinelander; St. Croix River, Douglas Co. Minnesota: Elk River; Moores Lake; Warren; St. Vincent. Saskatchewan: Glen Ewen. Manitoba: Carberry.

Lepus americanus pineus Dalquest

1942. *Lepus americanus pineus* Dalquest, Jour. Mamm., 23:178, June 3, type from Cedar Mtn., Latah Co., Idaho.

MARGINAL RECORDS.—British Columbia (Cowan and Guiguet, 1956:106): Trail; Creston. Idaho (Hall, 1951c:176): 5 mi. W Cocolalla; Troy. Washington (Hall, 1951c:176): Blue Mts., Columbia Co.; *Marcus.*

Lepus americanus seclusus Baker and Hankins

1950. *Lepus americanus seclusus* Baker and Hankins, Proc. Biol. Soc. Washington, 63:63, May 25, type from 12 mi. E and 2 mi. N Shell, 7900 ft., Bighorn Mts., Big Horn Co., Wyoming. Known from type locality only.

Lepus americanus struthopus Bangs

1898. *Lepus americanus struthopus* Bangs, Proc. Biol. Soc. Washington, 12:81, March 24, type from Digby, Nova Scotia.

MARGINAL RECORDS (Hall, 1951c:176).—Newfoundland: Bay of Islands; Bay of St. George. Nova Scotia: type locality. Maine: Bucksport. Quebec: S of St. Lawrence River. New Brunswick: Andover. Prince Edward Island: Alberton. Quebec: Grosse Isle, Magdalen Islands.

Lepus americanus tahoensis Orr

1933. *Lepus washingtonii tahoensis* Orr, Jour. Mamm., 14:54, February 14, type from ½ mi. S Tahoe Tavern, Placer Co., California.
1942. [*Lepus americanus*] *tahoensis,* Dalquest, Jour. Mamm., 23:176, June 3.

MARGINAL RECORDS (Hall, 1951c:176).—California: vicinity Mineral. Nevada: 350 yards NE junction of Nevada state line and N shore Lake Tahoe. California: Niagara Creek; Cisco.

Lepus americanus virginianus Harlan

1825. *Lepus virginianus* Harlan, Fauna Americana, p. 196. Type locality, Blue Mountains, northeast of Harrisburg, Pennsylvania.
1875. [*Lepus americanus*] var. *virginianus,* J. A. Allen, Proc. Boston Soc. Nat. Hist., 17:431, February 17.
1825. *Lepus wardii* Schinz, Das Thierreich . . . , 4:428, based on the snowshoe rabbit of the southern part of the United States (Warden, D. B., *in* A statistical, political, and historical account of the United States of North America . . . , 1:233, 1819).
1845. *Lepus borealis* Schinz, Synopsis mammalium, 2:286–287. No type or type locality mentioned. From Virginia and the Alleghenies.

MARGINAL RECORDS (Hall, 1951c:177).—Quebec: Megantic County. Maine: *Greenville;* Sebec Lake; Mt. Desert Island. *Massachusetts: Concord; Middleboro. Rhode Island: Washington County.* New York: Locust Grove. Pennsylvania: type locality. Tennessee: White Rock. Ohio: Ashtabula County. Ontario: Holland River; *Ottawa River.*

Lepus americanus washingtonii Baird

1855. *Lepus washingtonii* Baird, Proc. Acad. Nat. Sci. Philadelphia, 7:333, April, type from Steilacoom, Washington.
1875. [*Lepus americanus*] var. *Washingtoni,* J. A. Allen, Proc. Boston Soc. Nat. Hist., 17:431, February 17.

MARGINAL RECORDS (Hall, 1951c:177, unless otherwise noted).—British Columbia (Cowan and Guiguet, 1956:107): Point Grey, thence eastward along S. bank of Fraser River to *Chilliwack.* Washington: *Mt. Vernon;* Lake Kapowsin; White Salmon. Oregon: Drew; Florence; *Tillamook.* Washington: Sekiu River.

Lepus othus
Alaskan Hare

Total length, 565–690; tail, 53–104; hind foot, 147–189; ear from notch (dry), 75–78. Color brownish in summer, white in winter, but tips of ears always black. General comparisons indicate that this is the species which in Eurasia bears the name *Lepus timidus*. The possibility that *L. othus othus* intergrades with *L. arcticus andersoni* needs to be investigated.

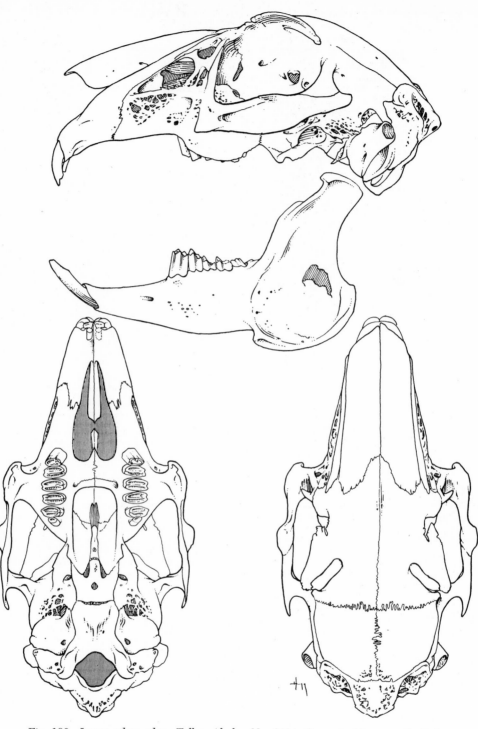

Fig. 186. *Lepus othus othus,* Teller, Alaska, No. 3194, Carnegie Museum, ♀, X 1.

Lepus othus othus Merriam

1900. *Lepus othus* Merriam, Proc. Washington Acad. Sci., 2:28, March 14, type from St. Michael, Norton Sound, Alaska.

MARGINAL RECORDS (Hall, 1951c:177, unless otherwise noted).—Alaska: Kuparuk River (Bee and Hall, 1956: 34); Killik River (*ibid.*); Kotzebue Sound; mts. NW Nulato River; Akiak; 75 mi. below Bethel; Wales (Rausch, 1953: 116).

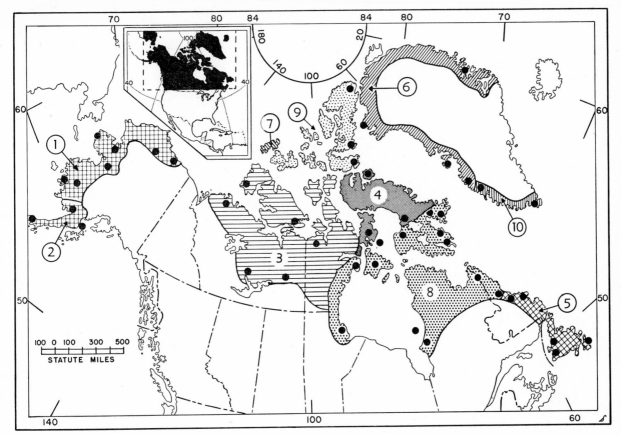

Map 190. *Lepus othus* and *Lepus arcticus*.

Guide to kinds	2. *L. othus poadromus*	5. *L. arcticus bangsii*	8. *L. arcticus labradorius*
1. *L. othus othus*	3. *L. arcticus andersoni*	6. *L. arcticus groenlandicus*	9. *L. arcticus monstrabilis*
	4. *L. arcticus arcticus*	7. *L. arcticus hubbardi*	10. *L. arcticus porsildi*

Lepus othus poadromus Merriam

1900. *Lepus poadromus* Merriam, Proc. Washington Acad. Sci., 2:29, March 14, type from Stepovak Bay, Alaska Peninsula, Alaska.

1936. *Lepus othus poadromus*, A. H. Howell, Jour. Mamm. 17:334, November 16.

MARGINAL RECORDS (Hall, 1951c:177).—Alaska: Nushagak; Kawatna Bay, Shelikof Strait; *Cold Bay; Chiknik; type locality; Sand Point*; 15 mi. W Pavlof Mtn.

Lepus arcticus
Arctic Hare

Revised by A. H. Howell, Jour. Mamm., 17:315–337, November 16, 1936. For the taxonomic status of the technical names *arcticus* and *glacialis* see Rhoads, Amer. Nat., 30:234–235, March, 1896; Merriam, Science, n. s., 3:564–565, April 10, 1896; Rhoads, Science, n. s., 3:843–845, June 5, 1896; Merriam, Science, n. s., 3:845, June 5, 1896.

Total length, 480–678; tail, 34–80; hind foot, 132–174; ear from notch (dry), 70–84. Upper parts gray in summer in southern subspecies; in others

white; in winter white in all subspecies, except black tips of ears. Weights of lean individuals reach 12 pounds. Hopping on the hind feet without touching the forefeet to the ground has repeatedly been recorded for this species. There are 4 to 8 young in a litter.

Lepus arcticus andersoni Nelson

1934. *Lepus arcticus andersoni* Nelson, Proc. Biol. Soc. Washington, 47:85, March 8, type from Cape Barrow, Coronation Gulf, Mackenzie.

MARGINAL RECORDS (Hall, 1951c:179, unless otherwise noted).—Franklin: Cape Kellett, Banks Island; Cambridge Bay, Victoria Island. Keewatin: Back River, 125 mi. NW Baker Lake (Gunderson, *et al.*, 1955:258). Mackenzie: Lake Hanbury; Fort Rae; Fort Anderson.

Lepus arcticus arcticus Ross

1819. *Lepus arcticus* Ross, A voyage of discovery . . . , ed. 2, vol. 2, appendix 4, p. 151, type locality Possession Bay, Bylot Island, lat. 73° 37′ N.

1819. *Lepus glacialis* Leach, *in* Ross, A voyage of discovery . . . , ed. 2, vol. 2, appendix 4, p. 170, type locality same as for *Lepus arcticus* Ross.

MARGINAL RECORDS (Hall, 1951c:178).—Franklin: type locality; Egukjuak, 8 mi. E Pond Inlet, Baffin Island;

west coast Baffin Island, 67° 30′; Winter Island, Melville Peninsula; Repulse Bay, Melville Peninsula.

Lepus arcticus bangsii Rhoads

1896. *Lepus arcticus bangsii* Rhoads, Amer. Nat., 30:253 [= 236 of March issue], author's separates (preprints)

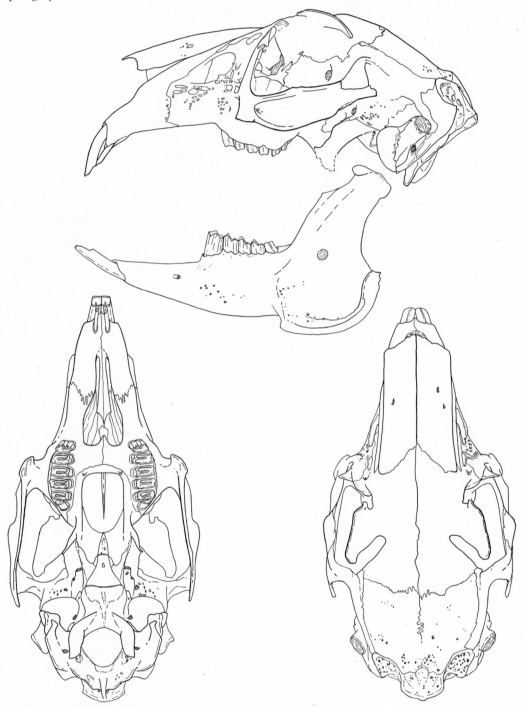

Fig. 187. *Lepus arcticus groenlandicus,* Cape Alexander, Greenland, No. 114850 U.S.N.M., ♂, X 1.

published February 20, 1896, type from Codroy, Newfoundland.

MARGINAL RECORDS (Hall, 1951c:179).—Labrador: Hopedale; Makkovik. Newfoundland: Saint Johns; type locality; Mt. St. Gregory.

Lepus arcticus groenlandicus Rhoads

1896. *Lepus groenlandicus* Rhoads, Amer. Nat., 30:254 [= 237 of March issue], author's separates (preprints) issued February 20, 1896, type from Robertson Bay, NW Greenland.
1934. [*Lepus arcticus*] *groenlandicus*, Nelson, Proc. Biol. Soc. Washington, 47:83, March 8.
1930. *Lepus variabilis hyperboreus* Pedersen, Medd. om Grønland, 77:363, no type or type locality designated but name applied to hares of east Greenland in the general vicinity of Scoresby Sound. Not *Lepus hyperboreas* Pallas, Zoogeographica Rosso-Asiatica, 1:152, 1811, a species of *Ochotona*.
1934. *Lepus arcticus persimilis* Nelson, Proc. Biol. Soc. Washington, 47:84, March 8, type from S side Clavering Island, east Greenland.

MARGINAL RECORDS (Hall, 1951c:179).—Greenland: Cape Alexander; on east coast to Francis Joseph Fiord; on west coast to *Nugsuak Peninsula*; Disko Island; Holsteinsborg.

Lepus arcticus hubbardi Handley

1952. *Lepus arcticus hubbardi* Handley, Proc. Biol. Soc. Washington, 65:199, November 5, type from near Cherie Bay, 5 mi. NE Mould Bay Station, Prince Patrick Island, Franklin. Known only from Prince Patrick Island.

Lepus arcticus labradorius Miller

1899. *Lepus labradorius* Miller, Proc. Biol. Soc. Washington, 13:39, May 29, type from Fort Chimo, Quebec.
1924. *Lepus arcticus labradorius*, G. M. Allen and Copeland, Jour. Mamm., 5:12, February 9.
1902. *Lepus arcticus canus* Preble, N. Amer. Fauna, 22:59, October 31, type from Hubbart Point, W coast Hudson Bay, Keewatin.

MARGINAL RECORDS (Hall, 1951c:179).—Franklin: Pangnirtung Fiord; Nunata, Kingua Fiord; Cumberland Sound, Blacklead Island; Weddell Harbor, Frobisher Bay. Labrador: Ramah; Solomons Island, near Davis Inlet. Quebec: *type locality*; Great Whale River, Hudson Bay; Belcher Islands. Manitoba: Fort Churchill; *Hubbart Point*. Keewatin: Cape Fullerton; Southampton Island. Franklin: *Cape Dorset*; Camp Kungovik, west coast Baffin Island, 65° 35′ N lat.; *Nettilling Fiord*.

Lepus arcticus monstrabilis Nelson

1934. *Lepus arcticus monstrabilis* Nelson, Proc. Biol. Soc. Washington, 47:85, March 8, type from Buchanan Bay, Ellesmere Island, Franklin.

MARGINAL RECORDS (Hall, 1951c:179).—Franklin: Cape Sheridan; Craig Harbor; Dundas Harbor, Devon Island.

Lepus arcticus porsildi Nelson

1934. *Lepus arcticus porsildi* Nelson, Proc. Biol. Soc. Washington, 47:83, March 8, type from near Julianehaab, lat. 61° 20′ N, Greenland.

MARGINAL RECORDS (Hall, 1951c:180).—Greenland: Sukkertoppen; *Neria, lat. 61° 36′ N*; lat. 60° 42′ N.

Lepus townsendii
White-tailed Jack Rabbit

X ⅙

Total length, 565–655; tail, 66–112; hind foot, 145–172; ear from notch (dry), 96–113. Upper parts grayish brown; tail all white or with dusky or buffy mid-dorsal stripe, which does not extend onto back; white in winter in northern parts of its range. Two adult males weighed 6½ and 5½ lbs. (Orr, 1940:43), and there are 3 to 6 young in a litter.

Lepus townsendii campanius Hollister

1837. *Lepus campestris* Bachman, Jour. Acad. Nat. Sci. Philadelphia, 7:349. Type locality, plains of the Saskatchewan, probably near Carlton House. Not *Lepus cuniculus campestris* Meyer, 1790.
1915. *Lepus townsendii campanius* Hollister, Proc. Biol. Soc. Washington, 28:70, March 12, a renaming of *L. campestris* Bachman.

MARGINAL RECORDS (Hall, 1951c:181).—Saskatchewan: Indian Head. Manitoba: Carberry. Ontario: Rainy River. Minnesota: Polk County; Otter Tail County; Sherburne County; Washington County. Illinois: Blanding, 6 mi. WNW Hanover. Kansas: Red Fork, 60 mi. W Fort Riley; Greensburg. New Mexico: near Taos; Hopewell. Colorado: Antonito; Fort Garland; Villa Grove; Salida; Como; *Denver*; Mt. Whitley, 25 mi. N Kremmling. Wyoming: Spring Creek; Big Piney; head Glenn Creek, Yellowstone National Park. Alberta: Great Plains region.

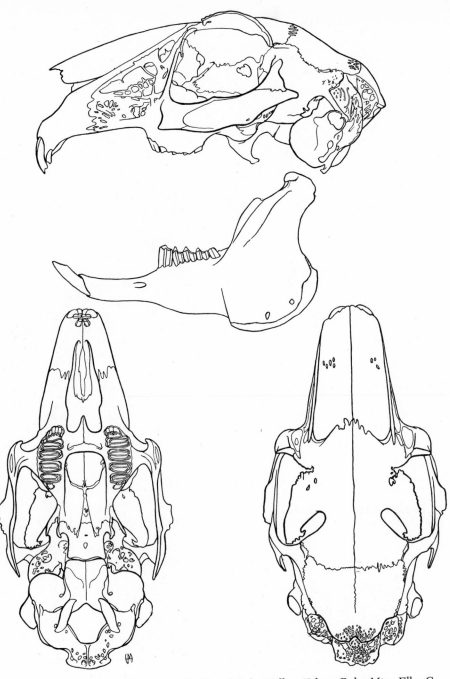

Fig. 188. *Lepus townsendii townsendii,* N end Ruby Valley, E base Ruby Mts., Elko Co., Nevada, No. 45746 K.U., ♀, X 1.

Lepus townsendii townsendii Bachman

1839. *Lepus townsendii* Bachman, Jour. Acad. Nat. Sci. Philadelphia, 8(pt. 1):90, pl. 2, type from Fort Walla Walla, near present town of Wallula, Walla Walla Co., Washington.

1904. *Lepus campestris sierrae* Merriam, Proc. Biol. Soc. Washington, 17:132, July 14, type from 7800 ft., Hope Valley, Alpine Co., California. Regarded as inseparable from *L. t. townsendii* by Orr, Occas. Papers, California Acad. Sci., 19:42, May 25, 1940.

MARGINAL RECORDS (Hall, 1951c:181, unless otherwise noted).—British Columbia: Okanagan Falls (Cowan and Guiguet, 1956:100). Idaho: Rathdrum Prairie; Lemhi River; Teton Basin. Wyoming: Hamsfork; Henrys Fork.

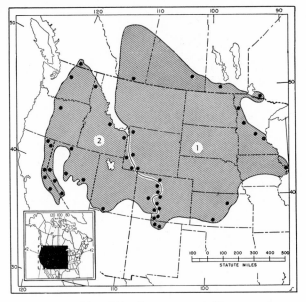

Map 191. *Lepus townsendii.*

1. *L. t. campanius*   2. *L. t. townsendii*

Colorado: Hot Sulphur Springs; Mt. Baldy; Crested Butte; Mill City. Utah: Kanab. Nevada: Hamilton; Desatoya Mts.; Santa Rosa Mts. California: Parker Creek, 6300 ft., Warner Mts. Nevada: 8600 ft., 3 mi. S Mt. Rose; 8900 ft., Lapon Canyon, Mt. Grant; Mt. Magruder. California: Tuolumne Meadows; Woodfords; Tahoe City; 4700 ft., Steele Meadows. Oregon: Antelope. Washington: Manson.

Lepus californicus
Black-tailed Jack Rabbit

Total length, 465–630; tail, 50–112; hind foot, 112–145; ear from notch (dry), 99–131. Upper

parts gray to blackish; tail with black mid-dorsal stripe extending onto back. On the tableland of Mexico and in the southwestern United States where this species occurs together with the white-sided jack rabbits, *L. californicus* can be recognized by the terminal black patch on the outside of each ear and by the less extensive area of white on the flank. To the eastward, in Tamaulipas, where only the black-tailed jack rabbit occurs, it too has extensively white flanks, and some individuals lack the terminal black patch on the ear.

A certain means for distinguishing the skulls of the black-tailed jack rabbit from those of all of the white-sided jack rabbits has not yet been discovered. The same is true of the skulls of the white-tailed jack rabbit and the black-tailed jack rabbit in the Great Basin region of Nevada. The skulls, at least of adults, of these two species in the region east of the Rocky Mountains can be readily distinguished by the pattern of infolding of the enamel on the front of the first upper incisor teeth; *L. townsendii* has a simple groove on the anterior face of the tooth and *L. californicus*, east of the Rocky Mountains, has a bifurcation, or even trifurcation, of the infold that can readily be seen by examining the occlusal surface of the incisor.

In Arizona, Vorhies and Taylor (1933:478) found the weight of 23 adult males to average 5.1 (4.4–6.1) lbs. In that state, 70 pregnant females averaged 2.24 (1–6) young per litter and the authors (*op. cit.*) thought that a female had 3 or 4 litters each year.

Lepus californicus altamirae Nelson

1904. *Lepus merriami altamirae* Nelson, Proc. Biol. Soc. Washington, 17:109, May 18, type from Alta Mira, Tamaulipas. Known from type locality only.
1951. *Lepus californicus altamirae*, Hall, Univ. Kansas Publ., Mus. Nat. Hist., 5:45, October 1.

Lepus californicus asellus Miller

1899. *Lepus asellus* Miller, Proc. Acad. Nat. Sci. Philadelphia, 51:380, September 29, type from San Luis Potosí, San Luis Potosí.
1909. *Lepus californicus asellus*, Nelson, N. Amer. Fauna, 29:150, August 31.

MARGINAL RECORDS (Hall, 1951c:182, unless otherwise noted).—Coahuila: (Baker, 1956:195): *3 mi. S and 3 mi. E Muralla, 3800 ft.*; Jaral; *41 mi. W and 15 mi. N Saltillo.* Nuevo León: Miquihuana. San Luis Potosí: Ciudad del Maíz (Dalquest, 1953b:75); Río Verde. Aguascalientes: Chicalote. Zacatecas: Valparaíso.

Lepus californicus bennettii Gray

1843. *Lepus bennettii* Gray, Zoology of the voyage of H.M.S. Sulphur . . . , p. 35, pl. 14, April, type from San Diego, San Diego Co., California.

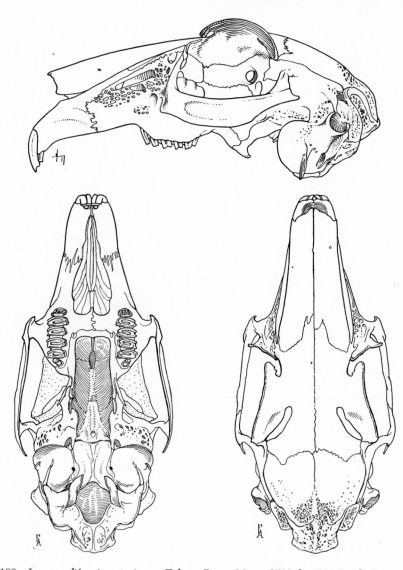

Fig. 189. *Lepus californicus texianus*, E base Burro Mesa, 3500 ft., Big Bend, Brewster Co., Texas, No. 81694 M.V.Z., ♂, X 1.

1909. *Lepus californicus bennetti*, Nelson, N. Amer. Fauna, 29:136, August 31.

MARGINAL RECORDS (Hall, 1951c:182).—California: Mt. Piños; Arroyo Seco, Pasadena; San Felipe Valley; Jacumba. Baja California: San Quintín. Northward along coast at least to California: Montalvo.

Lepus californicus californicus Gray

1837. *Lepus californica* Gray, Charlesworth's Mag. Nat. Hist., 1:586, type from "St. Antoine," California (probably on coastal slope of mts. near the Mission of San Antonio, Jolon, Monterey Co.).
1926. *Lepus californicus vigilax* Dice, Occas. Papers Mus. Zool., Univ. Michigan, 166:11, February 11, type from Balls Ferry, Shasta Co., California. Regarded as identical with *californicus* by Orr, Occas. Papers California Acad. Sci., 19:67, May 25, 1940.

MARGINAL RECORDS (Hall, 1951c:182).—Oregon: Drain; Grants Pass. California: Callahan, Scott River; 3300 ft., Lymans, NW of Lyonsville; Dry Creek, Oroville-Chico Road; Snelling; Hernandez; Morro; *Carmel Point; Bolinas Bay; Freestone; Sherwood; Ferndale;* 3 mi. W Arcata. Oregon: Rogue River Valley.

Lepus californicus curti Hall

1951. *Lepus californicus curti* Hall, Univ. Kansas Publ., Mus. Nat. Hist., 5:42, October 1, type from island 88 mi. S and 10 mi. W Matamoros, Tamaulipas. Known from type locality only.

Lepus californicus deserticola Mearns

1898. *Lepus texianus deserticola* Mearns, Proc. U.S. Nat. Mus., 18:564, June 24, type from western edge Colorado

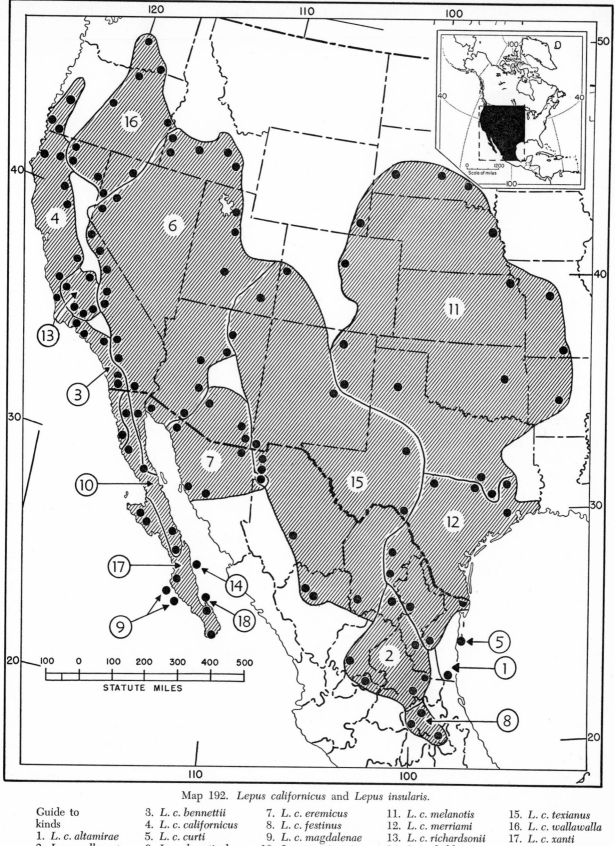

Map 192. *Lepus californicus* and *Lepus insularis*.

Guide to kinds
1. *L. c. altamirae*
2. *L. c. asellus*
3. *L. c. bennettii*
4. *L. c. californicus*
5. *L. c. curti*
6. *L. c. deserticola*
7. *L. c. eremicus*
8. *L. c. festinus*
9. *L. c. magdalenae*
10. *L. c. martirensis*
11. *L. c. melanotis*
12. *L. c. merriami*
13. *L. c. richardsonii*
14. *L. c. sheldoni*
15. *L. c. texianus*
16. *L. c. wallawalla*
17. *L. c. xanti*
18. *L. insularis*

283

Desert, at base of Coast Range Mts., Imperial Co., California.

1909. *Lepus californicus deserticola*, Nelson, N. Amer. Fauna, 29:137, August 31.

1932. *Lepus californicus depressus* Hall and Whitlow, Proc. Biol. Soc. Washington, 45:71, April 2, type from ½ mi. S Pocatello, Bannock Co., Idaho. (Regarded as inseparable from *L. c. deserticola* by Davis, The Recent mammals of Idaho, p. 359, April 5, 1939.)

MARGINAL RECORDS (Hall, 1951c:184).—Idaho: Boise River; Sawtooth National Forest; Arco; Blackfoot. Utah: Ogden; Provo; Loa. Arizona: San Francisco Mtn.; Fort Whipple; Phoenix; Rancho Bonito, Abra Valley. Sonora: El Doctor. Baja California: Calamahué [= Calamajue]; *Esperanza Canyon.* California: Coyote Wells; Kenworthy; Victorville; Farrington Ranch; 5 mi. SW Lone Pine; 10,000 ft., head Silver Canyon; Mono Mills; 5600 ft., near Woodfords. Nevada: Sutcliffe; ¾ mi. S Sulphur. Idaho: 6 mi. S Murphy.

Lepus californicus eremicus J. A. Allen

1894. *Lepus texianus eremicus* J. A. Allen, Bull. Amer. Mus. Nat. Hist., 6:347, December 7, type from Fairbank, Cochise Co., Arizona.

1909. *Lepus californicus eremicus*, Nelson, N. Amer. Fauna, 29:140, August 31.

MARGINAL RECORDS (Hall, 1951c:184).—Arizona: Casa Grande; Fort Bowie; 2 mi. E Portal. Chihuahua: San Bernardino Ranch (possibly Nelson should have placed this in Sonora); Colonia Garcia. Sonora: Hermosillo; La Libertad; Agua Dulce (of Sonora, not of Arizona).

Lepus californicus festinus Nelson

1904. *Lepus festinus* Nelson, Proc. Biol. Soc. Washington, 17:108, May 18, type from Irolo, Hidalgo.

1909. *Lepus californicus festinus* Nelson, N. Amer. Fauna, 29:151, August 31.

MARGINAL RECORDS (Hall, 1951c:184).—Hidalgo: Zimapán; *Tulancingo;* type locality. Querétaro: Tequisquiapam.

Lepus californicus magdalenae Nelson

1907. *Lepus californicus magdalenae* Nelson, Proc. Biol. Soc. Washington, 20:81, July 22, type from Magdalena Island, Baja California.

MARGINAL RECORDS (Hall, 1951c:184).—Baja California: type locality; Margarita Island.

Lepus californicus martirensis Stowell

1895. *Lepus martirensis* Stowell, Proc. California Acad. Sci., ser. 2, 5:51, May 28, type from the San Pedro Mártir Mountains of Baja California.

1909. *Lepus californicus martirensis*, Nelson, N. Amer. Fauna, 29:152, August 31.

MARGINAL RECORDS (Hall, 1951c:184).—Baja California: La Huerta; Calamahué [= Calamajue]; San Bruno; Rancho San José; San Simón.

Lepus californicus melanotis Mearns

1890. *Lepus melanotis* Mearns, Bull. Amer. Mus. Nat. Hist., 2:297, February 21, type from Independence, Kansas.

1909. *Lepus californicus melanotis*, Nelson, N. Amer. Fauna, 29:146, August 31.

MARGINAL RECORDS (Hall, 1951c:185, unless otherwise noted).—South Dakota: Lyman County; T. 101 N, R. 62 E, in Davison Co. (Schantz, 1957:419). Nebraska: Oakland. Kansas: near Doniphan Lake. Missouri: Saline Co.; 5 mi. E. Rockbridge. Arkansas: Lonsdale (Sealander, 1956:268). Oklahoma: 3 mi. E Wainwright. Texas: Brazos Co.; Golinda; Washburn. New Mexico: Santa Rosa; vicinity of Cimarron. Colorado: Semper. Wyoming: 3 mi. W Meriden along Horse Creek. South Dakota: 25 mi. E, 20 mi. S Rapid City (Findley, 1956a:2).

Lepus californicus merriami Mearns

1896. *Lepus merriami* Mearns, Preliminary diagnoses of new mammals from the Mexican border of the United States, p. 2, March 25 (preprint of Proc. U.S. Nat. Mus., 18:444, May 23, 1896), type from Fort Clark, Kinney Co., Texas.

1909. *Lepus californicus merriami*, Nelson, N. Amer. Fauna, 29:148, August 31.

MARGINAL RECORDS (Hall, 1951c:185, unless otherwise noted).—Texas: Mason; Lott; Antioch; Houston. Tamaulipas: Matamoros; Tamaulipeca, San Carlos Mts. Nuevo León: Santa Catarina. Coahuila (Baker, 1956:196): Monclova; Sabinas; *25 mi. S and 8 mi. E Piedra Blanca; 16 mi. N and 21 mi. E Piedra Blanca.*

Lepus californicus richardsonii Bachman

1839. *Lepus richardsonii* Bachman, Jour. Acad. Nat. Sci. Philadelphia, 8(pt. 1):88, type from California (exact locality unknown, but probably on interior slope of mts. near Jolon, Monterey Co.).

1909. *Lepus californicus richardsoni*, Nelson, N. Amer. Fauna, 29:133, August 31.

1904. *Lepus tularensis* Merriam, Proc. Biol. Soc. Washington, 17:136, July 14, type from Alila [= Earlimart], Tulare Co., California.

MARGINAL RECORDS (Hall, 1951c:185).—California: Minkler; Thompson Valley, Walker Basin; Kern Lake Basin; Carrizo Plains, 7 mi. SE Simmler; *2 mi. E Bryson;* Jolon.

Lepus californicus sheldoni Burt

1933. *Lepus californicus sheldoni* Burt, Proc. Biol. Soc. Washington, 46:37, February 20, type from Carmen Island [lat. 26° N, long. 111° 12' W, Gulf of California], Baja California. Known from type locality only.

Lepus californicus texianus Waterhouse

1848. *Lepus texianus* Waterhouse, A natural history of the Mammalia, 2:136, type locality unknown, but probably in western Texas.

1909. *Lepus californicus texianus*, Nelson, N. Amer. Fauna, 29:142, August 31.

1896. *Lepus texianus griseus* Mearns, Proc. U.S. Nat. Mus., 18:562, June 24, type from Fort Hancock, Texas.

1903. *Lepus* (*Macrotolagus*) *texianus micropus* J. A. Allen, Bull. Amer. Mus. Nat. Hist., 19:605, November 12, type from Río de las Bocas, northwestern Durango.

MARGINAL RECORDS (Hall, 1951c:185–186, unless otherwise noted).—Colorado: between Grand Junction and Utah boundary. New Mexico: Roswell. Texas: Colorado; Comstock. Coahuila (Baker, 1956:196): *18 mi. S and 14 mi. E Tanque Alvarez*; 8 mi. SE San Pedro de los Colonias, 3700 ft.; *3 mi. SE Torreón*. Durango: Río Sestín; Río de las Bocas. Chihuahua: Santa Rosalia; Pacheco; San Luis Mts. New Mexico: Guadalupe Ranch. Arizona: Painted Desert. Utah: Abajo (Blue Mts.).

Lepus californicus wallawalla Merriam

1904. *Lepus texianus wallawalla* Merriam, Proc. Biol. Soc. Washington, 17:137, July 14, type from Touchet, Plains of the Columbia, Walla Walla Co., Washington.
1909. *Lepus californicus wallawalla*, Nelson, N. Amer. Fauna, 29:132, August 31.

MARGINAL RECORDS (Hall, 1951c:186).—Washington: Moses Coulee; type locality. Oregon: Ontario. Nevada: 4100 ft., Quinn River Crossing; 4200 ft., 4½ mi. W Flanigan. California: 5000 ft., 7 mi. E Ravendale; 3600 ft., 1 mi. SE Weed; Hornbrook. Oregon: Hay Creek; Willow Junction.

Lepus californicus xanti Thomas

1898. *Lepus californicus Xanti* Thomas, Ann. and Mag. Nat. Hist., ser. 7, 1:45, January, type from Santa Anita, Baja California.

MARGINAL RECORDS (Hall, 1951c:186).—Baja California (southern part of the Peninsula): Santa Clara Mts., southward around range of *L. c. martirensis* to and down east coast; La Paz; Cape St. Lucas; San Jorgé; 20 mi. W San Ignacio.

Lepus insularis Bryant
Black Jack Rabbit

1891. *Lepus insularis* Bryant, Proc. California Acad. Sci., ser. 2, 3:92, April 23, type from Espíritu Santo Island, Gulf of California, Baja California. Known from Espíritu Santo Island only.
1895. *Lepus edwardsi* St.-Loup, Bull. Mus. Hist. Nat., Paris, 1:5, type from Espíritu Santo Island, Gulf of California, Baja California.

Total length, 574; tail, 96; hind foot, 121; ear from notch (dry), 105. This insular species, clearly a close relative of *Lepus californicus* of the adjacent peninsula of Baja California, is mainly glossy black on the upper parts but grizzled and suffused on sides of back and body, and in some specimens on head, with dark buffy or reddish brown; underparts dark cinnamon buffy or dusky brown; ears and sides of head grayish dusky; jugals heavier than in *Lepus californicus* of the adjacent peninsula of Baja California.

Lepus mexicanus Lichtenstein
White-sided Jack Rabbit

1830. *Lepus mexicanus* Lichtenstein, Abh. k. Akad. Wiss., Berlin, p. 101, prior to May, type from México (southern end of Mexican Tableland).
1830. *Lepus callotis* Wagler, Natürliches System der Amphibien . . . , p. 23, August, type from southern end of Mexican Tableland.
1833. *Lepus nigracaudatus* Bennett, Proc. Zool. Soc. London, p. 41, May 17, type from "that part of California which adjoins to Mexico" (probably southwestern part of Mexican Tableland).

Total length, 560; tail, 71; length of hind foot, 133; ear from notch (dry), 117. Upper parts dark, slightly pinkish, buff heavily washed with black; backs of ears mainly white without terminal patch of black; flanks white; rump iron gray.

MARGINAL RECORDS (Hall, 1951c:187).—Durango: Durango (city of). San Luis Potosí: Arenal. Hidalgo: Tulancingo. Oaxaca: Oaxaca (city of); Tlapancingo. Jalisco: Atenquiqui; Reyes.

Lepus flavigularis Wagner
Tehuantepec Jack Rabbit

1844. *Lepus callotis* var. γ *flavigularis* Wagner, *in* Schreber, Die Säugthiere . . . , Suppl., 4:106, type from México (probably near Tehuantepec City, Oaxaca).
1909. *Lepus flavigularis*, Nelson, N. Amer. Fauna, 29:125, August 31.

Total length, 595; tail, 77; hind foot, 133; ear from notch (dry), 112. Upper parts bright ochraceous buff strongly washed with black; ears entirely buff; nape with black stripe extending back from base of each ear and median stripe of buff; flanks and underparts of body white; rump iron gray; tympanic bullae smaller than in any other *Lepus* of México.

MARGINAL RECORDS (Hall, 1951c:188).—Oaxaca: Santa Efigenia; San Mateo del Mar; Huilotepec.

Lepus gaillardi
Gaillard's Jack Rabbit

Total length, 450–536; tail, 59–80; hind foot, 124–133; ear from notch (dry), 110–112. Coloration essentially as in *Lepus mexicanus* except that nape is plain buff, without a trace of black, and upper parts paler, more vinaceous buff.

Lepus gaillardi battyi J. A. Allen

1903. *Lepus* (*Microtolagus* [*sic*]) *gaillardi battyi* J. A. Allen, Bull. Amer. Mus. Nat. Hist., 19:607, November 12, type from Rancho Santuario, northwestern Durango.

MARGINAL RECORDS (Hall, 1951c:188).—Durango: Río Campo; type locality.

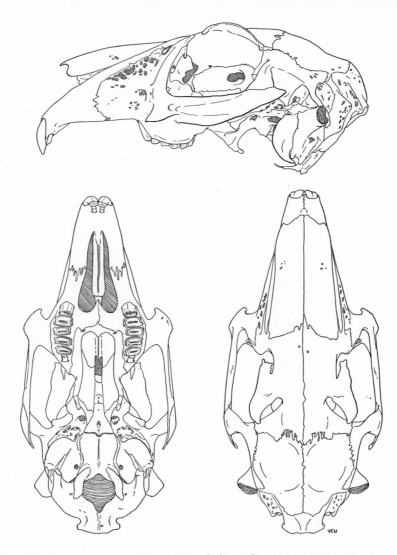

Fig. 190. *Lepus mexicanus*, 3½ mi. S Tecolotlán, Jalisco, No. 31842 K.U., ♀, X 1.

Lepus gaillardi gaillardi Mearns

1896. *Lepus gaillardi* Mearns, Proc. U.S. Nat. Mus., 18: 560, June 24, type from West Fork of Playas Valley, near monument No. 63, Mexican boundary line, Hidalgo Co., New Mexico.

MARGINAL RECORDS (Hall, 1951c:188).—New Mexico: Animas Valley. Chihuahua: Whitewater; Colonia Juarez. New Mexico: type locality.

Lepus alleni
Antelope Jack Rabbit

Total length, 553–670; tail, 48–76; hind foot, 127–150, ear from notch, in flesh, 138–173. Top and sides of head creamy buff, slightly washed on top with

black; tail white except for mid-dorsal line of black extending onto rump; sides of shoulders, flanks, sides of abdomen, rump, and outside of hind legs uniform iron gray. The average weight of 61 adult males from Arizona was 8.2 pounds. In that state 124 pregnant females had an average of 1.93 young (1–5) and Vorhies and Taylor (1933:580) thought that a female had 3 or 4 litters per year.

Lepus alleni alleni Mearns

1890. *Lepus alleni* Mearns, Bull. Amer. Mus. Nat. Hist., 2:294, February 21, type from Rillito, on the Southern Pacific Railroad, Pima Co., Arizona.

MARGINAL RECORDS (Hall, 1951c:189).—Arizona: Queen Creek; Cascabel; Calabasas. Sonora: Cerro Blanco;

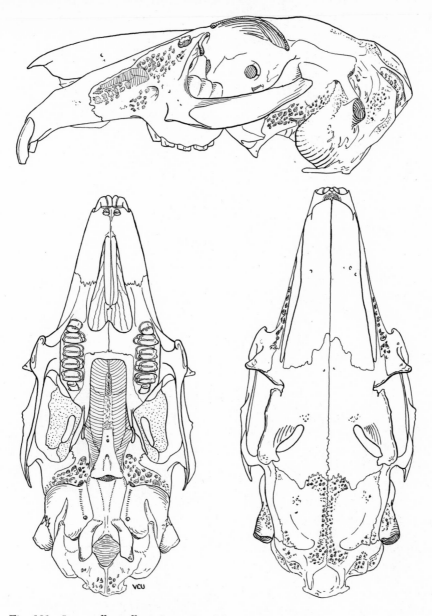

Fig. 191. *Lepus alleni alleni,* Santa Rita Mts., 30 mi. S Tucson, Pima Co., Arizona, No. 8621 K.U., ♂, X 1.

Oputo; Batamotal; La Libertad Ranch; Picu Pass. Arizona: 2 mi. W Quitovaquita; Casa Grande.

Lepus alleni palitans Bangs

1900. *Lepus (Macrotolagus) alleni palitans* Bangs, Proc. New England Zool. Club, 1:85, February 23, type from Aguacaliente [*sic*], about 40 mi. SE Mazatlán, Sinaloa.

MARGINAL RECORDS (Hall, 1951c:189).—Sonora: near San Bernardo on Río Mayo on Sonora side of Sonora-Chihuahua boundary; *Alamos*; Guirocoba. Nayarit: Acaponeta. Sinaloa: Esquinapa; *Rosario*; Culiacán. Sonora: near Navajoa.

Lepus alleni tiburonensis Townsend

1912. *Lepus alleni tiburonensis* Townsend, Bull. Amer. Mus. Nat. Hist., 31:120, June 14, type from Tiburón Island, Gulf of California, Sonora. Known from Tiburón Island only.

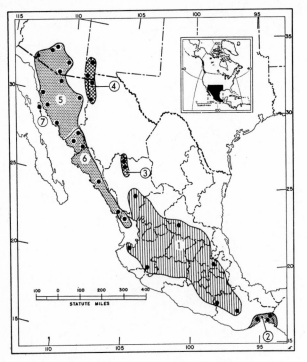

Map 193. *Lepus alleni* and allies.

Guide to kinds
1. *L. mexicanus*
2. *L. flavigularis*
3. *L. gaillardi battyi*
4. *L. gaillardi gaillardi*
5. *L. alleni alleni*
6. *L. alleni palitans*
7. *L. alleni tiburonensis*

Lepus europaeus
European Hare

Total length, 640–700; tail, 70–100; hind foot, 130–150; ear from notch (dry), 79–100; weight 6⅝ to 10 lbs. Upper parts tawny, mixed with blackish hairs on back; underparts white including under side of tail; upper side of tail and terminal patch at distal end of outside of ears black; upper side of feet tawny like sides (not white or whitish). This is an introduced species.

Lepus europaeus hybridus Desmarest

1822. *Lepus hybridus* Desmarest, Mammalogie . . . , pt. 1, p. 349, *in* Encyclopédie méthodique . . . , name based on "Russac" of Pallas, Novae species quadrupedum e glirium ordine . . . , p. 5, 1778. Type locality, central Russia.
1912. *Lepus europaeus hybridus,* Miller, Catalogue of the mammals of western Europe . . . , p. 508, November 23.

MARGINAL RECORDS (Peterson and Reynolds, 1954:6, unless otherwise noted).—Michigan: Ontonagon County (Burt, 1946:246). Ontario: Parry Sound District, Burk's Falls; Lindsay; *Highway No. 38 near Hartington* (Reynolds, 1955:15); Pittsburg Twp. (*ibid.*). Massachusetts: near North Adams. Connecticut: Washington. Ontario: Woodstock (Anderson, 1946:100); St. Thomas (*ibid.*); Highgate (Reynolds, 1955:15). Michigan: Sanilac County (Burt, 1946:246). See also Silver (1924:1134) for record of several introductions (possibly of subspecies other than *L. e. hybridus*) including one at Bethlehem in Pennsylvania, and one in 1888 at Jobstown in New Jersey.

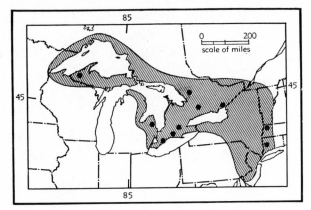

Map 194. *Lepus europaeus hybridus.*

Order **RODENTIA**—Rodents

The earliest known rodents (Family Ischyromyidae) are from the late Paleocene of North America. When they first appear they are already clearly rodents and there are no known fossils that are intermediate between rodents and the archaic mammalian groups. Further, although the rodents probably exceed all other orders combined in variety and actual numbers, the fossil record is disproportionately poor. Because of this lack of fossils and because there are many instances of convergence, divergence, and parallelism, the current taxonomic arrangements of the higher taxonomic groups are correspondingly unsatisfactory.

Rodents are terrestrial, fossorial, arboreal, glissant, or semiaquatic mammals having a generalized type of brain and placentation. The feet are clawed and the fibula does not articulate with the calcaneum. The masseter muscle is highly specialized and its arrangement serves as a basis for the recognition of the principal suborders. Only 4 incisors, 2 above and 2 below, are present, and these grow continuously. The maximum dental formula is: i. $\frac{1}{1}$, c. $\frac{0}{0}$, p. $\frac{2}{1}$, m. $\frac{3}{3}$ = 22 permanent teeth, for instance in several squirrels. The lower jaw is somewhat loosely articulated to the skull and considerable rotatory motion is employed in chewing. Molariform teeth may be either hypsodont or brachydont. The crowns of the molariform series display several patterns of the enamel and dentine that seem to be basically different, but the homologies of these are not known.

Rodents are primarily herbivores, but many kinds show a marked predilection for animal matter, and some seem to require at least some of it in their diet. Food consists of grasses, stems, roots, leaves, nuts, fruits, bark, various small forms of animal life, both invertebrate and vertebrate; even cannibalism occurs occasionally in some groups.

The Order Rodentia comprises a group remarkably homogeneous with respect to the ordinal characters. Yet in other characters the variation is great. Included are the volant flying squirrels, the almost wholly subterranean pocket gophers, the saltatorial genera of various families, the semiaquatic beavers and muskrats, the various arboreal squirrels and mice, and the vast assemblage of terrestrial kinds. Some are quick, slender, and agile, and others are slow, heavy-bodied, and clumsy. Collectively, rodents occupy nearly all available ecological situations except the air and the open seas. Some, like the sagebrush vole (*Lagurus*) are comparatively restricted ecologically; others—the deermice of the genus *Peromyscus*, for example—are among the terrestrially ubiquitous animals in North America.

Because of their great numbers and variety, rodents are of incalculable importance to man. Many of them serve as buffer species; that is, they are a source of food for predators and thus absorb much of the predator pressure that would otherwise be directed against more desirable species. A case in point is the lemming of the North. When lemmings are abundant they provide adequate food for the wolves; as a result, the caribou, which are of prime importance in the economies of Arctic peoples, obtain a respite and increase in numbers. When the lemmings (and hares) are in a low of their periodic cycles of abundance, caribou are subjected to more wolf predation (one of the strands in the web of forces that controls the size of the caribou population). The same relationship between rodents, predators, and livestock probably obtains to some extent in the western United States.

The food habits of many rodents make them highly desirable from man's point of view because the rodents destroy many noxious weeds and insects. Dietary predilections, however, at times make some rodents in localized areas serious and expensive nuisances. Voles, for example, sometimes destroy orchards in the northern states by girdling the trees. On the whole, however, the activities of rodents are beneficial to man, and control activities, when required, should be pursued with discretion and knowledge.

Occasionally certain rodents become important in disease control. All mammals harbor ectoparasites, but rodents are especially important because they are so numerous and widespread. Certain of the ectoparasites upon occasion transmit microscopic pathogenic organisms capable of producing epidemics in man. The devastating plagues of medieval Europe seem to have been cases in point; the non-native *Rattus* is thought to have become a vast reservoir of pathogenic microorganisms.

On the credit side of the ledger, the Order Rodentia contains some of the most important furbearers; beaver, muskrat, nutria, and chinchilla are examples. The search for furs, principally beaver pelts, was largely responsible for the early explorations of the western United States and Canada.

KEY TO SUBORDERS OF RODENTIA

1. Infraorbital canal not transmitting any part of medial masseter muscle (or at least not modified for transmission of the muscle).
                                        Sciuromorpha, p. 290
1'. Infraorbital canal transmitting medial masseter muscle and enlarged for that purpose.
  2. Infraorbital foramen greatly enlarged (see Fig. 432). . . Hystricomorpha, p. 779
  2'. Infraorbital canal moderately enlarged (see Fig. 321) except in Zapodidae.
                                        Myomorpha, p. 551

SUBORDER SCIUROMORPHA

Infraorbital canal not transmitting any part of masseter medialis; dentition, i. $\frac{1}{1}$, c. $\frac{0}{0}$, p. $\frac{2-1}{1}$, m. $\frac{3}{3}$ (except in a few extinct genera); 4th premolar usually large and important. Tibia and fibula variably free or extensively fused.

The zygomasseteric structure of this suborder is of at least 2 distinct types. In the more primitive type the origin of the masseter is wholly beneath the infraorbital foramen and no part of the muscle extends onto the rostrum. In the advanced type the zygomatic plate is broadened and tilted upward and a part of the lateral masseter originates above the infraorbital foramen and on the rostrum.

This suborder includes the most primitive living rodents and the earliest known fossil rodents.

KEY TO NORTH AMERICAN FAMILIES
OF SCIUROMORPHA

1. Skull broad, flat, and triangular in dorsal aspect; dentition, i. $\frac{1}{1}$, c. $\frac{0}{0}$, p. $\frac{2}{1}$, m. $\frac{3}{3}$; auditory bullae flask-shaped; angular process of mandible strongly inflected. Aplodontidae, p. 290
1'. Skull not broad and flat; dentition, i. $\frac{1}{1}$, c. $\frac{0}{0}$, p. $\frac{2 \text{ or } 1}{1}$, m. $\frac{3}{3}$; auditory bullae not flask-shaped; angular process not strongly inflected.
  2. Tail broad, flat, scaly; toes of hind feet webbed. . . . . . . Castoridae, p. 546
  2'. Tail not broad, flat, scaly; toes of hind feet not webbed.
    3. External fur-lined cheek pouches present.
      4. Frontal bone backing postorbital process; skull robust and angular; auditory bullae not greatly inflated. . . . . . Geomyidae, p. 411
      4'. Frontal bone bearing postorbital process; skull weak and smooth; auditory bullae inflated.
                                    Heteromyidae, p. 472
    3'. External fur-lined cheek pouches absent. . . . . . . Sciuridae, p. 292

FAMILY APLODONTIDAE—Mountain Beaver

Origin of masseter muscle wholly beneath infraorbital foramen and no part of muscle reaches rostrum; zygomatic plate narrow and horizontal; tibia and fibula always separate; angular process of mandible markedly inflected; skull widened and flattened posteriorly.

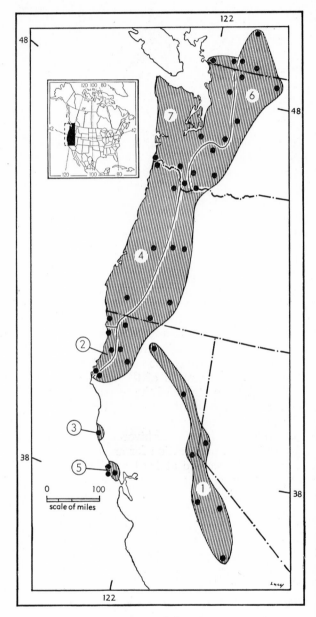

Map 195. *Aplodontia rufa.*

Guide to subspecies	
1. *A. r. californica*	4. *A. r. pacifica*
2. *A. r. humboldtiana*	5. *A. r. phaea*
3. *A. r. nigra*	6. *A. r. rainieri*
	7. *A. r. rufa*

Aplodontids are the oldest known group of living rodents, their time range being from late Paleocene to Recent. They have been regarded by some authors as including the ancestors of all later rodents, but this view is by no means universally accepted. There is only one living species, *Aplodontia rufa*.

Genus **Aplodontia** Richardson—Mountain Beaver

Revised by Taylor, Univ. California Publ. Zool., 17:435–504, May 29, 1918; see also Finley, Murrelet, 22:45–49, January 20, 1942, and Dalquest, Murrelet, 26:34–37, December 28, 1945.

1829. *Aplodontia* Richardson, Zool. Jour., 4:334, January. Type, *Aplodontia leporina* Richardson [= *Anisonyx rufa* Rafinesque]. Many variant spellings of *Aplodontia* are in the literature.

Skull unusually broad and flat, especially posteriorly; cheek-teeth, $\frac{5}{4}$, the first in upper series being a small simple peg; posterior cheek-teeth when slightly worn showing single simple basin; auditory bullae flask-shaped; palate extending posteriorly beyond tooth-rows; angular process of mandible greatly inflected; coronoid process high.

Aplodontia rufa
Mountain Beaver

X ⅕

External measurements: total length, 310–470; hind foot, 36–64. Body compact; legs short and stout; ears, eyes, and tail small; fur pinkish-cinnamon to brown, becoming grayish with age; relatively uniformly colored.

Mountain beavers or sewellels are confined to a limited part of the Pacific Northwest, both in forests and densely vegetated thickets, principally, but not always, at lower elevations. They seldom venture more than a few yards from cover. They are burrowing animals, the burrows varying from 4 to 10 inches in diameter and extending sometimes for 200 or 300 yards.

The food of the mountain beaver consists of almost any available vegetation, although deciduous vegetation is preferred. The animal does not hibernate, but does store food. The rut seemingly occurs in late winter or early spring and lasts approximately 6 weeks. The 2 or 3 blind young are born about a month later. Mountain beavers seldom survive in captivity for more than a few weeks.

Aplodontia rufa californica (Peters)

1864. *H[aplodon]. leporinus* var. *Californicus* Peters, Monatsb. preuss. Akad. Wiss., Berlin, p. 179, type assumed to be from the Sierra Nevada of California (Grinnell, Proc. California Acad. Sci., ser. 4, 3:344, August 28, 1913; Hall, Murrelet, 22:50, January 20, 1942); specimens from Blue Canyon in the central Sierra may be regarded as typical (Taylor, Univ. California Publ. Zool., 17:474, May 29, 1918).
1904. [*Aplodontia rufa*] *californica*, Trouessart, Catalogus mammalium . . . , Suppl., fasc. 2, p. 348.
1886. *Aplodontia major* Merriam, Ann. New York Acad. Sci., 3:316, May, type from Sierra Nevada, Placer Co., California.

MARGINAL RECORDS.—California: Mt. Shasta (Grinnell, 1933:194); mountains 12 mi. W Susanville (Taylor, 1918:475). Nevada: 2½ mi. W, ⅞ mi. S Lakeview (Hall, 1946:575). California: Mammoth (Taylor, 1918:475); Clover Creek (Grinnell, 1933:194); Chinquapin (Taylor, 1918:475); Lake Tahoe, Emerald Bay (*ibid.*).

Aplodontia rufa humboldtiana Taylor

1916. *Aplodontia humboldtiana* Taylor, Proc. Biol. Soc. Washington, 29:21, February 24, type from Carlotta, Humboldt Co., California.
1918. *Aplodontia rufa humboldtiana* Taylor, Univ. California Publ. Zool., 17:470, May 29.

MARGINAL RECORDS.—California: Requa (Grinnell, 1933:195); 12 mi. N Hoopa, 3 mi. SW Weitzpek (Taylor, 1918:470); Rio Dell (Finley, 1942:49); thence northward along coast to point of beginning.

Aplodontia rufa nigra Taylor

1914. *Aplodontia nigra* Taylor, Univ. California Publ. Zool., 12:297, April 15, type from Point Arena, Mendocino Co., California. Known only from the type locality.
1918. *Aplodontia rufa nigra* Taylor, Univ. California Publ. Zool., 17:479, May 29.

Aplodontia rufa pacifica Merriam

1899. *Aplodontia pacifica* Merriam, Proc. Biol. Soc. Washington, 13:19, January 31, type from Newport, mouth of Yaquina Bay, Lincoln Co., Oregon.
1918. *Aplodontia rufa pacifica*, Taylor, Univ. California Publ. Zool., 17:467, May 29.

MARGINAL RECORDS (Taylor, 1918:467, unless otherwise noted).—Oregon: Astoria; 11 mi. NW Linton (Finley, 1942:49); Eugene; Briggs Creek, 13 mi. SW Galice. California: 7 mi. ENE Smith River (Finley, 1941:49) thence northward along coast to Columbia River.

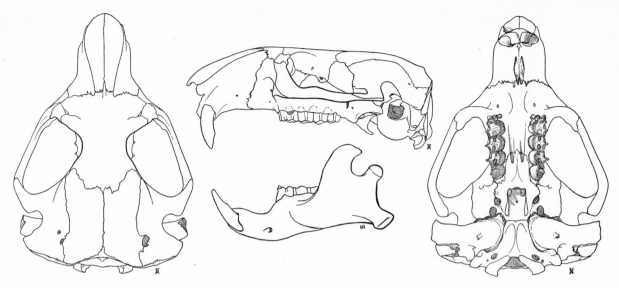

Fig. 192. *Aplodontia rufa californica*, ½ mi. S Marlette Lake, Nevada, No. 67066 M.V.Z., ♂, X 1.

Aplodontia rufa phaea Merriam

1899. *Aplodontia phaea* Merriam, Proc. Biol. Soc. Washington, 13:20, January 31, type from Point Reyes, Marin Co., California.
1918. *Aplodontia rufa phaea*, Taylor, Univ. California Publ. Zool., 17:480, May 29.

MARGINAL RECORDS.—California (Grinnell, 1933: 195): 5 mi. W Inverness; Lagunitas; 4 mi. S Olema.

Aplodontia rufa rainieri Merriam

1899. *Aplodontia major rainieri* Merriam, Proc. Biol. Soc. Washington, 13:21, January 31, type from Paradise Creek, 5200 ft., S side Mt. Rainier, Pierce Co., Washington.
1904. [*Aplodontia rufa*] *rainieri*, Trouessart, Catalogus mammalium . . . , Suppl., fasc. 2, p. 348.
1916. *Aplodontia californica columbiana* Taylor, Univ. California Publ. Zool., 12:499, May 6, type from Roabs Ranch, Hope, British Columbia. (Regarded as inseparable from *A. r. rainieri* by Dalquest, Univ. Kansas Publ., Mus. Nat. Hist., 2:369, April 9, 1948.)

MARGINAL RECORDS.—British Columbia: Nicola Valley near Merritt (Cowan and Guiguet, 1956:115); Sterling Creek near Hedley (Anderson, 1947:168). Washington (Dalquest and Scheffer, 1945:37, unless otherwise noted): Loomis; Mt. Adams; Skamania; Mt. St. Helens (Dalquest, 1948:369); Mt. Rainier (*ibid.*); Cascade Tunnel; Beaver Creek. British Columbia: mile 14 on the Hope-Princeton Highway (Cowan and Guiguet, 1956:115).

Aplodontia rufa rufa (Rafinesque)

1817 *Anisonyx? rufa* Rafinesque, Amer. Monthly Mag., 2: 45, November. Type locality, neighborhood Columbia River, Oregon. Specimens from Marmot, Clackamas Co., regarded as typical (Taylor, Univ. California Publ. Zool., 17:455, May 29, 1918).

1886. *Aplodontia rufa*, Merriam, Ann. New York Acad. Sci., 3:316, May.
1899. *Aplodontia olympica* Merriam, Proc. Biol. Soc. Washington, 13:20, January 31, type from Quinault Lake, Grays Harbor Co., Washington.
1914. *Aplodontia chryseola* L. Kellogg, Univ. California Publ. Zool., 12:295, April 15, type from Jackson Lake, Siskiyou Co., California.
1916. *Aplodontia rufa grisea* Taylor, Univ. California Publ. Zool., 12:497, May 6, type from Renton, near Seattle, King Co., Washington.

MARGINAL RECORDS.—British Columbia: Chilliwack (Anderson, 1947:167). Washington: Sauk (Taylor, 1918: 455); Easton (*ibid.*); Puyallup (*ibid.*); 1½ mi. W Yaclot (Finley, 1942:45). Oregon (Taylor, 1918:455–456): McKenzie Bridge; Ft. Klamath, Anna Creek Canyon; N base Ashland Peak. California: Canyon Creek (*ibid.*); Rio Dell (*ibid.*); 10 mi. W forks of Salmon River (*ibid.*); Poker Flat, 12 mi. NW Happy Camp (Finley, 1941:45). Oregon: Vida (Taylor, 1918:455). Washington (Dalquest and Scheffer, 1945:37): 6 mi. NE Kelso; along N side Columbia River, as at mouth of Bear River, 5 mi. NE Ilwaco, and up the coast to British Columbia: Aldergrove (Cowan and Guiguet, 1956:114).

FAMILY **SCIURIDAE**—Squirrels and Relatives

Skull never of truly fossorial type; cheek-teeth $\frac{5}{4}$ or $\frac{4}{4}$, cuspidate, rooted, and usually not simplified; auditory bullae prominent, but usually not specially modified; well-developed postorbital processes; fibula and tibia not fused; tail completely haired.

The oldest known terrestrial squirrels are from late Miocene (Barstovian) deposits. The tree-squirrel line extends back possibly to the Oligocene.

The family includes semi-fossorial, terrestrial, and volant species. The family is widely distributed and, within certain broad limitations imposed by structure, remarkably versatile ecologically. Although primarily herbivorous, upon occasion nearly all sciurids will accept animal food and some do so avidly.

As a whole, the true squirrels seem less subject to periodic fluctuations in populations than many other rodents.

KEY TO NORTH AMERICAN GENERA OF SCIURIDAE

1. Membrane present between foreleg and hind leg; modified for gliding; zygomatic plate low, little tilted upward. . . . . *Glaucomys*, p. 405
1'. Membrane not present between foreleg and hind leg; not modified for gliding; zygomatic plate (usually) tilted strongly upward.
   2. No antorbital canal, the antorbital foramen piercing the zygomatic plate of the maxillary.
      3. Keel on tip of baculum on dorsal side; P3 present; tail more than 40 per cent of total length.
          Eutamias, p. 296
      3'. Keel on tip of baculum on ventral side; P3 absent; tail less than 38 per cent of total length.
          Tamias, p. 293
   2'. Antorbital canal present.
      4. Zygomatic breadth more than 48; anterior lower premolar with a paraconulid. . *Marmota*, p. 320
      4'. Zygomatic breadth less than 48; anterior lower premolar without paraconulid.
         5. Zygomata not parallel, but converging anteriorly with anterior part twisted toward a horizontal plane.
            6. Maxillary tooth-rows strongly convergent posteriorly. . . . . *Cynomys*, p. 364
            6'. Maxillary tooth-rows not strongly convergent posteriorly.
               7. Small masseteric tubercle directly below narrowly oval infraorbital foramen; cranium subrectangular from dorsal aspect; cranium flattened and little inclined downward to supernuchal line; clavobrachialis muscle absent. . . . . . . *Ammospermophilus*, p. 330
               7'. Medium to large masseteric tubercle ventral and slightly lateral to oval or subtriangular infraorbital foramen; cranium not subrectangular from dorsal aspect; cranium inflated and inclined downward to supernuchal line; clavobrachialis muscle present.
                    Spermophilus, p. 335
         5'. Zygomata nearly parallel and nearly vertical throughout, that is to say, not twisted.
            8. Upper incisors projecting forward to or beyond tip of nasals.
               9. Upper incisors grooved; postorbital process anterior to vertical line through posterior zygomatic root. . . . . *Syntheosciurus*, p. 395
               9'. Upper incisors not grooved; postorbital process almost directly above posterior zygomatic root. . . . . *Microsciurus*, p. 396
            8'. Upper incisors not projecting to or beyond tip of nasals.
              10. Baculum present; P3 usually well developed. . . . . *Sciurus*, p. 368
              10'. Baculum absent; P3 usually vestigial or absent. . . . . *Tamiasciurus*, p. 398

Genus **Tamias** Illiger—Eastern Chipmunk

Revised by A. H. Howell, N. Amer. Fauna, 52:11–23, November 9, 1929. See J. A. White, Univ. Kansas Publ., Mus. Nat. Hist., 5:543–561, December 1, 1953, for status of genera of chipmunks.

1811. *Tamias* Illiger, Prodromus systematis mammalium et avium . . . , p. 83. Type, *Sciurus striatus* Linnaeus, 1758.

External measurements: 215–299; 78–113; 32–38. Greatest length of skull, 34.5–44.3. Skull lightly built, narrow; postorbital process small and weak; lacrimal not elongated; infraorbital foramen lacks canal, relatively larger than in most sciurids; P3 absent; head of malleus elongated; plane of manubrium of malleus forms 60 degree angle with plane of lamina; hypohyal and ceratohyal bones of hyoid apparatus fused in adults; conjoining tendon of anterior and posterior digastric muscles rounded in cross section; keel on ventral surface of tip of baculum, tip of baculum curved upward; tail less than 38 per cent of total length; five longitudinal dark and four longitudinal light stripes present but two dorsal light stripes at least twice as broad as other stripes; four lateral dark stripes short (after White, 1953:559).

American chipmunks dig their own burrows, construct a large nest of dry plant material, store food in summer and autumn, and in some areas are active for part of the winter although some individuals, at least, hibernate. Some animal matter is eaten but seeds, nuts, and fruits are the principal foods. Two to 6 embryos have been recorded.

Tamias striatus
Eastern Chipmunk

X ½

Characters as for the genus.

Tamias striatus fisheri A. H. Howell

1925. *Tamias striatus fisheri* A. H. Howell, Jour. Mamm., 6:51, February 9, type from Merritts Corners, 4 mi. W Ossining (Sing Sing), Westchester Co., New York.

MARGINAL RECORDS (A. H. Howell, 1929b:17, unless otherwise noted).—New York: Cohoes (Bole and Moulthrop, 1942:134). Connecticut: Plainfield (Goodwin, 1935:101). Rhode Island: Providence. New Jersey: 1 mi. NW New Gretna (Connor, 1953:232), thence southward along coast to Virginia: Suffolk; Mountain Lake. West Virginia (Kellogg, 1937:459): Odd, 2900 ft.; 1½ mi. S Big Creek; 5 mi. E Huntington. Ohio (A. H. Howell, 1932:166): Carpenter; Athens; Maysville; Bowerston. Pennsylvania: New Castle (Hamilton, 1943:216); Butler County (Richmond and Roslund, 1949:44); Tyrone; Flowing Spring; Cresson; Laughlintown; Summit Mills. West Virginia (Kellogg, 1937:459): 7 mi. E Philippi; Berkeley

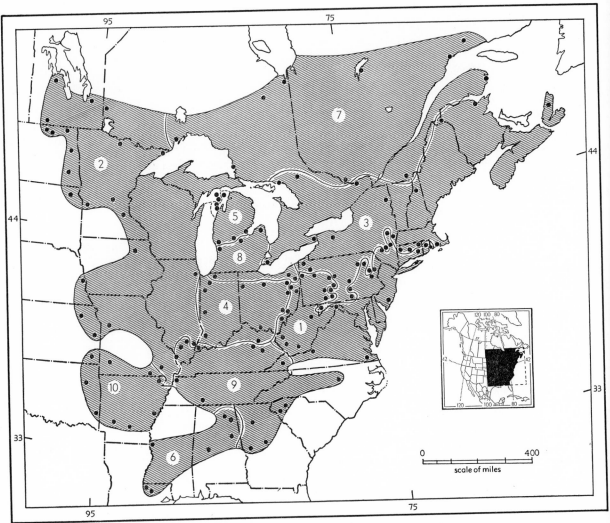

Map 196. *Tamias striatus.*

Guide to
subspecies
1. *T. s. fisheri*

2. *T. s. griseus*
3. *T. s. lysteri*
4. *T. s. ohionensis*

5. *T. s. peninsulae*
6. *T. s. pipilans*
7. *T. s. quebecensis*

8. *T. s. rufescens*
9. *T. s. striatus*
10. *T. s. venustus*

Springs. Pennsylvania: Carlisle; Harveys Lake; Saylorsburg; Bushkill Creek, 7 mi. E Cresco. New York: Lanesville; Kiskatom.

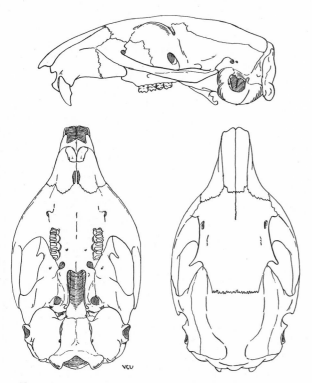

Fig. 193. *Tamias striatus griseus*, Missouri River bank, Doniphan Co., Kansas, No. 13701 K.U., ♀, X 1½.

Tamias striatus griseus Mearns

1891. *Tamias striatus griseus* Mearns, Bull. Amer. Mus. Nat. Hist., 3:231, June 5, type from Fort Snelling, Hennepin Co., Minnesota.

MARGINAL RECORDS.—Manitoba: Dauphin (Cameron, 1950:348); Pine Falls, Winnipeg River (Soper, 1946:142). Ontario: Ingolf (A. H. Howell, 1929b:21). Minnesota: Koochiching County (Swanson, 1945:79); Cook County (*ibid.*). Michigan: [North Fox Island] (Burt, 1946:184); South Fox Island (Hooper, 1942a:4). Illinois: River Forest (Necker and Hatfield, 1941:49); Mt. Carmel (*ibid.*). Missouri: Williamsville (A. H. Howell, 1929b:21); Independence (*ibid.*). Kansas (Cockrum, 1952:132): Peoria; Onaga. Nebraska: Fontenelle Forest Reserve, 2 mi. S Omaha (Velich, 1947:185). Iowa: Charles City (Scott, 1937:70). Minnesota: type locality; Stearns County (Swanson, 1945:79); Ortonville (A. H. Howell, 1929b:21). South Dakota: Fort Sisseton (*ibid.*). North Dakota (*ibid.*): Kathryn; Larimore; Walhalla; Fish Lake, Birchwood P.O.; Turtle Mts. Manitoba: Turtle Mtn. (Soper, 1946:142).

Tamias striatus lysteri (Richardson)

1829. *Sciurus (Tamias) lysteri* Richardson, Fauna Boreali-Americana, 1:181, pl. 15, June. Type locality, Penetanguishene, Ontario.

1886. *Tamias striatus lysteri,* Merriam, Amer. Nat., 20: 242, March.

MARGINAL RECORDS (A. H. Howell, 1929b:19, unless otherwise noted).—New Brunswick: Bathurst (Cameron, 1950:348). Nova Scotia: Cape Breton Island (Anderson, 1947:113), thence down the coast to Massachusetts: Wareham (Bole and Moulthrop, 1942:134). Connecticut (Goodwin, 1935:102): South Woodstock; Portland; Sharon Mtn. New York: Troy; Palensville [= Palenville]; *Kaaterskill Junction.* Pennsylvania: Mt. Pocono; Eaglesmere; Perry County (Gifford and Whitebread, 1951:57); Adams County (*ibid.*). Maryland: *Dans Mtn., 4 mi. NW Rawlings*; Accident; *Grantsville.* Pennsylvania: Summit (Grimm and Roberts, 1950:63); Tyronne; Venango County (Richmond and Roslund, 1949:44); Erie (*ibid.*). Ontario: Central Proton (Cameron, 1950:348); Point Pelee (*ibid.*); N end Georgian Bay (Anderson, 1947:113); S shore Lake Nipissing (Bole and Moulthrop, 1942:134); Ottawa (Cameron, 1950:348). New York: Plattsburg. New Hampshire: Pinkham Notch (11191 KU). New Brunswick: Edmundtson (Cameron, 1950:348).

Tamias striatus ohionensis Bole and Moulthrop

1942. *Tamias striatus ohionensis* Bole and Moulthrop, Sci. Publ. Cleveland Mus. Nat. Hist., 5(6):135, September 11, type from Cincinnati, Hamilton Co., Ohio.

MARGINAL RECORDS (Bole and Moulthrop, 1942: 137, unless otherwise noted).—Indiana: Hebron. Ohio: Payne; Bettsville; *Overton* (Hall and Kelson, 1952:352); Wooster (*ibid.*); Loudonville (*ibid.*); 7 mi. E Logan; Smoky Creek. Green Twp. Kentucky: Bath County. Indiana: Wheatland (Hall and Kelson, 1952:351); Parke County (Kirkpatrick and Conaway, 1948:133); Mt. Ayr.

Tamias striatus peninsulae Hooper

1942. *Tamias striatus peninsulae* Hooper, Occas. Papers Mus. Zool., Univ. Michigan, 461:1, September 15, type from Barnhart Lake, 3 mi. SE Millersburg, Presque Isle Co., Michigan.

MARGINAL RECORDS.—Michigan: Beaver Island (Hooper, 1942a:5); Bay County (Burt, 1946:184); Bass Lake (Hooper, 1942a:5); "near" Lake Michigan, N of Muskegon State Park (*ibid.*); South Manitou Island (Burt, 1946:184); North Manitou Island (*ibid.*).

Tamias striatus pipilans Lowery

1943. *Tamias striatus pipilans* Lowery, Occas. Papers. Mus. Zool., Louisiana State Univ., 13:235, November 22, type from 5 mi. S Tunica, West Feliciana Parish, Louisiana.

MARGINAL RECORDS (Lowery, 1943:237, unless otherwise noted).—Alabama: Woodville; Bucks Pocket; Talladega Mtn.; Greensboro (Hall and Kelson, 1952:352). Louisiana: Baines; type locality. Mississippi: Washington.

Tamias striatus quebecensis Cameron

1950. *Tamias striatus quebecensis* Cameron, Jour. Mamm., 31:347, August 21, type from St. Félicien, Lake St. John Co., Quebec.

MARGINAL RECORDS (Cameron, 1950:348, unless otherwise noted).—Ontario: S end James Bay (Anderson, 1947:113, as *T. s. griseus*). Quebec: Lake Albanel (Cameron and Morris, 1951:126); head Matamek River (Anderson, 1947:113, as *T. s. griseus*); Moisie Bay; Perce; Hatley; Parker. Ontario: Pancake Bay; Thunder Bay District; Kapuskasing.

Tamias striatus rufescens Bole and Moulthrop

1942. *Tamias striatus rufescens* Bole and Moulthrop, Sci. Publ. Cleveland Mus. Nat. Hist., 5(6):130, September 11, type from Chesterland Caves, Chester Twp., Geauga Co., Ohio.

MARGINAL RECORDS.—Michigan: Huron County (Burt, 1946:184). Ohio: Lisbon (Bole and Moulthrop, 1942:134); Evertt (*ibid.*). Indiana: La Porte County (Hall and Kelson, 1952:353). Michigan: Ottawa County (Burt, 1946:184); Gratiot County (*ibid.*).

Tamias striatus striatus (Linnaeus)

1758. [*Sciurus*] *striatus* Linnaeus, Syst. nat., ed. 10, 1:64, type locality fixed by A. H. Howell (N. Amer. Fauna, 52: 14, November 30, 1929) as upper Savannah River, South Carolina. A. H. Howell (*loc. cit.*) makes this restriction primarily on the basis of Catesby's account, and points out that Merriam (Amer. Nat., 20:238, 1886) states that a specimen in his collection from Sylva, North Carolina, "may be regarded as the type of *striatus*," but it is obviously impossible to fix the type locality at a point outside the region where Catesby is known to have traveled.
1857. *Tamias striatus*, Baird, 11th Ann. Rept. Smithsonian Inst., for 1856, p. 55.
1788. [*Sciurus striatus*] *americanus* Gmelin, Syst. nat., ed. 13, 1:150. Based on a number of earlier citations, among them the account of Catesby.

MARGINAL RECORDS.—Illinois: Olney (A. H. Howell, 1929b:16). Indiana: New Harmony (Bole and Moulthrop, 1942:134). Kentucky: Lexington (A. H. Howell, 1929b: 16); Quicksand (Hamilton, 1930:310). Virginia: Cleveland (Hooper and Cady, 1941:324). North Carolina: Chapel Hill (Engels, 1947:296). South Carolina: Greenville (Penney, 1950:85); Anderson (*ibid.*). Georgia: Roswell (9206 KU); Wesleyan College Campus, Rivoli (Knepton, 1955:136); 4 mi. N Geneva (Hall, 1939:766). Tennessee (Kellogg, 1939:271): 8 mi. NE Waynesboro; Reelfoot Lake, Samburg. Illinois: Wolf Lake (A. H. Howell, 1929b:16); Woodlawn (Cory, 1912:130).

Tamias striatus venustus Bangs

1896. *Tamias striatus venustus* Bangs, Proc. Biol. Soc. Washington, 10:137, December 28, type from Stilwell, Adair Co., Oklahoma.

MARGINAL RECORDS.—Kansas: Independence (Cockrum, 1952:132). Missouri: 8 mi. S Carthage (A. H. Howell, 1929b:23); 20 mi. SE Alton (Leopold and Hall, 1945: 144). Arkansas (Sealander, 1956:270, unless otherwise noted): Clay County; Phillips County; Dallas County; *Hempstead County*; Delight (A. H. Howell, 1929b:23). Oklahoma (Blair, 1939:112): 5 mi. W Smithville; Red Fork.

Genus Eutamias Trouessart—Western Chipmunks

The arrangement here followed is that of White, Univ. Kansas Publ., Mus. Nat. Hist., 5:543–561, 12 figs. in text, December 1, 1953.
1880. *Eutamias* Trouessart, Bull. Soc. d'Études Sci. d'Angers, 10(fasc. 1):86. Type, *Sciurus striatus asiaticus* Gmelin.

Skull lightly built, narrow; postorbital process light and weak; lacrimal not elongated; infraorbital foramen lacks canal, relatively larger than in most sciurids; P3 present; head of malleus not elongated; plane of manubrium of malleus at angle of 90° to plane of lamina; hypohyal and ceratohyal bones of hyoid apparatus fused in adults; conjoining tendon between anterior and posterior sets of digastric muscles ribbonlike; keel on dorsal side of tip of baculum; tail more than 40 per cent of total length; 5 longitudinal dark stripes evenly spaced and subequal in width; 2 lateral dark stripes short (after White, 1953:558).

Subgenus Neotamias A. H. Howell
Western Chipmunks

Revised by A. H. Howell, N. Amer. Fauna, 52:23–137, November 30, 1929.

1929. *Neotamias* A. H. Howell, N. Amer. Fauna, 52:26, November 30. Type, *Tamias asiaticus merriami* J. A. Allen.

Total length, 166–277; tail, 67–140. Greatest length of skull, 28.7–40.8. "Lambdoidal crest barely discernible; supraorbital notches even with, or posterior to, posterior notch of zygomatic plate; baculum with distinct keel on dorsal surface of tip which curves upward; pelage silky; ears long and pointed" (White, 1953:558).

KEY TO SPECIES OF NEOTAMIAS

1. Dorsal stripes (except median one) more or less indistinct.
    2. Occurring in California and Baja California. . . . . *E. merriami*, p. 310
    2′. Occurring east of the Californias. . . . . *E. dorsalis*, p. 308
1′. Dorsal stripes all distinctly marked.
    3. Greatest length of skull 37 or more.
        4. Occurring in Arizona, New Mexico, Texas, and México.
            5. Hind foot, 34–38; occurring in México, exclusive of Baja California. . . . . *E. bulleri*, p. 319
            5′. Hind foot, 32–35; occurring in Arizona, New Mexico, and Texas. . . . *E. cinereicollis*, p. 313
        4′. Occurring in British Columbia, Washington, Oregon, California, Baja California, and Nevada in Sierra Nevada.

6. Tail less bushy; backs of ears distinctly bicolor in all pelages; tips of nasals not separated by median notch.
 7. Ears relatively short, not pointed; submalar dark stripe not black below ear. . *E. townsendii*, p. 306
 7′. Ears long and pointed; submalar dark stripe expanding into conspicuous black area below ear; occurring in northern Sierra Nevada. . . . . *E. quadrimaculatus*, p. 314
6′. Tail more bushy; backs of ears unicolor or nearly so in summer pelage (bicolor in winter pelage); tips of nasals separated by small median notch.
 8. Color reddish; occurring north of San Francisco Bay and Mt. Lassen. . . . . *E. sonomae*, p. 308
 8′. Color grayish; occurring south of San Francisco Bay and American River. . . *E. merriami*, p. 308
3′. Greatest length of skull less than 37.
 9. Greatest length of skull, 34.5–37.
  10. Occurring in México.
   11. Occurring in Baja California. . . . . *E. merriami*, p. 308
   11′. Not occurring in Baja California. . . . . *E. bulleri*, p. 319
  10′. Occurring north of México.
   12. Occurring north and west of Yellowstone Nat'l Park.
    13. Baculum 5 mm. or more long. . . . . *E. ruficaudus*, p. 312
    13′. Baculum less than 5 mm. long. . . . . *E. amoenus*, p. 303
   12′. Occurring in Yellowstone Nat'l Park and south thereof in United States.
    14. Occurring in Texas, southern half of New Mexico and southern ⅔ of Arizona.
     E. cinereicollis, p. 313
    14′. Not occurring as above.
     15. Occurring in California and Nevada and with outer face of I describing arc having radius less than 5.3.
      16. Submalar dark stripe obsolete anteriorly; skull flattened dorsally.
       E. panamintinus, p. 316
      16′. Submalar dark stripe complete anteriorly; skull rounded dorsally.
       E. speciosus, p. 315
     15′. Occurring east of California or, in the southern Sierra Nevada of California, outer face of I describing arc having radius of more than 5.3.
      17. Occurring at higher elevations on Charleston Peak, Nevada, and Potosi Mtn. Range. . . . . *E. palmeri*, p. 319
      17′. Not occurring on Charleston Peak, Nevada, or other parts of Potosi Mtn. Range.
       18. Upper parts tawny; width of base of baculum less than ¼ length of shaft; angle formed by tip and shaft of baculum more than 115°.
        E. quadrivittatus, p. 311
       18′. Upper parts dark; width of base of baculum more than ⅓ length of shaft; angle formed by tip and shaft of baculum less than 115°.
        E. umbrinus, p. 317
9′. Greatest length of skull less than 34.5.
 19. Greatest length of skull less than 31.7.
  20. Underside of tail bright orange-yellow. . . . . *E. alpinus*, p. 298
  20′. Underside of tail not bright orange-yellow.
   21. Length of bent tip of baculum less than 28 per cent of length of shaft. *E. minimus*, p. 299
   21′. Length of bent tip of baculum more than 28 per cent of length of shaft.
    E. amoenus, p. 303
19′. Greatest length of skull more than 31.7.
 22. Occurring north of 45° 15′ and with baculum 5 mm. or more long. . . *E. ruficaudus*, p. 312
 22′. Occurring south of 45° 15′ and with baculum less than 5 mm. long.
  23. When in California and Nevada.
   24. Submalar dark stripe obsolete anteriorly; skull flattened dorsally; base of baculum markedly widened and base of keel of baculum ½ length of tip.
    E. panamintinus, p. 316
   24′. Submalar dark stripe complete anteriorly; skull rounded dorsally; base of baculum of variable width and base of keel of variable length.
    25. Combination of following: length of skull, 31.8–33.9; length of head and body, 106–127; incisive foramina small; inner pair of pale dorsal stripes relatively broad; tip of baculum 35 or fewer per cent of length of shaft; angle between tip and shaft of baculum more than 115°. . . . . *E. amoenus*, p. 303

Key continued on page 298

25′. Combination of following: length of skull, 33.5–36.7; length of head and body, 114–144; incisive foramina large; inner pair of pale dorsal stripes relatively narrow; tip of baculum 36 or more per cent of length of shaft; angle between tip and shaft of baculum less than 115°.

    26. Outer pale stripes not broader than inner pale stripes; dark submalar stripe without black center below eye; tip of upper incisor anterior to posterior border of alveolus when skull is placed on horizontal surface; distal ½ of shaft of baculum laterally compressed.

E. umbrinus, p. 317

    26′. Outer pale stripes broader than inner pale stripes; dark submalar stripe with black center below eye; tip of upper incisor posterior to posterior border of alveolus when skull is placed on horizontal surface; distal ⅔ of shaft of baculum laterally compressed.   .   *E. speciosus*, p. 315

23′. When outside of California and Nevada.

    27. Shaft of baculum thick, robust; keel of baculum at least ¼ as long as tip.

        28. Base of baculum markedly expanded; angle between tip and shaft of baculum less than 115°; upper parts of dark, somber hue. . . . . *E. umbrinus*, p. 317

        28′. Base of baculum not markedly expanded; angle between tip and shaft of baculum more than 115°; upper parts more brightly colored. . . . . *E. quadrivittatus*, p. 311

    27′. Shaft of baculum slender, light; keel of baculum less than ¼ as long as tip.

        29. Underside of tail grayish yellow; length of skull, 31.0–34.2; tip of baculum 28 per cent or less of length of shaft. . . . . *E. minimus*, p. 299

        29′. Underside of tail ochraceous; length of skull 33.0–35.6; tip of baculum more than 28 per cent of length of shaft. . . . . *E. amoenus*, p. 303

Eutamias alpinus (Merriam)
Alpine Chipmunk

1893. *Tamias alpinus* Merriam, Proc. Biol. Soc. Washington, 8:137, December 28, type from Big Cottonwood Meadows, 10,000 ft., just south of Mount Whitney, Tulare Co., California.

1897. *Eutamias alpinus* Merriam, Proc. Biol. Soc. Washington, 11:191, July 1.

External measurements: 166–195; 70–85; 28–31. Greatest length of skull, 28.9–31.7. Colors generally yellowish; light and dark stripes weakly contrasted. Skull broad and flattened. Smaller than other species of same area, except *E. minimus* from

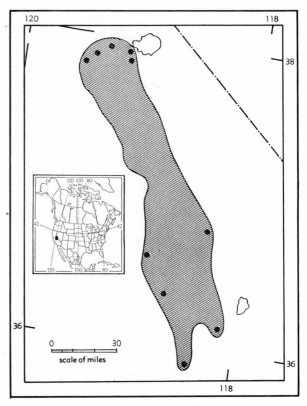

Map 197. *Eutamias alpinus*.

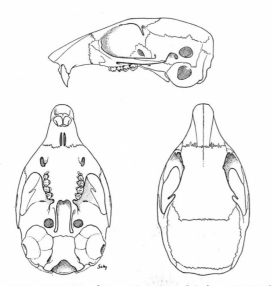

Fig. 194. *Eutamias alpinus*, Cottonwood Lakes, 11,000 ft., Inyo Co., California, No. 14942 M.V.Z., ♂, X 1½.

which *E. alpinus* differs in shorter tail that is more nearly flat in cross section and bright orange instead of dull grayish yellow beneath, longer and finer fur, paler dorsal coloration, more ochraceous in light dorsal stripes, larger and more flattened braincase, longer and blunter rostrum, wider palate and shorter incisors. Baculum: Shaft thin; keel low, ⅟₇ of length of tip; tip 39 per cent of length of shaft; angle formed by tip and shaft 135°; distal ⅓ of shaft slightly compressed laterally; base slightly wider than shaft; shaft short, 2.17 mm.

MARGINAL RECORDS.—California (Johnson, 1943:75, unless otherwise noted): Mt. Conness (A. H. Howell, 1929b: 35); Warren Fork of Leevining Creek, 9700–10,000 ft.; Independence Creek, 10,000 ft. (A. H. Howell, 1929b:35); Onion Valley; Olancha Peak, 9750–10,500 ft.; Horse Corral Meadows; Mineral King (A. H. Howell, 1929b:35); Mt. Clark, 10,000 ft.; Mt. Hoffman, 10,200–10,700 ft.; Cold Canyon, 8000 ft.

Eutamias minimus
Least Chipmunk

C. G. Pritchard × ¼

External measurements: 167–225; 70–114; 26–35. Greatest length of skull, 28.7–34.2. Stripes well defined. Skull having high, narrow braincase. Differences from *E. alpinus* are mentioned in the account of that species. The only other species with which *E. minimus* is likely to be confused is *E. amoenus*. Certain subspecies of these two species (for example *E. m. operarius* and *E. a. amoenus*) closely resemble each other. As yet no specific diagnosis has been framed that will serve to distinguish the two species in all parts of their geographic ranges. At any one place, however, the two are distinguishable. For example, in Nevada and California, *E. minimus* differs from *E. amoenus* as follows: smaller; paler; underside of tail yellowish instead of reddish; braincase less flattened; zygomatic arches less flattened; rostrum shorter; upper incisors less recurved. In Wyoming and southwestern Montana, and possibly in other areas, the tip of the baculum, in adult males, is less than 28 per cent of the length of the shaft (averages 24 per cent), whereas the tip is more than 28 per cent in *E. amoenus* (averages 34 per cent). For differences in

other areas where the two species occur reference should be made to A. H. Howell's (1929:36–77) "Revision of the American Chipmunks."

E. minimus lives in sagebrush far distant from conifers as well as in sagebrush where conifers occur. In our experience, the habitat of *E. amoenus* always includes conifers.

Eutamias minimus arizonensis A. H. Howell

1922. *Eutamias minimus arizonensis* A. H. Howell, Jour. Mamm., 3:178, August 4, type from Prieto Plateau, south end Blue Range, Greenlee Co., Arizona.

MARGINAL RECORDS.—Arizona (A. H. Howell, 1929b: 53): type locality; Alpine.

Eutamias minimus atristriatus V. Bailey

1913. *Eutamias atristriatus* V. Bailey, Proc. Biol. Soc. Washington, 26:129, May 21, type from Penasco Creek, 7400 ft., 12 mi. E Cloudcroft, Sacramento Mts., New Mexico.
1922. *Eutamias minimus atristriatus*, A. H. Howell, Jour. Mamm., 3:178, August 4.

MARGINAL RECORDS.—New Mexico (A. H. Howell, 1929b:52): 6 mi. E Cloudcroft; Penasco.

Eutamias minimus borealis (J. A. Allen)

1877. [*Tamias asiaticus*] var. *borealis* J. A. Allen, *in* Coues and Allen, Monogr. N. Amer. Rodentia, p. 793, August, type from Fort Liard, Mackenzie.
1922. *Eutamias minimus borealis*, A. H. Howell, Jour. Mamm., 3:183, August 4.

MARGINAL RECORDS (A. H. Howell, 1929b:57, unless otherwise noted).—Mackenzie: Fort Simpson (Banfield, 1951:117); Hay River (*ibid.*); Fort Resolution. Saskatchewan: Poplar Point, Athabasca Lake. Manitoba: The Pas (Anderson and Rand, 1944:133); Wekusko Lake, Eastside, District of The Pas (22116 KU); Oxford House. Ontario: Moose River (Anderson, 1940:64); Minaki. North Dakota: Fort Pembina; Turtle Mts. Montana: Zortman; Big Snowy Range (Anderson, 1947:114); 4 mi. W Tyler; Bear Paw Range (Anderson, 1947:114). Saskatchewan: Fort Walsh. British Columbia: Assiniboine Pass (Cowan and Guiguet, 1956:137); Tucheeda Lake; 8 mi. W Babine; head Finley River, near Thudade Lake; mouth Dease River, Alaska Highway (Rand, 1944:41).

In British Columbia, specimens from Tornado Pass are assigned by Cowan and Guiguet (1956:137) to this subspecies instead of to *oreocetes*.

Eutamias minimus cacodemus Cary

1906. *Eutamias pallidus cacodemus* Cary, Proc. Biol. Soc. Washington, 19:89, June 4, type from head of Corral Draw, Sheep Mtn., Big Badlands, South Dakota.
1922. *Eutamias minimus cacodemus*, A. H. Howell, Jour. Mamm., 3:183, August 4.

MARGINAL RECORDS.—South Dakota (A. H. Howell, 1929b:45, none of the localities have been found on any map and their exact positions are unknown): *Cheyenne River Badlands; Corral Draw*; type locality.

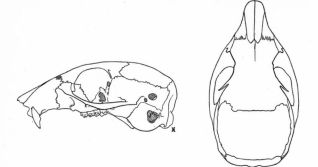

Fig. 195. *Eutamias minimus scrutator*, Wisconsin Creek, 7800 ft., Nevada, No. 45513 M.V.Z., ♀, X 1½.

Eutamias minimus caniceps Osgood

1900. *Eutamias caniceps* Osgood, N. Amer. Fauna, 19:28, October 6, type from Lake Laberge, Yukon.
1922. *Eutamias minimus caniceps,* A. H. Howell, Jour. Mamm., 3:184, August 4.

MARGINAL RECORDS (A. H. Howell, 1929b:58, unless otherwise noted).—Yukon: Sheldon Mtn. (Anderson, 1947: 114). Mackenzie: Nahanni River Mts. (*ibid.*). British Columbia: McDane Post, Dease River; near head Stikine River; Groundhog Mtn. (Cowan and Guiguet, 1956:137); Telegraph Creek; Atlin; Bennett City. Yukon: 1½ mi. S, 3 mi. E Dalton Post (Baker, 1951:100); 6 mi. SW Kluane, 2550 ft. (*ibid.*); Fort Selkirk (Rand, 1945b:48).

Eutamias minimus caryi Merriam

1908. *Eutamias minimus caryi* Merriam, Proc. Biol. Soc. Washington, 21:143, June 9, type from Medano Ranch, San Luis Valley, Alamosa Co., Colorado.

MARGINAL RECORDS.—Colorado (Warren, 1942:145): type locality; San Luis Lakes; Mosca.

Eutamias minimus confinis A. H. Howell

1925. *Eutamias minimus confinis* A. H. Howell, Jour. Mamm., 6:52, February 9, type from head of Trapper Creek, 8500 ft., W slope Bighorn Mts., Wyoming.

MARGINAL RECORDS (White, 1953:597).—Wyoming: Medicine Wheel Ranch, 9000 ft., 28 mi. E Lovell; 20 mi. from [W ?] Sheridan; 5½ mi. W, 1 mi. S Buffalo, 6500 ft.; *head North Fork Powder River*; 3 mi. SE Tensleep, 4300 ft.; type locality.

Eutamias minimus consobrinus (J. A. Allen)

1890. *Tamias minimus consobrinus* J. A. Allen, Bull. Amer. Mus. Nat. Hist., 3:112, June, type from Parleys Canyon, Wasatch Mts., near former site of Barclay, Utah.
1901. *Eutamias minimus consobrinus,* Miller and Rehn, Proc. Boston Soc. Nat. Hist., 30(1):42, December 27.
1905. *Eutamias lectus* J. A. Allen, Brooklyn Inst., Mus. Sci. Bull., 1:117, March 31, type from Beaver Valley, Beaver Co., Utah.

1918. *Eutamias consobrinus clarus* V. Bailey, Proc. Biol. Soc. Washington, 31:31, May 16, type from Swan Lake Valley, Yellowstone National Park, Wyoming.

MARGINAL RECORDS.—Montana: head Sage Creek, Pryor Mts. (21682 KU). Wyoming (White, 1953:594): Needle Mtn.; 12 mi. N Kendall; Lake Fork, Wind River Mts.; Moccasin Lake, 10,100 ft., 19 mi. W, 4 mi. N Lander; *3 mi. E, ½ mi. N South Pass City, 7900 ft.*; South Pass City; Big Sandy; 4 mi. W Pinedale, 7200 ft.; Stanley; Kemmerer; Cumberland, 14 mi. S, 1 mi. W Kemmerer, 6550 ft.; Fort Bridger; Lone Tree. Utah (Durrant, 1952:135): Summit Springs. Colorado (A. H. Howell, 1929b:47–48, unless otherwise noted): Lay; *Oak Creek*; Elkhead Mts., 20 mi. E Slater; Hahn Peak; Canadian Creek; Chambers Lake; Grand Lake; Twin Lakes; Almont; Coventry, 6800 ft. (Warren, 1942:146); Crawford; 14 mi. SE Dragon, Utah. Utah (Durrant, 1953:135): Nipple; SW slope Bald Peak, 10,500 ft., Uinta Mts.; near Soldier Summit; Baldy Ranger Station; Elkhorn G.S., 9400 ft., Fishlake Plateau, 14 mi. N Torrey; Wildcat R.S., 8700 ft., Boulder Mtn.; Bryce National Park; East Rim, just outside Zion National Park boundary; Cedar City; Beaver; 10 mi. E Sigurd; Ephraim; Butterfield Canyon, 3 mi. SW Butterfield Tunnel, 8000 ft. Idaho: Inkom (Davis, 1939:215); 12 mi. (via highway) NW Rea (21685 KU). Wyoming: Bunsen Peak, Yellowstone National Park (A. H. Howell, 1929b:48). Arizona: Bright Angel Spring, Kaibab Plateau (*op. cit.*, p. 47). Localities (A. H. Howell, 1929b:47–48) not found: Colorado: Coyote Basin; Cedar Springs.

Eutamias minimus grisescens A. H. Howell

1925. *Eutamias minimus grisescens* A. H. Howell, Jour. Mamm., 6:52, February 9, type from Farmer, Douglas Co., Washington.

MARGINAL RECORDS.—Washington (Dalquest, 1948: 253, unless otherwise noted): Douglas; Coulee City (A. H. Howell, 1929b:41); Moses Coulee (*ibid.*); Pasco; Vantage.

Eutamias minimus hudsonius Anderson and Rand

1944. *Eutamias minimus hudsonius* Anderson and Rand, Canadian Field-Nat., 57:133, January 24, type from Bird, Hudson Bay Railway, Mile 349, Manitoba.

MARGINAL RECORDS (Anderson, 1947:114).—Manitoba: Herchmer, Hudson Bay Railway, Mile 412; type locality; Thicket Portage, Hudson Bay Railway, Mile 165; Alberta Lake near Flin Flon. Anderson (*loc. cit.*) states that *E. m. hudsonius* "probably occurs in extreme northwestern Ontario and northeastern Saskatchewan."

Eutamias minimus minimus (Bachman)

1839. *Tamias minimus* Bachman, Jour. Acad. Nat. Sci. Philadelphia, 8:71, type from Green River, near mouth Big Sandy Creek, Sweetwater Co., Wyoming.
1901. *Eutamias minimus,* Miller and Rehn, Proc. Boston Soc. Nat. Hist., 30(1):42, December 27.

MARGINAL RECORDS.—Wyoming (White, 1953:592): 40 mi. E Dubois; 27 mi. N, 1 mi. E Powder River, 6075 ft.; Casper; Spring Creek, 10 mi. W Marshall; Sheep Creek; 30 mi. E Rawlins, 6750 ft.; Sulphur Springs. Colorado: Snake River, 20 mi. W Baggs, Wyoming (A. H. Howell, 1929b: 38); Sand Creek (Warren, 1942:144); *Lay* (A. H. Howell,

1929b:38); Lily (Warren, 1942:144); Ladore (A. H. Howell, 1929:38). Utah: just N of Linwood (Durrant, 1952:137). Wyoming (White, 1953:592): Henrys Fork, mouth of Burnt Fork; 15 mi. WSW Granger; Opal; Fontanelle; Big Piney; 60 mi. SE Jackson; 2 mi. SE Big Sandy; Little Sandy River; Ft. Washakie; Wind River, near mouth Meadow Creek; Jackeys Creek, 3 mi. S Dubois.

Eutamias minimus neglectus (J. A. Allen)

1890. *Tamias quadrivittatus neglectus* J. A. Allen, Bull. Amer. Mus. Nat. Hist., 3:106, June, type from Montreal River, Ontario.
1922. *Eutamias minimus neglectus,* A. H. Howell, Jour. Mamm., 3:184, August 4.

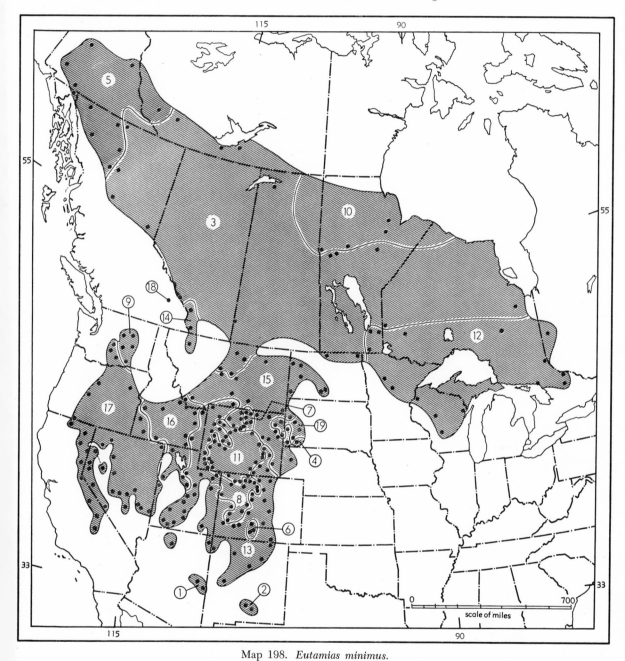

Map 198. *Eutamias minimus.*

Guide to subspecies
1. *E. m. arizonensis*
2. *E. m. atristriatus*
3. *E. m. borealis*
4. *E. m. cacodemus*
5. *E. m. caniceps*
6. *E. m. caryi*
7. *E. m. confinis*
8. *E. m. consobrinus*
9. *E. m. grisescens*
10. *E. m. hudsonius*
11. *E. m. minimus*
12. *E. m. neglectus*
13. *E. m. operarius*
14. *E. m. oreocetes*
15. *E. m. pallidus*
16. *E. m. pictus*
17. *E. m. scrutator*
18. *E. m. selkirki*
19. *E. m. silvaticus*

1925. *Eutamias minimus jacksoni* A. H. Howell, Jour. Mamm., 6:53, February 9, type from Crescent Lake, Oneida Co., Wisconsin. Anderson and Rand, Canadian Field-Nat., 57:134, January 24, 1944, regard *E. m. jacksoni* as a synonym of *E. m. neglectus*. White, Univ. Kansas Publ., Mus. Nat. Hist., 5:618, December 1, 1953, accepts the subspecies as valid.

MARGINAL RECORDS.—Ontario: Lake Seul (Anderson, 1947:114); Kapuskasing (*ibid.*). Quebec: 6 mi. N Authier Nord (Peterson, 1953:3). Ontario (*ibid.*): Temagami; Lister Twp., Algonquin Park; Cache Lake, Algonquin Park; French River. Wisconsin: Marinette (Cory, 1912:137); Camp Douglas (White, 1953:618); Thorp (Schmidt, 1931: 111); mouth of Namekagan River (Cory, 1921:137). Minnesota: Cass County (Swanson, *et al.*, 1945:79); Clearwater County (*ibid.*). Manitoba: Caddy Lake, Sandilands Forest Reserve (Anderson, 1947:114); Cedar Lake (Soper, 1946:142); Whiteshell Forest Reserve (*ibid.*). Localities not found: Red Rock Lake (Soper, 1946:142); Haveland Bay (Anderson, 1944:134).

Eutamias minimus operarius Merriam

1905. *Eutamias amoenus operarius* Merriam, Proc. Biol. Soc. Washington, 18:164, June 29, type from Gold Hill, 7400 ft., Colorado.
1922. *Eutamias minimus operarius*, A. H. Howell, Jour. Mamm., 3:183, August 4.

MARGINAL RECORDS.—Wyoming (White, 1953:598, 602): 6 mi. S, 2 mi. W Casper; Springhill, 12 mi. N Laramie Peak; 6 mi. W Islay. Colorado: Livermore (Warren, 1942:147); Littleton (A. H. Howell, 1929b:50); Elbert (*ibid.*); Hardscrabble Canyon, 7 mi. above Wetmore (*ibid.*); Fisher Peak (Warren, 1942:147). New Mexico (V. Bailey, 1932:90, unless otherwise noted): Raton Mts.; Halls Peak; 10 mi. NE Santa Fe (A. H. Howell, 1929:51); Gallinas Mts.; Jemez Mts.; Chuska Mts. Arizona: Tunitcha Mts. (A. H. Howell, 1929b:47, as *E. m. consobrinus*). Utah (Durrant, 1952:141): Gooseberry Ranger Station, 8300 ft., Elk Ridge; Uncompahgre Indian Reservation. Colorado (A. H. Howell, 1929b:50, unless otherwise noted): Somerset; Coventry; Silverton (Warren, 1942:147); Lake City; St. Elmo; Tennessee Pass (A. H. Howell, 1929b:50–51); Hot Springs, Middle Park; Longs Peak; North Park [Canadian Creek]. Wyoming (White, 1953:602): 5 mi. N, 5 mi. E Savery, 6900 ft.; 10 mi. E, 6 mi. S Saratoga, 8800 ft.

Eutamias minimus oreocetes Merriam

1897. *Eutamias oreocetes* Merriam, Proc. Biol. Soc. Washington, 11:207, July 1, type from Summit Mtn., at timberline, N of Summit Station, on Great Northern Railroad, Montana.
1922. *Eutamias minimus oreocetes*, A. H. Howell, Jour. Mamm., 3:183, August 4.

MARGINAL RECORDS.—Alberta (Anderson, 1947:115): Forget-me-not Mtn.; Waterton Lakes National Park. Montana: type locality.

Eutamias minimus pallidus (J. A. Allen)

1874. *Tamias quadrivitatus* var. *pallidus* J. A. Allen, Proc. Boston Soc. Nat. Hist., 16:289. Type locality, Camp Thorne, near Glendive, Montana.
1922. *Eutamias minimus pallidus*, A. H. Howell, Jour. Mamm., 3:183, August 4.

MARGINAL RECORDS.—North Dakota (A. H. Howell, 1929b:44): Williston; Goodall; Palace Buttes, 6 mi. N Cannon Ball; Parkin; Oakdale; Marmarth. Montana (A. H. Howell, 1929b:44): Alzada. South Dakota (*ibid.*): Belle Fourche. Wyoming (White, 1953:595–596): 4 mi. S, 3 mi. W Rocky Point; Pine Ridge; Newcastle. South Dakota (A. H. Howell, 1929b:44): 20 mi. N Elk Mtn., 6000 ft.; Edgemont. Nebraska: Glen (*ibid.*). Wyoming (White, 1953:595–596): *Laramie County*; 15 mi. SW Wheatland; Douglas; Merino; Sheridan. Montana: Little Bighorn River, 14 mi. S Crow Agency (A. H. Howell, 1929b:44). Wyoming (White, 1953:595–596): Greybull; *Hyattville*; 15 mi. W Tensleep; 10 mi. S Tensleep, near No Wood Creek; head Bridger Creek; Willow Creek, 10 mi. SW Thermopolis; 2 mi. S, 2 mi. E Meeteetse. Montana (A. H. Howell, 1929b: 44): Columbus; Dillon; Judith River; Jensen's Ranch; Darnell's Ranch, on Missouri River.

Eutamias minimus pictus (J. A. Allen)

1890. *Tamias minimus pictus* J. A. Allen, Bull. Amer. Mus. Nat. Hist., 3:115, June, type from Kelton, Utah.
1901. *Eutamias minimus pictus*, Miller and Rehn, Proc. Boston Soc. Nat. Hist., 30:42, December 27.
1890. *Tamias minimus melanurus* Merriam, N. Amer. Fauna, 4:22, October 8, type from W side Snake River, near Blackfoot, Idaho.

MARGINAL RECORDS.—Montana: Donovan (A. H. Howell, 1929b:40). Idaho (Davis, 1939:213): Dubois; Idaho Falls; Pocatello; Malad City. Utah (Durrant, 1952: 139): Fairfield; Nephi; Ibapah; type locality. Idaho (Davis, 1939:212): 1 mi. N Idavada; Deer Flat; Salmon Valley, near Sawtooth City; Lemhi.

Eutamias minimus scrutator Hall and Hatfield

1934. *Eutamias minimus scrutator* Hall and Hatfield, Univ. California Publ. Zool., 40(6):321, February 12, type from near Blanco Mtn. 10,500 ft., White Mts., Mono Co., California.

MARGINAL RECORDS.—Washington (Dalquest, 1948: 252): Ellensburg; Sunnyside. Oregon: Baker (A. H. Howell, 1929b:40). Idaho (Davis, 1939:213): Silver City; 2½ mi. E Jordan Valley. Nevada: Goose Creek, 2 mi. W Utah boundary (Hall, 1946:333). Utah: 4 mi. S Gandy (Durrant, 1952:139). Nevada (Hall, 1946:333, unless otherwise noted): Eagle Valley, 3½ mi. N Ursine, 5900 ft.; Garden Valley, 8½ mi. NE Sharp; Burned Corral Canyon, Quinn Canyon Mts.; 3 mi. W Hamilton, 8400 ft.; Fish Spring Valley, ½ mi. N Fish Lake, 6500 ft.; 2½ mi. NE Silverbow, 7000 ft., Kawich Mts.; Toquima Mts., 2 mi. W Meadow Valley Ranger Station; Cloverdale Creek; Smiths Creek, 6800 ft.; Eldorado Canyon, Humboldt Range; Quinn River Crossing, 4100 ft. (Hall, 1946:332); 12 mi. N and 2 mi. E Gerlach, 4000 ft. (*ibid.*). California: Warm Spring, 9 mi. E Amedee (Johnson, 1943:80). Nevada: Horse Canyon, Pahrum Peak, 5800 ft. (Hall, 1946:332); 2¾ mi. SW Pyramid (*ibid.*); 6 mi. NE Virginia City, 6000 ft. (*ibid.*); Cottonwood Canyon, Mt. Grant, 7400 ft. (Hall, 1946:333); N side Mt. Magruder, 7400 ft. (*ibid.*). California: Menache Meadows, 5 mi. SW Olancha Peak (A. H. Howell, 1929b: 40); Mazourka Canyon, Inyo Mts. (Johnson, 1943:80); Mammoth (A. H. Howell, 1929b:40); Diamond Valley, 1 mi. SE Woodfords (Johnson, 1943:80); Vinton (*ibid.*); Spaldings, Eagle Lake (*ibid.*); 10 mi. SW Alturas (*ibid.*); Mt. Hebron (Johnson, 1944:77). Oregon: Tule Lake (A. H.

Howell, 1929b:41); Fremont (*ibid.*, on geographic grounds); 2 mi. NE Prineville (Hall and Hatfield, 1934:325). Washington: Wiley City (Dalquest, 1948:252). Nevada: 1½ mi. NW Mountain Well, 6100 ft. (Hall, 1946:333).

Eutamias minimus selkirki Cowan

1946. *Eutamias minimus selkirki* Cowan, Proc. Biol. Soc. Washington, 59:113, October 25, type from Paradise Mine, near Toby Creek, 19 mi. W Invermere, British Columbia. Known only from the type locality.

Eutamias minimus silvaticus White

1952. *Eutamias minimus silvaticus* White, Univ. Kansas Publ., Mus. Nat. Hist., 5:261, April 10, type from 3 mi. NW Sundance, 5900 ft., Crook Co., Wyoming.

MARGINAL RECORDS.—Wyoming: 15 mi. N Sundance, Black Hills National Forest, 5500 ft. (White, 1953:598). South Dakota (A. H. Howell, 1929b:57, on geographic grounds): Fort Meade; Rapid City; Buffalo Gap. Wyoming (White, 1953:598): SE Newcastle; Devils Tower.

Eutamias amoenus
Yellow-pine Chipmunk

External measurements: 181–245; 73–108; 29–35. Greatest length of skull, 31.3–35.6. Some shade of reddish more prominent than in most subspecies of *E. minimus* (account of which see for comparison). Smaller, more tawny, and braincase more flattened than in *E. panamintinus*. Skull averaging smaller than in *E. umbrinus* or *E. speciosus*. In the Sierra Nevada of California where the three species occur in the same area, *E. amoenus* differs from *E. umbrinus* as follows: smaller; more reddish (less grayish) head and shoulders; broader inner light dorsal stripes; more ochraceous suffusion over light facial stripes and underparts; less massive skull with relatively broader braincase; less elevated rostrum; shorter upper incisors and less nearly parallel zygomatic arches; bent tip of baculum no more than, instead of more than, 35 per cent of length of shaft. From *E. speciosus*, *E. amoenus* differs as follows: smaller; shorter and broader-appearing ears; less sharply contrasting light and dark stripes; in *amoenus* the inner pair of light dorsal stripes is broader and the outer pair of light stripes, though not always narrower, is less conspicuous; light facial stripes more heavily washed with ochraceous; dark facial stripes less blackish; skull less massive; rostrum more pointed; incisive foramina smaller; bent tip of baculum no more than, instead of more than, 35 per cent of length of shaft (30 to 35 per cent in *amoenus* and 47 to 55 per cent in *speciosus*).

Eutamias amoenus albiventris Booth

1947. *Eutamias amoenus albiventris* Booth, Murrelet, 28 (1):7, April 30, type from Wickiup Spring, 23 mi. W Anatone, Asotin-Garfield County boundary, Washington.

MARGINAL RECORDS (Booth, 1947:8).—Washington: Dayton; Anatone. Oregon: Cornucopia; Bourne; Meacham. Washington: Wallula (?); Prescott.

Eutamias amoenus affinis (J. A. Allen)

1890. *Tamias quadrivittatus affinis* J. A. Allen, Bull. Amer. Mus. Nat. Hist., 3:103, June, type from Ashcroft, British Columbia.
1922. *Eutamias amoenus affinis*, A. H. Howell, Jour. Mamm., 3:184, August 4.

MARGINAL RECORDS (A. H. Howell, 1929b:73, unless otherwise noted).—British Columbia: Lac la Hache (Anderson, 1947:115); Black Pines (Cowan, 1946:109); Kamloops (*ibid.*); Schoonover Mtn., Okanagan Valley; Rossland (Anderson, 1947:115). Washington: Republic; Omak Lake; Chelan; Wenatchee; 10 mi. NW Ellensburg (Dalquest, 1948:257); Cleveland; 10 mi. N Grand Dalles; Mt. St. Helens; Easton; Wenatchee Lake; Hart Lake (Dalquest, 1948:257); Sheep Mts. British Columbia: Hedley (Cowan, 1946:109); Hope (Gordon's Ranch); Lillooet (Anderson, 1947:115); Clinton (Cowan, 1946:109). Cowan and Guiguet (1956:140–142) assign to the subspecies *ludibundus* some of the material mentioned immediately above.

Eutamias amoenus amoenus (J. A. Allen)

1890. *Tamias amoenus* J. A. Allen, Bull. Amer. Mus. Nat. Hist., 3:90, June, type from Fort Klamath, Oregon.
1913. *Eutamias amoenus*, Merriam, Proc. Biol. Soc. Washington, 11:94, July 11.
1913. *Eutamias amoenus propinquus* Anthony, Bull. Amer. Mus. Nat. Hist., 32:6, March 7, type from Ironside, Malheur Co., Oregon.

MARGINAL RECORDS.—Idaho (Davis, 1939:219, unless otherwise noted): vicinity of Riggins (Rust, 1946:318); Mill Creek, 14 mi. W Challis; Birch Creek, 10 mi. S Nicholia; mountains E of Birch Creek; Schutt's Mine; 8 mi. W Swan Lake; Malad. Utah (Durrant, 1952:142): Pine Canyon, 6600 ft., Raft River Mts., 17 mi. NW Kelton; S. Fork George Creek, 7000 ft., Raft River Mts., 5 mi. SE Yost. Nevada (Hall, 1946:335): summit between heads Copper and Coon creeks, Jarbidge Mts.; Cobb Creek, 6 mi. SW Mountain City. Oregon (A. H. Howell, 1929b:64): Cedar Mts.; Steens Mts. Nevada: 12-mile Creek, ½ mi. E California boundary (Hall, 1946:335). California: E face Warren Peak, 8700 ft., Warner Mts. (Johnson, 1943:85); 8 mi. S Susanville (Johnson, 1943:86); Millford (A. H. Howell, 1929b:63); 1½ mi. SE Sierraville (Johnson, 1943:86); Lincoln Creek, 6200 ft. (A. H. Howell, 1929b:63); Chaparal (*sic*) (*ibid.*); Sisson (Johnson, 1943:85); 3 mi. SW Weed (*ibid.*); near head Little Shasta River, 4000 ft., N side Goosenest Mtn. (*ibid.*). Oregon (A. H. Howell, 1929b:64): type locality; Diamond Lake; Sisters; Antelope; McEwen (A. H. Howell, 1929b:64).

Eutamias amoenus canicaudus Merriam

1903. *Eutamias canicaudus* Merriam, Proc. Biol. Soc. Washington, 16:77, May 29, type from Spokane, Washington.
1922. *Eutamias amoenus canicaudus*, A. H. Howell, Jour. Mamm., 3:184, August 4.

MARGINAL RECORDS.—Washington: Marcus (Anderson, 1947:115). Idaho: 5 mi. W Cocolalla (Davis, 1939:

222). Montana: Prospect Creek, near Thompson Falls (A. H. Howell, 1929b:71). Idaho: 2 mi. NE Weippe (Davis, 1939:222). Washington: Pullman (Dalquest, 1948: 258); Waterville (242470 BS); ½ mi. E Devil's Lake (Johnson, Cheney and Scheffer, 1951:40).

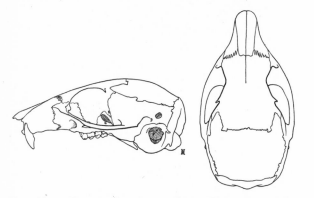

Fig. 196. *Eutamias amoenus celeris,* Pine Forest Mtn., Nevada, No. 7931 M.V.Z., ♂, X 1½.

Eutamias amoenus caurinus Merriam

1898. *Eutamias caurinus* Merriam, Proc. Acad. Nat. Sci. Philadelphia, 50:352, October 4, type from Olympic Mountains, Washington (timberline, near head of Soleduck River).
1922. *Eutamias amoenus caurinus,* A. H. Howell, Jour. Mamm., 3:184, August 4.

MARGINAL RECORDS.—Washington: Happy Lake, Olympic Mts. (A. H. Howell, 1929b:77); Deer Park (Dalquest, 1948:256); "near" head Dosewallips River (A. H. Howell, 1929b:77); type locality.

Eutamias amoenus celeris Hall and Johnson

1940. *Eutamias amoenus celeris* Hall and Johnson, Proc. Biol. Soc. Washington, 53:155, December 19, type from near head of Big Creek, 8000 ft., Pine Forest Mts., Humboldt Co., Nevada.

MARGINAL RECORDS (Hall, 1946:335).—Nevada: Alder Creek, 7000–8000 ft.; ridge "near" Pine Forest Mtn.

Eutamias amoenus cratericus Blossom

1937. *Eutamias amoenus cratericus* Blossom, Occas. Papers Mus. Zool., Univ. Michigan, 366:1, December 21, type from Grassy Cone, Craters of the Moon National Monument, 6000 ft., 26 mi. SW Arco, Butte Co., Idaho.

MARGINAL RECORDS (Davis, 1939:223).—Idaho: Sunset Cone; near Big Cinder Butte, Craters of the Moon; *30 mi. SW Arco, at S Base White Knob Mts.*

Eutamias amoenus felix (Rhoads)

1895. *Tamias quadrivittatus felix* Rhoads, Amer. Nat., 29: 941, October, type from Church Mountain, New Westminster district, British Columbia, near the international boundary.
1922. *Eutamias amoenus felix,* A. H. Howell, Jour. Mamm., 3:184, August 4.

MARGINAL RECORDS.—British Columbia: Fawn Bluff, Bute Inlet (Anderson, 1947:116); Tami Hy Creek (A. H. Howell, 1929b:76). Washington: Mt. Baker (*ibid.*).

Eutamias amoenus ludibundus Hollister

1911. *Eutamias ludibundus* Hollister, Smiths. Miscl. Coll. 56(26):1, December 5, type from Yellowhead Lake, 3700 ft., British Columbia.
1922. *Eutamias amoenus ludibundus,* A. H. Howell, Jour. Mamm., 3:184, August 4.

MARGINAL RECORDS.—British Columbia: Fraser River, near mouth N. Fork (A. H. Howell, 1929b:75). Alberta: head Smoky River (*op. cit.*:74); Henry House (*ibid.*); Astoria Creek (Cowan, 1946:110). British Columbia: Canim Lake (*ibid.*); Lillooet (A. H. Howell, 1929b:75); Hope (*ibid.*); Coalmont (*ibid.*). Washington: Hidden Lakes (*ibid.*); Lyman Lake (Dalquest, 1948:257); Mt. Stuart (A. H. Howell, 1929b:74); Lake Kachess (Dalquest, 1948: 257); Boulder Cave (*ibid.*); Glacier Basin, Mt. Rainier (A. H. Howell, 1929b:75); Mt. St. Helens (Dalquest, 1948: 257). Oregon (A. H. Howell, 1929b:75): Mt. Hood; Wapinitia; Three Sisters; O'Leary Mtn., 10 mi. S McKenzie Bridge. Washington: Winchester Mtn., Twin Lakes (A. H. Howell, 1929b:75). British Columbia: second summit, United States–Canada boundary, W of Skagit River (A. H. Howell, 1929b:75); McGillivary Creek, Lillooet District (*ibid.*); Quesnel (Cowan, 1946:110). Cowan and Guiguet (1956:140–142) assign specimens from some of the above mentioned localities to the subspecies *affinis.*

Eutamias amoenus luteiventris (J. A. Allen)

1890. *Tamias quadrivittatus luteiventris* J. A. Allen, Bull. Amer. Mus. Nat. Hist., 3:101, June, type from "Chief Mountain Lake" [= Waterton Lake], Alberta (3½ mi. N of the United States–Canada boundary).
1922. *Eutamias amoenus luteiventris,* A. H. Howell, Jour. Mamm., 3:179, August 4.

MARGINAL RECORDS (A. H. Howell, 1929b:68–69, unless otherwise noted).—British Columbia: Kinbasket Lake (Cowan, 1946:109). Alberta: Banff (Anderson, 1947:116); foothills 40 mi. W Calgary; Burmis. Montana: St. Marys Lake; Highwood Mts. (Anderson, 1947:116); Buffalo; Crazy Mts. (Anderson, 1947:116); Reed Point; Red Lodge. Wyoming (White, 1953:603): Valley; 3¾ mi. E, 1 mi. S Moran, 6200 ft.; Merna; head La Barge Creek, 9100 ft. Idaho (Davis, 1939:221): head Crow Creek, Preuss Mts.; Warm River; Salmon River Mts.; Fiddle Creek; Seven Devils Mts.; Craig Mts. Montana: Superior; Thompson Falls (Anderson, 1947:116). Washington: Newport (Dalquest, 1948: 258); 15 mi. W Marcus. British Columbia: Trail; Okanagan Landing; Rayleigh (Cowan, 1946:109).

Eutamias amoenus monoensis Grinnell and Storer

1916. *Eutamias amoenus monoensis* Grinnell and Storer, Univ. California Publ. Zool., 17:3, August 23, type from Warren Fork of Leevining Creek, 9200 ft., Mono Co., California.

MARGINAL RECORDS (Johnson, 1943:86, unless otherwise noted).—California: Mohawk, 4400 ft. Nevada: W side Truckee River, 1 mi. W Verde, 4900 ft. (Hall, 1946:336). California: Diamond Valley, 5500 ft., 1 mi. SE Woodfords; Swager Creek, 7600 ft., Sweetwater Range; Pine City, 8700 ft., near Mammoth; Long Valley, 7300 ft., near Convict Creek; Silver Lake (A. H. Howell, 1929b:66).

Eutamias amoenus ochraceus A. H. Howell

1925. *Eutamias amoenus ochraceus* A. H. Howell, Jour. Mamm., 6:54, February 9, type from Studhorse Canyon, 6500 ft., Siskiyou Mts., California.

MARGINAL RECORDS (Johnson, 1943:84–85, unless otherwise noted).—Oregon (A. H. Howell, 1929b:65): Ashland Peak; Siskiyou. California: head Deadfall Creek, W slope Mt. Eddy; Snow Mtn. (Johnson, 1947:65); W side Thomas Creek, South Yolla Bolly Mtn.; near Blake Lookout, South Fork Mtn., 5700 ft.; head Redcap Creek, 5800 ft., 10 mi. E, 4 mi. N Hoopa; head east fork Dunn Creek, Siskiyou Mts.

Eutamias amoenus septentrionalis Cowan

1946. *Eutamias amoenus septentrionalis* Cowan, Proc. Biol. Soc. Washington, 59:110, October 25, type from Ootsa Lake P.O., on north shore Ootsa Lake, British Columbia.

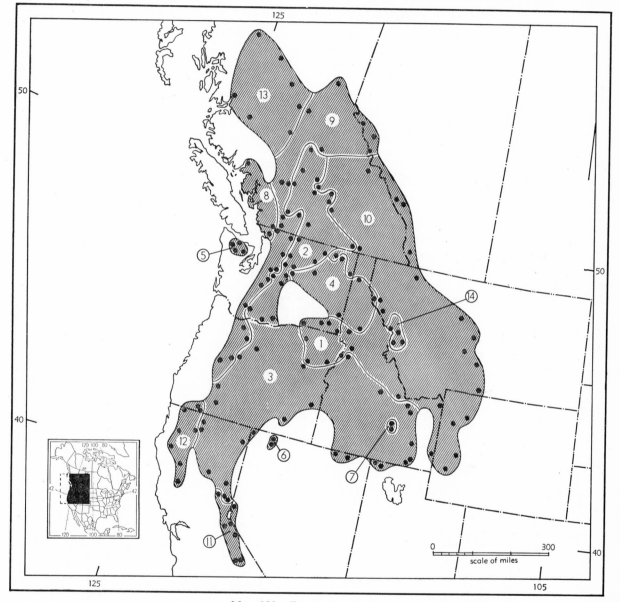

Map 199. *Eutamias amoenus.*

Guide to subspecies
1. *E. a. albiventris*
2. *E. a. affinis*
3. *E. a. amoenus*
4. *E. a. canicaudus*
5. *E. a. caurinus*
6. *E. a. celeris*
7. *E. a. cratericus*
8. *E. a. felix*
9. *E. a. ludibundus*
10. *E. a. luteiventris*
11. *E. a. monoensis*
12. *E. a. ochraceus*
13. *E. a. septentrionalis*
14. *E. a. vallicola*

MARGINAL RECORDS (Cowan, 1946:111, unless otherwise noted).—British Columbia: Rocher Deboule; Babine Lake; Sinkut Mts. (Munro, 1949:129); Puntchesakut Lake; Hanceville (Cowan and Guiguet, 1956:143); Rainbow Mts.; Kimsquit.

Eutamias amoenus vallicola A. H. Howell

1922. *Eutamias amoenus vallicola* A. H. Howell, Jour. Mamm., 3:179, August 4, type from Bass Creek, 3725 ft., near Stevensville, Montana.

MARGINAL RECORDS.—Montana: Lolo (A. H. Howell, 1929b:70); Skalkaho Road (Davis, 1937:24); Canyon Creek (*ibid.*); type locality.

Eutamias townsendii
Townsend's Chipmunk

External measurements: 227–277; 90–126; 34–39. Greatest length of skull, 36.8–40.8. In length of head and body (approximately 139) largest member of the subgenus *Neotamias*; average weight of adult males, 85 grams; "coloration varying from tawny or olivaceous with obscure stripes and tawny underparts . . . to grayish ochraceous with conspicuous stripes and white underparts. . . . Light and dark markings in general weakly contrasted, tending to blend at borders. Ochraceous pigments relatively dominant; light facial stripes and cheeks always more or less clouded. Backs of ears fully furred, with conspicuous white posterior third in all pelages. Dark facial stripes brown nearly throughout; submalar dark stripe continuous anteriorly with

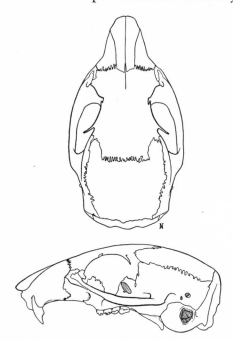

Fig. 197. *Eutamias townsendii senex*, Blue Canyon, 5000 ft., Placer Co., California, No. 18870 M.V.Z., ♂, X 1½.

ocular; concentration of ochraceous pigment on cheek suggesting incipient genal dark stripe. Dark dorsal stripes brown, central stripe nearly black. Inner pair of light dorsal stripes dull gray or brown; outer pair white, more or less clouded with gray or ochraceous. Tail relatively slender and sparsely haired, not so bushy as in *quadrimaculatus* and *sonomae*; reddish central area on underside of tail becoming darker toward base; submarginal black area on underside uniformly conspicuous laterally for entire length of tail, about 10 mm. in anteroposterior width terminally; edging white" (Johnson, 1943:112).

Skull massive, broad, and flattened. Braincase relatively small; zygomatic arches widely flaring and superior zygomatic process of squamosal nearly horizontal; outermost borders of zygomatic arches straight and nearly parallel; rostrum broad anteriorly; tips of nasals not separated by any terminal notch; incisive foramina approximately 3 mm. long.

Eutamias townsendii cooperi (Baird)

1855. *Tamias cooperi* Baird, Proc. Acad. Nat. Sci. Philadelphia, 7:334, type from Klickitat Pass, 4500 ft., Cascade Mts., Skamania Co., Washington (see Cooper, Amer. Nat., 2:531, December, 1868).
1919. *Eutamias townsendii cooperi,* Taylor, Proc. California Acad. Sci., ser. 4, 9:110, July 12.

MARGINAL RECORDS (A. H. Howell, 1929b:111–112, unless otherwise noted).—British Columbia: Roab's Ranch, near Hope (Anderson, 1947:117); *Lightning Lakes near Allison Pass* (Cowan and Guiguet, 1956:147). Washington: Barron; Stehekin; Entiat River, 20 mi. from mouth; mts. near Wenatchee; McAllister Meadows, Tieton River; 9 mi. SW Fort Simcoe; White Salmon. Oregon: Parkdale; Wapinitia; O'Leary Mtn., 10 mi. S McKenzie Bridge; Anchor; Glendale; Reston; Vida; Detroit. Washington: Skamania (Hall and Kelson, 1952:349); Yacolt (*ibid.*); White River, 3100 ft., Glacier National Park (Taylor and Shaw, 1927:92); Index Peak, 2700 ft.; Glacier. British Columbia: Huntingdon (Anderson, 1947:117, but Cowan and Guiguet, 1956:147 refer these specimens to the subspecies *townsendii*); Cultus Lake (*ibid.*). Washington: Chilliwack Creek, 30 mi. E Glacier. British Columbia: Chilliwack Lake.

Eutamias townsendii ochrogenys Merriam

1897. *Eutamias townsendii ochrogenys* Merriam, Proc. Biol. Soc. Washington, 11:195, 206, July 1, type from Mendocino, California.

MARGINAL RECORDS (Johnson, 1943:114, unless otherwise noted).—Oregon (A. H. Howell, 1929b:113): Port Orford; Rouge River Mts. California: Wimer Spring, 1800 ft., 7 mi. E town of Smith River; Coyote Peak, 3000 ft.; Fair Oaks; 5 mi. N Willits; Lake Leonard, 10 mi. NW Ukiah; Cazadero (A. H. Howell, 1929b:113); Freestone, thence up coast to point of beginning.

Eutamias townsendii senex (J. A. Allen)

1890. *Tamias senex* J. A. Allen, Bull. Amer. Mus. Nat. Hist., 3:83, June, type from summit of Donner Pass, Placer Co., California.

1922. *Eutamias townsendii senex*, A. H. Howell, Jour. Mamm., 3:181, August 4.

MARGINAL RECORDS.—Oregon (A. H. Howell, 1929b: 117): Mill Creek, 20 mi. W Warm Springs; Bend; Arnold Ice Cave; West Silver Creek, 4650 ft., Silver Lake; Naylox; Klamath Fall. California: Picard (A. H. Howell, 1929b: 116); 20 mi. NW Canby, 4500 ft. (Johnson, 1943:118); Lassen Creek (A. H. Howell, 1929b:116). Oregon: Lakeview (*op. cit.*:117). California (Johnson, 1943:118, unless otherwise noted): Fort Bidwell (A. H. Howell, 1929b: 116); head N. Fork Parker Creek, 5500 ft., Warner Mts.; 10 mi. N Canby (A. H. Howell, 1929b:116); Fort Crook (*ibid.*); 5 mi. N Fredonyer Peak, 5700 ft.; 8 mi. S Susanville; Sierra Valley (A. H. Howell, 1929b:116). Nevada: Glenbrook (Hall, 1946:345). California (Johnson, 1943: 118, unless otherwise noted): Silver Creek (A. H. Howell, 1929b:116); Mammoth; Shaver Ranger Station, 5300 ft.; "vicinity" Chinquapin, 6200–7500 ft.; Crane Flat, 6300 ft.; N. Fork Stanislaus River, 6700 ft. (A. H. Howell, 1929b: 116); Slipperyford (= Kyburz); [20 mi. SW] Quincy (A. H. Howell, 1929b:116); Lyonsville (*ibid.*); Baird (*ibid.*); Castle Lake, 5434 ft.; Mt. Tomhead, 5000 ft.; Grindstone Creek, 6500 ft. (A. H. Howell, 1929b:116); Snow Mtn. (Johnson, 1947:66); 4 mi. S South Yolla Bolly Mtn.; divide 12 mi. N North Yolla Bolly Mtn., 4400 ft.; Grizzly Creek, 5600 ft.; S. Fork Salmon River, 5000 ft.; head Rush Creek, 6400 ft.; Wildcat Peak, 7200 ft.; Shasta Valley (A. H. Howell, 1929b:116). Oregon (A. H. Howell, 1929b:117): Prospect; Crater Lake.

Eutamias townsendii siskiyou A. H. Howell

1922. *Eutamias townsendii siskiyou* A. H. Howell, Jour. Mamm., 3:180, August 4, type from near summit of White Mtn., 6000 ft., Siskiyou Mts., California.

MARGINAL RECORDS.—Oregon (A. H. Howell, 1929b: 114): W base Three Sisters; halfway between Drew and Crater Lake. California (Johnson, 1943:115): W. Fork Cottonwood Creek, 4000 ft., 4½ mi. SW Hilt; Donomore Meadow, 5800 ft., 15 mi. W Hilt; Preston Peak; Salmon Mts., S of Greenview; near Trinity Summit, 5000 ft., 10 mi. E Hoopa; Horse Ridge, 5500 ft., SE of Ruth; Van Dusen River, 12 mi. E Bridgeville; Horse Mtn., 4650–5200 ft.; White Mtn. Oregon (A. H. Howell, 1929b:114): Agness; Farren Ranger Station, Briggs Creek, 18 mi. SW Galice. Localities not found (Johnson, 1943:115) on South Fork Mtn., California: Kohenberger's Ranch; "vicinity" of Millers Spring; 2½ mi. NE Reilley's Ranch.

Eutamias townsendii townsendii (Bachman)

1839. *Tamias Townsendii* Bachman, Jour. Acad. Nat. Sci. Philadelphia, 8(pt. 1):68, type from lower Columbia River, near lower mouth of Willamette River, Oregon.
1897. *E[utamias]. townsendi*, Merriam, Proc. Biol. Soc. Washington, 11:192, July 1.
1842. *Tamias hindei* (typographical error for *hindsii*) Gray, Ann. Mag. Nat. Hist., ser. 1, 10:264, December, type locality not definitely known.
1903. *Tamias townsendii littoralis*, Elliot, Field. Columbian Mus., Publ. 74, Zool. Ser., 3(10):153, May 2, type from Marshfield, Oregon.

MARGINAL RECORDS (A. H. Howell, 1929b:109, unless otherwise noted).—British Columbia: Mt. Lehman (Anderson, 1947:117); Chilliwack (*ibid.*); Chilliwack Lake;

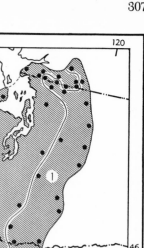

Map 200. *Eutamias townsendii.*

Guide to subspecies
1. *E. t. cooperi*
2. *E. t. ochrogenys*
3. *E. t. senex*
4. *E. t. siskiyou*
5. *E. t. townsendii*

Skagit (Anderson, 1947:117). Washington: Chilliwack Creek, Whatcom County. British Columbia: Huntingdon. Washington: Hamilton (Dalquest, 1948:262); North Bend; Mt. St. Helens. Oregon: Bissell; Eugene; Elk Head; Oakland; Myrtle Point; Empire, thence up coast to British Columbia: Esquimalt [introduced]; New Westminster.

Eutamias sonomae
Sonoma Chipmunk

External measurements: 220–272; 93–126; 32.0–39. Greatest length of skull, 36.6–39.7. Resembles *E. townsendii* but differs as follows: body paler; legs, tail, and ears longer; tail broader, more bushy; cheeks in winter, gray instead of brown; ears, in summer pelage, sparsely furred and unicolored instead of well-furred and bicolored; central reddish area on underside of tail becoming paler rather than darker anteriorly; skull narrower; braincase relatively larger and more inflated; zygomatic arches more closely appressed to skull; anterior tips of nasals separated from one another by notch; incisive foramina shorter; posterior edge of palate thickened and having short spine instead of terminating in long, slender (thin) spine; upper incisors more recurved and angle of notch across occlusal surfaces more acute; cheek-teeth smaller.

Eutamias sonomae alleni A. H. Howell

1922. *Eutamias townsendii alleni,* A. H. Howell, Jour. Mamm., 3:181, August 4, type from Inverness, Marin Co., California.

MARGINAL RECORDS (Johnson, 1943:126).—California: Point Reyes, 5 mi. W Inverness; type locality; Nicasio; Mailliard; Bolinas Ridge, 1350 ft., 2½ mi. S Lagunitas.

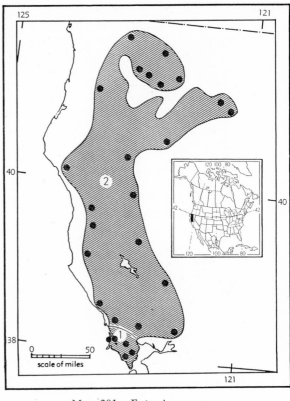

Map 201. *Eutamias sonomae.*

1. *E. s. alleni*					2. *E. s. sonomae*

Eutamias sonomae sonomae Grinnell

1915. *Eutamias sonomae* Grinnell, Univ. California Publ. Zool., 12:321, January 20, type from 1 mi. W Guerneville, Sonoma Co., California.

MARGINAL RECORDS (Johnson, 1943:125–126, unless otherwise noted).—California: Seiad Valley, 1400 ft.; Forest House, 3000 ft., 3 mi. S Yreka; 1 mi. S Weed; Scott Mts., W of Gazelle (A. H. Howell, 1929b:119); Scott River, 6 mi. NW Callahan; Salmon Mts., SW of Greenview; Dana; Fort Crook (A. H. Howell, 1929b:119); Redding (White, 1953:619); 3 mi. W Knob; coast Range, Tehama Co., 17 mi. W Paskenta (A. H. Howell, 1929b:119); Fouts Springs; Rumsey, 500 ft.; Vacaville (A. H. Howell, 1929b:119); Eldridge; Freestone, 300 ft.; 7 mi. W Cazadero; Christine (A. H. Howell, 1929b:118); Sherwood; Laytonville; Briceland (A. H. Howell, 1929b:118); Hoopa Valley. Californian localities not found are: Lime Gulch, 1 mi. E Castle Peak; Mt. Mill Hotel; Howell Mtn. (from Johnson, 1943:126), and Castle Peak; Hermitage; Kunz (from A. H. Howell, 1929b:119).

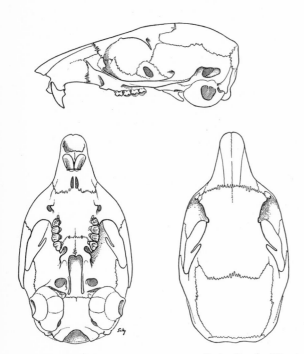

Fig. 198. *Eutamias sonomae sonomae,* Parks Creek, 1½ mi. SW Edgewood, 2900 ft., Siskiyou Co., California, No. 69197 M.V.Z., ♀, X 1½.

Eutamias merriami
Merriam's Chipmunk

External measurements: 208–277; 89–140; 32.5–39. Greatest length of skull, 35.5–40.1. Tail long and bushy (75 to 97 per cent of length of head and body); feet and ears long and slender; ears sparsely furred on convex surfaces in summer pelage; color grayish (notably ochraceous near coast); dorsal stripes all of approximately equal width; dark stripes gray or brown, seldom with black areas; light stripes grayish; cheeks and underparts white, more or less dulled by gray but in coastal areas usually suffused with ochraceous; tail-edging usually dull white but slightly buffy in some specimens; dorsal stripes more or less indistinct in winter pelage of three subspecies (*kernensis, obscurus* and *meridionalis*), in this respect resembling *E. dorsalis*; skull resembling that of *E. sonomae*. Large size distinguishes *E. merriami* from all species with which it shares its range except *E. quadrimaculatus* and *E. townsendii*. From the two last named it differs in longer and bushier tail, the edging of which is dull white or slightly buffy rather than pure white; narrower skull; more recurved incisors; presence of notch between anterior tips of nasals. Also, from *E. townsendii*, *E. merriami* differs in grayish instead of brownish cheeks, and from *E. quadrimaculatus* in much paler submalar stripes.

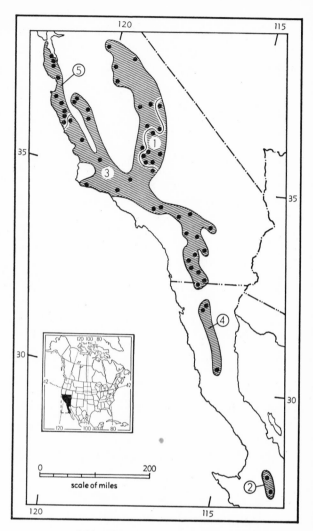

Map 202. *Eutamias merriami.*

Guide to subspecies
1. *E. m. kernensis*
2. *E. m. meridionalis*
3. *E. m. merriami*
4. *E. m. obscurus*
5. *E. m. pricei*

Eutamias merriami kernensis Grinnell and Storer

1916. *Eutamias merriami kernensis* Grinnell and Storer, Univ. California Publ. Zool., 17:5, August 23, type from Fay Creek, 4100 ft., 6 mi. N Weldon, Kern Co., California.

MARGINAL RECORDS (Johnson, 1943:134).—California: Onion Valley, 8500 ft., Sierra Nevada; W slope Walker Pass, 4600 ft.; 2 mi. N Sorell's Ranch, 4500 ft., Kelsoe Valley; French Gulch, 6700–7300 ft.; Kern River, 12 mi. below Bodfish; Kern River at Isabella; forks of Big and Little Kern rivers.

Eutamias merriami meridionalis Nelson and Goldman

1909. *Eutamias merriami meridionalis* Nelson and Goldman, Proc. Biol. Soc. Washington, 22:23, March 10, type from Aguaje de San Esteban, approximately 1200 ft., about 25 mi. NW San Ignacio, Baja California.

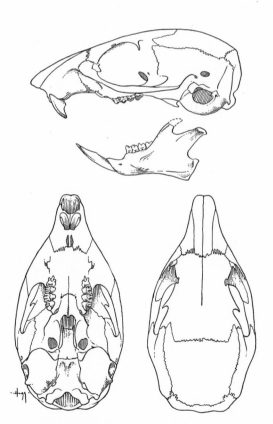

Fig. 199. *Eutamias merriami pricei*, Santa Cruz, Santa Cruz Co., California, No. 233 K.U., ♂, X 1½.

MARGINAL RECORDS.—Baja California: San Pablo (A. H. Howell, 1929b:131); type locality.

Eutamias merriami merriami (J. A. Allen)

1889. *Tamias asiaticus merriami* J. A. Allen, Bull. Amer. Mus. Nat. Hist., 2:176, October 21, type from San Bernardino Mts., 4500 ft., due north of San Bernardino, California.
1897. *E[utamias]. merriami*, Merriam, Proc. Biol. Soc. Washington, 11:191, July 1.
1916. *Eutamias merriami mariposae* Grinnell and Storer, Univ. California Publ. Zool., 17:4, August 23, type from El Portal, 2000 ft., Mariposa Co., California.

MARGINAL RECORDS (Johnson, 1943:133–134, unless otherwise noted).—California: ¼ mi. E Columbia; "vicinity" Columbia Point, 5000 ft.; Kings River Canyon, 5000 ft.; Jordan Hot Springs, 6700 ft.; Doyle's Camp; Glenville (A. H. Howell, 1929b:126); Tehachapi Peak (*ibid.*); Pine Flats, N. Fork San Gabriel River; Doble, 7000 ft.; Barkers Dam, 10 mi. SW Twenty Nine Palms; Hidden Lake, 9000 ft., "near" Round Valley; Toro Peak, 8000 ft.; Warner Pass; Laguna Mts.; Mountain Spring (A. H. Howell, 1929b:126). Baja California: Nachogüero Valley. California: Cuyamaca Mts.; Witch Creek; Poppet Flat, 3700–4000 ft., San Jacinto Mts.; Santa Ana River, 5500–6000 ft.; Mt. Wilson, 5700 ft.; Matilija; Bulitos Creek, 7 mi. W Gaviota; Mission Creek, 2 mi. N San Antonio Mission; Paso Robles (A. H. Howell, 1929b:126); head San Juan River, Carrizo Plains (*ibid.*); Waltham Creek, 1850 ft., 4½ mi. SE Priest Valley; near Cook P.O., 1300 ft., Bear Valley; Butts Ranch, 3000 ft., 5 mi. NNE San Benito; 1 mi. SE summit San Benito Mtn., 4400 ft.; Old Fort Tejon, 3200 ft.; 1 mi. S Dunlap; Raymond, 940 ft.; 1 mi. W Coulterville, 1600 ft. Localities not found in California: Smith Mtn., San Diego Co. (A. H. Howell, 1929b:126); Dark Canyon, Riverside Co. (Johnson, 1943:134).

Eutamias merriami obscurus (J. A. Allen)

1890. *Tamias obscurus* J. A. Allen, Bull. Amer. Mus. Nat. Hist., 3:70, June, type from Sierra San Pedro Mártir, near Vallecitos, Baja California.
1909. *E[utamias]. m[erriami]. obscurus*, Nelson and Goldman, Proc. Biol. Soc. Washington, 22:23, March 10.

MARGINAL RECORDS (A. H. Howell, 1929b:130).—Baja California: Hanson Laguna, Hanson Laguna Mts.; Rosarito Divide, San Pedro Mártir Mts.; El Rayo, Hanson Laguna Mts.

Eutamias merriami pricei (J. A. Allen)

1895. *Tamias pricei* J. A. Allen, Bull. Amer. Mus. Nat. Hist., 7:333, November 8, type from Portola, San Mateo Co., California.
1899. (*Eutamias Merriami*) *Pricei*. Trouessart, Catalogus mammalium . . . , fasc. 6 (appendix), p. 1312 (received June, 1899).

MARGINAL RECORDS (Johnson, 1943:132, 134, unless otherwise noted).—California: Redwood City (A. H. Howell, 1929b:128); Palo Alto; Arroyo Quito; Corralitos (A. H. Howell, 1929b:128); San Francisquito Ranch; Chews Ridge; 2 mi. SW Abbotts; Santa Lucia Peak; vicinity Chalk Peak.

Eutamias dorsalis
Cliff Chipmunk

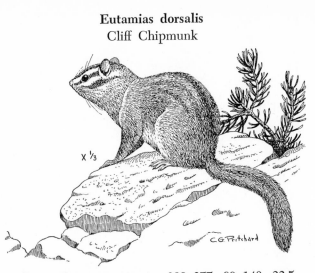

X ⅓

External measurements: 208–277; 89–140; 32.5–39.0. Greatest length of skull, 35.5–40.1. Upper parts smoke gray or neutral gray; dorsal stripes indistinct and in some stages of pelage obsolete; median stripe more pronounced than lateral stripes; postauricular patches grayish-white and poorly defined; upper side of tail fuscous-black overlain with tilleul buff; tail ochraceous-tawny, cinnamon or pinkish buff below, bordered with fuscous black and edged with tilleul buff or grayish white; underparts creamy white, in some specimens tinged with buff. Top of braincase flattened, but slightly less so than in *E. panamintinus*; incisive foramina diverging posteriorly rather than parallel.

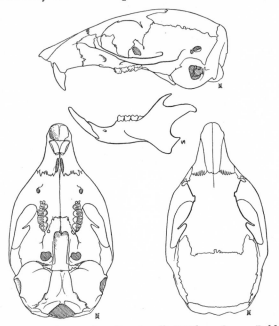

Fig. 200. *Eutamias dorsalis grinnelli*, SW base Groom Baldy, 7200 ft., Nevada, No. 47949 M.V.Z., ♂, X 1½.

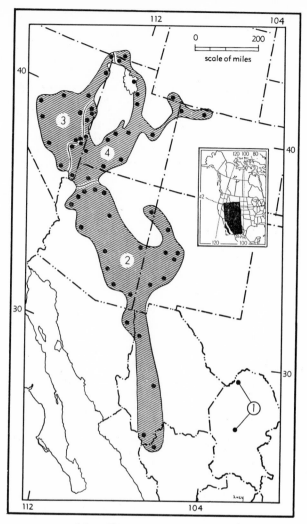

Map 203. *Eutamias dorsalis.*

1. *E. d. carminis*   3. *E. d. grinnelli*
2. *E. d. dorsalis*   4. *E. d. utahensis*

Eutamias dorsalis carminis Goldman

1938. *Eutamias dorsalis carminis* Goldman, Proc. Biol. Soc. Washington, 51:56, March 18, type from Carmen Mts., 7400 ft., Coahuila.

MARGINAL RECORDS.—Coahuila: type locality; Sierra de la Madera, 23 mi. S and 5 mi. W Ocampo, 7500 ft. (57778 KU).

Eutamias dorsalis dorsalis (Baird)

1855. *Tamias dorsalis* Baird, Proc. Acad. Nat. Sci., Philadelphia, 7:332, April, type from Fort Webster, coppermines of the Mimbres, near present site of Santa Rita, Grant Co., New Mexico.
1897. *E[utamias]. dorsalis,* Merriam, Proc. Biol. Soc. Washington, 11:210, July 1.

1904. *Eutamias canescens,* J. A. Allen, Bull. Amer. Mus. Nat. Hist., 20:208, May 28, type from Guanacevi, Durango.

MARGINAL RECORDS (A. H. Howell, 1929b:133, unless otherwise noted).—Arizona: S side Grand Canyon; Supai Village, Cataract Creek; Walnut, near Winona; Springerville. New Mexico: Datil Mts.; El Moro. Arizona: Fort Defiance. New Mexico: Riley; Magdalena Mts.; Kingston; Burro Mts. Chihuahua: Minaca. Durango: Guanacevi. Chihuahua: Sierra Madre, near Guadalupe y Calvo; Colonia Garcia. Sonora: above Santa María Mine, near El Tigre (Burt, 1938:38). Arizona: Chiricahua Mts. (Cahalane, 1939:428); Rincon Mts.; Oracle; Fish Creek, Tonto National Forest; Weaver Mts.; Hualpai Mts.; Peach Springs; Pine Spring, Hualpai Indian Reservation.

Eutamias dorsalis grinnelli Burt

1931. *Eutamias dorsalis grinnelli* Burt, Jour. Mamm., 12:300, August 24, type from Mormon Well, Sheep Mts., 6500 ft., Clark Co., Nevada.

MARGINAL RECORDS (Hall, 1946:349).—Nevada: Goose Creek, 2 mi. W Utah line, 5000 ft.; Pilot Peak, ½ mi. W Debbs Creek, 6000–9000 ft.; Water Canyon, 8–10 mi. N Lund; Eagle Valley, 3½ mi. N Ursine, 5600 ft.; 2 mi. SE Pioche, 6000 ft.; type locality; *Hidden Forest, Sheep Mts., 8500 ft.*; Belted Range, 5 mi. W White Rock Spring, 6950–7050 ft.; Manhattan; Wisconsin Creek, 7600 and 7800 ft.; 8 mi. W Eureka; Cherry Creek, 6800 ft.

Eutamias dorsalis utahensis Merriam

1897. *Eutamias dorsalis utahensis* Merriam, Proc. Biol. Soc. Washington, 11:210, July 1, type from Ogden, Utah.

MARGINAL RECORDS.—Idaho: near Bridge (Davis, 1939:225). Wyoming: Green River, 4 mi. NE Linwood, Utah (White, 1953:605). Colorado: W flank Cross Mtn. (Warren, 1942:150); Douglas Spring (A. H. Howell, 1929b:134). Utah (Durrant, 1952:151): 7 mi. N Greenriver, 4100 ft.; 8 mi. S Escalante, 5200 ft.; 2 mi. SW Cave Lake Canyon, 5 mi. NW Kanab. Arizona: Trumbull Mts. (A. H. Howell, 1929b:134). Nevada (Hall, 1946:352): Cedar Basin, 30 mi. SE St. Thomas, 3500 ft.; Meadow Valley Wash, 7 mi. S Caliente, 4000 ft.; 11 mi. E Panaca; Lehman Cave, 7500 ft.; Smith Creek, Mt. Moriah, 6600 ft.; Hendry Creek, 7½ mi. SE Mt. Moriah, 6800 ft.; ¼ mi. W Utah boundary, lat. 38° 17′ N, 7300 ft. Utah (Durrant, 1952:151): Hebron; Beaver; Clear Creek; 6.9 mi. SE Sigurd; Provo; Draper; type locality; George Creek rd. junction, 5 mi. SE Yost, Raft River Mts., 6700 ft.

Eutamias quadrivittatus
Colorado Chipmunk

External measurements: 197–235; 80–110; 28.4–35.0. Greatest length of skull, 33.4–36.8. Head smoke gray shaded with reddish; dorsal stripes distinct; underside of tail reddish; bent tip of baculum amounting to 30 to 44 per cent of length of shaft of baculum; cranial breadth averaging between 16.0 and 16.8 mm. (See Map 209.)

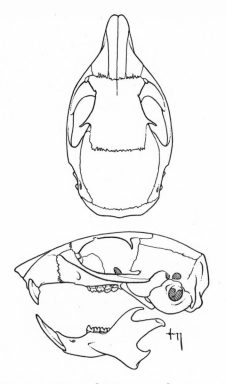

Fig. 201. *Eutamias quadrivittatus quadrivittatus*, 2 mi. S, 4 mi. W Coyote, 8100 ft., Rio Arriba Co., New Mexico, No. 41802 K.U., ♀, X 1½.

Eutamias quadrivittatus hopiensis Merriam

1905. *Eutamias hopiensis* Merriam, Proc. Biol. Soc. Washington, 18:165, June 29, type from Keam Canyon, Painted Desert, Arizona.
1922. *Eutamias quadrivittatus hopiensis*, A. H. Howell, Jour. Mamm., 3:184, August 4.

MARGINAL RECORDS (White, 1953:570–571, unless otherwise noted).—Colorado: White River; Roan Plateau, 14 mi. SE Dragon in Utah (A. H. Howell, 1929b:84); Atchee (*ibid.*); 8 mi. N Rifle (*ibid.*); Yarmany Creek, near McCoy (*ibid.*); McCoy; Eagle (A. H. Howell, 1929b:84); 1 mi. E Somerset, 6100 ft.; 1 mi. S Cortez, 5000 ft. Arizona: Wheatfield Creek, W slope Tunitcha Mts.; type locality. Utah: Zion National Park (Durrant, 1952:149); Fruita; 2 mi. W Orangeville (Kelson, 1951:45); E side confluence Green and White rivers, 1 mi. SE Ouray, 4700 ft.

Eutamias quadrivittatus quadrivittatus (Say)

1823. *Sciurus quadrivittatus* Say, *in* Long, Account of an exped. . . . to Rocky Mts. . . . , 2:45. Type locality, Arkansas River, Colorado, about 26 mi. below Cañon City.
1901. *Eutamias quadrivittatus*, Miller and Rehn, Proc. Boston Soc. Nat. Hist., 30(1):43, December 27.
1890. *Tamias quadrivittatus gracilis* J. A. Allen, Bull. Amer. Mus. Nat. Hist., 3:99, June, type from San Pedro, Socorro Co., New Mexico.

1909. *Eutamias quadrivittatus animosus* Warren, Proc. Biol. Soc. Washington, 22:105, June 25, type from Irwin Ranch, Las Animas Co., Colorado.

MARGINAL RECORDS (A. H. Howell, 1929b:82–83, unless otherwise noted).—Colorado: Elkhorn; Spring Canyon, 7 mi. SE Fort Collins; Palmer Lake; Colorado Springs; Wetmore, Hardscrabble Canyon; Gaume's Ranch; Baca County (White, 1953:568). Oklahoma: Kenton (*ibid.*). New Mexico: 4 mi. NW Tucumcari (*ibid.*); Cuervo; Manzano Mts.; Mt. Taylor, San Mateo Mts.; Bear Ridge, Zuni Mts. (White, 1953:568). Arizona: 12 mi. N Fort Defiance. New Mexico: Chuska Mts. (White, 1953:568); Blanco (*ibid.*). Colorado: Bondad, 15 mi. S Durango, 6050 ft. (White, 1953:568); Silverton; Sapinero (White, 1953:568); 5 mi. N, 22 mi. W Saguache, 10,000 ft. (*ibid.*); Cochetopa National Forest; St. Elmo; Buena Vista; W spur Lookout Mtn., near Golden (White, 1953:568); Boulder; Arkins.

Eutamias ruficaudus
Red-tailed Chipmunk

External measurements: 223–248; 101–121; 32–36. Greatest length of skull, 33.9–36.2. Upper parts and sides deep tawny; underside of tail ochraceous tawny to Sanford Brown; light dorsal stripes grayish brown, often mixed with ochraceous tawny; skull resembling that of *E. umbrinus umbrinus* but averaging smaller, with narrower rostrum and interorbital region; baculum 4 mm. or more long.

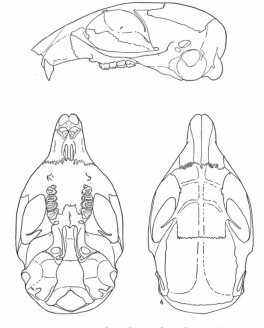

Fig. 202. *Eutamias ruficaudus ruficaudus*, Lolo Creek, 6½ mi. W Lolo, 3470 ft., Montana, No. 93358 M.V.Z., ♂, X 1½.

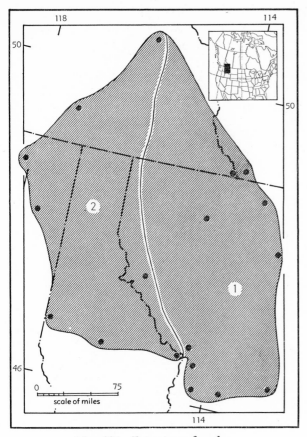

Map 204. *Eutamias ruficaudus.*

1. *E. r. ruficaudus*   2. *E. r. simulans*

Eutamias ruficaudus ruficaudus A. H. Howell

1920. *Eutamias ruficaudus* A. H. Howell, Proc. Biol. Soc. Washington, 33:91, December 30, type from Upper St. Marys Lake, Montana.

MARGINAL RECORDS (A. H. Howell, 1929:97, unless otherwise noted).—Alberta: Waterton Lake Park (Anderson, 1947:116). Montana: type locality; summit Great Northern Railroad; Deer Lodge (237 KU); mts. 15 mi. E Corvallis; Canyon Creek, near Hamilton (Davis, 1937:24); Bass Creek, Bitterroot Mts., NW Stevensville; 6½ mi. W Lolo (93358 MVZ); Upper Stillwater Lake. British Columbia (Cowan and Guiguet, 1956:145): *Akamina Pass*; Sage Pass.

Eutamias ruficaudus simulans A. H. Howell

1922. *Eutamias ruficaudus simulans* A. H. Howell, Jour. Mamm., 3:179, August 4, type from Coeur d'Alene, Kootenai Co., Idaho.

MARGINAL RECORDS.—British Columbia: Invermere (Anderson, 1947:117). Montana: Prospect Creek, near Thompson Falls (A. H. Howell, 1929b:98). Idaho: Packers Meadow (Davis, 1939:223); 12 mi. E Weippe (Rust, 1946: 318); Moscow (Davis, 1939:223). Washington: Loon Lake (A. H. Howell, 1929b:98); Marcus (*ibid.*). British Columbia: Nelson (Anderson, 1947:117). White (1953: 623) supposes that *E. r. simulans* does not intergrade with *E. r. ruficaudus* and is a distinct species.

Eutamias cinereicollis
Gray-collared Chipmunk

External measurements: 208–250; 90–115; 32–36. Greatest length of skull, 35.1–38.4. Resembles *E. umbrinus* but more grayish (less tawny), especially on shoulders; skull averaging longer.

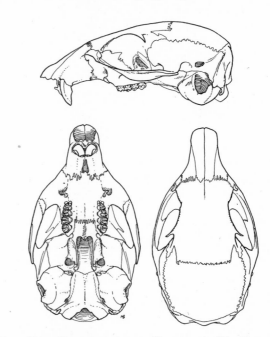

Fig. 203. *Eutamias cinereicollis cinereicollis*, Hannagan Meadows, 9500 ft., Arizona, No. 55373 M.V.Z., ♂, X 1½.

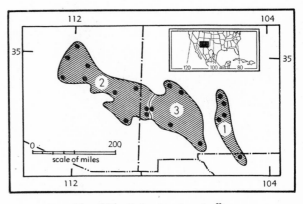

Map 205. *Eutamias cinereicollis.*

Guide to subspecies   2. *E. c. cinereicollis*
1. *E. c. canipes*   3. *E. c. cinereus*

Eutamias cinereicollis canipes V. Bailey

1902. *Eutamias cinereicollis canipes* V. Bailey, Proc. Biol. Soc. Washington, 15:117, June 2, type from Dog Canyon, 7000 ft., Guadalupe Mts., Texas.

MARGINAL RECORDS (A. H. Howell, 1929b:102, unless otherwise noted).—New Mexico: Jicarilla Mts.; Capitan Mts.; Ruidoso. Texas: The Bowl, 8200 ft. (Davis and Robertson, 1944:267). New Mexico: Mescalero.

Eutamias cinereicollis cinereicollis (J. A. Allen)

1890. *Tamias cinereicollis* J. A. Allen, Bull. Amer. Mus. Nat. Hist., 3:94, June, type from San Francisco Mtn., Arizona.
1901. *Eutamias cinereicollis,* Miller and Rehn, Proc. Boston Soc. Nat. Hist., 30(1):40, December 27.

MARGINAL RECORDS (A. H. Howell, 1929b:100, unless otherwise noted).—Arizona: Little Spring, NW base San Francisco Mtn. (V. Bailey, 1935:13); Anderson Mesa; Springerville. New Mexico: 10 mi. NE Mogollon (6832 KU); 8 mi. SE Mogollon (7014 KU). Arizona: Blue River; Mt. Thomas, White Mts.; Baker Butte; Mayer; Bill Williams Mtn.

Eutamias cinereicollis cinereus V. Bailey

1913. *Eutamias cinereicollis cinereus* V. Bailey, Proc. Biol. Soc. Washington, 26:130, May 21, type from Copper Canyon, 8200 ft., Magdalena Mts., New Mexico.

MARGINAL RECORDS (A. H. Howell, 1929b:101).—New Mexico: Datil Range, 22 mi. NW Fort Tularosa; type locality; Organ Mts.; Kingston; Mogollon Mts.

Eutamias quadrimaculatus (Gray)
Long-eared Chipmunk

1867. *Tamias quadrimaculatus* Gray, Ann. Mag. Nat. Hist., ser. 3, 20:435, December, type from Michigan Bluff, Placer Co., California.

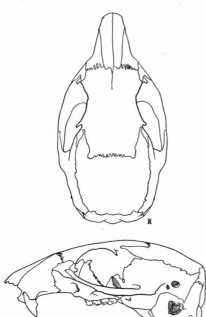

Fig. 204. *Eutamias quadrimaculatus,* 3 mi. S Mt. Rose, 8500 ft., Nevada, No. 88265 M.V.Z., ♂, X 1½.

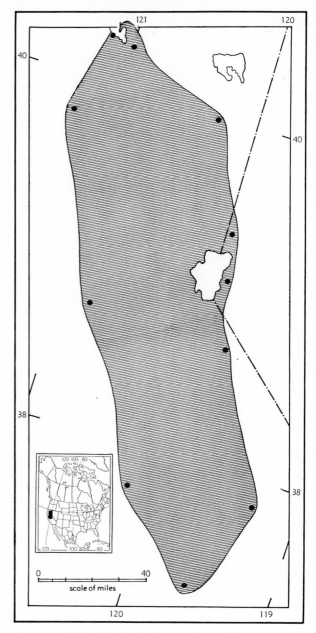

Map 206. *Eutamias quadrimaculatus.*

1897. *E[utamias]. quadrimaculatus,* Merriam, Proc. Biol. Soc. Washington, 11:191, July 1.
1886. *Tamias macrorhabdotes* Merriam, Proc. Biol. Soc. Washington, 3:25, January 27, type from Blue Canyon, Placer Co., California.

External measurements: 200–250; 85–118; 34–37. Greatest length of skull, 36.3–38.5. Resembles *E. townsendii,* but differs as follows: smaller; longer ears; more brightly colored; generally more reddish and less grayish with less grayish dulling of white areas; bushier tail with more conspicuous white edging; less massive skull; longer nasals; narrower and shallower rostrum; shorter incisive foramina; smaller molariform teeth.

MARGINAL RECORDS (Johnson, 1943:120–122, unless otherwise noted).—California: 1 mi. SSE Prattville (Tevis, 1955:72—his station No. 9): 8 mi. NW Greenville; Grizzly Mtn. Nevada (Hall, 1946:346): 3 mi. S Mt. Rose, 8500 ft.; 10 mi. NW Minden. California: Markleeville; near junction Sunrise Trail and Cloud's Rest Trail, 7000 ft.; Bass Lake; near Gentry's, Big Oak Flat Road; Placerville; Merrimac.

Eutamias speciosus
Lodgepole Chipmunk

External measurements: 197–241; 67–114; 30–36. Greatest length of skull, 33.5–36.1. This chipmunk lives in or near dense stands of lodgepole pine in the damper and more sheltered basins of the Sierra Nevada, whereas *E. umbrinus* there lives in the open forest of stunted limber pine and white bark pine on exposed and well-drained ridges and slopes near timber line. Differences between the two species are: in *E. speciosus*, slightly smaller size; longer ears and shorter tail; darker color; facial stripes darker, submalar stripe having, instead of lacking, black center below eye; subterminal black area on underside of tail 20, instead of 10, millimeters long; skull shorter and broader; upper incisors shorter and more recurved, their outer borders forming an arc of a circle having a radius of 5 instead of 5.7 mm. When the skull rests on a horizontal surface and is viewed from the side a perpendicular line through the posterior border of the alveolus falls

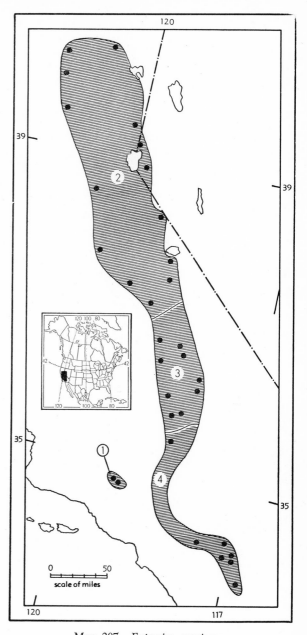

Map 207. *Eutamias speciosus.*

1. *E. s. callipeplus*   3. *E. s. sequoiensis*
2. *E. s. frater*   4. *E. s. speciosus*

anterior, rather than posterior, to the tip of the incisor. In *E. speciosus* the auditory bullae are smaller and the zygomatic arches converge anteriorly instead of being approximately parallel.

Eutamias speciosus callipeplus (Merriam)

1893. *Tamias callipeplus* Merriam, Proc. Biol. Soc. Washington, 8:136, December 28, type from Mt. Piños, 8800 ft. Ventura Co., California.

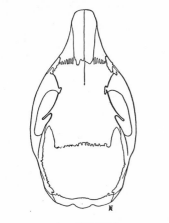

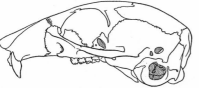

Fig. 205. *Eutamias speciosus frater,* Galena Creek, 8950 ft., Nevada, No. 88261 M.V.Z., ♂, X 1½.

1897. *Eutamias speciosus callipeplus* Merriam, Proc. Biol. Soc. Washington, 11:202, July 1.

MARGINAL RECORDS.—California (Johnson, 1943:107, unless otherwise noted): 1 mi. NE Mt. Piños, 8000 ft.; 3 mi. NW Frazier Borax Mine, 8100 ft.; *type locality*. Not found: Cañon de las Uvas (A. H. Howell, 1929b:91).

Eutamias speciosus frater (J. A. Allen)

1890. *Tamias frater* J. A. Allen, Bull. Amer. Mus. Nat. Hist., 3:88, June, type from Donner, California.
1897. *Eutamias speciosus frater,* Merriam, Proc. Biol. Soc. Washington, 11:194, July 1.

MARGINAL RECORDS.—California (Johnson, 1943:105); Eagle Lake; Campbell's Hot Springs, 5200 ft. Nevada (Hall, 1946:344): 3 mi. S Mt. Rose, 8500 ft.; Genoa (probably at higher elevation). California (Johnson, 1943:105, unless otherwise noted): Swager Creek, 7600 ft., Sweetwater Range; Mono Craters, 8000 ft.; near Mammoth; Huntington Lake, 7000 ft.; Devils Peak, 6500 ft., near Fish Camp; vicinity of Crane Flat; Wrights Lake; Chaparral (A. H. Howell, 1929b:87); Summit Creek, 5200 ft., 2 mi. E Mineral; Upper Lost Creek (A. H. Howell, 1929b:87).

Eutamias speciosus sequoiensis A. H. Howell

1922. *Eutamias speciosus sequoiensis* A. H. Howell, Jour. Mamm., 3:180, August 4, type from Mineralking, 7300 ft., east fork of Kaweah River, California.

MARGINAL RECORDS.—California (Johnson, 1943:106, unless otherwise noted): Hume, 5300 ft.; Kings River Canyon, 5000 ft.; Bubbs Creek; Little Cottonwood Creek, 9500 ft.; Little Brush Meadow, 9700 ft., E slope Olancha Peak; Taylor Meadow, 7000 ft.; Cannell Meadow, 7500 ft.; headwaters N. Tule River (A. H. Howell, 1929b:89); Alta Trail, Giant Forest.

Eutamias speciosus speciosus (Merriam)

1890. *Tamias speciosus* Merriam, *in* J. A. Allen, Bull. Amer. Mus. Nat. Hist., 3:86, June, type from Whitewater Creek, 7500 ft., San Bernardino Mts., California.
1897. *Eutamias speciosus* Merriam, Proc. Biol. Soc. Washington, 11:194, July 1.

MARGINAL RECORDS.—California (Johnson, 1943:107, except as otherwise noted): French Gulch, Piute Mts.; Fawnskin Park (A. H. Howell, 1929b:90); Sugarloaf; Dry Lake, 9000 ft.; Taquitz Valley, 8000 ft.; Mt. San Bernardino, 9000 ft.; Alpine City (A. H. Howell, 1929b:90).

Eutamias panamintinus
Panamint Chipmunk

External measurements: 192–220; 80–102; 28.4–32.5. Greatest length of skull, 33.1–34.8. The bright, tawny colors with conspicuously gray rump, and flattened braincase are outstanding characteristics. Differences from *E. minimus* of the same geographic areas are: size larger; color more reddish, especially in summer pelage; central area of underside of tail

more reddish and wider; skull larger and braincase more flattened. Differences from *E. amoenus* are: slightly shorter feet and ears; paler; gray rather than brown crown; narrower and paler facial stripes; less conspicuous dark dorsal stripes of which only part of the median one is black and the lateral pair almost obsolete; relatively narrower inner and broader outer stripes; skull, in general, broader; roof of braincase more nearly flat; nasals less prolonged anteriorly; incisive foramina longer; upper incisors less recurved. Differences from *E. quadrivittatus* are: lesser size; more reddish (less grayish) shoulders; less solidly black and less solidly white dorsal stripes; broader and more flattened braincase; shorter upper incisors; smaller cheekteeth; less nearly parallel zygomatic arches. From *E. palmeri*, *E. panamintinus* differs in essentially the same fashion as from *E. umbrinus*. From *E. speciosus*, *E. panamintinus* differs in color in approximately the same way as from *E. umbrinus* but more pronouncedly. The braincase is of approximately the same length but is more flattened in *E. panamintinus*, which has less divergent upper toothrows and more pointed rostrum. From *E. quadrimaculatus*, *E. panamintinus* can be distinguished by lesser size alone; also the tail has an edging of buff rather than white. Differences from *E. dorsalis* are: reddish instead of grayish upper parts; reddish and distinct, instead of grayish and indistinct, submedian dark dorsal stripes; more flattened braincase; parallel, instead of anteriorly convergent, incisive foramina.

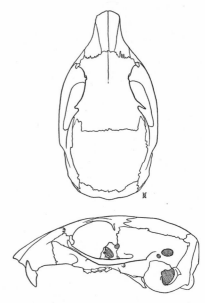

Fig. 206. *Eutamias panamintinus panamintinus*, ½ mi. W Wheeler Well, Nevada, No. 52149 M.V.Z., ♂, X 1½.

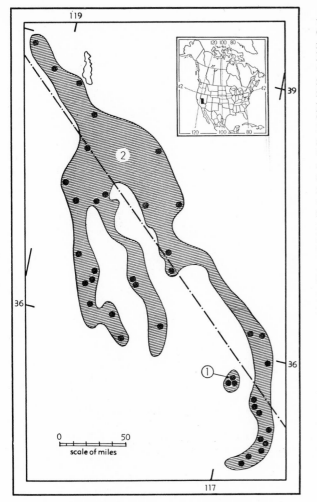

Map 208. *Eutamias panamintinus.*

1. *E. p. acrus*   2. *E. p. panamintinus*

Eutamias panamintinus acrus Johnson

1943. *Eutamias panamintinus acrus* Johnson, Univ. California Publ. Zool., 48:94, December 24, type from 1¼ mi. SE Horse Spring, 5000 ft., Kingston Range, northeastern San Bernardino Co., California.

MARGINAL RECORDS.—California (Johnson, 1943:94): Horse Spring, 4700 ft., Kingston Range; type locality; 2 mi. SW Horse Spring.

Eutamias panamintinus panamintinus (Merriam)

1893. *Tamias panamintinus* Merriam, Proc. Biol. Soc. Washington, 8:134, December 28, type from Johnson Canyon, near lower edge of piñon belt at approximately 5000 ft., in vicinity of Hungry Bill's Ranch, Panamint Mts., California.

1897. *Eutamias panamintinus* Merriam, Proc. Biol. Soc. Washington, 11:194, July 1.

1931. *Eutamias panamintinus juniperus* Burt, Jour. Mamm., 12:298, August 24, type from ½ mi. W Wheeler Well, W slope Charleston Mts., Clark Co., Nevada.

MARGINAL RECORDS.—Nevada (Hall, 1946:338–339, unless otherwise noted): Andersons Ranch; 2 mi. SW Pine Grove, 7250 ft.; Cottonwood Creek, Mt. Grant; Endowment Mine, Excelsior Mts.; Springdale Canyon, 6650 ft., Lone Mtn.; W side Stonewall Mtn., 6000 ft.; Kyle Canyon, Charleston Peak; N side Potosi Mtn., 5800–8000 ft. California (Johnson *et al.*, 1948:356): 5 mi. SW Ivanpah, 4500 ft.; Government Holes; 5 mi. NE Granite Well, 5400 ft.; pass between Granite Mts. and Providence Mts.; Mitchell's; Cedar Canyon, 5000–5300 ft.; Mescal Cave; SE side Clark Mtn., 6300 ft.; N side Clark Mtn., 5400 ft. Nevada: W slope Charleston Peak, Wheeler Well (Hall, 1946:339). California: Fall Canyon, 5600 ft., Grapevine Mts. (Johnson, 1943:93). Nevada (Hall, 1946:338–339): 2½ mi. E and 1 mi. S Grapevine Peak, 6700 ft.; Mt. Magruder. California (Johnson, 1943:93–94, unless otherwise noted): Roberts Ranch, 8250 ft., Wyman Creek; Hanaupah Canyon; 3 mi. E Jackass Spring; 3 mi. N Jackass Spring, 6000 ft.; 2½ mi. SE head Black Canyon, 8000 ft., White Mts.; Lone Pine (A. H. Howell, 1929b:79); Hockett Trail, vicinity Carrol Creek; Canyon, 5 mi. SW Olancha (A. H. Howell, 1929b:79); Coso Mts. (*ibid.*); Mountain Spring, Argus Mts.; Little Cottonwood Creek, 9000 ft., Sierra Nevada; Onion Valley; Bishop Creek, 7000 ft. (A. H. Howell, 1929b:79); Rock Creek, 6200 ft., near Sherwin Hill, 21 mi. NW Bishop; near Antelope Peak, 6500 ft., 5 mi. N Benton.

Eutamias umbrinus
Uinta Chipmunk

External measurements: 196–243; 73–115; 30–35. Greatest length of skull, 33.5–36.8. ". . . pelage dark; sides dark; narrow cranial breadth; baculum distinguishable from that of any other species (*E. palmeri* excepted) by the combination of width of base more than ⅓ of length of shaft, distal ½ of shaft

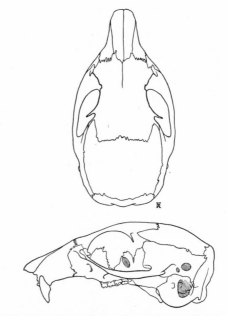

Fig. 207. *Eutamias umbrinus inyoensis,* mouth Pole Canyon, S side Baker Creek, E side Snake Mts., Nevada, No. 41574 M.V.Z., ♂, X 1½.

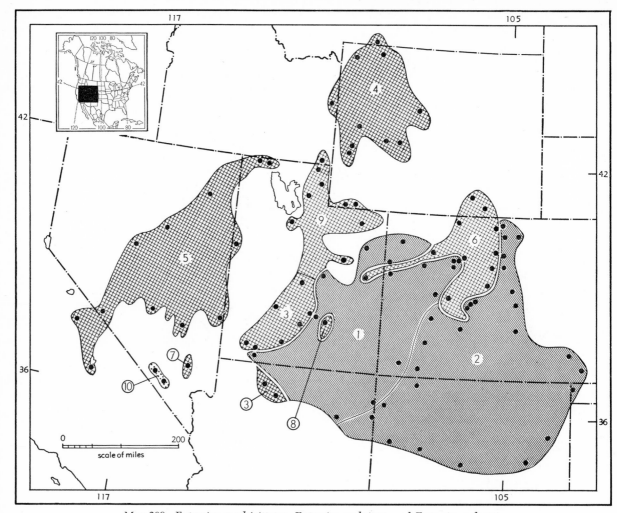

Map 209. *Eutamias quadrivittatus, Eutamias umbrinus,* and *Eutamias palmeri.*

Guide to   3. *E. umbrinus adsitus*   7. *E. umbrinus nevadensis*
kinds   4. *E. umbrinus fremonti*   8. *E. umbrinus sedulus*
1. *E. quadrivittatus hopiensis* 5. *E. umbrinus inyoensis*   9. *E. umbrinus umbrinus*
2. *E. quadrivittatus quadrivittatus* 6. *E. umbrinus montanus* 10. *E. palmeri*

laterally compressed, and keel ¼ of length of tip"
(White, 1953:571).

This species has long been confused with *E.
quadrivattatus* from which it can be distinguished
externally only by the most subtle means. The
bacula of the two species, however, differ sharply.
The geographic range probably is more extensive
than is now known; White (1953:620) remarks that
bacula from as far west as Lardo, Valley County,
Idaho, seem to be of this species.

Eutamias umbrinus adsitus J. A. Allen

1905. *Eutamias adsitus* J. A. Allen, Brooklyn Inst. Mus.
Science Bull., 1:118, March 31, type from Brigg's
[= Britt's] Meadow, 10,000 ft., Beaver Mts., Utah.

1953. *Eutamias umbrinus adsitus,* White, Univ. Kansas
Publ., Mus. Nat. Hist., 5:572, December 1.

MARGINAL RECORDS.—Utah (Durrant, 1952:148, un-
less otherwise noted): Great Basin Experiment Station;
Carcass Creek, Grover, 7255 ft. (Kelson, 1951:44); 18 mi.
N Escalante, 9500 ft.; Bryce Canyon, 8200 ft.; *Cedar
Breaks, 10,000 ft.*; West Rim, Zion National Park, 6500 ft.
(White, 1953:572); Pine Valley Mts.; type locality. Also
on the Kaibab Plateau, Arizona (White, 1953:572): De
Motte Park; Bright Angel Spring.

Eutamias umbrinus fremonti White

1953. *Eutamias umbrinus fremonti* White, Univ. Kansas
Publ., Mus. Nat. Hist., 5:576, December 1, type from 31
mi. N Pinedale, 8025 ft., Sublette Co., Wyoming.

MARGINAL RECORDS (White, 1953:576, unless otherwise noted).—Montana: Beartooth Mts. Wyoming: 16¼ mi.

N, 17 mi. W Cody, 5625 ft.; 12 mi. N, 3 mi. W Shoshoni, 4650 ft.; 17 mi. S, 6½ mi. W Lander, 8450 ft.; Big Sandy (on geographic grounds; A. H. Howell, 1929b:95); Merna (*ibid.*); 19 mi. W, 2 mi. S Big Piney, 7700 ft.; La Barge Creek. Idaho: Big Hole Mts., near Irwin. Wyoming: Yellowstone National Park.

Eutamias umbrinus inyoensis Merriam

1897. *Eutamias speciosus inyoensis* Merriam, Proc. Biol. Soc. Washington, 11:202, 208, July 1, type from Black Canyon, 8200 ft., White Mts., Inyo Co., California.
1953. *Eutamias umbrinus inyoensis,* White, Univ. Kansas Publ., Mus. Nat. Hist., 5:573, December 1.

MARGINAL RECORDS.—Utah: head George and Clear creeks, 8500 ft., 5 mi. S Stanrod, Raft River Mts. (White, 1953:574); Queen of Sheba Canyon, W side Deep Creek Mts., 8000 ft. (Durrant, 1952:146). Nevada (Hall, 1946:341): Eagle Valley, 3½ mi. N Ursine, 5800 ft.; E and N slopes Irish Mtn.; Kawich Mts., 2⅗ mi. E Silverbow, 7300 ft. California (Johnson, 1943:99): S slope Cirque Peak, 10,500 ft.; Mammoth Pass, 9800 ft. Nevada (Hall, 1946:341, unless otherwise noted): Chiatovich Creek, 8200 ft.; Smiths Creek, 7100 ft.; 4 mi. S Tonkin, Denay Creek, Roberts Mts.; head Ackler Creek (White, 1953:574).

Eutamias umbrinus montanus White

1953. *Eutamias umbrinus montanus* White, Univ. Kansas Publ., Mus. Nat. Hist., 5:576, December 1, type from ½ mi. E and 3 mi. S Ward, 9400 ft., Boulder Co., Colorado.

MARGINAL RECORDS (White, 1953:577, unless otherwise noted).—Wyoming: 3 mi. ESE Browns Peak, 10,000 ft.; 3½ mi. S Wood's Landing. Colorado: 2 mi. E Log Cabin, 7450 ft.; type locality; Davidson Mine, 3 mi. SW Idaho Springs; Tarryall Creek Camp, 8700 ft.; S side Crested Butte Mtn., 9500 ft.; McCoy (Kelson, 1951:43, on geographic grounds). Utah: PR Springs, 7950 ft., 43 mi. S Ouray. Colorado: 1 mi. NW Pagoda Peak, 10,400 ft.; Mt. Zirkel, 10,000 ft.

Eutamias umbrinus nevadensis Burt

1931. *Eutamias quadrivittatus nevadensis* Burt, Jour. Mamm., 12:299, August 24, type from Hidden Forest, 8500 ft., Sheep Mts., Clark Co., Nevada. Known only from the type locality.
1953. *Eutamias umbrinus nevadensis,* White, Univ. Kansas Publ., Mus. Nat. Hist., 5:574, December 1.

Eutamias umbrinus sedulus White

1953. *Eutamias umbrinus sedulus* White, Univ. Kansas Publ., Mus. Nat. Hist., 5:573, December 1, type from Mt. Ellen, Henry Mts., Garfield Co., Utah. Known only from the type locality.

Eutamias umbrinus umbrinus (J. A. Allen)

1890. *Tamias umbrinus* J. A. Allen, Bull. Amer. Mus. Nat. Hist., 3:96, June, type from Blacks Fork, approximately 8000 ft., Uinta Mts., Utah.
1901. *Eutamias umbrinus,* Miller and Rehn, Proc. Boston Soc. Nat. Hist., 30(1):45, December 27.

MARGINAL RECORDS (White, 1953:572, unless otherwise noted).—Idaho: ¼ mi. W Copenhagen Basin (Davis,

1939:224). Utah: Monte Cristo, 18 mi. W Woodruff, 8000 ft. Wyoming: 9 mi. S Robertson, 8000 ft.; Lonetree (A. H. Howell, 1929b:95). Utah: Paradise Park, 21 mi. W, 15 mi. N Vernal, 10,050 ft.; Junction Argyle and Minnie Maud creeks (Durrant, 1955b:74); Butterfield Canyon, 3 mi. SW Butterfield Tunnel, 8000 ft. (Durrant, 1952:145); Wasatch Mts., near Ogden (*ibid.*); Spring Hollow, Logan Canyon (*ibid.*).

Eutamias palmeri Merriam
Palmer's Chipmunk

1897. *Eutamias palmeri* Merriam, Proc. Biol. Soc. Washington, 11:208, July 1, type from Charleston Peak, 8000 ft., Clark Co., Nevada.

External measurements: 204–233; 74–101; 31–35. Greatest length of skull, 34.9–36.5. Dorsal stripes indistinct in winter pelage. From geographically adjoining populations of its closest relative, *E. umbrinus*, *E. palmeri* differs in browner (more reddish) dark dorsal stripes, more tawny color on underside of tail, shorter rostrum, and shorter upper incisors.

MARGINAL RECORDS.—Nevada: Deer Creek, 8250 ft. (Hall, 1946:344); type locality.

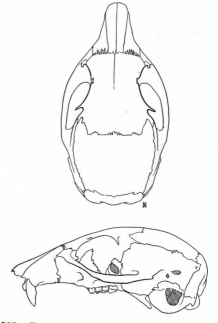

Fig. 208. *Eutamias palmeri*, 6 mi. N Charleston Park Resort, 7800 ft., Nevada, No. 86850 M.V.Z., ♂, X 1½.

Eutamias bulleri
Buller's Chipmunk

External measurements: 222–248; 93–113; 34–38. Greatest length of skull, 35.7–39.6. Facial markings broader and more blackish than in *E. cinereicollis*;

grayish collar present but faint in some specimens; dark dorsal stripes shaded with Mikado brown; light dorsal stripes white or shaded with reddish; sides with wash of cinnamon or brownish; ventral face of tail reddish; skull resembling that of *E. cinereicollis* but larger.

Eutamias bulleri bulleri (J. A. Allen)

1889. *Tamias asiaticus bulleri* J. A. Allen, Bull. Amer. Mus. Nat. Hist., 2:173, October 21, type from Sierra de Valparaiso, Zacatecas.
1901. *Eutamias bulleri*, Miller and Rehn, Proc. Boston Soc. Nat. Hist., 30(1):40, December 27.

MARGINAL RECORDS.—Zacatecas: Sierra Madre, SW Sombrerete (A. H. Howell, 1929b:103); type locality.

Eutamias bulleri durangae J. A. Allen

1903. *Eutamias durangae* J. A. Allen, Bull. Amer. Mus. Nat. Hist., 19:594, November 12, type from Arroyo de Bucy, approximately 7000 ft., Sierra de Candella, Durango.
1922. *Eutamias bulleri durangae*, A. H. Howell, Jour. Mamm., 3:184, August 4.
1905. *Tamias nexus* Elliot, Proc. Biol. Soc. Washington, 18:233, December 9, type from Coyotes, Durango.

MARGINAL RECORDS (A. H. Howell, 1929:104, unless otherwise noted).—Chihuahua: Sierra Madre, near Guadalupe y Calvo. Durango: type locality; Durango (city of): El Salto; 6 mi. ENE La Ciudad (Hooper, 1955:8); Cerro Huehuento (*ibid.*).

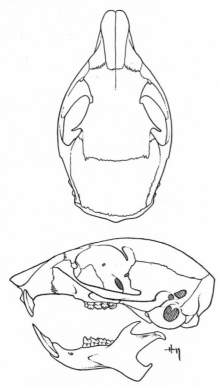

Fig. 209. *Eutamias bulleri durangae*, 9 mi. SW Las Adjuntas, 8900 ft., Durango, No. 54522 K.U., ♂, X 1½.

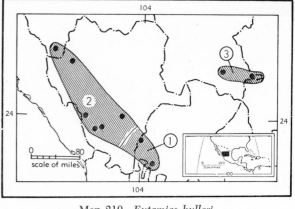

Map 210. *Eutamias bulleri.*

Guide to subspecies
1. *E. b. bulleri*
2. *E. b. durangae*
3. *E. b. solivagus*

Eutamias bulleri solivagus A. H. Howell

1922. *Eutamias bulleri solivagus* A. H. Howell, Jour. Mamm., 3:179, August 4, type from Sierra Guadalupe, Coahuila.

MARGINAL RECORDS.—Coahuila: type locality; 12 mi. E San Antonio de Alazanas, 9000 ft. (33099 KU).

Genus Marmota Blumenbach—Marmots

Revised by A. H. Howell, N. Amer. Fauna, 37:1–80, 15 pls., 3 figs. in text, April 7, 1915.

1777. *Glis* Erxleben, Systema regni animalis . . . , 1:358. Type not designated; included *Glis marmota, G. monax, G. canadensis, G. cricetus, G. tscherkessicus, G. citellus, G. zemni, G. lemmus, G. migratorius, G. barabensis, G. arenarius, G. lagurus,* and *G. oeconomicus.* Not *Glis* Brisson, 1762, a genus of dormouse.
1779. *Marmota* Blumenbach, Handbuch der Naturgeschichte, 1:79. Type, *Mus marmorata* Linnaeus. Not *Marmota* Frisch, 1775; Frisch names are unavailable.
1780. *Arctomys* Schreber, Die Säugthiere . . . , pl. 208. Type, *Mus monax* Linnaeus.
1780. *Lagomys* Storr, Prodromus methodi mammalium . . . , p. 39. No type designated; 24 species included; ". . . typified by species of *Arctomys*" (Gill, Bull. Philos. Soc. Washington, 2:viii(App.), 1880).
1811. *Lipura* Illiger, Prodromus systematis mammalium et avium . . . , p. 95. Type, *Hyrax hudsonius* Schreber [= *Glis canadensis* Erxleben].
1923. *Marmotops* Pocock, Proc. Zool. Soc. London, p. 1200, February 13. Type, *Mus monax* Linnaeus; proposed as a subgenus.

External measurements: 418–820; 100–252; 68–113. Five digits, thumb rudimentary but bearing nail; palm with 5 pads (3 at bases of digits) and sole with 6 (4 at bases of digits). Pelage brown, reddish, or black; some species with white markings. Rostrum and cranium subequal; interorbital region much wider than postorbital region; P4 as large as or larger than M1; cheek-teeth highcrowned; metaloph complete on each upper molar, and on M3 turns posteriad and joins posterior cingulum; p4 molariform, its protolophid a transverse crest between protoconid and parametaconid; m1 and m2 parallelogram-shaped in occlusal outline; cheek-pouch rudimentary and lacking retractor muscles.

Marmots are primarily cursorial, but at least *M. monax* and *M. flaviventris* climb to a limited degree. Marmots eat green plant material, hibernate for 4 to 8 months, have 1 litter per year of 2 to 9 young, molt once annually, and dig their own burrows. Abandoned burrows are the homes of many other kinds of mammals.

KEY TO NORTH AMERICAN SPECIES OF MARMOTA

1. Upper tooth-rows parallel; 8 mammae (only 1 pair abdominal). . . . . *M. monax*, p. 321
1'. Upper tooth-rows divergent anteriorly; 10 mammae (2 pairs abdominal).
  2. Feet buffy, hazel, or tawny; posterior pad on sole of hind foot oval in shape and situated near middle of sole; sides of neck with conspicuous buffy patches.
                    M. flaviventris, p. 324
  2'. Feet black or blackish brown; posterior pad on sole of hind foot subcircular and situated near edge of sole; sides of neck lacking buffy patches.
    3. Forepart of body predominately black and white; posterior part of body suffused with tawny; not occurring on Vancouver Island or Olympic Peninsula. . . . . . . *M. caligata*, p. 327
    3'. Forepart of body not predominately black and white and posterior parts not notably dissimilar; occurring on Vancouver Island or Olympic Peninsula.
      4. Upper parts brown mixed with whitish; posterior border of nasals shallowly U-shaped; occurring on Olympic Peninsula. *M. olympus*, p. 329
      4'. Upper parts uniformly brown; posterior border of nasals deeply V-shaped; confined to Vancouver Island. . . *M. vancouverensis*, p. 330

Marmota monax
Woodchuck

X 1/6

External measurements: 418–665; 100–155; 68–88. Eight mammae (2 pair pectoral, only 1 pair abdominal and 1 pair inguinal); posterior pad on sole of hind foot oval and situated near middle of sole. Color reddish or brownish; head without white except around nose; feet black or dark brown; interorbital region broad; postorbital processes projecting at right angles to long axis of skull or slightly forward of right angle; nasals, in posterior extent, usually noticeably wider than premaxillae; palate abruptly truncate at posterior border; incisive foramina widest posteriorly and narrowest anteriorly; maxillary tooth-rows approximately parallel instead of divergent anteriorly.

Marmota monax bunkeri Black

1935. *Marmota monax bunkeri* Black, Jour. Mamm., 16:319, November 15, type from 7 mi. SW of Lawrence, Douglas Co., Kansas.

MARGINAL RECORDS.—Nebraska (Swenk, 1938:350–351): Ashland; *NE of Weeping Water*. Kansas (Cockrum, 1952:119): Doniphan Lake; 5½ mi. SE Fontana; Hamilton. Nebraska: near Fairbury (Swenk, 1938:350).

Marmota monax canadensis (Erxleben)

1777. [*Glis*] *canadensis* Erxleben, Systema regni animalis . . . , 1:363, based primarily on the Quebec marmot of Pennant. From "Canada et ad fretum Hudsonis," but type locality fixed as Quebec, Quebec, Canada, by A. H. Howell, N. Amer. Fauna, 37:31, April 7, 1915.
1904. [*Marmota monax*] *canadensis*, Trouessart, Catalogus mammalium . . . , Suppl., p. 344.
1778. *Mus empetra* Pallas, Novae species quadrupedum e glirium ordine . . . , p. 75, based primarily on the Quebec marmot of Pennant.
1808. *Arctomys sibila* Wolf, Linne's Natursyst., 2:481, name proposed to include *Arctomys empetra* Pallas and *Arctomys pruinosa* Gmelin, 1788, supposed to be the same.
1820. *Arctomys melanopus* Kuhl, Beiträge zur Zoologie und vergleichenden Anatomie, p. 64. Type locality, Canada.

MARGINAL RECORDS.—Mackenzie: Simpson (Anderson, 1947:105); mouth Buffalo River, Great Slave Lake (Soper, 1942:133). Manitoba: York Factory (Anderson, 1947:106). Ontario: Moose River near Hudson Bay (A. H. Howell, 1915:32). Quebec: Eastmain River (Cameron and Morris, 1951:126); Temiscamie River, 15 mi. from Lake Albanel (*ibid.*); Malbaie River (Anderson, 1940:63); Ste. Anne de Monts (Goodwin, 1924:256). New Brunswick: Arthurette (A. H. Howell, 1915:32). Nova Scotia: Newport (*ibid.*); vicinity of Lake Kedgemakooge (Sheldon, 1936:212). Maine: Mount Desert Island (Manville, 1942:395). Vermont: Mt. Mansfield (Osgood, 1938:438). *Along the north bank of the Ottawa River* (Anderson, 1947:105), and W shores Lake Huron and Lake Superior to Minnesota: Carlton County (Swanson, 1945:75); Aitkin (Swenk, 1938:348); Thief River Falls (*ibid.*). North Dakota: Pembina (*ibid.*); Walhalla (*ibid.*). Saskatchewan: Moose Mtn. (Soper, 1946:140). Alberta: vicinity of Islay (Rand, 1948b:128); Red Deer River (*ibid.*); Entrance (*ibid.*). British Columbia: near head Finlay River (A. H. Howell, 1915:32). Mackenzie: Liard (Anderson, 1947:105).

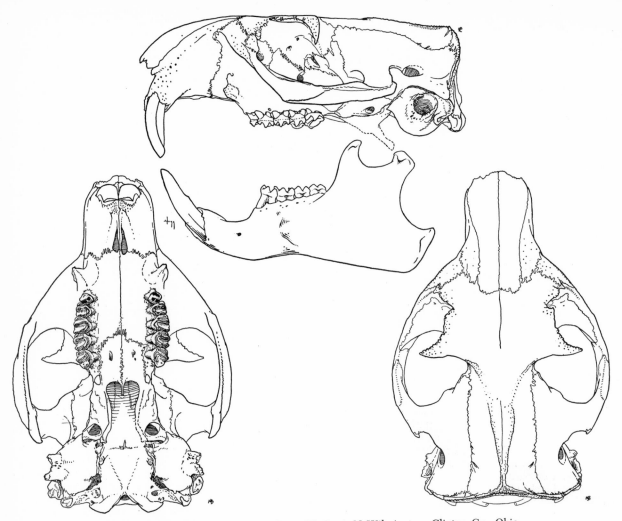

Fig. 210. *Marmota monax monax*, 3 mi. W, 3 mi. N Wilmington, Clinton Co., Ohio,
No. 81418 M.V.Z., ♀, X 1.

Marmota monax ignava (Bangs)

1899. *Arctomys ignavus* Bangs, Proc. New England Zool.
Club, 1:13, February 28, type from Black Bay, Strait of
Belle Isle, Labrador.
1904. [*Marmota monax*] *ignavus*, Trouessart, Catalogus
mammalium . . . , Suppl., p. 344.

MARGINAL RECORDS.—Labrador: Ailik, Peters Cove
(A. H. Howell, 1915:30); southward along coast to Point
Armour (209960 BS); head of Hamilton Inlet [= North-
west River] (A. H. Howell, 1915:30). Fort George on
Ungava Bay (Miller and Kellogg, 1955:182), is not plotted
on our map.

Marmota monax johnsoni Anderson

1943. *Marmota monax johnsoni* Anderson, Ann. Rept. Provancher Soc. Nat. Hist., Quebec, for 1942, p. 53, September 7, type from Percé, Gaspé Co., Quebec.

MARGINAL RECORDS (Anderson, 1947:106).—Quebec:
Gaspé Peninsula: *Federal Mine*; type locality; *Salmon
Branch, Grand Cascapedia River; Kelley's Camp, Berry
Mountain Brook, near head of Grand Cascapedia River.* Not
found: Near foot Mt. Lyall (Anderson, 1947:106).

Marmota monax monax (Linnaeus)

1758. [*Mus*] *monax* Linnaeus, Syst. nat., ed. 10, 1:60. Type
locality, Maryland.
1904. [*Marmota*] *monax*, Trouessart, Catalogus mammalium
. . . , Suppl., p. 344.

MARGINAL RECORDS.—Iowa: Dickinson County
(Swenk, 1938:349); 3 mi. NW Waukon (Stoner, 1922:260).
Illinois (Necker and Hatfield, 1941:48): *Grand Detour*;
Fox Lake. Michigan: Dowagiac (A. H. Howell, 1915:25).
Ohio: Hicksville (Bole and Moulthrop, 1942:129). Penn-
sylvania: Erie County (Richmond and Roslund, 1949:24);
Sullivan County (Roslund, 1951:29); Marple (A. H. Howell,
1915:25). New Jersey: Wading River (Connor, 1953:232).

Virginia: Doswell (A. H. Howell, 1915:25); Brunswick County (Handley and Patton, 1947:148); Grayson County (*ibid.*). North Carolina: Roan Mtn. (A. H. Howell, 1915: 25). South Carolina: Greenville (Penney, 1950:85). Alabama (A. H. Howell, 1921:61, unless otherwise noted): Piedmont; 16 mi. NW Prattville (Holt, 1924:67); Natural Bridge. Tennessee: Duck River, 6 mi. SW Waverly (Kellogg, 1939:269). Illinois: Ozark (Necker and Hatfield, 1941: 48). Arkansas (Sealander, 1956:269): Crawford County; Hempstead County; Lincoln County; Lee County; Clay County. Iowa: Union County (Swenk, 1938:349); Wall Lake (Scott, 1937:68).

Marmota monax ochracea Swarth

1911. *Marmota ochracea* Swarth, Univ. California Publ. Zool., 7:203, February 18, type from Forty-mile Creek, Alaska.
1915. *Marmota monax ochracea*, A. H. Howell, N. Amer. Fauna, 37:34, April 7.

MARGINAL RECORDS.—Alaska: Moose Creek, 30 mi. above Fairbanks (243607 BS); type locality. Yukon: Nisutlin River [Mile 40, Canol Road] (Rand, 1945b:44). British Columbia (Cowan and Guiguet, 1956:118): Lower Liard Crossing [Mile 213, Alaska Highway]; near junction of Liard

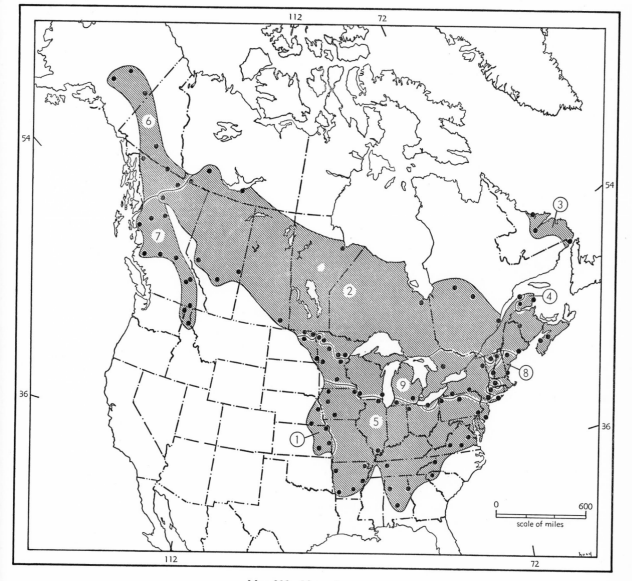

Map 211. *Marmota monax.*

1. *M. m. bunkeri*	4. *M. m. johnsoni*	7. *M. m. petrensis*
2. *M. m. canadensis*	5. *M. m. monax*	8. *M. m. preblorum*
3. *M. m. ignava*	6. *M. m. ochracea*	9. *M. m. rufescens*

and Trout rivers; Atlin. Alaska: Healy River (243814 BS); Fairbanks (247613 BS).

Marmota monax petrensis A. H. Howell

1915. *Marmota monax petrensis* A. H. Howell, N. Amer. Fauna, 37:33, April 7, type from Revelstoke, British Columbia.

MARGINAL RECORDS (Cowan and Guiguet, 1956: 118, unless otherwise noted).—British Columbia: Lynx Creek, Isaacs Lake (Hall, 1934:372); Glacier; Creston. Idaho: Thompson Pass (Anderson, 1947:106). Washington: Pend Oreille Mts. (Dalquest, 1948:263). British Columbia: type locality; Quesnel; Lonesome Lake; Salvus; Kispiox.

Marmota monax preblorum A. H. Howell

1914. *Marmota monax preblorum* A. H. Howell, Proc. Biol. Soc. Washington, 27:14, February 2, type from Wilmington, Middlesex Co., Massachusetts.

MARGINAL RECORDS.—Maine: Norway (A. H. Howell, 1915:28); Eliot (*ibid.*). Connecticut (Goodwin, 1935:98): *East Wallingford*; Sharon Mtn. Vermont: Saxtons River (Osgood, 1938:438).

Marmota monax rufescens A. H. Howell

1914. *Marmota monax rufescens* A. H. Howell, Proc. Biol. Soc. Washington, 27:13, February 2, type from Elk River, Sherburne Co., Minnesota.

MARGINAL RECORDS.—North Dakota: *Grafton* (Swenk, 1938:348). Minnesota: Marshall County (Swanson, 1945:75); Hubbard County (*ibid.*); Princeton (Swenk, 1938:348); *Pine County* (Swanson, 1945:75), thence along south shore of Lake Superior, thence almost due east to Ontario: Lake of Bays (A. H. Howell, 1915:27), *thence along south bank of Ottawa River* (Anderson, 1947:106). New York: Elizabethtown (A. H. Howell, 1915:27). Vermont: *Ferrisburg* (Osgood, 1938:438); Lunenburg (*ibid.*). Massachusetts: Easthampton (A. H. Howell, 1915:27). New York: Hastings (A. H. Howell, 1915:27); Miller Place (*ibid.*); Owego (*ibid.*); Allegheny State Park (Schoonmaker, 1929:248). Ohio (Bole and Moulthrop, 1942:129): *Geauga Lake*; Cleveland. Michigan: Ann Arbor (A. H. Howell, 1915:27). Wisconsin (*ibid.*): Racine; *Delavan*; Bridgeport. Minnesota: Nicollet County (Swanson, 1945: 75); Grant County (*ibid.*). North Dakota (Swenk, 1938: 348): Wahpeton; *Leonard*; Devils Lake.

Marmota flaviventris
Yellow-bellied Marmot

External measurements: 470–700; 130–220; 70–92. Ten mammae (2 pair pectoral, 2 pair abdominal, and 1 pair inguinal); posterior pad on sole of hind foot oval and situated near middle of sole. Color tawny, often frosted with white; white markings between eyes usual; sides of neck with conspicuous buffy patches; feet varying from light buff to hazel or dark brown (never black); interorbital region narrow; postorbital processes projecting back of a line drawn across their bases and at right angles

to long axis of skull; nasals no broader posteriorly than premaxillae; posterior border of palate beveled at obtuse angle; incisive foramina constricted posteriorly or of equal width throughout; maxillary tooth-rows slightly divergent anteriorly.

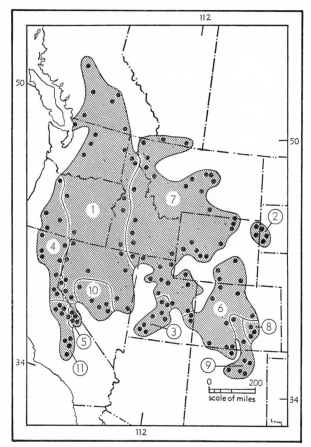

Map 212. *Marmota flaviventris*

Guide to subspecies	
1. *M. f. avara*	6. *M. f. luteola*
2. *M. f. dacota*	7. *M. f. nosophora*
3. *M. f. engelhardti*	8. *M. f. notiros*
4. *M. f. flaviventris*	9. *M. f. obscura*
5. *M. f. fortirostris*	10. *M. f. parvula*
	11. *M. f. sierrae*

Marmota flaviventris avara (Bangs)

1899. *Arctomys flaviventer avarus* Bangs, Proc. New England Zool. Club, 1:68, July 31, type from Okanagan, British Columbia.

1904. [*Marmota flaviventer*] *avarus*, Trouessart, Catalogus mammalium . . . , Suppl., p. 344.

MARGINAL RECORDS.—British Columbia: Williams Lake (Anderson, 1947:107); Sicamous (Cowan and Guiguet, 1956:120); Vernon (A. H. Howell, 1915:42); Trail (Anderson, 1947:107). Washington: Spokane Bridge (Rust, 1946:317). Idaho: 10 mi. N St. Maries (Davis, 1939: 159); 17 mi. N Prichard (Rust, 1946:318); Rapid River, near Riggins (Davis, 1939:159); Crane Creek, 15 mi. E Mid-

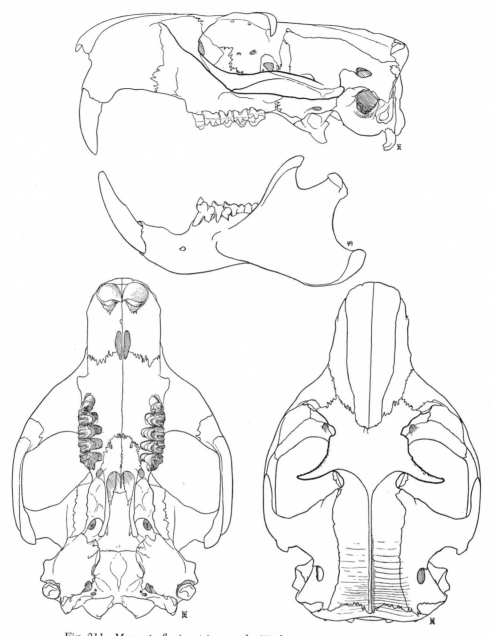

Fig. 211. *Marmota flaviventris parvula*, W slope Toquima Mtn., Nevada,
No. 57476 M.V.Z., ♂, X 1.

vale (*ibid.*); 1 mi. S Riddle (*ibid.*). Nevada (Hall, 1946:287): Mountain City; head of Ackler Creek, 6800 ft.; ½ mi. N Treasury Lake, 12,200 ft.; ¼ mi. W Hamilton; Granite Mtn.; Mt. Grant; Mt. Siegel; 3 mi. E Reno; Smoke Creek, 4300 ft.; 12-mile Creek, 1 mi. E California boundary, 5300 ft. Oregon: Adel (209035 BS); Prineville (242645 BS). Washington: Ellensburg (243744 BS); 5 mi. N Entiat (Dalquest, 1948:263); Twisp (234960 BS); just outside Bellingham (Edson, 1935:68). British Columbia: Hope (Anderson, 1947:107); *Lytton* (Cowan and Guiguet, 1956:120); Ashcroft (A. H. Howell, 1915:42).

Marmota flaviventris dacota (Merriam)

1889. *Arctomys dacota* Merriam, N. Amer. Fauna, 2:8, October 30, type from Custer, Custer Co., Black Hills, South Dakota.

1914. *M[armota]. f[laviventer]. dacota*, A. H. Howell, Proc. Biol. Soc. Washington, 27:15, February 2.

MARGINAL RECORDS.—Wyoming: 1 mi. S Warren Peak Lookout, 6000 ft. (19956 KU). South Dakota (A. H. Howell, 1915:50): Savoy; Tigerville, near Hill City; Custer. Wyoming: ½ mi. E Buckhorn, 6100 ft. (41640 KU).

Marmota flaviventris engelhardti J. A. Allen

1905. *Marmota engelhardti* J. A. Allen, Mus. Brooklyn Inst. Arts and Sci., Sci. Bull., 1:120, March 31, type from Briggs [= Britt's] Meadows, 10,000 ft., Beaver Range Mts., Beaver Co., Utah.

1915. *Marmota flaviventris engelhardti,* A. H. Howell, N. Amer. Fauna, 37:45, April 7.

MARGINAL RECORDS.—Utah (Durrant, 1952:104, unless otherwise noted): 5 mi. E Great Basin Exp. Station; head right fork Cottonwood Creek, Manti National Forest (243665 BS); Torrey, 6800 ft.; Long Valley, Markagunt Plateau 250612 BS); Duck Creek Sink, Cedar Mtn., 8300 ft.; Cedar Breaks, 10,000 ft.; type locality; Fish Lake.

Lange (1956:289–291) records bones of *Marmota flaviventris* from Indian archaeological sites from several places including the following; Arizona: Tse-an Olje Cave; Cylinder Cave; Tse-an Kaetan Cave; Tooth Cave; Government Cave, approximately 23 mi. W of Flagstaff; Woodchuck Cave; Keet Seel. These occurrences are not shown on Map 212.

Marmota flaviventris flaviventris (Aud. and Bach.)

1841. *Arctomys flaviventer* Audubon and Bachman, Proc. Acad. Nat. Sci. Philadelphia, 1:99, type locality, "Mountains between Texas and California," but fixed as Mt. Hood, Oregon, by A. H. Howell (N. Amer. Fauna, 37:39, 40, April 7, 1915).

1904. [*Marmota*] *flaviventer,* Trouessart, Catalogus mammalium . . . , Suppl., p. 344.

MARGINAL RECORDS.—Oregon: type locality; Summer Lake (A. H. Howell, 1915:41). California: Steele Swamp (Grinnell, 1933:119); Petes Valley, 4500 ft. (Grinnell, *et al.*, 1930:476); Donner (A. H. Howell, 1915:41). Nevada: 3 mi. S Mt. Rose, 8500 ft. (Hall, 1946:286). California: Hope Valley (A. H. Howell, 1915:41); Glen Alpine Springs (Grinnell, 1933:119); SW Black Butte, 6600 ft. (Grinnell, *et al.*, 1930:476); Hat Creek, 8000 ft. (*ibid.*); Penoyar (Grinnell, 1933:119). Oregon (A. H. Howell, 1915:41): Klamath Lake; Crater Lake.

Marmota flaviventris fortirostris Grinnell

1921. *Marmota flaviventris fortirostris* Grinnell, Univ. California Publ. Zool., 21:242, November 7, type from 11,800 ft., McAfee Meadow, White Mts., Mono Co., California.

MARGINAL RECORDS.—California: near White Mtn. Peak (Grinnell, 1933:120); type locality; near Blanco Mtn. (Grinnell, 1933:120); Big Prospector Meadow, 10,300–10,700 ft. (Grinnell, 1921:243).

Marmota flaviventris luteola A. H. Howell

1914. *Marmota flaviventer luteola* A. H. Howell, Proc. Biol. Soc. Washington, 27:15, February 2, type from Woods Post Office, 7500 ft., Medicine Bow Mts., Albany Co., Wyoming.

1914. *Marmota flaviventer warreni* A. H. Howell, Proc. Biol. Soc. Washington, 27:16, February 2, type from Smith Trail, 2 mi. W Crested Butte, 10,000 ft., Gunnison Co., Colorado. Regarded as inseparable from *M. f. luteola* by Warren, Jour. Mamm., 17:392, November 16, 1936.

1915. *Marmota flaviventer campioni* Figgins, Proc. Biol. Soc. Washington, 28:147, September 21, type from 8 mi.

NW Higho, Jackson Co., Colorado. Regarded as inseparable from *M. f. luteola* by Warren (*antea*).

MARGINAL RECORDS (A. H. Howell, 1915:52–53, unless otherwise noted).—Wyoming: Laramie Mts.; Sherman. Colorado: Estes Park; Pikes Peak (Warren, 1942: 113); 9 mi. S Cochetopa Pass; 4 mi. S, 23 mi. W Antonito, 9600 ft. (41644 KU). New Mexico: 5 mi. E Brazos Peak (7156 KU). Colorado: Osier (Warren, 1942:114); Florida (*ibid.*). Utah (Durrant, 1952:105): 4 mi. W Geyser Pass, 10,000 ft., La Sal Mts.; Warner R.S., 9750 ft., La Sal Mts. Colorado: Meeker; Elkhead Mts. Wyoming: 7½ mi. N, 18½ mi. E Savery, 8300 ft. (25302 KU); Bridgers Pass (Hall and Kelson, 1952:345).

Marmota flaviventris nosophora A. H. Howell

1914. *Marmota flaviventer nosophora* A. H. Howell, Proc. Biol. Soc. Washington, 27:15, February 2, type from Willow Creek, 4000 ft., 7 mi. E Corvallis, Ravalli Co., Montana.

MARGINAL RECORDS (A. H. Howell, 1915:48–49, unless otherwise noted).—Alberta (Moore, 1953:142): Waterton; near Aden. Montana: Como Lake; 4 mi. S Fort Logan, Camas Creek (233386 BS); 18 mi. N White Sulphur Springs (233384 BS); 5 mi. NW Hilger (123382 BS); Judith Mts., 7 mi. NE Lewiston (229841 BS); 7 mi. W Tyler (229839 BS); 5 mi. N mouth Big Timber Creek (225854 BS); Pryor Mts. Wyoming: 1 mi. E Acme (41416 KU); Sheridan; 9 mi. E, 5 mi. N Tensleep, 7400 ft. (19959 KU); 15 mi. NW Lost Cabin; 20 mi. S, 3½ mi. W Lander, 9000 ft. (37394 KU); Little Sandy Creek; 4 mi. E, 9 mi. N Pinedale, 9100 ft. (14844 KU); 12 mi. N Kendall; 19 mi. W, 2 mi. S Big Piney, 7700 ft. (14846 KU). Idaho: Pegram (215137 BS). Utah (Durrant, 1952:102): Laketown; Smith and Morehouse Creek, 8250 ft. Wyoming: 9 mi. S Robertson, 8000 ft. (25289 KU). Utah (Durrant, 1952:102, unless otherwise noted): Beaver Creek; Post Canyon, Book Cliffs, 75 mi. S Ouray (11426 CM); head right fork Cottonwood Creek, about 16 mi. NW Castledale (243663 BS); 6 mi. E Eureka; City Creek Canyon, 1½ mi. above forks, 4700 ft.; 6½ mi. W Brigham City, 4300 ft.; South Willow Canyon, 10,000 ft., base of Deseret Peak (Durrant, 1955b:73); 7½ mi. SE Yost, Raft River Mts., 6500 ft. Nevada: 1 mi. S Contact, 4800 ft. (Hall, 1946:287). Idaho: Salmon Creek, 8 mi. W Rogerson (Davis, 1939: 162); 2 mi. S Hagerman (*ibid.*); Lake Alturas (*ibid.*); Elk City (225145 BS). Montana: Weeksville; [8 mi. E] Horse Plains; N side Pinkham Creek, about 4 mi. SW Rexford (Wright and Conaway, 1950:32).

Marmota flaviventris notioros Warren

1934. *Marmota flaviventris notioros* Warren, Jour. Mamm., 15:62, February 15, type from 10,600 ft., near Marion Reservoir or Lake, Wet Mts., Custer Co., Colorado.

MARGINAL RECORDS.—Colorado (Warren, 1942:115): type locality; Greenhorn Mts.; Wet Mts. in Huerfano Co.

Marmota flaviventris obscura A. H. Howell

1914. *Marmota flaviventer obscura* A. H. Howell, Proc. Biol. Soc. Washington, 27:16, February 2, type from Wheeler Peak, 11,500 ft., 5 mi. S Twining, Taos Co., New Mexico.

MARGINAL RECORDS.—Colorado: head of Raspberry Creek, N of Villa Grove (Warren, 1942:114); Fort Massachusetts (probably = Sierra Blanca) (*ibid.*). New Mexico: Agua Fria Peak (Warren, 1936:397); 6 mi. W Rociada (225614 BS); 9 mi. NE Santa Fe (Holdenreid and Morlan, 1956:374); Panchuela, 8 mi. NW Pecos Baldy Lake (221869 BS); type locality.

Marmota flaviventris parvula A. H. Howell

1915. *Marmota flaviventer parvula* A. H. Howell, Proc. Biol. Soc. Washington, 27:14, February 2, type from Jefferson, Nye Co., Nevada.

MARGINAL RECORDS.—Nevada (Hall, 1946:289): Smiths Creek, 7500 ft.; Jefferson; Hot Creek Canyon, 6 mi. W Hot Creek P.O.; W slope Toquima Peak, 10,000 ft.; Arc Dome; Eastgate.

Marmota flaviventris sierrae A. H. Howell

1915. *Marmota flaviventris sierrae* A. H. Howell, N. Amer. Fauna, 37:43, April 7, type from 9300 ft., head of Kern River, Mt. Whitney, Tulare Co., California.

MARGINAL RECORDS.—California (A. H. Howell, 1915:44, unless otherwise noted): Tuolumne Meadows; Silver Lake, 7300 ft. (Grinnell, 1933:120); vicinity of Mammoth (A. B. Howell, 1924:33); Bishop Creek, 8000 ft.; Cottonwood Lakes; Monache Meadows, near Olancha Peak; Cannell Meadows (Grinnell, 1933:120); E. Fork Kaweah River; Big Meadows.

Marmota caligata
Hoary Marmot

External measurements: 620–820, 170–250, 90–113. Ten mammae (2 pair pectoral, 2 pair abdominal, and 1 pair inguinal); posterior pads on sole of hind foot subcircular and situated near edges of sole. Color mixed black and white, sometimes with brownish tinge especially on posterior half of upper parts; feet black or blackish brown, often with white markings on forefeet; interorbital region narrow; postorbital processes rarely projecting at right angles to long axis of skull and in most subspecies projecting back of line drawn across bases of processes and at right angle with long axis of skull; nasals narrowed posteriorly and averaging approximately same breadth as premaxillae; posterior border of palate beveled at obtuse angle; incisive foramina shaped differently depending on subspecies; maxillary tooth-rows divergent anteriorly.

Rausch (1953:116–120) arranges *M. caligata* and its subspecies as subspecies of the Eurasian species *M. marmota*. Until this arrangement has been studied in greater detail we prefer to retain the specific name *caligata*.

Marmota caligata broweri Hall and Gilmore

1934. *Marmota caligata broweri* Hall and Gilmore, Canadian Field-Nat., 48:57, April 2, type from Point Lay, Arctic Coast of Alaska; Rausch (Arctic, 6:117, July, 1953) states that the type locality is probably actually the head of Kukpowruk River, about 69° N lat.

MARGINAL RECORDS.—Alaska: 50 mi. inland from Wainwright (A. M. Bailey and Hendee, 1926:20); 30 to 35 mi. N Tulugak Lake (Rausch, 1951:178); *Hulahula River, in foothills S of Barter Island* (Bee and Hall, 1956:43); near Arctic Village, Chandalar River (*ibid.*); Big Squaw Lake (*ibid.*); mountains inland from Kotzebue Sound (A. M. Bailey and Hendee, 1926:20); Cape Thompson (Rausch, 1951:178); type locality.

Marmota caligata caligata (Eschscholtz)

1829. *Arctomys caligatus* Eschscholtz, Zoologischer Atlas, pt. 2, p. 1, pl. 6. Type locality, near Bristol Bay, Alaska.
1903. *Marmotta* [*sic*] *caligata*, J. A. Allen, Bull. Amer. Mus. Nat. Hist., 19:539, October 10.
1788. *Arctomys pruinosa* Gmelin, Syst. nat., ed. 13, 1:144, based on the hoary marmot of Pennant, may apply, at least in part, here but A. H. Howell (N. Amer. Fauna, 37:59, April 7, 1915), the reviser of the American marmots, rejects the name as unidentifiable.

MARGINAL RECORDS (A. H. Howell, 1915:61, unless otherwise noted).—Mackenzie: Black Mtn., SW of Aklavik (Porsild, 1945:14); mountain W of Fort Goodhope (Anderson, 1947:107). Yukon: Kalzas Creek (Rand, 1945b:45). British Columbia: Atlin (Rand, 1945b:45); Cheonee Mts. Alaska: Portland Canal (Anderson, 1947:107); Fort Snettisham; Yakutat Bay; Hinchinbrook Island; Cape Elizabeth; Kanatak, Portage Bay; Aleknagik Lake; Toklat River near head; hills back of Nome (Bailey and Hendee, 1926:20); Fort Yukon.

Marmota caligata cascadensis A. H. Howell

1914. *Marmota caligata cascadensis* A. H. Howell, Proc. Biol. Soc. Washington, 27:17, February 2, type from Mt. Rainier, Pierce Co., Washington.

MARGINAL RECORDS.—British Columbia (Cowan and Guiguet, 1956:122): McLean near Lillooet; Spences Bridge; Three Brothers Mtn. in Manning Park. Washington: Mt. Chopaka (Dalquest, 1948:265); near head Cascade River (A. H. Howell, 1915:69); mountains near Easton (*ibid.*); Mt. Adams (Dalquest, 1948:265); type locality; Mt. Baker (*ibid.*). British Columbia: Lihumitson Mts. near Chilliwack (Cowan and Guiguet, 1956:122); Howe Sound (Anderson, 1947:107); Alta Lake (Cowan and Guiguet, 1956:122).

Marmota caligata nivaria A. H. Howell

1914. *Marmota caligata nivaria* A. H. Howell, Proc. Biol. Soc. Washington, 27:17, February 2, type from 6100 ft., mountains near Upper St. Marys Lake, Glacier Co., Montana.

MARGINAL RECORDS.—Alberta (Anderson, 1947:107): Banff National Park; Mt. Forgetmenot. Montana: type locality. Idaho: St. Joe National Forest (Rust, 1946:318); Elk Summit, Salmon River Mts. (Davis, 1939:163); near Clarkia (Rust, 1946:318).

Marmota caligata okanagana (King)

1836. *Arctomys okanaganus* King, Narrative of a journey to the shores of the Arctic Ocean . . . , 2:236. Type

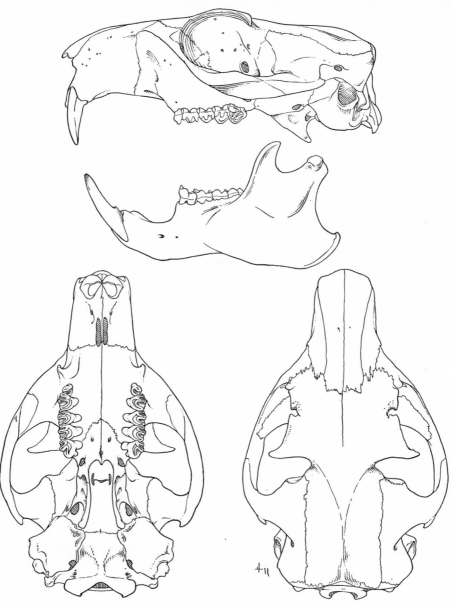

Fig. 212. *Marmota caligata broweri*, mouth Chamberlin Canyon, S end Lake Peters, 145° 08′ 34″, 69° 20′ 58″, 3690 ft., Brooks Range, Alaska, No. 50417 K.U., ♀, X 1.

locality, the region occupied by the Okanagan Indians on the borders of the Rocky Mts. between Columbia and Fraser rivers, subsequently fixed by A. H. Howell (Proc. Biol. Soc. Washington, 27:17, February 2, 1914) as Gold Range, British Columbia.

1915. *Marmota caligata okanagana*, A. H. Howell, N. Amer. Fauna, 37:64, April 7.

MARGINAL RECORDS.—Alberta: Henry House (76233 BS); 15 mi. S Henry House (Anderson, 1934:62). British Columbia: Field (*ibid.*); Spillimacheen River (*ibid.*); Mt. Evans (Cowan and Guiguet, 1956:124); Toby Creek (*ibid.*); Rossland group of Monashee Range, near Rossland

(Anderson, 1934:63); Shuswap Range (Anderson, 1947:108).

Marmota caligata oxytona Hollister

1912. *Marmota sibila* Hollister, Smiths. Miscl. Coll., 56(35):1, February 7, type from head Moose Pass branch of Smoky River, 7200 ft., Alberta. Not *Arctomys sibila* Wolf, 1808 [= *Glis canadensis* Erxleben].

1914. *Marmota oxytona* Hollister, Science, n.s., 39:251, February 13, a renaming of *M. sibila* Hollister.

1915. *Marmota caligata oxytona*, A. H. Howell, N. Amer. Fauna, 37:63, April 7.

MARGINAL RECORDS.—Yukon: S. Fork Macmillan River, Mile 268 (Rand, 1945a:36). Mackenzie: Fort Liard (A. H. Howell, 1915:64). British Columbia: Laurier Pass (*ibid.*); head Wapiti River (210235 BS). Alberta: type locality; Pobokton River (210830 BS). British Columbia: Barkerville (Anderson, 1947:108); Wells Gray Park (Cowan and Guiguet, 1956:125); mountains near Babine (A. H. Howell, 1915:64); Nine-mile Mtn., near Hazelton (Swarth, 1924:381); mountains near Klappan River (A. H. Howell, 1915:64); Sheslay River (*ibid.*). Yukon: Teslin Lake (Rand, 1945b:45). For British Columbia, Cowan and Guiguet (1956:125) refer specimens from Moose Pass and from Tonquin Pass to this subspecies instead of to *okanagana*; these authors (*loc. cit.*) refer to *oxytona* instead of to *nivaria* an occurrence at Level Mtn.

Marmota caligata raceyi Anderson

1932. *Marmota caligata raceyi* Anderson, Ann. Rept. Canadian Nat. Mus. for 1931, 70:112, November 24, type from 6500 ft., Itcha Mts., Chilcotin Plateau, lat. 52° 45′ N, long. 125° W, British Columbia.

MARGINAL RECORDS.—British Columbia: Wistaria (Anderson, 1947:108); type locality; 30 mi. E Bella Coola (Hall and Gilmore, 1934:58); Mt. Brilliant, 5500 ft., Rainbow Mts. (Anderson, 1947:108).

Marmota caligata sheldoni A. H. Howell

1914. *Marmota caligata sheldoni* A. H. Howell, Proc. Biol. Soc. Washington, 27:18, February 2, type from Montague Island, Alaska. Known only from the type locality.

Marmota caligata vigilis Heller

1909. *Marmota vigilis* Heller, Univ. California Publ. Zool., 5:248, February 18, type from W shore of Glacier Bay, Alaska. Known only from the type locality.
1915. *Marmota caligata vigilis,* A. H. Howell, N. Amer. Fauna, 37:61, April 7.

Marmota olympus (Merriam)
Olympic Mountain Marmot

1898. *Arctomys olympus* Merriam, Proc. Acad. Nat. Sci. Philadelphia, 50:352, October 4, type from timber line at head of Soleduc River, Olympic Mts., Clallam Co., Washington.
1904. [*Marmota*] *olympus,* Trouessart, Catalogus mammalium . . . , Suppl., p. 344.

External measurements: 680–785; 195–252; 94–112. Color brownish drab mixed with white; interorbital region and rostrum broad; otherwise closely resembling *M. caligata*.

Rausch (1953:120) considers *M. olympus*, as well as the several subspecies of *M. caligata*, to be only subspecifically differentiated from the Old World *Marmota marmota*; he employs for *olympus* the name *M[armota]. m[armota]. olympus*.

MARGINAL RECORDS.—Washington: Happy Lake (A. H. Howell, 1915:70); *Deer Park* (Dalquest, 1948:267); *Mt. Elinor* (A. H. Howell, 1915:70); *Mt. Steel* (*ibid.*); type locality.

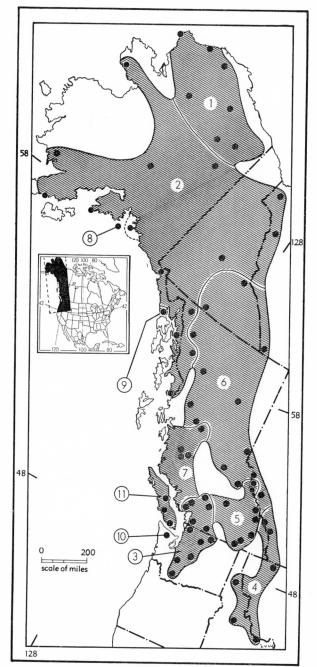

Map 213. *Marmota caligata* and allies.

Guide to kinds
1. *M. c. broweri*
2. *M. c. caligata*
3. *M. c. cascadensis*
4. *M. c. nivaria*
5. *M. c. okanagana*
6. *M. c. oxytona*
7. *M. c. raceyi*
8. *M. c. sheldoni*
9. *M. c. vigilis*
10. *M. olympus*
11. *M. vancouverensis*

Cranford, N. J.

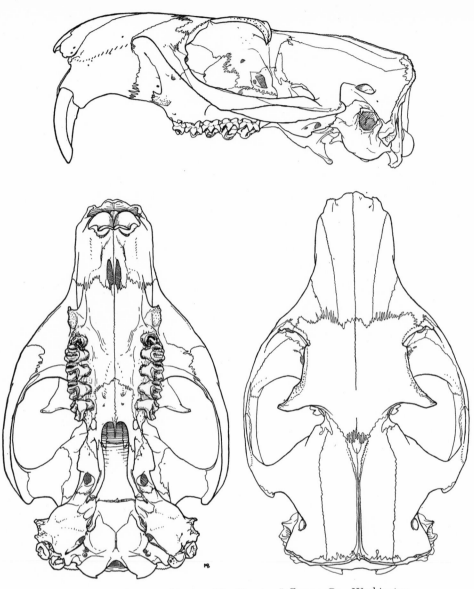

Fig. 213. *Marmota olympus,* Mt. Kimpta, Jefferson Co., Washington,
No. 84153 M.V.Z., ♀, X 1.

Marmota vancouverensis Swarth
Vancouver Marmot

1911. *Marmota vancouverensis* Swarth, Univ. California
Publ. Zool., 7:201, February 18, type from Mt. Douglas,
Vancouver Island, British Columbia.

External measurements: 670–750; 180–237; 91–
110. Color uniformly dark brown; posterior border
of nasals deeply V-shaped; otherwise closely resembles *M. caligata.*

Rausch (1953:120) states that *M. vancouverensis*
should probably be regarded as a subspecies of *M.*

marmota; he employs the name *M[armota].?*
m[armota]. vancouverensis.

MARGINAL RECORDS.—British Columbia, Vancouver
Island (Anderson, 1947:109, unless otherwise noted): Mt.
Washington (Hardy, 1955:361); *Mt. Strata* (*ibid.*); type
locality; *King Solomon Basin; Golden Eagle Basin; Green
Mtn.;* Jordan River (Cowan and Guiguet, 1956:126).

Genus Ammospermophilus Merriam—Antelope
Squirrels

Revised (under generic name *Citellus*) by A. H. Howell,
N. Amer. Fauna, 56:166–183, May 18, 1938. Bryant, Amer.

Midland Nat., 33:374–375, March, 1945, accords *Ammospermophilus* generic rank.

1892. *Ammospermophilus* Merriam, Proc. Biol. Soc. Washington, 7:27, April 13. Type, *Tamias leucurus* Merriam.

External measurements: 194–250; 54–94; 35–43. White stripe on each side of back extending from shoulder onto hip; upper parts otherwise grayish with ochraceous; tail usually curved over back exposing under surface. Small masseteric tubercle situated directly below oval infraorbital foramen; outer wall of this foramen inclined slightly mediad; interorbital region narrower than postorbital constriction; cranium nearly rectangular in dorsal outline; cheek-teeth low-crowned; metaloph on M1 and M2 does not join protocone; protolophid absent on p4; baculum with proximal end greatly enlarged and with a process on left side; clavobrachialis muscle absent.

Antelope ground squirrels eat seeds, instead of or in addition to green vegetation, have 2 annual molts, do not hibernate (at least in most areas), live in desertlike areas (Lower Sonoran and lower part of Upper Sonoran life-zones). In Nevada (Hall, 1946: 317), 10 females contained 5 to 11 embryos, the mode being 7 and the mean 7.8.

KEY TO SPECIES OF AMMOSPERMOPHILUS

1. Underside of tail having median area white.
  2. Occurring in San Joaquin Valley of California. . . . . A. *nelsoni*, p. 334
  2′. Not occurring in San Joaquin Valley of California.
    3. Occurring on Espíritu Santo Island, Baja California; anterior upper premolar absent or rudimentary.
                      A. *insularis*, p. 334
    3′. Not occurring on Espíritu Santo Island, Baja California; anterior premolar present and normal.
      4. Occurring in Coahuila, Texas, and E of Rio Grande in New Mexico.
                      A. *interpres*, p. 333
      4′. Not occurring in Coahuila, Texas, or E of Rio Grande in New Mexico. . . . . A. *leucurus*, p. 332
1′. Underside of tail lacking median white area.
                      A. *harrisii*, p. 331

Ammospermophilus harrisii
Harris' Antelope Squirrel

External measurements: 222–250; 74–94; 38–42. Greatest length of skull, 38.2–41.2. Upper parts in summer pinkish cinnamon more or less darkened with fuscous; in winter mouse gray; tail, above and

below, mixed black and white and hence lacking clear white undersurface of the other species of the genus; in both seasons having two white stripes down back.

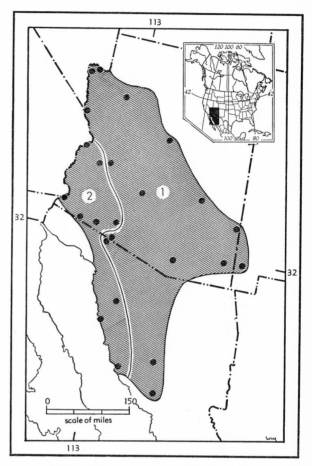

Map 214. *Ammospermophilus harrisii*.

1. *A. h. harrisii*   2. *A. h. saxicola*

Ammospermophilus harrisii harrisii (Aud. and Bach.)

1854. *Spermophilus harrisii* Audubon and Bachman, The viviparous quadrupeds of North America, 3:267. Type locality restricted by A. H. Howell (N. Amer. Fauna, 56: 167, May 18, 1938) in Santa Cruz Valley, Arizona, at the Mexican boundary.
1907. *Ammospermophilus harrisii*, Mearns, Bull. U.S. Nat. Mus., 56:viii, 303, April 13.

MARGINAL RECORDS (A. H. Howell, 1938:169, unless otherwise noted).—Arizona: Gold Basin; Peach Springs; Montezuma Well; Rice; Sheldon. New Mexico: 12 mi. NW Animas. Arizona: Chiricahua Mts. (Cahalane, 1939:427); 30 mi. S Tucson. Sonora: Hermosillo; Ortiz; Agua Dulce (Burt, 1938:37). Arizona: Quitobaquita; 20 mi. SW Phoenix; Harquahala Mts.; Fort Mohave; Dolan Spring.

Ammospermophilus harrisii saxicola (Mearns)

1896. *Spermophilus harrisii saxicolus* Mearns, Preliminary diagnoses of new mammals from the Mexican border of the United States, p. 2, March 25 (preprint of Proc. U.S. Nat. Mus., 18:444, May 23, 1896), type from Tinajas Altas, Yuma Co., Arizona.

1907. *Ammospermophilus harrisii saxicola,* Mearns, Bull. U.S. Nat. Mus., 56:viii, 306, April 13.

1937. *Ammospermophilus harrisii kinoensis* Huey, Trans. San Diego Soc. Nat. Hist., 8:352, June 15, type from Bahía Kino, Sonora.

MARGINAL RECORDS (A. H. Howell, 1938:170, unless otherwise noted).—Arizona: Parker; Vicksburg; 10 mi. N Ajo; Tule Wells. Sonora: 45 mi. NE Puerto Libertad (Burt, 1938:37); Bahía Kino; Puerto Libertad. Arizona: type locality; Yuma.

Ammospermophilus leucurus
White-tailed Antelope Squirrel

External measurements: 194–239; 54–87; 35–43. Upper parts brownish or cinnamon; 2 white stripes on back extending from sides to hips; tail broadly white or whitish below, bordered with fuscous black; in winter pelage more grayish.

Although there are 2 molts per year, the hair of the tail seems to be molted only in autumn.

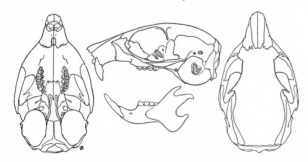

Fig. 214. *Ammospermophilus leucurus leucurus,* 14 mi. E Searchlight, Nevada, No. 61472 M.V.Z., ♂, X 1.

Ammospermophilus leucurus canfieldae Huey

1929. *Ammospermophilus leucurus canfieldae* Huey, Trans. San Diego Soc. Nat. Hist., 5:243, February 27, type from Punta Prieta, Baja California.

MARGINAL RECORDS (A. H. Howell, 1938:178).— Baja California: Jaraguay, 58 mi. SE San Fernando; Calamahue; Yubay, 30 mi. SE Calamahue; Campo Los Angeles; Santo Domingo; San Andrés.

Ammospermophilus leucurus cinnamomeus (Merriam)

1890. *Tamias leucurus cinnamomeus* Merriam, N. Amer. Fauna, 3:52, September 11, type from Echo Cliffs, Painted Desert, Coconino Co., Arizona.

1907. *Ammospermophilus leucurus cinnamomeus,* Mearns, Bull. U.S. Nat. Mus., 56:299, April 13.

MARGINAL RECORDS (A. H. Howell, 1938:175, unless otherwise noted).—Colorado: Grand Junction (Warren, 1942:134–135); Coventry (*ibid.*); Ashbaugh's Ranch, near McElmo. Arizona: Zuni River; Taylor; Winslow; Cedar Ranch Wash, Locket Tank. Utah (Durrant, 1952:125–126): 2 mi. W St. George; Little Castle Valley.

Ammospermophilus leucurus escalante (Hansen)

1955. *Citellus leucurus escalante* Hansen, Jour. Mamm., 36: 274, May 26, type from 2 mi. SE Escalante, 5400 ft., Garfield Co., Utah.

MARGINAL RECORDS (Hansen, 1955:274).—Utah: ½ mi. E Bicknell; Henry Mtns., Kings Ranch; 8 mi. S Escalante, 5200 ft.; Kanab; St. George; Beaverdam Wash; Leeds.

Ammospermophilus leucurus extimus Nelson and Goldman

1929. *Ammospermophilus leucurus extimus* Nelson and Goldman, Jour. Washington, Acad. Sci., 19:281, July 19, type from Saccaton (15 mi. N Cape San Lucas), Baja California.

MARGINAL RECORDS (A. H. Howell, 1938:180).— Baja California: Santana; San Bruno; San Juanico Bay; Aguaje de San Esteban.

Ammospermophilus leucurus leucurus (Merriam)

1889. *Tamias leucurus* Merriam, N. Amer. Fauna, 2:20, October 30, type from San Gorgonio Pass, Riverside Co., California.

1907. *Ammospermophilus leucurus* [*leucurus*], Mearns, Bull. U.S. Nat. Mus., 56:viii, 299, April 13.

1904. *Citellus l*[*eucurus*]. *vinnulus* Elliot, Field Columb. Mus., Publ. 79, Zool. Ser., 3:241, January 7, type from Keeler, Owens Lake, Inyo Co., California.

MARGINAL RECORDS.—Oregon: Vale (A. H. Howell, 1938:173). Idaho (Davis, 1939:206): Homedale; 5 mi. N Bruneau; Glenns Ferry. Nevada (Hall, 1946:318): Quinn River Crossing, 4100 ft.; S base Granite Peak, East Range; 8 mi. SE Eastgate; Hot Creek Range, 4 mi. N Hot Creek, 6400 ft.; N Lund; 1 mi. SE Smith Creek Cave, Mt. Moriah, 5800 ft.; 8 mi. S Wendover, 4700 ft. Utah (Durrant, 1952:123): Promontory Point; Elberta; Nephi; Monroe. Arizona: 6 mi. N Wolf Hole (A. H. Howell, 1938:172); Grand Wash, 8 mi. S Pakoon Spring (*ibid.*). Baja California: San Felipe (*ibid.*); Parral (Elliot, 1907:161). California (A. H. Howell, 1938:172): Jacumba; Radec, 12 mi. E Temecula; Banning; Hesperia; Mojave; Kern River Valley, near Kernville; Independence; 8 mi. W Bishop. Nevada (Hall, 1946:317–318): East Walker River, 2 mi. NW Morgan's Ranch, 5100 ft.; Washoe Lake. California (A. H. Howell, 1938:172): Amedee; Lower Alkali Lake. Nevada

(Hall, 1946:317–318): Smoke Creek, 9 mi. E California boundary, 3900 ft.; mouth Little High Rock Canyon; Virgin Valley, 5000 ft. Oregon (A. H. Howell, 1938:173): Adel; South Warner Lake; Tumtum Lake; Watson.

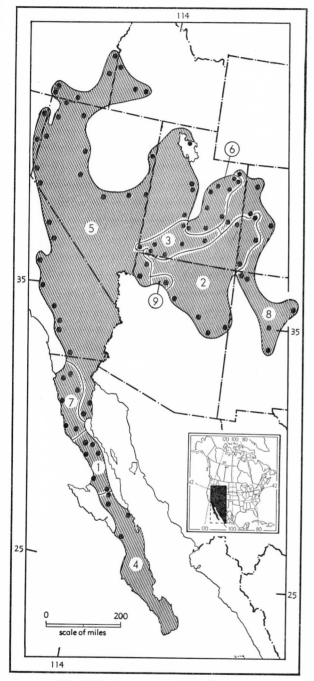

Map 215. *Ammospermophilus leucurus.*

Guide to subspecies
1. *A. l. canfieldae*
2. *A. l. cinnamomeus*
3. *A. l. escalante*
4. *A. l. extimus*
5. *A. l. leucurus*
6. *A. l. notom*
7. *A. l. peninsulae*
8. *A. l. pennipes*
9. *A. l. tersus*

Ammospermophilus leucurus notom (Hansen)

1955. *Citellus leucurus notom* Hansen, Jour. Mamm., 36: 274, May 26, type from Notom, Wayne Co., Utah.

MARGINAL RECORDS (Hansen, 1955:275).—Utah: 8 mi. S Vernal; 7 mi. SW Jensen, N bank Green River; Pariette Ranch, 8 mi. SW Ouray; 10 mi. S Greenriver; Hanksville; Torrey; Buckhorn Wash, San Rafael River; Wellington; Antelope Canyon, 10 mi. SW Myton.

Ammospermophilus leucurus peninsulae (J. A. Allen)

1893. *Tamias leucurus peninsulae* J. A. Allen, Bull. Amer. Mus. Nat. Hist., 5:197, August 18, type from San Telmo, Baja California.
1907. *Ammospermophilus leucurus peninsulae,* Mearns, Bull. U.S. Nat. Mus., 56:299, April 13.

MARGINAL RECORDS (A. H. Howell, 1938:177).— Baja California: Agua Escondido, near Hanson Laguna; Trinidad Valley; San Fernando; Rosario; type locality; San Rafael Valley, 20 mi. E Ojos Negros.

Ammospermophilus leucurus pennipes A. H. Howell

1931. *Ammospermophilus leucurus pennipes* A. H. Howell, Jour. Mamm., 12:162, May 14, type from Grand Junction, Colorado.

MARGINAL RECORDS.—Utah: Vernal (Durrant, 1952: 124). Colorado: White River, 20 mi. E Rangeley (A. H. Howell, 1938:176); Hotchkiss (*ibid.*). New Mexico (A. H. Howell, 1938:176, unless otherwise noted): Fruitland; Jemez; Socorro Mts. (Warren, 1942:135); 35 mi. W Albuquerque; Shiprock. Colorado: Fruita (Howell, 1938:176). Utah (Durrant, 1952:124): 1 mi. E Highway 160, 6 mi. S Valley City, 4500 ft.

Ammospermophilus leucurus tersus Goldman

1929. *Ammospermophilus leucurus tersus* Goldman, Jour. Washington Acad. Sci., 19:435, November 19, type from lower end of Prospect Valley, 4500 ft., Grand Canyon, Hualpai Indian Reservation, Arizona. Known only from the type locality.

Ammospermophilus interpres (Merriam)
Texas Antelope Squirrel

1890. *Tamias interpres* Merriam, N. Amer. Fauna, 4:21, October 8, type from El Paso, El Paso Co., Texas.
1905. *Ammospermophilus interpres,* V. Bailey, N. Amer. Fauna, 25:81, October 24.

External measurements: 220–235; 68–84; 36–40. Closely resembles *A. leucurus*; from the adjoining *A. leucurus pennipes, A. interpres* differs in having 2 black bands, instead of 1, on the hairs of the tail.

MARGINAL RECORDS (A. H. Howell, 1938:181, unless otherwise noted).—New Mexico: east foothills, Manzano Mts. Texas: 7 mi. N Pine Springs (Davis and Robert-

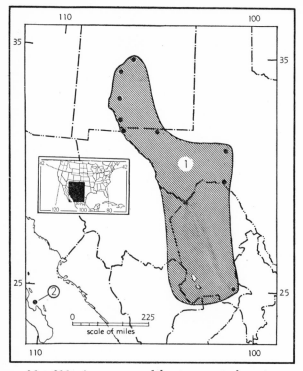

Map 216. *Ammospermophilus*, two nominal species.

1. *A. interpres*   2. *A. insularis*

son, 1944:266); Castle Mts.; High Bridge, mouth Pecos River. Coahuila: Jaral. Texas: El Paso. New Mexico: Organ Mts.; San Andres Mts.; 10 mi. NE Socorro.

Ammospermophilus insularis Nelson and Goldman
Espíritu Santo Island Antelope Squirrel

1909. *Ammospermophilus leucurus insularis* Nelson and Goldman, Proc. Biol. Soc. Washington, 22:24, March 10, type from Espíritu Santo Island, Baja California. Known only from Espíritu Santo Island.

External measurements: 210–240; 71–83; 36–40. Resembles *A. l. extimus* of adjoining mainland, but differs in larger size, darker flanks and legs, and absent or vestigial P3.

Ammospermophilus nelsoni (Merriam)
Nelson's Antelope Squirrel

1893. *Spermophilus nelsoni* Merriam, Proc. Biol. Soc. Washington, 8:129, December 28, type from Tipton, Tulare Co., California.
1909. *Ammospermophilus nelsoni*, Lyon and Osgood, Bull. U.S. Nat. Mus., 62:172.
1916. *Ammospermophilus nelsoni amplus* Taylor, Univ. California Publ. Zool., 17:15, October 3, type from 20 mi. S Los Baños, Merced Co., California.

External measurements: 218–240; 63–79; 40–43. Resembles *A. l. leucurus* but differs as follows:

larger, more buffy (less grayish), more widely spreading zygomatic arches and larger auditory bullae.

Hawbecker (1947:125) found that although the green parts of filaree and grass are eaten, both seeds and insects seem to be necessary as food. Adults become inactive (to exactly what extent is unknown) to avoid the heat of summer. The young, in summer, forage at the time of day when the temperature is lowest.

MARGINAL RECORDS (A. H. Howell, 1938:183).— California: Los Baños; Dos Palos; Firebaugh; Mendota; Huron; type locality; 8 mi. NE Bakersfield; Rose Station, 4 mi. E Fort Tejon; Cuyama Valley; 8 mi. E Simmler; Carriso Plains; Alcalde; Panoche Pass.

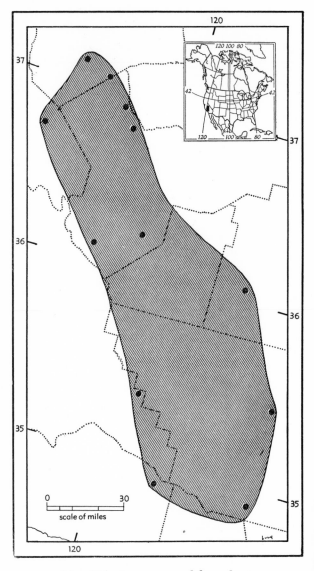

Map 217. *Ammospermophilus nelsoni*.

Genus **Spermophilus** Cuvier—Spermophiles and Ground Squirrels

Revised by A. H. Howell, N. Amer. Fauna, 56:1–256, May 18, 1938, under the name *Citellus*. Subgenera treated by Bryant, Amer. Midland Nat., 33:257–390, March, 1945.

1816. *Citellus* Oken, Lehrbuch der Naturgeschichte, pt. 3, 2:842. Type, *Mus citellus* Linnaeus. (Oken names not available under the Regles. See Hershkovitz, Jour. Mamm., 30:289–301, August 17, 1949.)

1817. *Anisonyx* Rafinesque, Amer. Monthly Mag., 2(1):45. Type, *Anisonyx brachiura* Rafinesque [= *Arctomys columbianus* Ord]. (Not *Anisonyx* Latreille, 1807, a coleopteran.)

1825. *Spermophilus* F. Cuvier, Des dents des mammifères, . . . , p. 255. Type, "*Mus citellus* Linn."

1830. *Citillus* Lichtenstein, Darstellung neuer oder wenig bekannter Säugethiere . . . , pl. 31, fig. 2 (not paged).

1844. *Colobotis* Brandt, Bull. Class. Phys.-Math. Acad. Imp. Sci. St. Petersbourg, 2(23 and 24):366. Type, *Arctomys fulvus* Lichtenstein.

1844. *Otocolobus* Brandt, Bull. Class. Phys.-Math. Acad. Imp. Sci. St. Petersbourg, 2(23 and 24):382. Equals *Colobotis*.

1874?. *Colobates* Milne-Edwards, Recherches Hist. Nat. Mamm., 1:157.

1927. *Urocitellus* Obolenskij, Comp. Rend. Acad. Sci. USSR., p. 188. Type, *Spermophilus eversmanni* Brandt.

External measurements: 167–520; 32–252; 27–68. Brown, reddish, black, black and white, striped, spotted, variegated, or of solid color. Five digits on each foot; each digit with a claw, or nail (pollex has flat nail); palm with 5 pads (3 interdigital and 2 metacarpal); sole with 4 interdigital pads and no metatarsal pads. Four to seven pairs of mammae. Masseteric tubercle of medium or large size, situated ventral and slightly lateral to infraorbital foramen; infraorbital foramen oval or triangular, relatively broader than in *Ammospermophilus*; a bend present in dorsal profile of skull at junction of rostrum and cranium; zygomatic arches expanded posteriorly but not appressed so closely as in *Ammospermophilus*, *Eutamias*, and *Tamias* and not spread so widely as in *Marmota*; upper tooth-rows parallel or diverging slightly posteriorly; M3 and m3 without complicated enamel folds in basins thus resembling *Ammospermophilus* and differing from *Cynomys*. Dentition: i. $\frac{1}{1}$, c. $\frac{1}{1}$, p. $\frac{1-2}{1}$, m. $\frac{3}{3}$. Clavobrachialis muscle present.

Ground squirrels are essentially herbivorous and spermophilous. They dig their own burrows, and some species live in colonies. Those species that live in and above the Upper Sonoran Life-zone hibernate. In the arid parts of the state of Nevada the species *S. townsendii* begins dormancy (aestivation) when green food dries up and the period of dormancy (aestivation and hibernation) may be as long as 8 months.

KEY TO SUBGENERA OF SPERMOPHILUS

1. Molars brachydont; parastyle ridge on M1 and M2 joining the protocone without abrupt change of direction.
  2. Anterior upper premolar simple; less than ¼ size of P4.
    3. Upper incisors stout and distinctly recurved; tail of adults longer than 128; upper parts variegated black, white and buff. . *Otospermophilus*, p. 351
    3'. Upper incisors slender and not distinctly recurved; tail of adults shorter than 128; upper parts plain or with 1 white stripe on each side of back extending from shoulder all of way onto hip.
      4. Postorbital process long and slender; golden mantle on head and white stripe on each side of back from shoulder onto hip. *Callospermophilus*, p. 359
      4'. Postorbital process short and thick; upper parts uniformly pinkish gray (not striped or spotted). *Xerospermophilus*, p. 357
  2'. Anterior upper premolar bearing two cusps and a functional cutting edge; more than ¼ size of P4. . . . *Poliocitellus*, p. 350
1'. Molars hypsodont; parastyle ridge on M1 and M2 joining protocone with abrupt change of direction.
  5. Metaloph on P4 continuous; upper parts reddish or with fine white spots on gray background. . . . . *Spermophilus*, p. 335
  5'. Metaloph on P4 not continuous; upper parts with nearly square white spots, in some species arranged in rows or upper parts clay color (*S. perotensis*). *Ictidomys*, p. 344

Subgenus **Spermophilus** Cuvier

1825. *Spermophilus* F. Cuvier, Des dents des mammifères . . . , p. 255. Type, "*Mus citellus* Linn."

External measurements: 167–495; 32–153; 29–68. Greatest length of skull, 32.4–65.8. Gray, reddish, or with fine white spots on gray background. Infraorbital foramen subtriangular, its lateral wall inclined ventrolaterad; masseteric tubercle situated more laterally than in *Otospermophilus*; interorbital and postorbital constrictions narrow and approximately equal in width; zygomatic arches expanded posteriorly; rostrum short and broad, expanded at tip and constricted at base; fossae anterolateral to incisive foramina shallow; anterior margin of alveolar border drops abruptly to join diastema instead of merging with diastema in a gradual curve as in other subgenera; cheek-teeth high-crowned;

M1 and M2 narrowly triangular in occlusal outline; anterior cingulum joins protocone with abrupt change of direction on M1 and M2; metaloph joins protocone on each upper molar; M3 much larger than M2; posterior cingulum of M3 bends abruptly posteriad from protocone; p4 molariform, protolophid large and extends obliquely ventromediad from protoconid; protoconid of this tooth much larger than hypoconid; trigonid on lower cheek-teeth much higher than talonid; occlusal outline of m1 and m2 parallelogram-shaped; baculum having wider and deeper spoon than in *Callospermophilus* and rows of spines on margin more divergent; baculum otherwise as in *Otospermophilus*; cheek pouches of medium size; atlantoscapularis dorsalis muscle absent.

KEY TO NORTH AMERICAN SPECIES OF SUBGENUS SPERMOPHILUS

1. Upper parts unspotted and unmottled.
    2. Hind foot longer than 39.
        3. Underside of tail grayish.
                                   S. *armatus*, p. 339
        3'. Underside of tail buffy or reddish.
            4. Underside of tail buffy.
                             S. *richardsonii*, p. 338
            4'. Underside of tail reddish.
                               S. *beldingi*, p. 340
    2'. Hind foot less than 39. . S. *townsendii*, p. 336
1'. Upper parts spotted or mottled.
    5. Hind foot more than 43.
        6. Dorsal spots whitish. . S. *undulatus*, p. 343
        6'. Dorsal spots buffy. S. *columbianus*, p. 341
    5'. Hind foot less than 43.
        7. Upper parts grayish. S. *washingtoni*, p. 337
        7'. Upper parts brownish. S. *brunneus*, p. 338

Spermophilus townsendii
Townsend's Ground Squirrel

External measurements: 167–271; 32–72; 29–38. Greatest length of skull, 32.4–43.3. Upper parts plain, smoke gray shaded with pinkish buff or pinkish cinnamon; underparts whitish; underside of tail reddish. Rostrum stout, its sides nearly parallel; supraorbital borders of skull slightly elevated; postorbital processes long, slender, decurved; temporal ridges lyrate, meeting posteriorly in old age and forming a slight sagittal crest.

Townsend's ground squirrel subsists on green vegetation. As soon as an individual becomes fat enough to enter the dormant condition it begins aestivation. In Nevada this is in July—a time when the vegetation often dries up. Normally the squirrel does not emerge until 7½ to 8 months later. If, however, the food supply is insufficient in spring and summer to fatten the squirrel in 120 to 135 days, it

may stay out longer or may emerge for a time in the autumn after only a short period of aestivation. Five to 15 embryos have been recorded; in 2 consecutive years the mode and mean were 10 in western Nevada, but in the 3rd year 8.

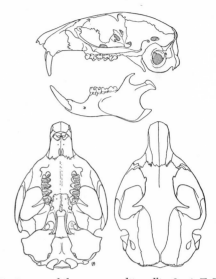

Fig. 215. *Spermophilus townsendii mollis*, 6 mi. E Stillwater, Nevada, No. 41525 M.V.Z., ♂, X 1.

Spermophilus townsendii artemesiae (Merriam)

1913. *Citellus mollis artemesiae* Merriam, Proc. Biol. Soc. Washington, 26:137, May 21, type from Birch Creek, about 10 mi. S Nicholia, Idaho.
1938. *Citellus townsendii artemesiae,* A. H. Howell, N. Amer. Fauna, 56:65, May 18.
1913. *Citellus mollus* [*sic*] *pessimus* Merriam, Proc. Biol. Soc. Washington, 26:138, May 21, type from lower part of Big Lost River, Butte Co., Idaho.

MARGINAL RECORDS (Davis, 1939:196–197).—Idaho: Birch Creek, 2 mi. SE Kaufman; near Taber; Pingree, thence westward on N side Snake River to 3 mi. W Bliss; 3 mi. SE Arco.

Spermophilus townsendii canus Merriam

1898. *Spermophilus mollis canus* Merriam, Proc. Biol. Soc. Washington, 12:70, March 24, type from Antelope, Wasco Co., Oregon.
1938. *Citellus townsendii canus,* A. H. Howell, N. Amer. Fauna, 56:67, May 18.

MARGINAL RECORDS (A. H. Howell, 1938:67, unless otherwise noted).—Oregon: 10 mi. N Baker; Cedar Mts. Nevada (Hall, 1946:300): Hot Spring; Virgin Valley; Long Valley Ranch. Oregon: Summer Lake; Fremont; Warmspring; 7 mi. E Antelope.

Spermophilus townsendii idahoensis (Merriam)

1913. *Citellus idahoensis* Merriam, Proc. Biol. Soc. Washington, 26:135, May 21, type from Payette, Idaho.
1939. *Citellus townsendii idahoensis,* Davis, Jour. Mamm., 20:182, May 15.

MARGINAL RECORDS (Davis, 1939:188, unless otherwise noted).—Idaho: 2 mi. S Payette; 14 mi. SE Boise; Glenns Ferry (A. H. Howell, 1938:69), thence along N side Snake River to point of beginning.

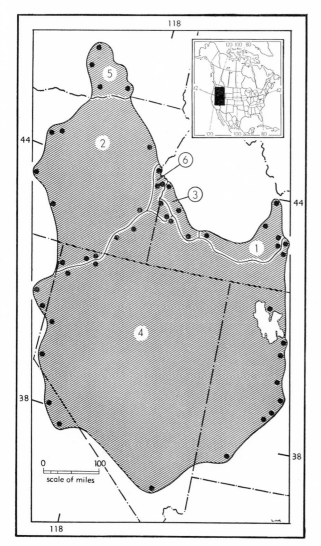

Map 218. *Spermophilus townsendii.*

1. *S. t. artemesiae*   4. *S. t. mollis*
2. *S. t. canus*   5. *S. t. townsendii*
3. *S. t. idahoensis*   6. *S. t. vigilis*

Spermophilus townsendii mollis Kennicott

1863. *Spermophilus mollis* Kennicott, Proc. Acad. Nat. Sci. Philadelphia, 15:157. Type locality, Camp Floyd [= Fairfield], Utah Co., Utah.
1938. *Citellus townsendii mollis*, A. H. Howell, N. Amer. Fauna, 56:63, May 18.
1898. *Spermophilus mollis stephensi* Merriam, Proc. Biol. Soc. Washington, 12:69, March 24, type from Queen Station, near head Owens Valley, Mineral Co., Nevada.

1913. *Citellus leurodon* Merriam, Proc. Biol. Soc. Washington, 26:136, May 21, type from Murphy, in hills W of Snake River, Owyhee Co., Idaho.
1913. *Citellus mollis washoensis* Merriam, Proc. Biol. Soc. Washington, 26:138, May 21, type from Carson Valley [Douglas Co.?], Nevada.

MARGINAL RECORDS.—Idaho: Murphy (A. H. Howell, 1938:64); Blackfoot (Davis, 1939:193); Ross Fork Creek (*ibid.*). Utah (Durrant, 1952:112–113): Promontory; Salt Lake City; 3 mi. N Saratoga Springs; Nephi; Manti; Salina; Richfield; 2 mi. W Cedar City. Nevada (Hall, 1946:303): Indian Springs. California (A. H. Howell, 1938:64): Long Valley; Mono Lake. Nevada (Hall, 1946:303): Carson City; Pyramid Lake. California (A. H. Howell, 1938:64): Honey Lake; Horse Lake. Nevada (Hall, 1946:303): mouth Little High Rock Canyon, 5000 ft.; Big Creek Ranch, Pine Forest Mts. Oregon (A. H. Howell, 1938:64–65): White Horse Sink; Rome.

Spermophilus townsendii townsendii Bachman

1839. *Spermophilus townsendii* Bachman, Jour. Acad. Nat. Sci. Philadelphia, 8:61. Type locality, "On the Columbia River, about 300 miles above its mouth," Washington (but see T. H. Scheffer, Jour. Mamm., 27:395, November 25, 1946).
1898. *Spermophilus mollis yakimensis* Merriam, Proc. Biol. Soc. Washington, 12:70, March 24, type from Mabton, Yakima Co., Washington.

MARGINAL RECORDS (A. H. Howell, 1938:63, unless otherwise noted).—Washington: Ellensburg; Kennewick (Dalquest, 1948:268); Bickleton; Wiley City.

Spermophilus townsendii vigilis (Merriam)

1913. *Citellus canus vigilis* Merriam, Proc. Biol. Soc. Washington, 26:137, May 21, type from Vale, Oregon.
1938. *Citellus townsendii vigilis*, A. H. Howell, N. Amer. Fauna, 56:66, May 18.

MARGINAL RECORDS.—Oregon (A. H. Howell, 1938:66): Huntington; Ontario. Idaho (Davis, 1939:190): Homedale; 2 mi. W Reynolds Creek. Oregon: type locality.

Spermophilus washingtoni (A. H. Howell)
Washington's Ground Squirrel

1938. *Citellus washingtoni washingtoni* A. H. Howell, N. Amer. Fauna, 56:69, May 18, type from Touchet, Walla Walla Co., Washington. (See T. H. Scheffer, Jour. Mamm., 27:395, November 26, 1946.)
1938. *Citellus washingtoni loringi* A. H. Howell, N. Amer. Fauna, 56:71, May 18, type from Douglas, Washington. Dalquest (Univ. Kansas Publ., Mus. Nat. Hist., 2:271, April 9, 1948) regards *S. w. loringi* as inseparable from *S. washingtoni.*

External measurements: 185–245; 32–65; 30–38. Greatest length of skull, 35.0–41.4. Upper parts smoke gray flecked with white spots; tail mixed fuscous and grayish white with blackish tip. Skull resembles that of *S. townsendii* but narrower in relation to length. Type of food and period of dormancy essentially as in *S. townsendii.*

MARGINAL RECORDS (A. H. Howell, 1938:71, unless otherwise noted).—Washington: Mansfield; Wilbur; Cheney; Wawawai. Oregon: Pilot Rock; Heppner; Willows. Washington: Pasco; Waterville (Dalquest, 1948:271).

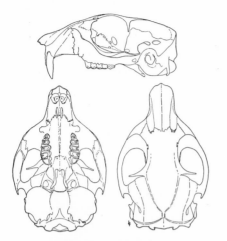

Fig. 216. *Spermophilus washingtoni*, 4 mi. W Pasco, Franklin Co., Washington, No. 93247 M.V.Z., ♂, X 1.

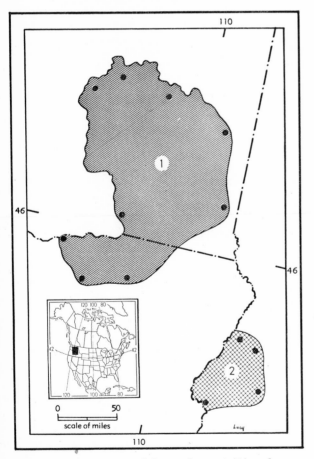

Map 219. *Spermophilus washingtoni* (1) and *Spermophilus brunneus* (2).

Spermophilus brunneus (A. H. Howell)
Idaho Ground Squirrel

1928. *Citellus townsendii brunneus* A. H. Howell, Proc. Biol. Soc. Washington, 41:211, December 18, type from New Meadows, Adams Co., Idaho.
1938. *Citellus brunneus* A. H. Howell, N. Amer. Fauna, 56: 72, May 18.

External measurements: 214–252; 46–61; 33–37. Greatest length of skull, 38.7–40.8. Upper parts dappled grayish brown, the brown predominating on lower part of back; nose, outer sides of hind legs, and ventral face of tail rusty brown; shoulders and forelegs ochraceous buff; underparts grayish fulvous; chin white; terminal hairs of tail with 5 to 8 alternating bands of black and white or fulvous. From S. *washingtoni* this species differs in ear larger (height from notch, 9–12), upper parts brown instead of gray and with smaller spots; pelage shorter and coarser; absence of distinct, white, ventrolateral stripe; auditory bullae smaller; rostrum shorter and broader; ratio of palatal to postpalatal length 82 as opposed to 70.5; sphenopalatine fissures smaller.

MARGINAL RECORDS (Davis, 1939:184).—Idaho: 1 mi. N Bear Creek R.S.; type locality; Van Wyck; Weiser.

Spermophilus richardsonii
Richardson's Ground Squirrel

External measurements: 253–337; 65–100; 39.5–49. Greatest length of skull, 42.0–48.6. Upper parts drab or smoke gray, more or less shaded with fuscous and dappled with cinnamon buff; under side of tail clay color, cinnamon buff, sayal brown, or ochraceous buff. Where the range of this species meets and overlaps that of S. *beldingi*, S. *richardsonii* can be recognized by relatively and actually longer tail, more intense cinnamon pigmentation on nose and underparts and ochraceous buff rather than reddish color on underside of tail. Where the ranges of S. *townsendii* and S. *richardsonii* overlap, the latter can be recognized by relatively and actually longer tail, cinnamon colored rather than whitish underparts, and tail with, rather than without, buffy white border. Where S. *armatus* and S. *richardsonii* occur together the latter can be recognized by the ochraceous buff instead of gray underside of the tail.

S. *richardsonii* hibernates. Seven and 8 embryos are numbers common in this species and as many as 11 embryos have been recorded. There seems to be only one litter per year.

Spermophilus richardsonii aureus (Davis)

1939. *Citellus elegans aureus* Davis, The Recent mammals of Idaho, Caxton Printers, Caldwell, Idaho, p. 177, April

5, type from Double Springs, 16 mi. NE Dickey, Custer Co., Idaho.

1943. *Citellus richardsonii aureus*, Hall, Amer. Midl. Nat., 29:378, March.

MARGINAL RECORDS.—Montana: Harrison (A. H. Howell, 1938:77). Idaho (Davis, 1939:182, unless otherwise noted): Henry Lake; near Teton Canyon; Patterson; Dickey; Forney (A. H. Howell, 1938:77). Montana (*ibid.*): Big Hole Bench, W of Wisdom; 9 mi. N Wisdom.

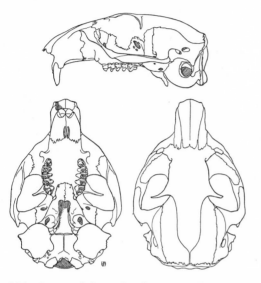

Fig. 217. *Spermophilus richardsonii nevadensis*, 4 mi. S Romano, Nevada, No. 70559 M.V.Z., ♂, X 1.

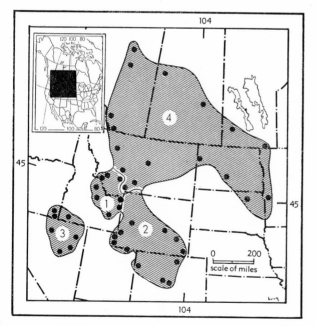

Map 220. *Spermophilus richardsonii*.

1. *S. r. aureus*
2. *S. r. elegans*
3. *S. r. nevadensis*
4. *S. r. richardsonii*

Spermophilus richardsonii elegans Kennicott

1863. *Spermophilus elegans* Kennicott, Proc. Acad. Nat. Sci. Philadelphia, 15:158, type from Fort Bridger, Wyoming.
1938. *Citellus richardsonii elegans*, A. H. Howell, N. Amer. Fauna, 56:76, May 18.

MARGINAL RECORDS (A. H. Howell, 1938:77, unless otherwise noted).—Wyoming: Poison Spider Creek; Bear Creek, near Eagle Peak; 2 mi. NE Cheyenne (14875 KU). Colorado: Fort Collins, Buckhorn R.S.; Garo; 10 mi. S Leadville; Rangeley (Cary, 1911:90). Utah: 2 mi. E Summit-Daggett Co. line, 2 mi. S Utah-Wyoming state line (Durrant, 1955b:74); Wasatch (Hansen, 1953:132); 1 mi. N Randolph (*ibid.*). Wyoming: Cokeville; 1½ mi. NE Pinedale (14856 KU).

Spermophilus richardsonii nevadensis (A. H. Howell)

1928. *Citellus elegans nevadensis* A. H. Howell, Proc. Biol. Soc. Washington, 41:211, December 18, type from Paradise, Humboldt Co., Nevada.
1938. *Citellus richardsonii nevadensis*, A. H. Howell, N. Amer. Fauna, 56:77, May 18.

MARGINAL RECORDS.—Oregon: head Rattlesnake Creek (A. H. Howell, 1938:78). Idaho: 1 mi. S Riddle (Davis, 1939:177). Nevada (Hall, 1946:305): Metropolis; Ruby Valley; 4 mi. S Romano, Diamond Valley; 1 mi. N Winnemucca. Oregon: Malheur Co., near McDermitt, Nevada (A. H. Howell, 1938:78).

Spermophilus richardsonii richardsonii (Sabine)

1822. *Arctomys richardsonii* Sabine, Trans. Linn. Soc. London, 13:589. Type locality, Carlton House, Saskatchewan.
1831. *Spermophilus richardsonii*, Cuvier, Supplément à l'histoire naturelle générale et particulière de Buffon, 1:323.

MARGINAL RECORDS (A. H. Howell, 1938:75, unless otherwise noted).—Alberta: S end Baptiste Lake (Soper, 1948:58). Saskatchewan: Livelong; Touchwood Hills (Hall, 1938:108). Manitoba: Petrel; 11 mi. E Emerson, 2 mi. N border (Soper, 1946:140). Minnesota: Lac qui Parle County (Swanson, 1945:76). South Dakota: Aberdeen. North Dakota: Bismarck; Buford. Montana: Tyler; Livingston; Lower Basin, West Gallatin River; Toston; Birch Creek. Alberta: Cardston Road, Waterton Lakes National Park (Banfield, 1950:38); 6 mi. E Maycroft (Crowe, 1943:398); Edmonton (Rand, 1948b:135).

Spermophilus armatus Kennicott
Uinta Ground Squirrel

1863. *Spermophilus armatus* Kennicott, Proc. Acad. Nat. Sci. Philadelphia, 15:158. Type locality, foothills of the Uinta Mts., near Fort Bridger, Wyoming.

External measurements: 280–303; 63–81; 42–45.5. Greatest length of skull, 46.3–48.5. Head, front of face, and ears cinnamon, sprinkled on crown with gray; sides of face and neck pale smoke gray; eye ring cartridge buff; front legs cinnamon buff, shading to pinkish buff on feet; general tone of dorsal area sayal brown or cinnamon buff, the hairs tipped with pinkish buff, bases of hairs fuscous; sides paler than back, mixed cartridge buff and fuscous; thighs cinnamon; hind feet pinkish buff; tail, above and below, fuscous black, mixed with pale buff or buffy white, and edged with pinkish buff; underparts pinkish buff, shaded with buffy white. Underside of tail gray instead of ochraceous buff as in S. *richardsonii elegans*. Skull resembling that of S. *richardsonii elegans* but larger.

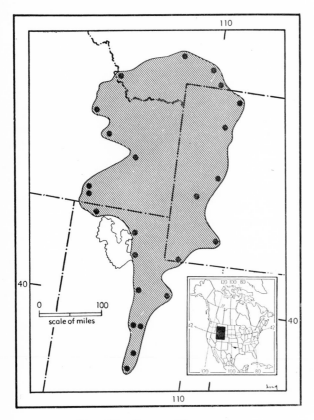

Map 221. *Spermophilus armatus.*

MARGINAL RECORDS (A. H. Howell, 1938:80–81, unless otherwise noted).—Montana: West Gallatin River; West Boulder Creek, 18 mi. SE Livingston; Cooke. Wyoming: 14¼ mi. N, 12 mi. W Cody (37409 KU); Valley; W end Half Moon Lake (14886 KU); Little Piney Creek, 8000 ft.; 5 mi. W Greenriver (Svihla, R. D., 1931:260); 1 mi. N Bridger Lake R.S. (25320 KU). Utah (Durrant, 1952:115, unless otherwise noted): Fruitland; Mt. Pleasant; 20 mi. E Salina (Kelson, 1951:27); Fish Lake; Maple Canyon; Mt. Timpanogos; Bountiful; Mantua; Pine Canyon, 17 mi. NE Kelton. Idaho: Wickel Ranch, Elba (Davis, 1939: 173); 4 mi. S Albion (*ibid.*); Blackfoot; Arco (Davis, 1939: 173); head Pahsimeroi River (*ibid.*). Montana: Donovan.

Spermophilus beldingi
Belding's Ground Squirrel

External measurements: 254–300; 55–76; 40–47. Greatest length of skull, 41.3–46.3. Upper parts smoke gray mixed with reddish brown or pinkish cinnamon; middorsal area darkened with Sayal Brown; forehead pinkish cinnamon; underparts grayish washed with pinkish cinnamon that is most pronounced on pectoral region, forelegs, forefeet, and hind feet; tail slightly darker than back on upper side but distinctly reddish, often hazel, beneath. Skull resembling that of S. *richardsonii*, but interorbital breadth greater relative to length of skull; in populations of S. *beldingi* geographically overlapping those of S. *richardsonii*, nasals averaging shorter relative to breadth of cranium. From S. *richardsonii*, S. *beldingi* is distinguished by shorter tail that is reddish rather than ochraceous buff beneath. Also, S. *beldingi* has more reddish in the pelage. From S. *townsendii*, *beldingi* is distinguished by larger size, cinnamon-colored rather than whitish underparts, maxillary tooth-row more, rather than less, than 8.9 mm.

Spermophilus beldingi beldingi Merriam

1888. *Spermophilus beldingi* Merriam, Ann. New York Acad. Sci., 4:317, December 28, type from Donner, Placer Co., California.

MARGINAL RECORDS (A. H. Howell, 1938:82, unless otherwise noted).—California: Independence Lake. Nevada (Hall, 1946:309): 3 mi. S Mt. Rose, 8500–8600 ft.; ¼ mi. E Zephyr Cove, 6300 ft.; 6 mi. S Minden, 4850 ft. California: Walker Lake; Mono Lake; Bishop Creek; Little Pete Meadows, near head Middle Fork, Kings River; Sand Meadow; Bear Valley; head South Fork, American River, near Silver Lake.

Spermophilus beldingi creber (Hall)

1940. *Citellus beldingi crebrus* Hall, Murrelet, 21:59, December 20, type from Reese River Valley, 7 mi. N Austin, Lander Co., Nevada.

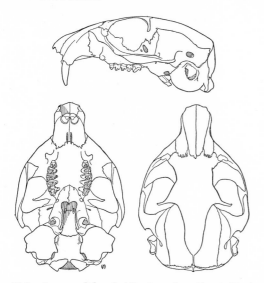

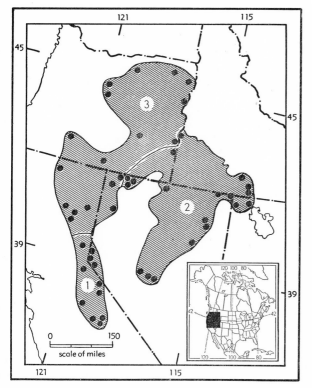

Fig. 218. *Spermophilus beldingi creber,* 7 mi. N Austin, Nevada, No. 70542 M.V.Z., ♂, X 1.

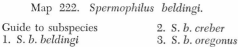

Map 222. *Spermophilus beldingi.*

Guide to subspecies
1. S. *b. beldingi*
2. S. *b. creber*
3. S. *b. oregonus*

MARGINAL RECORDS (Hall, 1946:310, unless otherwise noted).—Idaho (Hall, 1940:60): S bank Snake River, Homedale; S bank Snake River, 6 mi. S Rupert; 2 mi. S Malta; Bridge. Utah (Durrant, 1955, *et al.,* 73–74): Park Valley; *Grouse Creek Mts.;* Grouse Creek; *12 mi. NW Grouse Creek.* Nevada: Goose Cr., 2 mi. W Utah boundary; Cedar Creek, 10 mi. NE San Jacinto, 6000 ft.; Steels Creek, N end Ruby Mts., 7000 ft.; Jerry Creek, 6700 ft.; W side Ruby Lake, 3 mi. N White Pine Co. line, 6200 ft.; Antone Creek, 1½ mi. SE Meadow Valley R.S.; Toquima Range, Meadow Creek (Valley) R.S.; Bell's Ranch, Reese River, 6890 ft.; Calico Mtn.; Big Creek, Pine Forest Mts., 6000–7000 ft.; head Leonard Creek, Pine Forest Mts., 6500 ft.; Alder Creek, Pine Forest Mts., 5000 ft. Oregon: 2 mi. W Jordan Valley (Hall, 1940:60).

Spermophilus beldingi oregonus Merriam

1898. *Spermophilus oregonus* Merriam, Proc. Biol. Soc. Washington, 12:69, March 24, type from Swan Lake Valley, Klamath Basin, Oregon.
1938. *Citellus beldingi oregonus,* A. H. Howell, N. Amer. Fauna, 56:83, May 18.

MARGINAL RECORDS (A. H. Howell, 1938:84–85, unless otherwise noted).—Oregon: Elgin; Joseph; Home; Rockville. Nevada (Hall, 1946:309): Badger; Massacre Creek, 5800 ft.; Rock Creek, 7000–7425 ft. California: Horse Lake; 12 mi. NE Prattville; North Fork, Feather River; Mt. Lassen, probably near Black Butte; Grass Lake. Oregon: Ft. Klamath; Camas Prairie, E of Lakeview; Narrows; Prineville; Hay Creek; Heppner.

Spermophilus columbianus
Columbian Ground Squirrel

External measurements: 327–410; 80–116; 48–58. Greatest length of skull, 49.5–57. Nose and face tawny or hazel; occiput, nape, and sides of neck smoke gray; upper parts cinnamon buff or sayal brown, shaded with fuscous and in winter with smoke gray; hind legs and feet tawny or hazel; front feet ochraceous buff; tail gray or tawny; underparts ochraceous buff or tawny. Skull resembling that of S. *richardsonii* but longer and zygomatic arches less expanded posteriorly; dorsal outline more nearly flat; supraorbital margins of frontals not elevated or thickened; rostrum and nasals longer; upper tooth-rows nearly parallel instead of appreciably divergent anteriorly.

The late William T. Shaw in a long series of papers (for example 1925a and 1925b) recorded the results of his exhaustive study of the habits of this species; its natural history is thus better understood than that of the other species of the subgenus. S. *columbianus* is colonial, hibernates 7 to 8 months of the year, has a gestation period of approximately 24 days, and produces 2 to 7 young (average 3.5) per litter. The young leave the nest when approximately 4 weeks old. The hibernation-cell ordinarily is sealed by a plug of earth 2 feet or more in length in the burrow leading from the main burrow to the cell. Adult males, but not females or young, store some seeds of wild plants or bulbs in the lining of dry grass of the hibernation-cell and eat this stored food in spring (seemingly not in winter) when they emerge from hibernation. Adult males emerge a week to 10 days earlier than do females and immature animals. The time of emergence from hibernation of females and immature animals is thought to coincide with the first growth of plants that serve as green food.

Spermophilus columbianus columbianus (Ord)

1815. *Arctomys Columbianus* Ord, *in* Guthrie, A new geogr., hist., coml. grammar . . . , Philadelphia, Amer. ed. 2, 2:292 (described on p. 303). Based on Lewis's and Clark's description of animals taken on a camas prairie between the forks of the Clearwater and Kooskooskie rivers, Idaho.

1891. *Spermophilus columbianus*, Merriam, N. Amer. Fauna, 5:39, July 30.

1817. *Anisonyx brachiura* Rafinesque, Amer. Monthly Mag., 2:45. Based on same source as *Arctomys Columbianus* Ord.

1829. *Arctomys parryi* var. β., *erythrogluteia* Richardson, Fauna Boreali-Americana, p. 161. Type locality, "Rocky Mountains, near the sources of the Elk River" [= Wolf Plain, 30 mi. W Rock Lake, Alberta].

1884. *Cynomys columbianus* True, Proc. U.S. Nat. Mus., 7(App., Circ. 29):593, November 29. (Apparently based on *Arctomys Columbianus* Ord, 1815.)

1903. *Citellus columbianus albertae* J. A. Allen, Bull. Amer. Mus. Nat. Hist., 19:537, October 10, type from Canadian National Park, Banff, Alberta.

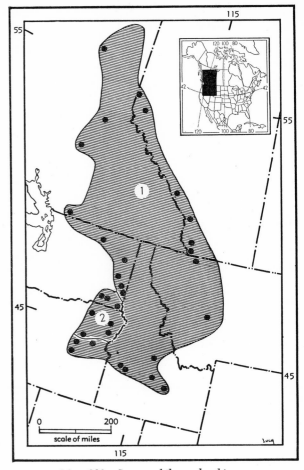

Map 223. *Spermophilus columbianus.*

1. *S. c. columbianus*   2. *S. c. ruficaudus*

MARGINAL RECORDS (A. H. Howell, 1938:89, unless otherwise noted).—British Columbia: mountains on E side lower Parsnip River (Anderson, 1947:109). Alberta: Two Lakes, near Hat Mtn. (Soper, 1947:151); Smoky River Valley, 50 mi. N Jasper (Anderson, 1947:110); Banff (Soper, 1947:151); Pincher Creek (Banfield, 1950:39); Mt. Forgetmenot; Waterton Lakes National Park (Banfield, 1950:38). Montana: St. Mary; Helena. Idaho: Mill Creek, 14 mi. W Challis (Davis, 1939:176); Ketchum (*ibid.*); Craters of the Moon (*ibid.*); Bald Mtn. R.S., 10 mi. S Idaho City; Shafer Butte. Oregon: 10 mi. N Harney; Strawberry Mts.; Ironside. Washington: Pullman (Dalquest, 1948:275); Colfax; Williams Lake; Loon Lake; 15 mi. E Tonasket (Dalquest, 1948:275). British Columbia: Ashnola River (Cowan and Guiguet, 1956:128); Lac la Hache (*ibid.*); Barkerville.

Spermophilus columbianus ruficaudus (A. H. Howell)

1928. *Citellus columbianus ruficaudus* A. H. Howell, Proc. Biol. Soc. Washington, 41:212, December 18, type from Wallowa Lake, Wallowa Co., Oregon.

MARGINAL RECORDS (A. H. Howell, 1938:90).—Washington: Dayton; Anatone. Oregon: type locality; Anthony, 6 mi. SW Cornucopia; Dixie Butte; Meacham. Washington: Prescott.

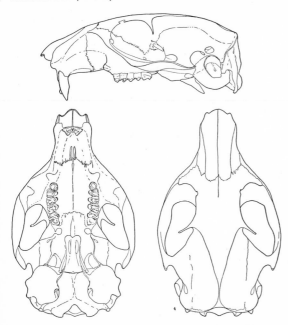

Fig. 219. *Spermophilus columbianus ruficaudus,* Cold Spring, 8 mi. E Austin, Grant Co., Oregon, No. 78467 M.V.Z., ♂, X 1.

Spermophilus undulatus
Arctic Ground Squirrel

External measurements: 332–495; 77–153; 50–68. Greatest length of skull, 50.7–65.8. Head tawny or cinnamon; rest of upper parts reddish brown, cinnamon or fuscous, more or less abundantly flecked with whitish spots; underparts ochraceous tawny to cinnamon buff in summer but ochraceous buff or grayish white in winter; tail above, ochraceous tawny, cinnamon or cinnamon buff, mixed with fuscous black; tail beneath, russet or tawny. Skull angular; highest at plane of postorbital processes; zygomata strongly twisted from the vertical plane; P3 ⅓ to ½ size of P4.

This species hibernates and is colonial. Seven embryos were found in a female taken on June 13 at Point Lake, Mackenzie. This species occurs in Asia as well as in North America.

Spermophilus undulatus ablusus (Osgood)

1903. *Citellus plesius ablusus* Osgood, Proc. Biol. Soc. Washington, 16:25, March 19, type from Nushagak, Alaska.
1953. *Citellus undulatus ablusus,* Rausch, Arctic, 6:123, July.
1903. *Citellus stonei* J. A. Allen, Bull. Amer. Mus. Nat. Hist., 19:537, October 10, type from Stevana Flats, near Port Müller, Alaska Peninsula; not Wrangell, Alaska (see J. A. Allen, *op. cit.*:xvii).

MARGINAL RECORDS (A. H. Howell, 1938:99–100, unless otherwise noted).—Alaska: Eschscholtz Bay; Savage River, Mt. McKinley National Park; Jennie Creek; Anchorage; Ushagat Island; Unimak Island; Unalakleet (Rausch, 1953:124); Golofnin Bay; Cooper Gulch (Quay, 1951:91); Cottonwood Creek (*ibid.*); Trail Creek (*ibid.*). Introduced also on Unalaska, Umnak, and Kavalga Islands of the Aleutian group, but these occurrences are not shown on our map.

Spermophilus undulatus kennicottii (Ross)

1861. *A[rctomys]. kennicottii* Ross, Canadian Nat. and Geol., 6:434, type from Fort Good Hope, Mackenzie.
1955. *Spermophilus undulatus kennicottii,* Bee and Hall, Univ. Kansas Mus. Nat. Hist., Miscl. Publ., 8:43, March 10.
1900. *Spermophilus barrowensis* Merriam, Proc. Washington Acad. Sci., 2:20, March 14, type from Point Barrow, Alaska.
1900. *Spermophilus beringensis* Merriam, Proc. Washington Acad. Sci., 2:20, March 14, type from Cape Lisburne, Alaska.

MARGINAL RECORDS.—Alaska: Point Barrow (A. H. Howell, 1938:96); eastward along Arctic Coast into Mackenzie: Fort Anderson (A. H. Howell, 1938:95). Alaska: Porcupine River, 12 mi. below Coleen River and near Salmon Trout River (*ibid.*, but see Bee and Hall, 1956:55–57); Anaktuvuk Pass (39381 KU); Chandler Lake (43232 KU); Cape Thompson (A. H. Howell, 1938:96).

Spermophilus undulatus kodiacensis J. A. Allen

1874. *Spermophilus parryi* Var. *kodiacensis* J. A. Allen, Proc. Boston Soc. Nat. Hist., 16:292, lectotype from Kodiak Island, Alaska. Known only from Kodiak Island.
1953. *Citellus undulatus kodiacensis,* Rausch, Arctic, 6:124, July.

Spermophilus undulatus lyratus (Hall and Gilmore)

1932. *Citellus lyratus* Hall and Gilmore, Univ. California Publ. Zool., 38:396, September 17, type from Iviktook Lagoon, about 35 mi. NW Northeast Cape, St. Lawrence Island, Bering Sea, Alaska.
1953. *Citellus undulatus lyratus,* Rausch, Arctic, 6:125, July.

MARGINAL RECORDS.—St. Lawrence Island, Alaska: type locality; *Kukuliak* (Cade, 1951:358).

Spermophilus undulatus nebulicola (Osgood)

1903. *Citellus nebulicola* Osgood, Proc. Biol. Soc. Washington, 16:26, March 19, type from Nagai Island, Shumagin Islands, Alaska.
1953. *C[itellus]. undulatus nebulicola,* Rausch, Arctic, 6:121, July.

MARGINAL RECORDS (A. H. Howell, 1938:101).—Shumagin Islands, Alaska: Koniuji Island; Simeonof Island; type locality.

Spermophilus undulatus osgoodi Merriam

1900. *Spermophilus osgoodi* Merriam, Proc. Washington Acad. Sci., 2:18, March 14, type from Fort Yukon, Alaska.
1953. *Citellus undulatus osgoodi,* Rausch, Arctic, 6:123, July.

MARGINAL RECORDS (A. H. Howell, 1938:105).—Alaska: type locality; 20 mi. above Circle; 10 mi. above Hess Creek.

Spermophilus undulatus parryii (Richardson)

1825. *Arctomys Parryii* Richardson, *in* Parry, Journal of a second voyage . . . , p. 316. Type locality, Five Hawser Bay, Lyon Inlet, Melville Peninsula, Hudson Bay, Canada.
1956. *Spermophilus undulatus parryii,* Harper, Univ. Kansas Mus. Nat. Hist., Miscl. Publ., 12:17, October 26.
1829. *Arctomys parryi* var. *phaeognatha* Richardson, Fauna Boreali-Americana, 1:161, type from Hudson Bay.

MARGINAL RECORDS.—Keewatin: *Melville Peninsula* (Anderson, 1947:110); Marble Island (Howell, 1938:95); about 25 mi. S Cape Eskimo, Hudson Bay (Anderson, 1947:110). Mackenzie: Kasba Lake (A. H. Howell, 1938:95); Artillery Lake (Anderson, 1947:110); Sekwi River (*ibid.*); Langton Bay (A. H. Howell, 1938:95) thence along Arctic Coast to point of beginning.

Spermophilus undulatus plesius Osgood

1900. *Spermophilus empetra plesius* Osgood, N. Amer. Fauna, 19:29, October 6, type from Bennett City, head of Lake Bennett, British Columbia.
1953. *Citellus undulatus plesius,* Rausch, Arctic, 6:123, July.

MARGINAL RECORDS (A. H. Howell, 1938:98, un-

Fig. 220. *Spermophilus undulatus kennicottii*, Bearpaw Creek, 1⁷⁄₁₀ mi. N, 1⁷⁄₁₀ mi. E Umiat, 152° 04′ 50″, 69° 23′ 30″, 550 ft., Alaska, No. 50437 K.U., ♂, X 1.

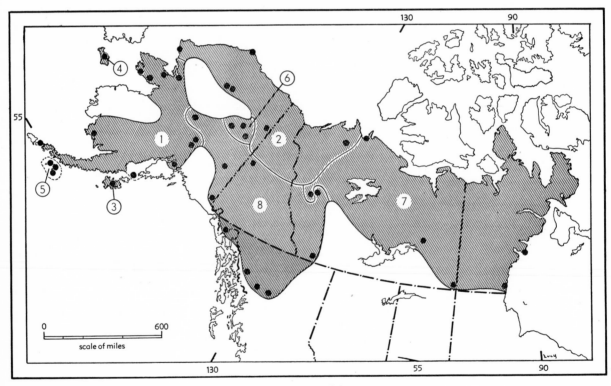

Map 224. *Spermophilus undulatus* in America.

1. *S. u. ablusus*	3. *S. u. kodiacensis*	5. *S. u. nebulicola*	7. *S. u. parryii*
2. *S. u. kennicottii*	4. *S. u. lyratus*	6. *S. u. osgoodi*	8. *S. u. plesius*

less otherwise noted).—Alaska: Tanana Hills. Yukon: head Coal Creek (Anderson, 1947:110). Mackenzie: mountains W of Fort Norman; Fort Liard (Anderson, 1947:110). British Columbia (Cowan and Guiguet, 1956:130): Tatletuey Lake; head Klappan River; Glenora Mtn.; Stonehouse Creek near junction with Kelsall River. Alaska: Chitina River Glacier; Tanana Crossing.

Subgenus **Ictidomys** J. A. Allen

1877. *Ictidomys* J. A. Allen, *in* Coues and Allen, Monogr. N. Amer. Rodentia, p. 821, August. Type, *Sciurus tridecemlineatus* Mitchill.
1907. *Ictidomoides* Mearns, Bull. U.S. Nat. Mus., 56:328, April 13. Type, *Sciurus mexicanus* Erxleben, 1777.

External measurements: 170–380; 55–166; 27–51. Greatest length of skull, 34.0–52.5. Upper parts with nearly square white spots, in some species arranged in rows, or upper parts (in S. *perotensis*) clay color. Anterolateral walls of cranium nearly vertical; least width of postorbital region slightly greater than width of interorbital region; ventral mandibular incisure deep and acutely arched as in *Xerospermophilus*; crowns of cheek-teeth higher than those of *Otospermophilus* and lower than those of subgenus *Spermophilus*; trigon of P4, M1, and M2 narrowly V-shaped; anterior cingulum of M1 and M2 joins protocone with abrupt change of direction; metaloph on M1 and M2 separated from protocone by sulcus; tendency toward fusion of metaconule and metacone on M1 and M2. Metaloph indistinct or absent on M3; M3 much larger than M2; posterior cingulum on M3 bends abruptly posteriad from protocone; p4 not molariform, protolophid small; occlusal outline of m1 and m2 rhomboidal; cheek pouches of medium size; atlanto-scapularis dorsalis muscle absent.

KEY TO SPECIES OF SUBGENUS ICTIDOMYS

1. Dorsal area striped. . S. *tridecemlineatus*, p. 345
1'. Dorsal area spotted or plain.
  2. Dorsal spots in linear series. S. *mexicanus*, p. 347
  2'. Dorsal spots not in linear series or upper parts plain.
    3. Underparts buffy; upper parts plain or spots buffy. . . . S. *perotensis*, p. 350
    3'. Underparts and dorsal spots white.
      S. *spilosoma*, p. 348

Spermophilus tridecemlineatus
13-lined Ground Squirrel

X ½

External measurements: 170–297; 60–132; 27–41. Greatest length of skull, 34.0–45.8. Upper parts marked with a series of alternating dark (brownish or blackish) and light longitudinal stripes; a row of nearly square white spots in each of the dark dorsal stripes; lowermost stripes on sides less well defined than on back; in some subspecies some of the light dorsal stripes are broken into spots. Skull long, narrow, and lightly built in comparison with that of S. *townsendii*; molariform tooth-rows only slightly convergent posteriorly.

The 13-lined ground squirrel lives chiefly in well-drained prairies and areas of short, non-native grass, and is solitary. The burrow lacks a mound of excavated earth at the entrance. Although the animals store seeds in large quantities, they hibernate for approximately 6 months of the year. Large quantities of insects are included in the diet. Much of the most detailed knowledge available on the hibernation of sciurids was worked out from a study of this species by G. E. Johnson (1931:439–461) and his students.

Spermophilus tridecemlineatus alleni Merriam

1898. *Spermophilus tridecemlineatus alleni* Merriam, Proc. Biol. Soc. Washington, 12:71, March 24, type from near head of Canyon Creek, 8000 ft., west slope Bighorn Mts., Wyoming.

MARGINAL RECORDS (A. H. Howell, 1938:115).—Wyoming: Bighorn Basin, head Kirby Creek; Miners Delight, near head Twin Creek; New Fork, Green River, Lander Road.

Spermophilus tridecemlineatus arenicola (A. H. Howell)

1928. *Citellus tridecemlineatus arenicola* A. H. Howell, Proc. Biol. Soc. Washington, 41:213, December 18, type from Pendennis, Kansas.
1955. *Spermophilus tridecemlineatus arenicola*, Hall, Univ. Kansas Mus. Nat. Hist., Misc. Publ., 7:92, December 13.

MARGINAL RECORDS.—Colorado: Greeley (A. H. Howell, 1938:112); Leroy (Warren, 1942:127). Kansas (Cockrum, 1952:125): Long Island; 7 mi. SW Sylvan Grove. Oklahoma (Blair, 1939:111): 3 mi. E Cherokee; 3 mi. W Orienta. Texas (A. H. Howell, 1938:112): Mobeetie; Lubbock. New Mexico: Roswell (*ibid.*); Loveless Lake, 10 mi. NW Capitan Mts. (*ibid.*); 4 mi. SW Cimarron (Hill, 1942:79), thence northward along the edge of the Great Plains to the point of beginning.

Spermophilus tridecemlineatus hollisteri (V. Bailey)

1913. *Citellus tridecemlineatus hollisteri* V. Bailey, Proc. Biol. Soc. Washington, 26:131, May 21, type from Elk Valley, 8000 ft., Mescalero Indian Reservation, Sacramento Mts., New Mexico.

MARGINAL RECORDS (A. H. Howell, 1938:116).—New Mexico: 35 mi. NW Cimarron; Maxwell; 12 mi. N Las Vegas; type locality.

Spermophilus tridecemlineatus monticola (A. H. Howell)

1928. *Citellus tridecemlineatus monticola* A. H. Howell, Proc. Biol. Soc. Washington, 41:214, December 18, type from Marsh Lake, 9000 ft., White Mts., Arizona. Known only from the type locality.

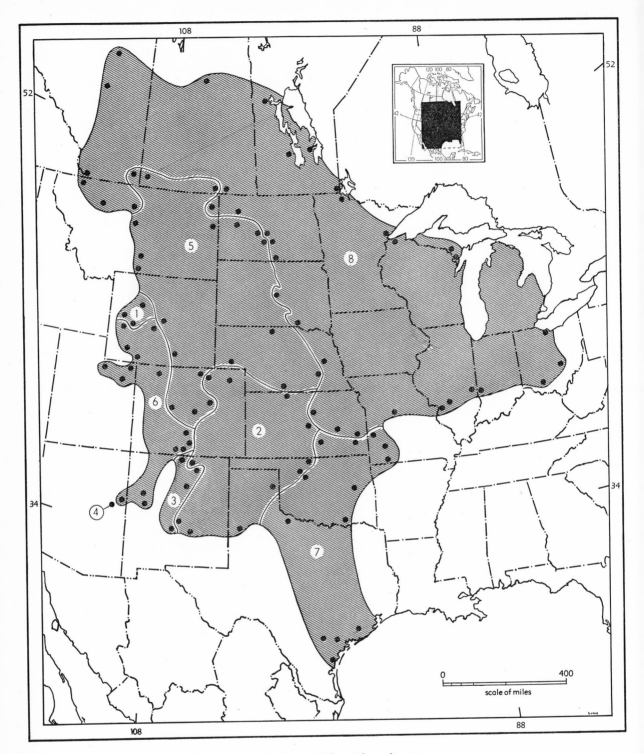

Map 225. *Spermophilus tridecemlineatus.*

1. *S. t. alleni*   3. *S. t. hollisteri*   5. *S. t. pallidus*   7. *S. t. texensis*
2. *S. t. arenicola*   4. *S. t. monticola*   6. *S. t. parvus*   8. *S. t. tridecemlineatus*

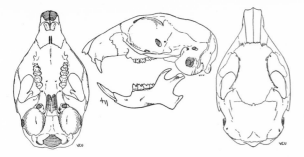

Fig. 221. *Spermophilus tridecemlineatus arenicola*, 6 mi. W Bird City, Cheyenne Co., Kansas, No. 12079 K.U., ♂, X 1.

Spermophilus tridecemlineatus pallidus J. A. Allen

1874. [*Spermophilus tridecemlineatus*] var. *pallidus* J. A. Allen, Proc. Boston Soc. Nat. Hist., 16:291, February 4, a *nomen nudum*. "Hab. The dry plains and deserts of the interior westward to the Great Basin."

1877. [*Spermophilus tridecemlineatus*] var. *pallidus* J. A. Allen, *in* Coues and Allen, Monogr. N. Amer. Rodentia, p. 872, August, 1877. Type locality, "Plains of lower Yellowstone River," Montana. (Specimen from mouth of Yellowstone River designated as lectotype by A. H. Howell, N. Amer. Fauna No. 56:112, footnote, May 18, 1938.)

1895. *Spermophilus tridecemlineatus olivaceous* J. A. Allen, Bull. Amer. Mus. Nat. Hist., 7:337, November 8, type from Custer, Custer Co., Black Hills, South Dakota.

MARGINAL RECORDS (A. H. Howell, 1938:114, unless otherwise noted).—Alberta: near Elkwater Lake (Soper, 1946:140). Saskatchewan: vicinity Kealy Springs, Cypress Hills, 14 mi. N Ravenscrag (*ibid.*); Salt Lake (*op. cit.*:141). Montana: type locality. North Dakota: Oakdale; Fort Clark; Mandan. Nebraska: Valentine; near head Blue River; Beaver City; Sidney. Colorado: Fort Collins; between Mattison and Resolis; Colorado Springs (Warren, 1942:127); Twin Lakes, near Leadville (*ibid.*). Wyoming: Medicine Bow Mts.; Casper. Montana: Pryor Mts.; Billings; 20 mi. NE Roy.

Spermophilus tridecemlineatus parvus J. A. Allen

1895. *Spermophilus tridecemlineatus parvus* J. A. Allen, Bull. Amer. Mus. Nat. Hist., 7:337, November 8, type from Kennedys Hole, Uncompahgre Indian Reservation, 20 mi. northeast of Ouray, Uintah Co., Utah.

MARGINAL RECORDS (A. H. Howell, 1938:118–119, unless otherwise noted).—Wyoming: Big Sandy Creek; Independence Rock. Colorado: Axial Basin, 12 mi. SE Lay; Westcliffe; Fort Garland (Warren, 1942:130); San Acacio; Antonito. New Mexico: Datil Mts., 12 mi. NW Datil; St. Augustine Plains, near Monica Spring. Arizona: Springerville (Warren, 1942:130). Utah (Durrant, 1952:117): Pariette Bench, 12 mi. S Ouray; Red Creek, 2 mi. N Fruitland; Diamond Mtn. Wyoming: 33 mi. S Bitter Creek, 6900 ft. (14928 KU); Green River.

Spermophilus tridecemlineatus texensis Merriam

1898. *Spermophilus tridecemlineatus texensis* Merriam, Proc. Biol. Soc. Washington, 12:71, March 24, type from Gainesville, Cooke Co., Texas.

1899. *Spermophilus* (*Ictidomys*) *tridecemlineatus badius* Bangs, Proc. New England Zool. Club, 1:1, February 8, type from Stotesbury, Vernon Co., Missouri.

MARGINAL RECORDS (A. H. Howell, 1938:110–111, unless otherwise noted).—Missouri: Stotesbury; Golden City; Washburn. Oklahoma: 3 mi. E Wainwright (Blair, 1939:111); 5 mi. N Colbert (McCarley, 1952:106). Texas: Richmond; Port Lavaca (Strecker, 1926:19); Corpus Christi (Blair, 1952:239); Bee County; Vernon. Oklahoma: 5 mi. SW Canton (Blair, 1939:111). Kansas (Cockrum, 1952:126): Garden Plains; Neosho Falls.

Spermophilus tridecemlineatus tridecemlineatus (Mitchill)

1821. *Sciurus tridecem-lineatus* Mitchill, Med. Repos. (n.s.), 6(21):248. Type locality, central Minnesota (see J. A. Allen, Bull. Amer. Mus. Nat. Hist., 7:338, November 8, 1895).

1849. *Spermophilus tridecem lineatus,* Audubon and Bachman, The viviparous quadrupeds of North America, 1:294.

1822. *Arctomys hoodii* Sabine, Trans. Linn. Soc. London, 13:590, type from Carlton House, Saskatchewan. (Regarded by A. H. Howell, N. Amer. Fauna, 56:107, May 18, 1938, as inseparable from S. *t. tridecemlineatus* but arranged by Anderson, Bull. Nat. Mus. Canada, 102:111, January 24, 1947, as a tenable subspecies.)

MARGINAL RECORDS (A. H. Howell, 1938:109–110, unless otherwise noted).—Alberta: near NE angle Baptiste Lake (Soper, 1948:58). Saskatchewan: Prince Albert. Manitoba: Bell River, a few mi. E Mafeking (Criddle, 1939:1); McCreary (*ibid.*); Geyser (*ibid.*); near W end Whitemouth Lake (Soper, 1946:140). Minnesota (Swanson, 1945:76): Williams; Duluth. Wisconsin: Herbster. Michigan (Burt, 1946:179): Dickinson County; Menominee County. Ohio: Sandusky County (Bole and Moulthrop, 1942:130); Muskingum County (*ibid.*); Bainbridge. Indiana: 5 mi. S Terre Haute (Evermann and Butler, 1894:128). Illinois: Kansas; Hillsboro (Chiasson, 1953:510); Madison County (*ibid.*). Missouri: Saline County (Enders, 1932:118). Kansas (Cockrum, 1952:125–126): Anderson County; 3 mi. SW Burdick; 3½ mi. W, ½ mi. S Beloit. Nebraska: Columbus. South Dakota: Fort Randall; Pierre. North Dakota: Zeeland; Bismark; Washburn; Fort Berthold. Montana: Johnson Lake. Saskatchewan: Estevan (Soper, 1946:140). Montana: Bear Paw Mts., 20 mi. SE Fort Assiniboine; Choteau; St. Mary Lake (Anderson, 1947:111). Alberta: Chief Mountain Lake; Red Deer (Anderson, 1947:111).

Spermophilus mexicanus
Mexican Ground Squirrel

External measurements: 280–380; 110–166; 38–51. Greatest length of skull, 41.0–52.5. Upper parts wood brown or buffy brown to sayal brown or snuff brown, with nearly square white spots arranged in longitudinal rows, usually 9 in number, the spots in some animals partly confluent and in others faint; head buffy brown or wood brown, sprinkled with white; nose clay color or cinnamon buff; feet, sides, and underparts white to pinkish buff; tail above, mixed fuscous and grayish or buffy white; tail beneath, avellaneous to cinnamon buff, more or less obscured by grayish or buffy white. Skull resembling that of *S. tridecemlineatus* but larger, braincase less elongate, and zygomata more widely expanded.

Ground squirrels of this species seem not to hibernate, but in cold spells plug the entrances to their burrows after going in and remain underground for considerable periods. The food seems to be seeds and insects in approximately equal proportions. The burrows are on sandy plains.

Spermophilus mexicanus mexicanus (Erxleben)

1777. [*Sciurus*] *mexicanus* Erxleben, Systema regni animalis . . . , 1:428. Type locality, Toluca, México, by restriction (see Mearns, Preliminary diagnoses of new mammals from the Mexican border of the United States, p. 1, March 25, 1896).
1843. *Spermophilus mexicanus,* Wagner, *in* Schreber, Die Säugthiere . . . , Suppl., 3:250.

MARGINAL RECORDS (A. H. Howell, 1938:120, unless otherwise noted).—Jalisco: 1 mi. NE Villa Hidalgo (38327 KU); Lagos. Querétaro: Tequisquiapan. Hidalgo: Irolo. Tlaxcala: Huamantla. Puebla: San Andrés, Chalchicomula; Atlixco. Distrito Federal: Tlalpam. Jalisco: 10 mi. SW Tepatitlán (Hooper, 1955:8); Zapotlán; Atemajac; 21 mi. SW Guadalajara (38326 KU).

Spermophilus mexicanus parvidens Mearns

1896. *Spermophilus mexicanus parvidens* Mearns, Preliminary diagnoses of new mammals from the Mexican border of the United States, p. 1, March 25 (preprint of Proc. U.S. Nat. Mus., 18:443, May 23, 1896), type from Fort Clark, Kinney Co., Texas.

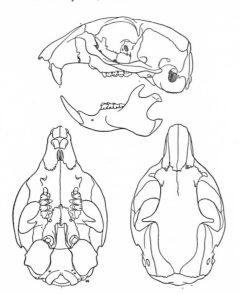

Fig. 222. *Spermophilus mexicanus parvidens,* ½ mi. NE Del Rio, Val Verde Co., Texas, No. 93789 M.V.Z., ♀, X 1.

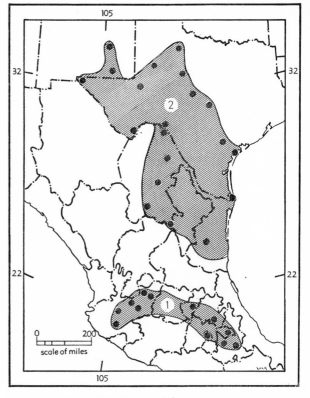

Map 226. *Spermophilus mexicanus.*

1. *S. m. mexicanus*   2. *S. m. parvidens*

MARGINAL RECORDS (A. H. Howell, 1938:121–122, unless otherwise noted).—New Mexico: Roswell: Carlsbad. Texas: Monahans; Lamesa (Blair, 1954b:245); Guthrie (*ibid.*); Colorado; San Angelo; Mason; 12 mi. N Beeville (Blair, 1952:239); Rockport; Port Isabel. Tamaulipas: Victoria. Coahuila: 8 mi. N LaVentura (33096 KU); 1 mi. N Parras (Baker, 1956:205); 5 mi. N, 2 mi. W Monclova (35724 KU); Sabinas; Las Vacas. Texas: Del Rio; Black Gap Wildlife Management Area (Tamsitt, 1954:48); El Paso.

Spermophilus spilosoma
Spotted Ground Squirrel

External measurements: 185–253; 55–92; 28–38. Greatest length of skull, 34.1–42.7. Upper parts drab, cinnamon drab, avellaneous, smoke gray, fawn, wood brown, snuff brown, or verona brown, more or less spotted with "squarish" white spots; tail

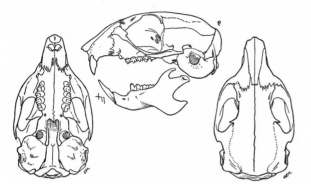

Fig. 223. *Spermophilus spilosoma marginatus*, N end Mariscal Mtn., 2300 ft., Brewster Co., Texas, No. 80346 M.V.Z., ♀, × 1.

above usually resembling back but having fuscous black at tip; tail beneath some shade of cinnamon. Skull resembles that of *S. tridecemlineatus* but relatively broader, especially in rostrum and interorbital region; auditory bullae much larger.

Ground squirrels of this species prefer dry sandy soils. At least in the southern part of their geographic range, they do not hibernate long, if at all. The food is thought to be mostly green vegetation and seeds.

Spermophilus spilosoma annectens Merriam

1893. *Spermophilus spilosoma annectens* Merriam, Proc. Biol. Soc. Washington, 8:132, December 28, type from "The Tanks," 12 miles from Point Isabel, Padre Island, Texas.

MARGINAL RECORDS.—Texas: mouth Pecos River (A. H. Howell, 1938:128); Mustang Island (Blair, 1952:239). Tamaulipas: 89½ mi. S, 10 mi. W Matamoros (Hall, 1951a:38).

Spermophilus spilosoma cabrerai (Dalquest)

1951. *Citellus spilosoma cabrerai* Dalquest, Proc. Biol. Soc. Washington, 64:106, August 24, type from 10 km. NNW Nuñez, San Luis Potosí.

MARGINAL RECORDS.—San Luis Potosí: 6 km. S Matehuala (Dalquest, 1953b:93); 2 mi. NW Tepeyac, 3400 ft., 14 mi. N, 29 mi. W C. del Maiz (39760 KU); 6 km. SSW Nuñez (Dalquest, 1953b:93).

Spermophilus spilosoma canescens Merriam

1890. *Spermophilus canescens* Merriam, N. Amer. Fauna, 4:38, October 8, type from Willcox, Cochise Co., Arizona.
1932. *Citellus spilosoma canescens*, V. Bailey, N. Amer. Fauna, 53:109, March 1.
1890. *Spermophilus spilosoma macrospilotus* Merriam, N. Amer. Fauna, 4:38, October 8, type from Oracle, Pinal Co., Arizona.
1901. [*Spermophilus spilosoma*] *microspilotus* Elliot, Field Columb. Mus., Publ. 45, Zool. Ser., 2:96, an accidental renaming of *macrospilotus*.

1902. *Spermophilus spilosoma arens* V. Bailey, Proc. Biol. Soc. Washington, 15:118, June 2, type from El Paso, El Paso Co., Texas.

MARGINAL RECORDS (A. H. Howell, 1938:126, unless otherwise noted).—Arizona: Pima. New Mexico: Apache. Texas: El Paso (Davis and Robertson, 1944:266); Fort Hancock. Chihuahua: Lake Palomas; Chihuahua; Casas Grande; Whitewater, Mexican boundary line. Sonora: La Noria. Arizona: Buenas Aires; Oracle.

Spermophilus spilosoma cryptospilotus Merriam

1890. *Spermophilus cryptospilotus* Merriam, N. Amer. Fauna, 3:57, September 11, type from "Tenebito" [=Dinnebito] Wash, Painted Desert, Coconino Co., Arizona.
1938. *Citellus spilosoma cryptospilotus*, A. H. Howell, N. Amer. Fauna, 56:130, May 18.

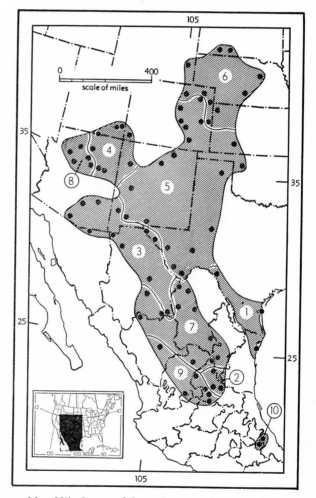

Map 227. *Spermophilus spilosoma* and *Spermophilus perotensis*.

1. S. s. annectens
2. S. s. cabrerai
3. S. s. canescens
4. S. s. cryptospilotus
5. S. s. marginatus

6. S. s. obsoletus
7. S. s. pallescens
8. S. s. pratensis
9. S. s. spilosoma
10. S. perotensis

MARGINAL RECORDS.—Utah (Durrant, 1952:117): Monticello; Lockerby. Colorado: McElmo Creek, S of Cortez (A. H. Howell, 1938:130). New Mexico: Thoreau (Warren, 1942:132). Arizona: Holbrook (*ibid.*); Winslow (A. H. Howell, 1938:130); Moa Ave (*ibid.*). Utah: 5 mi. S summit Navajo Mtn. (Durrant, 1952:117).

Spermophilus spilosoma marginatus V. Bailey

1890. *Spermophilus spilosoma major* Merriam, N. Amer. Fauna, 4:39, October 8, type from Albuquerque, Bernalillo Co., New Mexico. Not *Mus citellus* var. *major* Pallas, 1779 [= *Spermophilus major*], from near Samara, Russia.
1902. *Spermophilus spilosoma marginatus* V. Bailey, Proc. Biol. Soc. Washington, 15:118, June 2, type from Alpine, Brewster Co., Texas.

MARGINAL RECORDS (A. H. Howell, 1938:127–128, unless otherwise noted).—Colorado: Akron; Hugo. Kansas: Kinsley (Cockrum, 1952:128). Oklahoma: 5 mi. SW Canton (Blair, 1939:110). Texas: Mobeetie; Colorado; E base mountains at Fort Stockton (V. Bailey, 1905:88); area of La Mota (Tamsitt, 1954:48); Presidio County; Van Horn. New Mexico: Mesilla; 8 mi. E Deming; St. Augustine Plains, 12 mi. N Monica Spring; Espanola; 4 mi. SW Cimarron (Hill, 1942:79). Colorado: 18 mi. S La Junta; Pueblo (Warren, 1942:131); near Lytle (*ibid.*); Barr Lake.

Spermophilus spilosoma obsoletus Kennicott

1863. *Spermophilus obsoletus* Kennicott, Proc. Acad. Nat. Sci. Philadelphia, 15:157. Type locality, restricted by A. H. Howell (N. Amer. Fauna, 56:131, May 18, 1938) to "50 miles west of Fort Kearney, Nebraska."
1955. *Spermophilus spilosoma obsoletus*, Hall, Univ. Kansas Mus. Nat. Hist., Misc. Publ., 7:94, December 13.

MARGINAL RECORDS (A. H. Howell, 1938:131, unless otherwise noted).—South Dakota: S. Fork White River; Bennett County (Over and Churchill, 1945:26). Nebraska: Neligh; type locality. Kansas: 9 mi. NW St. Francis (Cockrum, 1952:128). Colorado: Tuttle; Wray (Warren, 1942: 132); Sterling (*ibid.*); Greeley. Wyoming: Wheatland.

Spermophilus spilosoma pallescens (A. H. Howell)

1928. *Citellus spilosoma pallescens* A. H. Howell, Proc. Biol. Soc. Washington, 41:212, December 18, type from La Ventura, Coahuila.
1956. *Spermophilus spilosoma pallescens*, Baker, Univ. Kansas Publ., Mus. Nat. Hist., 9:205, June 15.

MARGINAL RECORDS.—Coahuila: 2 mi. S, 3 mi. E Hechicero, 4450 ft. (54503 KU); 11 mi. E Acebuches (54505 KU); 3 mi. NW Cuatro Ciénegas, 2450 ft. (Baker, 1956:207); 1 mi. N Saltillo, 5000 ft. (34926 KU). Nuevo León: Doctor Arroyo (A. H. Howell, 1938:125). San Luis Potosí: Salado (Dalquest, 1953b:92). Zacatecas: Cañitas (A. H. Howell, 1938:125). Durango: Río Ocampo (J. A. Allen, 1904:209). Chihuahua (A. H. Howell, 1938:125): Santa Rosalía; Escalón. Coahuila: 3 mi. NE Sierra Mojada (40858 KU).

Spermophilus spilosoma pratensis Merriam

1890. *Spermophilus spilosoma pratensis* Merriam, N. Amer. Fauna, 3:55, September 11, type from pine plateau at N foot of San Francisco Mtn., Coconino Co., Arizona.

1890. *Spermophilus spilosoma obsidianus* Merriam, N. Amer. Fauna, 3:56, September 11, type from cedar belt, NE of San Francisco Mtn., Coconino Co., Arizona.

MARGINAL RECORDS (A. H. Howell, 1938:129).— Arizona: Grand Canyon; Deadmans Flat, NE San Francisco Mtn.; Walnut Canyon, Coconino National Forest; Seligman; Aubrey Valley, Hualpai Indian Reservation.

Spermophilus spilosoma spilosoma Bennett

1833. *Spermophilus spilosoma* Bennett, Proc. Zool. Soc. London, p. 40, May 17. Type locality, Durango, México (see A. H. Howell, N. Amer. Fauna, 56:122, May 18, 1938).

MARGINAL RECORDS.—Durango: 4 mi. E Durango, 6200 ft. (38328 KU). San Luis Potosí: 2 km. E Illescas (Dalquest, 1953b:92); Hacienda la Parada (*ibid.*); 10 mi. NE San Luis Potosí (39762 KU); Jesús María (Dalquest, 1953b:92). Aguascalientes: Chicalote (A. H. Howell, 1938: 124).

Spermophilus perotensis
Perote Ground Squirrel

1893. *Spermophilus perotensis* Merriam, Proc. Biol. Soc. Washington, 8:131, December 28, type from Perote, Veracruz.

External measurements: 243–261; 57–78; 38–40. Greatest length of skull, 42.2–44.5. Upper parts clay color to wood brown or drab and indistinctly sprinkled with pinkish buff on hinder back; sides of body pinkish buff or cartridge buff; underparts and feet similar or slightly paler; tail above like back but pinkish buff below and bordered at distal end with blackish. Braincase high, narrow.

MARGINAL RECORDS.—Veracruz: type locality; *2 km. E Perote* (23972 KU); *2 km. W Limón* (30001 KU). Puebla: 4 km. N San Salvador del Seco, 8000 ft. (Davis, 1944:383).

Subgenus Poliocitellus A. H. Howell

1938. *Poliocitellus* A. H. Howell, N. Amer. Fauna, 56:42, May 18. Type, *Arctomys franklinii* Sabine, 1822.

External measurements: 381–397; 136–153; 53.0–57.5. Greatest length of skull, 52.1–55.1. Head grayish; dorsum tawny olive or clay color; tail above and below blackish mixed with buff, overlaid and bordered with creamy white; underparts pinkish buff or buffy white. Skull long and narrow; postorbital and interorbital constrictions of approximately equal width; molars higher crowned than in *Otospermophilus* and lower crowned than in subgenus *Spermophilus*; M1 and M2 subquadrate in occlusal outline; trigon on P4, M1, and M2 broadly V-shaped; anterior cingulum usually joins protocone with abrupt change of direction; metalophs complete and mesostyles present on P4, M1, and M2; M3 slightly larger than M2; occlusal outline of m1 and m2 rhomboidal; spoon of baculum relatively larger than in subgenus *Spermophilus* but baculum otherwise similar; cheek pouches large; atlantoscapularis dorsalis muscle absent.

Spermophilus franklinii (Sabine)
Franklin's Ground Squirrel

X ¼

1822. *Arctomys franklinii* Sabine, Trans. Linn. Soc. London, 13:587, type from Carlton House, Saskatchewan.
1827. *Spermophilus Franklini*, Lesson, Manuel de Mammalogie . . . , p. 244.

Characters as for the subgenus.

Franklin's ground squirrel occurs in areas of dense high (10 inches or more) grass or weedy vegetational cover and not on closely grazed or mowed fields. Three to 10 burrows widely spaced form a colony of sorts. Approximately ⅔ of the food is plant material and the other ⅓ animal matter. Several months are spent in hibernation. There are 5 to 10 young in a litter.

MARGINAL RECORDS (A. H. Howell, 1938:134–135, unless otherwise noted).—Alberta: Athabasca Landing (Rand, 1948b:134). Saskatchewan: Prince Albert National Park (Anderson, 1947:111). Manitoba: *Lake Winnipeg* (*ibid.*); Whitemouth Lake (Soper, 1946:141). Ontario: Emo (Anderson, 1947:111). Minnesota: Cass Lake; Chisago County (Swanson, 1945:78). Wisconsin: Delevan. Illinois: Grayslake (Necker and Hatfield, 1941:49). Indiana: North Liberty; between Battle Ground and Ash Grove (Kirkpatrick and Conaway, 1948:133). Illinois (Necker and Hatfield, 1941:49): Charleston; St. Clair County. Kansas (Cockrum, 1952:130): 5½ mi. N Moran; Neosho Falls; Hamilton; 1 mi. S, ½ mi. W Lindsborg; 9 mi. W Wakeeney. Nebraska: Kearney; 2 mi. NW Lisco (Jones, 1954:483); Niobrara, thence northward in the *Missouri Valley of North Dakota, and South Dakota*. Saskatchewan: Oxbow. Alberta: Edmonton (Rand, 1948b:134); Sturgeon River, 25 mi. N Edmonton.

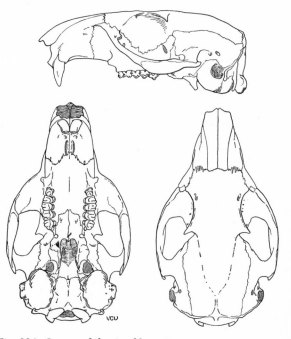

Fig. 224. *Spermophilus franklinii*, 5 mi. N Moran, Allen Co., Kansas, No. 8640 K.U., ♂, X 1.

Subgenus Otospermophilus Brandt—Rock Squirrels

1844. *Otospermophilus* Brandt, Bull. Class. Phys.-Math. Acad. Imp. Sci. St. Pétersbourg, 2:379, March. Type, *Sciurus grammurus* Say.
1938. *Notocitellus* A. H. Howell, N. Amer. Fauna, 56:44, May 18. Type, *Spermophilus annulatus* Audubon and Bachman. *Notocitellus* arranged as a synonym of *Otospermophilus* by Bryant (1945:377).

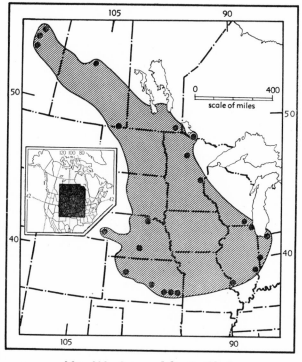

Map 228. *Spermophilus franklinii*.

External measurements: 315–540, 138–252; 43–65. Variegated pattern of black, white, and buff; infra-orbital foramen oval; masseteric tubercule situated nearly ventral to infraorbital foramen; width at post-orbital constriction slightly more than interorbital width; fossae anterolateral to incisive foramina deep; upper cheek-teeth low-crowned; M1 and M2 sub-quadrate in occlusal outline; metaloph on P4–M2 separated from protocone by sulcus; M3 slightly larger than M2; metaloph on M3 absent; proto-lophid on p4 absent and protoconid slightly larger than hypoconid; baculum with proximal end en-larged into a knob; check pouches large; atlanto-scapularis dorsalis muscle present. For additional characters see Bryant (1945:376).

KEY TO SPECIES OF SUBGENUS OTOSPERMOPHILUS

1. Supraorbital foramen open; sides of head grayish (or mixed black and white); not in Tropical Life-zone.
   2. Nape and shoulders with dark median area; in United States occurring west of line from Toyabe Mts. (Central Nevada) to Providence Mts. (SE California) and in México confined to Baja California.
      3. Dark median area on shoulders united with equally dark area on top of head; occurring south of 28° in Baja California. . . S. *atricapillus*, p. 355
      3'. Dark median area on shoulders darker than top of head; occurring north of 28°. . . . S. *beecheyi*, p. 354
   2'. Nape and shoulders without dark median area; in United States occurring east of a line passing through westernmost parts of Toyabe Mts. (Central Nevada) and Providence Mts. (SE California); in México not occurring in Baja California. S. *variegatus*, p. 352
1'. Supraorbital foramen closed; sides of head tawny or buffy; confined to Tropical Life-zone (Nayarit south into Guerrero).
   4. Cheeks tawny; tail ringed; nasals longer than 15.3. . . . . S. *annulatus*, p. 356
   4'. Cheeks buffy; tail not ringed; nasals shorter than 15.3. . . . S. *adocetus*, p. 357

Spermophilus variegatus
Rock Squirrel

External measurements: 430–525; 172–252; 53–65. Greatest length of skull, 56.0–67.7. Upper parts variegated black and white, often with buff; head and forepart of back black in many subspecies; tail mixed black or brown and buffy white.

The partiality for rocks was emphasized when Villa found this species in Michoacán, México, on still warm lava (Hall and Villa, 1949:450). The species stores food. We do not know if it hiber-nates or aestivates.

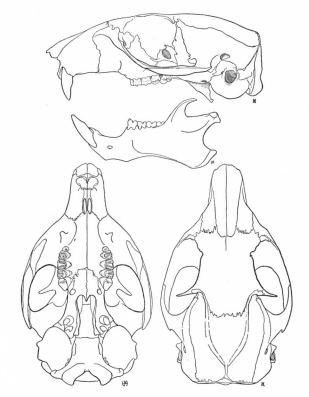

Fig. 225. *Spermophilus variegatus grammurus*, Baker Creek, 7300 ft., Nevada, No. 41517 M.V.Z., ♂, X 1.

Spermophilus variegatus buckleyi Slack

1861. *Spermophilus buckleyi* Slack, Proc. Acad. Nat. Sci. Philadelphia, 13:314, type from Packsaddle Mountain, Llano Co., Texas.
1905. *Citellus variegatus buckleyi*, V. Bailey, N. Amer. Fauna, 25:84, October 24.

MARGINAL RECORDS.—Texas: San Saba River (A. H. Howell, 1938:141); Bull Creek (*op. cit.*:142); head Nueces River (Strecker, 1926:18); Rocksprings (A. H. Howell, 1938:142).

Spermophilus variegatus couchii Baird

1855. *Spermophilus couchii* Baird, Proc. Acad. Nat. Sci. Philadelphia, 7:332, April, type from Santa Catarina, a few miles W of Monterrey, Nuevo León.
1955. *Spermophilus variegatus couchii*, Baker, Univ. Kansas Publ., Mus. Nat. Hist., 9:207, June 15.

MARGINAL RECORDS (A. H. Howell, 1938:141, un-less otherwise noted).—Texas: Green Gulch, 5200 ft., Chisos Mts. (Borell and Bryant, 1942:20); Boquillas (*ibid.*). Nuevo León: type locality. Tamaulipas: Victoria. Coahuila: Sierra Encarnación; Sierra Guadalupe.

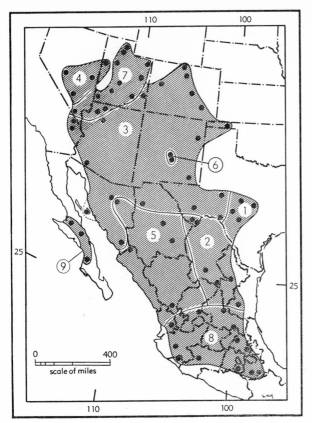

Map 229. *Spermophilus variegatus* and *S. atricapillus.*

Guide to kinds
1. S. v. *buckleyi*
2. S. v. *couchii*
3. S. v. *grammurus*
4. S. v. *robustus*
5. S. v. *rupestris*
6. S. v. *tularosae*
7. S. v. *utah*
8. S. v. *variegatus*
9. *S. atricapillus*

Spermophilus variegatus grammurus (Say)

1823. S[*ciurus*]. *grammurus* Say, *in* Long, Account of an exped. . . . to the Rocky Mts. . . . , 2:72, type from Purgatory River, near mouth of Chacuaco Creek, Las Animas Co., Colorado.
1952. *Spermophilus variegatus grammurus*, Hall and Kelson, Univ. Kansas Publ., Mus. Nat. Hist., 5:346, December 15.
1913. *Citellus variegatus juglans* V. Bailey, Proc. Biol. Soc. Washington, 26:131, May 21, type from Glenwood, 5000 ft., Rio San Francisco, Catron Co., New Mexico.

MARGINAL RECORDS (A. H. Howell, 1938:144–145, unless otherwise noted).—Colorado: Larimer County, about 10 mi. from Wyoming line (Warren, 1942:118); Lyons; Colorado Springs (Warren, 1942:117); 18 mi. S La Junta. Oklahoma: Beaver County (Blair, 939:110). New Mexico: Mosquero; Carlsbad. Texas: Castle Mts.; Devils River; Davis Mts. Chihuahua: Colonia Garcia. Sonora: Providencia Mines; Camoa (Laurie, 1953:385); Tiburon Island (Burt, 1938:35). Arizona: Bates Well, 20 mi. S Ajo. California (Johnson, *et al.*, 1948:353): Mitchell's; NW side Clark Mtn. Arizona: Grand Canyon (Durrant and Hansen, 1954:269). Utah: Castle Valley, 18 mi. NE Moab, 6000 ft. (*ibid.*). Colorado: Rifle.

Spermophilus variegatus robustus (Durrant and Hansen)

1954. *Citellus variegatus robustus*, Durrant and Hansen, Proc. Biol. Soc. Washington, 67:264, November 15, type from Pass Creek, Deep Creek Mountains, 8000 ft., Juab Co., Utah.

MARGINAL RECORDS (Durrant and Hansen, 1954: 268).—Utah: type locality. Nevada: Cherry Creek, 6800 ft.; 2 mi. S Oak Spring, 5800 ft.; Kingston Canyon, 6350 ft.

Spermophilus variegatus rupestris (J. A. Allen)

1903. *Citellus* (*Otospermophilus*) *grammurus rupestris* J. A. Allen, Bull. Amer. Mus. Nat. Hist., 19:595, November 12, type from Río Sestín, northwestern Durango.
1904. [*Citellus variegatus*] *rupestris*, Elliot, Field Columb. Mus., Publ. 95, Zool. Ser., 4:150.

MARGINAL RECORDS (A. H. Howell, 1938:139).—Sonora: Oposura. Chihuahua: Chihuahua; Santa Rosalía. Durango: Guazamota. Sinaloa: Sierra de Choix, 50 mi. NE Choix.

Spermophilus variegatus tularosae (Benson)

1932. *Citellus grammurus tularosae* Benson, Univ. California Publ. Zool., 38:336, April 14, type from French's Ranch, 5400 ft., 12 mi. northwest of Carrizozo, Lincoln Co., New Mexico.
1938. *Citellus variegatus tularosae*, A. H. Howell, N. Amer. Fauna, 56:145, May 18.

MARGINAL RECORDS.—New Mexico: type locality; Malpais Lava Beds (A. H. Howell, 1938:146).

Spermophilus variegatus utah (Merriam)

1903. *Citellus grammurus utah* Merriam, Proc. Biol. Soc. Washington, 16:77, May 29, type from foot of Wasatch Mts., near Ogden, Weber Co., Utah.
1905. *Citellus variegatus utah*, Elliot, Field Columb. Mus., Publ. 105, Zool. Ser., 6:115, December 6.

MARGINAL RECORDS.—Utah: Logan (Durrant, 1952: 120); along Green River, 15 mi. S Ouray, 4500 ft. (Durrant and Hansen, 1954:268); Florence Canyon, 35 mi. E Greenriver (Durrant, 1952:120); Moki Tanks, Circle Cliffs (Durrant and Hansen, 1954:269). Arizona: Big Spring, above Ryan, Kaibab Plateau (Durrant and Hansen, 1954:268); 3 mi. S Trumbull Spring, Trumbull Mts. (*ibid.*). Nevada: Charleston Park, 8000 ft. (*ibid.*). Utah: Pine Valley (Durrant, 1952:121); Parowan (*ibid.*); Beaver (*ibid.*); Willow Springs (*ibid.*); Ogden (*ibid.*).

Spermophilus variegatus variegatus (Erxleben)

1777. [*Sciurus*] *variegatus* Erxleben, Systema regni animalis . . . , 1:421. Type locality, Valley of México, near City of México (see Nelson, Science, n.s., 8:897, December 23, 1898).
1898. *Spermophilus variegatus*, Nelson, Science, n.s., 8:898, December 23.
1830. *Sciurus buccatus* Lichtenstein, Abh. Akad. Wiss., Berlin, 1827, p. 117. Based on a specimen in the Berlin Museum, probably from México.
1833. *Spermophilus macrourus* Bennett, Proc. Zool. Soc. London, p. 41, May 17, type from west México.

MARGINAL RECORDS (A. H. Howell, 1938:138, unless otherwise noted).—San Luis Potosí (Dalquest, 1953b: 95); Puerto de Lobos; Hda. Capulín. Hidalgo: Encarnación; Tulancingo. Puebla: Tehuacán (Davis and Russell, 1954:72); 33 km. W Tehuacán, 8000 ft. (Davis, 1944: 383). Morelos: Tetela del Volcán (Davis and Russell, 1954:72). Michoacán: Tancítaro (Hall and Villa, 1949: 450). Colima: Hda. San Antonio, base Volcán de Colima. Jalisco: Plantinar. Nayarit: Tepic. Zacatecas: Berriozabal.

Spermophilus beecheyi
California Ground Squirrel

External measurements: 357–500; 145–200; 50–64. Greatest length of skull, 51.6–62.4. Head cinnamon or brown; upper parts brown flecked with whitish or buffy; sides of neck and shoulders white or whitish, this color extending backward in two divergent stripes separated by triangular area of dark color. Skull averaging smaller than in S. *variegatus* but otherwise indistinguishable.

This species has been extensively studied by Linsdale (1946), Fitch (1948), and others. The squirrels thrive on grazing lands and much land that is cultivated. Costly, long-continued, and damaging (to other wildlife) methods of control by agricultural agencies have been aimed at the species. It was a matter of interest when Linsdale (*op. cit.*) found that allowing the grass to mature on an area for three consecutive seasons eliminated the squirrels; they cannot persist in areas where the grass is so tall that they cannot see over it. Seven young in a litter is the rule, and the mean is 7.2 (Grinnell and Dixon, 1919:619). Animals more than one year old aestivate and hibernate but those less than a year old, ordinarily at least, remain active above ground all winter.

Spermophilus beecheyi beecheyi (Richardson)

1829. *Arctomys (Spermophilus) beecheyi* Richardson, Fauna Boreali-Americana, 1:170, type from "neighborhood of San Francisco and Monterey, in California"; restricted to Monterey, Monterey Co., California, Grinnell Univ. California Publ. Zool., 40:120, Sept. 26, 1933.
1831. *Spermophilus beecheyi*, Cuvier, Supplément à l'histoire naturelle générale et particulière de Buffon, 1:331.

MARGINAL RECORDS (A. H. Howell, 1938:150).—California: Walnut Creek; Corral Hollow, 8 mi. SW Tracy; Bitterwater; Idria Mines; Pozo; San Rafael Mts.; Heninger Flats, San Gabriel Mts.; Lytle Creek; Temescal [Canyon]; Point Firmin, San Pedro.

Spermophilus beecheyi douglasii (Richardson)

1829. *Arctomys ? (Spermophilus?) douglasii* Richardson, Fauna Boreali-Americana, 1:172. Type locality, bank of Columbia River, Oregon.
1913. *Citellus beecheyi douglasi*, Grinnell, Proc. California Acad. Sci., ser. 4, 3:345, August 28.

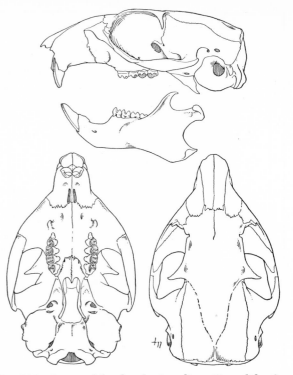

Fig. 226. *Spermophilus beecheyi nudipes*, Escondido, San Diego Co., California, No. 45956 K.U., ♂, X 1.

MARGINAL RECORDS (A. H. Howell, 1938:152–153, unless otherwise noted).—Washington: Satus Creek, 6 mi. N Yakima County border (Clanton and Johnson, 1954:15); 21 mi. E Goldendale (*ibid.*). Oregon: Warm Springs River; 10 mi. E McKenzie Bridge; Fort Klamath. California: Goose Lake; Lake City; Merrillville; Chico; Cherokee; Davis; Elmira; Fairfield. Thence northward along coast to Oregon: Tillamook; Portland. Washington: White Salmon River (Dalquest, 1948:276).

Spermophilus beecheyi fisheri Merriam

1893. *Spermophilus beecheyi fisheri* Merriam, Proc. Biol. Soc. Washington, 8:133, December 28, type from South Fork of Kern River, 3 mi. above Onyx, California.

MARGINAL RECORDS (A. H. Howell, 1938:156, unless otherwise noted).—California: Susanville. Nevada (Hall, 1946:314): 1 mi. SW Pyramid Lake; 5 mi. WSW Fallon; 1 mi. N Virginia City; Carson River, 5 mi. SE Minden, 5900 ft.; 6½ mi. S Minden, 4900 ft. California: Greenville; Nevada City; Coulterville; Soquel Mill, head North Fork San Joaquin River; Mt. Whitney; Walker Pass; Tehachapi Peak; Mono Flats; Cuyama Valley; Dos Palos; Pacheco Pass; Modesto; Tracy; 6 mi. E Colusa; Yankee Hill; Oroville.

Spermophilus beecheyi nesioticus (Elliot)

1904. *Citellus nesioticus* Elliot, Field Columb. Mus., Publ. 90, Zool. Ser., 3:263, March 7, type from [near Avalon] Santa Catalina Island, California. Known from Santa Catalina Island only.
1913. *Citellus beecheyi nesioticus*, Grinnell, Proc. California Acad. Sci., ser. 4, 3:346, August 28.

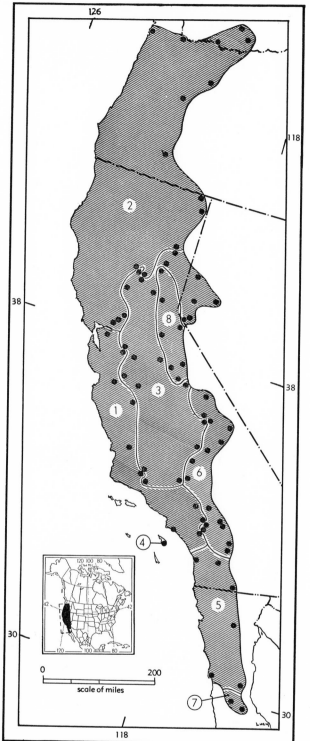

Map 230. *Spermophilus beecheyi.*

1. *S. b. beecheyi*   4. *S. b. nesioticus*   7. *S. b. rupinarum*
2. *S. b. douglasii*   5. *S. b. nudipes*   8. *S. b. sierrae*
3. *S. b. fisheri*   6. *S. b. parvulus*

Spermophilus beecheyi nudipes (Huey)

1931. *Citellus beecheyi nudipes* Huey, Trans. San Diego Soc. Nat. Hist., 7(2):18, October 6, type from Hanson Laguna, Sierra Juárez, 5200 ft., Baja California.

MARGINAL RECORDS (A. H. Howell, 1938:159, unless otherwise noted).—California: Oceanside; Grapevine Spring; Mountain Spring, 4 mi. N Monument 231, Mexican boundary line. Baja California: type locality; Mattomi [= Matomi] (Elliot, 1903:211); San Quentín.

Spermophilus beecheyi parvulus (A. H. Howell)

1931. *Citellus beecheyi parvulus* A. H. Howell, Jour. Mamm., 12:160, May 14, type from Shepherd Canyon, Argus Mts., California.

MARGINAL RECORDS (A. H. Howell, 1938:157–158, unless otherwise noted).—California: Owens Valley; Jackass Spring, Panamint Range; Argus Range; Little Lake; Victorville; Doble (Grinnell, 1908:143); Fish Creek (*ibid.*); Palm Springs; Thomas Mtn. (source of record mislaid after map was engraved); Riverside; San Bernardino; Cameron; Piute Mts.; Lone Pine; NE base Mt. Williamson.

Spermophilus beecheyi rupinarum (Huey)

1931. *Citellus beecheyi rupinarum* Huey, Trans. San Diego Soc. Nat. Hist., 7(2):17, October 6, type from Cataviña, Baja California.

MARGINAL RECORDS.—Baja California: San Fernando (A. H. Howell, 1938:160); type locality.

Spermophilus beecheyi sierrae (A. H. Howell)

1938. *Citellus beecheyi sierrae* A. H. Howell, N. Amer. Fauna, 56:153, May 18, type from Emerald Bay, Lake Tahoe, El Dorado Co., California.

MARGINAL RECORDS (A. H. Howell, 1938:154).—California: Quincy; Markleeville; Little Yosemite; Wawona; near head Merced River; Big Trees; Blue Canyon.

Spermophilus atricapillus W. E. Bryant
Baja California Rock Squirrel

1889. *Spermophilus grammurus atricapillus* W. E. Bryant, Proc. California Acad., 2(ser. 2):26, June 20. Type locality, Comondú, Baja California.

External measurements: 410–465; 185–210; 55–60. Greatest length of skull, 54.8–58.5. Closely resembles *S. beecheyi* but darker, especially on head and anterior half of back; tail averages longer and skull averages smaller. (See Map 229.)

The geographic range of *S. atricapillus* seems to be separated from that of *S. beecheyi* by a 40-mile wide area uninhabited by any species of the subgenus *Otospermophilus.*

MARGINAL RECORDS (A. H. Howell, 1938:162).—Baja California: San Pablo; type locality; San Ignacio.

Spermophilus annulatus
Ring-tailed Ground Squirrel

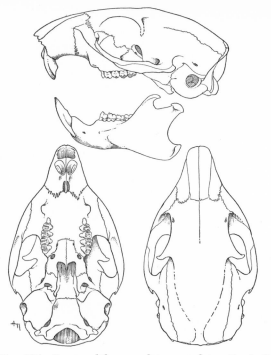

Fig. 227. *Spermophilus annulatus annulatus*, 5 mi. S Purificación, Jalisco, No. 33438 K.U., ♀, X 1.

External measurements: 383–470; 186–238; 50–64. Greatest length of skull, 51.6–57.0. Upper parts nearly uniform mixed fuscous black and cinnamon buff or pale pinkish buff, blackish color often predominating on head and in some specimens on back; chin, throat, and sides of nose and face ochraceous buff; sides of neck, shoulders, and forelimbs hazel; ears and hind legs hazel or tawny; underparts warm buff or pinkish buff; tail mixed pinkish buff and black above, hazel beneath; tail approximately same length as head and body, distichous, narrow, not bushy, and with approximately 15 blackish annulations. Interorbital breadth more than 42 per cent of zygomatic breadth; anteroposterior diameter of upper incisors more than in the larger-skulled S. *beecheyi*.

Spermophilus annulatus annulatus Audubon and Bachman

1842. *Spermophilus annulatus* Audubon and Bachman, Jour. Acad. Nat. Sci. Philadelphia, 8:319, type from an unknown locality; subsequently designated as Manzanillo, Colima, by A. H. Howell (N. Amer. Fauna, 56:163, May 18, 1938).

MARGINAL RECORDS (A. H. Howell, 1938:164).—Colima: Hda. San Antonio, base of Volcán de Colima. Guerrero: El Naranjo; La Unión, thence northward along coast to Colima: type locality. Jalisco: 5 mi. S Purificación (33438 KU).

Spermophilus annulatus goldmani Merriam

1902. *Spermophilus annulatus goldmani* Merriam, Proc. Biol. Soc. Washington, 15:69, March 22, type from Santiago, Nayarit.

MARGINAL RECORDS (A. H. Howell, 1938:165).—Nayarit: type locality; Compostela; Arroyo de San Juan Sanches, about 40 mi. SW Compostela; San Blas.

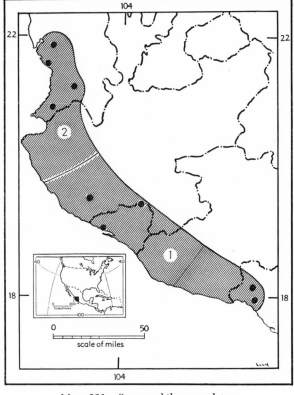

Map 231. *Spermophilus annulatus.*

1. *S. a. annulatus*   2. *S. a. goldmani*

Spermophilus adocetus
Lesser Tropical Ground Squirrel

External measurements: 315–353; 138–168; 43–48. Greatest length of skull, 41.6–46.2. Resembles *S. annulatus* but smaller, paler (less reddish); tail without annulations; rostrum shorter and broader; interorbital region averaging 49 instead of 45 per cent of zygomatic breadth.

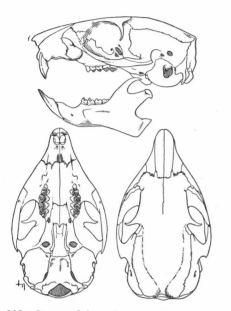

Fig. 228. *Spermophilus adocetus adocetus*, 9 mi. S Lombardia, 1500 ft., Michoacán, No. 38346 K.U., ♂, X 1.

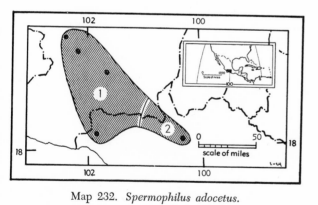

Map 232. *Spermophilus adocetus.*

1. *S. a. adocetus*   2. *S. a. arceliae*

Spermophilus adocetus adocetus (Merriam)

1903. *Citellus adocetus* Merriam, Proc. Biol. Soc. Washington, 16:79, May 29, type from La Salada, 40 mi. S Uruapan, Michoacán.

MARGINAL RECORDS.—Michoacán: near Tancítaro (Hall and Villa, 1949:450); Volcán Jarullo (A. H. Howell,

1938:166). Guerrero: La Escondida, about 20 mi. SE Balsas (*ibid.*). Michoacán: Apatzingan, 1040 ft. (Hall and Villa, 1949:450).

Spermophilus adocetus arceliae (Villa)

1942. *Citellus adocetus arceliae* Villa, Anales Inst. Biol., 13(1):357, October, type from Rancho El Limón, 4 km. S Arcelia, Guerrero. Known only from the type locality.

Subgenus Xerospermophilus Merriam

1892. *Xerospermophilus* Merriam, Proc. Biol. Soc. Washington, 7:27, April 13. Type, *Spermophilus mohavensis* Merriam.

External measurements: 210–266; 57–107; 32–40. Greatest length of skull, 34.9–40.0. Upper parts pinkish gray (in *S. mohavensis*) and under surface of tail white, or (in *S. tereticaudus*) upper parts vinaceous cinnamon, pinkish cinnamon, light drab, cinnamon drab, or ecru drab; tail beneath drab or buff; upper parts without mottling. Skull short and broad; postorbital region wider than interorbital region; rostrum not constricted at base or expanded at tip; coronoid process of mandible and P3 smaller than in any other subgenus of the genus; molar teeth low crowned; M1 and M2 subquadrate in occlusal outline; trigon on P4, M1, and M2 broadly V-shaped; anterior cingulum usually joins protocone with abrupt change of direction on M1 and M2; metaloph on P4, M1, and M2 separated from protocone by sulcus as in *Otospermophilus* and *Ictidomys*; M3 slightly larger than M2; posterior cingulum of M3 does not bend sharply posteriad from protocone as in subgenera *Spermophilus* and *Ictidomys*; P4 not molariform; trigonid on lower cheek-teeth slightly higher than talonid; occlusal outline of m1 and m2 rhomboidal as in *Otospermophilus*; baculum resembles that of subgenus *Spermophilus* but spoon relatively larger and entire baculum "stouter"; cheek pouches large; atlanto-scapularis dorsalis muscle absent.

KEY TO SPECIES OF SUBGENUS XEROSPERMOPHILUS

1. Underside of tail white. . *S. mohavensis*, p. 357
1'. Underside of tail not white (usually cinnamon). . . . . *S. tereticaudus*, p. 358

Spermophilus mohavensis Merriam
Mohave Ground Squirrel

1889. *Spermophilus mohavensis* Merriam, N. Amer. Fauna, 2:15, October 30, type from near Rabbit Springs, about 15 mi. E Hesperia, San Bernardino Co., California (Grinnell and Dixon, Monthly Bull. California Comm. Hort., 7:667, January 27, 1919).

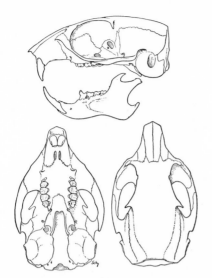

Fig. 229. *Spermophilus mohavensis*, 1 mi. NW Lovejoy Springs, 2300 ft., California, No. 44285 M.V.Z., ♀, X 1.

External measurements: 210–230; 57–72; 32–38. Greatest length of skull, 38.1–40.0. In coloration resembles S. *townsendii mollis*, but upper parts more pinkish without trace of mottling; tail beneath whitish. Cranial characters as given for the subgenus.

This squirrel lives on the lower parts of the desert. It carries its tail over its back after the manner of an *Ammospermophilus*, but does not twitch the tail. Six embryos were recorded in one female.

MARGINAL RECORDS (A. H. Howell, 1938:185).— California: Haiwee Meadow, 10 mi. S Owens Lake; Salt Wells Valley, N end Mohave Desert; Oro Grande; Mohave River (= Rabbit Springs, 15 mi. E Hesperia); Hesperia; Palmdale; Mojave; Little Lake.

Spermophilus tereticaudus
Round-tailed Ground Squirrel

External measurements: 204–266; 60–107; 32–40. Greatest length of skull, 34.9–39.3. In winter, upper parts pinkish cinnamon, underparts white; in summer, upper parts brighter pinkish cinnamon and pelage shorter and harsher (there are 2 annual molts); tail long and slender and not broadly haired. Skull resembles that of S. *mohavensis* but smaller.

This is a shy, secretive ground squirrel that often has to be looked for to be found on the wind-drifted sand in the Lower Sonoran Life-zone. The mouth of the burrow is directly below some part of the periphery of a mesquite or creosote bush. This squirrel seldom is seen above ground in cold weather and whether it hibernates is not known. Six to 12 embryos have been found.

Spermophilus tereticaudus apricus (Huey)

1927. *Citellus tereticaudus apricus* Huey, Trans. San Diego Soc. Nat. Hist., 5(7):85, October 10, type from Valle de la Trinidad (lat. 31° 20′ N; long. 115° 40′ W), Baja California. Known only from the type locality.

Spermophilus tereticaudus chlorus (Elliot)

1904. *Citellus chlorus* Elliot, Field Columb. Mus., Publ. 87, Zool. Ser., 3:242, January 7, type from Palm Springs, Riverside Co., California.

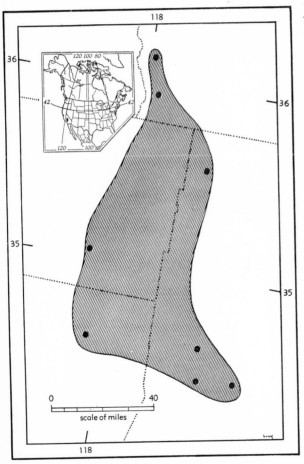

Map 233. *Spermophilus mohavensis*.

1913. *Citellus tereticaudus chlorus,* Grinnell, Proc. California Acad. Sci., ser. 4, 3:347, August 28.

MARGINAL RECORDS (A. H. Howell, 1938:189).—California: Cabazon; Whitewater Station; Coachella; Mecca; Agua Caliente.

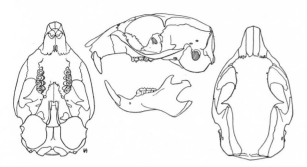

Fig. 230. *Spermophilus tereticaudus tereticaudus,* Furnace Creek Ranch, Death Valley, 178 ft. below sea level, Inyo Co., California, No. 27381 M.V.Z., ♀, X 1.

Spermophilus tereticaudus neglectus Merriam

1889. *Spermophilus neglectus* Merriam, N. Amer. Fauna, 2:17, October 30, type from Dolans Spring, 12 mi. NW Chloride, Mohave Co., Arizona.
1938. *Citellus tereticaudus neglectus,* A. H. Howell, N. Amer. Fauna, 56:187, May 18.
1891. *Spermophilus sonoriensis* Ward, Amer. Nat., 25:158, February, type from Hermosillo, Sonora.
1918. *Citellus tereticaudus arizonae* Grinnell, Proc. Biol. Soc. Washington, 31:105, November 29, type from Tempe, Maricopa Co., Arizona.

MARGINAL RECORDS (A. H. Howell, 1938:188, unless otherwise noted).—Arizona: type locality; Hackberry; 2 mi. N Wickenburg (Hatfield, 1942:150); Tempe; 10 mi. N Rillito; Rillito Creek, 5 mi. N Tucson; W base Santa Rita Mts. Sonora: Querobabi; Hermosillo; Ortiz; Camoa, Río Mayo; Obregon; Guaymas; Ciénega Well, 30 mi. S Mon. 204. Arizona: Colorado River at Mon. 204, thence northward on E side of Colorado River to at least *Fort Mohave.*

Spermophilus tereticaudus tereticaudus Baird

1858. *Spermophilus tereticaudus* Baird, Mammals, *in* Repts. Expl. Surv. . . . , 8(1):315, July 14, type from Old Fort Yuma, Imperial Co., California.
1904. *Citellus eremonomus* Elliot, Field Columb. Mus., Publ. 87, Zool. Ser., 3:243, January 7, type from Furnace Creek, Death Valley, Inyo Co., California.
1926. *Citellus tereticaudus vociferans* Huey, Proc. Biol. Soc. Washington, 39:29, July 30, type from San Felipe, Baja California.

MARGINAL RECORDS (A. H. Howell, 1938:187, unless otherwise noted).—Nevada (Hall, 1946:319): Bunkerville; ½ mi. E St. Thomas, 2100 ft., thence southward on W side of Colorado River to Baja California: San Felipe Bay; San Felipe. California: Coyote Well; La Puerta; Baregas Spring (= Borego); Daggett; Barstow; type locality. Nevada (Hall, 1946:319): Ash Meadows; 4 mi. NW Las Vegas, 2100 ft.

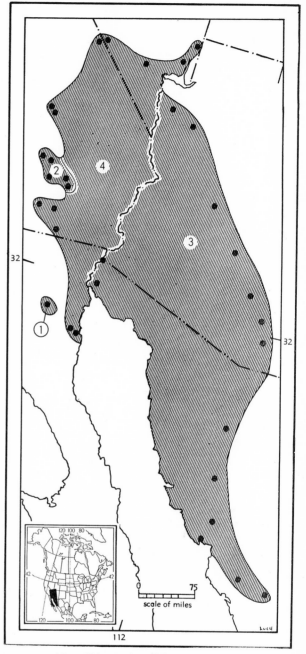

Map 234. *Spermophilus tereticaudus.*

1. *S. t. apricus*   3. *S. t. neglectus*
2. *S. t. chlorus*   4. *S. t. tereticaudus*

Subgenus Callospermophilus Merriam
Golden-mantled Ground Squirrels

1897. *Callospermophilus* Merriam, Proc. Biol. Soc. Washington, 11:189, July 1. Type, *Sciurus lateralis* Say.

External measurements: 215–315; 52–118; 35–49. Greatest length of skull, 39.6–48.3. A white stripe from shoulder to hip on each side of back; white stripe bordered below, and in most subspecies above, by black stripe; back gray, buff, cinnamon, or fawn; "mantle" on head and shoulders varying from cinnamon buff to tawny or russet; except in color and smaller size, closely resembling subgenus *Otospermophilus* but differing as follows: interorbital region relatively narrower in comparison with width at postorbital constriction; angular process of mandible relatively shorter; metaloph on M1 and M2 joins protocone; small protolophid present, instead of absent, on p4; atlantoscapularis dorsalis muscle present.

These ground squirrels can be distinguished from chipmunks by absence of stripes on side of head. Golden-mantled ground squirrels hibernate but store food. We do not know if the food is used. Preferred habitat is open timber or edges of meadows bordered by timber. Four to 8 embryos have been found; 5 and 6 are the usual numbers.

KEY TO SPECIES OF SUBGENUS CALLOSPERMOPHILUS

1. Occurring S of United States–Mexican boundary. . . . . . . S. *madrensis*, p. 363
1'. Occurring N of United States–Mexican boundary.
   2. Occurring in Cascade Mts. of S British Columbia and Washington. S. *saturatus*, p. 363
   2'. Not occurring in Cascade Mts. of British Columbia and Washington. S. *lateralis*, p. 360

Spermophilus lateralis
Golden-mantled Ground Squirrel

X ⅓

External measurements: 230–308; 63–118; 35–46. Greatest length of skull, 39.6–45.6. Color as described for the subgenus.

Fig. 231. *Spermophilus lateralis trepidus*, Kingston Ranger Station, 7500 ft., Nevada, No. 45473 M.V.Z., ♀, X 1.

Spermophilus lateralis arizonensis (V. Bailey)

1913. *Callospermophilus lateralis arizonensis* V. Bailey, Proc. Biol. Soc. Washington, 26:130, May 21, type from Little Spring, 8250 ft., San Francisco Mtn., Arizona.

MARGINAL RECORDS (A. H. Howell, 1938:197).— Arizona: type locality; Springerville. New Mexico: head Mimbres River; Big Rocky Creek, Mimbres Mts. Arizona: Prieto Plateau; Montezuma Well; Williams.

Spermophilus lateralis caryi (A. H. Howell)

1917. *Callospermophilus lateralis caryi* A. H. Howell, Proc. Biol. Soc. Washington, 30:105, May 23, type from 7 mi. S Fremont Peak, 10,400 ft., Wind River Mts., Fremont Co., Wyoming.

MARGINAL RECORDS (A. H. Howell, 1938:198).— Wyoming: Bobcat Ridge; Jakey's Creek, 5 mi. S Dubois; Bull Lake; 5 mi. E, 9 mi. N Pinedale, 9100 ft. (14941 KU).

Spermophilus lateralis bernardinus Merriam

1893. *Spermophilus chrysodeirus brevicaudus* Merriam, Proc. Biol. Soc. Washington, 8:134, December 28, type from San Bernardino Peak, San Bernardino Co., California. Not *Spermophilus brevicauda* Brandt, 1844, type from southern Altai.
1898. *Spermophilus (Callospermophilus) bernardinus* Merriam, Science, n.s., 8:782, December 2, a renaming of S. c. *brevicaudus* Merriam.
1938. *Citellus lateralis bernardinus*, A. H. Howell, N. Amer. Fauna, 56:209, May 18.

MARGINAL RECORDS (Grinnell, 1908:141–142).— California: Holcomb Valley; Sugarloaf; San Gorgonio Peak; head S. Fork Santa Ana River.

Spermophilus lateralis castanurus (Merriam)

1890. *Tamias castanurus* Merriam, N. Amer. Fauna, 4:19, October 8, type from Park City, Wasatch Mts., Summit Co., Utah.

1938. *Citellus lateralis castanurus,* Howell, N. Amer. Fauna, 56:201, May 18.

MARGINAL RECORDS (A. H. Howell, 1938:202–203, unless otherwise noted).— Idaho: Big Hole Mts. Wyoming:

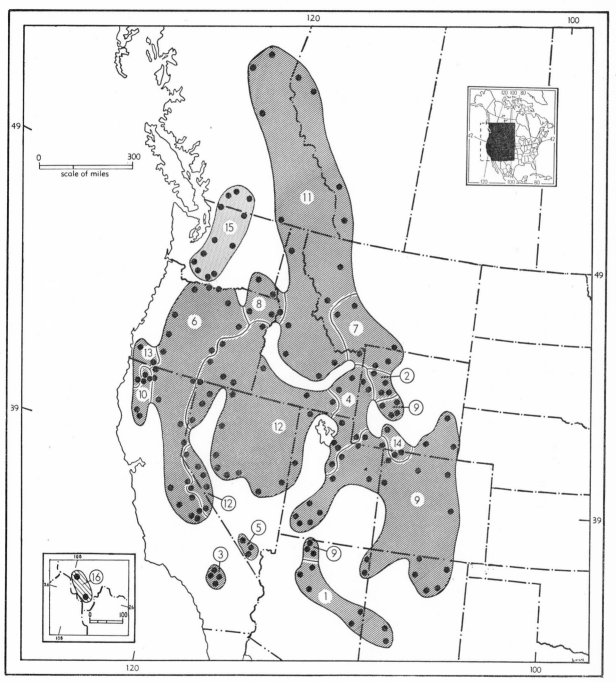

Map 235. *Spermophilus lateralis* and allies.

1. *S. l. arizonensis*	5. *S. l. certus*	9. *S. l. lateralis*	13. *S. l. trinitatis*
2. *S. l. caryi*	6. *S. l. chrysodeirus*	10. *S. l. mitratus*	14. *S. l. wortmani*
3. *S. l. bernardinus*	7. *S. l. cinerascens*	11. *S. l. tescorum*	15. *S. saturatus*
4. *S. l. castanurus*	8. *S. l. connectens*	12. *S. l. trepidus*	16. *S. madrensis*

head Flat Creek; 12 mi. NW Kendall; head Smiths Fork. Utah (Durrant, 1952:128): type locality; Santaquin Canyon, upper sawmill, N of Mt. Nebo; Barclay; Tony Grove, Logan Canyon. Idaho: 8 mi. NE Inkom.

Spermophilus lateralis certus (Goldman)

1921. *Callospermophilus lateralis certus* (Goldman, Jour. Mamm., 2:232, November 29, type from north base Charleston Peak, Clark Co., Nevada.

MARGINAL RECORDS (Hall, 1946:326).—Nevada: Wheeler Well; Charleston Peak; N side Potosi Mtn., 7000 ft., Spring Mts.

Spermophilus lateralis chrysodeirus (Merriam)

1890. *Tamias chrysodeirus* Merriam, N. Amer. Fauna, 4:19, October 8, type from Fort Klamath, Klamath Co., Oregon.
1936. *Citellus lateralis chrysodeirus*, A. H. Howell, N. Amer. Fauna, 56:203, May 18.

MARGINAL RECORDS (A. H. Howell, 1938:204–205, unless otherwise noted).—Oregon: Willows; Meacham; Rock Creek; 10 mi. SW Silver Lake. California: Goose Lake; Sierra Valley. Nevada (Hall, 1946:322): 2 mi. W Mt. Rose summit; *1½ mi. N and 3 mi. E Edgewood*. California: Mono Lake; near head San Joaquin River; Mt. Whitney; Mulkey Meadows, 15 mi. S Mt. Whitney; E. Fork Kaweah River, Sequoia National Park; Dinkey Creek, North Fork, Kings River; Merced River, Fish Camp, S. Fork; Shingletown; Mt. Shasta; Beswick. Oregon: Four-mile Lake; Diamond Lake; McKenzie Bridge; Mt. Hood; Miller, mouth of Deschutes River.

Spermophilus lateralis cinerascens (Merriam)

1890. *Tamias cinerascens* Merriam, N. Amer. Fauna, 4:20, October 8, type from Helena, 4500 ft., Lewis and Clark Co., Montana.
1938. *Citellus lateralis cinerascens*, A. H. Howell, N. Amer. Fauna, 56:198, May 18.

MARGINAL RECORDS (A. H. Howell, 1938:199, unless otherwise noted).—Montana: Helena; Beartooth Mts. Wyoming: Pahaska Tepee, Whirlwind Peak; Yellowstone National Park. Idaho: Henrys Lake (Davis, 1939:201). Montana: Deer Lodge County.

Spermophilus lateralis connectens (A. H. Howell)

1931. *Callospermophilus chrysodeirus connectens* A. H. Howell, Jour. Mamm., 12:161, May 14, type from Homestead, Oregon.
1938. *Citellus lateralis connectens* A. H. Howell, N. Amer. Fauna, 56:205, May 18.

MARGINAL RECORDS (A. H. Howell, 1938:206, unless otherwise noted).—Washington: Dayton; Anatone. Idaho: ½ mi. E Black Lake (Davis, 1939:202). Oregon: type locality; Anthony.

Spermophilus lateralis lateralis (Say)

1823. S[*ciurus*]. *lateralis* Say, *in* Long, Account of an exped. . . . to the Rocky Mts. . . . , 2:46. Type locality, Arkansas River, near Canyon City, Colorado (about 26 mi.

below Canyon City, Merriam, Proc. Biol. Soc. Washington, 18:163, June 29, 1905).
1831. *Spermophilus lateralis*, Cuvier, Supplément à l'histoire naturelle générale et particulière de Buffon, 1:335.

MARGINAL RECORDS (A. H. Howell, 1938:194, unless otherwise noted).—Isolated northern segment in Wyoming: Mosquito Park R. S., 17½ mi. W, 2½ mi. N Lander, 9500 ft. (32372 KU); Miners Delight, 3 mi. NE Atlantic City; 25 mi. S, 3 mi. W Lander, 9200 ft. (37431 KU); Big Sandy. Main segment of range, Wyoming: Springhill, 12 mi. N Laramie Peak; 2⅛ mi. W Horse Creek P.O., 6600 ft. (14934 KU). Colorado: ½ mi. E, 3 mi. S Ward, 9400 ft. (19974 KU); Manitou. New Mexico: Cimarron; 10 mi. N Pecos; Santa Fe; Jemez Mts.; Tierra Amarilla. Arizona: 12 mi. NW Fort Defiance, 7800 ft.; Lukachukai Mts. Colorado: 28 mi. N, 5 mi. W Mack, 7250 ft. (41680 KU). Utah (Durrant, 1952:130): PR Springs, 7950 ft., 43 mi. S Ouray; 18 mi. N Escalante; Bryce National Park; Duck Creek, 9000 ft., Cedar Mtn.; Brian Head, 11,000 ft.; Britts Meadow, Beaver Range, 8500 ft.; Maple Canyon; Currant Creek, Uinta National Forest; Henrys Fork. Wyoming: 9 mi. S Robertson, 8000 ft. (25373 KU); Maxon. Colorado: Escalante Hills, 20 mi. SE Ladore; 5 mi. S Pagoda Peak, 9100 ft. (19969 KU). Wyoming: 5 mi. N, 5 mi. E Savery, 6900 ft. (14934 KU). Isolated southern segment in Arizona: Jacob Lake; Greenland Spring; V. T. Park.

Spermophilus lateralis mitratus (A. H. Howell)

1931. *Callospermophilus chrysodeirus mitratus* A. H. Howell, Jour. Mamm., 12:161, May 14, type from South Yolla Bolly Mtn., California.
1938. *Citellus lateralis mitratus* A. H. Howell, N. Amer. Fauna, 56:210, May 18.

MARGINAL RECORDS (A. H. Howell, 1938:211).—California: Salmon Mts.; Castle Lake; Coast Range, 17 mi. W Paskenta; type locality; Salmon River, South Fork, Siskiyou Mts.

Spermophilus lateralis tescorum (Hollister)

1911. *Callospermophilus lateralis tescorum* Hollister, Smiths. Misc. Coll., 56(26):2, December 5, type from head of Moose Pass, branch of the Smoky River, 7000 ft., Alberta (near Moose Pass, British Columbia).

MARGINAL RECORDS (A. H. Howell, 1938:200–201, unless otherwise noted).—British Columbia: Sukunka River. Alberta: Wapiti River (Anderson, 1947:112); Grand Cache River, 70 mi. N Jasper House; Canmore; Maycroft (Crowe, 1943:398). Montana: Bear Creek; Bass Creek, near Stevensville. Idaho: Birch Creek (Davis, 1939:201); Craters of the Moon National Monument (*ibid.*); Edna (Anderson, 1947:112); Warren; 5 mi. W Cocolalla (Davis, 1939:201). British Columbia: Rossland (Anderson, 1947:112); Barkerville; head of Parsnip River (Cowan and Guiguet, 1956:133).

Spermophilus lateralis trepidus (Taylor)

1910. *Callospermophilus trepidus* Taylor, Univ. California Publ. Zool., 5(6):283, February 12, type from head of Big Creek, 8000 ft., Pine Forest Mts., Humboldt Co., Nevada.
1938. *Citellus lateralis trepidus*, A. H. Howell, N. Amer. Fauna, 56:206, May 18.

1918. *Callospermophilus chrysodeirus perpallidus* Grinnell, Univ. California Publ. Zool., 17:429, April 25, type from near Big Prospector Meadow, 10,300 ft., White Mts., Mono Co., California.

MARGINAL RECORDS (A. H. Howell, 1938:207–208, unless otherwise noted).—Oregon: Home. Idaho: Silver City; Albion; Bannock Mts., 8 mi. W Swan Lake. Utah: Clear Creek, 5 mi. SW Nafton (Durrant, 1952:127); Deep Creek Mts. (Durrant, 1955b:74). Nevada (Hall, 1946:323, 326): Baker Creek, 8675 ft.; Quinn Canyon Mts., Burned Corral Canyon, 6700 ft.; Greenmonster Canyon, Monitor Range, 7500–9000 ft.; N slope Toquima Mtn., 9000 ft.; Shoshone Mts., 2 mi. W Indian Valley, 9000 ft.; 3 mi. W Carroll Summit, E of Eastgate; El Dorado Canyon, 8000 ft., Humboldt Range; 13 mi. N Paradise Valley, 6700 ft. Oregon: McDermitt Creek, 8 mi. NE McDermitt, Nevada; Steens Mts. Nevada (Hall, 1946:323, 326): type locality; ½ mi. S Rock Creek, 6000 ft.; Horse Canyon, Pahrum Peak, 5800 ft.; 12-mile Creek, ½ mi. E Calif. boundary, 5300 ft. Oregon: Mt. Warner [= Hart Mtn.]; Burns. Isolated southwestern segment of range, Nevada: Edgewood; Lapon Canyon, Mt. Grant, 8900 ft. (Hall, 1946:323); Endowment Mine, 6500 ft., Excelsior Mts. (*ibid.*); Chiatovich Creek, 8200 ft. (*ibid.*). California: Inyo Mts.; Mammoth Lakes.

Spermophilus lateralis trinitatis (Merriam)

1901. *Callospermophilus chrysodeirus trinitatis* Merriam, Proc. Biol. Soc. Washington, 14:126, July 19, type from E of Hoopa Valley, 5700 ft., Trinity Mts., California.
1938. *Citellus lateralis trinitatis*, A. H. Howell, N. Amer. Fauna, 56:211, May 18.

MARGINAL RECORDS (A. H. Howell, 1938:212).—Oregon: Briggs Creek, 13 mi. SW Galice; Siskiyou. California: type locality.

Spermophilus lateralis wortmani (J. A. Allen)

1895. *Tamias wortmani* J. A. Allen, Bull. Amer. Mus. Nat. Hist., 7:335, November 8, type from Kinney Ranch, Bitter Creek, Sweetwater Co., Wyoming.
1911. *Callospermophilus lateralis wortmani*, Cary, N. Amer. Fauna, 33:84, August 17.

MARGINAL RECORDS (A. H. Howell, 1938:195).—Wyoming: Superior. Colorado: Snake River, 20 mi. below Baggs, Wyoming; Snake River, 5 mi. above Lily.

Spermophilus saturatus (Rhoads)
Cascade Golden-mantled Ground Squirrel

1895. *Tamias lateralis saturatus* Rhoads, Proc. Acad. Nat. Philadelphia, 47:43, April 9, type from Lake Kichelos [= Keechelus], 8000 ft., Kittitas Co., Washington.
1938. *Citellus saturatus*, A. H. Howell, N. Amer. Fauna, 56:212, May 18.

External measurements: 286–315; 92–118; 43–49. Greatest length of skull, 44.0–48.3. Closely resembles S. *lateralis* but larger. Mantle poorly defined; inner pair of dark stripes obsolete or much reduced; outer pair of dark stripes reduced in length and obscurely defined.

MARGINAL RECORDS (A. H. Howell, 1938:213, unless otherwise noted).—British Columbia: Tulameen (Anderson, 1947:112); Hedley. Washington: Bauerman Ridge (Dalquest, 1948:281); Wenatchee; Cleveland (Dalquest, 1948:281); Goldendale (*ibid.*); Trout Lake; Mt. St. Helens; Spray Park; type locality; Hannegan Pass. British Columbia: Skagit River (Cowan and Guiguet, 1956:131).

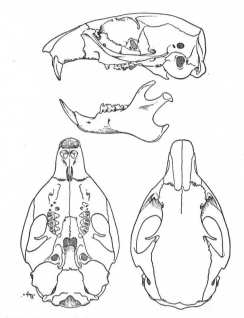

Fig. 232. *Spermophilus saturatus*, Stephens Pass, King Co., Washington, No. 22150 K.U., ♂, X 1.

Spermophilus madrensis (Merriam)
Sierra Madre Mantled Ground Squirrel

1901. *Callospermophilus madrensis* Merriam, Proc. Washington Acad. Sci., 3:563, November 29, type from Sierra Madre, 7000 ft., near Guadalupe y Calvo, Chihuahua. Known only from the type locality.

External measurements: 215–243; 52–66; 37–40. Greatest length of skull, 44.1–44.4. Closely resembles S. *lateralis* but smaller, tail shorter, colors much duller with scarcely a trace of mantle, black stripes short and poorly defined (tending to become obsolete), white stripes reaching nearly to base of tail; skull narrower and braincase more highly arched.

MARGINAL RECORDS.—Chihuahua: Batopilas (Miller and Kellogg, 1955:216); type locality.

Genus Cynomys Rafinesque—Prairie Dogs

Revised by Hollister, N. Amer. Fauna, 40:1–36, 7 pls., 2 figs. in text, June 20, 1916.

1817. *Cynomys* Rafinesque, Amer. Monthly Mag., 2:45, November. Type, *Cynomys socialis* Rafinesque [= *Arctomys ludoviciana* Ord].

1819. *Monax* Warden, Statistical, political and historical account of the United States . . . , 1:226. Type, *Monax missouriensis* Warden [= *Arctomys ludoviciana* Ord].
1827. *Cynomis* Lesson, Manuel de mammalogie . . . , p. 244, a *lapsus*.
1894. *Cynomomus* Osborn, Science, 23:103, February 23, a *lapsus plumae* for *Cynomys*.

External measurements: 305–430; 30–115; 52–67. Condylobasal length, 51.9–64.0. Wrist and heel furred; manus with 5 distinct claws; mammae, 8–12. Skull broad and robust; occipital crest well developed; sagittal crest moderate anteriorly but well developed posteriorly; squamosal root of zygoma widespreading; antorbital foramen subtriangular, with prominent tubercle; tooth-rows strongly convergent posteriorly; individual cheek-teeth large and expanded laterally; 1st premolar large, nearly equalling 2nd; cheek-teeth more hypsodont than in *Spermophilus*, especially protocone; M3 with additional transverse ridge. Color pattern not sharply bicolor, usually grayish, brownish, or buffy.

Prairie-dogs are social animals and usually live in "towns" or colonies, some of which formerly extended for many miles. Social traits are the more marked in the subgenus *Cynomys*. The common name alludes to the "barking" of alarmed animals. Food consists mainly of green vegetation. Overgrazing by domestic livestock improves conditions for prairie-dogs. Now the prairie-dog is gone from much of its former range, having been intentionally eliminated by man.

There are two annual molts in all species except *C. mexicanus*, and except on the tail where replacement of hair occurs only once annually.

KEY TO SPECIES OF CYNOMYS

1. Tail tipped with black; jugal heavy, thick, the outer surface at angle of ascending ramus presenting a broad, triangular surface.
   2. Black on tail covering most of distal half; posterior border of inflected angle of mandible nearly at right angles to axis of jaw. . . . . *C. mexicanus*, p. 366
   2'. Black on tail confined to distal third; posterior border of inflected angle of mandible at angle of approximately 45° to axis of jaw. . . . *C. ludovicianus*, p. 364
1'. Tail tipped with white; jugal weak, thin, flat, the outer surface at angle of ascending ramus only slightly thickened, the margin rounded, not distinctly triangular.
   3. Terminal half of tail white, without dark center.
      4. Color in summer reddish (Tawny-Olive to Clay Color); postorbital breadth great (14.2 in adult males);

supraorbital notch prominent, almost foramenlike. . . . . *C. parvidens*, p. 367
      4'. Color in summer grayish (Pinkish Buff to Pale Smoke Gray); postorbital breadth small (13.2 in adult males); supraorbital notch obsolete. . . . . *C. leucurus*, p. 366
   3'. Terminal half of tail with gray center.
      C. gunnisoni, p. 368

Subgenus **Cynomys** Rafinesque

1817. *Cynomys* Rafinesque, Amer. Monthly Mag., 2:45. Type, *Cynomys socialis* Rafinesque [= *Arctomys ludoviciana* Ord].

Tail comparatively long, averaging more than ⅓ of total length; tipped with black. Skull massive; occipital region ovoid from posterior aspect; jugal thick and heavy, its outer surface at angle of ascending branch broad, triangular, with inferior vertex produced downward; maxillary root of zygoma correspondingly strengthened, the shelf and the suprajugal arm much thickened. Cheek-teeth larger, more expanded laterally than in subgenus *Leucocrossuromys*.

Cynomys ludovicianus
Black-tailed Prairie Dog

× ⅓

External measurements: 355–415; 72–115; 57–67. Condylobasal length, 56.6–64. Upper parts (summer) approximately dark pinkish cinnamon finely lined with black and buff; upper lip, sides of nose, and eye ring buffy or whitish; tail above like back for proximal ⅔, black or blackish brown distally; tail below vinaceous-cinnamon proximally, with distal ⅓ blackish or dark brown; underparts whitish or buffy white. See account of subgenus for diagnostic cranial characters.

Characteristically, animals of this species build a ridge of hard-packed soil around the mouth of the burrow; the mouth of the burrow is at the apex of the cone of earth. They seem not to hibernate and flourish where grass is short.

Two to 10 young (mode and mean, 5) are born in the period from April to July.

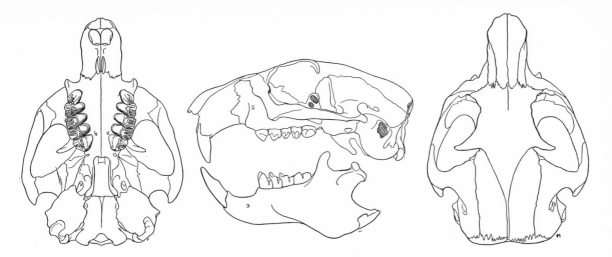

Fig. 233. *Cynomys ludovicianus ludovicianus*, Higgens, Lipscomb Co., Texas, No. 44365 M.V.Z., ♀, X 1.

Cynomys ludovicianus arizonensis Mearns

1890. *Cynomys arizonensis* Mearns, Bull. Amer. Mus. Nat. Hist., 2:305, February 21, type from Point of Mountain, near Willcox, Cochise Co., Arizona.
1892. *C[ynomys]. ludovicianus arizonensis,* Merriam, Proc. Biol. Soc. Washington, 7:158, July 27.

MARGINAL RECORDS (Hollister, 1916:21, unless otherwise noted).—New Mexico: San Pedro; Santa Rosa; Roswell; 8 mi. SW Carlsbad (7130 KU). Texas: 2 mi. E Sheffield (Hermann, 1950:374); [30 mi. S] Sheffield. Chihuahua: Juarez; Colonia Juarez. Sonora: Río San Pedro (Burt, 1938: 37). Arizona: Fort Huachuca; Bonita. New Mexico: Cactus Flat, 20 mi. N Cliff; Jornada del Muerto; east foothills, Manzano Mts.

Cynomys ludovicianus ludovicianus (Ord)

1815. *Arctomys ludoviciana* Ord, *in* Guthrie, A new geogr., hist., coml. grammar . . . , Philadelphia, Amer. ed. 2, 2:292 (description on p. 302). Type locality, "Upper Missouri River" ("vicinity of the Missouri, and throughout the greater part of Louisiana").
1858. *Cynomys ludovicianus,* Baird, Mammals, *in* Repts. Expl. and Surv. . . . , 8(1):xxxix, 331, July 14.
1817. *Cynomys socialis* Rafinesque, Amer. Monthly Mag., 2:45, November. Type locality, "Plains of the Missouri."
1817. *Cynomys ? grisea* Rafinesque, Amer. Monthly Mag., 2:45, November. Type locality, "On the Missouri."
1819. *Monax missouriensis* Warden, Statistical, political and historical account of the United States . . . , 1:226. Type locality, "The Missouri country." Based largely on the account of "Major Pike, in his expedition through Louisiana."
1825. *Arctomys latrans* Harlan, Fauna Americana, p. 306. Type locality, "Plains of the Missouri."
1829. *C[ynomys]. cinereus* Richardson, Fauna Boreali-Americana, pt. 1, p. 155 (pro *grisea* Rafinesque, 1817).
1905. *Cynomys pyrrotrichus* Elliot, Proc. Biol. Soc. Washington, 18:139, April 18, type from White Horse Spring, Woods Co., Oklahoma.

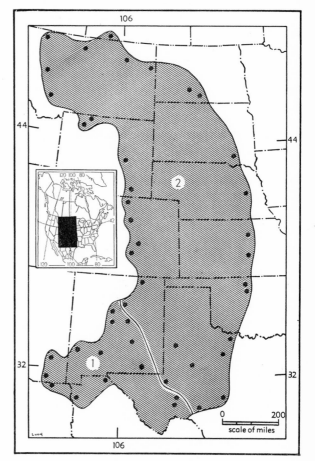

Map 236. *Cynomys ludovicianus.*

1. *C. l. arizonensis* 2. *C. l. ludovicianus*

MARGINAL RECORDS (Hollister, 1916:18–19, unless otherwise noted).—Saskatchewan: approximately 7½ mi. SE Val Marie (Soper, 1946:141). Montana: near mouth Milk River; Boxelder Creek. North Dakota: Glenullin; 4 mi. N Cannonball (209782 NM). South Dakota: Armour (54151 BS). Nebraska: Columbus. Kansas (Cockrum, 1952:122): Clay County; Marion County. Oklahoma (Blair, 1939:111): Ponca Agency; 1 mi. N and 7 mi. W Stillwater. Texas: Henrietta; Fort Belknap (V. Bailey, 1905:89); Mason; head Devils River (V. Bailey, 1905:89); Monahans; Colorado; Llano Estacado. New Mexico: Pecos; Koehler Junction. Colorado: Soda Springs; near Colorado Springs (Warren, 1942:136); Boulder (Cary, 1911:94); Livermore (ibid.). Wyoming: Pole Creek; Fort Fetterman; Sage Creek; Isha-wooa. Montana: 3 mi. NW Three Forks (Davis, 1937:24); 10 mi. NW Craig; Shelby Junction; Fort Assiniboine.

Cynomys mexicanus Merriam
Mexican Prairie Dog

1892. *Cynomys mexicanus* Merriam, Proc. Biol. Soc. Washington, 7:157, July 27, type from La Ventura, Coahuila.

External measurements: 390–430; 89–115; 59.0–68.5. Condylobasal length, 58.4–60.5. Upper parts as in *C. ludovicianus*, but less reddish and more grayish and vinaceous-buff; black hairs more numerous, giving a more grizzled effect; tail above like back in proximal half, black distally, the black extending proximally as a border; tail below as in *C. ludovicianus*, except for greater extent of black; underparts whitish. Selected characters in which the skull differs from that of *C. ludovicianus* are: auditory bullae more inflated; cheek-teeth triangular; nasals broad and usually posteriorly truncate; triangular plate of jugal especially well developed and greatly produced at downward point.

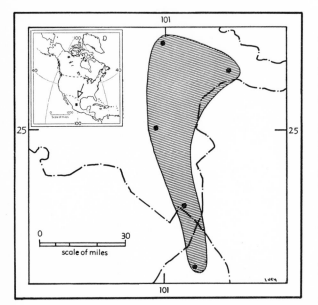

Map 237. *Cynomys mexicanus*.

The molt of this species is reported to be complex. Hollister (1916:22) thinks that "there are three complete renewals of the pelage . . . annually."

MARGINAL RECORDS.—Coahuila (Baker, 1956:203): Saltillo; 3 mi. N, 4 mi. W San Antonio de las Alzanas; type locality. San Luis Potosí: Vanegas (Miller and Kellogg, 1955:188). Coahuila: 3 mi. N Gómez Farías, 7000 ft.

Subgenus Leucocrossuromys Hollister

1916. *Leucocrossuromys* Hollister, N. Amer. Fauna, 40:23, June 20. Type, *Spermophilus gunnisoni* Baird.

Tail comparatively short, averaging less than ⅕ total length; tipped with white. Skull not so massive as in subgenus *Cynomys*; occipital region elliptical-ovoid from posterior aspect; jugal weak, thin, flat, its outer surface at angle of ascending ramus only slightly thickened, and margin rounded, not triangular; maxillary root of zygoma correspondingly weak, the shelf and suprajugal arm not markedly thickened. Cheek-teeth smaller, less expanded laterally than in *Cynomys*.

Cynomys leucurus Merriam
White-tailed Prairie Dog

1890. *Cynomys leucurus* Merriam, N. Amer. Fauna, 3:59, September 11, type from Fort Bridger, Uinta Co., Wyoming.
1898. *Cynomys lewisii*, J. A. Allen, Bull. Amer. Mus. Nat. Hist., 10:55, November 10. Not *Arctomys lewisii* Audubon and Bachman, 1854, a *Marmota* from the "shores of the Columbia River" (see Hollister, N. Amer. Fauna, 40:26, June 20, 1916).

External measurements: 340–370; 40–60; 60–65. Condylobasal length, 56.0–61.3. Upper parts pinkish buff mixed with black, which is heaviest on middorsal region and on rump; spots above eyes and cheeks brownish black; nose yellowish; upper side of tail proximally like rump but distal half white; underparts pale pinkish buff, slightly darker in axillary and inguinal regions. Skull large, robust; zygomatic arches widespread; postorbital processes robust and sharply decurved; tympanic bullae large and well inflated; cheek-teeth large, especially in transverse dimension.

This species occurs at higher elevations than *C. ludovicianus*, is less inclined to form large colonies, and hibernates.

MARGINAL RECORDS (Hollister, 1916:27, unless otherwise noted).—Montana: Clarks Fork; Sage Creek. Wyoming: Spring Creek; 17 mi. NNW Casper, 5650 ft. (14968 KU); Garrett; W of Cheyenne. Colorado: Canadian Creek; Crawford. Utah (Durrant, 1952:107): N side Colorado River, 4500 ft.; Ferron; Emma Park, head Price River,

Fig. 234. *Cynomys leucurus*, W side Green River, 1 mi. N Utah border, Sweetwater Co., Wyoming, No. 16802 K.U., ♂, X 1.

near Colton; 8 mi. E Sunnyside, 6700 ft.; Duchesne; 1½ mi. N Tridell, 6700 ft. Colorado: Escalante Hills. Utah (Durrant, 1952:107): Linwood; Uinta Mts.; eastern Morgan County. Wyoming: Fossil; 2 mi. N Big Piney, 6900 ft. (14965 KU); Dubois; Ishawooa.

Cynomys parvidens J. A. Allen
Utah Prairie Dog

1905. *Cynomys parvidens* J. A. Allen, Mus. Brooklyn Inst. Arts and Sci., Sci. Bull., 1:119, March 31, type from Buckskin Valley, Iron Co., Utah.

External measurements: 305–360; 30–57; 55–61. Condylobasal length of skull, 53.0–57.9. Upper parts cinnamon or clay color with mixture of buff and black-tipped hairs, usually slightly darker on rump; chin, sides of nose, and lips buffy white; upper side of tail proximally like rump, distal half white; underparts Cinnamon-Buff, grading to Cinnamon on pectoral and inguinal regions. Skull angular and robust; interorbital region broad; postorbital processes not abruptly projecting.

So far as known, this species represents the isolated western outpost of the genus. *C. parvidens* is clearly a member of the white-tailed group and is thought by some mammalogists to be a subspecies of *C. leucurus*. It is here retained as a separate species since intergradation has never been demonstrated and it is distinguished by trenchant morphological characters (see Kelson, 1951:23–25).

MARGINAL RECORDS (Durrant, 1952:109, unless otherwise noted).—Utah: Ivie Farm, Salina; Coal Mine Flat, 20 mi. E Salina, 4875 ft.; Widtsoe (249294 BS); U. S. Highway 89, ¼ mi. N Garfield-Kane County line; Pine Valley; head Buckthorn Flat, 1 mi. S Beaver–Iron County line, 6000 ft.; W of Cedar City.

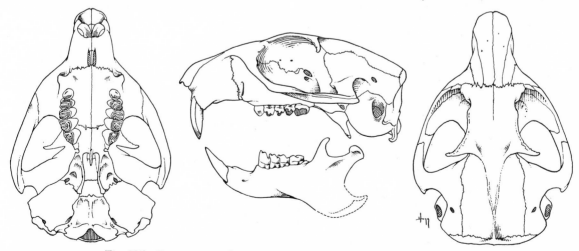

Fig. 235. *Cynomys parvidens*, 1 mi. W Cedar City, 5800 ft., Iron Co., Utah, No. 15962 K.U., ♂, X 1.

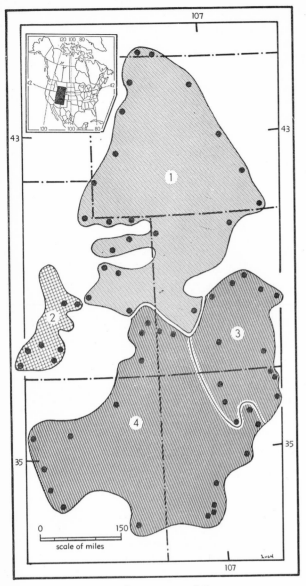

Map 238. Three species of *Cynomys*.

1. *Cynomys leucurus*   3. *Cynomys gunnisoni gunnisoni*
2. *Cynomys parvidens*   4. *Cynomys gunnisoni zuniensis*

Cynomys gunnisoni
Gunnison's Prairie Dog

External measurements: 309–373; 39–68; 52.0–62.5. Condylobasal length of skull, 51.9–57.8. Upper parts approximately Cinnamon-Buff, darkest in mid-dorsal region and rump, lightly to moderately overlaid with black hairs; upper side of tail proximally like rump, distally mixed gray and white, bordered and tipped with white; underparts near Pale Cinnamon, often somewhat buffy. Skull differs from that of *C. leucurus* and *C. parvidens* in certain selected characters as follows: maxillary arm of zygomatic arch more broadly spreading; mastoids smaller and more obliquely placed; audital bullae smaller.

The breeding season is April and May. There are 3 to 6 young (mean, 4.8).

Cynomys gunnisoni gunnisoni (Baird)

1855. *Spermophilus gunnisoni* Baird, Proc. Acad. Nat. Sci. Philadelphia, 7:334, April, type from Cochetopa Pass, Saguache Co., Colorado.
1858. *Cynomys gunnisonii*, Baird, Mammals, *in* Repts. Expl. Surv. . . . , 8(1):xxxix, July 14.

MARGINAL RECORDS (Hollister, 1916:31, unless otherwise noted).—Colorado: Tarryall Creek; Divide; NW of Colorado City; Fort Garland. New Mexico: Costilla Pass; 16 mi. SW Cimmaron, 9500–10,500 ft. (Hill, 1942:79); Coyote Creek; Jemez Mts.; Gallinas Mts.; La Jara Lake. Colorado: Wagon Wheel Gap (Warren, 1942:140); near Crested Butte (Cary, 1911:95); Leadville (*ibid.*).

Cynomys gunnisoni zuniensis Hollister

1916. C[ynomys]. g[unnisoni]. *zuniensis* Hollister, N. Amer. Fauna, 40:29, June 20, type from Wingate, McKinley Co., New Mexico.

MARGINAL RECORDS (Hollister, 1916:34, unless otherwise noted).—Utah: 25 mi. SE Moab (249293 BS). Colorado: Bedrock; Coventry. New Mexico: Espanola; Pecos; Manzano Mts.; Magdalena; Ojo Caliente; Fairview; Chloride (210358 BS). Arizona: 9-mile Spring, Ash Flat (222894 BS); Agua Fria Valley; 6 mi. S Yarnell, Peeples Valley (Hatfield, 1942:150); Simmons (209452 BS); Aubrey Valley; Kendrick Park; Tonalea (251045 BS). Utah (Durrant, 1952:110): 2 mi. S Blanding, Galbraith Ranch; Hewit Ranch, East Canyon.

Genus **Sciurus** Linnaeus—Tree Squirrels

Mexican and Central American species revised by Nelson, Proc. Washington Acad. Sci., 1:15–106, May 9, 1899.

1758. *Sciurus* Linnaeus, Syst. nat., ed. 10, 1:63. Type, *Sciurus vulgaris* Linnaeus.

Braincase strongly depressed posteriorly and without prominent ridges; palate broad, almost square posteriorly and terminating immediately behind tooth-rows; infraorbital foramen always forming canal; masseteric tubercle weak; M1 and M2 with 4 transverse crests, the 2nd and 3rd being most prominent and terminating in well-marked cusps; M3 with 1 prominent transverse crest; P3 present or absent and, when present, usually vestigial; size moderate; tail always bushy; ears prominent and sometimes tufted.

It is not yet possible to construct a satisfactory key to separate the species of *Sciurus* occurring in Central America and México; the present key includes only those species occurring north of México.

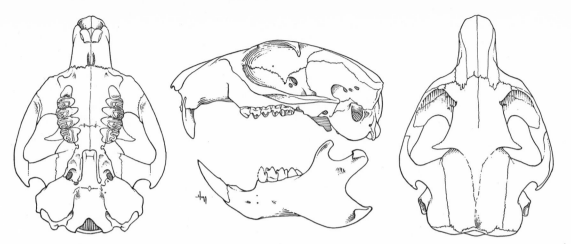

Fig. 236. *Cynomys gunnisoni gunnisoni*, 8 mi. N El Rito, Rio Arriba Co., New Mexico, No. 6236 K.U., ♀, X 1.

KEY TO SPECIES OF SCIURUS OCCURRING
NORTH OF MÉXICO

1. Premolars $\frac{1}{1}$.
    2. Occurring in eastern half of United States. . . . . *S. niger*, p. 386
    2′. Occurring in western half of United States.
        3. Underparts white. . *S. arizonensis*, p. 393
        3′. Underparts not white.
            4. Occurring in Chiricahua Mts., Arizona. . . . *S. chiricahuae*, p. 392
            4′. Not occurring in Chiricahua Mts., Arizona. . . . . *S. apache*, p. 392
1′. Premolars ordinarily $\frac{2}{1}$.
    5. P4 usually broader than long. *S. griseus*, p. 382
    5′. P4 usually not broader than long.
        6. Interorbital breadth usually more than postorbital constriction; ears tufted.
            7. Underparts white; tail dark above. . . . . . *S. aberti*, p. 384
            7′. Underparts dark; tail white above. . . . *S. kaibabensis*, p. 386
        6′. Interorbital breadth less than postorbital constriction; ears not tufted.
            S. carolinensis, p. 369

Subgenus **Neosciurus** Trouessart

1880. *Neosciurus* Trouessart, Le Naturaliste, 2:292, October. Type, *Sciurus carolinensis* Gmelin.
1880. *Echinosciurus* Trouessart, *ibid.* Type, *Sciurus hypopyrrhus* Wagler [= *Sciurus aureogaster* Cuvier].
1899. *Baiosciurus* Nelson, Proc. Washington Acad. Sci., 1:31, May 9. Type, *Sciurus deppei* Peters.

This possibly composite subgenus has never been carefully described nor morphologically delimited. Although inadequate, the remarks of A. H. Howell (1938:48–49) in this connection seem the most pertinent. He characterized the subgenus as fol-

lows: Skull relatively long, especially rostral part; braincase relatively shallow (as compared with subgenus *Sciurus*); postorbital processes relatively short and stout; premolars $\frac{2}{1}$; P4 subtriangular rather than quadrangular.

This subgenus contains the eastern gray squirrel and the large assemblage of Mexican and Central American squirrels, the taxonomic status and phylogenetic affinities of which are poorly known. The 13 nominal species probably belong to 6 or possibly 7 species at most. Much of the formerly forested parts of México where these squirrels occurred is now denuded of trees, and the natural geographic distribution of the animals is much altered by constriction and fragmentation. Intergrades between certain morphologically distinct populations probably no longer exist and it is likely that the systematic relationships of the mid-American squirrels can never be satisfactorily resolved except inferentially.

Sciurus carolinensis
Gray Squirrel

External measurements: 430–500; 210–240; 60–70. Weight, 400–710 grams. Upper parts normally grizzled dark to light gray, usually with buffy under-fur, buffy tone more pronounced on head, back, feet, and shoulders; underparts dark to light gray, usually with strong buffy suffusion; tail long, bushy, and of same general tone as body. Melanism and albinism, both partial and complete, are common in the species, and have led to much nomenclatural confusion. Cranial characters as for the subgenus.

The distribution of this gray squirrel is closely correlated with the distribution of the eastern hardwood trees, especially oak, hickory, and formerly chestnut. The nuts of these trees comprise the bulk of the diet. Food is stored but usually not in large caches; nuts, for example, are usually stored individually in holes and crevices. The species formerly displayed mass migrations of many thousands of individuals; migrations in modern times are mostly small and localized.

The gray squirrel is a highly aboreal animal. It is more secretive than the fox squirrel and is an excellent and much hunted game animal. The gray squirrel is usually found in heavily forested bottomland. Nests are usually in a hole in a tree, but leaf nests are not uncommon.

Mating takes place in mid-winter and the young —1-4, usually 2 or 3—are born after a gestation period of 44 days. A second litter is produced in late summer.

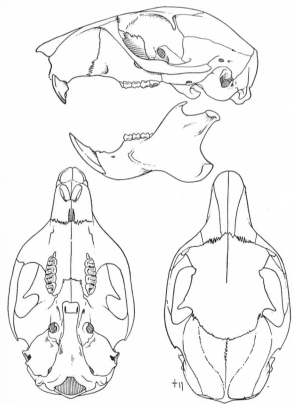

Fig. 237. *Sciurus carolinensis carolinensis*, 5 mi. NW Fall River, Greenwood Co., Kansas, No. 9637 K.U., ♂, X 1.

Sciurus carolinensis carolinensis Gmelin

1788. [*Sciurus*] *carolinensis* Gmelin, Syst. nat., ed. 13, 1:148. Type locality, Carolina.

MARGINAL RECORDS.—Indiana: Denver (Bangs, 1896:154). Ohio: Smoky Creek (Bole and Moulthrop, 1942:138). Kentucky: Carter Caves (Welter and Sollberger, 1939:80); Quicksand (Hamilton, 1930:310). Tennessee: Poor Valley Ridge, 1200 ft., 3 mi. NE Rutledge (Kellogg, 1939:273); Walden Ridge, near Soddy (*ibid.*). South Carolina: Richland (Penney, 1950:85). North Carolina: Statesville (Bangs, 1896:154). Virginia (Patton, 1939:76): Charlotte Court House; Suffolk; Eastville. Florida (Sherman, 1937:113–114): Micco; St. Petersburg. Alabama (A. H. Howell, 1921:64): Point Clear; Carlton. Louisiana (Lowery, 1943:239): Bogalusa; Holden; Magnolia Crossing, near Denham Springs; Lindsay; Tunica; Lotus; Anacoco. Texas (V. Bailey, 1905:78): mouth of Colorado River; Cuervo; Austin; Brazos. Oklahoma: Dougherty (36157/48501 BS); Mohawk Park (Blair, 1939:112). Kansas: Cedar Vale (Cockrum, 1952:113); 1 mi. SW Hamilton (*ibid.*); Osborne (Black, 1937:179). Nebraska: mouth of Platte River (Jones, 1954:482). Illinois: Union County (Necker and Hatfield, 1941:50). Indiana (Lyon, 1936:203, unless otherwise noted): *Sullivan County; Vigo County; Parke County; Montgomery County*; Tippecanoe County (Kirkpatrick and Conaway, 1948:133); *Carroll County; Cass County.*

Sciurus carolinensis extimus Bangs

1896. *Sciurus carolinensis extimus* Bangs, Proc. Biol. Soc. Washington, 10:158, December 28, type from Miami, Dade Co., Florida.

MARGINAL RECORDS.—Florida: Eau Gallie (Sherman, 1937:114); type locality.

Sciurus carolinensis fuliginosus Bachman

1839. *Sciurus fuliginosus* Bachman, Proc. Zool. Soc. London, 1838, p. 97, February 7, type from near New Orleans, Louisiana.
1895. *Sciurus carolinensis fuliginosus*, Bangs, Proc. Boston Soc. Nat. Hist., 26:543, July 31.

MARGINAL RECORDS (Lowery, 1943:239, unless otherwise noted).—Louisiana: Jonesville; Port Allen; Ponchatoula. Alabama (A. H. Howell, 1921:64): Stiggins Lake, 3 mi. E Mt. Vernon; Chuckvee Bay; Bayou Labatre. Louisiana: Egan.

Sciurus carolinensis hypophaeus Merriam

1886. *Sciurus carolinensis hypophaeus* Merriam, Science, 7:351, April 16, type from Elk River, Sherburne Co., Minnesota.

MARGINAL RECORDS.—Manitoba: East Selkirk (Anderson, 1947:122); Lake Jessie, Winnipeg River (Soper, 1946:142). Minnesota (Swanson, 1945:79–80): Williams; Duluth; Anoka County; 2 mi. N Sartell; Grant County. North Dakota: Fargo (V. Bailey, 1927:45); 1 mi. N Kathryn (Hibbard, 1957:530); 2 mi. S Bismarck (*ibid.*); 4 mi. SW Velva (*ibid.*). Manitoba: a few mi. N Treesbank (Soper, 1946:142); Portage la Prairie (Anderson, 1947:112).

Map 239. *Sciurus carolinensis.*

1. S. c. carolinensis   3. S. c. fuliginosus   5. S. c. matecumbei
2. S. c. extimus   4. S. c. hypophaeus   6. S. c. pennsylvanicus

Sciurus carolinensis matecumbei H. H. Bailey

1937. *Sciurus carolinensis minutus* H. H. Bailey, Bailey Mus.
Libr. Nat. Hist., Bull. 12 [p. 4], January 15, type from
Key Largo, Monroe Co., Florida. Not *Sciurus minutus*
du Chaillu, 1861. Known only from the type locality.
1937. *Sciurus carolinensis matecumbei* H. H. Bailey, Jour.
Mamm., 18:516, November 22, a renaming of *Sciurus
carolinensis minutus* H. H. Bailey.

Sciurus carolinensis pennsylvanicus Ord

1815. *Sciurus Pennsylvanica* Ord, *in* Guthrie, A new geogr.,
hist., coml. grammar . . . , Philadelphia, Amer. ed. 2,
2:292. Type locality, Pennsylvania W of the Allegany
Ridge.
1894. *Sciurus carolinensis pennsylvanicus*, Rhoads, Appendix
of reprint of Ord (*supra*), p. 19.
1815. *Sciurus hiemalis* Ord, *in* Guthrie, A new geogr., hist.,

coml. grammar . . . , Philadelphia, Amer. ed. 2, 2:292. Type locality, near Tuckerton, near Little Egg Harbor, New Jersey.

1830. *Sciurus leucotis* Gapper, Zool. Jour., 5:206, type from region between York (Toronto) and Lake Simcoe, Ontario.

1849. *Sciurus migratorius* Audubon and Bachman, The viviparous quadrupeds of North America, 1:265. Based on *S. leucotis* Gapper, 1830.

MARGINAL RECORDS.—Ontario: Ottawa (Rand, 1945c:124). Quebec: area of Montreal (Cameron, 1953:64). New Hampshire: Chocorua, 13 mi. N Ossipee Center (8559 KU). Maine: Mount Desert Island (Manville, 1942:395). New Jersey: Wading River (Connor, 1953:232). Virginia: Hampstead (Patton, 1939:76); Amelia County (Handley and Patton, 1947:152); Blacksburg (Patton, 1939:76). Tennessee (Kellogg, 1939:273): Sheeds Creek, 12 mi. W Copperhill, 1600 ft.; 4 mi. NE Shady Valley, 3800 ft. Virginia: head Moccasin Creek (Hooper and Cady, 1941:324). West Virginia: 4 mi. E Huntington (Kellogg, 1937:461); Jacksons Mill (Barbour, 1951:370); Clinton (*ibid.*). Ohio (Bole and Moulthrop, 1942:139): North Chagrin Metropolitan Park; Mud Creek. Indiana: Marshall County (Lyon, 1936:203). Illinois (Necker and Hatfield, 1941:50): Newton; Peoria. Iowa (Stoner, 1918:25): Muscatine; Des Moines; Clay County. Minnesota (Swanson, 1945:80): *McLeod County*; near St. Cloud. Wisconsin: Prescott (Cory, 1912:122). Ontario: Mount Forest (Bangs, 1896:156).

Sciurus aureogaster
Red-bellied Squirrel

Reviewed by Kelson, Univ. Kansas Publ., Mus. Nat. Hist., 5:243–250, April 10, 1952.

External measurements: 470–573; 235–276; 63–70. Normal color of upper parts light to dark grizzled gray; patches of bright ferruginous to dark brown variable in extent either on nuchal- and rump-region or only on shoulder region; underparts ochraceous to dark brown or of various shades of gray depending on subspecies; tail usually bushy with basal ring colored like back; remainder of upper side of tail blackish grizzled with white; underside of tail same as upper side but with ferruginous median stripe. Melanism and phaeanism, partial or complete, common, especially southwardly.

The species occupies a wide variety of habitats from the humid lowland jungles to open, pine-clad forests at high altitudes. Food is varied according to the habitat. Known foods include principally fruits such as mangos, green figs, jubo plums, tamarind pods, chico zapote, and maize. Individuals of this species are highly arboreal and seldom descend to the ground except to seek food.

A female with 2 nearly term fetuses was taken on March 3, 8 km. N of Potrero, Veracruz, in the Lower Tropical Life-zone. A male obtained 7 km. NW of Potrero on January 9 had enlarged testes.

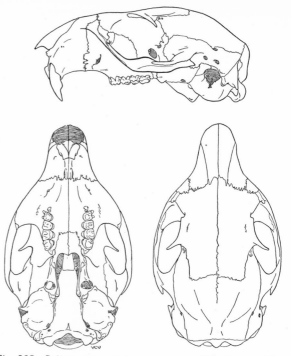

Fig. 238. *Sciurus aureogaster aureogaster*, Río Atoyac, 8 km. NW Potrero, Veracruz, No. 17910 K.U., ♂, X 1.

Sciurus aureogaster aureogaster Cuvier

1829. [*Sciurus?*] *aureogaster* Cuvier, *in* Geoffroy St.-Hilaire, and F. Cuvier, Hist. Nat. Mamm., 6, livr. 59, pl. with text, September (binomial published only at end of work, table générale et méthodique, 7:4, 1842), type from "California"; restricted to Altamira, Tamaulipas, by Nelson (Proc. Washington Acad. Sci., 1:38, May 9, 1899).

1830. *Sciurus rafiventer* Lichtenstein, Abh. k. Akad. Wiss., Berlin, p. 116 (1827). Based on a red-bellied, North American *Sciurus*.

1831. *Sciurus leucogaster* F. Cuvier, supplément à l'histoire naturelle générale et particulière de Buffon, 1:300.

1831. *Sciurus hypopyrrhus* Wagler, Oken's Isis, p. 510, type from "Mexico"; restricted to Minatitlán, Veracruz, by Nelson (*op. cit.*:42).

1841. *Sciurus mustelinus* Audubon and Bachman, Proc. Acad. Nat. Sci. Philadelphia, p. 100. Based on a melanistic individual "received from California."

1841. *Sciurus ferruginiventris* Audubon and Bachman, Proc. Acad. Nat. Sci. Philadelphia, p. 101. Allegedly from California.

1845. *Sciurus ferrugineiventris* Schinz, Synopsis mammalium, 2:14, a variant spelling of *ferruginiventris*.

1855. *Sciurus hypoxanthus* (Lichtenstein MS) Geoffroy, Voyage de la Vénus, Zool. (text), p. 158 (on labels of squirrels from Berlin Museum, *fide* Nelson, *op. cit.*:38).

1855. *Sciurus chrysogaster* Giebel, Säugethiere, p. 650, an etymological substitute for *aureogaster*.

1867. *Sciurus hypopyrrhous* Gray, Ann. Mag. Nat. Hist., ser. 3, 20:424, a variant spelling of *hypopyrrhus*.

1867. *Macroxus morio* Gray, Ann. Mag. Nat. Hist., ser. 3, 2:424. Type locality unknown.

1887. *Sciurus rufiventris* ? Rovirosa, La Naturaleza, 7:360 (1885–1886).

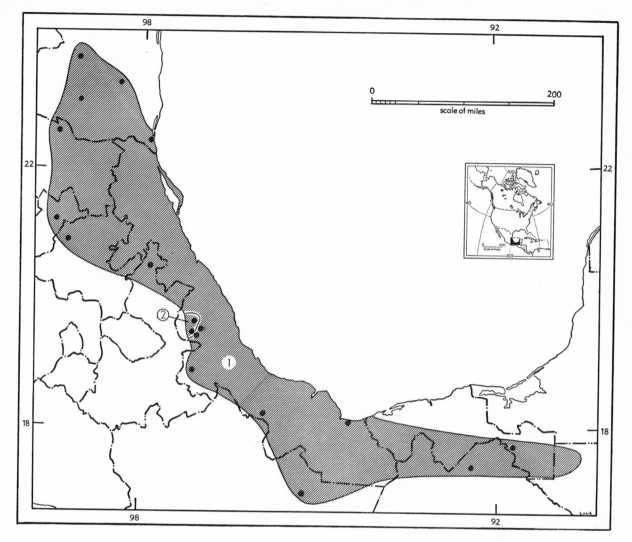

Map 240. *Sciurus aureogaster.* (1) *S. aureogaster aureogaster;* (2) *S. aureogaster frumentor.*

MARGINAL RECORDS (Kelson, 1952:249, unless otherwise noted).—Tamaulipas: Victoria; Santa María (Goodwin, 1954:8); type locality, thence down coast to Veracruz: Coatzocoalcos. Tabasco: Monte Cristo. Guatemala: *extreme NW Petén* (Handley, 1950:151). Chiapas: *Laguna Ocotal* (Burnett and Lyman, 1957:293); Tumbalá. Oaxaca: mountains near Santo Domingo. Veracruz: Otatitlán; Orizaba; Jico; Jalapa; Puebla; Metlaltoyuca. Hidalgo: Sierra Encarnación. Querétaro: Pinal de Amoles. San Luis Potosí: Cuesta de los Cedros (Dalquest, 1953b:84). Tamaulipas: Goméz Farías (Goodwin, 1954:8).

Sciurus aureogaster frumentor Nelson

1898. *Sciurus aureogaster frumentor* Nelson, Proc. Biol. Soc. Washington, 12:154, June 3, type from Las Vigas, Veracruz.

MARGINAL RECORDS (Kelson, 1952–249).—Veracruz: type locality; Jico.

Sciurus poliopus
Mexican Gray Squirrel

External measurements: 490–530; 230–250; 67–72. Upper parts light to dark grizzled gray with yellowish to rusty suffusion; nape and rump patches usually present and varying from tawny to brown; underparts varying from rich ferruginous to yellowish white, but usually gray with ochraceous suffusion; tail above blackish with white wash, below of various shades of gray with median rusty to tawny stripe.

Mexican gray squirrels live in hardwood- and especially pine-forests, eat acorns, pine nuts, and, probably other plant foods, are shy, and usually seek safety in flight rather than concealment.

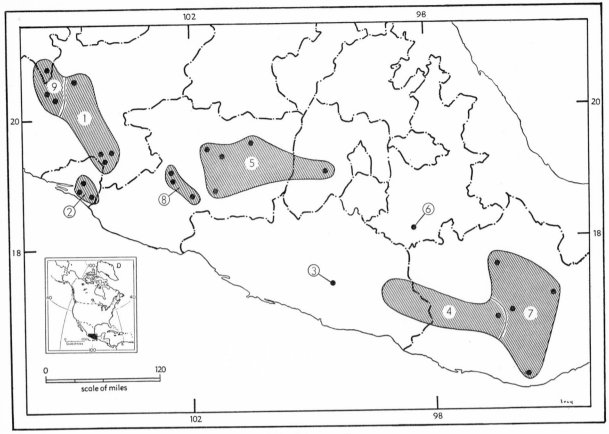

Map 241. *Sciurus poliopus.*

1. S. *p. cervicalis*	4. S. *p. hernandezi*	7. S. *p. poliopus*
2. S. *p. colimensis*	5. S. *p. nemoralis*	8. S. *p. senex*
3. S. *p. effugius*	6. S. *p. perigrinator*	9. S. *p. tepicanus*

Sciurus poliopus cervicalis J. A. Allen

1890. *Sciurus cervicalis* J. A. Allen, Bull. Amer. Mus. Nat. Hist., 3:183, December 10, type from Hda. San Marcos, Tonila, Jalisco.
1899. *Sciurus poliopus cervicalis,* Nelson, Proc. Washington Acad. Sci., 1:51, May 9.

MARGINAL RECORDS (J. A. Allen, 1906:243, unless otherwise noted).—Jalisco: Ameca (Nelson, 1899b:52); Tuxpan; type locality; Las Canoas.

Sciurus poliopus colimensis Nelson

1898. *Sciurus albipes colimensis* Nelson, Proc. Biol. Soc. Washington, 12:152, June 3, type from Hacienda Magdalena, Colima.
1899. *Sciurus poliopus colimensis* Nelson, Proc. Washington Acad. Sci., 1:52, May 9.

MARGINAL RECORDS (Nelson, 1899b:54).—Colima: type locality; Armería, Río Coahu[a]yana.

Sciurus poliopus effugius Nelson

1898. *Sciurus albipes effugius* Nelson, Proc. Biol. Soc. Washington, 12:152, June 3, type from high mountains

[15 mi.] west of Chilpancingo, Guerrero. Known only from the type locality.
1899. *Sciurus poliopus effugius* Nelson, Proc. Washington Acad. Sci., 1:54, May 9.

Sciurus poliopus hernandezi Nelson

1898. *Sciurus albipes quercinus* Nelson, Proc. Biol. Soc. Washington, 12:150, June 3, type from mountains 15 mi. W of Oaxaca, Oaxaca. Not *Sciurus quercinus* Erxleben, 1777.
1898. [*Sciurus albipes*] *hernandezi* Nelson, Science, n.s., 8:783, December 2, a renaming of *Sciurus albipes quercinus* Nelson.
1899. *Sciurus poliopus hernandezi* Nelson, Proc. Washington Acad. Sci., 1:48, May 9.

MARGINAL RECORDS (Nelson, 1899b:49).—Guerrero: southeastern Guerrero; type locality.

Sciurus poliopus nemoralis Nelson

1898. *Sciurus albipes nemoralis* Nelson, Proc. Biol. Soc. Washington, 12:151, June 3, type from Pátzcuaro, Michoacán.
1899. *Sciurus poliopus nemoralis* Nelson, Proc. Washington Acad. Sci., 1:50, May 9.

MARGINAL RECORDS (Hall and Villa, 1949:450, unless otherwise noted).—Michoacán: 20 mi. E Morelia, 7300 ft. México: N slope Volcán Toluca (Nelson, 1899b:51). Michoacán: 1½ km. N San Juan, 2250 m.; Nahuatzen; type locality.

Sciurus poliopus perigrinator Nelson

1904. *Sciurus poliopus perigrinator* Nelson, Proc. Biol. Soc. Washington, 17:149, October 6, type from Piaxtla, Puebla. Known only from the type locality.

Sciurus poliopus poliopus Fitzinger

1867. [*Sciurus variegatus*] *poliopus* Fitzinger, Sitzungsber. k. Akad. Wiss., Wien, 55:478, March. Based on *Sciurus varius* var. β Wagner, 1843. Type locality by subsequent designation, Cerro San Felipe, Oaxaca.
1899. *Sciurus poliopus*, Nelson, Proc. Washington Acad. Sci., 1:46, May 9.
1837. *Sciurus albipes* Wagner, Abh. math.-phys., 101, bayerisch. Akad. Wiss. München, 2:501. Not *Sciurus albipes*, Kerr, 1792.
1843. *Sciurus varius* Wagner, *in* Schreber, Die Säugthiere . . . , Suppl., 3:168. Not *Sciurus varius* Pallas, 1831.
1867. *Sciurus variegatus rufipes* Fitzinger, Sitzungsber. k. Akad. Wiss., Wien, 55:478, March. Based on *S. varius* var. γ Wagner, 1843.
1867. *Macroxus leucops* Gray, Ann. Mag. Nat. Hist., ser. 3, 20:427, December, type from Oaxaca, México.
1898. *Sciurus wagneri* J. A. Allen, Bull. Amer. Mus. Nat. Hist., 10:453, November 10, a renaming of *Sciurus albipes* Wagner and *S. varius* Wagner.

MARGINAL RECORDS (Nelson, 1899b:48).—Oaxaca: [Pápalo Santos] Reyes; Mt. Zempoaltepec; Pluma [Hidalgo]; type locality.

Sciurus poliopus senex Nelson

1904. *Sciurus poliopus senex* Nelson, Proc. Biol. Soc. Washington, 17:148, October 6, type from La Salada, 40 mi. S of Uruapan, Michoacán.

MARGINAL RECORDS (Hall and Villa, 1949:451).—Michoacán: Tancítaro, 6000 ft.; type locality; Apatzingán, 1040 ft.

Sciurus poliopus tepicanus J. A. Allen

1906. *Sciurus poliopus tepicanus* J. A. Allen, Bull. Amer. Mus. Nat. Hist., 22:243, July 25, type from Rancho Palo Amarillo, near Amatlán de Cañas, Nayarit.

MARGINAL RECORDS (J. A. Allen, 1906:244).—Nayarit: type locality. Jalisco: La Laja; Wakenakili Mts. [= Sierra de Tapalpa]. Other record-stations of occurrence reported by Allen (*loc. cit.*) can not be located precisely, but are in the immediate vicinity of the type locality.

Sciurus nelsoni
Nelson's Squirrel

External measurements: 510–525; 250–260; 65–72. Upper parts grizzled sooty-grayish or blackish brown with pale yellowish or buffy suffusion; tip of head, ears, legs, and feet variously grayish, brown-

ish, or blackish; underparts varying from grayish to blackish-brown with rusty wash; tail above blackish with wash of white, below yellowish gray usually with tawny to ferruginous median stripe and white margin. Color highly variable geographically and individually.

Nelson's squirrels live in forests at high elevations and many populations are isolated from others.

Sciurus nelsoni hirtus Nelson

1898. *Sciurus nelsoni hirtus* Nelson, Proc. Biol. Soc. Washington, 12:153, June 3, type from Tochimilco, Puebla.

MARGINAL RECORDS.—México: 5 km. W Río Frío, 10,000 ft. (19325 KU); Monte Río Frío, 45–55 km. ESE Mexico City, 10,500 ft. (Davis, 1944:384); Volcán Iztaccíhuatl (Nelson, 1898:153); N slope Mt. Popocatepetl, 10,000–13,500 ft. (Davis, 1944:384). Puebla: type locality. Morelos: Tetela de Volcán (Davis and Russell, 1954:72).

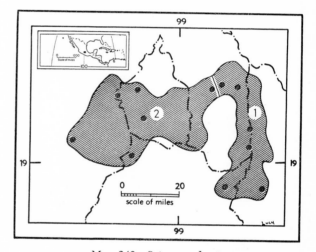

Map 242. *Sciurus nelsoni.*

1. *S. nelsoni hirtus*   2. *S. nelsoni nelsoni*

Sciurus nelsoni nelsoni Merriam

1893. *Sciurus nelsoni* Merriam, Proc. Biol. Soc. Washington, 8:144, December 29, type from Huitzilac, Morelos.

MARGINAL RECORDS (Nelson, 1899b:56, unless otherwise noted).—Distrito Federal: Cruz de Coloxtitla, 3600 m. (Hooper, 1947:44); Ajusco. México: Rancho Córdoba (Hooper, 1947:44). Morelos: type locality. México: Tenango del Valle; Salazar.

Sciurus colliaei
Collie's Squirrel

External measurements: 498–542; 264–272; 65–71. Upper parts yellowish gray coarsely grizzled and heavily overlaid with black; sides paler than back; nape, shoulders, legs, and ears variable, but usually either dark gray or of some shade approximating rufous; underparts white; base of tail like back; remainder black above with wash of white, below grizzled grayish or blackish yellow edged with white.

Collie's squirrels live on the lowlands along the west coast of México, seldom above 2500 feet, and are reported to eat a variety of fruits.

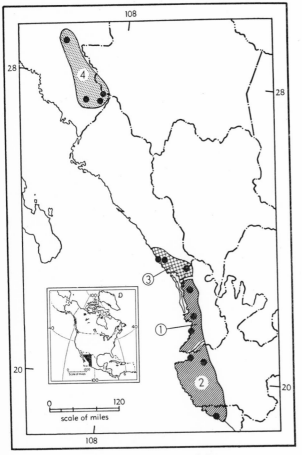

Map 243. Three species of *Sciurus*.

1. S. *colliaei colliaei*   3. S. *sinaloensis*
2. S. *colliaei nuchalis*   4. S. *truei*

Sciurus colliaei colliaei Richardson

1839. *Sciurus colliaei* Richardson, *in* Beechey, The zoology of Capt. Beechey's voyage . . . , p. 8, type from San Blas, Nayarit. (*Sciurus colliaei* Bachman, 1838, is a *nomen nudum*.)

MARGINAL RECORDS.—Nayarit: Acaponeta (Nelson, 1899b:59); Santiago (*ibid.*); 5 mi. S Las Varas, 150 ft. (39767 KU).

Sciurus colliaei nuchalis Nelson

1899. *Sciurus colliaei nuchalis* Nelson, Proc. Washington Acad. Sci., 1:59, May 9, type from Manzanillo, Colima.

MARGINAL RECORDS (Nelson, 1899b:60).—Jalisco: Ixtapa; Mascota. Colima: type locality.

Sciurus sinaloensis Nelson
Sinaloan Squirrel

1899. *Sciurus sinaloensis* Nelson, Proc. Washington Acad. Sci., 1:60, May 9, type from Mazatlán, Sinaloa.

External measurements: 524; 255; 62. Upper parts pale reddish yellow mixed with black; neck, shoulders, flanks, legs, and feet grayish to whitish; underparts white or nearly so; tail above grizzled yellowish brown with white wash, below similar with white edge.

This nominal species belongs in a group with S. *colliaei* and S. *truei*; S. *sinaloensis* probably is but a subspecies of S. *colliaei*, differs from S. *colliaei* in pale yellowish or reddish (instead of blackish) back, like S. *colliaei* lives in the lowlands and its geographic range is continuous with that of S. *colliaei colliaei*.

MARGINAL RECORDS (Nelson, 1899b:61).—Sinaloa: type locality; Tatemales; Plomosas.

Sciurus truei Nelson
Sonoran Squirrel

1899. *Sciurus truei* Nelson, Proc. Washington Acad. Sci., 1:61, May 9, type from Camoa, Río Mayo, Sonora.

External measurements: 487; 247; 67. Upper parts of head and body dark yellowish grizzled with black; outside of legs and feet dark gray; underparts white; basal tail-ring above like back but washed with pale yellow below; remainder of tail above grizzled black and buff with wash of white, below dark yellowish grizzled with black and narrowly edged with white.

Although belonging to the *colliaei* group, this nominal species differs from *colliaei* in: generally broader, heavier, more flattened skull; especially broad jugals; larger tympanic bullae; and more or less uniform dark yellowish color above. Unlike *colliaei*, *truei* occurs inland and usually at higher elevations. It inhabits riparian and sylvan situations.

MARGINAL RECORDS (Burt, 1938:38).—Sonora: San Javier; Baromico; Guirocoba; Chinobampo.

Sciurus socialis
Sociable Squirrel

External measurements: 418–525; 256–272; *ca.* 67. Upper parts dingy whitish gray over ground color of yellowish to rusty; patch (sometimes present) on nape tawny to rich rufous; rump patch obsolete but sometimes well-marked by various tones of ochraceous to rufous; base of tail like rump, distally black heavily washed with white above and varying from pale fulvous gray to rich, dark rusty with a white edge below; head, sides, flanks, legs, and feet variable but of varying shades of gray in most specimens; underparts varying from almost white to dark rusty. Melanism is common but usually is incomplete. Skull closely resembles that of S. *aureogaster*.

As now understood, S. *socialis* is confined to the lowlands of the Pacific slope of the Isthmus of Tehuantepec, whereas S. *aureogaster* occupies the Atlantic slope. Further study probably will disclose that S. *socialis*, S. *aureogaster*, S. *yucatanensis*, and S. *griseoflavus* belong to one species-group or even one species. The southern "species" have relatively thin, coarse, and harsh pelage.

Squirrels of the species *Sciurus socialis* were so named because they were reported to occur in groups. Many species of tree squirrels occur in groups in the breeding season. S. *socialis* lives in lowland scrub forests and occasionally raids fields of ripening corn and coconut groves.

Sciurus socialis cocos Nelson

1898. *Sciurus socialis cocos* Nelson, Proc. Biol. Soc. Washington, 12:155, June 3, type from Acapulco, Guerrero.

MARGINAL RECORDS.—Guerrero: Río Aguacatello, 30 km. N Acapulco, 1000 ft. (Davis, 1944:384). Oaxaca: Jamiltepec (Nelson, 1899b:67). Guerrero: type locality.

Sciurus socialis littoralis Nelson

1907. *Sciurus socialis littoralis* Nelson, Proc. Biol. Soc. Washington, 20:87, December 11, type from Puerto Angel, Oaxaca. Known only from the type locality.

Sciurus socialis socialis Wagner

1837. *Sciurus socialis* Wagner, Abh. math.-phys., 101, bayerisch. Akad. Wiss. München, 2:504, type from near Tehuantepec, Oaxaca.

MARGINAL RECORDS (Nelson, 1899b:65, unless otherwise noted).—Chiapas: Tuxtla. Guatemala: Nenton (Handley, 1950:151). Chiapas: Calera; Tonalá. Oaxaca: Colotepec; Santa Efigenia.

Sciurus griseoflavus
Guatemalan Gray Squirrel

External measurements: 500–550; 250–270; *ca.* 68. Upper parts grizzled yellowish-brown or distinctly grayish, usually thinly washed with white; tail, above black washed with white, and below with median stripe of grizzled yellowish to rusty brown

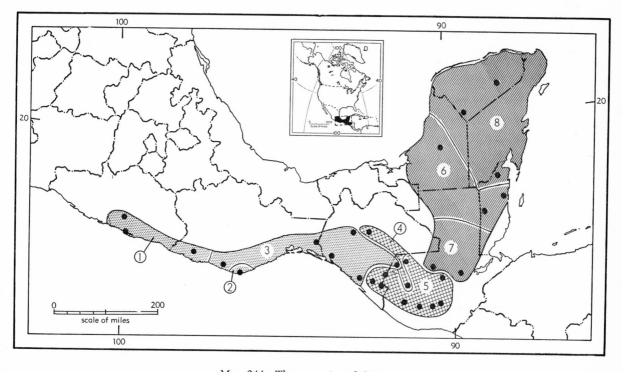

Map 244. Three species of *Sciurus*.

1. S. *socialis cocos*
2. S. *socialis littoralis*
3. S. *socialis socialis*

4. S. *griseoflavus chiapensis*
5. S. *griseoflavus griseoflavus*

6. S. *yucatanensis baliolus*
7. S. *yucatanensis phaeopus*
8. S. *yucatanensis yucatanensis*

with white edge; underparts bright or dark, dull rufous to grayish white with ochraceous suffusion. Color in this species varies greatly seasonally, individually, and geographically. Certain of the differences in color are genetic and others result from wear. In "average" pelage S. *griseoflavus* is distinguishable by heavy body, and the combination of grizzled yellowish-brown back with reddish brown venter, and lack of patches on nape and rump.

The coloration of squirrels from the western highlands of Guatemala strongly suggests intergradation between S. *socialis* and S. *griseoflavus*, but we have not seen sufficient material to warrant placing S. *griseoflavus* as a subspecies of S. *socialis*.

S. *griseoflavus* is a highland species and occurs principally in pine and oak forests. Because of its large size, delectable meat, and extreme wariness, this squirrel is a highly esteemed game animal.

Sciurus griseoflavus chiapensis Nelson

1899. *Sciurus griseoflavus chiapensis* Nelson, Proc. Washington Acad. Sci., 1:69, May 9, type from San Cristóbal, Chiapas.

MARGINAL RECORDS.—Chiapas: type locality. Guatemala: Cerro Calel (Handley, 1950:152).

Sciurus griseoflavus griseoflavus (Gray)

1867. *Macroxus griseoflavus* Gray, Ann. Mag. Nat. Hist., ser. 3, 20:427, December, type from Guatemala; restricted to Dueñas by Nelson, Proc. Washington Acad. Sci., 1:67, May 9, 1899.
1878. *Sciurus griseoflavus*, Alston, Proc. Zool. Soc. London, p. 660, September.

MARGINAL RECORDS.—Guatemala (Goodwin, 1934:26, unless otherwise noted): San Mateo; La Primavera; vicinity of Guatemala City (Nelson, 1899b:69); Antigua; San Lucas; Volcán Santa María (Nelson, 1899:69). Chiapas: Pinabete (*ibid.*); Finca Juárez, 1200 m. (Hooper, 1947:45); Volcán de Tacaná, 2600–3800 m. (*ibid.*).

Sciurus yucatanensis
Yucatán Squirrel

External measurements: 450–500; 220–255; 55–65. Upper parts grizzled black and gray with suffusion of yellow to ochraceous buff; underparts varying from dirty white through a grizzled yellowish-gray to black; tail above black with wash of white, below with median stripe of dull gray fulvous or black and gray bordered with black and edged with white; ear tufts (sometimes present) dingy white; pelage thin, coarse, and stiff. Skull averages smaller (basal length *ca.* 45) than neighboring species.

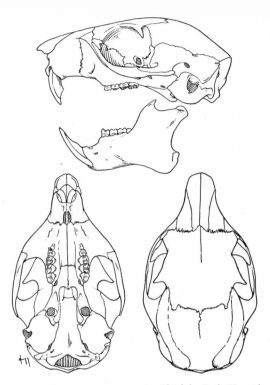

Fig. 239. *Sciurus yucatanensis*, Chichén Itzá, Yucatán, No. 108179 U.S.N.M., ♂, X 1.

Sciurus yucatanensis baliolus Nelson

1901. *Sciurus yucatanensis baliolus* Nelson, Proc. Biol. Soc. Washington, 14:131, August 9, type from Apazote, Campeche.

MARGINAL RECORDS.—Campeche: type locality. British Honduras (A. Murie, 1935:24): Belize; El Cayó. Guatemala: *Petén* (Handley, 1950:152).

Sciurus yucatanensis phaeopus Goodwin

1932. *Sciurus yucatanensis phaeopus* Goodwin, Amer. Mus. Novit., 574:1, October 22, type from Secanquim, 1600 ft., Alta Vera Paz, Guatemala.

MARGINAL RECORDS (Goodwin, 1934:27).—Guatemala: type locality; Finca Chama [1200 ft., 30 mi. NW Cobán].

Sciurus yucatanensis yucatanensis J. A. Allen

1877. [*Sciurus carolinensis*] var. *yucatanensis* J. A. Allen, *in* Coues and Allen, Monogr. N. Amer. Rodentia, p. 705, August, cotypes from Mérida, Yucatán.
1897. *Sciurus yucatanensis* J. A. Allen, Bull. Amer. Mus. Nat. Hist., 9:5, February 23.

MARGINAL RECORDS.—Yucatán: Chichén Itzá (108179 USNM). British Honduras: Orange Walk (Gaumer, 1917:101). Yucatán: San Anselmo (*ibid.*).

Sciurus variegatoides
Variegated Squirrel

C.G. Pritchard

×¼

Revised by Harris, Miscl. Publ. Mus. Zool., Univ. Michigan, 38:7–39, September 4, 1937.

External measurements: 510–560; 245–280; 60–66. Weight, 450–520 grams. Upper parts highly variable, from blackish to grizzled yellowish gray; tail black above with heavy wash of white, sometimes appearing faintly annulated; tail below with median area of tawny to dark rufous, bordered with black and edged with white; underparts white to rich cinnamon-buff; when underparts not entirely white, white inguinal, axillary, and gular patches usually present; rump patch absent; dorsal patch on shoulder usually absent, and when present faintly expressed; pelage shiny, coarse, and bristly. S. variegatoides is distinguishable from S. griseoflavus, a neighboring, and perhaps overlapping, species, by: shorter, harsher pelage; richly rufescent, rather than obscure and pale, postauricular patches; and the color of the back that in rare specimens is never grizzled yellowish brown as in griseoflavus. S. variegatoides differs from the adjacent S. yucatanensis in: larger skull and lack of black postauricular patches. The white underparts or white patches thereon are sufficient to distinguish S. variegatoides from S. aureogaster.

This squirrel is one of the most conspicuous and abundant small mammals throughout its geographic range. It inhabits both humid lowland situations and dry woodlands on uplands. Its food consists of a variety of herbaceous materials such as fruits, nuts, and tender shoots. In general its habits are the same as those of Sciurus deppei. See account of of that species.

Sciurus variegatoides adolphei (Lesson)

1842. *Macroxus adolphei* Lesson, Nouveau tableau du régne animal . . . mammifères, p. 112, type from Realejo, Nicaragua.
1920. *Sciurus variegatoides adolphei*, Goldman, Smiths. Miscl. Coll., 69(5):136, April 24.
?1905. *Sciurus boothiae annalium* Thomas, Ann. Mag. Nat. Hist., ser. 7, 16:309, September, type from Honduras.

MARGINAL RECORDS (Harris, 1937:17).—Nicaragua: Volcán Chinandega [= Volcán El Viejo]; Corinto; *type locality*.

Sciurus variegatoides atrirufus Harris

1930. *Sciurus adolphei atrirufus* Harris, Occas. Papers Mus. Zool., Univ. Michigan, 219:2, October 15, type from Tambor, Nicoya Peninsula, Costa Rica. Known only from the type locality.
1937. *Sciurus variegatoides atrirufus* Harris, Miscl. Publ. Mus. Zool., Univ. Michigan, 38:19, September 4.

Sciurus variegatoides bangsi Dickey

1928. *Sciurus variegatoides bangsi* Dickey, Proc. Biol. Soc. Washington, 41:7, February 1, type from Barra de Santiago, Dept. Ahuachapán, El Salvador.

MARGINAL RECORDS (Harris, 1937:12, unless otherwise noted).—El Salvador: San José del Sacare, 3600 ft.; Hda. Chilata; *type locality*. Guatemala: *eastern part Pacific Coast* (Handley, 1950:153). El Salvador: El Tablón, 1450 ft.

Sciurus variegatoides belti Nelson

1899. *Sciurus boothiae belti* Nelson, Proc. Washington Acad. Sci., 1:78, May 9, type from Escondido River, 50 miles from Bluefields, Nicaragua.
1937. *Sciurus variegatoides belti*, Harris, Miscl. Publ. Mus. Zool., Univ. Michigan, 38:13, September 4.

MARGINAL RECORDS (Harris, 1937:16, unless otherwise noted).—Honduras: Yoro (Goodwin, 1942:153). Nicaragua: Greytown; Los Sabalos, Río San Juan; Chontales; Matagalpa. Not found: Lancetilla; Ca[r]melina, Honduras.

Sciurus variegatoides boothiae Gray

1843. *Sciurus boothiae* Gray, List of the . . . Mammalia in the . . . British Museum, p. 139, type from Honduras (restricted to San Pedro Sula by Nelson, Proc. Washington Acad. Sci., 1:77, May 9, 1899).
1937. *Sciurus variegatoides boothiae* Harris, Miscl. Publ. Mus. Zool., Univ. Michigan, 38:12, September 4.
1842. *Sciurus richardsoni* Gray, Ann. Mag. Nat. Hist., ser. 1, 10:264. Not *Sciurus richardsoni* Bachman, 1838.
1845. *Sciurus fuscovariegatus* Schinz, Synopsis mammalium, 2:15.

MARGINAL RECORDS (Harris, 1937:13, unless otherwise noted).—Honduras: type locality. Nicaragua: Jalapa; San Juan [de Murra]; Jicaro. Honduras: El Jaral (Goodwin, 1942:153). Guatemala: *along border of Honduras, on Caribbean Coast* (Handley, 1950:153). Not found: Laguna, Honduras.

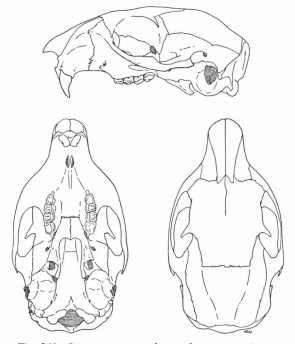

Fig. 240. *Sciurus variegatoides rigidus*, Agua Caliente, Cartago, Costa Rica, No. 16533 K.U., ♂, X 1.

Sciurus variegatoides dorsalis Gray

1849. *Sciurus dorsalis* Gray, Proc. Zool. Soc. London, for 1848, p. 138, June 1, type erroneously assumed to be from Caracas, Venezuela. Nelson (Proc. Washington Acad. Sci., 1:7, May 9, 1899) regards specimens from Liberia, Costa Rica, as typical.
1920. *Sciurus variegatoides dorsalis*, Goldman, Smiths. Miscl. Coll., 69(5):136, April 24.

MARGINAL RECORDS (Goodwin, 1946:361, unless otherwise noted).—Nicaragua: Tipitapa (Harris, 1937:22). Costa Rica: Miravalles; Chomes; Las Huacas; San Juanillo; La Cruz.

Sciurus variegatoides goldmani Nelson

1898. *Sciurus goldmani* Nelson, Proc. Biol. Soc. Washington, 12:149, June 3, type from Huehuetán, Chiapas.
1928. *Sciurus variegatoides goldmani*, Dickey, Proc. Biol. Soc. Washington, 41:8, February 1.

MARGINAL RECORDS.—Chiapas: Finca Esperanza, 250 m. (Hooper, 1947:45). Guatemala: Finca Cipres, 2000 ft. (Goodwin, 1934:28); Concepción del Mar (Harris, 1937:11); Hda. California (Goodwin, 1934:28). Chiapas: type locality.

Sciurus variegatoides helveolus Goldman

1912. *Sciurus variegatoides helveolus* Goldman, Smiths. Miscl., Coll., 56(36):3, February 19, type from Corozal, Canal Zone, Panamá.

MARGINAL RECORDS.—Panamá: near Panama City (Harris, 1937:27); Santiago de Colorado (*op. cit.*:26); *Province Veraguas* (*ibid.*); Chorrera (Goldman, 1920:136).

Sciurus variegatoides managuensis Nelson

1898. *Sciurus boothiae managuensis* Nelson, Proc. Biol. Soc. Washington, 12:150, June 3, type from Río Managua, Guatemala.
1937. *Sciurus variegatoides managuensis*, Harris, Miscl. Publ. Mus. Zool., Univ. Michigan, 38:17, September 4.

MARGINAL RECORDS (Harris, 1937:18).—Guatemala: Quiragua; "probably" Zacapa. Not found: Bobos.

Sciurus variegatoides melania (Gray)

1867. *Macroxus melania* Gray, Ann. Mag. Nat. Hist., ser. 3, 20:425, December, type from Point Burica, Costa Rica.
1920. *Sciurus variegatoides melania*, Goldman, Smiths. Miscl. Coll., 69(5):136, April 24.

MARGINAL RECORDS.—Panamá: Boquete (Goldman, 1920:137); Remedios (Harris, 1937:26); coastal lowlands [of Mariato River district, Azuero Peninsula] (Bole, 1937: 163). Costa Rica: type locality. Panamá: Divalá (Harris, 1937:26).

Sciurus variegatoides rigidus Peters

1863. *Sciurus rigidus* Peters, Monatsb. preuss. Akad. Wiss., Berlin, p. 652, type from San José, Costa Rica.
1937. *Sciurus variegatoides rigidus*, Harris, Miscl. Publ. Mus. Zool., Univ. Michigan, 38:22, September 4.
1867. *Sciurus intermedius* Gray, Ann. Mag. Nat. Hist., ser. 3, 20:421, type from Guatemala.
1867. *Macroxus nicoyana* Gray, *op. cit.*:423, type from Nicoya, Costa Rica.
1933. *Sciurus variegatoides austini* Harris, Occas. Papers Mus. Zool., Univ. Michigan, 266:1, June 28, type from Las Agujas, Puntarenas, Costa Rica. Regarded as inseparable from *S. v. rigidus* by Hall and Kelson, Univ. Kansas Publ., Mus. Nat. Hist., 5:356, December 15, 1952.

MARGINAL RECORDS (Hall and Kelson, 1952:356, unless otherwise noted).—Costa Rica: Zarcéro; Juan Viñas (Goodwin, 1946:362); San Isidro (*ibid.*); Las Agujas; Chomes.

Sciurus variegatoides thomasi Nelson

1899. *Sciurus thomasi* Nelson, Proc. Washington Acad. Sci., 1:71, May 9, type from Talamanca, Costa Rica.
1937. *Sciurus variegatoides thomasi*, Harris, Miscl., Publ. Mus. Zool., Univ. Michigan, 38:24, September 4.

MARGINAL RECORDS (Goodwin, 1946:362, unless otherwise noted).—Costa Rica: San Carlos; Guápiles; Pacuare; Cuábre; Pozo Azul (J. A. Allen, 1904:44); La Carpintera; Perálta; Villa Quesada.

Sciurus variegatoides underwoodi Goldman

1932. *Sciurus boothiae underwoodi* Goldman, Jour. Washington Acad. Sci., 22(10):275, May 19, type from Monte Redondo, 5100 ft., "about" 30 miles northwest of Tegucigalpa, Honduras.
1937. *Sciurus variegatoides underwoodi*, Harris, Miscl. Publ. Mus. Zool., Univ. Michigan, 38:9, September 4.

MARGINAL RECORDS (Harris, 1937:10-11, unless otherwise noted).—Honduras: El Caliche Cedros (Goodwin, 1942:152). Nicaragua: San Rafael del Norte; Matagalpa. Costa Rica: Port Parker Bay (Goodwin, 1946:360). Nica-

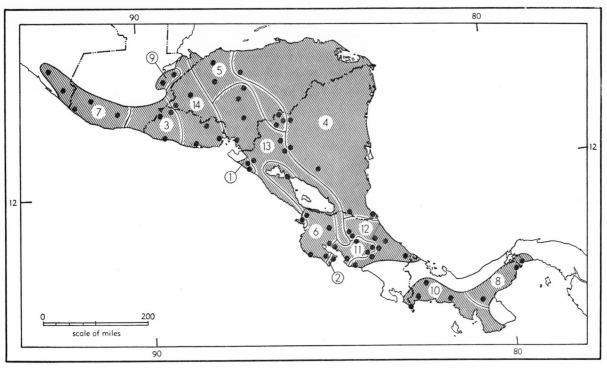

Map 245. *Sciurus variegatoides.*

Key to subspecies	3. *S. v. bangsi*	7. *S. v. goldmani*	11. *S. v. rigidus*
1. *S. v. adolphei*	4. *S. v. belti*	8. *S. v. helveolus*	12. *S. v. thomasi*
2. *S. v. atrirufus*	5. *S. v. boothiae*	9. *S. v. managuensis*	13. *S. v. underwoodi*
	6. *S. v. dorsalis*	10. *S. v. melania*	14. *S. v. variegatoides*

ragua: Volcán El Viejo. Honduras: Cantarranas; Sabana Grande (Goodwin, 1942:152); type locality.

Sciurus variegatoides variegatoides Ogilby

1839. *Sciurus variegatoides* Ogilby, Proc. Zool. Soc. London, p. 117, December, type from El Salvador.
1842. *Macroxus pyladei* Lesson, Nouveau tableau du régne animal . . . mammifères, p. 112, type from San Carlos, El Salvador.
1843. *Sciurus griseocaudatus* Gray, *in* The zoology of the H. M. S. Sulphur . . . , 2(Mamm.):34, type from west coast of Central America.

MARGINAL RECORDS (Harris, 1937:9, unless otherwise noted).—Guatemala: *highlands along border El Salvador and Honduras* (Handley, 1950:153). Honduras: Las Flores (Goodwin, 1942:152). El Salvador: Monte Cacaguatique; La Unión; Puerto del Triunfo. Honduras: Plan del Rancho (Goodwin, 1942:152).

Sciurus deppei
Deppe's Squirrel

External measurements: 343–387; 162–188; 54–58. Upper parts varying from grizzled dark rusty brown to yellowish brown and even grayish brown; outside of legs and feet usually dark gray; tail above black thinly washed with white, below varying from ochraceous to rich ferruginous, bordered with black and edged with white or pale yellow; underparts usually white or yellowish to dull rufous, but buffy patches of inguinal, axillary and gular regions extend well onto venter of some specimens. Small size distinguishes this squirrel from other species of the subgenus except *S. negligens*. The gray upper parts of *S. negligens* distinguish it from *S. deppei.*

Sciurus deppei usually lives in dense vegetation in humid lowlands and in dry more open forests of higher elevations. This species is essentially arboreal, but spends much time on the ground seeking nuts, seeds, buds, insects, and fruits. Nests are in hollow tree-trunks and in balls of leaves and twigs among the higher branches. Deppe's squirrels are agile, move rapidly through trees, and leap remarkably long distances from one branch to another. They breed throughout the year and have 2 to 8 (usually 4) young.

Sciurus deppei deppei Peters

1863. *Sciurus deppei* Peters, Monatsb. preuss. Akad. Wiss., Berlin, p. 654, type from Papantla, Veracruz.

1867. *Macroxus tephrogaster* Gray, Ann. Mag. Nat. Hist., ser. 3, 20:431, type from México.

1867. *Macroxus taeniurus* Gray, *ibid.*, type from Guatemala.

MARGINAL RECORDS (Nelson, 1899b:104, unless otherwise noted).—Puebla: Metlaltoyuca. Veracruz: type locality; Catemaco. Chiapas: Tumbalá; *6 mi. SE Palenque* (Kuns and Tashian, 1954:101). Guatemala (Goodwin, 1934:25): La Perla; Secanquim. Honduras (Goodwin, 1942:154): Catacombas; Las Peinitas; Rancho Quemado; Comayaguela; La Florida; Belén Gaucho. Guatemala (Goodwin, 1934:25): Volcán San Lucas; Finca Carolina. Chiapas: Cerro Ovando, 1800–2100 m. (Hooper, 1947:44); Triunfo, 1950 m. (*ibid.*); Ocuilapa. Oaxaca: mountains near Santo Domingo; Reyes. Veracruz: Córdoba; Jico; Las Vigas. Puebla: Huachinango.

Sciurus deppei matagalpae J. A. Allen

1908. *Sciurus deppei matagalpae* J. A. Allen, Bull. Amer. Mus. Nat. Hist., 24:660, October 13, type from San Rafael del Norte, Nicaragua.

MARGINAL RECORDS (J. A. Allen, 1910:104).— Nicaragua: Río Coco; Peña Blanca; type locality.

Sciurus deppei miravallensis Harris

1931. *Sciurus miravallensis* Harris, Occas. Papers Mus. Zool., Univ. Michigan, 277:1, June 4, type from Volcán de Miravalles, 1500 ft., Cordillera de Guanacaste, Costa Rica.

1943. *Sciurus deppei miravallensis* Harris, Occas. Papers Mus. Zool., Univ. Michigan, 476:10, October 8.

MARGINAL RECORDS (Goodwin, 1946:363).—Costa Rica: Hda. Alemania; Hacienda Santa María; Vijagua; type locality; *Volcán Orosi*.

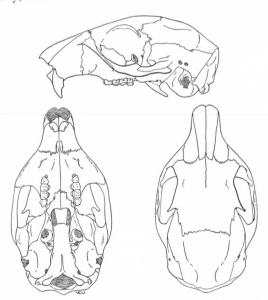

Fig. 241. *Sciurus deppei*, 9 km. E Papantla, 300 ft., Veracruz, No. 23952 K.U., ♂, X 1.

Sciurus deppei negligens Nelson

1898. *Sciurus negligens* Nelson, Proc. Biol. Soc. Washington, 12:147, June 3, type from Altamira, Tamaulipas.

1953. *Sciurus deppei negligens,* Hooper, Occas. Papers Mus. Zool., Univ. Michigan, 544:4, March 25.

MARGINAL RECORDS.—Tamaulipas (Nelson, 1899b: 105): Victoria; type locality. San Luis Potosí (Dalquest, 1953b:88–89): *12 mi. E Tamazunchale*; 1 mi. S Tamazunchale; Cerro Conejo; 10 km. E Platanito.

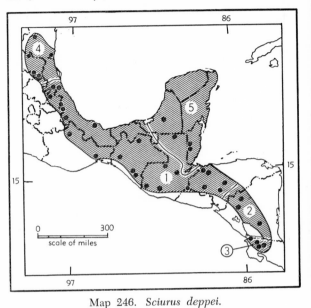

Map 246. *Sciurus deppei.*

Guide to subspecies	
1. S. d. deppei	3. S. d. miravallensis
2. S. d. matagalpae	4. S. d. negligens
	5. S. d. vivax

Sciurus deppei vivax Nelson

1901. *Sciurus deppei vivax* Nelson, Proc. Biol. Soc. Washington, 14:131, August 9, type from Apazote, Campeche.

MARGINAL RECORDS.—Peninsula of Yucatán southward to Campeche: type locality. British Honduras (A. Murie, 1935:24): near El Cayo; transition area bordering Mountain Pine Ridge. Guatemala: Uaxactún (*ibid.*); *Petén* (Handley, 1950:151).

Subgenus Hesperosciurus Nelson

1899. *Hesperosciurus* Nelson, Proc. Washington Acad. Sci. 1:27, May 9. Type, *Sciurus griseus* Ord.

Large squirrel; jugals relatively "weak" and relatively little twisted from vertical plane; skull broad, especially across parietals; nasals terminating posteriorly subequally with posterior tongues of premaxillae; molars massive.

Sciurus griseus
Western Gray Squirrel

External measurements: 510–570; 265–290; 74–80. Upper parts varying from dark gray to light gray with yellowish or ochraceous wash; underparts varying from white to gray with tawny suffusion; tail gray but often with blackish or tawny suffusion.

The western gray squirrel lives in forested areas of the mountains and lowlands of the Pacific Coastal states. Principal foods are acorns, nuts and tender twigs and shoots. This arboreal squirrel forages on the ground more than the eastern gray squirrel does, is active throughout the year, stores little food, and builds nests well above the ground preferably in holes in trees but sometimes among branches. Scarcity of food causes migrations in some years and local populations vary much for this reason and because of disease. The annual litter of 3 to 5 young is born in late winter or spring.

Sciurus griseus anthonyi Mearns

1897. *Sciurus fossor anthonyi* Mearns, Preliminary diagnoses of new mammals of the genera *Sciurus, Castor, Neotoma,* and *Sigmodon,* from the Mexican border of the United States, p. 1, March 5 (preprint of Proc. U. S. Nat. Mus., 20:501, January 19, 1898), type from Campbells Ranch, Laguna Mts., San Diego Co., California.
1907. *Sciurus griseus anthonyi* Mearns, Bull. U. S. Nat. Mus., 56:264, April 13.

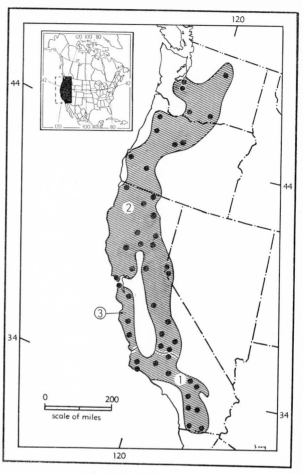

Map 247. *Sciurus griseus.*

Guide to subspecies   2. S. g. *griseus*
1. S. g. *anthonyi*   3. S. g. *nigripes*

MARGINAL RECORDS (BS specimens, unless otherwise noted).—California: Tehachapi Peak (66599); Little Bear Valley (32957/44979); San Bernardino Peak (56683); Santa Rosa Peak (Grinnell and Swarth, 1913:324); Laguna Mts. (Mearns, 1907:267); type locality; Smith Mtn. (35281/47546); San Gorgonio Pass (193930 NM); Oak Knoll, near Pasadena (Grinnell, 1933:135); Gaviota Pass (31691/43830); 7 mi. NE Santa Ynez (243178); vicinity Mt. Piños (Grinnell, 1933:135).

Sciurus griseus griseus Ord

1818. *Sciurus griseus* Ord, Jour. Physique, Chimie, Hist. Nat. Arts, 87:152. Type locality, The Dalles, Columbia River, Wasco Co., Oregon.
1841. *Sciurus leporinus* Audubon and Bachman, Proc. Acad. Nat. Sci. Philadelphia, p. 101, having habitat in "Northern parts of California."
1848. *Sciurus fossor* Peale, Mammalia and ornithology, *in* U. S. Expl. Exped. . . . , 8:55, from "southern parts of Oregon [where] there is a species of pine (*Pinus Lambertii,* Douglass,) which produces a cone about fifteen inches long, and eighteen in circumference."

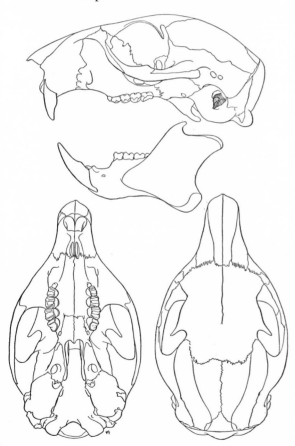

Fig. 242. *Sciurus griseus griseus,* French Gulch, Kern Co., California, No. 60026 M.V.Z., ♂, X 1.

1852. *Sciurus heermanni* Le Conte, Proc. Acad. Nat. Sci. Philadelphia, 6:149, September, type from California, probably central Sierran foothills in vicinity of Calaveras River, Calaveras Co.

MARGINAL RECORDS (BS specimens, unless otherwise noted).—Washington: Lake Chelan (Dalquest, 1948:284); Cleveland (89139). Oregon: Wapinitia (89013); Mill Creek, 20 mi. W Warm Springs (206958); Anchor (222568). California: Beswick (139237); Etna Mills (90519); Bear Creek Valley, W of Dana (95498); Battle Creek Meadows (98479); Quincy (95764). Nevada: Verdi (Richardson, 1954:578); 3 mi. S, 5 mi. W Carson City (Johnson, 1955: 578). California: S. Fork Kings River Canyon (30107/ 42123); Walker Pass (29288); Piute Mts. (151201); Greenhorn Mts. (Grinnell, 1933:134); headwaters Tule River (66598); Raymond (64838); Placerville (55957); 8 mi. E Chico (147594); Tehama (58038); Bartlett Mtn. (65730); near Vacaville (Grinnell, 1933:134); Mt. Tamalpais (*ibid.*); Shelley Creek (91492). Oregon: Coquille (12590 NM); Salem (57584); 3½ mi. E Newberg (11452 KU). Washington: Trout Lake (89006); Roy (249613); "near" Tacoma (Dalquest, 1948:284).

Sciurus griseus nigripes Bryant

1889. *Sciurus fossor nigripes* Bryant, Proc. California Acad. Sci., ser. 2, 2:25, June 20, type from the coast region of San Mateo Co., California.
1894. [*Sciurus*] *griseus nigripes*, Rhoads, Amer. Nat., 28: 525, June.

MARGINAL RECORDS.—California: near San Francisco (5647 MCZ); Scott Creek, Mt. Hamilton Range (Grinnell, 1933:135); Tassajara Creek, 6 mi. below Tassajara Springs (117696 BS); San Simeon (31587/43460 BS).

Subgenus Otosciurus Nelson

1899. *Otosciurus* Nelson, Proc. Washington Acad. Sci., 1:28, May 9. Type, *Sciurus aberti* Woodhouse.

Size large; ears long, broad with pronounced tufts (reduced in summer pelage); feet large; tail comparatively short and broad; upper parts mainly gray; lateral line usually black and distinct; skull short and broad; frontal area flattened; braincase wide and depressed; rostrum narrow and laterally compressed; nasals long (equalling interorbital breadth); premolars $\frac{2}{1}$.

The species of this subgenus are known collectively as the tassel-eared squirrels. They are found in the southern Rocky Mountains of Colorado and New Mexico, the Sierra Madre Occidental of western México, and on several isolated mountains in southern Utah and Arizona. These squirrels live between 6000 and 10,000 feet elevation and almost never venture beyond the yellow-pine forest.

Food consists of pine nuts, some acorns, but principally of the cambium of terminal pine twigs. Sometimes succulent forbs, berries, and various roots and tubers are eaten, and occasionally bird nests are plundered.

Ordinarily these squirrels are silent, but upon occasion become vociferous. Although seldom abundant, even locally, they are often seen because of their conspicuous markings, large size, and the openness of their habitat.

The nest usually is among the branches of a tall pine, is made of twigs and pine needles, and seldom is in a hole in a tree, perhaps because holes are scarce in yellow pines. The 3 or 4 young are born usually in April or May. There is often more than 1 litter a year, especially in the southern parts of the range of the subgenus.

Sciurus aberti
Abert's Squirrel

External measurements: 463–584; 195–255; 65–80. Back dark grizzled iron gray; sides usually black; indistinct median dorsal stripe varying from rufous to chocolate brown; tail above same as back but overlaid with wash of white; tail below white (plumbeous underfur sometimes shows through guard hairs) except for grizzled gray basal band. The geographic variation in this species is in color and extent of median dorsal stripe, and to a lesser extent in the proportions of the skull.

Sciurus aberti aberti Woodhouse

1853. *Sciurus dorsalis* Woodhouse, Proc. Acad. Nat. Sci. Philadelphia, 6:110. Not *Sciurus dorsalis* Gray, 1848.
1853. *Sciurus aberti* Woodhouse, Proc. Acad. Nat. Sci. Philadelphia, 6(1852):220, type from San Francisco Mtn., Coconino Co., Arizona, a renaming of *S. dorsalis* Woodhouse.
1855. *Sciurus castanotus* Baird, Proc. Acad. Nat. Sci. Philadelphia, 7:332, type from "the Mimbres" [= "Coppermines" according to Baird, Mammals, *in* Repts. Expl. Surv. . . . , 8(1):266, July 14, 1858], New Mexico.
1858. *Sciurus castanonotus* Baird, Mammals, *in* Repts. Expl. Surv. . . . , 8(1):xxxvii, July 14. (An emendation; *castanotus* stated to have been a typographical error for *castanonotus*.)
1867. *Sciurus alberti* Gray, Ann. Mag. Nat. Hist., ser. 3, 20:417, a *lapsus* for *aberti*.

MARGINAL RECORDS (BS specimens, unless otherwise noted).—Arizona: Grandview (227708); type locality; Springerville (24648/32041). New Mexico: Datil Range (V. Bailey, 1932:69); Magdalena Mts. (*ibid.*); about 4 mi. SE Kingston, 9000 ft. (167583); head Meadow Creek, about 8500 ft., Piños Altos Mts. (51297). Arizona: Prieto Plateau, S end Blue Range (205565); Apache Maid Mtn. (223072); Williams (2086 KU).

Sciurus aberti barberi J. A. Allen

1904. *Sciurus aberti barberi* J. A. Allen, Bull. Amer. Mus. Nat. Hist., 20:207, May 28, type from Colonia García, Chihuahua. Known only from the type locality.

MARGINAL RECORDS.—Chihuahua: type locality. ?Sonora: Burt (1938:38) cites Baird who quotes Clark as having seen this species about *Santa Cruz* and thinks that the *Santa Cruz* was in northern Sonora instead of New Mexico.

Sciurus aberti chuscensis Goldman

1931. *Sciurus aberti chuscensis* Goldman, Proc. Biol. Soc. Washington, 44:133, October 17, type from Chusca Mts., 9000 ft., New Mexico.

MARGINAL RECORDS.—Arizona: Tunitcha Mts. (Goldman, 1931:134). New Mexico: Tohatchi Mtn. (6216 KU). Arizona: 12 mi. N Fort Defiance (Goldman, 1931:134).

Sciurus aberti durangi Thomas

1893. *Sciurus aberti durangi* Thomas, Ann. Mag. Nat. Hist., ser. 6, 11:50, January, type from Ciudad Ranch, 100 mi. W Durango City, Durango.

MARGINAL RECORDS (Nelson, 1899b:86, unless otherwise noted).—Chihuahua: Sierra Madre, near Guadalupe y Calvo. Durango: Laguna del Progreso (Goodwin, 1954:8); El Salto; type locality; Cerro Huehueto, 3000 m. (Goodwin, 1954:8). The statement by Brand (1937:53) that *Sciurus aberti durangi* occurs in northwestern Chihuahua is in error; he was probably referring to *S. a. barberi*.

Sciurus aberti ferreus True

1894. *Sciurus aberti concolor* True, Diagnosis of new North American mammals, p. 1, April 26 (preprint of Proc. U. S. Nat. Mus., 17:241, November 15, 1894), type from Loveland, Larimer Co., Colorado. Not *Sc[iurus]. concolor* Blyth, 1855 [= *Callosciurus caniceps concolor*], type from Malacca.
1900. [*Sciurus aberti*] *ferreus* True, Proc. Biol. Soc. Washington, 13:183, November 30, a renaming of *S. a. concolor* True, 1894.

MARGINAL RECORDS.—Colorado: Livermore (Kelson, 1951:11); type locality; Manitou Peak (6943 KU); Mosca Pass (Warren, 1942:153); 2½ mi. SW Estes Park (8604 KU).

Sciurus aberti mimus Merriam

1904. *Sciurus aberti mimus* Merriam, Proc. Biol. Soc. Washington, 17:130, June 9, type from Hall Peak, at south end of Cimarron Mountains, Mora Co., New Mexico.

MARGINAL RECORDS.—Colorado: Pagosa Springs (Warren, 1942:152); San Juan Mts., 10 mi. W Antonito (*ibid.*). New Mexico: 8 mi. W Cimarron, 7800–8500 ft. (Hill, 1942:78); type locality; Las Vegas (154 KU); Ranchos Vallejos (Hooper, 1941:26); Jemez Mts. (V. Bailey, 1932:72). Colorado: Florida (Warren, 1942:152).

Sciurus aberti navajo Durrant and Kelson

1947. *Sciurus aberti navajo* Durrant and Kelson, Proc. Biol. Soc. Washington, 60:79, July 2, type from 1 mi. E Kigalia Ranger Station, 30 mi. W Blanding, Natural Bridges National Monument Road, 8000 ft., San Juan Co., Utah.

MARGINAL RECORDS.—Utah: *Verdure* (Kelson, 1951:11); type locality.

Sciurus aberti phaeurus J. A. Allen

1904. *Sciurus aberti phaeurus* J. A. Allen, Bull. Amer. Mus.

Nat. Hist., 20:205, May 28, type from La Ciénega, 7500 ft., Durango.

MARGINAL RECORDS (J. A. Allen, 1904:206).—Chihuahua: Guadalupe y Calvo. Durango: type locality; Ciénega Corrales, 7000 ft.

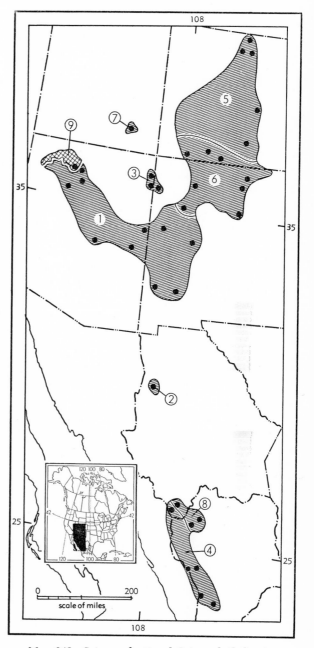

Map 248. *Sciurus aberti* and *Sciurus kaibabensis*.

Guide to kinds	
1. *S. a. aberti*	5. *S. a. ferreus*
2. *S. a. barberi*	6. *S. a. mimus*
3. *S. a. chuscensis*	7. *S. a. navajo*
4. *S. a. durangi*	8. *S. a. phaeurus*
	9. *S. kaibabensis*

Sciurus kaibabensis Merriam
Kaibab Squirrel

1904. *Sciurus kaibabensis* Merriam, Proc. Biol. Soc. Washington, 17:129, June 9, type from Bright Angel Creek, top of Kaibab Plateau, N side Grand Canyon of Colorado River, Coconino Co., Arizona. Known only from the Kaibab Plateau.

Similar in size to *Sciurus aberti*. Upper parts dark grizzled gray, usually with rufous or rusty median dorsal area; tail white above and below, sometimes with few blackish hairs; underparts dark gray to black.

The Kaibab squirrel is confined to the Kaibab Plateau of the northern side of the Grand Canyon of Arizona. The area is approximately 40 miles long and 20 miles wide. Efforts to introduce the animals elsewhere—southern Utah, for example—happily have thus far proved unsuccessful.

Subgenus **Parasciurus** Trouessart

1880. *Parasciurus* Trouessart, Le Naturaliste, 2(37):292, October. Type, *Sciurus niger* Linneaus.
1899. *Araeosciurus* Nelson, Proc. Washington Acad. Sci., 1:29, May 9. Type, *Sciurus oculatus* Peters.

The fox squirrels and their immediate relatives lack P3 (as in the subgenus *Guerlinguetus*); otherwise most closely resembling subgenus *Neosciurus*; skull resembling that of *Neosciurus* but shallower and broader. Other characters are: frontals slightly elevated posteriorly; interorbital notch distinct; notch in premaxillary plate opposite middle or posterior half of M1; P4 subtriangular (not quadrangular) in cross section. See also account of the subgenus *Guerlinguetus*.

The Mexican and Central American species of the subgenus *Parasciurus* are perhaps better known taxonomically, as a whole, than those of some other subgenera; nevertheless the species S. *apachi*, S. *alleni*, and S. *chiricahuae* may be only subspecies of a single species.

Sciurus niger
Fox Squirrel

Subspecies occurring in United States reviewed by Osgood, Proc. Biol. Soc. Washington, 20:44–47, April 18, 1907; southern subspecies reviewed by Lowery and Davis, Occas. Papers Mus. Zool., Louisiana State Univ., 9:153–172, March 4, 1942.

External measurements: 454–698; 200–330; 51–82. Highly variable in color both individually and geographically. There are three basic color phases, red or buff, gray, and black. Although these are individual color phases, one of them usually predominates locally. In one phase upper parts may be buffy or one of several shades of gray, but usually pale, sometimes with strong suffusion of black; toes, nose and sometimes ears and tip of tail marked with white; tail above and below essentially same as upper parts and underparts of body, respectively; underparts like back but seldom with pronounced black suffusion. In the second color phase, upperparts yellowish or yellowish brown suffused with varying amounts of black; toes, nose, ears and tail usually not marked with white; underparts ordinarily yellowish to rufous, but in some individuals darker and in others whitish. Melanism is frequent in either of the two more nearly "normal" phrases, and may be partial or complete. This extreme polychromatism is principally responsible for so much confusion taxonomically within this species and between it and certain other species.

Open hardwood forests on uplands seem to be preferred, but fox squirrels are considerably tamer than gray squirrels and adapt themselves readily to urban habitats.

Perhaps because of their large size, fox squirrels are not so agile and sure-footed as the gray squirrels, and forage more on the ground. The staple food is seeds and especially nuts, but in season a great variety of vegetable matter, and some animal food, is eaten. Occasionally bird nests are robbed, and in spring, sap of trees is sometimes heavily utilized—so much so, in fact, that the trees, especially maples, may be seriously damaged. Much food is buried and more is recovered than by many other kinds of mammals that bury food.

Summer nests are large balls of leaves and twigs rather flimsily constructed and placed high in trees. One animal often makes several in a season. The winter nest is carefully made, weather-proof and in a hole in a tree or high on the branches.

The fox squirrel mates in mid-winter and often again in late spring. The 1 to 6 (usually 3) naked and blind young are born about 45 days later. Fox squirrels first breed at about 11 months and the normal life span is 4 to 6 years.

Sciurus niger avicennia A. H. Howell

1919. *Sciurus niger avicennia* A. H. Howell, Jour. Mamm., 1:37, November 28, type from Everglade[s], Collier Co., Florida.

MARGINAL RECORDS (Moore, 1956:61, unless otherwise noted).—Florida: Fort Myers; Immokalee; The Big Cypress, Collier County, a few miles from the borders of Hendry and Broward counties (*op. cit.*:62); Florida City; Chokoloskee; type locality.

Sciurus niger bachmani Lowery and Davis

1942. *Sciurus niger bachmani* Lowery and Davis, Occas. Papers Mus. Zool., Louisiana State Univ., 9:156, March 4, type from 10 mi. NW Enon, Washington Parish, Louisiana.

MARGINAL RECORDS.—Mississippi: Michigan City (A. H. Howell, 1909:59). Alabama (A. H. Howell, 1921: 66–67): Sand Mtn., near Carpenter; Piedmont; Castleberry; Orange Beach. Louisiana (Lowery, 1943:240): Nott; 10 mi. E Baton Rouge. Mississippi: 5 mi. N Woodville (Lowery and Davis, 1942:162); Minter City (179464 BS).

Sciurus niger cinereus Linnaeus

1758. [*Sciurus*] *cinereus* Linnaeus, Syst. nat., ed. 10, p. 64. Type locality restricted to Cambridge, Dorchester Co., Maryland, by Barkalow (Proc. Biol. Soc. Washington, 69:13, May 21, 1956).
1877. *Sciurus niger* Var. *cinereus,* J. A. Allen, *in* Coues and Allen, Monogr. N. Amer. Rodentia, p. 717, August.
1867. *Macroxus neglectus* Gray, Ann. Mag. Nat. Hist., ser. 3, 20:425, December, type from Wilmington, Newcastle Co., Delaware.
1920. *Sciurus niger bryanti* H. H. Bailey, Bull. Bailey Mus. and Lib. Nat. Hist., 1:1, August 1 (?), type from Dorchester County, Maryland.

MARGINAL RECORDS.—Delaware: Wilmington (type locality of *Macroxus neglectus*). Maryland: type locality.

Sciurus niger limitis Baird

1855. *Sciurus limitis* Baird, Proc. Acad. Nat. Sci. Philadelphia, 7:331, April, type from Devils River, Valverde Co., Texas.
1907. S[*ciurus*]. n[*iger*]. *limitis,* Osgood, Proc. Biol. Soc. Washington, 20:45, April 18.

MARGINAL RECORDS (Lowery and Davis, 1942:172, unless otherwise noted).—Texas: Vernon (V. Bailey, 1905: 77); Giddings; 30 mi. SW Eagle Lake; Aransas Refuge; mouth Nueces River (Blair, 1952:239). Coahuila: 2 mi. S, 3 mi. E San Juan de Sabinas, 1160 ft. (48439 KU); 8 mi. N, 4 mi. W Muzquiz, 1800 ft. (44865 KU); Fortín, 330 ft., 33 mi. N, 1 mi. E San Geronimo (44798 KU). Texas: Independence Creek (Hermann, 1950:374).

Sciurus niger ludovicianus Custis

1806. *Sciurus ludovicianus* Custis, Philadelphia Med. Phys. Jour., 2:47. Type locality, Red River of Louisiana; restricted to Natchitoches Parish by Lowery and Davis (Occas. Papers Mus. Zool., Louisiana State Univ., 9:164, March 4, 1942).
1839. *Sciurus texianus* Bachman, Proc. Zool. Soc. London, p. 86, for 1838, February 7, type from "Mexico."
1877. [*Sciurus niger*] var. *ludovicianus,* J. A. Allen, *in* Coues and Allen, Monogr. N. Amer. Rodentia, p. 718, August.

MARGINAL RECORDS (Lowery, 1943:240, unless otherwise noted).—Arkansas: Delight (Lowery and Davis, 1942: 166). Louisiana: Ruston; Cypress; Oberlin; Crowley. Texas: Jefferson (V. Bailey, 1905:76); near Beaumont (*op. cit.*: 75); 2 mi. E Sheldon (Lowery and Davis, 1942:166); Brenham (V. Bailey, 1905:75); 16 mi. SW College Station (Lowery and Davis, 1942:166); Milano (V. Bailey, 1905: 75); Groesbeck (Lowery and Davis, 1942:166); Texarkana (V. Bailey, 1905:75).

Sciurus niger niger Linnaeus

1758. [*Sciurus*] *niger* Linnaeus, Syst. nat., ed. 10, 1:64 (based on Catesby's Black Fox Squirrel). Type locality, probably southern South Carolina.
1758. [*Sciurus*] *cinereus* Linnaeus, Syst. nat., ed. 10, 1:64. Type locality, "America septentrionali"—may have applied in part to this subspecies, *niger.* Because of the early uncertainty of the application of the name, *cinereus* has been employed by one author or another as the name of almost every subspecies of both S. *niger* and S. *carolinensis,* although probably none of the post-Linnaean authors intended that *his* usage was to be regarded as a *new* name. Erroneous employment of the name arose through both misunderstanding of the original application and misidentification of specimens. No effort is made herein to allocate properly the many different usages of the name since several of them are of uncertain application. The name, however, has been used in at least 12 quite different senses, and probably there are others. Now, of course, the name [*Sciurus*] *cinereus* Linnaeus is applied to the subspecies of *Sciurus niger* occurring at Cambridge, Dorchester County, Maryland.

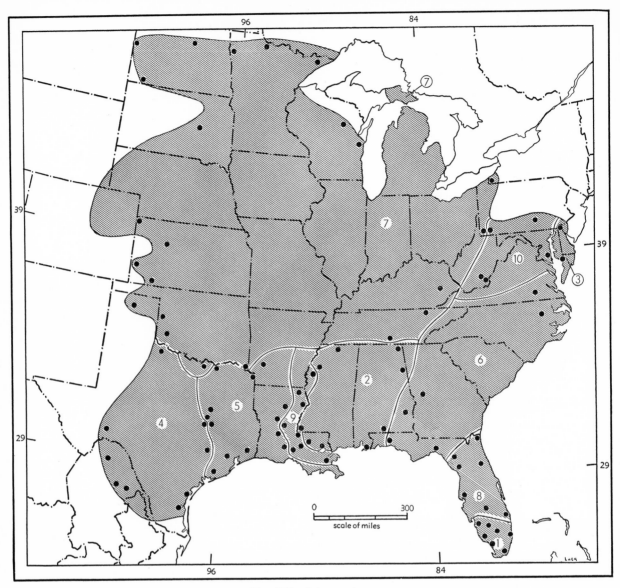

Map 249. *Sciurus niger*.

1. *S. n. avicennia*	3. *S. n. cinereus*	5. *S. n. ludovicianus*	7. *S. n. rufiventer*	9. *S. n. subauratus*
2. *S. n. bachmani*	4. *S. n. limitis*	6. *S. n. niger*	8. *S. n. shermani*	10. *S. n. vulpinus*

1802. *Sciurus capistratus* Bosc, Bull. Soc. Philom, Paris, No. 67, 3(7):145, October, type from Charleston, South Carolina.

MARGINAL RECORDS.—Virginia: Prince George County (Handley and Patton, 1947:154). North Carolina: Tarboro (Bangs, 1896:148). Florida: Jefferson County (Moore, 1956:57, on map, fig. 4); Okaloosa County (*ibid.*). Alabama: Abbeville (A. H. Howell, 1921:65). Georgia: 1 mi. W Junction City (14613 KU).

Sciurus niger rufiventer É. Geoffroy St.-Hilaire

1803. *Sciurus rufiventer* É. Geoffroy St.-Hilaire, Catalogue des mammifères du Museum National d'Histoire Naturelle,

Paris, p. 176. Type locality, Mississippi Valley probably between southern Illinois and central Tennessee (Osgood, Proc. Biol. Soc. Washington, 20:44, April 18, 1907).

1907. *Sciurus niger rufiventer*, Osgood, Proc. Biol. Soc. Washington, 20:44, April 18.

1820. *Sciurus ruber* Rafinesque, Ann. Nat., p. 4. Type locality, Missouri Territory.

1823. *Sciurus macroura* Say, *in* Long, Account of an exped. . . . to the Rocky Mts. . . . , 1:115. Type locality, northeastern Kansas. Not *Sciurus macrourus* Pennant, 1769 [= *Ratufa macroura macroura* from highlands of Ceylon].

1825. *Sciurus magnicaudatus* Harlan, Fauna Americana, p. 178, a renaming of *S. macroura* Say.

1851. *Sciurus rubicaudatus* Audubon and Bachman, The viviparous quadrupeds of North America, 2:pl. 55; text in letterpress, 2:30. Type locality, Kentucky.

1851. *Sciurus sayii* Audubon and Bachman, The viviparous quadrupeds of North America, 2:pl. 89, text in letterpress, 2:274. Type locality, somewhere in bottomlands of Wabash, Illinois, or Missouri rivers or in Michigan.

MARGINAL RECORDS.—Minnesota (Gunderson and Beer, 1953:86): Koochiching County; Cook County. Wisconsin: Menominee Indian Reservation (Komarek, 1932:206); Brookville [= Brockville] (Cory, 1912:113), along southern shores of Great Lakes to New York: Chautauqua County (Hamilton, 1943:233). Pennsylvania: Greene County (Grimm and Roberts, 1950:65). Kentucky: Jackson (A. H. Howell, 1910:25). Tennessee (Kellogg, 1939:274): Highcliff, 3 mi. E Jellico; 3 mi. S Fayetteville. Oklahoma: 10 mi. SE Broken Bow (Blair, 1939:113). Texas (Russell, 1953:456): Gainesville; *2 mi. S Marysville*. Oklahoma (Blair, 1939:113): Wichita National Forest; 3 mi. W Cheyenne. Texas: Stinnett (Blair, 1954b:243). Kansas (Cockrum, 1952:115–116, unless otherwise noted): 14 mi. SW Meade; Hamilton County, sec. 27, R. 39, T. 25 (Hall, 1955b:83); Trego County; 23 mi. NW St. Francis. South Dakota: 2 mi. S, 3 mi. E Fort Thompson, 1370 ft. (41631 KU). North Dakota: 1½ mi. W Reeder (Hibbard, 1957:527); 2 mi. S Dore (*op. cit.*:530); Pleasant Lake (*ibid.*). Minnesota: Polk County (Gunderson and Beer, 1953:86). Introduced in upper peninsula of Michigan (Burt, *in verbis*). Range extended into northeastern Colorado through natural invasion and introduction (Hoover and Yeager, 1953:359).

Sciurus niger shermani Moore

1956. *Sciurus niger shermani* Moore, Amer. Midl. Nat., 55:56, January, type from 2 mi. E of University of Florida Conservation Reserve, Welaka, Putnam Co., Florida.

MARGINAL RECORDS (Moore, 1956:56–57).—Florida: Nassau County; type locality; Jupiter; Highland[s] County; Hillsborough County; Levy County; Gilchrist County.

Sciurus niger subauratus Bachman

1839. *Sciurus subauratus* Bachman, Proc. Zool. Soc. London, p. 87, for 1838, February 7. Type locality restricted to Iberville Parish, Louisiana, by Lowery and Davis, Occas. Papers. Mus. Zool., Louisiana State Univ., 9:166, March 4, 1942.

1942. *Sciurus niger subauratus*, Lowery and Davis, Occas. Papers Mus. Zool., Louisiana State Univ., 9:166, March 4.

1839. *Sciurus auduboni* Bachman, *ibid.*, p. 97, February 7. Type obtained at market, New Orleans, Louisiana; melanistic specimen of *S. n. subauratus*.

MARGINAL RECORDS (Lowery, 1943:240, unless otherwise noted).—Mississippi: Moorehead (Lowery and Davis, 1942:169). Louisiana: Tallulah; St. Francisville area; 5 mi. S [Louisiana State] University; Toca Village; New Iberia; Valentine Lake; Oakgrove.

Sciurus niger vulpinus Gmelin

1788. [*Sciurus*] *vulpinus* Gmelin, Syst. nat., ed. 13, p. 147, based on specimens from the eastern United States including the Blue Mountains (of Pennsylvania).

1954. *Sciurus niger vulpinus*, Barkalow, Jour. Elisha Mitchell Sci. Soc., 70:25, June.

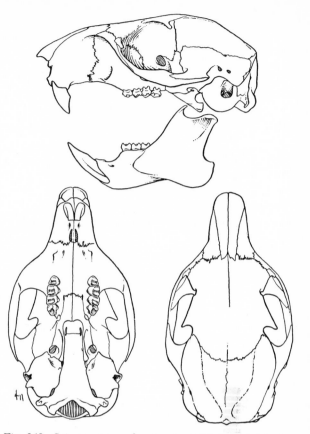

Fig. 243. *Sciurus niger rufiventer*, 6 mi. W, 6 mi. S Oberlin, Decatur Co., Kansas, No. 19027 K.U., ♂, X 1.

1896. *Sciurus ludovicianus vicinus* Bangs, Proc. Biol. Soc. Washington, 10:150, December 28, type from White Sulphur Springs, West Virginia.

MARGINAL RECORDS.—Pennsylvania: Carlisle (Bangs, 1896:153). Maryland: Calvert County (Poole, 1944:316). West Virginia: White Sulphur Springs (Bangs, 1896:150); Lewisburg (Poole, 1944:316). Pennsylvania: Rothruck (Bangs, 1896:153).

Sciurus oculatus
Peters' Squirrel

External measurements: 530–560; 254–269; 68–73. Upper parts either uniform grizzled gray or with median band or strong suffusion of black; ears and orbital ring dull white to buffy; tail above black with heavy white suffusion; tail below grizzled gray to yellowish brown bordered with black and edged with white; underparts varying from white with pale yellowish suffusion to rich ochraceous buff. Superficially this species resembles *S. carolinensis*, especially the more southern subspecies of the eastern gray squirrel. The most obvious difference is the absence of P3 in *S. oculatus. S. alleni* and *S.*

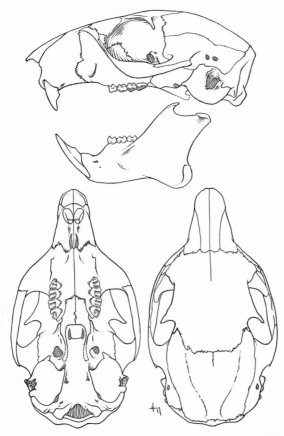

Fig. 244. *Sciurus oculatus oculatus*, Tulancingo, Hidalgo, No. 55609 U.S.N.M., ♂, X 1.

oculatus closely resemble each other but *oculatus* can be distinguished as follows: larger; usually buffy, rather than white, venter; and, prominent postauricular patches that are at most only faintly marked in S. *alleni*.

S. *oculatus* is most abundant in the pine forests of the Transition and boreal life-zones, but occurs at lower elevations (5000 ft.) in oak forests. It eats pine seeds and twigs where they are available, but accepts also acorns, wild figs, and other fruits.

Sciurus oculatus oculatus Peters

1863. *Sciurus oculatus* Peters, Monatsb. preuss. Akad. Wiss., Berlin, p. 653, type from México, probably near Las Vigas, Veracruz.
1830. *Sciurus capistratus* Lichtenstein, Abh. k. Akad. Wiss., Berlin, p. 116. Based on a North American *Sciurus* lacking a red belly. Not *Sciurus capistratus* Bosc, 1802.
1890. *Sciurus niger melanonotus* Thomas, Proc. Zool. Soc. London, p. 73, June, type from Las Vigas, Veracruz.

MARGINAL RECORDS (Dalquest, 1950:6).—Queretaro: Pinal de Amoles. Veracruz: Las Vigas. Puebla: Mt. Orizaba. Hidalgo: Tulancingo; Real del Monte; Encarnación.

Sciurus oculatus shawi Dalquest

1950. *Sciurus oculatus shawi* Dalquest, Occas. Papers Mus. Zool., Louisiana State Univ., 23:4, July 10, type from Rancho San Francisco, 38 km. ESE city of San Luis Potosí, San Luis Potosí.

MARGINAL RECORDS.—San Luis Potosí: Villar (Dalquest, 1950:6–7); vicinity Cerro Conejo at Llano de Garzas (*ibid.*); Cerro Campanario (Dalquest, 1953b:86); type locality.

Sciurus oculatus tolucae Nelson

1898. *Sciurus oculatus tolucae* Nelson, Proc. Biol. Soc. Washington, 12:148, June 3, type from north slope of the Volcano of Toluca, State of México.

MARGINAL RECORDS (Dalquest, 1950:6, unless otherwise noted).—Guanajuato: Guanajuato City. Querétaro: Tequisquiapan. Distrito Federal: Parres (Villa, 1953:368). México: type locality.

Sciurus alleni Nelson
Allen's Squirrel

1898. *Sciurus alleni* Nelson, Proc. Biol. Soc. Washington, 12:147, June 3, type from Monterrey, Nuevo León.

External measurements: total length, 471; tail, 217. Upper parts yellowish brown, lightly grizzled,

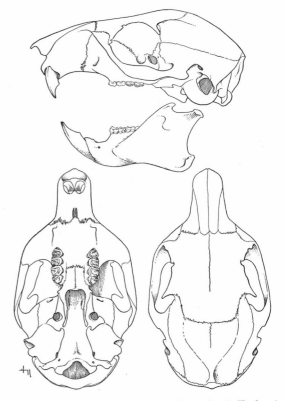

Fig. 245. *Sciurus alleni*, Diamante Pass, 4 mi. E, 3 mi. S Saltillo, 8200 ft., Coahuila, No. 35741 K.U., ♀, X 1.

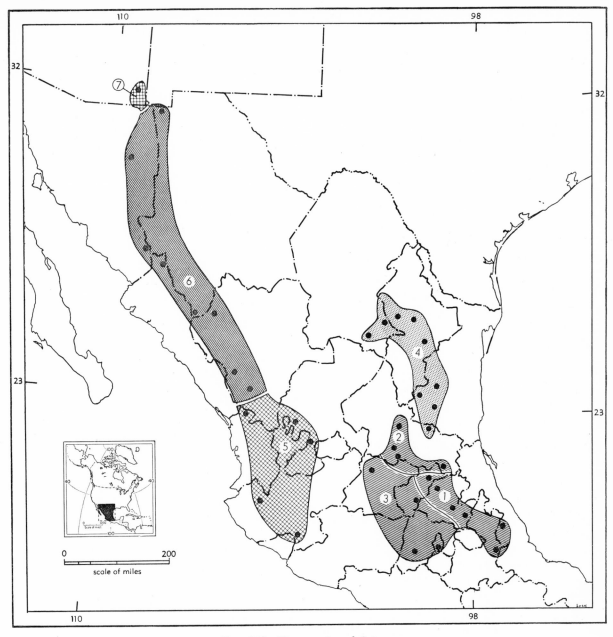

Map 250. Five species of *Sciurus*.

Guide to	2. *S. oculatus shawi*	5. *S. nayaritensis*
kinds	3. *S. oculatus tolucae*	6. *S. apache*
1. *S. oculatus oculatus*	4. *S. alleni*	7. *S. chiricahuae*

and darker medially than on sides; postauricular patch brownish gray; tail above black washed with white, sometimes with buffy undertone; tail below, except for basal band like upper parts, yellowish brown to yellowish gray bordered with black and edged with white; underparts white or nearly so. See remarks under *S. oculatus*.

Allen's squirrels inhabit forests of oak, pine, and madroña mainly between 3000 and 5000 feet altitude but are reported from altitudes between 2000 and 8200 feet. Food consists of acorns, pine seeds, and other herbaceous items. Dice (1937:252) reported a female containing four 20-mm. embryos on July 21 in Tamaulipas and another with four 37-mm.

embryos on August 10. A nest in a hollow branch of a jaboncillo tree contained young on August 23.

MARGINAL RECORDS (KU specimens, unless otherwise noted).—Nuevo León: type locality; Río de San Juan (Mearns, 1907:270); Linares, 1200 ft. (17908). Tamaulipas: near Victoria (Mearns, 1907:270); La Joya de Salos (Goodwin, 1954:8). San Luis Potosí: 2 mi. S Pendencia (Dalquest, 1953b:87). Tamaulipas: near Miquihuana (Mearns, 1907:270). Coahuila: 10 mi. S General Cepeda (Baker, 1956:215); Diamante Pass, 8200 ft., Sierra Guadalupe, 4 mi. E, 3 mi. S Saltillo (ibid.).

Sciurus nayaritensis J. A. Allen
Nayarit Squirrel

1889. Sciurus alstoni J. A. Allen, Bull. Amer. Mus. Nat. Hist., 2:167, October 21, type from Sierra Valparaíso, Zacatecas. Not Sciurus alstoni Anderson, 1879 [= Callosciurus alstoni], type from ?Borneo.
1890. [Sciurus] nayaritensis J. A. Allen, Bull. Amer. Mus. Nat. Hist., 2:vii, footnote, February, a renaming of S. alstoni J. A. Allen, 1889.

Average external measurements of 5 topotypes are: 566; 272; 78. Upper parts dark grizzled gray with rusty yellow undertone; tail above, except for complete basal ring of color of upper parts, black with heavy wash of white; tail below rusty with black border and white edge, usually faintly washed with white; underparts and feet white, sometimes faintly yellowish, but rarely rusty.

This squirrel lives at altitudes of between 6500 and 9000 feet in forests of pine and oak in the Transition Life-zone of the western Sierra Madre of the Republic of México.

MARGINAL RECORDS (Nelson, 1899b:94).—Nayarit: Sierra Madre. Zacatecas: type locality; Plateado. Jalisco: Barranca Beltram, E base Sierra Nevada de Colima; Sierra de Juanacatlán.

Sciurus apache J. A. Allen
Apache Squirrel

1893. Sciurus apache J. A. Allen, Bull. Amer. Mus. Nat. Hist., 5:29, March 16, type from western slope of the Sierra de Nacori, 6300 ft., in eastern Sonora (van Rossem, Jour. Mamm., 17:417, November 16, 1936).

External measurements (5 adults from northern Chihuahua): 540–575; 260–295; 75–79. Upper parts dark grizzled gray sometimes lightly washed with yellow or buffy; crown and median area of back sometimes blackish; ears gray sometimes suffused with buffy; postauricular patches of dull or orange buff sometimes present; tail above black with wash varying from yellowish white to rusty yellow; tail below varying from yellowish rusty to dull rusty rufous, bordered with black and edged with pale yellow or rusty rufous; underparts vary-

ing from dark dull buffy yellow to rich orange yellow, sometimes suffused with rusty.

The Apache squirrel varies less in color than most other Mexican tree squirrels. Superficially it resembles S. niger but can be distinguished by details of color. The Apache squirrel lives in oak-pine forests of western México—seldom in pure stands of pines. Nests are usually in hollow oaks and one report indicated 3 young in a litter.

MARGINAL RECORDS (Nelson, 1899b:96, unless otherwise noted).—Chihuahua: Turkey Canyon, San Luis Mts. (Mearns, 1907:172). Durango: Arroyo de Bucy (J. A. Allen, 1903:594); El Salto (Goldman, 1933:72); Laguna del Progreso (Goodwin, 1954:8). Chihuahua: near Guadalupe y Calvo. Sinaloa: Sierra de Choix. Sonora: Baromico (Burt, 1938:38); type locality.

Sciurus chiricahuae Goldman
Chiricahua Squirrel

1933. Sciurus chiricahuae Goldman, Proc. Biol. Soc. Washington, 46:71, April 27, type from Cave Creek, Chiricahua Mts., Cochise Co., Arizona, 5200 ft. Known only from the Chiricahua Mts., Arizona.

External measurements: 530–556; 250–275; 73–80. Upper parts grizzled light ochraceous buff; orbital rings, postauricular patches, tip of nose, lips, and

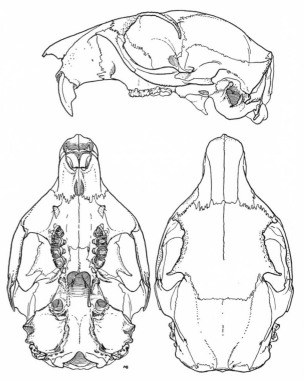

Fig. 246. Sciurus chiricahuae, Chiricahua Mts., 8200 ft., Cochise Co., Arizona, No. 64959 M.V.Z., ♀, X 1.

underparts light tawny; tail above ochraceous buff mixed with black; tail below light tawny, bordered with black, edged with light ochraceous buff.

The Chiricahua squirrel is closely related to—in fact, probably only a subspecies of—*S. apache* and differs in more brilliant color, more evenly rounded dorsal profile of braincase, and less flattened profile of frontal area.

S. chiricahuae is known only from the Chiricahua Mountains of southeastern Arizona and is rare there. It prefers the thickets of the canyon bottoms and generally avoids the oak-covered slopes. Although it spends little time on the ground, it is, for a tree squirrel, a poor climber and often slips or falls. Food consists of seeds of trees, acorns in season, roots, bulbs, and buds.

Sciurus arizonensis
Arizona Gray Squirrel

External measurements: 506–568; 240–310; 66–77. Upper parts uniform grizzled gray with tawny suffusion (in winter with pronounced ochraceous or fulvous dorsal stripe); postauricular patches of rusty yellow sometimes present; tail above black washed with white; tail below grizzled yellow-orange to rusty brown medially, bordered with

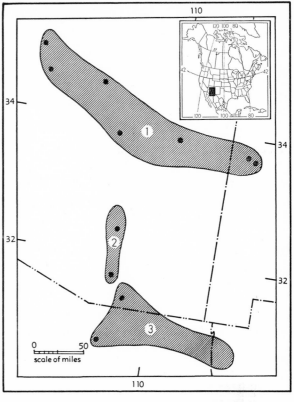

Map 251. *Sciurus arizonensis.*

Guide to subspecies
1. *S. a. arizonensis*
2. *S. a. catalinae*
3. *S. a. huachuca*

black and edged with white; underparts white or nearly so. For tree squirrels, these animals differ much seasonally in color, being grayer in winter. Some authors have mistaken the striking seasonal difference of molting animals for geographic variation. Further, it is known (Mearns, 1907:279) that walnuts, a preferred food, stain the pelage, especially the feet and underparts—a fact that has led at times to erroneous descriptions of color of the species.

The species occupies the lower elevations of the mountains, but ranges as high as the pine forests. Nowhere is it abundant except where concentrated temporarily in an area of favorable food supply. Food consists of pine seeds, nuts, fruits, and to a lesser extent other herbaceous materials. In habits it closely resembles the eastern gray squirrel, *Sciurus carolinensis.* Nests are built among branches of trees and in hollow tree-trunks.

Sciurus arizonensis arizonensis Coues

1867. *Sciurus arizonensis* Coues, Amer. Nat., 1:357, September, type from Fort Whipple, Yavapai Co., Arizona.

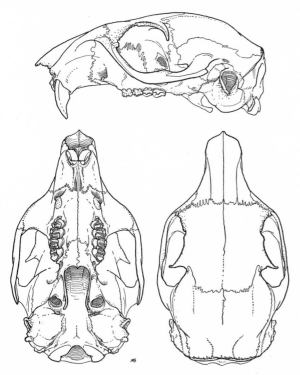

Fig. 247. *Sciurus arizonensis arizonensis*, Carr's Ranch, 5410 ft., Sierra Ancha, Arizona, No. 25500 M.V.Z., ♀, X 1.

MARGINAL RECORDS (V. Bailey, 1932:74, unless otherwise noted).—Arizona: Pine Creek (Mearns, 1907:276); Fossil Creek (*op. cit.*:277); near Fort Apache (J. A. Allen, 1895:245). New Mexico: headwaters San Francisco River, near Reserve; Negrito Creek, 10 mi. E Reserve. Arizona: Carr's Ranch, Sierra Ancha (Doutt, 1931:271); type locality.

Sciurus arizonensis catalinae Doutt

1931. *Sciurus arizonensis catalinae* Doutt, Ann. Carnegie Mus., 20:271, June 6, type from near Soldier Camp, 8000 ft., Santa Catalina Mts., Pima Co., Arizona.

MARGINAL RECORDS (Doutt, 1934:260).—Arizona: type locality; [Old Baldy Peak, 9400 ft.], Santa Rita Mts. See Burt (1933:117) on identity of specimens from the Santa Rita Mountains.

Sciurus arizonensis huachuca J. A. Allen

1894. *Sciurus arizonensis huachuca* J. A. Allen, Bull. Amer. Mus. Nat. Hist., 6:349, December 7, type from Huachuca Mts., southern Arizona.

MARGINAL RECORDS.—Arizona: type locality. Chihuahua: *northwestern Chihuahua* (Brand, 1937:53). Sonora: 32 mi. S Nogales (Nelson, 1899b:97).

Subgenus **Guerlinguetus** Gray

1821. *Guerlinguetus* Gray, London Med. Repos., 15:304, April. Type, *Sciurus guerlinguetus* Gray [= *Sciurus aestuans* Linnaeus].
1823. *Macroxus* F. Cuvier, Des dents des mammifères . . . , p. 161. Type by subsequent designation (Thomas, Proc. Zool. Soc. London, p. 933 for 1897, April, 1898), *Sciurus aestuans* Linnaeus.
1915. *Leptosciurus* J. A. Allen, Bull. Amer. Mus. Nat. Hist., 34:199, May 17. Type, *Sciurus rufoniger* Pucheran, 1845 [= *Macroxus pucheranii* Fitzinger, 1867, a name substituted for *rufoniger* Pucheran, *rufoniger* Pucheran being preoccupied by *Sciurus rufoniger* Gray, 1842].
1915. *Mesosciurus* J. A. Allen, *op. cit.*:212. Type, *Sciurus aestuans* var. *hoffmanni* Peters, 1863.
1915. *Histriosciurus* J. A. Allen, *op. cit.*:236. Type, *Sciurus gerrardi* Gray, 1861.
1915. *Simosciurus* J. A. Allen, *op. cit.*:280. Type, *Sciurus stramineus* Eydoux and Souleyet, 1841.

Resembles *Tamiasciurus hudsonicus* in shape and size of skull but cranium deeper and more highly arched; rostrum short and strongly "pinched in"; zygomata nearly parallel to axis of skull; postorbital processes short and slender; frontals swollen posteriorly; notch in maxillary plate opposite hinder part of P4 or division between P4 and M1; P3 absent; P4 subcircular or quadrate, instead of subtriangular as in *Parasciurus* and *Tamiasciurus*; differs further from *Parasciurus* in shorter rostrum, more swollen braincase, and position of notch in maxillary plate of zygoma (after A. H. Howell, 1938:50–51).

Sciurus granatensis
Tropical Red Squirrel

External measurements: 382–440; 180–190; 50–56. Color varies so much individually and geographically that it is difficult to frame a description that includes all variants. The following description will serve for the great majority of specimens: Upper parts mixed yellowish or rusty brown and black, with median area sometimes darker brown or even black; tail above varying from (1) color of upper parts but heavily overlaid with bright ferruginous (2) through intense rusty red to (3) black overlaid with white, with or without pronounced black tip; tail below with median area of dark yellowish brown but sometimes distinctly light yellowish or dark reddish brown; underparts dull rusty buff to deep ferruginous, often marked with white, especially on axial region and inguinal region.

These squirrels occur from sea level to more than 5000 feet elevation mostly in tropical jungles, in comparatively localized populations, and like the chickarees, *Tamiasciurus*, of the northern latitudes, sometimes are extremely shy and cautious and sometimes overtly bold. They are excellent climbers and make spectacular leaps from tree to tree in the normal course of their activities, but often flee from danger by running off through the forest on the ground. The seldom-heard call is a short series of rasping barks.

Sciurus granatensis chiriquensis Bangs

1902. *Sciurus* (*Guerlinguetus*) *aestuans chiriquensis* Bangs, Bull. Mus. Comp. Zool., 39(2):22, April, type from Divalá, Chiriquí, Panamá.
1947. [*Sciurus granatensis*] *chiriquensis*, Hershkovitz, Proc. U. S. Nat. Mus., 97:7, August 25.

MARGINAL RECORDS (Goodwin, 1946:364–365, unless otherwise noted).—Costa Rica: Cataratos San Carlos;

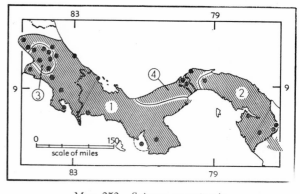

Map 252. *Sciurus granatensis.*

1. *S. g. chiriquensis*
2. *S. g. choco*
3. *S. g. hoffmanni*
4. *S. g. morulus*

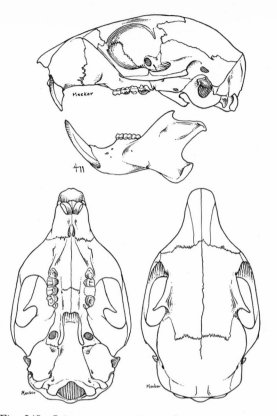

Fig. 248. *Sciurus granatensis morulus,* Barro Colorado Island, Canal Zone, Panamá, No. 45101 K.U., ♀, X 1.

Limón (Harris, 1931:3). Panamá: Almirante (*ibid.*); Cerro Viejo, Azuero Peninsula (Bole, 1937:162); Cébaco Island, Montijo Bay (*ibid.*); type locality. Costa Rica: Punta Jiménez; Palmar; El General; Pozo Azul Pirrís; *San Gerónimo Pirris*; Peralta; Santa Clara; Zarcéro.

Sciurus granatensis choco Goldman

1913. *Sciurus variabilis choco* Goldman, Smiths. Miscl. Coll., 60(22):4, February 28, type from Cana, 3500 ft., Pirri Mts., eastern Panamá.
1955. *Sciurus granatensis choco,* Miller and Kellogg, Bull. U. S. Nat. Mus., 205:257, March 3.

MARGINAL RECORDS (Goldman, 1920:140).—Panamá: Cerro Azul; Tacarcuna; Tapalisa; Mt. Pirre; Chepigana.

Sciurus granatensis hoffmanni Peters

1863. *Sciurus aestuans* var. *hoffmanni* Peters, Monatsb. preuss. Akad. Wiss., Berlin, p. 654, type from Costa Rica, subsequently restricted to Agua Caliente by Harris (Occas. Papers Mus. Zool., Univ. Michigan, 476:9, October 8, 1943).
1947. [*Sciurus granatensis*] *hoffmanni,* Hershkovitz, Proc. U.S. Nat. Mus., 97:7, August 25.
1867. *Macroxus xanthotus* Gray, Ann. Mag. Nat. Hist., ser. 3, 20:429, type from Cordillera de Tale, Veragua, Costa Rica.

MARGINAL RECORDS (Harris, 1931:3, unless otherwise noted).—Costa Rica: Santa Clara; Rancho de Río Jiménez (Goodwin, 1946:364); W side Turrialba; Buena Vista; Escazú Heights (Goodwin, 1946:364); Volcán Poás (*ibid.*).

Sciurus granatensis morulus Bangs

1900. *Sciurus variabilis morulus* Bangs, Proc. New England Zool. Club, 2:43, September 20, type from Loma del León, Panamá.
1955. *Sciurus granatensis morulus,* Miller and Kellogg, Bull. U.S. Nat. Mus., 205:257, March 3.

MARGINAL RECORDS (Goldman, 1920:141).—Panamá: Portobello; Tabernilla; Gatún.

Sciurus richmondi Nelson
Richmond's Squirrel

1898. *Sciurus richmondi* Nelson, Proc. Biol. Soc. Washington, 12:146, June 3, type from Escondido River, 50 miles above Bluefields, Nicaragua.

Average external measurements of 5 adult topotypes are: 361; 169; 52. Upper parts, including nose and base of tail, ochraceous or rusty brown, darker medially, purest on sides and lateral surfaces of legs; tail above black faintly suffused with tawny or rufous; tail below grizzled yellow-brown, bordered with black, and edged with ochraceous or yellow; underparts varying from dull yellow to dull buffy or ferruginous; yellowish postauricular patch sometimes present. Differs from *S. granatensis hoffmanni* principally in color, especially of underparts.

Sciurus richmondi inhabits dense humid jungles.

MARGINAL RECORDS (J. A. Allen, 1910:104).— Nicaragua: Río Tuma; type locality; Vijagua.

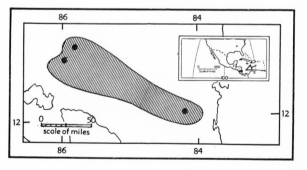

Map 253. *Sciurus richmondi.*

Genus **Syntheosciurus** Bangs—Montane Squirrels

1902. *Syntheosciurus* Bangs, Bull. Mus. Comp. Zool., 39:25, April. Type, *Syntheosciurus brochus* Bangs.
1904. *Synthetosciurus* Elliot, Field Columb. Mus., Publ. 95, Zool. Ser., 4:91, August 2, a renaming of *Syntheosciurus* Bangs.

Skull resembles that of *Microsciurus* but cranium more highly arched; frontals swollen; upper incisors projected forward; molariform teeth relatively large, P3 reaching crown of P4; auditory bullae small; postorbital processes slender (after A. H. Howell, 1938:52); skull thin and papery.

Various authors (Goodwin, 1946:365, for example) do not accord *Syntheosciurus* generic rank; some retain it as a subgenus. Certainly the characters allegedly diagnostic of the genus scarcely seem to indicate generic rank. Nevertheless, we here retain the group as a genus because the paucity of specimens does not as yet permit a critical analysis of the characters. This group, regardless of its nomenclatural status, seems to occupy a position intermediate between the genus *Sciurus* and the genus *Microsciurus*.

KEY TO SPECIES OF SYNTHEOSCIURUS

1. Upper inscisors with a pronounced longitudinal groove. . . . . . *S. brochus*, p. 396
1'. Upper incisors lacking longitudinal groove. *S. poasensis*, p. 396

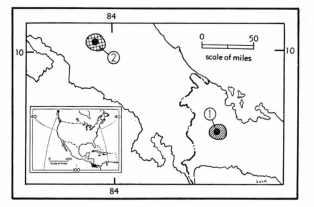

Map 254. *Syntheosciurus.*

1. *S. brochus*   2. *S. poasensis*

Syntheosciurus brochus Bangs
Boquete Mountain Squirrel

1902. *Syntheosciurus brochus* Bangs, Bull. Mus. Comp. Zool., 39:25, April, type from Boquete, 7000 ft., Chiriquí, Panamá. Known only from the type locality.

Measurements and description of the type follow. Total length, 320; tail, 150; hind foot, 46. "Upper parts finely mixed olivaceous bistre and dull tawny olive . . . ; orbital ring, sides of nose, and chin tawny olive; tail similar to back, fringed along sides with pale rusty and slightly more reddish, less olivaceous below; underparts, especially along middle line, strongly suffused with orange rufous . . ." (Bangs, 1902:25).

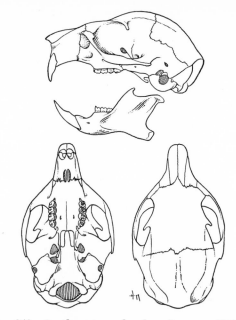

Fig. 249. *Syntheosciurus brochus*, Boquete, 7000 ft., Chiriquí, Panamá, No. 10402 M.C.Z., ♂, X 1. (After Bangs, Bull. Mus. Comp. Zool., 39:26, April, 1902.)

Syntheosciurus poasensis (Goodwin)
Poás Mountain Squirrel

1942. *Sciurus poasensis* Goodwin, Amer. Mus. Novit., 1218:1, February 11, type from Volcán Poás, 6700 ft., Alajuela, Costa Rica. Known only from the type locality.

Measurements and description of the type and only known specimen are: length of head and body, 155; tail, 140; hind foot without claws, 40 (in dried skin including claws, 43.7). Upper parts, including top of head, ears, sides of body, and legs and feet, finely mixed Cinnamon-Buff and black, darkest medially; tail similar to upper parts and fringed with reddish Cinnamon-Buff (after Goodwin, 1946:365). This species is readily distinguishable from *S. brochus* by the lack of a groove on the upper incisor.

Genus **Microsciurus** J. A. Allen—Pygmy Squirrels

1895. *Microsciurus* J. A. Allen, Bull. Amer. Mus. Nat. Hist., 7:332, November 8. Type, *Sciurus* (*Microsciurus*) *alfari* J. A. Allen.

Smallest of the North and Central American tree squirrels; skull strongly depressed posteriorly, and postorbital process situated nearly or exactly over posterior zygomatic root; frontals broad; nasals short; jugal broad; upper incisors pro-odont, usually extending beyond plane of tip of nasals; palate normal; bullae small; cheek-teeth as in *Sciurus*, but small outer (3rd) cusp of upper molars is often barely traceable; p3 present, and rather well developed (after Ellerman, 1940:319).

This group was originally described as a subgenus of *Sciurus* and was so treated by authors until Goldman (1912a:4) accorded it generic rank. Since J. A. Allen's (1915:188) review of the South American squirrels, the generic rank has not been seriously questioned.

Little has been published on the natural history of the microsciurine squirrels. The remarks of L. E. Miller (*in* J. A. Allen, 1915:189), who collected a number of specimens of this genus in Colombia, are perhaps the best general statement. "I have always found the *Microsciuri* much rarer than other squirrels, and usually in pairs. They seem to prefer the palm forests that are so abundant on the hillsides, where they feed on the various kinds of palm fruits and nuts. They invariably evince considerable curiosity, and can be approached to within a short distance before taking fright and hiding in the palm leaves. They move rapidly and gracefully, making long, daring leaps."

KEY TO NORTH AMERICAN SPECIES OF MICROSCIURUS

1. Upper parts coarsely grizzled black and pale orange buff or buffy yellow. . *M. isthmius*, p. 398
1'. Upper parts not as above.
  2. Upper parts uniform olivaceous brown with wash of dull yellow, the olivaceous tone being pronounced; confined to elevations above 4000 ft. in extreme western Panamá. . . . . . *M. boquetensis*, p. 398
  2'. Upper parts usually not olivaceous brown or when olivaceous tones present, not occurring in western Panamá.

                          M. alfari, p. 397

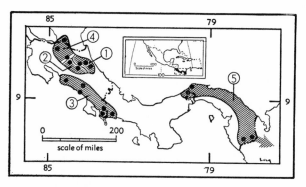

Map 255. *Microsciurus alfari.*

Guide to subspecies
1. *M. a. alfari*
2. *M. a. alticola*
3. *M. a. browni*
4. *M. a. septentrionalis*
5. *M. a. venustulus*

Microsciurus alfari
Alfaro's Pygmy Squirrel

External measurements: 232–260; 75(?)–120; 33–40. There are 2 fairly distinct "color phases." So far as known, all specimens of *M. a. alticola* and *M. a. septentrionalis* have upper parts that are dull olive-brown or olive-black; specimens of other subspecies have upper parts that are finely mixed ochraceous-tawny on black. Tail above varies from ochraceous-tawny to cinnamon rufous, sometimes with grayish wash, usually black-tipped; tail below distinctly buffy; underparts varying from dull ochraceous buff to dull gray with yellowish wash.

The texture of the hair varies with the altitudinal occurrence of the subspecies. In those occurring at higher elevations the pelage is long, dense, and soft; the converse is true in those occurring at or near sea level.

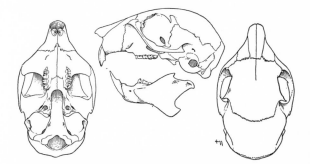

Fig. 250. *Microsciurus alfari browni*, Pozo Azul, Costa Rica, No. 140948 U.S.N.M., ♀, X 1.

Microsciurus alfari alfari (J. A. Allen)

1895. *Sciurus (Microsciurus) alfari* J. A. Allen, Bull. Amer. Mus. Nat. Hist., 7:333, November 8, type from Jiménez, Costa Rica.
1912. [*Microsciurus*] *alfari* Goldman, Smiths. Miscl. Coll., 56(36):4, February 19.

MARGINAL RECORDS (Goodwin, 1946:367).—Costa Rica: type locality; Siquirres; Carrillo.

Microsciurus alfari alticola Goodwin

1943. *Microsciurus alfari alticola* Goodwin, Amer. Mus. Novit., 1218:2, February 11, type from Lajos [*sic*], Villa Quesada, 5000 ft., Alajuela, Costa Rica.

MARGINAL RECORDS.—Costa Rica: type locality; La Hondura (Goodwin, 1946:368).

Microsciurus alfari browni (Bangs)

1902. *Sciurus (Microsciurus) browni* Bangs, Bull. Mus. Comp. Zool., 39:24, April, type from Bugaba, 600 ft., Chiriquí, Panamá.
1914. *Microsciurus alfari browni*, J. A. Allen, Bull. Amer. Mus. Nat. Hist., 33:151, February 26.

MARGINAL RECORDS (Goodwin, 1946:368).—Costa Rica: San Gerónimo; El General; Agua Buena. Panamá: type locality. Costa Rica: Coto; Puerta Uvita; *Pozo Azul.*

Microsciurus alfari septentrionalis Anthony

1920. *Microsciurus septentrionalis* Anthony, Jour. Mamm., 1:81, March 2, type from Sábalos, on Río San Juan, at junction of Río Sábalos, Nicaragua.
1946. *Microsciurus alfari septentrionalis*, Goodwin, Bull. Amer. Mus. Nat. Hist., 87:367, December 31.

MARGINAL RECORDS (Goodwin, 1946:367).—Nicaragua: type locality. Costa Rica: La Vieja de San Carlos; La Vijagua.

Microsciurus alfari venustulus Goldman

1912. *Microsciurus alfari venustulus* Goldman, Smiths. Miscl. Coll., 56(36):4, February 19, type from Gatún, Canal Zone, Panamá.
1920. M[*icrosciurus*]. *i*[*sthmicus*]. *venustulus*, Goldman, Smiths. Miscl. Coll., 69(5):143, April 24, a *lapsus.*

MARGINAL RECORDS (Goldman, 1920:143, unless otherwise noted).—Panamá: Porto Bello [= Portobelo]; Mt. Tacarcuna; Cana; Barro Colorado Island (Enders, 1930:288).

Microsciurus boquetensis (Nelson)
Boquete Pygmy Squirrel

1903. *Sciurus (Microsciurus) boquetensis* Nelson, Proc. Biol. Soc. Washington, 16:121, September 30, type from Boquete, Chiriquí, Panamá. Known only from the type locality.
1912. *Microsciurus boquetensis*, Miller, Bull. U.S. Nat. Mus., 79:338, December 31.

Measurements of the overstuffed, dry type are: 257; 116; 37. Upper parts uniform olivaceous-brown with dull yellow wash; tail dull tawny-olive with black wash and narrowly edged with pale yellow; throat and chest rusty rufous grading to dull grizzled brown on posterior underparts.

This squirrel probably is only subspecifically distinct from *M. alfari*; the characters—for example, long, dense pelage and olivaceous color—alleged to indicate specific status, occur also to some extent in the subspecies of *M. alfari, alticola* and *septentrionalis,* that occur at higher elevations.

Microsciurus isthmius
Isthmian Pygmy Squirrel

External measurements of the type, a female, are: 260; 113; 38. Upper parts coarsely grizzled black and pale orange buff or buffy yellow, purest on cheeks and sides; tail above coarsely grizzled black and pale buff; tail below tawny ochraceous bordered with black and edged with grayish buff, becoming pure black at tip; underparts orange buffy, clearest on throat, chest, and inner surfaces of legs

and lighter medially. Rostrum slenderer and premaxillae narrower than in holotype of *M. i. isthmius.*

This species is distinguished from *M. a. venustulus,* which occurs in the same region, but at lower elevations, by: "much paler, more coarsely grizzled color of upper parts . . . , the maxillae encroach farther on the frontals between the lachrymals and premaxillae, and the interparietal is subtriangular instead of rectangular" (Goldman, 1912b:5). Only one subspecies of the *isthmius*-group occurs within the geographic scope of this work.

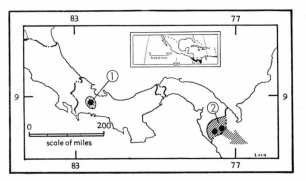

Map 256. Two species of *Microsciurus.*

1. *M. boquetensis*   2. *M. isthmius vivatus*

Microsciurus isthmius vivatus Goldman

1912. *Microsciurus isthmius vivatus* Goldman, Smiths. Miscl. Coll., 60(2):4, September 20, type from near Cana, 3500 ft., eastern Panamá.

MARGINAL RECORDS.—Panamá: Mt. Tacarcuna (Goldman, 1920:144); type locality.

Genus Tamiasciurus Trouessart—Red Squirrels

Revised by J. A. Allen, Bull. Amer. Mus. Nat. Hist., 10: 249–298, July 22, 1898.

1880. *Tamiasciurus* Trouessart, Le Naturaliste, 2(37):292, October. Type, *Sciurus hudsonicus* Erxleben.

Notch in zygomatic plate opposite anterior margin of M1 or posterior part of P4 and is farther forward than in *Sciurus.* Baculum vestigial and confined to glans penis. As determined by a study of the osteological and myological features, *Tamiasciurus* bears approximately the same relation to *Sciurus* as the genus *Tamias* does to the subgenus *Neotamias* of the genus *Eutamias.* The differences in the reproductive system are here considered to be of generic significance. However, insufficient work has been done on the reproductive systems of squirrels to provide a basis for an adequate interpretation of value of this system in determining phylogenetic relationships within the group (modified from Bryant, 1945:383).

The red squirrel, or chickaree, occupies a wide geographic range in North America extending from Alaska and northern Quebec southward, in the Rockies, to southern New Mexico and, in the Appalachians, to South Carolina. Within this range it occupies a fairly wide variety of sylvan habitats; it occurs in the hardwood forests of eastern North America, the coniferous forests of the west and north, and in the far north is at home among the dwarf conifers. It is an excellent climber and races through the trees with surprising speed and agility. Although it does not hibernate, inclement weather will cause it to remain in the nest often for several days. Contrariwise, it is sometimes active on full-moon nights. Red squirrels accept a wide variety of plant foods and store food in quantity. The usual arrangement is 1 or 2 main food caches and innumerable smaller caches. The larger caches are usually made in damp places, sometimes even in water. Moisture probably prevents the seeds from dropping from stored cones. These major storage sites, or midden heaps, are a prominent feature of many forested areas, and some attain a diameter of 15 to 18 feet and a depth of 3 feet.

Red squirrels sometimes migrate and at such times do not hesitate to take to the water and swim distances of several miles.

Nests of chickarees are of 3 sorts. The 1st is made in a hole in a tree trunk—a hole that the squirrel seldom makes itself. The 2nd is a tightly constructed mass of twigs, leaves, mosses, and lichens situated among the densest foliage of a tree and is an alternative winter nest and is almost completely weather-tight. A 3rd kind of nest is a loose mass of twigs and leafy debris in a high tree and is used mainly in periods of good weather. Each squirrel usually has several nests in various places throughout its home range. Many nests, and often the occupants, are heavily infested with a large variety of ectoparasites. At times burrows are constructed, especially under stones or stumps, chiefly, it seems, for food storage.

Ordinarily solitary, red squirrels pair for mating in late winter or spring according to the latitude. The 3 to 7 (usually 5 or 6) young are born blind and naked after a gestation period of between 36 and 40 days. Melanism is rare in this genus and albinism is uncommon.

There are 2 species currently recognized, *Tamiasciurus hudsonicus* and *T. douglasii*. The form *fremonti*, formerly regarded as a species, is here considered to be a subspecies of *T. hudsonicus*.

There is doubt as to the names correctly to apply to certain of the subspecies of *Tamiasciurus* and whether certain named kinds warrant nomencla-

tural recognition. We here employ essentially the arrangement used by R. M. Anderson (1947).

KEY TO SPECIES OF TAMIASCIURUS

1. Underparts white or nearly so. *T. hudsonicus*, p. 399
1'. Underparts more or less rust colored.
T. douglasii, p. 403

Tamiasciurus hudsonicus
Red Squirrel

External measurements: 270–385; 92–158; 35–57. Upper parts rusty reddish, brownish, or olivaceous gray, usually purest on sides; black or blackish lateral line usually present; tail above yellowish-rusty to rufous, usually lightly (but sometimes heavily) washed or grizzled with black and white; tail below yellowish-rufous or yellowish-gray to rusty red, edged with white- to fulvous-tipped hairs; underparts varying from white to grayish-white, or faintly washed with yellow.

Tamiasciurus hudsonicus abieticola (A. H. Howell)

1929. *Sciurus hudsonicus abieticola* A. H. Howell, Jour. Mamm., 10:75, February 11, type from Highlands, North Carolina.
1937. *Tamiasciurus hudsonicus abieticola*, Kellogg, Proc. U.S. Nat. Mus., 84:459, October 7.

MARGINAL RECORDS.—West Virginia: Cheat Mtn., 3 mi. W Cheat Bridge, 3900 ft. (Kellogg, 1937:459). North Carolina: Roan Mtn. (A. H. Howell, 1929a:76). South Carolina: Oconee (Penney, 1950:85). North Carolina: type locality. Tennessee: Buck Fork, Little Pigeon River (Kellogg, 1939:271).

Tamiasciurus hudsonicus baileyi (J. A. Allen)

1898. *Sciurus hudsonicus baileyi* J. A. Allen, Bull. Amer. Mus. Nat. Hist., 10:261, July 22, type from Bighorn Mountains, near head of Kirby Creek, 8400 ft., Washakie Co., Wyoming.
1940. *Tamiasciurus hudsonicus baileyi*, Hayman and Holt, in Ellerman, The families and genera of living rodents, British Mus., 1:346, June 8.

MARGINAL RECORDS (J. A. Allen, 1898:262, unless otherwise noted).—Montana: Bear Creek, Bear Paw Mts.; Pryor Mts. Wyoming: head Smiths Fork, E base Bighorn Mts.; Sherman. Montana: Big Snowy Mts. (Hatt, 1929:17).

Tamiasciurus hudsonicus columbiensis A. H. Howell

1936. *Tamiasciurus hudsonicus columbiensis* A. H. Howell, Proc. Biol. Soc. Washington, 49:135, August 22, type from Raspberry Creek, about 30 mi. SE Telegraph Creek, northern British Columbia.

MARGINAL RECORDS.—Yukon: S fork Macmillan River, Canol Road (Rand, 1945a:38). British Columbia:

1 mi. NW junction Irons Creek and Liard River (Baker, 1951:97); Muncho Lake (Rand, 1944:42); Summit Pass (Cowan and Guiguet, 1956:151); Fort Grahame (*ibid.*). Alberta (Soper, 1947:152): Folding Mtn.-Roche; Canmore. British Columbia: Lake La Hache (A. H. Howell, 1936: 136); Chilcotin River (Anderson, 1947:118); Hagensborg (Cowan and Guiguet, 1956:151); 10 mi. from Glenora (*ibid.*). Yukon: McIntyre Creek, 2250 ft., 3 mi. NW White-horse (Baker, 1951:97); vicinity Lake Laberge (Anderson, 1947:118).

Tamiasciurus hudsonicus dakotensis (J. A. Allen)

1894. *Sciurus hudsonicus dakotensis* J. A. Allen, Bull. Amer. Mus. Nat. Hist., 6:325, November 7, type from Squaw Creek, Black Hills, Custer Co., South Dakota.

1940. *Tamiasciurus hudsonicus dakotensis,* Hayman and Holt, *in* Ellerman, The families and genera of living rodents, British Mus., 1:346, June 8.

MARGINAL RECORDS (J. A. Allen, 1898:260).— Wyoming: Belle Fourche. South Dakota: type locality.

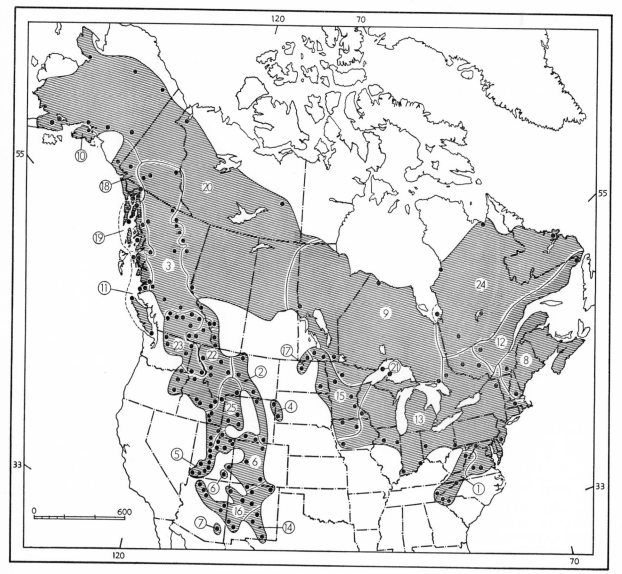

Map 257. *Tamiasciurus hudsonicus.*

Guide to subspecies			
1. *T. h. abieticola*	5. *T. h. dixiensis*	12. *T. h. laurentianus*	19. *T. h. picatus*
2. *T. h. baileyi*	6. *T. h. fremonti*	13. *T. h. loquax*	20. *T. h. preblei*
3. *T. h. columbiensis*	7. *T. h. grahamensis*	14. *T. h. lychnuchus*	21. *T. h. regalis*
4. *T. h. dakotensis*	8. *T. h. gymnicus*	15. *T. h. minnesota*	22. *T. h. richardsoni*
	9. *T. h. hudsonicus*	16. *T. h. mogollonensis*	23. *T. h. streatori*
	10. *T. h. kenaiensis*	17. *T. h. pallescens*	24. *T. h. ungavensis*
	11. *T. h. lanuginosus*	18. *T. h. petulans*	25. *T. h. ventorum*

Tamiasciurus hudsonicus dixiensis Hardy

1942. *Tamiasciurus fremonti dixiensis* Hardy, Proc. Biol. Soc. Washington, 55:87, June 25, type from near Further Water, 9500 ft., Dixie National Forest, Pine Valley Mts., Washington Co., Utah.
1950. *T[amiasciurus]. h[udsonicus]. dixiensis,* Hardy, Proc. Biol. Soc. Washington, 63:14, April 26.

MARGINAL RECORDS (Durrant and Hansen, 1954: 95).—Utah: Elkhorn Guard Station, 9400 ft., 14 mi. N Torrey, Fishlake Plateau; Donkey Lake, 10,000 ft., Boulder Mtn.; Cyclone Lake, Aquarius Plateau; *Duck Creek, 9000 ft., Cedar Mtn.;* 2 mi. W Navajo Lake; *1 mi. up Middle Fork from Pine Valley Camp, Dixie National Forest;* type locality; Parowan Canyon; Puffer Lake, 9500 ft.

Tamiasciurus hudsonicus fremonti (Audubon and Bachman)

1853. *Sciurus fremonti* Audubon and Bachman. The viviparous quadrupeds of North America, 3(30):pl. 149, fig. 2; text, 3:237. Type locality, "Rocky Mountains," probably in the park region of central Colorado.
1950. *T[amiasciurus]. hudsonicus fremonti,* Hardy, Proc. Biol. Soc. Washington, 63:14, April 26.
1950. *Tamiasciurus hudsonicus wasatchensis* Hardy, Proc. Biol. Soc. Washington, 63:13, April 26, type from about 10,000 ft., in spruce-fir area along Skyline Drive east of Mt. Nebo, Juab Co., near Juab-Utah Co. line, Utah. Arranged as a synonym of *fremonti* by Durrant and Hansen, Jour. Mamm., 35:91, February 10, 1954.

MARGINAL RECORDS.—Wyoming (J. A. Allen, 1898: 288–289): Bridgers Pass; Woods P.O., Medicine Bow Mts. Colorado: Arkins (*ibid.*); Fort Garland (*ibid.*). New Mexico: Chama (V. Bailey, 1932:75). Utah (Durrant and Hansen, 1954:94): *1 mi. W Geyser Pass, 9700 ft., La Sal Mts.; 3 mi. W Geyser Pass, 10,000 ft., La Sal Mts.;* Mt. Tomaski; *Clark Lake, La Sal Mts.* Colorado: Coal Creek Canyon (9146 KU). Utah (Durrant and Hansen, 1954:94): Hacking Lake, 15 mi. due NW Vernal, 9000 ft.; 2 mi. E Duchesne; Strawberry Reservoir; 5 mi. E Ferron Reservoir; *Bear Canyon Picnic Grounds, SE of Mt. Nebo;* Tinnys Flat, Santaquin Canyon; Smith and Morehouse Creek, Weber River. Wyoming: Fort Bridger (J. A. Allen, 1898:289). Utah: junction Deep and Carter creeks, 7900 ft. (Durrant and Hansen, 1954:94);—also 1 mi. E Jackson Camp, 21 mi. N Blanding, Abajo Mts., 10,200 ft. (*ibid.*).

Tamiasciurus hudsonicus grahamensis (J. A. Allen)

1894. *Sciurus hudsonicus grahamensis* J. A. Allen, Bull. Amer. Mus. Nat. Hist., 6:350, December 7, type from Graham Mountains, Graham Co., Arizona. Known only from the Graham Mts.
1951. *T[amiasciurus]. h[udsonicus]. grahamensis,* Kelson, Univ. Utah Biol. Ser., 11(3):17, February 15.

Tamiasciurus hudsonicus gymnicus (Bangs)

1899. *Sciurus hudsonicus gymnicus* Bangs, Proc. New England Zool. Club, 1:28, March 31, type from Greenville, near Moosehead Lake, Piscataquis Co., Maine.
1938. *Tamiasciurus hudsonicus gymnicus,* F. L. Osgood, Jour. Mamm., 19:438, November 14.

MARGINAL RECORDS.—Quebec: North Hatley (Anderson, 1942:33). New Hampshire: Amherst (Hatt, 1929:16).

Tamiasciurus hudsonicus hudsonicus (Erxleben)

1777. [*Sciurus vulgaris*] *hudsonicus* Erxleben, Systema regni animalis . . . , 1:416. Based on the Hudson Bay Squirrel of Pennant, 1771. Type locality, mouth of the Severn River, Ontario (see A. H. Howell, Proc. Biol. Soc. Washington, 49:134, August 22, 1936).
1923. *Tamiasciurus hudsonicus,* Pocock, Proc. Zool. Soc. London, p. 213, July 6.
1788. [*Sciurus*] *hudsonius* Gmelin, Syst. nat., ed. 13, 1:147. Based on several earlier citations, among them the Hudson Bay Squirrel of Pennant, 1771.
1822. *Sciurus rubrolineatus* Desmarest, Mammalogie . . . , 2:333, *in* Encyclopédie méthodique. . . . Based on "*Écureuil rouge,* Warden, Descript des Etats-Unis, tom. 5, p. 630."

MARGINAL RECORDS (according to the geographic range outlined by Anderson, 1947:118).—Ontario: type locality; Georgian Bay (Anderson, 1947:118). Minnesota: Itasca County (Cahn, 1921:72). Manitoba: Sandilands Forest Reserve (Soper, 1946:142); vicinity of Cormorant Lake, Mile 42 from The Pas (Breckenridge, 1936:62).

Tamiasciurus hudsonicus kenaiensis A. H. Howell

1936. *Tamiasciurus hudsonicus kenaiensis* A. H. Howell, Proc. Biol. Soc. Washington, 49:136, August 22, type from Hope, Cook Inlet, Alaska. Known only from the Kenai Peninsula.

Tamiasciurus hudsonicus lanuginosus (Bachman)

1839. *Sciurus lanuginosus* Bachman, Proc. Zool. Soc. London, p. 101, for 1838, February 7, type from Fort McLoughlin, Campbell Island, British Columbia (see McCabe and Cowan, Trans. Royal Canadian Inst., Toronto, 25:164, February, 1945).
1956. *Tamiasciurus hudsonicus lanuginosus,* Cowan and Guiguet, British Columbia Prov. Mus., Handbook, 11: 151, July 15.
1890. *Sciurus hudsonius* [*sic*] *vancouverensis* J. A. Allen, Bull. Amer. Mus. Nat. Hist., 3:165, November 14, type from Duncan Station, Vancouver Island, British Columbia. Not taxonomically distinct from *T. h. lanuginosus* according to McCabe and Cowan, Trans. Royal Canadian Inst., pp. 164, 165, February, 1945.

MARGINAL RECORDS (Cowan and Guiguet, 1956: 151, 156).—British Columbia: Porcher Island; mouth of Skeena River; Hagensborg; Owikeno Lake; Calvert Island; all of Vancouver Island. Not found: Arran Rapids and Little Gillard Island, all in British Columbia.

Tamiasciurus hudsonicus laurentianus Anderson

1942. *Tamiasciurus hudsonicus laurentianus* Anderson, Ann. Rept. Provancher Soc. Nat. Hist., Quebec, for 1941, p. 31, July 14, type from Lac Marchant, near Moisie Bay, Saguenay Co., north shore of Gulf of St. Lawrence, Quebec.

MARGINAL RECORDS (Anderson, 1947:118).—N shore of Gulf of St. Lawrence and St. Lawrence River from Quebec (?): Strait of Belle Isle SW to St. Maurice River.

Tamiasciurus hudsonicus loquax (Bangs)

1896. *Sciurus hudsonicus loquax* Bangs, Proc. Biol. Soc. Washington, 10:161, December 28, type from Liberty Hill, New London Co., Connecticut.
1936. *Tamiasciurus hudsonicus loquax*, A. H. Howell, Occas. Papers Mus. Zool., Univ. Michigan, 338:1, July 7.

MARGINAL RECORDS.—Quebec (Anderson, 1941:33): Parker; Kamika Lake. New York: Heart Lake (Schoonmaker, 1929:151). Massachusetts: Worcester (12528 KU); New Jersey: Wading River (Connor, 1953:232), thence down the coast to Virginia (Handley and Patton, 1947:151): Henrico County; Buckingham County. West Virginia: Berkeley Springs (Kellogg, 1937:460); Ogelbay Park (Barbour, 1951:370). Ohio: 1 mi. E Ansonia (2859 KU). Indiana (Lyon, 1936:198): Jefferson County; Vanderburg County. Illinois (Necker and Hatfield, 1941:50): Onarga; Lawn Ridge. Iowa: Atlantic (Stoner, 1918:26). Minnesota: Oronoco (J. A. Allen, 1898:258). Michigan: Keeweenaw County (Burt, 1946:188). Ontario: Lake Nipissing (Anderson, 1947:119).

Tamiasciurus hudsonicus lychnuchus (Stone and Rehn)

1903. *Sciurus fremonti lychnuchus* Stone and Rehn, Proc. Acad. Nat. Sci. Philadelphia, 55:18, May 5, type from Forks of Ruidoso, Lincoln Co., New Mexico.
1955. *Tamiasciurus hudsonicus lychnuchus* Miller and Kellogg, Bull. U.S. Nat. Mus., 205:262, March 3.
1929. *S[ciurus]. f[remonti]. ruidoso* Hatt, Roosevelt Wildlife Ann., 2(1): map facing p. 16, March. Name appears only on a map (not in the text) and is a *lapsus* and *nomen nudum*.

MARGINAL RECORDS (V. Bailey, 1932:80).—New Mexico: Capitan Mts.; Guadalupe Mts.; type locality.

Tamiasciurus hudsonicus minnesota (J. A. Allen)

1899. *Sciurus hudsonicus minnesota* J. A. Allen, Amer. Nat., 33:640, August, type from Fort Snelling, Hennepin Co., Minnesota.
1940. *Tamiasciurus hudsonicus minnesota*, Hayman and Holt, *in* Ellerman, The families and genera of living rodents, British Mus., Volume 1. Rodents other than Muridae, p. 346, June 8.
1943. *Tamiasciurus hudsonicus murii* A. H. Howell, Proc. Biol. Soc. Washington, 56:67, June 16, type from Moorehead, Clay Co., Minnesota.

MARGINAL RECORDS.—Manitoba (A. H. Howell, 1943:68): Carberry; Red River. Minnesota: S end Ten Mile Lake (Leraas, 1942:344); Elk River (B. Bailey, 1929:159); type locality. Iowa (Scott, 1937:70): Charles City; Dickinson County. North Dakota: Lisbon (A. H. Howell, 1943:68).

Tamiasciurus hudsonicus mogollonensis (Mearns)

1890. S[ciurus]. hudsonius [sic] mogollonensis Mearns, Auk, 7:49, January, type from Quaking Asp settlement, near summit of Mogollon Mts., Coconino Co., Arizona.
1951. T[amiasciurus]. h[udsonicus]. mogollonensis, Kelson, Univ. Utah Biol. Ser., 11(3):17, February 15.
1898. *Sciurus fremonti neomexicanus* J. A. Allen, Bull. Amer. Mus. Nat. Hist., 10:291, July 22, type from Rayado Canyon, Colfax Co., New Mexico. (Regarded as inseparable from *mogollonensis* by V. Bailey, N. Amer. Fauna, 53:75, March 1, 1932.)

MARGINAL RECORDS (V. Bailey, 1932:76, unless otherwise noted).—New Mexico: Raton Mts.; Manzano Mts.; Mimbres Mts.; 10 mi. S Mogollon (7550 KU). Arizona (J. A. Allen, 1898:292, unless otherwise noted): White Mts.; Bakers Butte; San Francisco Mtn.; Kaibab Plateau (V. Bailey, 1935:8); Springerville. New Mexico: Chuska Mts.; Mt. Taylor; San Juan Mts.

Tamiasciurus hudsonicus pallescens A. H. Howell

1942. *Tamiasciurus hudsonicus pallescens* A. H. Howell, Proc. Biol. Soc. Washington, 55:13, May 12, type from 8 mi. E Upham, McHenry Co., North Dakota.

MARGINAL RECORDS.—Manitoba: Max Lake, Turtle Mts. (Anderson, 1947:119). North Dakota: Towner (A. H. Howell, 1942:14).

Tamiasciurus hudsonicus petulans (Osgood)

1900. *Sciurus hudsonicus petulans* Osgood, N. Amer. Fauna, 19:27, October 6, type from Glacier, 1870 ft., White Pass, southern Alaska.
1936. *Tamiasciurus hudsonicus petulans*, A. H. Howell, Proc. Biol. Soc. Washington, 49:136, August 22.

MARGINAL RECORDS (Anderson, 1947:119, unless otherwise noted).—Yukon: Burwash Landing, Kluane Lake. Alaska: type locality; Chilkat Valley (Swarth, 1921:93); Glacier Bay (*ibid.*); head Chitina River.

Tamiasciurus hudsonicus picatus (Swarth)

1921. *Sciurus hudsonicus picatus* Swarth, Jour. Mamm., 2:92, May 2, type from Kupreanof Island, 25 mi. S Kake Village, at southern end of Keku Straits, S.E. Alaska.
1947. *Tamiasciurus hudsonicus picatus*, Anderson, Bull. Nat. Mus. Canada, Biol. Ser., 102:120, January 24.

MARGINAL RECORDS.—Alaska: Lynn Canal (Anderson, 1947:120). British Columbia (Cowan and Guiguet, 1956:153): Flood Glacier; Hazelton. Alaska: type locality; Kulu Island (Anderson, 1947:120).

Tamiasciurus hudsonicus preblei A. H. Howell

1936. *Tamiasciurus hudsonicus preblei* A. H. Howell, Proc. Biol. Soc. Washington, 49:133, August 22, type from Fort Simpson, Mackenzie District, Northwest Territories.

MARGINAL RECORDS.—Alaska: vicinity Arctic Village (Rausch, 1953:126). Mackenzie: Aklavik (Banfield, 1951:117); Artillery Lake (*ibid.*). Manitoba: *North Saskatchewan River* (Anderson, 1947:120). Alberta: Torrens Mtn. (Soper, 1947:152). British Columbia (Cowan and Guiguet, 1956:153): Aylard Creek; Redfern Lake; Lower Liard Crossing. Alaska: Yerrick Creek, 21 mi. W, 4 mi. N Tok Junction (Baker, 1951:98); *Swede Lake, Little Tok River*, various points between Paxson and Valdez (Strecker, *et al.*, 1952:478); Tyonek (Osgood, 1901:63); Lake Iliamanna (J. A. Allen, 1898:256); Naknek Lake (Schilling and Rausch, 1956:197); Kowak River (J. A. Allen, 1898:256); near Anaktuvuk Pass (Rausch, 1953:126).

Tamiasciurus hudsonicus regalis A. H. Howell

1936. *Tamiasciurus regalis* A. H. Howell, Occas. Papers Mus. Zool., Univ. Michigan, 338:1, July 7, type from Belle Isle, Isle Royale, Michigan. Known only from Isle Royale.

1943. *Tamiasciurus hudsonicus regalis,* Burt, Occas. Papers Mus. Zool., Univ. Michigan, 481:6, November 10.

Tamiasciurus hudsonicus richardsoni (Bachman)

1839. *Sciurus richardsoni* Bachman, Proc. Zool. Soc. London, for 1838, p. 100, February 7, type from head Big Lost River, Custer Co., Idaho (restricted by Merriam, N. Amer. Fauna, 5:50, July 30, 1891).
1939. *Tamiasciurus hudsonicus richardsoni,* Davis, The recent mammals of Idaho, Caxton Printers, Caldwell, Idaho, p. 227, April 5.

MARGINAL RECORDS (Davis, 1939:227, unless otherwise noted).—British Columbia (Cowan and Guiguet, 1956:154): Assiniboin. Alberta: a few mi. NW Crowsnest Lake (Soper, 1947:154); Waterton Lakes National Park (Anderson, 1947:120). Montana: Summit (J. A. Allen, 1898:267); 9 mi. S Monarch (18244 KU). Idaho: Birch Creek; Lost River Mts.; Baker Creek, 12 mi. N Ketchum; Alturas Lake. Oregon: East Camp Creek, Unity (3347 KU); Meacham (J. A. Allen, 1898:267). Washington: Blue Mts. (Dalquest, 1948:289). Idaho: Castle Creek R.S. Montana: Bitterroot Valley (J. A. Allen, 1898:267); Missoula (Dice, 1922:263); Thompson Pass (J. A. Allen, 1898:267). British Columbia (Cowan and Guiguet, 1956:154): *Rossland;* Deer Park; Nelson; Invermere.

Tamiasciurus hudsonicus streatori (J. A. Allen)

1898. *Sciurus hudsonicus streatori* J. A. Allen, Bull. Amer. Mus. Nat. Hist., 10:267, July 22, type from Ducks, British Columbia.
1936. *T[amiasciurus]. h[udsonicus]. streatori,* A. H. Howell, Proc. Biol. Soc. Washington, 49:135, August 22.

MARGINAL RECORDS (Cowan and Guiguet, 1956:154, unless otherwise noted).—British Columbia: 30 mi. N Mt. Revelstoke; Glacier; Monashee Pass. Washington: Marcus (Hatt, 1929:19). Idaho (Rust, 1946:319): NE Idaho County; Lewis County. Washington: Fort Spokane (Hatt, 1929:18); head Lake Chelan (Dalquest, 1948:289); Ruby Creek (*ibid.*). British Columbia: Bridge River; Pavilion; Black Pines; Mt. Todd.

Tamiasciurus hudsonicus ungavensis Anderson

1942. *Tamiasciurus hudsonicus ungavensis* Anderson, Ann. Rept. Provancher Soc. Nat. Hist., Quebec, for 1941, p. 33, July 14, type from Lake Waswanipi ("Woswonaby Post," Hudson's Bay Company), Abitibi District, Quebec, about 180 mi. SE of intersection of Quebec-Ontario interprovincial boundary with James Bay.

MARGINAL RECORDS (Anderson, 1942:34, unless otherwise noted).—Quebec: Chimo. Labrador: Rigoulette [sic] (Bangs, 1898:497, on geographic grounds). Quebec: Lake Albanel (Cameron and Morris, 1951:126); type locality; Charlton Island, James Bay; Great Whale River.

Tamiasciurus hudsonicus ventorum (J. A. Allen)

1898. *Sciurus hudsonicus ventorum* J. A. Allen, Bull. Amer. Mus. Nat. Hist., 10:263, July 22, type from South Pass City, Wind River Mts., Fremont Co., Wyoming.
1939. *Tamiasciurus hudsonicus ventorum,* Davis, The Recent mammals of Idaho, Caxton Printers, Caldwell, Idaho, p. 229, April 5.

MARGINAL RECORDS.—Montana: Mystic Lake (Hatt, 1929:17). Wyoming: Bull Lake, E base Wind River Range (J. A. Allen, 1898:264); type locality; LaBarge Creek, Thompsons Plateau (*ibid.*). Utah (Durrant and Hansen, 1954:91): Old Canyon, 6 mi. W Randolph; Aspen Grove, Mt. Timpanogos; The Dam, Parleys Canyon; *Mt. Willard, Weber-Boxelder Co. line.* Idaho (Davis, 1939:229): Malad City; Indian Creek, 4 mi. S Pocatello; N fork Pocatello Creek, 6½ mi. NE Pocatello; Henrys Lake.

Tamiasciurus douglasii
Douglas' Squirrel

External measurements: 270–348; 102–156; 45–55. Weights of 5 males and 5 females from eastern Oregon are, respectively, 256 and 255 grams. The color varies individually, geographically, and seasonally. Upper parts dark olivaceous brown to brownish gray, usually with broad median band of dark ferruginous to chestnut; tail above usually like median part of back for proximal ⅔, then becoming black or blackish; tail below approximately grizzled rusty bordered with black and edged with buffy- or white-tipped hairs; underparts strong buffy gray through ochraceous tones to reddish orange with strong black wash.

Tamiasciurus douglasii albolimbatus (J. A. Allen)

1890. *Sciurus hudsonius* [sic] *californicus* J. A. Allen, Bull. Amer. Mus. Nat. Hist., 3:165, November 14, type from Blue Canyon, Placer Co., California. Not *Sciurus californicus* Lesson, 1847 [= ?*Citellus beecheyi*], type locality, "California."
1898. *Sciurus douglasii albolimbatus* J. A. Allen, Bull. Amer. Mus. Nat. Hist., 10:453, November 10, a renaming of *Sciurus hudsonius* [sic] *californicus* J. A. Allen, 1890.
1940. *Tamiasciurus douglasii albolimbatus,* Hayman and Holt, *in* Ellerman, The families and genera of living rodents, British Mus., 1:347, June 8.

MARGINAL RECORDS (J. A. Allen, 1898:280–281, unless otherwise noted).—Oregon: 10 mi. W Wapineta; Strawberry Butte; 10 mi. N Harney; Warner Mts. California:

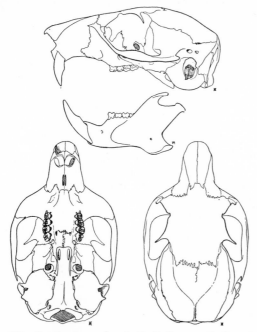

Fig. 251. *Tamiasciurus douglasii albolimatus*, Incline Creek, 6500 ft., Nevada, No. 65215 M.V.Z., ♀, X 1.

Camp Bidwell; Big Valley Mts.; Honey Lake. Nevada: 3 mi. S Mt. Rose, 8500 ft. (Hall, 1946:353). California: Markleeville; vicinity of Mammoth (A. B. Howell, 1924:35); Cottonwood Lakes (Grinnell, 1933:134); Kern River; E fork Kaweah River; S fork Merced River; Snow Mtn. (Grinnell, 1933:134); Sanhedrin Mtn. (*ibid.*); Siskiyou Mts. (*ibid.*). Oregon: Prospect; Diamond Lake.

Tamiasciurus douglasii douglasii (Bachman)

1836. *Sciurus douglasii* Gray, Proc. Zool. Soc. London, p. 88, a *nomen nudum.*

1839. *Sciurus douglasii* Bachman, Proc. Zool. Soc. London, p. 99, for 1838, Feb. 7, type from "shores of the Columbia River" (Audubon and Bachman, The viviparous quadrupeds of North America, 1:371, 1841), subsequently restricted by J. A. Allen (Bull. Amer. Mus. Nat. Hist., 10:284, July 22, 1898) to the mouth of the Columbia River.

1940. *Tamiasciurus douglasii douglasii*, Hayman and Holt, *in* Ellerman, The families and genera of living rodents, British Mus., 1:347, June 8.

1842. *Sciurus belcheri* Gray, Ann. Mag. Nat. Hist., ser. 1, 10:263, type from mouth of the Columbia River.

1855. *Sciurus suckleyi* Baird, Proc. Acad. Nat. Sci. Philadelphia, 7:333, April, type from Steilacoom, Puget Sound, Washington.

MARGINAL RECORDS (J. A. Allen, 1898:275, unless otherwise noted).—Washington: Simiahmoo [Bay]; Sauk; Tacoma; Kalama. Oregon: Eagle Creek; Scottsburgh; Marshfield (Elliot, 1907:140); thence northward along coast to point of beginning.

Tamiasciurus douglasii mollipilosus (Aud. and Bach.)

1841. *Sciurus molli-pilosus* Audubon and Bachman, Proc. Acad. Nat. Sci. Philadelphia, 1:102, October. Type

locality, coast of northern California ("Most probably somewhere in Oregon" according to Grinnell, Univ. California Publ. Zool., 40:133, September 26, 1933).

1940. *Tamiasciurus douglasii mollipilosus*, Hayman and Holt, *in* Ellerman, The families and genera of living rodents, British Mus., 1:347, June 8.

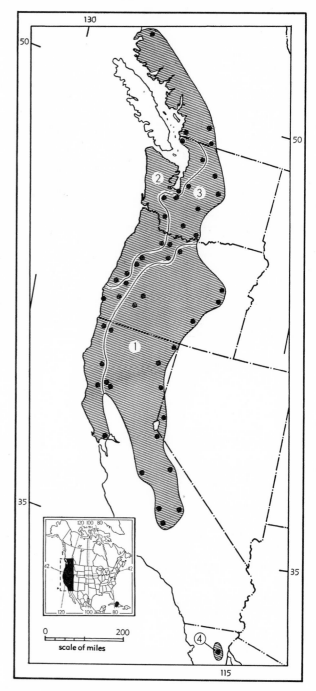

Map. 258. *Tamiasciurus douglasii.*

Guide to subspecies
1. *T. d. albolimbatus*
2. *T. d. douglasii*
3. *T. d. mollipilosus*

1897. *Sciurus hudsonicus orarius* Bangs, Proc. Biol. Soc. Washington, 11:281, December 30, type from Philo, Mendocino Co., California.
1898. *Sciurus douglasii cascadensis* J. A. Allen, Bull. Amer. Mus. Nat. Hist., 10:277, July 22, type from Mt. Hood, Oregon (for status see V. Bailey, N. Amer. Fauna, 55:122, August 29, 1936, and Anderson, Bull. Nat. Mus. Canada, 102:121, January 24, 1937).

MARGINAL RECORDS (J. A. Allen, 1898:278, unless otherwise noted).—British Columbia (Cowan and Guiguet, 1956:156): Owikeno Lake at head of Rivers Inlet; Spuzzum; 1 mi. E Pinewoods. Washington: head Lake Chelan; Wenatchee (Dalquest, 1948:290); Natchez River; Goldendale. Oregon: Bald Mtn., head Clackamas River, Glendale. California: Gasduct [= Gasquet] (J. A. Allen, 1898:276); South Fork Mtn. (Grinnell, 1933:133); Willets, 1700–2000 ft. (J. A. Allen, 1898:276); Petaluma (Anderson, 1947: 121), thence northward along coast to Oregon: Port Orford (*ibid.*); Elk Head; Eugene; Sweet Home; Mt. Hood. Washington: Tenino; Roy; Snoqualmie Falls. British Columbia (Cowan and Guiguet, 1956:156): Vancouver, thence along coast, including *Bowen, Gambier* and *Stuart* islands, to *Rivers Inlet.*

Tamiasciurus douglasii mearnsi (Townsend)

1897. *Sciurus hudsonius mearnsi* Townsend, Proc. Biol. Soc. Washington, 11:146, June 9, type from San Pedro Mártir Mts., about 7000 ft., Baja California.
1940. *Tamiasciurus douglasii mearnsi*, Hayman and Holt, *in* Ellerman, The families and genera of living rodents, British Mus., 1:348, June 8.

MARGINAL RECORDS (Elliot, 1907:142).—Baja California: Vallecitos, Sierra San Pedro Mártir; *La Grulla.*

Genus **Glaucomys** Thomas—American Flying Squirrels

Revised by A. H. Howell, N. Amer. Fauna, 44:1–64, June 13, 1918.

1908. *Glaucomys* Thomas, Ann. Mag. Nat. Hist., ser. 8, 1:5, January. Type, *Mus volans* Linnaeus.

Fore- and hind-limbs connected from wrists to ankles by loose fold of fully haired skin; tail broad, flattened, almost parallel-sided, and tip rounded. Skull lightly constructed and somewhat flattened; nasals abruptly depressed at tip; dorsal profile of skull from nasals to postfrontal region nearly straight, abruptly depressed to occiput; frontals long and narrow; interorbital region narrow; infraorbital foramen oval, vertical, and situated near P3; zygomatic plate tilted upward at angle of approximately 65° to basicranial axis; zygomata appressed, slightly convergent anteriorly, with nearly vertical sides; postorbital process broad at base, tapering abruptly to a point, and depressed at tip. Dentition, i. $\frac{1}{1}$, c. $\frac{0}{0}$, p. $\frac{2}{1}$, m. $\frac{3}{3}$.

Flying squirrels are the only North American sciurids that are essentially nocturnal.

Flying squirrels do not fly, but glide by means of the fold of skin between the foreleg and hind leg.

By varying the tension on the gliding membranes and by altering the position of the tail, they control the direction of the glide and change direction in mid-air to some extent.

The animals are highly social and several often live together. The nest is constructed in hollow trees, but bird houses, barns, and even houses occupied by man are occupied by these squirrels. They eat plants and animals and are more carnivorous than the tree squirrels. This trait often is a disadvantage because in suitable habitats they commonly succumb to meat-baited traps placed for furbearers. In some places flying squirrels must be trapped out of an area before a fur trapper can obtain, say, marten.

The animals thrive in captivity and quickly become gentle. The breeding season seems to vary with the species. *Glaucomys sabrinus* usually breeds only once a year, in late winter or early spring. *G. volans* often breeds twice, first in late winter and again in late spring. The 3 to 6 young are born blind and naked.

There seems to be only one complete molt; this occurs from September to November.

KEY TO SPECIES OF GLAUCOMYS

1. Size larger (total length more than 260; greatest length of skull more than 36); hairs on underparts gray basally. . *G. sabrinus*, p. 407
1'. Size smaller (total length less than 260; greatest length of skull less than 36); hairs on underparts white or almost so basally.
G. volans, p. 405

Glaucomys volans
Southern Flying Squirrel

x ½

External measurements: 211–253; 81–120; 28–33; greatest length of skull, 32.0–35.9. Upperparts drab, pinkish cinnamon, sayal brown, snuff brown,

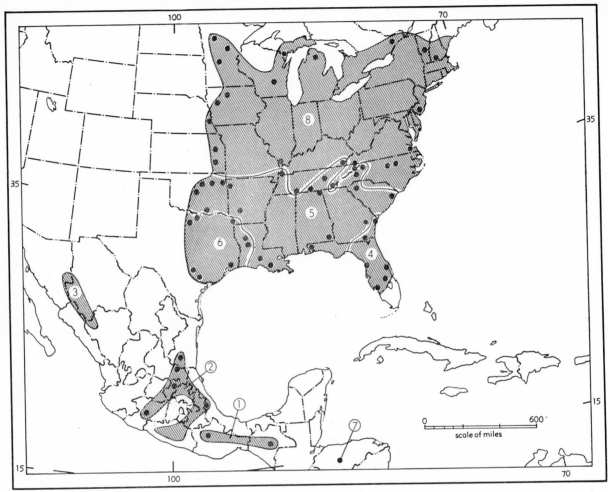

Map 259. *Glaucomys volans.*

1. *G. v. goldmani*	3. *G. v. madrensis*	5. *G. v. saturatus*	7. *G. v. underwoodi*
2. *G. v. herreranus*	4. *G. v. querceti*	6. *G. v. texensis*	8. *G. v. volans*

hair-brown, or yellowish wood brown according to season and subspecies; sides of face smoke gray, often washed with fuscous or buff; tail above hair-brown, snuff brown, verona brown, fuscous, or drab; tail below pinkish cinnamon, vinaceous-cinnamon, or pinkish buff; underparts white or creamy-white, often with cinnamon or pinkish buff sides; hairs of underparts white or whitish to base, except on glissant membranes and hind legs where plumbeous basally.

In some areas (for example, in New York and Virginia) where *G. volans* and *G. sabrinus* occur together, certain specimens are identifiable to species only with difficulty. In every case, however, a consideration of *all* characters that usually serve to identify the species will permit recognition whereas reliance on one or a few characters may not.

Glaucomys volans goldmani (Nelson)

1904. *Sciuropterus volans goldmani* Nelson, Proc. Biol. Soc. Washington, 17:148, October 6, type from 20 mi. SE Teopisca, Chiapas.
1918. *Glaucomys volans goldmani*, A. H. Howell, N. Amer. Fauna, 44:28, June 13.

MARGINAL RECORDS.—Oaxaca: Cerro San Felipe (Hooper, 1952d:110). Chiapas: type locality.

Glaucomys volans herreranus Goldman

1936. *Glaucomys volans herreranus* Goldman, Jour. Washington Acad. Sci., 26:463, November 15, type from mts. of Veracruz.

MARGINAL RECORDS.—Tamaulipas: Aserradero del Infernillo (Goodwin, 1954:9). San Luis Potosí: 8 mi. by road E Santa Barbarita (Dalquest, 1953b:97). Veracruz: Los Pescados, Cofre de Perote (Hooper, 1952d:110). Querétaro: Pinal de Amoles (*op. cit.*:109). A sight record from 9 km. (by highway) S Pátzcuaro, Michoacán (*op. cit.*:110), possibly pertains to this subspecies.

Glaucomys volans madrensis Goldman

1936. *Glaucomys volans madrensis* Goldman, Jour. Washington Acad. Sci., 26:463, November 15, type from Sierra Madre, Chihuahua. *Known only from the type locality.*

Glaucomys volans querceti (Bangs)

1896. *Sciuropterus volans querceti* Bangs, Proc. Biol. Soc. Washington, 10:166, December 28, type from Citronelle, Citrus Co., Florida.
1918. *Glaucomys volans querceti*, A. H. Howell, N. Amer. Fauna, 44:26, June 13.

MARGINAL RECORDS.—Georgia: Montgomery (A. H. Howell, 1918:27). Florida: Lake Harney (Sherman, 1937:114); Shell Hammock (A. H. Howell, 1918:27); Fort Myers (Sherman, 1937:114); type locality. Georgia: Okefinokee Swamp (Harper, 1927:334).

Glaucomys volans saturatus A. H. Howell

1915. *Glaucomys volans saturatus* A. H. Howell, Proc. Biol. Soc. Washington, 28:110, May 27, type from Dothan, Houston Co., Alabama.

MARGINAL RECORDS (A. H. Howell, 1918:25–26, unless otherwise noted).—Kentucky: Big Black Mtn. (Barbour, 1951:105). Tennessee: 7 mi. SW Crossville (Kellogg, 1939:275). Alabama: Sand Mtn., near Carpenter. North Carolina: Magnetic City, foot of Roan Mtn.; Cranberry. South Carolina: Greenville (Penney, 1950:85); Plantersville. Georgia: Reidsville. Alabama: type locality. Florida: Milton (Sherman, 1937:114). Louisiana: Powhatan Plantation, near Gibson; Bryceland (Lowery, 1943:241). Arkansas: Delight. Oklahoma (Blair, 1939:113, unless otherwise noted): 5 mi. SW Colbert (McCarley, 1952:106); Oklahoma City; Stillwater; Twin Lakes; Scraper. Arkansas: 1 mi. N Winslow (7830 KU). Kentucky: Hickman. Tennessee: 6 mi. SW Frankewing (Kellogg, 1939:275).

Glaucomys volans texensis A. H. Howell

1915. *Glaucomys volans texensis* A. H. Powell, Proc. Biol. Soc. Washington, 28:110, May 27, type from 7 mi. NE Sour Lake, Hardin Co., Texas.

MARGINAL RECORDS.—Texas: Gainesville (Russell, 1953:456); Texarkana (A. H. Howell, 1918:28). Louisiana (Lowery, 1943:241): Flora; Simpson. Texas: type locality; Cuero (A. H. Howell, 1918:27); Guadalupe River, 40 mi. E San Antonio (J. A. Allen, 1896:67); Aledo (A. H. Howell, 1918:27).

Glaucomys volans underwoodi Goodwin

1936. *Glaucomys volans underwoodi* Goodwin, Amer. Mus. Novit., 898:1, December 31, type from Zambrano, 4500 ft., Tegucigalpa, Honduras. *Known only from the type locality.*

Glaucomys volans volans (Linnaeus)

1758. [*Mus*] *volans* Linnaeus, Syst. nat., ed. 10, 1:63. Type locality fixed by Elliot (Field Columb. Mus., Zool. Ser., 2:109, 1901) as Virginia.
1915. [*Glaucomys*] *volans*, A. H. Howell, Proc. Biol. Soc. Washington, 28:109, May 27.

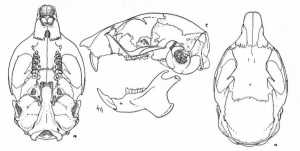

Fig. 252. *Glaucomys volans saturatus*, 4 mi. SE Bergman, Boone Co., Arkansas, No. 95369 M.V.Z., ♀, X 1.

1778. *Sciurus volucella* Pallas, Novae species quadrupedum e glirium . . . , p. 351, seemingly a renaming of *Mus volans* Linnaeus.
1808. *Pteromys virginianus* Tiedemann, Zoologie . . . , p. 451, a renaming of *Mus volans* Linnaeus.
1816. *Pteromys americana* Oken, Lehrbuch der Naturgeschichte, 2:865, a renaming of *Sciurus volucella* Pallas. Oken 1816 names are, in any case, non-Linnaean and not available under the *Regles*.
1829. ? *Pteromys cucullatus* Fischer, Synopsis mammalium, p. 365. Type locality, Virginia (?). Based on "*Sciurus, Virginianus, volans*" Seba.
1896. *Sciuropterus silus* Bangs, Proc. Biol. Soc. Washington, 10:163, December 28, type from top of Katis Mtn., 3200 ft., near White Sulphur Springs, West Virginia.
1915. *Pteromys volans nebrascensis* Swenk, Univ. Nebraska Studies, 15:151, September 25, type from Nebraska City, Otoe Co., Nebraska.

MARGINAL RECORDS.—Minnesota: Clearwater County (Gunderson and Beer, 1953:88); Aitkin (A. H. Howell, 1918:23). Wisconsin: Beaver Dam (A. H. Howell, 1918:24). Michigan: Menominee County (Burt, 1946:196); Otsego County (*ibid.*). Ontario: Clayton, about 45° N (Anderson, 1947:123). Vermont: Rutland County (Osgood, 1938:438). New Hampshire: Hancock (A. H. Howell, 1918:23). New Jersey: 4 mi. NW New Gretna (Connor, 1953:232), thence down the coast to Virginia: Suffolk (A. H. Howell, 1918:24). North Carolina: Raleigh (Goodwin, 1935:113); Apex (A. H. Howell, 1918:23). Tennessee (Kellogg, 1939:276): Wautauga Valley; Roan Mtn., 4100 ft.; Big Frog Mtn., 12 mi. W Copperhill, 2000 ft.; 8 mi. N Waynesboro. Illinois: Olive Branch (Necker and Hatfield, 1941:51). Kansas (Cockrum, 1952:134): Woodson County; Topeka. Nebraska: [Nebraska City] Otoe Co. (Goodwin, 1935:113). Iowa (Stoner, 1918:18): Wall Lake; Humboldt. Minnesota: Stearns County (Swanson, 1945:82).

Glaucomys sabrinus
Northern Flying Squirrel

External measurements: 263–368; 115–180; 34–45. Greatest length of skull, 37.3–44.2. Upper parts varying from cinnamon to pecan brown according to subspecies; tail above from cinnamon to fuscous or even blackish, usually darkest near tip; tail below varying from pinkish cinnamon to nearly black; underparts white or creamy white, often washed

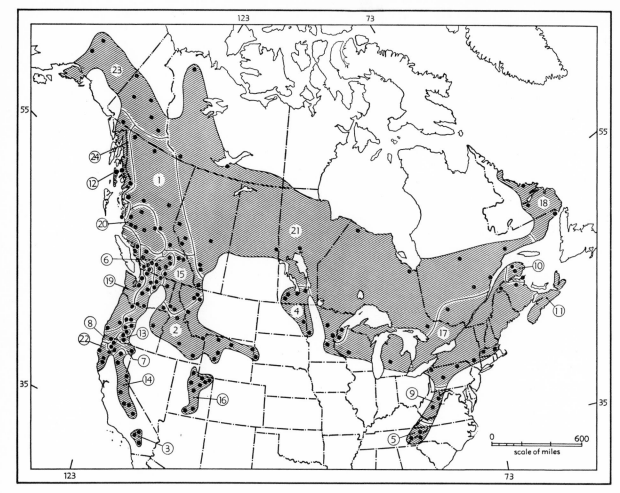

Map 260. *Glaucomys sabrinus.*

1. *G. s. alpinus*	7. *G. s. flaviventris*	13. *G. s. klamathensis*	19. *G. s. oregonensis*
2. *G. s. bangsi*	8. *G. s. fuliginosus*	14. *G. s. lascivus*	20. *G. s. reductus*
3. *G. s. californicus*	9. *G. s. fuscus*	15. *G. s. latipes*	21. *G. s. sabrinus*
4. *G. s. canescens*	10. *G. s. goodwini*	16. *G. s. lucifugus*	22. *G. s. stephensi*
5. *G. s. coloratus*	11. *G. s. gouldi*	17. *G. s. macrotis*	23. *G. s. yukonensis*
6. *G. s. columbiensis*	12. *G. s. griseifrons*	18. *G. s. makkovikensis*	24. *G. s. zaphaeus*

with some shade of buffy or yellowish; sides of head and sometimes face gray, often with wash of buff, cinnamon, or fuscous.

Glaucomys sabrinus alpinus (Richardson)

1828. *Pteromys alpinus* Richardson, Zool. Jour., 3:519. Type locality, Jasper House, Alberta. (See A. H. Howell, N. Amer. Fauna, 44:40, June 13, 1918.)
1918. *Glaucomys sabrinus alpinus,* A. H. Howell, N. Amer. Fauna, 44:40, June 13.

MARGINAL RECORDS.—British Columbia: Warm Springs, 15 mi. S Atlin (Baker, 1951:100); Lower Liard Crossing (Anderson, 1947:124); Peace River Canyon, near Hudsons Hope (A. H. Howell, 1918:41). Alberta: Wildhay River country (Soper, 1947:154); type locality; Henry

House (Anderson, 1947:124). British Columbia: Henry Creek (Cowan and Guiguet, 1956:160); Ten-mile Lake (Cowan, 1936:58); Babine Lake (Cowan and Guiguet, 1956:160); Salvus (Cowan and Guiguet, 1956:158).

Glaucomys sabrinus bangsi (Rhoads)

1897. *Sciuropterus alpinus bangsi* Rhoads, Proc. Acad. Nat. Sci. Philadelphia, 49:321, July 19, type from Raymond, Bear Lake Co., Idaho.
1918. *Glaucomys sabrinus bangsi,* A. H. Howell, N. Amer. Fauna, 44:38, June 13.
1915. *Glaucomys bullatus* A. H. Howell, Proc. Biol. Soc. Washington, 28:113, May 27, type from Sawtooth (=Alturas) Lake, E base Sawtooth Mts., Idaho. Regarded as inseparable from *G. s. bangsi* by Mayer (Murrelet, 22:31, September 15, 1941).

MARGINAL RECORDS.—Montana: Paola (A. H. Howell, 1918:40); Willow Creek (Davis, 1937:24). Idaho: 7 mi. W Yellowstone, 7000 ft. (33923 KU). Wyoming: 31½ mi. N, 36 mi. W Cody, 6900 ft. (37518 KU); Bear Lodge Mts. (King, 1951:469); ½ mi. N, 3 mi. E Buckhorn, 6200 ft. (41803 KU). South Dakota: Black Hills (King, 1951:469). Wyoming: Wind River Mts. near Dubois (A. H. Howell, 1918:40); 10 mi. NE Pinedale, 8000 ft. (15079 KU). Idaho: Justice Park (Davis, 1939:234); Ketchum (*ibid.*). Oregon: Beech Creek (A. H. Howell, 1918:52). Washington: Wildcat Spring (Dalquest, 1948:295). Idaho: Golden (Orr, 1943:528).

Glaucomys sabrinus californicus (Rhoads)

1897. *Sciuropterus alpinus californicus* Rhoads, Proc. Acad. Nat. Sci. Philadelphia, 49:323, July 19, type from near Squirrel Inn, 5200 ft., San Bernardino Mts., San Bernardino Co., California.
1918. *Glaucomys sabrinus californicus*, A. H. Howell, N. Amer. Fauna, 44:56, June 13.

MARGINAL RECORDS.—California: vicinity Red Ant Creek, Big Bear Lake (Sumner, 1927:315); Idyllwild, Strawberry Valley, San Jacinto Mts. (Grinnell and Swarth, 1913:328); type locality.

Glaucomys sabrinus canescens A. H. Howell

1915. *Glaucomys sabrinus canescens* A. H. Howell, Proc. Biol. Soc. Washington, 28:111, May 27, type from Portage la Prairie, Manitoba.

MARGINAL RECORDS (Anderson, 1947:124).—Manitoba: Poplar Point, S end Lake Winnipeg. Minnesota: Breckinridge. North Dakota: Portland. Manitoba: Treesbank; Carberry; type locality.

Glaucomys sabrinus coloratus Handley

1953. *Glaucomys sabrinus coloratus* Handley, Proc. Biol. Soc. Washington, 66:191, December 2, type from Bald Knob, 5000 ft., 3½ mi. S summit Mt. Mitchell, Yancey Co., North Carolina.

MARGINAL RECORDS (Handley, 1953:194).—Tennessee: Roan Mtn., 5500 ft. North Carolina: Mt. Mitchell, 5000 ft. Tennessee: Blanket Mtn., 4000 ft.

Glaucomys sabrinus columbiensis A. H. Howell

1915. *Glaucomys sabrinus columbiensis* A. H. Howell, Proc. Biol. Soc. Washington, 28:111, May 27, type from Okanagan, British Columbia.

MARGINAL RECORDS (Cowan and Guiguet, 1956:160, unless otherwise noted).—British Columbia: Salmon River; Lumby; Canyon Creek in Kettle Valley; *Bridesville*. Washington: Molson (Dalquest, 1948:296); Lake Chelan (Anderson, 1947:124); Stehekin (Dalquest, 1948:296). British Columbia: Hedley; eastern Manning Park; *Falkland*.

Glaucomys sabrinus flaviventris A. H. Howell

1915. *Glaucomys sabrinus flaviventris* A. H. Howell, Proc. Biol. Soc. Washington, 28:112, May 27, type from head Bear Creek, 6400 ft., Trinity Co., California.

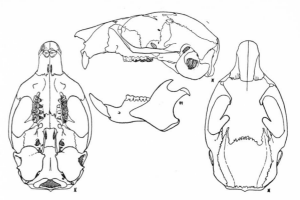

Fig. 253. *Glaucomys sabrinus lascivus*, Marlette Lake, 8000 ft., Nevada, No. 69640 M.V.Z., ♂, X 1.

MARGINAL RECORDS.—California: head Parker Creek, 7300 ft., Warner Mts. (Grinnell, 1933:136); Trinity Mts. (*ibid.*); Grizzly Creek, 6000 ft. (A. H. Howell, 1918:55); Salmon Mts. (Grinnell, 1933:136).

Glaucomys sabrinus fuliginosus (Rhoads)

1897. *Sciuropterus alpinus fuliginosus* Rhoads, Proc. Acad. Nat. Sci. Philadelphia, 49:321, July 19, type from Cascade Mts., near Martin Station, about 8000 ft., Kittitas Co., Washington.
1918. *Glaucomys sabrinus fuliginosus*, A. H. Howell, N. Amer. Fauna, 44:47, June 13.

MARGINAL RECORDS.—British Columbia (Cowan and Guiguet, 1956:160–161): Blackwater Lake near Lillooet; Manning Park. Washington: Entiat River (Dalquest, 1948:296); Easton (A. H. Howell, 1918:48); Potato Hill, 15 mi. N Goldendale (*ibid.*). Oregon: Belknap Springs (V. Bailey, 1936:164); Crater Lake (*ibid.*). California: Preston Peak, Siskiyou Mts. (Grinnell, 1933:135). Oregon: Vida (V. Bailey, 1936:164). Washington: Carson (Dalquest, 1948:296); Glacier Basin (Cowan, 1937:81); Mt. Baker (*ibid.*). British Columbia (Cowan and Guiguet, 1956:160–161): Alta Lake; *Seton Lake*.

Glaucomys sabrinus fuscus Miller

1936. *Glaucomys sabrinus fuscus* Miller, Proc. Biol. Soc. Washington, 49:143, August 22, type from Cranberry Glades, 3300 ft., Pocahontas Co., West Virginia.

MARGINAL RECORDS (Handley, 1953:194).—West Virginia: Bickle Knob, 3900 ft., 7⁹⁄₁₀ mi. NE Elkins; *Cheat Bridge, 3900–4000 ft.*; type locality; *Mill Pt., Cranberry River, 3450 ft.*

Glaucomys sabrinus goodwini Anderson

1943. *Glaucomys sabrinus goodwini* Anderson, Ann. Rept. Provancher Soc. Quebec, for 1942, p. 55, September 7, type from Berry Mtn. Camp, junction Berry Mtn. Brook and Grand Cascapedia River, about 1500 ft., Matane Co., Quebec.

MARGINAL RECORDS (Anderson, 1943:56).—Quebec: Mt. Albert; type locality; Tracadie.

Glaucomys sabrinus gouldi Anderson

1943. *Glaucomys sabrinus gouldi* Anderson, Ann. Rept. Provancher Soc. Quebec, for 1942, p. 56, September 7, type from Frizzleton, Inverness Co., Cape Breton Island, Nova Scotia.

MARGINAL RECORDS (Anderson, 1947:125).—*Cape Breton Island, Nova Scotia.*

Glaucomys sabrinus griseifrons A. H. Howell

1934. *Glaucomys sabrinus griseifrons* A. H. Howell, Jour. Mamm., 15:64, February 15, type from Lake Bay, Prince of Wales Island, Alaska. Known only from the type locality.

Glaucomys sabrinus klamathensis (Merriam)

1897. *Sciuropterus alpinus klamathensis* Merriam, Proc. Biol. Soc. Washington, 11:225, July 15, type from Fort Klamath, 4200 ft., Klamath Co., Oregon.
1918. *Glaucomys sabrinus klamathensis,* A. H. Howell, N. Amer. Fauna, 44:52, June 13.

MARGINAL RECORDS (V. Bailey, 1936:165).—Oregon: Pauline Lake; Upper Klamath Lake; type locality; Crater Peak, 4 mi. S Crater Lake.

Glaucomys sabrinus lascivus (Bangs)

1899. *Sciuropterus alpinus lascivus* Bangs, Proc. New England Zool. Club, 1:69, July 31, type from Tallac, El Dorado Co., California.
1918. *Glaucomys sabrinus lascivus,* A. H. Howell, N. Amer. Fauna, 44:55, June 13.

MARGINAL RECORDS (A. H. Howell, 1918:56, unless otherwise noted).—California: Dana. Nevada: Marlette Lake, 8000 ft. (Hall, 1946:356). California: Kings River Canyon; Sherman Creek, Sequoia National Park (Grinnell, 1933:136); Fresno (mountains near?); Dudley, Smith Creek, 3000 ft. (Grinnell, 1933:136); Mill Creek, S base Mt. Lassen.

Glaucomys sabrinus latipes A. H. Howell

1915. *Glaucomys sabrinus latipes* A. H. Howell, Proc. Biol. Soc. Washington, 28:112, May 27, type from Glacier, British Columbia.

MARGINAL RECORDS.—British Columbia: Field (Cowan and Guiguet, 1956:161). Alberta: Waterton Lakes National Park (Anderson, 1947:125, as *fuliginosus*). Montana (A. H. Howell, 1918:49): Nyack; Stanton Lake. Idaho (Davis, 1939:234): Orofino; Cedar Mtn. Washington: Loon Lake (Dalquest, 1948:296). British Columbia (Cowan and Guiguet, 1956:161): Westbridge; Shuswap.

Glaucomys sabrinus lucifugus Hall

1934. *Glaucomys sabrinus lucifugus* Hall, Occas. Papers Mus. Zool., Univ. Michigan, 296:1, November 2, type from 12 mi. E Kamas, Summit Co., Utah.

MARGINAL RECORDS (Durrant, 1952:153, unless otherwise noted).—Utah: near Peterson; Henrys Fork, 8000 ft.; junction Deep and Carter creeks, 7900 ft.; Paradise Park, 10,000 ft., Uinta Mts.; 15 mi. N Mountain Home (11687 CM); Ephraim [mts. near?] (262651 BS); S point,

top Boulder Mtn., 11,000 ft.; Bryce National Park; Mt. Timpanogos.

Glaucomys sabrinus macrotis (Mearns)

1898. *Sciuropterus sabrinus macrotis* Mearns, Proc. U.S. Nat. Mus., 21:353, November 4, type from Hunter Mtn., 3300 ft., Catskill Mts., Greene Co., New York.
1915. *G[laucomys]. s[abrinus]. macrotis,* A. H. Howell, Proc. Biol. Soc. Washington, 28:111, May 27.

MARGINAL RECORDS.—New Brunswick (Anderson, 1947:126): Edmundston; Miramichi Road, Gloucester Co., thence down the coast to Massachusetts: Wilmington (A. H. Howell, 1918:37); Mt. Greylock (Copeland, 1912:159). New York: type locality. Pennsylvania: Alba (Roslund, 1951:44); McGees Mills (*ibid.*); Eire (mountains near?) (A. H. Howell, 1918:37). Michigan: Montcalm County (Burt, 1946:199). Wisconsin: Worden Twp., Clark Co. (Schmidt, 1931:110). Minnesota: Elk River (Anderson, 1947:126), thence eastward on the southern shores of lakes Superior and Huron and peninsular Ontario to Quebec: Blue Sea Lake (*ibid.*).

Glaucomys sabrinus makkovikensis (Sornborger)

1900. *Sciuropterus sabrinus makkovikensis* Sornborger, Ottawa Naturalist, 14:48, June 6, type from Makkovik, Labrador.
1918. *Glaucomys sabrinus makkovikensis,* A. H. Howell, N. Amer. Fauna, 44:34, June 13.

MARGINAL RECORDS (Anderson, 1947:126).—Labrador: type locality. Quebec: Saguenay Co., near Belle Isle Strait. Labrador: Northwest River.

Glaucomys sabrinus oregonensis (Bachman)

1839. *Pteromys oregonensis* Bachman, Jour. Acad. Nat. Sci. Philadelphia, 8:101, type from pine woods of the Columbia, near the sea. Probably near St. Helens, Columbia Co., Oregon. (See Rhoads, Proc. Acad. Nat. Sci. Philadelphia, 49:324, June, 1897.)
1918. *Glaucomys sabrinus oregonensis,* A. H. Howell, N. Amer. Fauna, 44:44, June 13.
1899. *Sciuropterus alpinus olympicus* Elliot, Field Columb. Mus., Publ. 30, Zool. Ser., 1:225, February 2, type from Happy Lake, Clallam Co., Washington. Regarded as inseparable from *G. s. oregonensis* by Dalquest (Univ. Kansas Publ., Mus. Nat. Hist., 2:295, April 9, 1948).

MARGINAL RECORDS.—British Columbia (Cowan and Guiguet, 1956:162): Butte Inlet; Agassiz; Upper Skagit River. Washington: Camp Skagit (A. H. Howell, 1918:45); Cottage Lake (Dalquest, 1948:295). Oregon (A. H. Howell, 1918:45): Marmot; Elk Head; Gold Beach; thence northward along the coast to British Columbia: Loughborough Inlet (Cowan and Guiguet, 1956:162).

Glaucomys sabrinus reductus Cowan

1937. *Glaucomys sabrinus reductus* Cowan, Proc. Biol. Soc. Washington, 50:79, June 22, type from Lonesome Lake, Atnarko River, approximately 52° 10′ N and 125° 45′ W, British Columbia.

MARGINAL RECORDS (Cowan and Guiguet, 1956: 162).—British Columbia: Wistaria; *Ootsa Lake*; Quesnel; Chezacut; type locality; Hagensborg; Kimsquit.

Glaucomys sabrinus sabrinus (Shaw)

1788. [*Sciurus*] *hudsonius* Gmelin, Syst. nat., ed. 13, 1:153. Type locality, mouth of Severn River, Ontario. A homonym of *Sciurus hudsonius* Gmelin, *antea*, p. 147, and possibly of *Sciurum hudsonium* Pallas, 1778.
1801. *Sciurus Sabrinus* Shaw, General zoology, 2:157, a renaming of *Sciurus hudsonius* Gmelin.
1915. [*Glaucomys*] *sabrinus*, A. H. Howell, Proc. Biol. Soc. Washington, 28:111, May 27.
1803. ?*Pteromys canadensis* É. Geoffroy St.-Hilaire, Catal. Mamm. Mus. Hist. Nat., Paris, p. 170, type from North America, probably Quebec (*fide* A. H. Howell, N. Amer. Fauna, 44:31, June 13, 1918).

MARGINAL RECORDS (A. H. Howell, 1918:34, unless otherwise noted).—Mackenzie, N.W.T.: Fort Anderson; Fort Resolution. Ontario: type locality; Moose Factory. Quebec: Kallio Lake (Cameron and Morris, 1951:127); Matamek River (Anderson, 1940:66); Tadousac; Lake Edward (Anderson, 1947:123). Ontario: Trout Creek. Wisconsin: Gordon; Nemakagan River. Minnesota (Swanson, 1945:82): Hinckley; Itasca County. Manitoba: Norway House. Saskatchewan: Cumberland House. Alberta: Calgary (Anderson, 1947:123); Didsbury; Edmonton (Anderson, 1947:123). Mackenzie: Fort Liard.

Glaucomys sabrinus stephensi (Merriam)

1900. *Sciuropterus oregonensis stephensi* Merriam, Proc. Biol. Soc. Washington, 13:151, June 13, type from Sherwood, 2500 ft., Mendocino Co., California.
1918. *Glaucomys sabrinus stephensi*, A. H. Howell, N. Amer. Fauna, 44:57, June 13.

MARGINAL RECORDS (Grinnell, 1933:136).—California: Cecilville; Dos Rios; type locality; Eureka.

Glaucomys sabrinus yukonensis (Osgood)

1900. *Sciuropterus yukonensis* Osgood, N. Amer. Fauna, 19:25, October 6, type from Camp Davidson, Yukon River, near Alaska-Canada boundary, Yukon.
1918. *Glaucomys sabrinus yukonensis*, A. H. Howell, N. Amer. Fauna, 44:41, June 13.

MARGINAL RECORDS.—Alaska: 8 mi. N Tanana (Dice, 1921:26). Yukon, N.W.T.: type locality; Mayo Lake, near head Stewart River (A. H. Howell, 1918:41); Frances Lake (Rand, 1945b:50); Lapie River (Canol Road, Mile 132, near junction Pelly and Ross rivers) (Anderson, 1947:127); Selkirk, junction Pelly and Lewes rivers (*ibid.*). Alaska: *Cook Inlet district* (24348 BS); head Toklat River (Anderson, 1947:127).

Glaucomys sabrinus zaphaeus (Osgood)

1905. *Sciuropterus alpinus zaphaeus* Osgood, Proc. Biol. Soc. Washington, 18:133, April 18, type from Helm Bay, Cleveland Peninsula, southeastern Alaska.
1918. *Glaucomys sabrinus zaphaeus*, A. H. Howell, N. Amer. Fauna, 44:43, June 13.

MARGINAL RECORDS.—Yukon: 1½ mi. S, 3 mi. E Dalton Post, 2500 ft. (Baker, 1951:100). British Columbia (Cowan and Guiguet, 1956:162): Nass River; Princess Royal Island. Alaska: *type locality*; Etolian Island (Cowan,

1937:81). Reference to any detailed map of southeastern Alaska will show that for each of the two localities last mentioned, the dot on Map 260 is misplaced slightly more than one millimeter.

FAMILY GEOMYIDAE—Pocket Gophers

Medium-sized rodents (132 to 400 mm.) with thickset bodies and little if any external evidence of a neck; strongly modified for fossorial life by having, for instance, small eyes, small ears, and stout, strong-clawed forelegs; large fur-lined cheek pouches that open externally; tail usually short and naked or sparsely haired; color relatively uniform in an individual, but varying from black to almost white depending on the kind. Skull massive and rugose; occiput large; auditory bullae relatively small; squamosals usually having pronounced ridges that often unite to form sagittal crest; zygomatic arches strong and widely flaring; interorbital constriction narrower than rostrum; squamosals large and comprising much of braincase at expense of frontals and parietals; occipitals broad, and paroccipital processes pronounced; mandible heavy and provided with large coronoid process; root of lower incisor forming prominent process between condyle and angular process. Dentition, i. $\frac{1}{1}$, c. $\frac{0}{0}$, p. $\frac{1}{1}$, m. $\frac{3}{3}$. Cheek-teeth evergrowing and having enamel greatly reduced.

The members of this family are widely distributed in North and Central America and the family has a temporal range from Lower Miocene to Recent.

Pocket gophers lead an almost completely subterranean existence and are only rarely seen above ground and then only momentarily. The burrow systems are often extensive and usually marked by a series of mounds of earth. The mounds are not conical as are those of the moles because the excavated earth is brought to the surface through an inclined lateral tunnel rather than a vertical shaft. Digging is accomplished mainly by means of the strong claws of the forefeet but the large upper incisor teeth also are used. The loose earth is compacted against the gopher's chest and the animal pushes the soil to the surface like an animated bulldozer might do.

Food consists mainly of the underground parts of plants, especially the succulent portions. Forbs, however, are often cut back above ground around the mouth of a burrow. Stems are cut in short lengths and transported in the cheek pouches to storage chambers, that are lateral pockets of the burrow system, for later use. Pocket gophers do not hibernate.

They are decidedly unsocial; except for a short time when the young are in the mother's burrow and when copulation takes place, any burrow system is occupied by only one animal. When two adults are placed together they fight viciously.

Pocket gophers have many natural enemies and to protect themselves they keep all entrances to a burrow closed with earthen plugs. It is thus easy for the collector to ascertain whether a given burrow is occupied; he need merely remove a plug and if there is an occupant, a new plug will be in place soon—sometimes, in fact, immediately.

Pocket gophers are relatively sedentary and live where there is suitable soil for burrowing. In many parts of their range, they are found in localized, isolated areas. Possibly because of their discontinuous distribution and great genetic plasticity, there are a great many kinds known. Indeed, in many areas, each individual population possesses some degree of uniqueness. Which of these populations are to be recognized nomenclaturally is often a highly subjective matter. Because of their remarkably great variability, more than 300 kinds of pocket gophers have been formally named.

KEY TO GENERA OF GEOMYIDAE

1. No enamel on posterior face of upper premolar.
  2. Posterior enamel plate present on 1st and 2nd upper molars.
    3. Upper incisor bisulcate. . . . . *Geomys*, p. 448
    3'. Upper incisor unisulcate.
      4. Frontal bone strongly constricted (biconcave) between orbits; external measurements less than 290,90,37; Jalisco and Nayarit. . . . . *Pappogeomys*, p. 463
      4'. Frontal bone parallel-sided (not constricted) between orbits; external measurements more than 290,90,37; Michoacán southward to Honduras. . . . . *Orthogeomys, p. 456
  2'. Posterior enamel plate absent on 1st and 2nd upper molars. . . . . *Cratogeomys*, p. 464
1'. Enamel present on posterior face of upper premolar.
  5. Posterior enamel plate of P4 restricted to inner side (posterior enamel plate present and complete on M1 and M2).
    6. Frontal bone broad and parallel-sided (not constricted) between orbits; pterygoids long.
                                     *Orthogeomys, p. 456
    6'. Frontal strongly constricted between orbits; pterygoids short.
      7. Postorbital processes absent; palatopterygoids long and slender (pterygoid part narrow).
                                   Heterogeomys, p. 458
      7'. Postorbital processes strongly marked; palatopterygoids short and broad (pterygoid part broad). . . . . *Macrogeomys*, p. 460
  5'. Posterior enamel plate of P4 complete.
    8. Posterior enamel plate present on inner (lingual) side only of M1 and M2; zygomatic arch complete without jugal (jugal inferior); incisors bisulcate. . . . . *Zygogeomys*, p. 455
    8'. Posterior enamel plate present and complete on M1, M2, and M3; zygomatic arch made up of jugal in middle extent; incisors not grooved or with only a fine sulcus on inner side. *Thomomys*, p. 412

* Merriam (1895a:23) writes that the posterior enamel plate of P4 "is evidently disappearing; it is present on the inner side in *O. latifrons* but is altogether absent or reduced to a very narrow strip in *O. grandis* and *scalops.*"

Genus **Thomomys** Wied-Neuwied—Smooth-toothed Pocket Gophers

Revised by V. Bailey, N. Amer. Fauna, 39:1–136, November 15, 1915.

1839. *Thomomys* Wied-Neuwied, Nova acta phys. med. acad. Leop.-Carol., 19(pt. 1):377. Type, *Thomomys rufescens* Wied-Neuwied.
1903. *Megascapterus* Elliot, Field Columb. Mus., Publ., 76, Zool. Ser., 3(11):190, July 25. Type, *Diplostoma bulbivorum* Richardson.

External measurements: average of 5 adult males of *T. bulbivorus*, the largest species, 300, 90, 42; type, adult male, of *T. talpoides pygmaeus*, the smallest subspecies, 177, 46, 22. Black to pale cream, usually nearly unicolor above and below. Upper and lower molars with anterior and posterior enamel plates; upper incisors bearing a minute groove near medial edge of anterior surface, which is otherwise smooth. Forefeet slenderer and relatively weaker than in other genera of pocket gophers; claws of forefeet much weaker than in other genera.

KEY TO THE SPECIES OF THOMOMYS

1. Sphenoidal fissure absent (see Fig. 254a).
  2. Height of ear from notch less than 7.
                    T. talpoides, p. 436
  2'. Height of ear from notch more than 7.
                    T. monticola, p. 445

1'. Sphenoidal fissure present (see Fig. 254a).
  3. Pterygoids concave on inner surface and convex on outer surface; confined to western Oregon. . . *T. bulbivorous*, p. 447
  3'. Pterygoids straight or nearly so; only *T. umbrinus* occurs in western Oregon and it is not confined thereto.
    4. Occurring in shaded area shown in Map 261. . . . . *T. umbrinus*, p. 413
    4'. Occurring in black areas shown in Map 261. From north to south these are:
      a. Parts of Oregon, Idaho, California and Nevada. . . *T. townsendii*, p. 435
      b. Parts of Arizona, New Mexico, Texas and Chihuahua. *T. baileyi*, p. 435

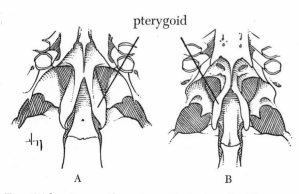

Fig. 254a. Anterolateral views of orbits of two skulls showing absence of sphenoidal fissure in *Thomomys talpoides bridgeri* (Pocatello, Idaho, 6731 K.U., ♀), upper, and presence of sphenoidal fissure in *Thomomys umbrinus ruidosae* (Ruidosa, New Mexico, 35157 K.U., ♀), lower, x 1½.

pterygoid

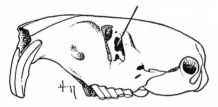

A   B

Fig. 254b. Pterygoid regions, X 3, in: A, *Thomomys bulbivorous*, Benton Co., Oregon, No. 50385 K.U., ♀; B, *Thomomys townsendii elkoensis*, Elburz, Nevada, No. 46460 K.U., ♀.

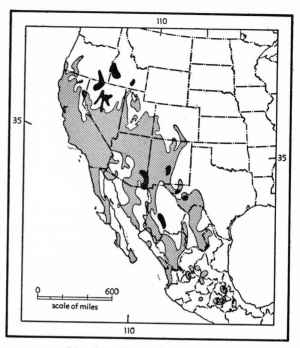

Map 261. Geographic ranges of:

a) *Thomomys umbrinus* (shaded areas)
b) *Thomomys townsendii* (black areas in Oregon, Idaho, California and Nevada)
c) *Thomomys baileyi* (black areas in Arizona, New Mexico, Texas, and Chihuahua)

Thomomys umbrinus
Southern Pocket Gopher

External measurements: 132–272; 43–100; 22–37. Color varies from black to almost white according to subspecies (and in *T. u. albicaudatus*, individually); not sharply bicolored, but underparts paler than upper parts. Sphenoidal fissure present; incisive foramina posterior to anterior opening of infraorbital canal; anterior prism of p4 rounded; interparietal relatively small; lambdoidal suture usually approximately straight in region of interparietal.

In Nevada, 63 pregnant females contained an average of 4.8 embryos (2–11; mode 4) (Hall, 1946: 458). In the latitude of central Nevada there is probably only 1 litter per year.

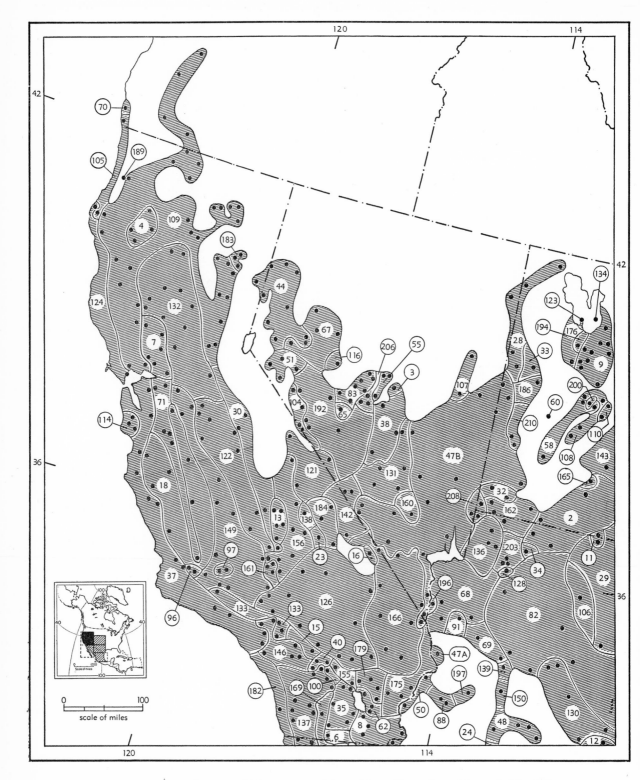

Map 262. Some subspecies of *Thomomys umbrinus*. For guide see legend beneath Map 263.

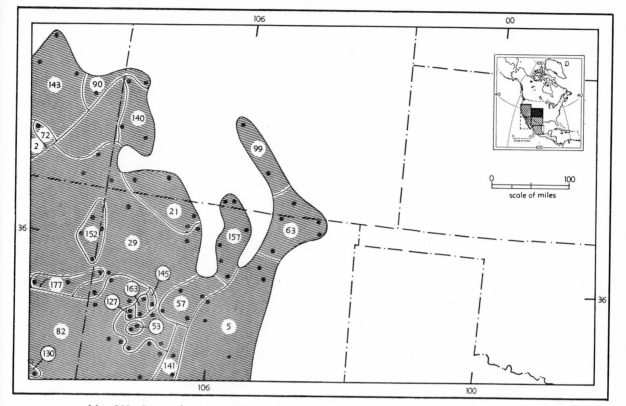

Map 263. Some subspecies of *Thomomys umbrinus*. Names following numerals comprise a
guide to both Map 262 and Map 263.

Guide to subspecies

2. *T. u. absonus*	47B. *T. u. centralis*	107. *T. u. latus*	152. *T. u. peramplus*
3. *T. u. abstrusus*	48. *T. u. cervinus*	108. *T. u. lenis*	155. *T. u. perpallidus*
4. *T. u. acrirostratus*	50. *T. u. chrysonotus*	109. *T. u. leucodon*	156. *T. u. perpes*
5. *T. u. actuosus*	51. *T. u. cinereus*	110. *T. u. levidensis*	157. *T. u. pervagus*
6. *T. u. affinis*	53. *T. u. collis*	114. *T. u. lorenzi*	160. *T. u. phelleoecus*
7. *T. u. agricolaris*	55. *T. u. concisor*	116. *T. u. lucrificus*	161. *T. u. piutensis*
8. *T. u. albatus*	57. *T. u. connectens*	121. *T. u. melanotis*	162. *T. u. planirostris*
9. *T. u. albicaudatus*	58. *T. u. contractus*	122. *T. u. mewa*	163. *T. u. planorum*
11. *T. u. alexandrae*	60. *T. u. convexus*	123. *T. u. minimus*	165. *T. u. powelli*
12. *T. u. alienus*	62. *T. u. crassus*	124. *T. u. minor*	166. *T. u. providentialis*
13. *T. u. alpinus*	63. *T. u. cultellus*	126. *T. u. mohavensis*	169. *T. u. puertae*
15. *T. u. altivallus*	65. *T. u. curtatus*	127. *T. u. morulus*	175. *T. u. riparius*
16. *T. u. amargosae*	67. *T. u. depressus*	128. *T. u. muralis*	176. *T. u. robustus*
18. *T. u. angularis*	68. *T. u. desertorum*	130. *T. u. mutabilis*	177. *T. u. rufidulus*
21. *T. u. apache*	69. *T. u. desitus*	131. *T. u. nanus*	179. *T. u. rupestris*
23. *T. u. argusensis*	70. *T. u. detumidus*	132. *T. u. navus*	182. *T. u. sanctidiegi*
24. *T. u. aridicola*	71. *T. u. diaboli*	133. *T. u. neglectus*	183. *T. u. saxatilis*
28. *T. u. aureiventris*	72. *T. u. dissimilus*	134. *T. u. nesophilus*	184. *T. u. scapterus*
29. *T. u. aureus*	82. *T. u. fulvus*	136. *T. u. nicholi*	186. *T. u. sevieri*
30. *T. u. awahnee*	83. *T. u. fumosus*	137. *T. u. nigracans*	189. *T. u. silvifugus*
32. *T. u. birdseyei*	88. *T. u. harquahalae*	138. *T. u. operarius*	192. *T. u. solitarius*
33. *T. u. bonnevillei*	90. *T. u. howelli*	139. *T. u. operosus*	194. *T. u. stansburyi*
34. *T. u. boreorarius*	91. *T. u. hualpaiensis*	140. *T. u. optabilis*	196. *T. u. suboles*
35. *T. u. boregoensis*	96. *T. u. infrapallidus*	141. *T. u. opulentus*	197. *T. u. subsimilis*
37. *T. u. bottae*	97. *T. u. ingens*	142. *T. u. oreoecus*	198. *T. u. supernus*
38. *T. u. brevidens*	99. *T. u. internatus*	143. *T. u. osgoodi*	200. *T. u. tivius*
40. *T. u. cabezonae*	100. *T. u. jacinteus*	145. *T. u. paguatae*	203. *T. u. trumbullensis*
44. *T. u. canus*	104. *T. u. lacrymalis*	146. *T. u. pallescens*	206. *T. u. vescus*
47A. *T. u. cedrinus*	105. *T. u. laticeps*	149. *T. u. pascalis*	208. *T. u. virgineus*
	106. *T. u. latirostris*	150. *T. u. patulus*	210. *T. u. wahwahensis*

The subspecies that recently have been assigned to the species *Thomomys bottae* (Eydoux and Gervais, 1836) all are here arranged as subspecies of the earlier named *Thomomys umbrinus* (Richardson, 1829) because Hoffmeister (1954:95, 96–100) arranged *Thomomys bottae hueyi* Goldman and *Thomomys burti proximus* Burt and Campbell [= *Thomomys umbrinus proximus* of authors] as subspecies of a single species. Although Hoffmeister used the specific name *bottae* (and not *umbrinus*)

he did not show that the subspecies *proximus* was specifically distinct from other subspecies of *Thomomys umbrinus* and in effect, nomenclaturally, united the two species *umbrinus* and *bottae*.

Thomomys umbrinus abbotti Huey

1928. *Thomomys bottae abbotti* Huey, Trans. San Diego Soc. Nat. Hist., 5:89, January 18, type from 1 mi. E El Rosario, Baja California (river bottom association), lat. 30° 03′ N, long. 115° 48′ W.

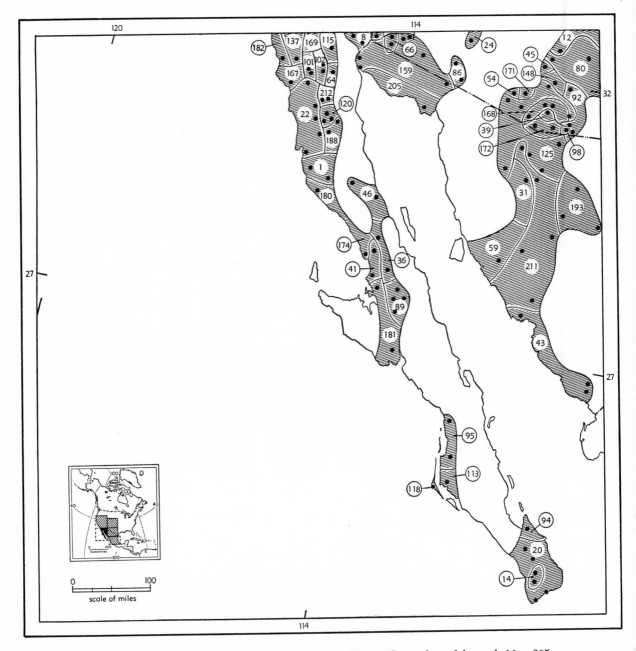

Map 264. Some subspecies of *Thomomys umbrinus*. For guide see legend beneath Map 265.

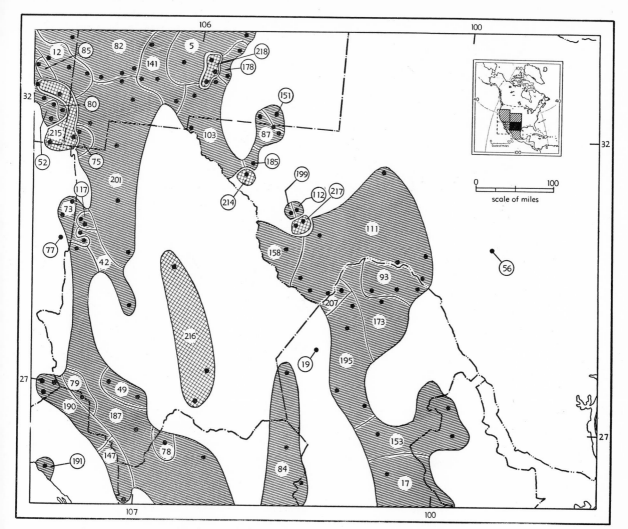

Map 265. Some subspecies of *Thomomys umbrinus* and all subspecies of *Thomomys baileyi*.
Names following numerals are a guide to both Map 264 and Map 265.

Guide
to kinds

1. *T. u. abbotti*	56. *T. u. confinalis*	103. *T. u. lachuguilla*	174. *T. u. rhizophagus*
5. *T. u. actuosus*	59. *T. u. convergens*	111. *T. u. limitaris*	178. *T. u. ruidosae*
8. *T. u. albatus*	64. *T. u. cunicularius*	112. *T. u. limpiae*	180. *T. u. ruricola*
12. *T. u. alienus*	66. *T. u. depauperatus*	113. *T. u. litoris*	181. *T. u. russeolus*
14. *T. u. alticolus*	73. *T. u. divergens*	115. *T. u. lucidus*	182. *T. u. sanctidiegi*
17. *T. u. analogus*	75. *T. u. emotus*	117. *T. u. madrensis*	185. *T. u. scotophilus*
19. *T. u. angustidens*	77. *T. u. estanciae*	118. *T. u. magdalenae*	187. *T. u. sheldoni*
20. *T. u. anitae*	78. *T. u. evexus*	120. *T. u. martirensis*	188. *T. u. siccovallis*
22. *T. u. aphrastus*	79. *T. u. eximius*	125. *T. u. modicus*	190. *T. u. simulus*
24. *T. u. aridicola*	80. *T. u. extenuatus*	137. *T. u. nigricans*	191. *T. u. sinaloae*
31. *T. u. basilicae*	82. *T. u. fulvus*	141. *T. u. opulentus*	193. *T. u. sonoriensis*
36. *T. u. borjasensis*	84. *T. u. goldmani*	147. *T. u. parviceps*	195. *T. u. sturgisi*
39. *T. u. burti*	85. *T. u. grahamensis*	148. *T. u. parvulus*	199. *T. u. texensis*
41. *T. u. cactophilus*	86. *T. u. growlerensis*	151. *T. u. pectoralis*	201. *T. u. toltecus*
42. *T. u. caliginosus*	87. *T. u. guadalupensis*	153. *T. u. perditus*	205. *T. u. vanrossemi*
43. *T. u. camoae*	89. *T. u. homorus*	158. *T. u. pervarius*	207. *T. u. villai*
45. *T. u. catalinae*	92. *T. u. hueyi*	159. *T. u. phasma*	211. *T. u. winthropi*
46. *T. u. catavinensis*	93. *T. u. humilis*	167. *T. u. proximarinus*	212. *T. u. xerophilus*
49. *T. u. chihuahuae*	94. *T. u. imitabilis*	168. *T. u. proximus*	214. *T. b. baileyi*
52. *T. u. collinus*	95. *T. u. incomptus*	169. *T. u. puertae*	215. *T. b. mearnsi*
54. *T. u. comobabiensis*	98. *T. u. intermedius*	171. *T. u. pusillus*	216. *T. b. nelsoni*
	101. *T. u. jojobae*	172. *T. u. quercinus*	217. *T. b. spatiosus*
	102. *T. u. juarezensis*	173. *T. u. retractus*	218. *T. b. tularosae*

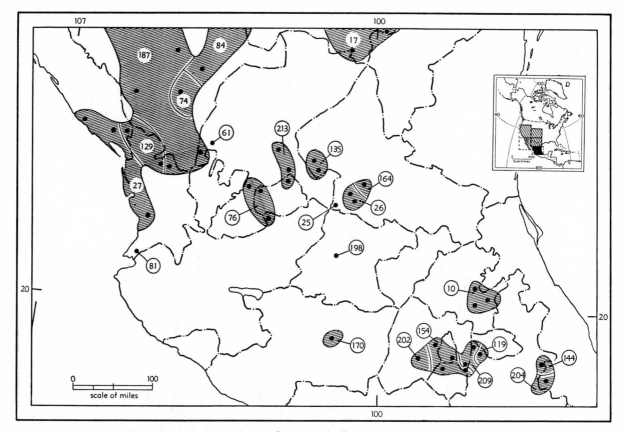

Map 266. Some subspecies of *Thomomys umbrinus*.

Guide to subspecies	76. *T. u. enixus*	164. *T. u. potosinus*
10. *T. u. albigularis*	81. *T. u. extimus*	170. *T. u. pullus*
17. *T. u. analogus*	84. *T. u. goldmani*	187. *T. u. sheldoni*
25. *T. u. arriagensis*	119. *T. u. martinensis*	198. *T. u. supernus*
26. *T. u. atrodorsalis*	129. *T. u. musculus*	202. *T. u. tolucae*
27. *T. u. atrovarius*	135. *T. u. newmani*	204. *T. u. umbrinus*
61. *T. u. crassidens*	144. *T. u. orizabae*	209. *T. u. vulcanius*
74. *T. u. durangae*	154. *T. u. peregrinus*	213. *T. u. zacatecae*

MARGINAL RECORDS.—Baja California: type locality; San Fernando Mission (Huey, 1949:54).

Thomomys umbrinus absonus Goldman

1931. *Thomomys perpallidus absonus* Goldman, Jour. Washington Acad. Sci., 21:425, October 19, type from Jacobs Pools, 4000 ft., Houserock Valley, Coconino Co., Arizona.

MARGINAL RECORDS.—Utah (Durrant, 1952:226): Escalante, 5258 ft. Arizona: type locality; near Kanab Wash, southern boundary Kaibab Indian Reservation (Hall and Davis, 1934:52). Utah (Durrant, 1952:226): Kanab, 4925 ft.

Thomomys umbrinus abstrusus Hall and Davis

1935. *Thomomys bottae abstrusus* Hall and Davis, Univ. California Publ. Zool., 40:391, March 13, type from Fish Spring Valley, 2 mi. SE Tulle Peak, 7000 ft., Nye Co., Nevada. Known only from the type locality.

Thomomys umbrinus acrirostratus Grinnell

1935. *Thomomys bottae acrirostratus* Grinnell, Univ. California Publ. Zool., 40:408, November 14, type from valley of Mad River, 2700 ft., 7 mi. above Ruth, Trinity Co., California.

MARGINAL RECORDS (Grinnell, 1935:408).—California: Helena, 1400 ft.; Deer Lick Springs, 3000 ft.; near Mad River bridge, SW base South Fork Mtn., 3000–3200 ft.; type locality.

Thomomys umbrinus actuosus Kelson

1951. *Thomomys bottae actuosus* Kelson, Univ. Kansas Publ., Mus. Nat. Hist., 5:67, October 1, type from Corona, Lincoln Co., New Mexico.

MARGINAL RECORDS (Kelson, 1951:70).—New Mexico: 10 mi. S Mora, 7300 ft.; Las Vegas; type locality; NE slope Capitan Mts.; *SW foothills Capitan Mts.; near W end summit of ridge, Capitan Mts.*; Bear Canyon, San Andres

Mts.; *E slope San Andres Mts.; E slope near S end Manzano Mts.*; E slope middle distance of range, Manzano Mts.; *E foothills near N end, Manzano Mts.*; San Pedro; *Pecos, 6800 ft.*

Thomomys umbrinus affinis Huey

1945. *Thomomys bottae affinis* Huey, Trans. San Diego Soc. Nat. Hist., 10:254, August 31, type from Jacumba, San Diego Co., California.

MARGINAL RECORDS.—California: type locality; *Mountain Spring* (we have not been able to locate the specimen from Mountain Spring assigned by V. Bailey, 1915:57, to *T. b. nigricans;* it is almost surely better assigned to *T. u. affinis*).

Thomomys umbrinus agricolaris Grinnell

1935. *Thomomys bottae agricolaris* Grinnell, Univ. California Publ. Zool., 40:409, November 14, type from Stralock Farm, 3 mi. W Davis, Yolo Co., California.

MARGINAL RECORDS.—California: Rumsey (Grinnell, 1935:409); Knights Landing (*ibid.*); type locality; Rio Vista Junction (Hooper, 1944:41); Denverton (*op. cit.*:40); 3 mi. W Vacaville (Grinnell, 1935:409).

Thomomys umbrinus albatus Grinnell

1912. *Thomomys albatus* Grinnell, Univ. California Publ. Zool., 10:172, June 7, type from W side Colorado River, at old Hanlon Ranch, near Pilot Knob, Imperial Co., California.

MARGINAL RECORDS.—California (Chattin, 1941: 278): Alamo Duck Preserve, 8 mi. NW Calipatria; Brawley, −109 ft.; 2 mi. SW Potholes. Arizona: Yuma (Goldman, 1947:20); 1 mi. N San Luis (Grinnell and Hill, 1936:3). Baja California: Colorado River, 20 mi. SW Pilot Knob (*ibid.*); 5 mi. E Cerro Prieto (*ibid.*). California: El Centro (Miller, 1946:350).

Thomomys umbrinus albicaudatus Hall

1930. *Thomomys perpallidus albicaudatus* Hall, Univ. California Publ. Zool., 32:444, July 8, type from Provo, 4510 ft., Utah Co., Utah.

MARGINAL RECORDS (Durrant, 1952:194).—Utah: Bountiful, 4500 ft.; Draper, 4500 ft.; type locality; 7 mi. SW Nephi, 6000 ft.; 2 mi. W Murray, 4300 ft.; Rose Canyon, Oquirrh Mts., 5650 ft.; Vernon, 4300 ft.; Little Valley, Sheeprock Mts., 5500 ft.; Clover Creek, Onaqui Mts., 5500 ft.; Bauer, 4500 ft.; thence northward east of Great Salt Lake to point of beginning.

Thomomys umbrinus albigularis Nelson and Goldman

1934. *Thomomys umbrinus albigularis* Nelson and Goldman, Jour. Mamm., 15:106, May 15, type from El Chico, 9800 ft., Sierra de Pachuca, Hidalgo.

MARGINAL RECORDS (Nelson and Goldman, 1934: 108).—Hidalgo: type locality; Tulancingo; Real del Monte.

Thomomys umbrinus alexandrae Goldman

1933. *Thomomys alexandrae* Goldman, Jour. Washington Acad. Sci., 23:464, October 15, type from plain 5 mi. SW

Rainbow Lodge, near Navajo Mtn., 6200 ft., Coconino Co., Arizona.

MARGINAL RECORDS.—Utah: Soldier Spring, Navajo Mtn., 8600 ft. (Durrant, 1952:227). Arizona: type locality.

Thomomys umbrinus alienus Goldman

1938. *Thomomys bottae alienus* Goldman, Jour. Washington Acad. Sci., 28:338, July 15, type from Mammoth, 2400 ft., San Pedro River, Pinal Co., Arizona.

MARGINAL RECORDS.—Arizona: Rice [= San Carlos] (Hall and Kelson, 1952:356); Safford (Goldman, 1938b: 339); Duncan (*ibid.*). New Mexico: Redrock (Goldman, 1947:19). Arizona: type locality.

Thomomys umbrinus alpinus Merriam

1897. *Thomomys alpinus* Merriam, Proc. Biol. Soc. Washington, 11:216, July 15, type from Big Cottonwood Meadows, 10,000 ft., 8 mi. SE Mt. Whitney peak, High Sierra, Inyo Co., California.

MARGINAL RECORDS.—California (Grinnell, 1933: 142, unless otherwise noted): Whitney Creek, 10,650 ft.; Cottonwood Creek, 9500 ft. (V. Bailey, 1915:64); Olancha Peak; Siretta Meadows, 9000 ft.; Jordan Hot Springs.

Thomomys umbrinus alticolus J. A. Allen

1899. *Thomomys fulvus alticolus* J. A. Allen, Bull. Amer. Mus. Nat. Hist., 12:13, March 4, type from Sierra Laguna, 7000 ft., Baja California.

MARGINAL RECORDS.—Baja California: 7 mi. NW San Bartolo (Huey, 1945:265); type locality.

Thomomys umbrinus altivallis Rhoads

1895. *Thomomys altivallis* Rhoads, Proc. Acad. Nat. Sci. Philadelphia, 47:34, February 21, type from San Bernardino Mts., 5000 ft., California.

MARGINAL RECORDS.—California (Grinnell, 1933: 142, unless otherwise noted): *Doble; Fish Creek* (Grinnell, 1908:150); *Seven Oaks;* Fawnskin Valley.

Thomomys umbrinus amargosae Grinnell

1921. *Thomomys perpallidus amargosae* Grinnell, Univ. California Publ. Zool., 21:239, November 7, type from Shoshone, 1560 ft., Amargosa River, Inyo Co., California. Known only from the type locality.

Thomomys umbrinus analogus Goldman

1938. *Thomomys umbrinus analogus* Goldman, Proc. Biol. Soc. Washington, 51:59, March 18, type from Sierra Guadalupe, about 12 mi. S General Cepeda, Coahuila.

MARGINAL RECORDS.—Coahuila (Baker, 1956:218): Jaral; 12 mi. E San Antonio de las Alazanas, 9000 ft.; Sierra Encarnación; *Sierra de Guadalupe, 7000 ft.*

Thomomys umbrinus angularis Merriam

1897. *Thomomys angularis* Merriam, Proc. Biol. Soc. Washington, 11:214, July 15, type from Los Baños, Merced Co., California.

MARGINAL RECORDS.—California: 8 mi. S Tracy (Grinnell, 1933:139); type locality; Coalinga (*ibid.*); Paso Robles (V. Bailey, 1915:53); Kings City (*ibid.*); Salinas (*ibid.*); San Benito (*ibid.*).

Thomomys umbrinus angustidens Baker

1953. *Thomomys bottae angustidens* Baker, Univ. Kansas Publ., Mus. Nat. Hist., 5:508, June 1, type from Sierra del Pino, 5250 ft., 6 mi. N, 6 mi. W Acebuches, Coahuila. Known only from the vicinity of the type locality.

Thomomys umbrinus anitae J. A. Allen

1898. *Thomomys fulvus anitae* J. A. Allen, Bull. Amer. Mus. Nat. Hist., 10:146, April 12, type from Santa Anita, Baja California.

MARGINAL RECORDS.—Baja California: Tres Pachitas (V. Bailey, 1915:59); Triunfo (*ibid.*); type locality; Cape San Lucas (Burt, 1940:3).

Thomomys umbrinus apache V. Bailey

1910. *Thomomys apache* V. Bailey, Proc. Biol. Soc. Washington, 23:79, May 4, type from Lake La Jara, 7500 ft., Jicarilla Apache Indian Reservation, New Mexico.

MARGINAL RECORDS.—Colorado: Bayfield (Warren, 1942:160). New Mexico (V. Bailey, 1932:241–242): Horse Lake; Stinking Spring Lake. Colorado: Florida (15974 KU).

Thomomys umbrinus aphrastus Elliot

1903. *Thomomys aphrastus* Elliot, Field Columb. Mus., Publ. 79, Zool. Ser., 3:219, August 15, type from San[to] Tomás, Baja California.

MARGINAL RECORDS.—Baja California: type locality; extreme west end El Valle de la Trinidad (Huey, 1945:260); San Antonio (Hall and Kelson, 1952:357); Rosarito (on geographic grounds, from V. Bailey, 1915:58, specimens not seen); Socorro (*ibid.*).

Thomomys umbrinus argusensis Huey

1931. *Thomomys argusensis* Huey, Trans. San Diego Soc. Nat. Hist., 7:43, December 19, type from Junction Ranch, Argus Mts., Inyo Co., California.

MARGINAL RECORDS.—California (Huey, 1931:44): type locality; *Mountain Spring; Orando (Arando) Mine.*

Thomomys umbrinus aridicola Huey

1937. *Thomomys bottae aridicola* Huey, Trans. San Diego Soc. Nat. Hist., 8:354, June 15, type from Ajo Railroad right-of-way, about 2 mi. N Black Gap, 10 mi. S Gila Bend, Maricopa Co., Arizona. Known only from the type locality.

Thomomys umbrinus arriagensis Dalquest

1951. *Thomomys umbrinus arriagensis* Dalquest, Jour. Washington Acad. Sci., 41:361, November 14, type from 1 km. S Arriaga, San Luis Potosí. Known only from the type locality.

Thomomys umbrinus atrodorsalis Nelson and Goldman

1934. *Thomomys umbrinus atrodorsalis* Nelson and Goldman, Jour. Mamm., 15:111, May 15, type from Alvarez, 8000 ft., San Luis Potosí.

MARGINAL RECORDS.—San Luis Potosí: San Luis Potosí (Nelson and Goldman, 1934:112); *1 km. N Arenal* (Dalquest, 1953b:100); type locality.

Thomomys umbrinus atrovarius J. A. Allen

1898. *Thomomys atrovarius* J. A. Allen, Bull. Amer. Mus. Nat. Hist., 10:148, April 12, type from Tatemales (near Rosario), Sinaloa.
1934. *Thomomys umbrinus atrovarius*, Nelson and Goldman, Jour. Mamm., 15:119, May 15.

MARGINAL RECORDS.—Sinaloa: Mazatlán (Miller, 1924:247); Rosario (V. Bailey, 1915:96). Nayarit: Navarete (*ibid.*), thence northward along coast to point of beginning.

Thomomys umbrinus aureiventris Hall

1930. *Thomomys perpallidus aureiventris* Hall, Univ. California Publ. Zool., 32:444, July 8, type from Fehlman Ranch, 3 mi. N Kelton, 4225 ft., Boxelder Co., Utah.

MARGINAL RECORDS (Durrant, 1952:182, unless otherwise noted).—Utah: type locality; Utah-Nevada boundary, E side Tacoma Range, 4300 ft. Nevada: 15 mi. S Montello, 4 mi. W Pilot Peak (Chamberlain, 1957:267). Utah: Ibapah, 5000 ft.; *Queen of Sheba Canyon, W side of Deep Creek Mts., 5600 ft.;* Trout Creek.

Thomomys umbrinus aureus J. A. Allen

1893. *Thomomys aureus* J. A. Allen, Bull. Amer. Mus. Nat. Hist., 5:49, April 28, type from Bluff City, San Juan Co., Utah.

MARGINAL RECORDS.—Utah: Monticello (Durrant, 1952:217). Colorado: Montezuma County, 3500 ft. (Warren, 1942:159). New Mexico (Kelson, 1951:70): Fruitland; Chama River, Gallina; near El Vado; Riley; St. Augustine Plains; Acoma; Wingate; Pueblo of Zuni. Arizona: Winslow (Durrant, 1946:73). Utah: type locality.

Thomomys umbrinus awahnee Merriam

1908. *Thomomys alpinus awahnee* Merriam, Proc. Biol. Soc. Washington, 21:146, June 9, type from Yosemite Valley, 4000 ft., near old Sentinel Hotel, Mariposa Co., California.

MARGINAL RECORDS.—California (V. Bailey, 1915:65, unless otherwise noted): type locality; Mineral King; *Kern River Lakes;* Taylor Meadow (Grinnell, 1933:142); *Tehachapi Peak* (*ibid.*); *E fork Kaweah River, 5600 ft.;* Wawona; *S fork Merced River, 4000 ft.*

Thomomys umbrinus basilicae Benson and Tillotson

1939. *Thomomys bottae occipitalis* Benson and Tillotson, Proc. Biol. Soc. Washington, 52:151, October 11, type from La Misión, 2 mi. W Magdalena, Sonora. Not *Thomomys bottae occipitalis* Dice, 1925, type a fossil, from Rancho La Brea deposits, California.
1940. *Thomomys bottae basilicae* Benson and Tillotson, Proc. Biol. Soc. Washington, 53:93, June 28, a renaming of *T. b. occipitalis.* Known only from the type locality.

Thomomys umbrinus birdseyei Goldman

1937. *Thomomys bottae birdseyei* Goldman, Proc. Biol. Soc. Washington, 50:134, September 10, type from Pine Valley Mts., 5 mi. E Pine Valley, 8300 ft., Washington Co., Utah.

MARGINAL RECORDS (Durrant, 1952:218).—Utah: Hebron; type locality; ¾ *mi. E town of Pine Valley, 6500 ft.; Pine Valley Campground, 6800 ft.*

Thomomys umbrinus bonnevillei Durrant

1946. *Thomomys bottae bonnevillei* Durrant, Univ. Kansas Publ., Mus. Nat. Hist., 1:141, August 15, type from Fish Springs, 4400 ft., Juab Co., Utah. Known only from the type locality.

Thomomys umbrinus boregoensis Huey

1939. *Thomomys bottae boregoensis* Huey, Trans. San Diego Soc. Nat. Hist., 9:70, December 8, type from Beatty Ranch, Borego Valley, San Diego Co., California.
1939. *Thomomys bottae aderrans* Huey, Trans. San Diego Soc. Nat. Hist., 9:71, December 8, type from Carrizo Creek, San Diego Co., California.

MARGINAL RECORDS (Chattin, 1941:277).—California: 2 mi. N Oasis, near Thermal; Mecca; Harpers Well; Coyote Wells; Carrizo Creek; E side San Felipe Narrows.

Thomomys umbrinus boreorarius Durham

1952. *Thomomys bottae boreorarius* Durham, Jour. Mamm., 33:498, November 19, type from Swamp Point, 7522 ft., 18½ mi. NW Bright Angel Point, North Rim of Grand Canyon, Coconino Co., Arizona.

MARGINAL RECORDS (Durham, 1952:498).—Arizona: *Powell Spring, 6209 ft.; NE end Powell Plateau, 7650 ft.;* type locality.

Thomomys umbrinus borjasensis Huey

1945. *Thomomys bottae borjasensis* Huey, Trans. San Diego Soc. Nat. Hist., 10:262, August 31, type from San Borjas Mission, lat. 28° 52′ N, long. 113° 53′ W, Baja California.

MARGINAL RECORDS.—Baja California: Yubay (on geographic grounds from V. Bailey, 1915:58, specimens not seen); type locality.

Thomomys umbrinus bottae (Eydoux and Gervais)

1836. *Oryctomys* (*Saccophorus*) *bottae* Eydoux and Gervais, Mag. de Zool., Paris, 6:23. Type locality, coast of California; name applied by Baird (Proc. Acad. Nat. Sci. Philadelphia, 7:335, April 1855) to the gopher occurring in the vicinity of Monterey.

MARGINAL RECORDS (V. Bailey, 1915:46, unless otherwise noted).—California: Walnut Creek (Hooper, 1944:37); San Jose; Salinas Valley; Jamesburg; Jolon; Pleyto; Santa Margarita; Big Pine Mts.; Matilija; Santa Paula; Santa Monica; Alhambra, thence northward along coast (excepting the range of *T. b. lorenzi*) to point of beginning.

Thomomys umbrinus brevidens Hall

1932. *Thomomys bottae brevidens* Hall, Univ. California Publ. Zool., 38:330, February 27, type from Breen Creek, 7000 ft., Kawich Range, Nye Co., Nevada.

MARGINAL RECORDS (Hall, 1946:470).—Nevada: 1 mi. N Fish Lake, 6500 ft., Fish Spring Valley; 5 mi. E Nyala, 6000 ft.; Cactus Flat, 5700 ft., 7½ mi. SW Silverbow.

Thomomys umbrinus burti Huey

1932. *Thomomys burti* Huey, Trans. San Diego. Soc. Nat. Hist., 7:158, July 28, type from Madera Canyon, 6000 ft., Santa Rita Mts., Arizona. Known only from the type locality.
1934. *Thomomys umbrinus burti*, Nelson and Goldman, Jour. Mamm., 15:117, May 15.

Thomomys umbrinus cabezonae Merriam

1901. *Thomomys cabezonae* Merriam, Proc. Biol. Soc. Washington, 14:110, July 19, type from Cabezon, San Gorgonio Pass, Riverside Co., California.

MARGINAL RECORDS.—California: Banning (Grinnell, 1933:141); Whitewater (*ibid.*); Schains Ranch (*ibid.*); *Vallevista, 1800 ft.* (Grinnell and Swarth, 1913:351).

Thomomys umbrinus cactophilus Huey

1929. *Thomomys bottae cactophilus* Huey, Trans. San Diego Soc. Nat. Hist., 5:241, February 27, type from Punta Prieta, lat. 28° 56′ N, long. 114° 12′ W, Baja California.

MARGINAL RECORDS.—Baja California: type locality; Santa Rosalía Bay (Huey, 1945:262).

Thomomys umbrinus caliginosus Nelson and Goldman

1934. *Thomomys umbrinus caliginosus* Nelson and Goldman, Jour. Mamm., 15:116, May 15, type from 8 mi. W Altamirano, 8000 ft., Sierra Madre, Chihuahua.

MARGINAL RECORDS.—Chihuahua: Colonia García (Nelson and Goldman, 1934:116); type locality.

Thomomys umbrinus camoae Burt

1937. *Thomomys bottae camoae* Burt, Occas. Papers Mus. Zool., Univ. Michigan, 344:1, January 5, type from Camoa, Río Mayo, Sonora.

MARGINAL RECORDS (Burt, 1938:42).—Sonora: San José de Guaymas; type locality; Tesia.

Thomomys umbrinus canus V. Bailey

1910. *Thomomys canus* V. Bailey, Proc. Biol. Soc. Washington, 23:79, May 4, type from Deep Hole, N end Smoke Creek Desert, Washoe Co., Nevada.

MARGINAL RECORDS (Hall, 1946:460, unless otherwise noted).—Nevada: Granite Creek; type locality; 2 mi. N Nixon; Fallon; 7 mi. S, 3½ mi. E Fallon; N side Carson River, 4300 ft., 1 mi. E Dayton; N side Truckee River, 9½ mi. E Reno, 4500 ft.; 4½ mi. S Flanagan, 4100 ft. California: Amedee (Hall, 1946:454). Nevada: Smoke Creek.

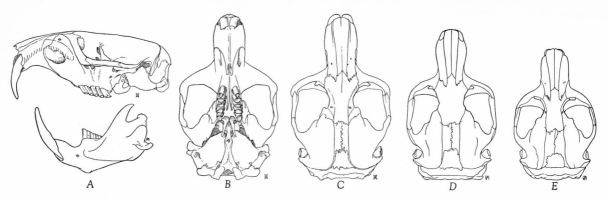

Fig. 255. *Thomomys umbrinus canus*, Deep Hole, Nevada, *A, B, C*, No. 41652 M.V.Z., ♂, X 1., and *D* No. 41660 ♀, X 1. *E* is *Thomomys umbrinus phelleoecus*, Hidden Forest, Nevada, No. 93119 M.V.Z., ♂, X 1. Note secondary sexual difference between *C* and *D*, and geographic (subspecific) difference between *C* and *E*.

Thomomys umbrinus catalinae Goldman

1931. *Thomomys fulvus catalinae* Goldman, Jour. Washington Acad. Sci., 21:419, October 19, type from Summerhaven, Santa Catalina Mts., 7500 ft., Pima Co., Arizona.

MARGINAL RECORDS.—Arizona: type locality; *Sabino Canyon, near Summerhaven* (Dice and Blossom, 1937:25).

Thomomys umbrinus catavinensis Huey

1931. *Thomomys bottae catavinensis* Huey, Trans. San Diego Soc. Nat. Hist., 7:45, December 19, type from Cataviña, lat. 29° 54′ N, long. 114° 57′ W, Baja California.

MARGINAL RECORDS.—Baja California: type locality; San Francisquito (on geographic grounds from V. Bailey, 1915:58, specimens not seen).

Thomomys umbrinus cedrinus Huey

1955. *Thomomys bottae cedrinus* Huey, Trans. San Diego Soc. Nat. Hist., 12:100, February 10, type from summit of Crossman Peak (Juniper-Piñon Belt), Chemehuevis Mts., Mohave Co., Arizona. Known only from the type locality and Lucky Star Mine lower on the mountain range.

Thomomys umbrinus centralis Hall

1930. *Thomomys perpallidus centralis* Hall, Univ. California Publ. Zool., 32:445, July 8, type from 2½ mi. E Baker (1¼ mi. W Nevada–Utah boundary on 39th parallel), 5700 ft., White Pine Co., Nevada.

MARGINAL RECORDS.—Utah (Durrant, 1952:199): 1 mi. SE Gandy, 5000 ft.; White Valley (Tule Spring), 60 mi. W Delta; 5 mi. S Garrison, 5400 ft.; Cedar City. Nevada (Hall, 1946:473): Meadow Valley Wash, 7 mi. S Caliente; Black Canyon; Boulder City; Durban Ranch, Colorado River, 14 mi. E Searchlight; ½ mi. N California–Nevada Monument, Colorado River, 500 ft. California: Colorado River, 500 ft. (Chattin, 1941:272). Nevada (Hall, 1946:473): Trout Canyon, 6500 ft.; Amargosa River, 3½ mi. NE Beatty,

3400 ft.; Springdale, N end Oasis Valley; Indian Springs; Coyote Spring, 2800 ft.; Crystal Spring to ¾ mi. S thereof, 4000 ft., Pahranagat Valley; Grant Mts., 19½ mi. WSW Sunnyside; Cleveland Ranch, 6000 ft., Spring Valley.

Thomomys umbrinus cervinus J. A. Allen

1895. *Thomomys cervinus* J. A. Allen, Bull. Amer. Mus. Nat. Hist., 7:203, June 29, type from Phoenix, Maricopa Co., Arizona.

MARGINAL RECORDS.—Arizona: type locality; Tempe (V. Bailey, 1915:79); Sacaton (*ibid.*); Gila Bend (Goldman, 1947:18).

Thomomys umbrinus chihuahuae Nelson and Goldman

1934. *Thomomys umbrinus chihuahuae* Nelson and Goldman, Jour. Mamm., 15:114, May 15, type from Sierra Madre, 7000 ft., about 65 mi. E Batopilas, Chihuahua.

MARGINAL RECORDS.—Chihuahua: Mojarachic (Knobloch, 1942:298); type locality.

Thomomys umbrinus chrysonotus Grinnell

1912. *Thomomys chrysonotus* Grinnell, Univ. California Publ. Zool., 10:174, June 7, type from Ehrenberg, Yuma Co., Arizona.
1931. *Thomomys fulvus flavidus* Goldman, Jour. Washington Acad. Sci., 21:417, October 19, type from Parker, 350 ft., Yuma Co., Arizona.

MARGINAL RECORDS.—Arizona: Parker (Goldman, 1947:16); 3 mi. S Ehrenberg (Grinnell and Hill, 1936:6).

Thomomys umbrinus cinereus Hall

1932. *Thomomys bottae cinereus* Hall, Univ. California Publ. Zool., 38:327, February 27, type from West Walker River, Smiths Valley, 4700 ft., Lyon Co., Nevada.

MARGINAL RECORDS (Hall, 1946:463).—Nevada: ½ mi. N Yerington; 3 mi. S Schurz, 4100 ft.; 9 mi. NE Wellington, 4800 ft.; East Walker River, 5000 ft., 5 mi. NW Morgans Ranch.

Thomomys umbrinus collinus Goldman

1931. *Thomomys fulvus collinus* Goldman, Jour. Washingman Acad. Sci., 21:421, October 19, type from Fly Park, 9000 ft., Chiricahua Mts., Cochise Co., Arizona.
1934. *Thomomys umbrinus chiricahuae* Nelson and Goldman, Jour. Mamm., 15:117, May 15, type from Pinery Canyon, 7500 ft., Chiricahua Mts., Arizona.

MARGINAL RECORDS.—Arizona: mouth of Turkey Creek, Chiricahua Mts. (Goldman, 1947:27); Rucker Canyon, Chiricahua Mts. (Goldman, 1931:422).

Thomomys umbrinus collis Hooper

1940. *Thomomys bottae collis* Hooper, Occas. Papers Mus. Zool., Univ. Michigan, 422:7, November 14, type from Shuman's Ranch, 30 mi. S Grants, T. 6 N, R. 10 W, sec. 30, Valencia Co., New Mexico.

MARGINAL RECORDS.—New Mexico: type locality; Point of Malpais, 12 mi. E Trechado (Kelson, 1951:70).

Thomomys umbrinus comobabiensis Huey

1937. *Thomomys bottae comobabiensis* Huey, Trans. San Diego Soc. Nat. Hist., 8:354, June 15, type from 5 mi. NW Sells, 2400 ft., Pima Co., Arizona. Known only from the type locality.

Thomomys umbrinus concisor Hall and Davis

1935. *Thomomys bottae concisor* Hall and Davis, Univ. California Publ. Zool., 40:390, March 13, type from Pott's Ranch, 6900 ft., Monitor Valley, Nye Co., Nevada.

MARGINAL RECORDS (Hall, 1946:469).—Nevada: Wilson Creek, 7200 ft.; type locality; 8 mi. N Pine Creek Ranch, 7050 ft.

Thomomys umbrinus confinalis Goldman

1936. *Thomomys lachuguilla confinalis* Goldman, Jour. Washington Acad. Sci., 26:119, March 15, type from 35 mi. E Rock Springs, 2450 ft., Texas. Known only from the type locality.

Thomomys umbrinus connectens Hall

1936. *Thomomys bottae connectens* Hall, Jour. Washington Acad. Sci., 26:296, July 15, type from Clawson Dairy, 5 mi. N Albuquerque, 4943 ft., Bernalillo Co., New Mexico.

MARGINAL RECORDS (Kelson, 1951:70).—New Mexico: Juan Tafoya; Bernalillo; Belen; Laguna.

Thomomys umbrinus contractus Durrant

1946. *Thomomys bottae contractus* Durrant, Univ. Kansas Publ., Mus. Nat. Hist., 1:50, August 15, type from Scipio, 5315 ft., Millard Co., Utah.

MARGINAL RECORDS (Durrant, 1952:206).—Utah: Oak City, 5000 ft.; type locality; Beaver, 6000 ft.

Thomomys umbrinus convergens Nelson and Goldman

1934. *Thomomys bottae convergens* Nelson and Goldman, Jour. Mamm., 15:123, May 15, type from Costa Rica Ranch, delta of Sonora River, SW of Hermosillo, Sonora. Known only from the type locality.

Thomomys umbrinus convexus Durrant

1939. *Thomomys bottae convexus* Durrant, Proc. Biol. Soc. Washington, 52:159, October 11, type from E side Clear Lake, 4600 ft., Millard Co., Utah. Known only from the type locality.

Thomomys umbrinus crassidens Nelson and Goldman

1934. *Thomomys umbrinus crassidens* Nelson and Goldman, Jour. Mamm., 15:113, May 15, type from Sierra de Valparaíso, 8700 ft., Zacatecas. Known only from the type locality.

Thomomys umbrinus crassus Chattin

1941. *Thomomys bottae crassus* Chattin, Trans. San Diego Soc. Nat. Hist., 9:274, April 30, type from 1½ mi. W Niland, −180 ft., Imperial Co., California.

MARGINAL RECORDS (Chattin, 1941:275).—California: Salt Creek; type locality; 5 mi. SW Niland, −212 ft.

Thomomys umbrinus cultellus Kelson

1951. *Thomomys bottae cultellus* Kelson, Univ. Kansas Publ., Mus. Nat. Hist., 5:64, October 1, type from Halls Peak, Mora Co., New Mexico.

MARGINAL RECORDS (Kelson, 1951:70).—Colorado: Fisher Peak. New Mexico: Oak Canyon; Sierra Grande; type locality; Long Canyon, 3 mi. N Catskill.

Thomomys umbrinus cunicularius Huey

1945. *Thomomys bottae cunicularius* Huey, Trans. San Diego Soc. Nat. Hist., 10:252, August 31, type from Los Palmitos (western end Pattie Basin), on southeastern basin of Sierra Juárez (desert slope), lat. 31° 44' N, long. 115° 36' W, Baja California. Known only from the type locality.

Thomomys umbrinus curtatus Hall

1932. *Thomomys bottae curtatus* Hall, Univ. California Publ. Zool., 38:329, February 27, type from San Antonio, 5400 ft., Nye Co., Nevada. Known only from the type locality.

Thomomys umbrinus depauperatus Grinnell and Hill

1936. *Thomomys perpallidus depauperatus* Grinnell and Hill, Jour. Mamm., 17:4, February 17, type from E base Tinajas Atlas Mts., 7 mi. S Raven Butte, 1150 ft., Yuma Co., Arizona.

MARGINAL RECORDS.—Arizona: type locality; proximity of Tinajas Atlas (Huey, 1937:354).

Thomomys umbrinus depressus Hall

1932. *Thomomys bottae depressus* Hall, Univ. California Publ. Zool., 38:326, February 27, type from Dixie Meadows (at south end of Humboldt Salt Marsh), 3500 ft., Churchill Co., Nevada.

MARGINAL RECORDS (Hall, 1946:461).—Nevada: 1⅔ mi. NE Ocala, 3900 ft.; type locality; 15 mi. SW Fallon, 5000 ft.; 1 mi. W Mountain Well.

Thomomys umbrinus desertorum Merriam

1901. *Thomomys desertorum* Merriam, Proc. Biol. Soc. Washington, 14:114, July 19, type from Mud Spring, Detrital Valley, Mohave Co., Arizona.

MARGINAL RECORDS.—Arizona: Mineral Park, Detrital Valley (V. Bailey, 1915:84); Big Sandy Creek, 2000 ft. (*ibid.*); type locality.

Thomomys umbrinus desitus Goldman

1936. *Thomomys bottae desitus* Goldman, Jour. Washington Acad. Sci., 26:113, March 15, type from Big Sandy River, 2000 ft., near Owen, Mohave Co., Arizona.

MARGINAL RECORDS.—Arizona: type locality; Kirkland (Goldman, 1947:15).

Thomomys umbrinus detumidus Grinnell

1935. *Thomomys bottae detumidus* Grinnell, Univ. California Publ. Zool., 40:405, November 14, type from 1½ mi. S (town of) Pistol River, 250 ft., Curry Co., Oregon. Known only from the type locality.

Thomomys umbrinus diaboli Grinnell

1914. *Thomomys diaboli* Grinnell, Univ. California Publ. Zool., 12:313, November 21, type from Sweeney's Ranch, 22 mi. [by road] SW Los Baños, Diablo Range, Merced Co., California.

MARGINAL RECORDS.—California: Bryon (Storer and Gregory, 1934:303); Pacheco Pass (V. Bailey, 1915:52); type locality; divide W of McKittrick, 3000 ft. (Grinnell, 1933:140); Gilroy (Hooper, 1944:39); Mt. Diablo (*ibid.*).

Thomomys umbrinus dissimilis Goldman

1931. *Thomomys perpallidus dissimilis* Goldman, Jour. Washington Acad. Sci., 21:425, October 19, type from E slope Mt. Ellen, 8000 ft., Henry Mts., Garfield Co., Utah. Known only from the type locality.

Thomomys umbrinus divergens Nelson and Goldman

1934. *Thomomys bottae divergens* Nelson and Goldman, Jour. Mamm., 15:122, May 15, type from 4 mi. W Huachinera, 4000 ft., Río Bavispe, Sonora.

MARGINAL RECORDS.—Sonora: Bacerac (Burt, 1938:42). Chihuahua: Chuichupa (Nelson and Goldman, 1934:123). Sonora: type locality.

Thomomys umbrinus durangi Nelson and Goldman

1934. *Thomomys umbrinus durangi* Nelson and Goldman, Jour. Mamm., 15:114, May 15, type from Durango, Durango.

MARGINAL RECORDS.—Durango: *8 mi. NE Durango, 6200 ft.* (34299 KU); type locality.

Thomomys umbrinus emotus Goldman

1933. *Thomomys fulvus emotus* Goldman, Proc. Biol. Soc. Washington, 46:76, April 27, type from Animas Peak, 8000 ft., Animas Mts., New Mexico. Known only from the upper slopes of the Animas Mts., New Mexico.
1934. *Thomomys umbrinus emotus,* Nelson and Goldman, Jour. Mamm., 15:116, May 15.

Thomomys umbrinus enixus Nelson and Goldman

1934. *Thomomys umbrinus enixus* Nelson and Goldman, Jour. Mamm., 15:112, May 15, type from Sierra Moroni, 8500 ft., near Plateado, Zacatecas.

MARGINAL RECORDS.—Zacatecas: type locality. Jalisco: 1 mi. NE Villa Hidalgo, 6500 ft. (39794 KU).

Thomomys umbrinus estanciae Benson and Tillotson

1939. *Thomomys bottae estanciae* Benson and Tillotson, Proc. Biol. Soc. Washington, 52:152, October 11, type from La Estancia, 6 mi. N Nacori, Sonora. Known only from the type locality.

Thomomys umbrinus evexus Nelson and Goldman

1934. *Thomomys umbrinus evexus* Nelson and Goldman, Jour. Mamm., 15:115, May 15, type from Mt. San Gabriel, vicinity of Rosario, 10 mi. NW Villa Ocampo, Río Florida between 7000 and 9000 ft., Durango. Known only from the type locality.

Thomomys umbrinus eximius Nelson and Goldman

1934. *Thomomys umbrinus eximius* Nelson and Goldman, Jour. Mamm., 15:118, May 15, type from Sierra de Choix, about 20 mi. NE Choix, Sinaloa. Known only from the type locality.

Thomomys umbrinus extenuatus Goldman

1935. *Thomomys bottae extenuatus* Goldman, Proc. Biol. Soc. Washington, 48:149, October 31, type from Willcox, 4000 ft., Cochise Co., Arizona.

MARGINAL RECORDS.—Arizona: Fort Grant (Goldman, 1947:24); type locality; E of Portal (Cahalane, 1939:430); Fort Bowie, near W base Chiricahua Mts. (Goldman, 1935:150); Oracle (Goldman, 1947:25).

Thomomys umbrinus extimus Nelson and Goldman

1934. *Thomomys umbrinus extimus* Nelson and Goldman, Jour. Mamm., 15:119, May 15, type from Colomo, 600 ft., Nayarit. Known only from the type locality.

Thomomys umbrinus fulvus (Woodhouse)

1852. *Geomys fulvus* Woodhouse, Proc. Acad. Nat. Sci. Philadelphia, 6:201, type from San Francisco Mtn., Coconino Co., Arizona.
1932. *Thomomys bottae nasutus* Hall, Proc. Biol. Soc. Washington, 45:96, June 21, type from west fork Black River, 7550 ft., Apache Co., Arizona. Regarded as inseparable from *T. u. fulvus* by Goldman (Proc. Biol. Soc. Washington, 48:156, October 31, 1935).

MARGINAL RECORDS.—Arizona: 5 mi. N Pine Spring, 7000 ft. (V. Bailey, 1915:81); type locality. New Mexico (Kelson, 1951:70–71): Zuni River; Ft. Wingate; Mt. Sedgwick; Largo Canyon, 10 mi. SW Quemado; Gallina Mts.; Copper Canyon, 8200 ft., Magdalena Mts.; Water Canyon, 6500 ft., Magdalena Mts.; 10 mi. E Chloride; about 4 mi. NW Kingston, 9500 ft.; Rio Mimbres; Burro Mts. Arizona: Prieto Plateau, S end Blue Range, 7500–9000 ft. (V. Bailey, 1915:81); NW slope Baker Butte (Kelson, 1951:70); Bradshaw City (V. Bailey, 1915:81); Prescott (*ibid.*).

Thomomys umbrinus fumosus Hall

1932. *Thomomys bottae fumosus* Hall, Univ. California Publ. Zool., 38:329, February 27, type from Milman Ranch, Moores Creek, 19 mi. SE Millett P.O., Nye Co., Nevada.

MARGINAL RECORDS (Hall, 1946:466).—Nevada: Kingston Ranch, 16 mi. N Millett P.O.; Daniels Ranch, 12 mi. NE Millett P.O.; type locality; Peavine Ranch, 7 mi. N San Antonio, 6000 ft.; Cloverdale Ranch; South Twin River, 7000 ft.; Millett P.O.

Thomomys umbrinus goldmani Merriam

1901. *Thomomys goldmani* Merriam, Proc. Biol. Soc. Washington, 14:108, July 19, type from Mapimí, 3800 ft., Durango.
1934. *Thomomys umbrinus goldmani*, Nelson and Goldman, Jour. Mamm., 15:115, May 15.

MARGINAL RECORDS.—Coahuila: 3 mi. NE Sierra Mojada, 4100 ft. (Baker, 1953:512; 3 mi. SE Torreón, 3800 ft. (*ibid.*); *4 mi. WSW Lerdo, 3800 ft.* (*ibid.*). Durango: San Gabriel (V. Bailey, 1915:95); *1 mi. WSW Mapimí, 3800 ft.* (Baker, 1953:512); type locality.

Thomomys umbrinus grahamensis Goldman

1931. *Thomomys fulvus grahamensis* Goldman, Jour. Washington Acad. Sci., 21:420, October 19, type from Graham Mts. (Pinaleno Mts. on some maps), 9200 ft., Graham Co., Arizona. Known only from the upper slopes of the Graham Mts.

Thomomys umbrinus growlerensis Huey

1937. *Thomomys bottae growlerensis* Huey, Trans. San Diego Soc. Nat. Hist., 8:353, June 15, type from 7 mi. E Papago Well, Pima Co., Arizona.

MARGINAL RECORDS.—Arizona: Bates Well, Growler Pass (Goldman, 1947:22); S end Puerto Blanco Mts. (Huey, 1942:360).

Thomomys umbrinus guadalupensis Goldman

1936. *Thomomys bottae guadalupensis* Goldman, Jour. Washington Acad. Sci., 26:117, March 15, type from McKittrick Canyon, 7800 ft., Guadalupe Mts., Texas.

MARGINAL RECORDS.—New Mexico: Dog Canyon, Guadalupe Mts., 6800 ft. (Goldman, 1936:118). Texas: mouth Pine Springs Canyon, 5800 ft. (Davis and Robertson, 1944:267); Burned Cabin, head McKittrick Canyon, 7500 ft. (*ibid.*).

Thomomys umbrinus harquahalae Grinnell and Hill

1936. *Thomomys harquahalae* Grinnell and Hill, Jour. Mamm., 17:7, February 17, type from Ranegras Plain, 10 mi. W Hope, Yuma Co., Arizona.

MARGINAL RECORDS.—Arizona: type locality; base of Harquahala Mts., 5 mi. S Salome (Grinnell and Hill, 1936:7). One of us (Hall) examined the holotype and three other specimens at the time when Grinnell and Hill were preparing the original description of *T. harquahalae* and ascertained that the differences between *harquahalae* and *T. u. suboles* and between *harquahalae* and *T. u. subsimilis* were, in kind and degree, of the sort that differentiate subspecies and not species of *Thomomys*. Because one of us has personally studied the specimens, we depart in the case of *harquahalae* from our practice of merely reporting taxonomic status in the literature for the kind of animal concerned, and assign subspecific status to this heretofore nominal species. The particular reasons which caused Grinnell to employ the binomial instead of the trinomial for *harquahalae*, and also for some other kinds written about at the same time, were stated by him (see Grinnell and Hill, 1936:9).

Thomomys umbrinus homorus Huey

1949. *Thomomys bottae homorus* Huey, Trans. San Diego Soc. Nat. Hist., 11:55, January 31, type from 1 mi. E Rancho Lagunitas, lat. 28° 20′ N, long. 113° 15′ W, Baja California.

MARGINAL RECORDS.—Baja California: type locality; Rancho Unión, 15 mi. E Calmallí (Huey, 1949:55); Santana (on geographic grounds from V. Bailey, 1915:59, specimens not seen); Calmallí (Huey, 1949:55).

Thomomys umbrinus howelli Goldman

1936. *Thomomys bottae howelli* Goldman, Jour. Washington Acad. Sci., 26:116, March 15, type from Grand Junction, 4600 ft., Mesa Co., Colorado.

MARGINAL RECORDS.—Colorado: type locality. Utah: 10 mi. N Moab (Durrant, 1952:212).

Thomomys umbrinus hualpaiensis Goldman

1936. *Thomomys bottae hualpaiensis* Goldman, Jour. Washington Acad. Sci., 26:114, March 15, type from Hualpai Peak, Hualpai Mts., 7000 ft., Mohave Co., Arizona. Known only from the type locality.

Thomomys umbrinus hueyi Goldman

1938. *Thomomys bottae hueyi* Goldman, Jour. Washington Acad. Sci., 28:340, July 15, type from Spud Rock Ranger Station, 7400 ft., Rincon Mts., Pima Co., Arizona.

MARGINAL RECORDS (Goldman, 1947:27).—Arizona: type locality; Ramsay Canyon, 7000 ft., Huachuca Mts.; head Miller Canyon, Huachuca Mts.

Thomomys umbrinus humilis Baker

1953. *Thomomys bottae humilis* Baker, Univ. Kansas Publ., Mus. Nat. Hist., 5:503, June 1, type from 3 mi. W Hda. San Miguel, 2200 ft., Coahuila.

MARGINAL RECORDS (Baker, 1953:505).—Coahuila: 1 mi. S, 9 mi. W Villa Acuña; type locality; Cañon del Cochino, 3200 ft., 16 mi. N, 21 mi. E Piedra Blanca.

Thomomys umbrinus imitabilis Goldman

1939. *Thomomys bottae imitabilis* Goldman, Proc. Biol. Soc. Washington, 52:30, March 11, type from La Paz, Baja California. Known only from the type locality.

Thomomys umbrinus incomptus Goldman

1939. *Thomomys bottae incomptus* Goldman, Proc. Biol. Soc. Washington, 52:29, March 11, type from San Jorge, near Pacific Coast W of Pozo Grande, about 25 mi. SW Comondú, Baja California.

MARGINAL RECORDS.—Baja California: type locality; Matancita (Burt, 1940:3).

Thomomys umbrinus infrapallidus Grinnell

1914. *Thomomys infrapallidus* Grinnell, Univ. California Publ. Zool., 12:314, November 21, type from 7 mi. SE Simmler, Carrizo Plain, San Luis Obispo Co., California.

MARGINAL RECORDS.—California: type locality; 5 mi. N Painted Rock, Carrizo Plain (V. Bailey, 1915:56).

Thomomys umbrinus ingens Grinnell

1932. *Thomomys bottae ingens* Grinnell, Univ. California Publ. Zool., 38:405, September 20, type from E side levee, 290 ft., 2 mi. due W of Millux, Buena Vista Lake, Kern Co., California.

MARGINAL RECORDS.—California: 12 mi. S, 8 mi. W Bakersfield (Grinnell, 1932:406); type locality.

Thomomys umbrinus intermedius Mearns

1897. *Thomomys fulvus intermedius* Mearns, Proc. U.S. Nat. Mus., 19:719, July 30, type from summit Huachuca Mts., 9000 ft., Arizona. Known only from the type locality.
1934. *Thomomys umbrinus intermedius,* Nelson and Goldman, Jour. Mamm., 15:117, May 15.

Thomomys umbrinus internatus Goldman

1936. *Thomomys bottae internatus* Goldman, Jour. Washman Acad. Sci., 26:115, March 15, type from Salida, 7000 ft., Chaffee Co., Colorado.

MARGINAL RECORDS.—Colorado: type locality; Gardner (Goldman, 1936:115).

Thomomys umbrinus jacinteus Grinnell and Swarth

1914. *Thomomys jacinteus* Grinnell and Swarth, Proc. California Acad. Sci., ser. 4, 4:154, December 30, type from Round Valley, 9000 ft., San Jacinto Mts., Riverside Co., California.

MARGINAL RECORDS.—California: San Jacinto Peak, 10,200 ft. (Grinnell, 1933:141); *type locality; Tahquitz Valley, 8000 ft.* (*ibid.*); *Tamarack Valley, 9400 ft.* (V. Bailey, 1915:67).

Thomomys umbrinus jojobae Huey

1945. *Thomomys bottae jojobae* Huey, Trans. San Diego Soc. Nat. Hist., 10:256, August 31, type from Sangre de Cristo, lat. 31° 52′ N, long. 116° 06′ W, Baja California.

MARGINAL RECORDS.—Baja California: La Huerta (Hall and Kelson, 1952:357); type locality.

Thomomys umbrinus juarezensis Huey

1945. *Thomomys bottae juarezensis* Huey, Trans. San Diego Soc. Nat. Hist., 10:255, August 31, type from Laguna Hanson, Sierra Juárez, Baja California.

MARGINAL RECORDS.—Baja California: type locality; El Rayo, Sierra Juárez (Huey, 1945:256).

Thomomys umbrinus lachuguilla V. Bailey

1902. *Thomomys aureus lachuguilla* V. Bailey, Proc. Biol. Soc. Washington, 15:120, June 2, type from arid foothills near El Paso, El Paso Co., Texas.

MARGINAL RECORDS.—New Mexico: Alamagordo (Kelson, 1951:71). Texas: El Paso (V. Bailey, 1932:238). New Mexico: Organ (Kelson, 1951:70).

Thomomys umbrinus lacrymalis Hall

1932. *Thomomys bottae lacrymalis* Hall, Univ. California Publ. Zool., 38:328, February 27, type from Arlemont [Chiatovich Ranch, Fish Lake Valley], 4900 ft., Esmeralda Co., Nevada.

MARGINAL RECORDS (Hall, 1946:464).—Nevada: Cat Creek, 4 mi. W Hawthorne; 1 mi. W Candelaria Junction, 5500 ft.; type locality; (upper) McNett Ranch, 5 mi. SW Arlemont, 5600 ft.

Thomomys umbrinus laticeps Baird

1855. *Thomomys laticeps* Baird, Proc. Acad. Nat. Sci. Philadelphia, 7:335, April, type from Humboldt Bay, Humboldt Co., California.

MARGINAL RECORDS.—Oregon: near Chetco (V. Bailey, 1936:253), thence southward along coast to California: Rio Dell, on Eel River (Grinnell, 1933:137).

Thomomys umbrinus latirostris Merriam

1901. *Thomomys latirostris* Merriam, Proc. Biol. Soc. Washington, 14:107, July 19, type from Tanner Crossing, about 3 mi. above Cameron, Little Colorado River, Coconino Co., Arizona. (For status see Hoffmeister, Jour. Washington Acad. Sci., 45:127, April 25, 1955.) Known only from 3, 4½, and 5 mi. N Cameron.

Thomomys umbrinus latus Hall and Davis

1935. *Thomomys bottae latus* Hall and Davis, Univ. California Publ. Zool., 40:393, March 13, type from Cherry Creek, 6500 ft., White Pine Co., Nevada.

MARGINAL RECORDS (Hall, 1946:471).—Nevada: type locality; 6½ mi. SE Ely, 6400 ft.

Thomomys umbrinus lenis Goldman

1942. *Thomomys townsendii lenis* Goldman, Proc. Biol. Soc. Washington, 55:75, June 25, type from Richfield, 5308 ft., Sevier Co., Utah.

MARGINAL RECORDS (Durrant, 1952:208).—Utah: Lynndyl, 4796 ft.; U. B. (= Yuba) Dam, 5000 ft.; Salina, 4375 ft.; type locality.

Thomomys umbrinus leucodon Merriam

1897. *Thomomys leucodon* Merriam, Proc. Biol. Soc. Washington, 11:215, July 15, type from Grant Pass, Rogue River Valley, Oregon.

MARGINAL RECORDS (V. Bailey, 1915:48–49, unless otherwise noted).—Oregon: Cottage Grove (Gabrielson, 1923:189); W slope Grizzly Peak. California: Goosenest Mtn., Shasta Valley; Edgewood; Fort Jones; Baird; Battle Creek; Dana; Old Fort Crook; Big Valley Mts.; Pit River Forest Service Station (Grinnell, 1933:138); Hayden Hill; Turner's (Grinnell, *et al.,* 1930:496); Mountain House; Prattville (Grinnell, 1934:195); Greenville; Genesee; Downieville; Blue Canyon; Fyffe [= Fyfee]; Placerville (Grinnell, 1933:138); 3 mi. W summit Mt. Sanhedrin; Lower Lake; Calistoga; Vacaville; Novato; Ukiah; Laytonville; Briceland; Cuddeback (= Carlotta) (Grinnell, 1933: 138); Hoopa Valley. Oregon: type locality; Umpqua Valley, near Roseburg (Gabrielson, 1923:189). Not found: Bartlett Mtn.; Picard; Post Creek; Slippery Ford (all from V. Bailey, 1915:48–49).

Thomomys umbrinus levidensis Goldman

1942. *Thomomys bottae levidensis* Goldman, Proc. Biol. Soc. Washington, 55:76, June 25, type from Manti, about 5500 ft., Sanpete Co., Utah.

MARGINAL RECORDS.—Utah (Durrant, 1952:209): Spring City; type locality.

Thomomys umbrinus limitaris Goldman

1936. *Thomomys lachuguilla limitaris* Goldman, Jour. Washington Acad. Sci., 26:118, March 15, type from 4 mi. W Boquillas, Brewster Co., Texas.

MARGINAL RECORDS (Baker, 1953:505).—Texas: Castle Mts.; Devils River, 13 mi. below Juno; Comstock; Samuels, 17 mi. W Langtry; Boquillas; Glenn Spring, 2606 ft.; E base Burro Mesa, 3500 ft.; 15 mi. S Marathon.

Thomomys umbrinus limpiae Blair

1939. *Thomomys bottae limpiae* Blair, Occas. Papers Mus. Zool., Univ. Michigan, 403:2, June 16, type from Limpia Canyon, 1 mi. N Fort Davis, 4700 ft., Jeff Davis Co., Texas.

MARGINAL RECORDS.—Texas: type locality; *2 mi. NW Fort Davis, 4800 ft., Limpia Canyon* (Blair, 1940:27).

Thomomys umbrinus litoris Burt

1940. *Thomomys bottae litoris* Burt, Occas. Papers Mus. Zool., Univ. Michigan, 424:1, November 29, type from Stearns Point, Magdalena Bay, Baja California. Known only from the type locality.

Thomomys umbrinus lorenzi Huey

1940. *Thomomys bottae lorenzi* Huey, Trans. San Diego. Soc. Nat. Hist., 9:219, July 31, type from 7 mi. N Boulder Creek, Santa Cruz Co., California.

MARGINAL RECORDS (Huey, 1940:220).—California: type locality; Scott Valley; Ben Lomond.

Thomomys umbrinus lucidus Hall

1932. *Thomomys bottae lucidus* Hall, Proc. Biol. Soc. Washington, 45:67, April 2, type from Las Palmas Canyon, 200 ft., W side Laguna Salada (N of 32° N latitude), Baja California. Known only from the type locality.

Thomomys umbrinus lucrificus Hall and Durham

1938. *Thomomys bottae lucrificus* Hall and Durham, Proc. Biol. Soc. Washington, 51:15, February 18, type from Eastgate, Churchill Co., Nevada.

MARGINAL RECORDS.—Nevada: type locality; *along creek flowing from Desatoya Mts. to Eastgate, 5025 ft.* (Hall, 1946:462).

Thomomys umbrinus madrensis Nelson and Goldman

1934. *Thomomys umbrinus madrensis* Nelson and Goldman, Jour. Mamm., 15:115, May 15, type from Pilares Canyon, 6400 ft., 10 mi. NE Colonia García, and about 25 mi. SW Casas Grandes, Chihuahua.

MARGINAL RECORDS.—Chihuahua: Pacheco (Nelson and Goldman, 1934:116); type locality.

Thomomys umbrinus magdalenae Nelson and Goldman

1909. *Thomomys magdalenae* Nelson and Goldman, Proc. Biol. Soc. Washington, 22:24, March 10, type from Magdalena Island, Baja California. Known only from the type locality.

Thomomys umbrinus martinensis Nelson and Goldman

1934. *Thomomys umbrinus martinensis* Nelson and Goldman, Jour. Mamm., 15:108, May 15, type from San Martín Texmelucán, 7400 ft., Puebla. Known only from the type locality.

Thomomys umbrinus martirensis J. A. Allen

1898. *Thomomys fulvus martirensis* J. A. Allen, Bull. Amer. Mus. Nat. Hist., 10:147, April 12, type from La Grulla Meadow, Sierra San Pedro Mártir, 7400 ft., Baja California (see Huey, Trans. San Diego Soc. Nat. Hist., 5:89, January 18, 1928).

MARGINAL RECORDS.—Baja California: Piñon, W slope San Pedro Mártir Mts. (Hall and Kelson, 1952:358); La Grulla, Sierra San Pedro Mártir (Huey, 1945:258); Valladares Creek, Sierra San Pedro Mártir (*ibid.*).

Thomomys umbrinus melanotis Grinnell

1918. *Thomomys melanotis* Grinnell, Univ. California Publ. Zool., 17:425, April 25, type from Big Prospector Meadow, 10,500 ft., White Mts., California.

MARGINAL RECORDS.—California: Benton (Grinnell, 1933:144). Nevada: Lida, 6100 ft. (Hall, 1946:476). California: Independence (Grinnell, 1933:144).

Thomomys umbrinus mewa Merriam

1908. *Thomomys mewa* Merriam, Proc. Biol. Soc. Washington, 21:146, June 9, type from Raymond, Madera Co., California.

MARGINAL RECORDS.—California: Chinese (Grinnell, 1933:138); 3 mi. NE Coulterville (Storer and Gregory, 1934:303); Wawona (V. Bailey, 1915:50); Shaver Ranger Station (Grinnell, 1933:138); Three Rivers (V. Bailey, 1915:50); Kernville (Grinnell, 1933:138); 8 mi. E Porterville (V. Bailey, 1915:50); Merced (*ibid.*); Lagrange (Grinnell, 1933:138).

Thomomys umbrinus minimus Durrant

1939. *Thomomys bottae minimus* Durrant, Proc. Biol. Soc. Washington, 52:161, October 11, type from Stansbury Island, Great Salt Lake, Tooele Co., Utah. Known only from the type locality.

Thomomys umbrinus minor V. Bailey

1914. *Thomomys bottae minor* V. Bailey, Proc. Biol. Soc. Washington, 27:116, July 10, type from Fort Bragg, Mendocino Co., California.

MARGINAL RECORDS.—California: Ferndale (V. Bailey, 1915:51), thence down coast to near San Rafael (Hooper, 1944:41).

Thomomys umbrinus modicus Goldman

1931. *Thomomys fulvus modicus* Goldman, Jour. Washington Acad. Sci., 21:418, October 19, type from La Osa (near Mexican boundary), southern end of Altar Valley, Pima Co., Arizona.

MARGINAL RECORDS.—Arizona: Tucson (Burt, 1933: 117); Fort Huachuca (Goldman, 1947:28). Sonora (Burt, 1938:40–41): Río Santa Cruz; Cerro Blanco; 35 mi. NW Magdalena; 5 mi. E Piquito. Arizona: Sells (Goldman, 1947:28); Fresnall Canyon, Baboquivari Canyon, just below Allison Dam (Dice and Blossom, 1937:25).

Thomomys umbrinus mohavensis Grinnell

1918. *Thomomys perpallidus mohavensis* Grinnell, Univ. California Publ. Zool., 17:427, April 25, type from Mohave River bottom near Victorville, 2700 ft., San Bernardino Co., California.

MARGINAL RECORDS (Chattin, 1941:270, unless otherwise noted).—California: Lone Willow Spring (Hall and Kelson, 1952:358); Riggs Wash, 5½ mi. NE Silver Lake, 1900 ft.; 2½ mi. E Ludlow, 1842 ft.; Sheep Hole Mts., 21½ mi. S Amboy, 2300 ft.; Barker's Reservoir, 10 mi. S Twentynine Palms; Quail Spring, 17 mi. E Morongo Valley; Cushenbury Springs (Grinnell, 1933:143); 8 mi. SSE Hesperia; Granite Wells, 3950 ft.; Fairmont (Grinnell, 1918:427); Grapevine Ranch (Hall and Kelson, 1952:359); 33 mi. E Mohave; 21 mi. SW Trona, 3050 ft.

Thomomys umbrinus morulus Hooper

1940. *Thomomys fulvus morulus* Hooper, Occas. Papers Mus. Zool., Univ. Michigan, 422:9, November 14, type from Bill Porter's Ranch, 8 mi. SE Paxton, Valencia Co., New Mexico.

MARGINAL RECORDS.—New Mexico: type locality; NW side Flagpole Crater (Kelson, 1951:70).

Thomomys umbrinus muralis Goldman

1936. *Thomomys muralis* Goldman, Jour. Washington Acad. Sci., 26:112, March 15, type from lower end Prospect Valley, 4500 ft., Hualpai Indian Reservation, Grand Canyon, Arizona. Known only from the type locality.

Thomomys umbrinus musculus Nelson and Goldman

1934. *Thomomys umbrinus musculus* Nelson and Goldman, Jour. Mamm., 15:119, May 15, type from Pedro Pablo, 3500 ft., about 22 mi. E Acaponeta, Sierra de Teponahuaxtla, Nayarit.

MARGINAL RECORDS.—Sinaloa: Plomosas (Nelson and Goldman, 1934:119). Nayarit: type locality.

Thomomys umbrinus mutabilis Goldman

1933. *Thomomys fulvus mutabilis* Goldman, Proc. Biol. Soc. Washington, 46:75, April 27, type from Camp Verde, Yavapai Co., Arizona.
1938. *Thomomys bottae pinalensis* Goldman, Jour. Washington Acad. Sci., 28:342, July 15, type from Oak Flat, 5 mi. E Superior, Pinal Mts., Pinal Co., Arizona. Considered inseparable from *T. u. mutabilis* by Hall and Kelson, Univ. Kansas Publ., Mus. Nat. Hist., 5:360, December 15, 1952.

MARGINAL RECORDS.—Arizona: Montezuma Well, near Camp Verde (Goldman, 1933:76); H-bar Ranch, 10 mi. S Payson (*ibid.*); Cazador Spring, S base Nanton Plateau (*ibid.*); Gila Mts. (Goldman, 1947:17); Oak Flat, 5 mi. E Superior, Pinal Mts. (Hall and Kelson, 1952:360); type locality.

Thomomys umbrinus nanus Hall

1932. *Thomomys bottae nanus* Hall, Univ. California Publ. Zool., 38:331, February 27, type from S end Belted Range, 5½ mi. NW White Rock Spring, 7200 ft., Nye Co., Nevada.

MARGINAL RECORDS (Hall, 1946:475).—Nevada: Quinn Canyon Mts., Burned Corral Canyon, 6700–8700 ft.; N slope Irish Mtn., 7000–8000 ft.; Summit Spring, 4800 ft.; type locality; Kawich Range, 6000 ft., 1½ mi. E Kawich P.O.

Thomomys umbrinus navus Merriam

1901. *Thomomys leucodon navus* Merriam, Proc. Biol. Soc. Washington, 14:112, July 19, type from Red Bluff, Tehama Co., California.

MARGINAL RECORDS (V. Bailey, 1915:50, unless otherwise noted).—California: Payne; Chico; 6 mi. E Oroville; Wheatland; Mokelumne Hill (Grinnell, 1933:138); Sacramento; Colusa; 5 mi. W Leesville; Sites; Willows; Battle Creek (Grinnell, 1933:138).

Thomomys umbrinus neglectus V. Bailey

1914. *Thomomys neglectus* V. Bailey, Proc. Biol. Soc. Washington, 27:117, July 10, type from Bear Flat Meadows, 6400 ft., San Antonio Peak, San Gabriel Mts., Los Angeles Co., California.

MARGINAL RECORDS.—California: Mt. Piños (Grinnell, 1933:140); Bouquet Canyon (*ibid.*); Mt. Islip, 7500 ft. (Burt, 1932:370); type locality.

Thomomys umbrinus nesophilus Durrant

1936. *Thomomys bottae nesophilus* Durrant, Bull. Univ. Utah, 27(2):2, October 3, type from Antelope Island, Great Salt Lake, Davis Co., Utah. Known only from the type locality.

Thomomys umbrinus newmani Dalquest

1951. *Thomomys umbrinus newmani* Dalquest, Jour. Washington Acad. Sci., 41:361, November 14, type from 7 km. NW Palma (village 12 km. NW Salinas), San Luis Potosí.

MARGINAL RECORDS (Dalquest, 1953b:99).—San Luis Potosí: type locality; Cerro Peñón Blanco.

Thomomys umbrinus nicholi Goldman

1938. *Thomomys bottae nicholi* Goldman, Jour. Washington Acad. Sci., 28:337, July 15, type from 20 mi. S Wolf Hole (road to Parashonts), 5000 ft., Shivwits Plateau, Mohave Co., Arizona. Regarded as inseparable from *T. u. trumbullensis* by Durrant, Univ. Kansas Publ., Mus. Nat. Hist., 6:224, August 10, 1952.

MARGINAL RECORDS.—Arizona: type locality; 6 mi. N Wolf Hole (Goldman, 1938b:338); 3 mi. NW Diamond Butte (*ibid.*).

Thomomys umbrinus nigricans Rhoads

1895. *Thomomys fulvus nigricans* Rhoads, Proc. Acad. Nat. Sci. Philadelphia, 47:36, February 21, type from Witch Creek, 2753 ft., 7 mi. W Julian, San Diego Co., California.

MARGINAL RECORDS.—California: Schains Ranch, W base San Jacinto Mts. (Grinnell, 1933:141); Kenworthy (V. Bailey, 1915:57); Santa Rosa Peak (*ibid.*); Julian (*ibid.*); Laguna Mts. (Huey, 1945:254). Baja California (Huey, 1945:254): Nachogüero Valley; Las Cruces; S end Valles de las Palmas. California (V. Bailey, 1915:57): Jamul Creek; Poway; Escondido; Hemet Valley.

Thomomys umbrinus operarius Merriam

1897. *Thomomys operarius* Merriam, Proc. Biol. Soc. Washington, 11:215, July 15, type from Keeler, E side Owens Lake, Inyo Co., California. Known only from the type locality.

Thomomys umbrinus operosus Hatfield

1942. *Thomomys bottae operosus* Hatfield, Bull. Chicago Acad. Sci., 6:151, January 12, type from Peeples Valley, 4400 ft., 6 mi. N Yarnell, Yavapai Co., Arizona. Known only from the type locality.

Thomomys umbrinus optabilis Goldman

1936. *Thomomys bottae optabilis* Goldman, Jour. Washington Acad. Sci., 26:116, March 15, type from Coventry, 6500 ft., Naturita Creek Valley, Montrose Co., Colorado.

MARGINAL RECORDS (Warren, 1942:159).—Colorado: Sieber Ranch, Little Dolores River; type locality; Bedrock, Dolores River.

Thomomys umbrinus opulentus Goldman

1935. *Thomomys bottae opulentus* Goldman, Proc. Biol. Soc. Washington, 48:150, October 31, type from Las Palomas, on the Rio Grande, Sierra Co., New Mexico.

MARGINAL RECORDS (Kelson, 1951:70).—New Mexico: Socorro; San Marcial; Las Cruces; Garfield; Lake Valley; Cuchillo.

Thomomys umbrinus oreoecus Burt

1932. *Thomomys oreoecus* Burt, Trans. San Diego Soc. Nat. Hist., 7:154, July 28, type from Greenwater [Black Mountains, 8 mi. SW Ryan], 4300 ft., Inyo Co., California.

MARGINAL RECORDS (Hall, 1946:477).—Nevada: Thorps Mill. California: type locality. Nevada: 4³⁄₁₀ mi. E California boundary, 4200 ft.

Thomomys umbrinus orizabae Merriam

1893. *Thomomys orizabae* Merriam, Proc. Biol. Soc. Washington, 8:145, December 29, type from Mt. Orizaba, 9500 ft., Puebla.
1915. *Thomomys umbrinus orizabae*, V. Bailey, N. Amer. Fauna, 39:90, November 15.

MARGINAL RECORDS.—Puebla: type locality; *10–16 km. NNE San Andrés, W slope Mt. Orizaba, 10,000–11,000 ft.* (Davis, 1944:385).

Thomomys umbrinus osgoodi Goldman

1931. *Thomomys perpallidus osgoodi* Goldman, Jour. Washington Acad. Sci., 21:424, October 19, type from Hanksville, Wayne Co., Utah.

MARGINAL RECORDS (Durrant, 1952:210).—Utah: ½ mi. N Spring Glen, 6150 ft.; Price River, 2 mi. SE Woodside, 4600 ft.; Notom, 6200 ft.; 5 mi. S Castle Dale, 5600 ft.

Thomomys umbrinus paguatae Hooper

1940. *Thomomys bottae paguatae* Hooper, Occas. Papers Mus. Zool., Univ. Michigan, 422:4, November 14, type from ½ mi. N Cebolleta (Seboyeta P.O.), Valencia Co., New Mexico. Known only from the type locality.

Thomomys umbrinus pallescens Rhoads

1895. *Thomomys bottae pallescens* Rhoads, Proc. Acad. Nat. Sci. Philadelphia, 47:36, February 21, type from Grapeland, San Bernardino Valley, San Bernardino Co., California.

MARGINAL RECORDS.—California: Palmdale (Burt, 1932:370); San Bernardino (Grinnell, 1933:140); El Casco (V. Bailey, 1915:55); Riverside (Grinnell, 1933:140); Los Angeles (*ibid.*); Saugus (Burt, 1932:370).

Thomomys umbrinus parviceps Nelson and Goldman

1934. *Thomomys simulus parviceps* Nelson and Goldman, Jour. Mamm., 15:121, May 15, type from Chacala, 3000 ft., Durango. Known only from the type locality. Reasons for here using the specific name *umbrinus* instead of *simulus* are given in the account of *Thomomys umbrinus simulus* beyond.

Thomomys umbrinus parvulus Goldman

1938. *Thomomys bottae parvulus* Goldman, Jour. Washington Acad. Sci., 28:339, July 15, type from pass between Santa Catalina and Rincon Mts., 4500 ft., Pima Co., Arizona. Known only from the type locality.

Thomomys umbrinus pascalis Merriam

1901. *Thomomys angularis pascalis* Merriam, Proc. Biol. Soc. Washington, 14:111, July 19, type from Fresno, San Joaquin Valley, Fresno Co., California.

MARGINAL RECORDS (Grinnell, 1933:139, unless otherwise noted).—California: vicinity of Stockton; Oakdale (V. Bailey, 1915:54); type locality; Tulare (V. Bailey, 1915:54); Bodfish (*ibid.*); Tehachapi; Tejon Pass; N flank Mt. Piños; Cuyama Valley; Buttonwillow (V. Bailey, 1915:54); Lemoore (*ibid.*); Modesto (Storer and Gregory, 1934:302).

Thomomys umbrinus patulus Goldman

1938. *Thomomys bottae patulus* Goldman, Jour. Washington Acad. Sci., 28:341, July 15, type from bottomland along Hassayampa River, 2000 ft., 2 mi. below Wickenburg, Maricopa Co., Arizona. Known only from the type locality.

Thomomys umbrinus pectoralis Goldman

1936. *Thomomys pectoralis* Goldman, Jour. Washington Acad. Sci., 26:120, March 15, type from vicinity of Carlsbad Cave, Carlsbad Cave National Monument, Eddy Co., New Mexico.

MARGINAL RECORDS.—New Mexico: type locality. Texas: *Bell Canyon, 1 mi. N, 1 mi. E Nickel* (52212 KU—the large size of the specimen provides evidence of intergradation between *Thomomys bottae* [now *umbrinus*] *guadalupensis* and *Thomomys pectoralis* and it is for this reason that the latter is here accorded only subspecific rank under the species *Thomomys umbrinus*).

Thomomys umbrinus peramplus Goldman

1931. *Thomomys fulvus peramplus* Goldman, Jour. Washington Acad. Sci., 21:423, October 19, type from Wheatfields Creek, 7000 ft. [about 27 mi. E Chin Lee], W slope Tunitcha Mts., Apache Co., Arizona.

MARGINAL RECORDS.—Arizona: type locality. New Mexico: Chusca Mts. (Kelson, 1951:70). Arizona: St. Michaels, E side Defiance Plateau (Goldman, 1947:12); Canyon de Chelly, 7 mi. above mouth (Goldman, 1931:424).

Thomomys umbrinus perditus Merriam

1901. *Thomomys perditus* Merriam, Proc. Biol. Soc. Washington, 14:108, July 19, type from Lampazos, Nuevo León.
1934. *Thomomys umbrinus perditus*, Nelson and Goldman, Jour. Mamm., 15:115, May 15.

MARGINAL RECORDS (Baker, 1953:511).—Nuevo León: type locality; Villadama. Coahuila: 2 mi. N, 18 mi. W Santa Teresa, 7500 ft.

Thomomys umbrinus peregrinus Merriam

1893. *Thomomys peregrinus* Merriam, Proc. Biol. Soc. Washington, 8:146, December 29, type from Salazar, 10,300 ft., México.
1915. *Thomomys umbrinus peregrinus*, V. Bailey, N. Amer. Fauna, 39:91, November 15.

MARGINAL RECORDS.—México: type locality. Distrito Federal: 2 mi. SSW Parres, 9000 ft. (38367 KU). México: Volcán Popocatépetl (Goodwin, 1954:9). Morelos: 5 km. N Tres Cumbres (Davis and Russell, 1954:72). México: *1 mi. ESE Salazar, 9500 ft.* (Villa, 1953:390).

Thomomys umbrinus perpallidus Merriam

1886. *Thomomys talpoides perpallidus* Merriam, Science, 8:588, December 24, type from Palm Springs, Riverside Co., California.

MARGINAL RECORDS.—California: Whitewater (Grinnell, 1933:142); ½ mi. SE Thermal (Chattin, 1941:269).

Thomomys umbrinus perpes Merriam

1901. *Thomomys aureus perpes* Merriam, Proc. Biol. Soc. Washington, 14:111, July 19, type from Lone Pine, Owens Valley, Inyo Co., California.

MARGINAL RECORDS (Grinnell, 1933:144, unless otherwise noted).—California: Bishop (V. Bailey, 1915:73); type locality; Coso (*ibid.*); vicinity Freeman; Kelso Pass; Isabella; S. Fork Kern River, near Onyx (V. Bailey, 1915:73); Haway Meadows, S of Owens Lake (*ibid.*).

Thomomys umbrinus pervagus Merriam

1901. *Thomomys aureus pervagus* Merriam, Proc. Biol. Soc. Washington, 14:110, July 19, type from Española, Rio Arriba Co., New Mexico.

MARGINAL RECORDS.—Colorado: Antonito (V. Bailey, 1932:234). New Mexico (Kelson, 1951:70): Questa; 10 mi. N Santa Fe; Santa Clara Canyon; Chama Canyon, 6100 ft. Colorado: Conejos River, 6 mi. W Antonito (V. Bailey, 1915:83).

Thomomys umbrinus pervarius Goldman

1938. *Thomomys bottae pervarius* Goldman, Proc. Biol. Soc. Washington, 51:57, March 18, type from Lloyd Ranch, 35 mi. S Marfa, 4200 ft., Presidio Co., Texas. Known only from the type locality.

Thomomys umbrinus phasma Goldman

1933. *Thomomys fulvus phasma* Goldman, Proc. Biol. Soc. Washington, 46:72, April 27, type from 2 mi. S Tule

Tank, Tule Desert, near Mexican boundary, Yuma Co., Arizona.

MARGINAL RECORDS.—Arizona: Tacna (Goldman, 1933:74); Tule Well (Huey, 1937:353). Sonora: Quitobaquita (Burt, 1938:42); Cienega Well, 30 mi. S Monument 204 (*ibid.*); Colorado River, 20 mi. S Mexican boundary (*ibid.*). Arizona: Wellton (Goldman, 1947:21).

Thomomys umbrinus phelleoecus Burt

1933. *Thomomys phelleoecus* Burt, Jour. Mamm., 14:56, February 14, type from Hidden Forest, 8500 ft., Sheep Mts., Clark Co., Nevada.

MARGINAL RECORDS (Hall, 1946:475).—Nevada: Hidden Forest, 7700 ft.; *ridge N Wiregrass* (= *Wire*) *Spring, 8250 ft.; Hidden Forest road, 5300 and 5450 ft.*

Thomomys umbrinus piutensis Grinnell and Hill

1936. *Thomomys bottae piutensis* Grinnell and Hill, Proc. Biol. Soc. Washington, 49:103, August 22, type from French Gulch, 6700 ft., Piute Mts., 2½ mi. NE Claraville, Kern Co., California.

MARGINAL RECORDS (Grinnell and Hill, 1936:104).—California: type locality; Kelso Valley; Walker Basin.

Thomomys umbrinus planirostris Burt

1931. *Thomomys perpallidus planirostris* Burt, Proc. Biol. Soc. Washington, 44:38, May 8, type from Zion National Park, Washington Co., Utah.

MARGINAL RECORDS (Durrant, 1952:225, unless otherwise noted).—Utah: East Entrance, 5725 ft., Zion National Park. Arizona: Fredonia (Goldman, 1947:9). Utah: 6 mi. S St. George, 2700 ft.; Santa Clara Creek.

Thomomys umbrinus planorum Hooper

1940. *Thomomys bottae planorum* Hooper, Occas. Papers Mus. Zool., Univ. Michigan, 422:5, November 14, type from 1½ mi. SW San Mateo, Valencia Co., New Mexico.

MARGINAL RECORDS (Kelson, 1951:70).—New Mexico: Horace Mesa, 1½ mi. S Canyon Lobo Ranger Station; 11 mi. SSE Grants.

Thomomys umbrinus potosinus Nelson and Goldman

1934. *Thomomys umbrinus potosinus* Nelson and Goldman, Jour. Mamm., 15:111, May 15, type from La Tinaja, 6000 ft. (at or near present town of Ventura), about 20 mi. NE San Luis Potosí, San Luis Potosí. Known only from the type locality.

Thomomys umbrinus powelli Durrant

1955. *Thomomys bottae powelli* Durrant, Proc. Biol. Soc. Washington, 68:79, August 3, type from Hall Ranch, Salt Gulch, 8 mi. W Boulder, 6000 ft., Garfield Co., Utah. Known only from the type locality.

Thomomys umbrinus providentialis Grinnell

1931. *Thomomys providentialis* Grinnell, Univ. California Publ. Zool., 38:1, October 17, type from Purdy, 4500 ft.,

6 mi. SE New York Mtn., Providence Range, San Bernardino Co., California.

MARGINAL RECORDS.—California: Twelve Mile Spring (on geographic grounds from V. Bailey, 1915:73, specimens not seen). Nevada (Hall, 1946:477): N side Potosi Mtn., 5800 ft.; 8 mi. SE Dead Mtn., 1900 ft. California: junction Piute Springs and Searchlight roads, 2130 ft. (Chattin, 1941:271); Turtle Mts., 12 mi. NE Sablon, 2492 ft. (*ibid.*); 7½ mi. NE Chubbuck, 2320 ft. (*ibid.*); pass between Granite and Providence Mts., 4000 ft. (*ibid.*); 5 mi. N Kelso Peak (Johnson, *et al.*, 1948:358).

Thomomys umbrinus proximarinus Huey

1945. *Thomomys bottae proximarinus* Huey, Trans. San Diego Soc. Nat. Hist., 10:261, August 31, type from Boca la Playa, mesa bordering the sea, lat. 31° 32′ N, long. 116° 38′ W, 16 mi. W Santo Tomás, Baja California. Known only from the type locality.

Thomomys umbrinus proximus Burt and Campbell

1934. *Thomomys burti proximus* Burt and Campbell, Jour. Mamm., 15:151, May 15, type from Old Parker Ranch (Pickett's Ranch on U.S.G.S. Topographic sheet, Patagonia Quadrangle, edition of August, 1905), 4800 ft., W slope Santa Rita Mts., Pima Co., Arizona.

1943. *Thomomys umbrinus proximus*, Goldman, Jour. Washington Acad. Sci., 33:147, May 15.

MARGINAL RECORDS (Goldman, 1947:34).—Arizona: Empire Ranch, E of Santa Rita Mts.; Fort Huachuca; Arivaca; type locality.

Thomomys umbrinus puertae Grinnell

1914. *Thomomys nigricans puertae* Grinnell, Univ. California Publ. Zool., 12:315, November 21, type from La Puerta (Mason's Ranch), 5 mi. W Vallecitos, at lower end of La Puerta Valley, San Diego Co., California. Known only from the type locality.

Thomomys umbrinus pullus Hall and Villa

1948. *Thomomys umbrinus pullus* Hall and Villa, Univ. Kansas Publ., Mus. Nat. Hist., 1:251, July 26, type from 5 mi. S Pátzcuaro, 7800 ft., Michoacán.

MARGINAL RECORDS (Hall and Villa, 1949:451).—Michoacán: *3 mi. S Pátzcuaro, 7800 ft.*; type locality.

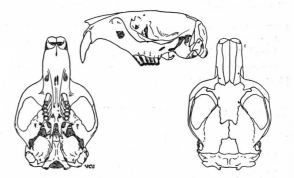

Fig. 256. *Thomomys umbrinus pullus*, 5 mi. S Pátzcuaro, Michoacán, No. 100515 M.V.Z., ♂, X 1.

Thomomys umbrinus pusillus Goldman

1931. *Thomomys fulvus pusillus* Goldman, Jour. Washington Acad. Sci., 21:422, October 19, type from Coyote Mts., 3000 ft., Pima Co., Arizona. Known only from the type locality.

Thomomys umbrinus quercinus Burt and Campbell

1934. *Thomomys burti quercinus* Burt and Campbell, Jour. Mamm., 15:150, May 15, type from Peña Blanca Spring, Pajarito Mts., Arizona.
1943. *Thomomys umbrinus quercinus,* Goldman, Jour. Washington Acad. Sci., 33:147, May 15.

MARGINAL RECORDS.—Arizona: type locality; pass over summit Patagonia Mts. (Goldman, 1947:35).

Thomomys umbrinus retractus Baker

1953. *Thomomys bottae retractus* Baker, Univ. Kansas Publ., Mus. Nat. Hist., 5:507, June 1, type from Fortín, 3300 ft., 20 mi. N, 2 mi. E San Gerónimo, Coahuila (see Baker, Univ. Kansas Publ., Mus. Nat. Hist., 9:220, June 15, 1956). Known only from the vicinity of the type locality (see Baker, *loc. cit.*).

Thomomys umbrinus rhizophagus Huey

1949. *Thomomys bottae rhizophagus* Huey, Trans. San Diego Soc. Nat. Hist., 11:54, January 31, type from Las Flores, lat. 28° 50' N, long. 113° 32' W, 7 mi. S Bahía de Los Angeles, Baja California. Known only from the type locality.

Thomomys umbrinus riparius Grinnell and Hill

1936. *Thomomys perpallidus riparius* Grinnell and Hill, Jour. Mamm., 17:4, February 17, type from Blythe, Riverside Co., California.

MARGINAL RECORDS (Chattin, 1941:274).—California: 13 mi. NE Blythe; type locality; Ford Dry Lake, 21½ mi. W Blythe.

Thomomys umbrinus robustus Durrant

1946. *Thomomys bottae robustus* Durrant, Univ. Kansas Publ., Mus. Nat. Hist., 1:30, August 15, type from Orr's Ranch, 4300 ft., Skull Valley, Tooele Co., Utah. Known only from the type locality.

Thomomys umbrinus rufidulus Hoffmeister

1955. *Thomomys bottae rufidulus* Hoffmeister, Jour. Washington Acad. Sci., 45:126, April 25, type from 2 mi. E Joseph City, Navajo Co., Arizona.

MARGINAL RECORDS (Hoffmeister, 1955:127).—New Mexico: Gallup. Arizona: Navajo; type locality.

Thomomys umbrinus ruidosae Hall

1932. *Thomomys bottae ruidosae* Hall, Proc. Biol. Soc. Washington, 45:96, June 21, type from Ruidoso, 6700 ft., Lincoln Co., New Mexico.

MARGINAL RECORDS (Kelson, 1951:71).—New Mexico: type locality; Cloudcroft, 9000 ft.; *8 mi. NW Cloudcroft, 7000 ft.; Mescalero.*

Thomomys umbrinus rupestris Chattin

1941. *Thomomys bottae rupestris* Chattin, Trans. San Diego Soc. Nat. Hist., 9:272, April 30, type from 2 mi. E Clemens Well, 1131 ft., Riverside Co., California.

MARGINAL RECORDS (Chattin, 1941:273).—California: 4 mi. SW Desert Center, 1020 ft.; Corn Spring, Chuckwalla Mts., 1573 ft.; Chocolate Mts., 11 mi. NE Niland; 3 mi. S Cottonwood Spring, 2400 ft.

Thomomys umbrinus ruricola Huey

1949. *Thomomys bottae ruricola* Huey, Trans. San Diego Soc. Nat. Hist., 11:53, January 31, type from 4 mi. N Santa Catarina Landing, lat. 29° 35' N, long. 115° 17' W, Baja California. Known only from the type locality.

Thomomys umbrinus russeolus Nelson and Goldman

1909. *Thomomys bottae russeolus* Nelson and Goldman, Proc. Biol. Soc. Washington, 22:25, March 10, type from San Angel, WSW San Ignacio, Baja California.

MARGINAL RECORDS.—Baja California: Campo Los Angeles, Viscaino Desert (Huey, 1949:55); type locality.

Thomomys umbrinus sanctidiegi Huey

1945. *Thomomys bottae sanctidiegi* Huey, Trans. San Diego Soc. Nat. Hist., 10:258, August 31, type from Balboa Park, San Diego, California.

MARGINAL RECORDS.—California: La Jolla (Huey, 1945:259); southward along coast to Baja California: Ensenada (Hall and Kelson, 1952:361).

Thomomys umbrinus saxatilis Grinnell

1934. *Thomomys bottae saxatilis* Grinnell, Proc. Biol. Soc. Washington, 47:193, October 2, type from 1 mi. N Susanville, 4400 ft., Lassen Co., California.

MARGINAL RECORDS.—California: type locality; edge Faulkner Ranch, adjacent to Gold Run, 4200 ft., 4½ mi. S Susanville (Grinnell, 1934:194); close to highway 9 mi. W Susanville, 4800 ft. (*ibid.*).

Thomomys umbrinus scapterus Elliot

1904. *Thomomys scapterus* Elliot, Field Columb. Mus., Publ. 87, Zool. Ser., 3:248, January 7, type from Hannopee Canyon, 7500 ft., Panamint Mts., Inyo Co., California.

MARGINAL RECORDS (Grinnell, 1933:145).—California: Jackass Spring, Panamint Mts.; Johnson Canyon, Panamint Mts.; near Lee Mine, 12 mi. N Darwin.

Thomomys umbrinus scotophilus Davis

1940. *Thomomys bottae scotophilus* Davis, Jour. Mamm., 21:204, May 16, type from 1½ mi. W Bat Cave, Sierra Diablo, Hudspeth Co., Texas.

MARGINAL RECORDS.—Texas: *Bat Cave, about 2 mi. S head Victoria Canyon* (Davis and Robertson, 1944:267); type locality.

Thomomys umbrinus sevieri Durrant

1946. *Thomomys bottae sevieri* Durrant, Univ. Kansas Publ., Mus. Nat. Hist., 1:45, August 15, type from Swasey Spring, 6500 ft., House Mtn., Millard Co., Utah. Known only from the type locality.

Thomomys umbrinus sheldoni V. Bailey

1915. *Thomomys sheldoni* V. Bailey, N. Amer. Fauna, 39:93, November 15, type from Santa Teresa, 6800 ft., Sierra del Nayarit, Nayarit.
1934. *Thomomys umbrinus sheldoni*, Nelson and Goldman, Jour. Mamm., 15:113, May 15.

MARGINAL RECORDS (V. Bailey, 1915:94).—Chihuahua: Chuichupa; near Guadalupe y Calvo. Durango: Río Sestín; La Boca. Zacatecas: Sierra Madre, 8500 ft. Nayarit: type locality. Durango: El Salto, 8400 ft.

Thomomys umbrinus siccovallis Huey

1945. *Thomomys bottae siccovallis* Huey, Trans. San Diego Soc. Nat. Hist., 10:258, August 31, type from El Cajón Canyon, 3200 ft., E base Sierra San Pedro Mártir, lat. 30° 54′ N, long. 115° 10′ W, Baja California.

MARGINAL RECORDS.—Baja California: type locality; Mattomi [= Matomi] (Hall and Kelson, 1952:362).

Thomomys umbrinus silvifugus Grinnell

1935. *Thomomys bottae silvifugus* Grinnell, Univ. California Publ. Zool., 40:406, November 14, type from 16 mi. due E Patricks Point, near Coyote Peak, 3000 ft., Humboldt Co., California. Known only from the type locality.

Thomomys umbrinus simulus Nelson and Goldman

1934. *Thomomys simulus simulus* Nelson and Goldman, Jour. Mamm., 15:120, May 15, type from Alamos, 1200 ft., Sonora.

MARGINAL RECORDS (Burt, 1938:40).—Sonora: type locality; Baromico; 7 mi. SW Guirocoba. Our examination of 2 topotypes (24857 and 24859 KU) and comparison of these with specimens of subspecies of *Thomomys umbrinus* from higher elevations to the eastward leads us to depart, in the case of *T. simulus,* from our practice of merely reporting the taxonomic status as it exists in the literature and to arrange *Thomomys simulus simulus* as a subspecies of *Thomomys umbrinus.* The variable number of pectoral mammae, the straightness of the suture on the dorsal surface of the skull where the anterior arm of the zygomatic arch meets the frontal, and all other morphological features studied in *T. simulus* fall well within the limits of variation shown by other subspecies of the species *Thomomys umbrinus.*

Thomomys umbrinus sinaloae Merriam

1901. *Thomomys sinaloae* Merriam, Proc. Biol. Soc. Washington, 14:108, July 19, type from Altata, Sinaloa. Known only from the type locality.

Thomomys umbrinus solitarius Grinnell

1926. *Thomomys solitarius* Grinnell, Univ. California Publ. Zool., 39:177, December 10, type from Fingerrock Wash, 5400 ft., Stewart Valley, Mineral Co., Nevada.

MARGINAL RECORDS (Hall, 1946:465).—Nevada: type locality; Lone Mtn., 6600 ft., 12½ mi. W, 2½ mi. S Tonopah; 4 mi. NE Arlemont, 4800 ft.; 7 mi. N Arlemont, 5500 ft.; S end Walker Lake, 4100 ft.

Thomomys umbrinus sonoriensis Nelson and Goldman

1934. *Thomomys umbrinus sonoriensis* Nelson and Goldman, Jour. Mamm., 15:118, May 15, type from 10 mi. E Chinapa, 3000 ft., Sonora.

MARGINAL RECORDS (Burt, 1938:39).—Sonora: type locality; Huásabas; Providencia Mines.

Thomomys umbrinus stansburyi Durrant

1946. *Thomomys bottae stansburyi* Durrant, Univ. Kansas Publ., Mus. Nat. Hist., 1:36, August 15, type from South Willow Creek, Stansbury Mts., 7500 ft., Tooele Co., Utah. Known only from the type locality.

Thomomys umbrinus sturgisi Goldman

1938. *Thomomys sturgisi* Goldman, Proc. Biol. Soc. Washington, 51:56, March 18, type from Sierra del Carmen, 6000 ft., Coahuila.

MARGINAL RECORDS (Baker, 1953:510).—Coahuila: type locality; Sierra de la Encantada, 4100 ft., 37 mi. S, 21 mi. E Boquillas; 3 mi. NW Cuatro Cienegas, 2450 ft.; 2 mi. N, 1 mi. W Ocampo, 4050 ft.

Thomomys umbrinus suboles Goldman

1928. *Thomomys fulvus suboles* Goldman, Proc. Biol. Soc. Washington, 41:203, December 18, type from Old Searchlight Ferry, Colorado River (northwest of Kingman), Arizona. Known only from the type locality.

Thomomys umbrinus subsimilis Goldman

1933. *Thomomys fulvus subsimilis* Goldman, Proc. Biol. Soc. Washington, 46:74, April 27, type from Harquahala Mts., 3000 ft., Yuma Co., Arizona. Known only from the type locality.

Thomomys umbrinus supernus Nelson and Goldman

1934. *Thomomys umbrinus supernus* Nelson and Goldman, Jour. Mamm., 15:110, May 15, type from Santa Rosa, between 9500 and 10,000 ft., about 7 mi. NE Guanajuato, Guanajuato. Known only from the type locality.

Thomomys umbrinus texensis V. Bailey

1902. *Thomomys fulvus texensis* V. Bailey, Proc. Biol. Soc. Washington, 15:119, June 2, type from head of Limpia Creek, 5500 ft., Davis Mts., Jeff Davis Co., Texas. Known only from the type locality.
1939. *Thomomys umbrinus texensis*, Blair, Occas. Papers Mus. Zool., Univ. Michigan, 403:2, June 16.

Thomomys umbrinus tivius Durrant

1937. *Thomomys bottae tivius* Durrant, Bull. Univ. Utah, 28(4):5, August 18, type from Oak Creek Canyon, 6 mi. E Oak City, 6000 ft., Millard Co., Utah. Known only from the type locality.

Thomomys umbrinus toltecus J. A. Allen

1893. *Thomomys toltecus* J. A. Allen, Bull. Amer. Mus. Nat. Hist., 5:52, April 28, type from Colonia Juárez, 4500 ft., Casas Grandes River, Chihuahua.

MARGINAL RECORDS.—New Mexico (Kelson, 1951: 71): Rio Mimbres; Deming. Chihuahua: Espía (V. Bailey, 1915:86); Casas Grandes (*ibid.*); Colonia Díaz (Huey, 1932:159). New Mexico: Adobe Ranch, N base Animas Mts. (Kelson, 1951:71).

Thomomys umbrinus tolucae Nelson and Goldman

1934. *Thomomys umbrinus tolucae* Nelson and Goldman, Jour. Mamm., 15:109, May 15, type from N slope Volcán de Toluca, 9500 ft., México. Known only from the type locality.

Thomomys umbrinus trumbullensis Hall and Davis

1934. *Thomomys bottae trumbullensis* Hall and Davis, Proc. Biol. Soc. Washington, 47:51, February 9, type from 3 mi. S Nixon Spring, Mt. Trumbull, Mohave Co., Arizona.

MARGINAL RECORDS.—Arizona: type locality; head Toroweap Valley (Hall and Davis, 1934:53); Mt. Logan (Goldman, 1947:10).

Thomomys umbrinus umbrinus (Richardson)

1829. *Geomys umbrinus* Richardson, Fauna Boreali-Americana, 1:202. Type locality, southern México; probably the vicinity of Boca del Monte, Veracruz; type said to have come from "Cadadaguois, a town in southwestern Louisiana"; see V. Bailey, Proc. Biol. Soc. Washington, 19:3–6, January 29, 1906.
1855. *Thomomys umbrinus*, Baird, Proc. Acad. Nat. Sci. Philadelphia, 7:332.

MARGINAL RECORDS.—Veracruz: type locality; *Xuchil* [*in Puebla?*] (Miller, 1924:246).

Thomomys umbrinus vanrossemi Huey

1934. *Thomomys bottae vanrossemi* Huey, Trans. San Diego Soc. Nat. Hist., 8:1, August 10, type from Punta Peñascosa, Sonora. Known only from the type locality.

Thomomys umbrinus vescus Hall and Davis

1935. *Thomomys bottae vescus* Hall and Davis, Univ. California Publ. Zool., 40:389, March 13, type from S slope Mt. Jefferson, Toquima Range, 9000 ft., Nye Co., Nevada.

MARGINAL RECORDS (Hall, 1946:468).—Nevada: 1 mi. E Jefferson, 7600 ft.; 5 mi. E Meadow Canyon R.S.; Meadow Canyon R.S.

Thomomys umbrinus villai Baker

1953. *Thomomys bottae villai* Baker, Univ. Kansas Publ., Mus. Nat. Hist., 5:505, June 1, type from 7 mi. S, 2 mi. E Boquillas, 1800 ft., Coahuila. Known only from the type locality.

Thomomys umbrinus virgineus Goldman

1937. *Thomomys bottae virgineus* Goldman, Proc. Biol. Soc. Washington, 50:133, September 10, type from Beaverdam Creek, 1500 ft., near confluence with Virgin River at Littlefield, Arizona.

MARGINAL RECORDS.—Utah: Beaverdam Wash, 8 mi. N Utah–Arizona border (Durrant, 1952:220). Arizona: type locality. Nevada: Mesquite, 1750 ft. (Hall, 1946:474).

Thomomys umbrinus vulcanius Nelson and Goldman

1934. *Thomomys umbrinus vulcanius* Nelson and Goldman, Jour. Mamm., 15:109, May 15, type from Volcán de Popocatépetl, 12,900 ft., México.

MARGINAL RECORDS (Davis, 1944:385).—Puebla: Río Otlatí, 8700 ft., 15 km. NW San Martín [Texmelucán]. México: N slope Mt. Popocatépetl, 13,500 ft.

Thomomys umbrinus wahwahensis Durrant

1937. *Thomomys bottae wahwahensis* Durrant, Bull. Univ. Utah, 28(4):3, August 18, type from Wah Wah Springs, 30 mi. W Milford, 6500 ft., Beaver Co., Utah.

MARGINAL RECORDS.—Utah: Desert Range Experiment Station, U.S. Forest Service, Sec. 9 T. 25 S, R. 17 W, Salt Lake base meridian (Durrant, 1952:214); type locality.

Thomomys umbrinus winthropi Nelson and Goldman

1934. *Thomomys bottae winthropi* Nelson and Goldman, Jour. Mamm., 15:122, May 15, type from Hermosillo, Sonora.

MARGINAL RECORDS (Burt, 1938:42).—Sonora: Saric; Magdalena; Ures; Ortiz; type locality.

Thomomys umbrinus xerophilus Huey

1945. *Thomomys bottae xerophilus* Huey, Trans. San Diego Soc. Nat. Hist., 10:257, August 31, type from near Diablito Spring, summit San Matías Pass between Sierra Juárez and Sierra San Pedro Mártir, Baja California.

MARGINAL RECORDS.—Baja California: type locality; Aguajita Spring, El Valle de la Trinidad (Huey, 1945:257).

Thomomys umbrinus zacatecae Nelson and Goldman

1934. *Thomomys umbrinus zacatecae* Nelson and Goldman, Jour. Mamm., 15:112, May 15, type from Berriozábal, 6600 ft., Zacatecas.

MARGINAL RECORDS.—Zacatecas: 5 mi. NW Zacatecas, 7600 ft. (39780 KU); type locality. Aguascalientes: 12 mi. N Rincón de Romos, 6500 ft. (39790 KU).

Thomomys baileyi
Bailey's Pocket Gopher

External measurements: 196–220; 65–69; 27–31. Upper parts brownish to buffy according to subspecies, often overlaid more or less with blackish; underparts washed with buffy or ochraceous shades. Skull small, weak, comparatively short and wide; upper incisors strongly procumbent and lightly but appreciably grooved; posterior ends of nasals depressed between premaxillae and terminating subequally to them; molariform dentition small and weak. Two pairs pectoral mammae and 2 pairs inguinal. This species is closely allied to *T. umbrinus* and we shall not be surprised if *T. baileyi* and *T. umbrinus* are found to intergrade, thereby showing that the named kinds of *Thomomys baileyi* are subspecies of the species *Thomomys umbrinus*.

Thomomys baileyi baileyi Merriam

1901. *Thomomys baileyi* Merriam, Proc. Biol. Soc. Washington, 14:109, July 19, type from Sierra Blanca, Hudspeth Co., Texas. Known only from the type locality.

Thomomys baileyi mearnsi V. Bailey

1914. *Thomomys mearnsi* V. Bailey, Proc. Biol. Soc. Washington, 27:117, July 10, type from Grays Ranch, 5000 ft., Animas Valley, Grant Co., New Mexico.
1934. *Thomomys baileyi mearnsi*, Nelson and Goldman, Jour. Mamm., 15:124, May 15.

MARGINAL RECORDS (Goldman, 1947:32).—Arizona: near Willcox, Sulphur Springs Valley. New Mexico: type locality. Arizona: San Bernardino; San Simeon Valley.

Thomomys baileyi nelsoni Merriam

1901. *Thomomys nelsoni* Merriam, Proc. Biol. Soc. Washington, 14:109, July 19, type from Parral, Chihuahua.
1934. *Thomomys baileyi nelsoni*, Nelson and Goldman, Jour. Mamm., 15:124, May 15.

MARGINAL RECORDS.—Chihuahua (Baker, 1953:512): Gallego; 1 mi. NW Camargo, 4000 ft.; type locality.

Thomomys baileyi spatiosus Goldman

1938. *Thomomys baileyi spatiosus* Goldman, Proc. Biol. Soc. Washington, 51:58, March 18, type from Alpine, 4500 ft., Brewster Co., Texas.

MARGINAL RECORDS.—Texas: type locality; Paisano (Goldman, 1938a:59).

Thomomys baileyi tularosae Hall

1932. *Thomomys baileyi tularosae* Hall, Univ. California Publ. Zool., 38:411, September 20, type from Cook Ranch, ½ mi. W Tularosa, Otero Co., New Mexico.

MARGINAL RECORDS.—New Mexico: type locality; about 2 mi. N Alamagordo (Blair, 1941:221); 11 mi. SW Alamagordo (*ibid.*).

Thomomys townsendii
Townsend's Pocket Gopher

Revised by Davis, Jour. Mamm., 18:145–158, May 12, 1937.

External measurements: 230–340; 53–113; 31–45. Basilar length, 36.7–50.0. Upper parts brownish or brownish-gray often strongly washed with black; underparts lighter than upper parts but not sharply bicolor. Ears short (5–8) and rounded; mammae usually 8; sphenoidal fissure present in skull; anterior opening of infraorbital canal anterior to, or even with, anterior palatine foramen; occlusal face of anterior prism of P4 rounded and less than ¾ the area of occlusal surface of posterior prism.

This species closely approaches *T. umbrinus* in its morphological characters and geographic distribution. In Nevada the closest approach, from both standpoints, seems to be between the subspecies *T. t. bachmani* and *T. u. canus*. Owing to a lack of intergrades, the two kinds are considered to belong to different species (Hall, 1946:455).

Thomomys townsendii bachmani Davis

1937. *Thomomys townsendii bachmani* Davis, Jour. Mamm., 18:150, May 12, type from Quinn River Crossing, 4100 ft., Humboldt Co., Nevada.

MARGINAL RECORDS (Hall, 1946:452, unless otherwise noted).—Oregon: 5 mi. SW Narrows (Davis, 1937: 151). Nevada: McDermitt; type locality; 17½ mi. S, 5 mi. W Quinn River Crossing; 11½ mi. E, 22 mi. N Gerlach; Flowing Springs, 7 mi. E, 3½ mi. N Division Peak, 4200 ft.; Big Creek Ranch. Oregon: Tum Tum Lake (Davis, 1937: 151); Lake Alvord (*ibid.*). Also Nevada: Paradise; 1 mi. E Golconda, 4000 ft.; 18 mi. NE Iron Point, 4600 ft.; Argenta; Battle Mtn.; 18 mi. W Battle Mtn.; Lovelock; Toulon; 1 mi. N Winnemucca.

Thomomys townsendii elkoensis Davis

1937. *Thomomys townsendii elkoensis* Davis, Jour. Mamm., 18:151, May 12, type from Evans, Eureka Co., Nevada.

MARGINAL RECORDS (Hall, 1946:453).—Nevada: 2 mi. W Halleck, 5200 ft.; 3 mi. S Halleck, 5200 ft.; type locality; 4 mi. S Romano; Winzell; Independence Valley.

Thomomys townsendii nevadensis Merriam

1897. *Thomomys nevadensis* Merriam, Proc. Biol. Soc. Washington, 11:213, July 15, type from Reese River Valley, 5 mi. W Austin, Lander Co., Nevada.
1915. *Thomomys townsendi nevadensis*, V. Bailey, N. Amer. Fauna, 39:44, November 15.

MARGINAL RECORDS.—Nevada: type locality; E side Reese River, 8 mi. W, 5 mi. S Austin (Hall, 1946:453).

Thomomys townsendii owyhensis Davis

1937. *Thomomys townsendii owyhensis* Davis, Jour. Mamm., 18:154, May 12, type from Castle Creek, 8 mi. S Oreana, Owyhee Co., Idaho.

MARGINAL RECORDS (Davis, 1939:248).—Idaho: Sinker Creek, 7 mi. SE Murphy; Indian Cove; type locality.

Thomomys townsendii relictus Grinnell

1926. *Thomomys relictus* Grinnell, Univ. California Publ. Zool., 30:2, August 18, type from 2 mi. S Susanville, valley of Susan River, Lassen Co., California.
1933. *Thomomys townsendii relictus* Grinnell, Univ. California Publ. Zool., 40:137, September 26.

MARGINAL RECORDS.—California: E. B. Coffin Ranch, 4½ mi. NE (a bit east) Susanville, 4600 ft. (Grinnell, 1934:196); 4 mi. ESE Amedee (Davis, 1937:150); 3 mi. S Susanville (*ibid.*).

Thomomys townsendii similis Davis

1937. *Thomomys townsendii similis* Davis, Jour. Mamm., 18:155, May 12, type from Pocatello, Bannock Co., Idaho.

MARGINAL RECORDS (Davis, 1939:251).—Idaho: 1 mi. E Pingree; Fort Hall Indian School, 10 mi. N Pocatello; type locality; American Falls; 4 mi. NW American Falls.

Thomomys townsendii townsendii (Bachman)

1839. *Geomys townsendii* Bachman, Jour. Acad. Nat. Sci. Philadelphia, 8:105. Type locality, erroneously given as "Columbia River," but probably near Nampa, Canyon Co., Idaho, where Townsend's party camped to trade with Indians, August 22, 1834 (V. Bailey, N. Amer. Fauna, 39:42, November 15, 1915).
1893. *Thomomys townsendii*, J. A. Allen, Bull. Amer. Mus. Nat. Hist., 5:61, April 28.

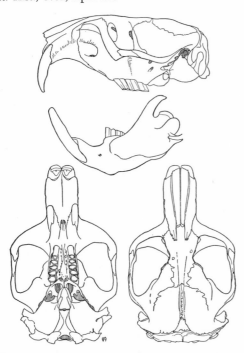

Fig. 257. *Thomomys townsendii nevadensis*, Malloy Ranch, 5 mi. W Austin, Nevada, No. 37073 M.V.Z., ♂, X 1.

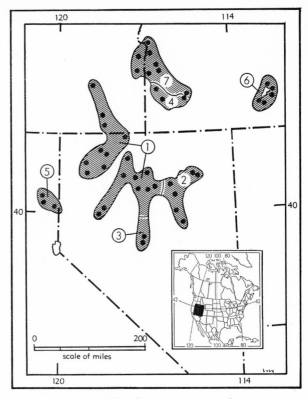

Map 267. *Thomomys townsendii.*

Guide to subspecies
1. *T. t. bachmani*
2. *T. t. elkoensis*
3. *T. t. nevadensis*
4. *T. t. owyhensis*
5. *T. t. relictus*
6. *T. t. similis*
7. *T. t. townsendii*

1914. *Thomomys nevadensis atrogriseus* V. Bailey, Proc. Biol. Soc. Washington, 27:118, July 10, type from Nampa, Idaho.

MARGINAL RECORDS.—Idaho (Davis, 1939:247): Weiser; 2 mi. S Payette; Caldwell; Nampa; Hammett; Homedale. Oregon (Davis, 1937:153): Owyhee; Vale.

Thomomys talpoides
Northern Pocket Gopher

External measurements: 165–253; 40–75; 20–31. Color highly variable according to subspecies; in most subspecies rich, dark brown, sometimes lightly washed with blackish; less often pale grayish to plumbeous. Underparts paler usually washed with buffy or ochraceous. Skull robust; zygomatic arches usually widely spreading; sphenoidal fissure absent; incisive foramina anterior to infraorbital canal; anterior prism of P4 triangular; occlusal face of anterior prism of P4 with distinct anteromedial notch and area of occlusal face of anterior prism ¾ or more that of posterior prism.

Over much of their geographic range, animals of this species occur in montane meadows, but in the northern parts of the range are found also in lowland situations. Overgrazed range conditions are, in most cases, indicated by, not caused by, an abundance of these gophers. In most uncultivated areas, they are distinctly beneficial to soil formation and vegetational productivity over a period of years.

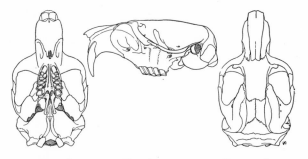

Fig. 258. *Thomomys talpoides monoensis*, Lapon Canyon, Mount Grant, Nevada, No. 63697 M.V.Z., ♂, X 1.

Thomomys talpoides aequalidens Dalquest

1942. *Thomomys talpoides aequalidens* Dalquest, Murrelet, 23:3, May 14, type from Abel Place, 2200 ft., 6 mi. SSE Dayton, Columbia Co., Washington.

MARGINAL RECORDS (Dalquest and Scheffer, 1944: 437, unless otherwise noted).—Washington: Clarkston; Asotin (on geographic grounds, from V. Bailey, 1915:107); *Jim Creek, 3200 ft., 11 mi. SE Dayton;* 6½ mi. SE Walla Walla (Drake and Booth, 1952:49); *1.9 mi. SE Walla Walla (ibid.);* Dayton (*ibid.*).

Thomomys talpoides agrestis Merriam

1908. *Thomomys talpoides agrestis* Merriam, Proc. Biol. Soc. Washington, 21:144, June 9, type from Medano Ranch, San Luis Valley, Colorado.

MARGINAL RECORDS (Warren, 1942:163, unless otherwise noted).—Colorado: 12 mi. W Saguache; Crestone; Fort Garland (V. Bailey, 1915:106); San Acacio; type locality.

Thomomys talpoides andersoni Goldman

1939. *Thomomys talpoides andersoni* Goldman, Jour. Mamm., 20:235, May 15, type from Medicine Hat, South Saskatchewan River, Alberta.

MARGINAL RECORDS.—Alberta: type locality; Milk River [Ranch, sec. 30, T.2, R. 9 W of 4th meridian] (Anderson, 1947:128).

Thomomys talpoides attenuatus Hall and Montague

1951. *Thomomys talpoides attenuatus* Hall and Montague, Univ. Kansas Publ., Mus. Nat. Hist., 5:29, February 28, type from 3½ mi. W Horse Creek P.O., 7000 ft., Laramie Co., Wyoming.

MARGINAL RECORDS (Hall and Montague, 1951:30). —Wyoming: 10 mi. N Hatcreek P.O., 5300 ft.; Little Bear Creek, 20 mi. SE Chugwater; 2 mi. S, ½ mi. E Pine Bluffs, 5200 ft. Colorado: Chimney Canyon, 10 mi. NE Avalo, 5100 ft.; Pawnee Buttes, 5300 ft. Wyoming: Arcola, 5200 ft.; 6 mi. W Islay; 5 mi. W, 1 mi. N Horse Creek P.O., 7200 ft.; 5 mi. SW Wheatland.

Thomomys talpoides bridgeri Merriam

1901. *Thomomys bridgeri* Merriam, Proc. Biol. Soc. Washington, 14:113, July 19, type from Harvey's Ranch, Smith Fork, 6 mi. SW Old Fort Bridger, Uinta Co., Wyoming.
1939. *Thomomys talpoides bridgeri,* Goldman, Jour. Mamm., 20:234, May 14.

MARGINAL RECORDS.—Idaho (Davis, 1939:260): 3 mi. SW Victor; 10 mi. SE Irwin. Wyoming: 19 mi. W, 2 mi. S Big Piney, 7700 ft. (15084 KU); type locality; 4 mi. S Lonetree (V. Bailey, 1915:113); 14 mi. S, 2 mi. E Robertson, 9300 ft. (25667 KU); 14½ mi. S, 1 mi. E Evanston, 6900 ft. (25536 KU). Idaho (Davis, 1939:260): Strawberry Creek (Canyon), 20 mi. NE Preston; Bridge; Indian Springs, 4 mi. S American Falls; Shelley; S side South Fork, 3 mi. W Swan Valley.

Thomomys talpoides bullatus V. Bailey

1914. *Thomomys talpoides bullatus* V. Bailey, Proc. Biol. Soc. Washington, 27:115, July 10, type from Powderville, Custer Co., Montana.

MARGINAL RECORDS (Swenk, 1941:4, unless otherwise noted).—Saskatchewan: Cypress Hills (Anderson, 1947: 128); Dollard (Soper, 1946:143). Montana: Johnson Lake. North Dakota: Buford. Montana: Glendive; type locality. Wyoming: Devils Tower (V. Bailey, 1915:102); Newcastle (*ibid.*); 23 mi. SW Newcastle, 4500 ft. (20229 KU); Clearmont; Parkman (= Pass) (Hall and Kelson, 1952: 363). Montana: Fort Custer; Red Lodge; Piney Buttes; Fort Assiniboine.

Thomomys talpoides caryi V. Bailey

1914. *Thomomys talpoides caryi* V. Bailey, Proc. Biol. Soc. Washington, 27:115, July 10, type from head of Trapper Creek, 9500 ft., Bighorn Mts., Bighorn Co., Wyoming.

MARGINAL RECORDS.—Wyoming: 12 mi. E, 2 mi. N Shell, 7500 ft. (20195 KU); *17½ mi. E, 4½ mi. S Shell, 8500 ft.* (20192 KU); 9 mi. E, 4 mi. N Tensleep, 7000 ft. (20230 KU). Probably also in Bighorn Mts. of Montana.

Thomomys talpoides cheyennensis Swenk

1941. *Thomomys talpoides cheyennensis* Swenk, Missouri Valley Fauna, 4:5, March 1, type from 2 mi. S Dalton, Cheyenne Co., Nebraska.

MARGINAL RECORDS.—Nebraska (Swenk, 1941:5): 9 mi. S Kimball; type locality; 4 mi. N Sidney; 10 mi. N Kimball, Wyoming (Hall and Montague, 1951:30): 1 mi. W Pine Bluffs, 5000 ft.; 12 mi. N, ½ mi. W Pine Bluffs.

Thomomys talpoides clusius Coues

1875. *Thomomys clusius* Coues, Proc. Acad. Nat. Sci. Philadelphia, 27:138, June 15, type from Bridger Pass, 18 mi. SW Rawlins, Carbon Co., Wyoming.
1915. *Thomomys talpoides clusius,* V. Bailey, N. Amer. Fauna, 39:100, November 15.

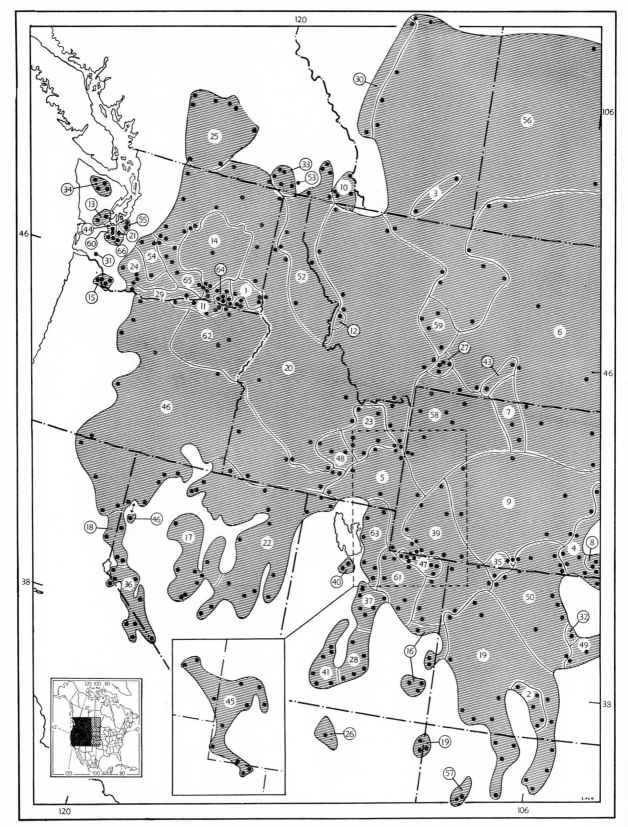

Map 268. Some subspecies of *Thomomys talpoides*. See guide to Map 269.

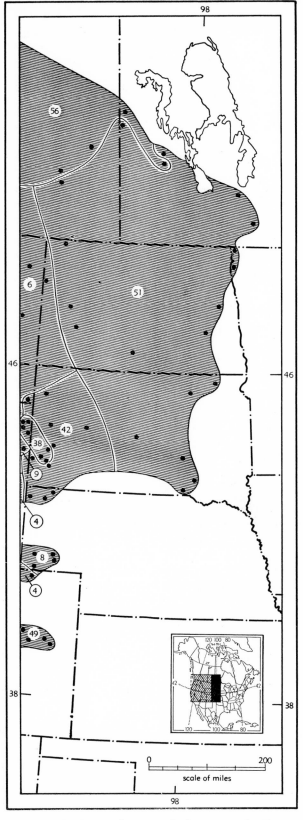

Map 269. Some subspecies of *Thomomys talpoides*.

(Names following numerals are a guide to maps 268, 269.)

1. *T. talpoides aequalidens*
2. *T. talpoides agrestis*
3. *T. talpoides andersoni*
4. *T. talpoides attenuatus*
5. *T. talpoides bridgeri*
6. *T. talpoides bullatus*
7. *T. talpoides caryi*
8. *T. talpoides cheyennensis*
9. *T. talpoides clusius*
10. *T. talpoides cognatus*
11. *T. talpoides columbianus*
12. *T. talpoides confinus*
13. *T. talpoides couchi*
14. *T. talpoides devexus*
15. *T. talpoides douglasii*
16. *T. talpoides durranti*
17. *T. talpoides falcifer*
18. *T. talpoides fisheri*
19. *T. talpoides fossor*
20. *T. talpoides fuscus*
21. *T. talpoides glacialis*
22. *T. talpoides gracilis*
23. *T. talpoides idahoensis*
24. *T. talpoides immunis*
25. *T. talpoides incensus*
26. *T. talpoides kaibabensis*
27. *T. talpoides kelloggi*
28. *T. talpoides levis*
29. *T. talpoides limosus*
30. *T. talpoides loringi*
31. *T. talpoides louiei*
32. *T. talpoides macrotis*
33. *T. talpoides medius*
34. *T. talpoides melanops*
35. *T. talpoides meritus*
36. *T. talpoides monoensis*
37. *T. talpoides moorei*
38. *T. talpoides nebulosus*
39. *T. talpoides ocius*
40. *T. talpoides oquirrhensis*
41. *T. talpoides parowanensis*
42. *T. talpoides pierreicolus*
43. *T. talpoides pryori*
44. *T. talpoides pugetensis*
45. *T. talpoides pygmaeus*
46. *T. talpoides quadratus*
47. *T. talpoides ravus*
48. *T. talpoides relicinus*
49. *T. talpoides retrorsus*
50. *T. talpoides rostralis*
51. *T. talpoides rufescens*
52. *T. talpoides saturatus*
53. *T. talpoides segregatus*
54. *T. talpoides shawi*
55. *T. talpoides tacomensis*
56. *T. talpoides talpoides*
57. *T. talpoides taylori*
58. *T. talpoides tenellus*
59. *T. talpoides trivialis*
60. *T. talpoides tumuli*
61. *T. talpoides uinta*
62. *T. talpoides wallowa*
63. *T. talpoides wasatchensis*
64. *T. talpoides whitmani*
65. *T. talpoides yakimensis*
66. *T. talpoides yelmensis*

MARGINAL RECORDS (Swenk, 1941:8, unless otherwise noted).—Wyoming: Redbank; Felterman; Rawhide Butte, 5400 ft.; 15 mi. SW Wheatland, 5200 ft.; Rock Creek; type locality; Green Mountains, 8000 ft.; JK Ranch, 5900 ft., Meadow Creek (Hall and Kelson, 1952:363).

Thomomys talpoides cognatus Johnstone

1955. *Thomomys talpoides cognatus* Johnstone, Canadian Field-Nat., 68:163, September 17, type from Crowsnest Pass, British Columbia.

MARGINAL RECORDS.—British Columbia (Johnstone, 1955:163): type locality; Flathead River, 20 mi. N U.S. boundary (*op. cit.*:157); East Newgate; Baynes Lake.

Thomomys talpoides columbianus V. Bailey

1914. *Thomomys fuscus columbianus* V. Bailey, Proc. Biol. Soc. Washington, 27:117, July 10, type from Touchet, Walla Walla Co., Washington.
1939. *Thomomys talpoides columbianus*, Goldman, Jour. Mamm., 20:234, May 15.

MARGINAL RECORDS.—Washington: Prescott (Dalquest and Scheffer, 1944:436); 7 mi. S Dixie, 4300 ft. (*ibid.*); 2½ *mi. S College Place, S side Walla Walla River* (Drake and Booth, 1952:47–48); *4 mi. S Walla Walla* (*ibid.*). Oregon: 1⁶⁄₁₀ mi. S Milton (*ibid.*); 7 mi. SW Milton (*ibid.*); Pendleton (V. Bailey, 1915:107); Willows (V. Bailey, 1936:261); Umatilla (*ibid.*). Washington: Fort Walla Walla (V. Bailey, 1915:107); 2 mi. E junction Snake and Columbia rivers, 350 ft. (Dalquest and Scheffer, 1944:436); 8 mi. E Eureka (Drake and Booth, 1952:47).

Thomomys talpoides confinis Davis

1937. *Thomomys talpoides confinis* Davis, Murrelet, 18:25, September 4, type from Gird Creek, near Hamilton, Ravalli Co., Montana.

MARGINAL RECORDS.—Montana: Hamilton (Davis, 1937:26); *type locality.*

Thomomys talpoides couchi Goldman

1939. *Thomomys talpoides couchi* Goldman, Jour. Mamm., 20:243, May 15, type from 4 mi. N Shelton, Mason Co., Washington.

MARGINAL RECORDS.—Washington: type locality; Lost Lake Prairie, near Satsop (Dalquest, 1948:314).

Thomomys talpoides devexus Hall and Dalquest

1939. *Thomomys talpoides devexus* Hall and Dalquest, Murrelet, 20:3, April 30, type from 1 mi. WSW Neppel, Grant Co., Washington.
1939. *Thomomys talpoides ericaeus* Goldman, Jour. Mamm., 20:243, May 15, type from Badger Mts., 8 mi. SW Waterville, Douglas Co., Washington. (Regarded as inseparable from *devexus* by Dalquest and Scheffer, Amer. Nat., 78:434, September, 1944.)

MARGINAL RECORDS (Dalquest and Scheffer, 1944:435).—Washington: Badger Mts.; type locality; 2½ mi. E, 1½ mi. S Pasco, 400 ft.; 4 mi. W Pasco, 350 ft.

Thomomys talpoides douglasii (Richardson)

1829. *Geomys douglasii* Richardson, Fauna Boreali-Americana, 1:200. Type locality, near mouth of Columbia River, probably near Vancouver, Washington.
1939. *Thomomys talpoides douglasii*, Goldman, Jour. Mamm., 20:234, May 15.

MARGINAL RECORDS.—Washington: Brush Prairie (Dalquest and Scheffer, 1944:444); type locality. Oregon: Scapoose, Columbia River, 20 mi. NW Portland (V. Bailey, 1936:254). Washington: 5 mi. E Vancouver (22254 KU).

Thomomys talpoides durranti Kelson

1949. *Thomomys talpoides durranti* Kelson, Proc. Biol. Soc. Washington, 62:143, August 23, type from Johnson Creek, 14 mi. N Blanding, 7500 ft., San Juan Co., Utah.

MARGINAL RECORDS (Durrant, 1952:174).—Utah: Oak Spring, middle fork Willow Creek, 15 mi. N Thompson; 1 mi. SE Mesa R.S., 9200 ft.; Warner R.S., La Sal Mts., 9750 ft., and discontinuously in the Abajo Mt. area at Gooseberry R.S., Elk Ridge, 8300 ft.; Dalton Spring, 5 mi. W Monticello, Abajo (= Blue) Mts., 8300 ft.; type locality.

Thomomys talpoides falcifer Grinnell

1926. *Thomomys falcifer* Grinnell, Univ. California Publ. Zool., 30:180, December 10, type from Bells Ranch, 6890 ft., Reese River Valley, Nye Co., Nevada.
1939. *Thomomys talpoides falcifer*, Goldman, Jour. Mamm., 20:234, May 15.

MARGINAL RECORDS (Hall, 1946:450).—Nevada: 2 mi. E Unionville, 4500 ft.; Malloy Ranch, 5 mi. W Austin, 5500 ft., Reese River; Silver Creek, N Austin; Birch Creek Ranch, Big Smoky Valley, 5650 ft.; Kingston R.S., 7500 ft.; Arc Dome; Slys Ranch, 7400 ft., Indian Valley, Shoshone Mts.; Cherry Valley (Meadows), 6450 ft.

Thomomys talpoides fisheri Merriam

1901. *Thomomys fuscus fisheri* Merriam, Proc. Biol. Soc. Washington, 14:111, July 19, type from Beckwith, Sierra Valley, Plumas Co., California.
1939. *Thomomys talpoides fisheri*, Goldman, Jour. Mamm., 20:234, May 15.

MARGINAL RECORDS.—Nevada (Hall, 1946:449): Cottonwood Creek, Virginia Mts., 4400 ft.; 6 mi. NE Virginia City, 6000 ft.; 8 mi. S Reno. California: type locality.

Thomomys talpoides fossor J. A. Allen

1893. *Thomomys fossor* J. A. Allen, Bull. Amer. Mus. Nat. Hist., 5:51, April 28, type from Florida, 7200 ft., La Plata Co., Colorado.
1939. *Thomomys talpoides fossor*, Goldman, Jour. Mamm., 20:234, May 15.

MARGINAL RECORDS (V. Bailey, 1915:112, unless otherwise noted).—Colorado: White River Plateau; Meeker; Blue Lake (Warren, 1935:153). New Mexico: Costilla Pass; Halls Peak; Pecos River Mts. (V. Bailey, 1932:230); Pecos Baldy. Colorado: Garretson's Ranch, Muddy Creek (Warren, 1942:164); Wasson Ranch, 3 mi. E Creede (13203 KU). New Mexico: Hopewell; head Santa Clara Creek, Jemez Mts.; Gallinas Mts.; Horse Lake. Colorado:

Pagosa Springs; type locality; La Plata City (Kelson, 1949: 144); Uncompahgre Plateau; Baxter Pass, Book Plateau. Isolated segment of range, Arizona: Lukachukai Mts. (Goldman, 1947:33). New Mexico: Chusca Mts. Arizona: Tunitcha Mts. (Goldman, 1947:33).

Thomomys talpoides fuscus Merriam

1891. *Thomomys clusius fuscus* Merriam, N. Amer. Fauna, 5:69, July 30, type from Summit Creek in mountains at head of Big Lost River, Custer Co., Idaho.
1939. *Thomomys talpoides fuscus*, Davis, The Recent mammals of Idaho, The Caxton Printers, Caldwell, Idaho, p. 253, April 5.
1901. *Thomomys myops* Merriam, Proc. Biol. Soc. Washington, 14:112, July 19, type from Conconully, E base Cascade Range, Okanogan Co., Washington.

MARGINAL RECORDS (V. Bailey, 1915:127–128, unless otherwise noted).—British Columbia: Westbridge (Anderson, 1947:128); Trail (*ibid.*). Washington: Round Top Mtn. (Dalquest and Scheffer, 1944:439). Idaho (Davis, 1939:255): Hoodoo Valley; Mission. Montana: Corvallis; Lolo; Thompson Falls; Tobacco Plains; summit W of Blackfoot Station; W of Benton; Livingston (Smith, 1940: 220); Fort Ellis; Lakeview (21723 KU). Idaho (Davis, 1939:255–256): Taylor Creek, 5 mi. S Montana Line at Sheridan Mtn.; 3 mi. SW Victor; 5 mi. W St. Anthony; Salmon Rivers Mts.; type locality; 16 mi. N Shoshone; 2 mi. E Acequia; 2 mi. S Hagerman; Crane Creek, 15 mi. E Midvale; Lewiston. Washington (following geographic arrangement of Dalquest, 1948:308): Wawawai (Dalquest and Scheffer, 1944:439); Cheney; Loon Lake; Sherman Creek Pass (Dalquest and Scheffer, 1944:439); Duley Lake (*ibid.*); Douglas; Wenatchee (Dalquest and Scheffer, 1944: 439); 5 mi. NE Cle Elum (*op. cit.*:440); Easton (Goldman, 1939:242); Mt. Stuart (*ibid.*); Lucerne (Dalquest and Scheffer, 1944:439); Barron (*op. cit.*:440).

Thomomys talpoides glacialis Dalquest and Scheffer

1942. *Thomomys talpoides glacialis* Dalquest and Scheffer, Proc. Biol. Soc. Washington, 55:97, August 13, type from prairie 2 mi. S Roy, Pierce Co., Washington. Known only from Roy Prairie, Washington.

Thomomys talpoides gracilis Durrant

1939. *Thomomys quadratus gracilis* Durrant, Bull. Univ. Utah, 29(6):3, February 28, type from Pine Canyon, 6600 ft., 17 mi. NW Kelton, Boxelder Co., Utah.
1939. *Thomomys talpoides gracilis* Durrant, Bull. Univ. Utah, 30(5):6, October 24.

MARGINAL RECORDS.—Idaho: S fork Owyhee River, 12 mi. N Nevada line (on geographic grounds from Davis, 1939:258). Nevada (Hall, 1946:448): ½ mi. W Jarbidge. Utah (Durrant, 1952:159): Yost; Park Valley; Etna. Nevada (Hall, 1946:448): Cleve Creek, 8100–8600 ft., Shell Creek Range; E side Shelbourne Pass, 6800 ft.; 1 mi. E Illipah, 6100 ft.; 3 mi. SW Hamilton, 8400 ft.; Nay Ranch, 7200 ft., Monitor Valley; Greenmonster Canyon, 7500–8200 ft., Monitor Range; Eureka; 5 mi. E Raines, Sulphur Spring Mts.; head Ackler Creek; Marys River, 5800 ft., 25 mi. N Deeth; 13 mi. N Paradise Valley, 6700 ft.; 5 mi. W Paradise Valley P.O.; Cottonwood Range.

Thomomys talpoides idahoensis Merriam

1901. *Thomomys idahoensis* Merriam, Proc. Biol. Soc. Washington, 14:114, July 19, type from Birch Creek, Clark Co., Idaho.
1939. *Thomomys talpoides idahoensis*, Davis, The Recent mammals of Idaho, The Caxton Printers, Caldwell, Idaho, p. 251, April 5.

MARGINAL RECORDS (Davis, 1939:252, unless otherwise noted).—Idaho: type locality; Dubois; N side South Fork, 3 mi. W Swan Valley; Idaho Falls; W Blackfoot (Davis, 1939:256); Big Butte; Big Lost River, near sink.

Thomomys talpoides immunis Hall and Dalquest

1939. *Thomomys talpoides immunis* Hall and Dalquest, Murrelet, 20:4, April 30, type from 5 mi. S Trout Lake, Klickitat Co., Washington.

MARGINAL RECORDS.—Washington: Mt. St. Helens (Dalquest and Scheffer, 1944:442); Morrison Springs Ranger Station (Dalquest, 1948:311); Gotchen Creek Ranger Station (Dalquest and Scheffer, 1944:442); type locality.

Thomomys talpoides incensus Goldman

1939. *Thomomys talpoides incensus* Goldman, Jour. Mamm., 20:240, May 15, type from Shuswap, Yale District, British Columbia.

MARGINAL RECORDS (Johnstone, 1955:161).—British Columbia: type locality; Salmon Arm; Monashee; Keremeos; Manning Park; Ashcroft; Savona; Kamloops.

Thomomys talpoides kaibabensis Goldman

1938. *Thomomys fossor kaibabensis* Goldman, Jour. Washington Acad. Sci., 28:333, July 15, type from De Motte Park, 9000 ft., Kaibab Plateau, Coconino Co., Arizona. Known only from the Kaibab Plateau.
1939. *Thomomys talpoides kaibabensis* Goldman, Jour. Mamm., 20:234, May 15.

Thomomys talpoides kelloggi Goldman

1939. *Thomomys talpoides kelloggi* Goldman, Jour. Mamm., 20:237, May 15, type from West Boulder Creek, Absaroka Mts., 18 mi. SE Livingston, Park Co., Montana.

MARGINAL RECORDS.—Montana: Boulder Creek, 8 mi. S Bigtimber (Goldman, 1939:238); type locality; 12 mi. E, 7 mi. S Livingston, 4500 ft., West Boulder River (21743 KU); 15 mi. E, 4 mi. S Livingston, 4400 ft., West Boulder River (21738 KU).

Thomomys talpoides levis Goldman

1938. *Thomomys fossor levis* Goldman, Jour. Washington Acad. Sci., 28:336, July 15, type from Seven Mile Flat, 10,000 ft., 5 mi. N Fish Lake, Fish Lake Plateau, Sevier Co., Utah.
1939. *Thomomys talpoides levis* Goldman, Jour. Mamm., 20:234, May 15.

MARGINAL RECORDS (Durrant, 1952:177).—Utah: type locality; Elkhorn Guard Station, 14 mi. N Torrey, 9400 ft., Fish Lake Plateau; Grover; 18 mi. N Escalante; summit Birch Creek, Escalante Mts.

Thomomys talpoides limosus Merriam

1901. *Thomomys limosus* Merriam, Proc. Biol. Soc. Washington, 14:116, July 19, type from White Salmon, Gorge of the Columbia, Klickitat Co., Washington.
1939. *Thomomys talpoides limosus*, Goldman, Jour. Mamm., 20:235, May 15.

MARGINAL RECORDS.—Washington (Dalquest and Scheffer, 1944:443): Paterson, 250 ft., thence westwardly along north side of Columbia River to 5 mi. W White Salmon.

Thomomys talpoides loringi V. Bailey

1914. *Thomomys fuscus loringi* V. Bailey, Proc. Biol. Soc. Washington, 27:118, July 10, type from South Edmonton, Alberta.
1939. *Thomomys talpoides loringi*, Goldman, Jour. Mamm., 20:234, May 14.

MARGINAL RECORDS.—Alberta: type locality; Moose Mtn. (Anderson, 1947:128).

Thomomys talpoides louiei Gardner

1950. *Thomomys talpoides louiei* Gardner, Jour. Mamm., 31:92, February 21, type from 12 mi. NNE Cathlamet (Crown-Zellerbach's Cathlamet Tree Farm), 2500 ft., Wahkiakum Co., Washington. Known only from the type locality.

Thomomys talpoides macrotis F. W. Miller

1930. *Thomomys talpoides macrotis* F. W. Miller, Proc. Colorado Mus. Nat. Hist., 9(3):41, December 14, type from D'Arcy Ranch, 2 mi. N Parker, Douglas Co., Colorado. Known only from the type locality.

Thomomys talpoides medius Goldman

1939. *Thomomys talpoides medius* Goldman, Jour. Mamm., 20:241, May 15, type from Silver King Mine, summit Toad Mtn., 6 mi. S Nelson, West Kootenay District, British Columbia.

MARGINAL RECORDS.—British Columbia: Ward's Ferry (Bonnington on Kootenay River, about 10 mi. below Nelson [Anderson, 1947:129]); Nelson (on geographic grounds; from V. Bailey, 1915:127); type locality; West Creston (Johnstone, 1955:157); Fruitvale (*ibid.*); Hall Creek (*ibid.*).

Thomomys talpoides melanops Merriam

1899. *Thomomys melanops* Merriam, Proc. Biol. Soc. Washington, 13:21, January 31, type from timberline at head of Soleduc River, Olympic Mts., Clallam Co., Washington.
1939. *Thomomys talpoides melanops*, Goldman, Jour. Mamm., 20:235, May 15.

MARGINAL RECORDS (Dalquest and Scheffer, 1944:448).—Washington: type locality; Happy Lake Ridge; Cat Creek, 4500 ft.; Canyon Creek, divide at head Bogachiel River.

Thomomys talpoides meritus Hall

1951. *Thomomys talpoides meritus* Hall, Univ. Kansas Publ., Mus. Nat. Hist., 5:221, December 15, type from 8 mi. N, 19½ mi. E Savery, 8800 ft., Carbon Co., Wyoming.

MARGINAL RECORDS (Hall, 1951d:222).—Wyoming: type locality; 17 mi. E, 7 mi. N Savery. Colorado: Elkhead Mts., 20 mi. SE Slater.

Thomomys talpoides monoensis Huey

1934. *Thomomys quadratus monoensis* Huey, Trans. San Diego Soc. Nat. Hist., 7:373, May 31, type from Dexter Creek Meadow, 6800 ft., at confluence of Dexter and Wet creeks, Mono Co., California.
1939. *Thomomys talpoides monoensis*, Goldman, Jour. Mamm., 20:234, May 15.

MARGINAL RECORDS (Hall, 1946:450, unless otherwise noted).—Nevada: N side Carson River, 4700 ft., 4½ mi. NE Genoa; 2 mi. SW Pine Grove, 7250 ft.; Cottonwood Creek, Mt. Grant; Chiatovich Creek, 8200 ft. California: type locality; Woodfords (Grinnell, 1933:146); Leevining (*ibid.*); Convict Creek (*ibid.*). Nevada: 6 mi. S Minden. The three localities last mentioned from California stand in the literature as places where *T. t. fisheri* occurs but the specimens need restudy in the light of the later naming of *T. t. monoensis*.

Thomomys talpoides moorei Goldman

1938. *Thomomys fossor moorei* Goldman, Jour. Washington Acad. Sci., 28:335, July 15, type from 1 mi. S Fairview, 6000 ft., Sanpete Co., Utah.
1939. *Thomomys talpoides moorei* Goldman, Jour. Mamm., 20:234, May 15.

MARGINAL RECORDS (Durrant, 1952:171).—Utah: near Payson Lake; Colton; Lake Creek, 11 mi. E Mt. Pleasant; Ephraim; mouth of Reddicks Canyon, Wales (= San Pitch) Mts., 7500 ft.; Mt. Nebo, 10,000 ft., 25 mi. SE Payson.

Thomomys talpoides nebulosus V. Bailey

1914. *Thomomys talpoides nebulosus* V. Bailey, Proc. Biol. Soc. Washington, 27:116, July 10, type from Jack Boyden's Ranch, 3750 ft., Sand Creek Canyon, 15 mi. NE Sundance, Crook Co., Wyoming.

MARGINAL RECORDS (V. Bailey, 1915:103, unless otherwise noted).—Wyoming: Bear Lodge Mts. (Swenk, 1941:4); 1 mi. E, ½ mi. N Beulah, 3550 ft. (20206 KU). South Dakota: Spring Creek; Beaver Creek; Custer. Wyoming: head of Rattlesnake Creek, 6000 ft., Black Hills; Sundance.

Thomomys talpoides ocius Merriam

1901. *Thomomys clusius ocius* Merriam, Proc. Biol. Soc. Washington, 14:114, July 19, type from Mountainview, Smiths Fork, 4 mi. (airline) SE Fort Bridger, Uinta Co., Wyoming.
1946. *Thomomys talpoides ocius*, Durrant, Univ. Kansas Publ., Mus. Nat. Hist., 1:17, August 15.

MARGINAL RECORDS.—Wyoming: Green River, junction of New Fork (V. Bailey, 1915:108); Eden (*ibid.*);

Kinney Ranch, 21 mi. S Bitter Creek (15110 KU). Colorado (Warren, 1942:162): Snake River, 20 mi. W Baggs; Craig; Douglas Spring. Utah (Durrant, 1952:170): PR Springs, 43 mi. S Ouray, 7950 ft.; Brown Corral, 20 mi. S Ouray, 6250 ft.; Vernal. Colorado: Ladore (Warren, 1942: 162). Wyoming: 5 mi. SW Maxon (V. Bailey, 1915:108); 3 mi. W Green River, 2 mi. N Utah border (17040 KU); Henrys Fork; type locality; Cumberland, 6500 ft. (21816 KU); Fontenelle (V. Bailey, 1915:108).

Thomomys talpoides oquirrhensis Durrant

1939. *Thomomys talpoides oquirrhensis* Durrant, Bull. Univ. Utah, 30(5):3, October 24, type from Settlement Creek, 6500 ft., Oquirrh Mts., Tooele Co., Utah.

MARGINAL RECORDS.—Utah: Rose Canyon, Oquirrh Mts., 5650 ft. (Durrant, 1952:163); type locality.

Thomomys talpoides parowanensis Goldman

1938. *Thomomys fossor parowanensis* Goldman, Jour. Washington Acad. Sci., 28:334, July 15, type from Brian Head, 11,000 ft., Parowan Mts., Iron Co., Utah.
1939. *Thomomys talpoides parowanensis* Goldman, Jour. Mamm., 20:234, May 15.

MARGINAL RECORDS (Durrant, 1952:176).—Utah: Britts Meadows, Beaver Mts., 8500 ft.; Puffer Lake, Beaver Mts.; ¼ mi. W Sunset Point, Bryce National Park, 8000 ft.; Duck Creek, Cedar Mts., 9000 ft.; type locality; Beaver Mts., Iron Co.

Thomomys talpoides pierreicolus Swenk

1941. *Thomomys talpoides pierreicolus* Swenk, Missouri Valley Fauna, 4:2, March 1, type from Wayside, Dawes Co., Nebraska.

MARGINAL RECORDS (Swenk, 1941:2–3).—South Dakota: Crow Buttes; Smithville. Nebraska: 5 mi. NW Chadron; Sand Creek Valley, near Horn; Indian Creek, N of Story. South Dakota: Elk Mtn.; Buffalo Gap; Rapid City; Fort Meade. Montana: Alzada.

Thomomys talpoides pryori V. Bailey

1914. *Thomomys pryori* V. Bailey, Proc. Biol. Soc. Washington, 27:116, July 10, type from head of Sage Creek, 6000 ft., Pryor Mts., Carbon Co., Montana.
1915. *Thomomys talpoides pryori,* V. Bailey, N. Amer. Fauna, 39:104, November 15.

MARGINAL RECORDS.—Montana: Bighorn River, W side, near Fort Custer (V. Bailey, 1915:105); type locality.

Thomomys talpoides pugetensis Dalquest and Scheffer

1942. *Thomomys talpoides pugetensis* Dalquest and Scheffer, Proc. Biol. Soc. Washington, 55:96, August 13, type from 4 mi. S Olympia, Thurston Co., Washington. Known only from the type locality.

Thomomys talpoides pygmaeus Merriam

1901. *Thomomys pygmaeus* Merriam, Proc. Biol. Soc. Washington, 14:115, July 19, type from Montpelier Creek, 6700 ft., about 10 mi. NE Montpelier, Bear Co., Idaho.
1939. *Thomomys talpoides pygmaeus,* Davis, The Recent mammals of Idaho, The Caxton Printers, Caldwell, Idaho, p. 252, April 5.

MARGINAL RECORDS.—Idaho (Davis, 1939:254): 5 mi. E Shelley. Wyoming (V. Bailey, 1915:110): Merna; Surveyors Park, 8000 ft., 12 mi. NE Pinedale; Big Sandy; Big Piney, 6400 ft.; Fossil, 6600 ft. Utah (Durrant, 1952: 165): Sheep Creek; Granite Park, 24 mi. S Manila. Wyoming (V. Bailey, 1915:110): 5 mi. W Lonetree, Henrys Fork, 7400 ft.; Bear River and Bear River divide, 6600–7500 ft., 14 mi. N Evanston. Idaho: type locality; Blackfoot (Davis, 1939:254). This subspecies occurs in the same geographic area as other subspecies of *talpoides*, but seems to be separated from them by local ecological (or microgeographical) differences.

Thomomys talpoides quadratus Merriam

1897. *Thomomys quadratus* Merriam, Proc. Biol. Soc. Washington, 11:214, July 15, type from The Dalles, Wasco Co., Oregon.
1939. *Thomomys talpoides quadratus,* Goldman, Jour. Mamm., 20:234, May 15.

MARGINAL RECORDS.—Oregon: type locality; Ochoco Ranger Station, 4000 ft., in Crook Co. (Hall and Orr, 1933: 42). Ironside, 4000 ft. (V. Bailey, 1915:115). Idaho (Davis, 1939:258): Reynolds Creek, 12 mi. S Snake River; S side Snake River, 2 mi. S Hagerman; Raft River, 2 mi. S Snake River; S side Snake River, 19 mi. SW American Falls; Elba; 1 mi. S Riddle. Nevada (Hall, 1946:447): meadow, Big Creek, 7000 ft., Pine Forest Mts.; Summit Lake; Soldier Meadows, 4600 ft.; 5 mi. E, 3½ mi. N Granite Peak, 3900 ft.; Smoke Creek, California–Nevada boundary, 4300 ft. California: Secret Valley, 4500 ft. (Grinnell, *et al.*, 1930:497); 4 mi. S Susanville (V. Bailey, 1915:115); Bieber (*ibid.*); Macdoel (Grinnell, 1933:145). Oregon (V. Bailey, 1915:115): Merrill; Fremont; Matoleus River; Wapinitia. Specimens from Oregon, for example from Huntington, that stand in the literature (see V. Bailey, 1915:127) as *T. [t.] fuscus* need re-examination because they probably are *T. t. wallowa* or *T. t. quadratus.*

Thomomys talpoides ravus Durrant

1946. *Thomomys talpoides ravus* Durrant, Univ. Kansas Publ., Mus. Nat. Hist., 1:15, August 15, type from 19 mi. N Vernal, 8000 ft., Uintah Co., Utah.

MARGINAL RECORDS (Durrant, 1952:167).—Utah: Henrys Fork, 8300 ft.; Hoop Lake, 8000 ft., Ashley National Forest; junction Deep and Carter creeks, 7900 ft.; Vernal-Manila road, 4 mi. W Greens Lake, 7500 ft.; type locality; Taylor Peak, 17 mi. N Vernal; E fork Blacks Fork, 31 mi. SSW Fort Bridger.

Thomomys talpoides relicinus Goldman

1939. *Thomomys talpoides relicinus* Goldman, Jour. Mamm., 20:239, May 15, type from Twin Springs, 20 mi. N Minidoka, Snake River Desert, Minidoka Co., Idaho.

MARGINAL RECORDS (Goldman, 1939:239–240).—Idaho: Laidlaw Park, 35 mi. NW Minidoka; type locality; Sparks Well, 23 mi. NE Minidoka.

Thomomys talpoides retrorsus Hall

1951. *Thomomys talpoides retrorsus* Hall, Univ. Kansas Publ., Mus. Nat. Hist., 5:83, October 1, type from Flagler, Kit Carson Co., Colorado.

MARGINAL RECORDS (Hall, 1951b:84–85).—Colorado: 8 mi. NE Elbert; type locality; 8 mi. S Seibert; Limon; Bijou Creek, near El Paso Co. line; Colorado Springs.

Thomomys talpoides rostralis Hall and Montague

1951. *Thomomys talpoides rostralis* Hall and Montague, Univ. Kansas Publ., Mus. Nat. Hist., 5:27, February 28, type from 1 mi. E Laramie, 7164 ft., Albany Co., Wyoming.

MARGINAL RECORDS (Hall and Montague, 1951:29). —Wyoming: 5 mi. N Laramie, 7200 ft.; 15 mi. SE Laramie, Pole Mtn., 8200 ft.; Sherman. Colorado: Estes Park; Gold Hill; Golden; 2½ mi. N Colorado Springs, 6000 ft.; Como, South Park, 9800 ft.; Hayden; Hahns Peak; Pearle, North Park, 9000 ft. Wyoming: 8 mi. S, 6 mi. E Saratoga; 2 mi. E, ½ mi. S Medicine Bow Peak, 10,800 ft. Not found: Colorado: Elkhorn, 7000 ft., Larimer Co.; Montgomery; Coulter, Grand Co.

Thomomys talpoides rufescens Wied-Neuwied

1839. *Thomomys rufescens* Wied-Neuwied, Nova Acta Phys.-Med. Acad. Caes. Leop.-Carol., 19(pt. 1):378, type from Minnetaree Village, now Old Fort Clark, about 6 mi. S Stanton, Mercer Co., North Dakota.
1915. *Thomomys talpoides rufescens,* V. Bailey, N. Amer. Fauna, 39:98, November 15.

MARGINAL RECORDS.—Manitoba: Marchand (Anderson, 1947:129); Lake Dauphin (*ibid.*); Selkirk Settlement (*ibid.*); Benito (Criddle, 1930:266). Minnesota: Humboldt (Swanson, 1945:82); Robbin (*ibid.*). North Dakota: Portland (V. Bailey, 1927:130); Valley City (*ibid.*). South Dakota (V. Bailey, 1915:99): Fort Sisseton; Aberdeen; White Lake; Armor; Fort Randall; Pierre. North Dakota: Cannon Ball (V. Bailey, 1927:131); Dickinson (V. Bailey, 1915:99); Killdeer Mts. (V. Bailey, 1927:131); Crosby (*ibid.*). Saskatchewan: Red Fox Lake, NE Kendal (Anderson, 1947:129).

Thomomys talpoides saturatus V. Bailey

1914. *Thomomys fuscus saturatus* V. Bailey, Proc. Biol. Soc. Washington, 27:117, July 10, type from Silver, near Saltese, Coeur d'Alene Mts., Missoula Co., Montana.
1939. *Thomomys talpoides saturatus,* Davis, The Recent mammals of Idaho, The Caxton Printers, Caldwell, Idaho, p. 253, April 5.

MARGINAL RECORDS.—British Columbia (Johnstone, 1955:159): Wasa; Fort Steele; Linklater Creek. Montana: Prospect Creek (V. Bailey, 1915:128). Idaho (Davis, 1939: 256): 2 mi. NE Weippe; Coeur d'Alene; 5 mi. W Cocolalla. British Columbia: Goatfell (Anderson, 1947:129); St. Mary's Prairie (Johnstone, 1955:159).

Thomomys talpoides segregatus Johnstone

1955. *Thomomys talpoides segregatus* Johnstone, Canadian Field-Nat., 68:161, September 17, type from Goat Mtn. on E side Kootenay River, near Wynndel, British Columbia.

MARGINAL RECORDS.—British Columbia (Johnstone, 1955:163): type locality; *Creston.*

Thomomys talpoides shawi Taylor

1921. *Thomomys douglasii shawi* Taylor, Proc. Biol. Soc. Washington, 34:121, June 30, type from Owyhigh Lake, 5100 ft., Mt. Rainier, Pierce Co., Washington.
1939. *Thomomys talpoides shawi,* Hall and Dalquest, Murrelet, 20:4, April 30.

MARGINAL RECORDS (Dalquest and Scheffer, 1944: 441–442).—Washington: Bumping Lake, 3 mi. NE Goose Prairie; Signal Peak, 4000 ft.; Glacier Basin, 5935 ft., Mt. Rainier.

Thomomys talpoides tacomensis Taylor

1919. *Thomomys douglasii tacomensis* Taylor, Proc. Biol. Soc. Washington, 32:169, September 30, type from 6 mi. S Tacoma, Pierce Co., Washington.
1939. *Thomomys talpoides tacomensis,* Goldman, Jour. Mamm., 20:235, May 15.

MARGINAL RECORDS.—Washington: Tacoma (Dalquest and Scheffer, 1944:445); type locality.

Thomomys talpoides talpoides (Richardson)

1828. *Cricetus talpoides* Richardson, Zool. Jour., 3:518. Type locality fixed at near Fort Carlton (Carlton House), Saskatchewan River, Saskatchewan.
1858. *Thomomys talpoides,* Baird, Mammals, in Repts. Expl. Surv. . . . , 8(1):403, July 14.
1837. *Geomys borealis* Richardson, Sixth Ann. Rept. British Assn. for 1836, 5:150. Type locality, plains of the Saskatchewan.
1843. *Geomys unisulcatus* Gray, List of the . . . Mammalia in the . . . British Museum, p. 149, a *nomen nudum.*

MARGINAL RECORDS (V. Bailey, 1915:98, unless otherwise noted).—Alberta: St. Albert; Elk Island National Park (Anderson, 1947:127). Saskatchewan (Anderson, 1947:127): Prince Albert National Park. Manitoba (*ibid.*): Swan River; Riding Mtn. Saskatchewan (*ibid.*): Yorkton; Indian Head; Moose Jaw. Montana: Bearpaw Mts.; Zortman; Big Snowy Mts.; Highwood; Blackfoot. Alberta: Calgary; Didsbury; Red Deer.

Thomomys talpoides taylori Hooper

1940. *Thomomys talpoides taylori* Hooper, Occas. Papers Mus. Zool., Univ. Michigan, 422:11, November 14, type from 6 mi. NE summit Mt. Taylor, about 8900 ft., near Fernandez summer camp, Valencia Co., New Mexico.

MARGINAL RECORDS.—New Mexico: type locality; Mirabel Spring, [SW slope] Mt. Taylor (Hooper, 1941:27).

Thomomys talpoides tenellus Goldman

1939. *Thomomys talpoides tenellus* Goldman, Jour. Mamm., 20:238, May 15, type from Whirlwind Peak, 10,500 ft., Absaroka Range, Park Co., Wyoming.

MARGINAL RECORDS (Goldman, 1939:239, unless otherwise noted).—Montana: Beartooth Mts. Wyoming: Pat O'Hara Creek, NE base Black Mtn.; Ishawooa Creek (Swenk, 1941:4, listed this as *T. t. bullatus* but may have overlooked the range assigned to *T. t. tenellus* when it was named by Goldman). Red Star Lodge, 3 mi. W, 6 mi. S Whirlwind Peak, 6700 ft. (21792 KU); 3¾ mi. E Moran, 6300 ft. (16974 KU); Jackson, 6300 ft. (15086 KU); Teton Pass; Old Faithful, Yellowstone National Park; Lamar River, Yellowstone National Park.

Thomomys talpoides trivialis Goldman

1939. *Thomomys talpoides trivialis* Goldman, Jour. Mamm., 20:236, May 15, type from near head Big Timber Creek, 5200 ft., about 15 mi. NW Big Timber, Crazy Mts., Sweetgrass Co., Montana.

MARGINAL RECORDS (Goldman, 1939:237).—Montana: various local stations, Little Belt Mts.; type locality; 4 mi. S White Sulphur Springs, Castle Mts.; Camas Creek, 4 mi. S Fort Logan, Big Belt Mts.

Thomomys talpoides tumuli Dalquest and Scheffer

1942. *Thomomys talpoides tumuli* Dalquest and Scheffer, Proc. Biol. Soc. Washington, 55:96, August 13, type from 7 mi. N Tenino, Thurston Co., Washington.

MARGINAL RECORDS.—Washington: type locality; 5 *mi. N Tenino* (22250 KU).

Thomomys talpoides uinta Merriam

1901. *Thomomys uinta* Merriam, Proc. Biol. Soc. Washington, 14:112, July 19, type from Blacks Fork, 10,000 ft., N base Gilbert Peak, Uinta Mts., Summit Co., Utah.
1939. *Thomomys talpoides uinta*, Goldman, Jour. Mamm., 20:234, May 15.

MARGINAL RECORDS (Durrant, 1952:164).—Utah: Smith and Morehouse Creek; 2 mi. S junction Bear River and Haydens Fork; Petty Mtn., 15 mi. N Mountain Home, 9500 ft.; Christensen Ranch, Nine Mile Canyon, 10 mi. E Summit, 6300 ft.; Forks, Sunnyside, 9000 ft.; Currant Creek, Uinta Mts.

Thomomys talpoides wallowa Hall and Orr

1933. *Thomomys quadratus wallowa* Hall and Orr, Proc. Biol. Soc. Washington, 46:41, March 24, type from Catherine Creek, 3500 ft., 7 mi. E Telocaset, Union Co., Oregon.
1939. *Thomomys talpoides wallowa*, Goldman, Jour. Mamm., 20:234, May 15.

MARGINAL RECORDS.—Washington: Mountain Top, 4500 ft. (Dalquest and Scheffer, 1944:438); Twin Buttes Ranger Station, 25 mi. SE Dayton (*ibid.*). Oregon: type locality; Anthony (Hall and Orr, 1933:42); Tollgate (Drake and Booth, 1952:51); Little Meadows, 20 mi. SE Walla Walla (*ibid.*). Washington: *Blue Creek Ridge, 20 mi. E Walla Walla* (*ibid.*); Hompeg Falls (Dalquest and Scheffer, 1944:42). Specimens from northeastern Oregon, for example from Bingham Prairie, Elgin and Huntington that stand in the literature as *T.* [*t.*] *fuscus* (V. Bailey, 1915:127) need re-examination because they probably are *T. t. wallowa.* (Those from Huntington possibly are *T. t. quadratus.*)

Thomomys talpoides wasatchensis Durrant

1946. *Thomomys talpoides wasatchensis* Durrant, Univ. Kansas Publ., Mus. Nat. Hist., 1:8, August 15, type from Midway, 5500 ft., Wasatch Co., Utah.

MARGINAL RECORDS (Durrant, 1952:161).—Utah: Logan Canyon, Beaver Basin, Utah–Idaho line; Logan Mts., 20 mi. E Logan; head Grove Creek; Mt. Timpanogos, 1 mi. N Aspen Grove; mouth Big Cottonwood Canyon; Ogden; Avon.

Thomomys talpoides whitmani Drake and Booth

1952. *Thomomys talpoides whitmani* Drake and Booth, Walla Walla College Publ. Dept. Biol. Sci. Biol. Sta., 1(3):52, November 25, type from Whitman National Monument, 750 ft., 6 mi. W Walla Walla, Walla Walla Co., Washington.

MARGINAL RECORDS (Drake and Booth, 1952:53–56). —Washington: 7½ mi. N Walla Walla; 1½ *mi. E Walla Walla*; 1 mi. S College Place; 2½ *mi. SW College Place; 4 mi. W College Place*; 1 mi. W Lowden.

Thomomys talpoides yakimensis Hall and Dalquest

1939. *Thomomys talpoides yakimensis* Hall and Dalquest, Murrelet, 20:4, April 30, type from Selah, Yakima Co., Washington.
1939. *Thomomys talpoides badius* Goldman, Jour. Mamm., 20:242, May 15, type from Wenatchee, Chelan Co., Washington.

MARGINAL RECORDS.—Washington: Natches River, 40 mi. above mouth (Goldman, 1939:242); Ellensburg (*ibid.*); 2 mi. NW Richland, 400 ft. (Dalquest and Scheffer, 1944:440); Kennewick (Goldman, 1939:242); Zillah (Dalquest and Scheffer, 1944:440); type locality; Cowiche (*ibid.*).

Thomomys talpoides yelmensis Merriam

1899. *Thomomys douglasi yelmensis* Merriam, Proc. Biol. Soc. Washington, 13:21, January 31, type from Tenino, Yelm Prairie, Thurston Co., Washington.
1939. *Thomomys talpoides yelmensis,* Goldman, Jour. Mamm., 20:235, May 15.

MARGINAL RECORDS.—Washington: type locality; 1 mi. W Vail (Dalquest and Scheffer, 1944:447); 2 mi. N Rochester (*ibid.*).

Thomomys monticola
Mountain Pocket Gopher

External measurements: 167–273; 42–97; 22–36. Upper parts vary from bright yellowish hazel to russet or Mars brown; underparts vary from dull buffy to richly ochraceous; feet light colored; tip of tail usually whitish. Skull comparatively slender; markedly and smoothly arched in profile between incisors and molariform series; zygomata slender; nasals long and slender; tympanic bullae small; sphenoidal fissure absent; incisive foramina anterior to infraorbital canal; anterior prism of P4 not less than ¾ of that of posterior prism.

Thomomys monticola and *T. talpoides* may intergrade in Oregon and therefore would be one species. Where the 2 species occupy adjoining ranges in California and Nevada they have been found to meet without intergradation.

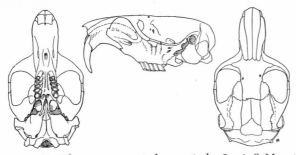

Fig. 259. *Thomomys monticola monticola*, 3 mi. S Mount Rose, 8600 ft., Nevada, No. 65219 M.V.Z., ♂, X 1.

Thomomys monticola helleri Elliot

1903. *Thomomys helleri* Elliot, Field Columb. Mus., Publ. 74, Zool. Ser., 3:165, May 7, type from Goldbeach, mouth of Rogue River, Curry Co., Oregon.
1915. *Thomomys monticola helleri,* V. Bailey, N. Amer. Fauna, 39:126, November 15.

MARGINAL RECORDS.—Oregon: *Wedderburn* (V. Bailey, 1936:258); type locality.

Thomomys monticola hesperus Merriam

1901. *Thomomys hesperus* Merriam, Proc. Biol. Soc. Washington, 14:116, July 19, type from Tillamook, Tillamook Co., Oregon.
1943. *Thomomys monticola hesperus,* Goldman, Jour. Washington Acad. Sci., 33(5):146, May 15.

MARGINAL RECORDS (V. Bailey, 1936:255, unless otherwise noted).—Oregon: Elsie; Forest Grove (Gabrielson, 1923:190); Grande Ronde (*ibid.*); Philomath, W of Corvallis; Alsea; Oretown (Gabrielson, 1923:189); type locality.

Thomomys monticola mazama Merriam

1897. *Thomomys mazama* Merriam, Proc. Biol. Soc. Washington, 11:214, July 15, type from Anna Creek, 6000 ft., near Crater Lake, Mt. Mazama, Klamath Co., Oregon.
1915. *Thomomys monticola mazama,* V. Bailey, N. Amer. Fauna, 39:123, November 15.

MARGINAL RECORDS (V. Bailey, 1915:123–124, unless otherwise noted).—Oregon: W slope Mt. Hood, 6000 ft.; S base Mt. Hood, Summit House; Three Sisters; Diamond Lake; type locality. California: 6 mi. SW Beswick, 6000 ft.; N fork Coffee Creek, 4500 ft.; head Bear Creek, 6400 ft.; Grizzly Creek [6000 ft.] (Grinnell, 1933:147); S fork Salmon River, 5000 ft. Oregon: Siskiyou Mts.; Prospect; Pengra (Hall and Kelson, 1952:363).

Thomomys monticola monticola J. A. Allen

1893. *Thomomys monticolus* J. A. Allen, Bull. Amer. Mus. Nat. Hist., 5:48, April 28, type from Mt. Tallac, 7500 ft., El Dorado Co., California.
1899. *Thomomys monticola pinetorum* Merriam, N. Amer. Fauna, 16:97, October 28, type from Sisson, Siskiyou Co., California.
1914. *Thomomys monticola premaxillaris* Grinnell, Univ. California Publ. Zool., 12:312, November 21, type from 2 mi. S South Yolla Bolly Mtn., 7500 ft., Tehama Co., California.

MARGINAL RECORDS.—California: Butte Creek, NE of Mt. Shasta (Grinnell, 1933:146); 12 mi. NE McCloud (V. Bailey, 1915:122); Eagle Lake Resort (Grinnell, *et al.*, 1930:497); Milford (V. Bailey, 1915:122); Willow Ranch, Long Valley (*ibid.*). Nevada (Hall, 1946:451): W side

Truckee River, ½ mi. W Verdi, 4900 ft.; 3 mi. S Mt. Rose, 8500 and 8600 ft.; Carson (W of City?). California (V. Bailey, 1915:122–123, unless otherwise noted): Markleeville; Sonora Pass; Mt. Dana; vicinity Mammoth, above 8000 ft. (A. B. Howell, 1924:31); Mono Pass; Huntington Lake (Grinnell, 1933:146); Tenaya Lake; Big Trees; head S fork American River; Heather Lake; Blue Canyon; Buck's Ranch; Mineral, 4900 ft. (Grinnell, *et al.*, 1930:497); Manzanita Lake, 6000 ft. (*ibid.*); 12 mi. W Burney; Sisson (Grinnell, 1933:146). Western segment of range, all in California: 12 mi. N North Yolla Bolly Mtn., 4400 ft. (*ibid.*); 2 mi. S South Yolla Bolly Mtn., 7500 ft. (*ibid.*).

Thomomys monticola nasicus Merriam

1897. *Thomomys nasicus* Merriam, Proc. Biol. Soc. Washington, 11:216, July 15, type from Farewell Bend, Deschutes River, Deschutes Co., Oregon.
1915. *Thomomys monticola nasicus,* V. Bailey, N. Amer. Fauna, 39:125, November 15.

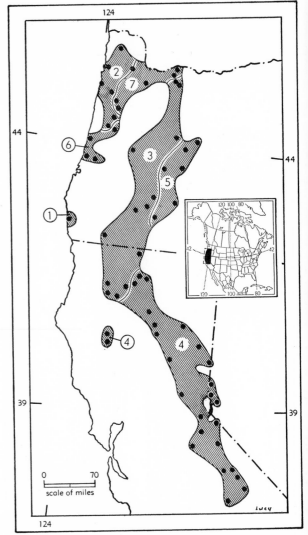

Map 270. *Thomomys monticola.*

Guide to subspecies   3. *T. m. mazama*   6. *T. m. niger*
1. *T. m. helleri*   4. *T. m. monticola* 7. *T. m. oregonus*
2. *T. m. hesperus*   5. *T. m. nasicus*

MARGINAL RECORDS.—Oregon: type locality; Paulina Lake (V. Bailey, 1915:125); Yamsey Mts. (V. Bailey, 1936:259); Fort Klamath (*ibid.*); mouth Davis Creek, Deschutes River (V. Bailey, 1915:125); Bend (*ibid.*).

Thomomys monticola niger Merriam

1901. *Thomomys niger* Merriam, Proc. Biol. Soc. Washington, 14:117, July 19, type from Seaton (= Mapleton), near mouth Umpqua River (= head of tidewater on Siuslaw River), Lane Co., Oregon. (See Miller and Kellogg, Bull. U.S. Nat. Mus., 205:325, March 3, 1955.)
1943. *Thomomys monticola niger,* Goldman, Jour. Washington Acad. Sci., 33(5):146, May 15.

MARGINAL RECORDS.—Oregon: Benton-Lane County line (Moore, 1927:309); 2 mi. E Scottsburg (V. Bailey, 1936:256); Seton (*ibid.*); Mercer (Storer and Gregory, 1934:302).

Thomomys monticola oregonus Merriam

1901. *Thomomys douglasi oregonus* Merriam, Proc. Biol. Soc. Washington, 14:115, July 19, type from Ely, near Oregon City, Willamette Valley, Clackamas Co., Oregon.
1943. *Thomomys monticola oregonus,* Goldman, Jour. Washington Acad. Sci., 33(5):146, May 15.

MARGINAL RECORDS (V. Bailey, 1936:254, unless otherwise noted).—Oregon: Summit; 2 mi. W Parkdale; near Canby; Pedee; Black Rock (Moore, 1927:309); Forest Grove.

Thomomys bulbivorus (Richardson)
Camas Pocket Gopher

1829. *Diplostoma bulbivorum* Richardson, Fauna Boreali-Americana, 1:206, type from "Banks of the Columbia

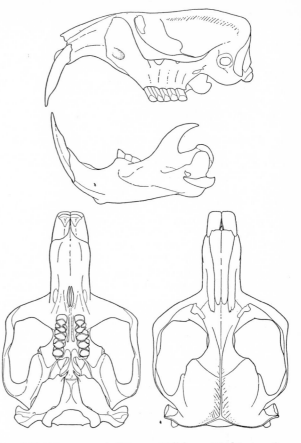

Fig. 260. *Thomomys bulbivorus,* Hillsboro, Washington Co., Oregon, No. 63479 M.V.Z., ♂, X 1.

River, Oregon," probably Portland, the only place near the Columbia River where it has been taken since. The type was reported as in the Hudson Bay Museum but has not been found (*fide* V. Bailey, N. Amer. Fauna, 39:40, November 15, 1915).
1855. *Thomomys bulbivorus,* Brandt, Beiträge zur nähern Kenntniss der Säugethiere Russland's, p. 188.

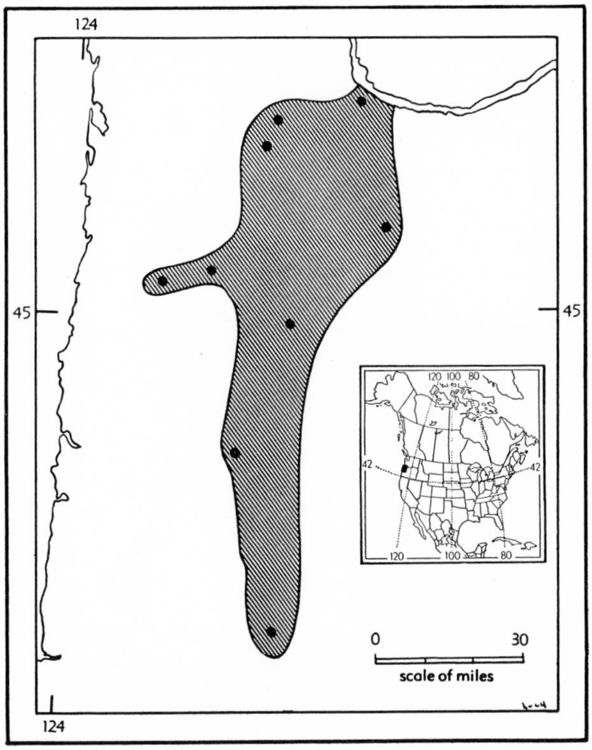

Average external measurements of 5 males: 300, 90, 42. Size large for the genus. Color dark sooty brown, the plumbeous basal hairs showing through on underparts. Skull short and wide; zygomatic arches usually widest posteriorly; nasals short; pterygoids convexly inflated and divided by narrow interpterygoid space; tympanic bullae relatively small; auditory meatus comparatively large; upper incisors markedly procumbent; molariform dentition weak.

MARGINAL RECORDS.—Oregon: Portland (V. Bailey, 1936:249); Mulino (V. Bailey, 1915:42); Salem (*ibid.*); Eugene (V. Bailey, 1936:249); Corvallis (Scheffer, 1938:222); Grande Ronde (V. Bailey, 1915:42); Sheridan (*ibid.*); Gaston (*ibid.*); Forest Grove (V. Bailey, 1936:249).

Map 271. *Thomomys bulbivorus.*

Genus **Geomys** Rafinesque—Eastern Pocket Gophers

Revised: Merriam, N. A. Fauna, 8:109–145, Jan. 31, 1895.

1817. *Geomys* Rafinesque, Amer. Monthly Mag., 2:45, November. Type, *Geomys pinetis* Rafinesque.
1817. *Diplostoma* Rafinesque, Amer. Monthly Mag., 2:44, November. Included *Diplostoma fusca* Rafinesque [= *Mus bursarius* Shaw] and *D. alba* Rafinesque [= *Mus bursarius* Shaw] from the Missouri River region.
1820. *Saccophorus* Kuhl, Beiträge zur Zoologie und vergleichenden Anatomie, pp. 65, 66. Type, *Mus bursarius* Shaw.
1823. *Pseudostoma* Say, *in* Long, Account of an exped. . . . to the Rocky Mts. . . . , 1:406. Type, *Mus bursarius* Shaw.
1825. *Ascomys* Lichtenstein, Abh. k. Acad. Wiss., Berlin, for 1822, p. 20, fig. 2. Type, *Ascomys canadensis* Lichtenstein [= *Mus bursarius* Shaw] nominally from Canada.

External measurements: in males, 217–357, 57–121, 27–43; in females, 187–316, 51–109, 23–39. Pale brown to black, usually paler below than above. P4 with only 3 enamel plates and decidedly larger than p4 (subequal in other genera); M1 and M2 each with 2 enamel plates; I1 bisulcate, principal sulcus on outer side of median line.

KEY TO SPECIES OF GEOMYS

1. Rostrum wider than basioccipital is long; occurring in Texas, New Mexico, and México.
    2. Squamosal arm of zygoma ending in prominent knob over middle of jugal; occurring in New Mexico. . *G. arenarius*, p. 452
    2'. Squamosal arm of zygoma lacking prominent knob over middle of jugal; occurring in southern Texas and Tamaulipas.
    G. personatus, p. 452
1'. Rostrum wider than basioccipital is long; north and east of Texas and New Mexico as well as in those states.
    3. Nasals not hour-glass shaped (only slightly, if at all, constricted near middle); not occurring in Alabama, Georgia, or Florida. . . . . . *G. bursarius*, p. 448
    3'. Nasals hour-glass shaped (strongly constricted near middle); occurring in Alabama, Georgia, and Florida.
        4. Occurring on Cumberland Island, Georgia. . . . *G. cumberlandius*, p. 455
        4'. Not occurring on Cumberland Island.
            5. Fontanel on each side of skull between parietal and squamosal bones. . . . . *G. fontanelus*, p. 455
            5'. No fontanel between parietal and squamosal bones.
                6. Interpterygoid space broadly U-shaped; nasals little constricted at middle. *G. colonus*, p. 455
                6'. Interpterygoid space broadly V-shaped; nasals much constricted at middle. *G. pinetis*, p. 453

Geomys bursarius
Plains Pocket Gopher

External measurements: in males, 217–357, 57–107, 27–43; in females, 187–316, 51–102, 23–39. Largest in north; smallest in south. Brown or black. Rostrum wider than basioccipital is long.

× ¼

Geomys bursarius ammophilus Davis

1940. *Geomys breviceps ammophilus* Davis, Texas Agric. Exp. Station Bull., 590:16, October 23, type from Cuero, De Witt Co., Texas.
1951. *Geomys bursarius ammophilus*, Baker and Glass, Proc. Biol. Soc. Washington, 64:57, April 13.

MARGINAL RECORDS.—Texas (Davis, 1940:17): type locality; Inez; Victoria; 8 mi. SE Cuero.

Geomys bursarius attwateri Merriam

1895. *Geomys breviceps attwateri* Merriam, N. Amer. Fauna, 8:135, January 31, type from Rockport, Texas.
1951. *Geomys bursarius attwateri*, Baker and Glass, Proc. Biol. Soc. Washington, 64:57, April 13.

MARGINAL RECORDS (Davis, 1940:16, unless otherwise noted).—Texas: 4 mi. SE Luling (Blair, 1952:239–240); 3 mi. SW Victoria; Matagorda; 8 mi. SW Rockport; 11 mi. E Beeville (Blair, 1952:239–240); 2 mi. NW Campbellton; 1 mi. N Moore; 18 mi. S San Antonio.

Geomys bursarius brazensis Davis

1938. *Geomys breviceps brazensis* Davis, Jour. Mamm., 19:489, November 14, type from 5 mi. E Kurten, *in* Grimes Co., Texas.
1951. *Geomys bursarius brazensis*, Baker and Glass, Proc. Biol. Soc. Washington, 64:57, April 13.

MARGINAL RECORDS.—Texas (Davis, 1940:15, unless otherwise noted): Terrell; Mineola; 4 mi. NE Carthage; 1 mi. N Trinity; 4 mi. N Huffman; 2½ mi. N Hockley; Eagle Lake (18445 KU); Brenham; 17 mi. E Caldwell; 5 mi. E Bastrop; Milano; 1 mi. SE Reagan; Palestine.

Geomys bursarius breviceps Baird

1855. *Geomys breviceps* Baird, Proc. Acad. Nat. Sci. Philadelphia, 7:335, type from Prairie Mer Rouge, Louisiana. Known only from the type locality.
1951. *Geomys bursarius breviceps*, Baker and Glass, Proc. Biol. Soc. Washington, 64:57, April 13.

Geomys bursarius bursarius (Shaw)

1800. *Mus bursarius* Shaw, Trans. Linn. Soc. London, 5:227. Type locality, somewhere in upper Mississippi Valley.

1829. *Geomys bursarius*, Richardson, F. Bor.-Amer., 1:203.
1817. *Diplostoma fusca* Rafinesque, Amer. Monthly Mag., 2:44, November. Type locality, Missouri River region.
1817. *Diplostoma alba* Rafinesque (*ibid.*). Type loc. same.
1825. *Ascomys canadensis* Lichtenstein, Abh. k. Akad. Wiss., Berlin, for 1822, p. 20, type from "Canada."

MARGINAL RECORDS.—Manitoba: 2¹⁄₁₀ mi. N border, 11½ mi. ENE Emerson (Anderson, 1947:130). Minnesota (Swanson, 1945:83): eastern Kittson County; Clearwater County; Cass County; Carlton County. Wisconsin: Solon Springs (232896 BS); 4 mi. E Iron River (Davis, 1955: 143); Anson Township, Chippewa Co. (Schmidt, 1931: 116); Mentor Township (*ibid.*). Missouri (Merriam, 1895a: 123): Williamsville; Hunter. Iowa: Ames (Scott, 1937:72). South Dakota (Merriam, 1895a:123): Scotland; Flandreau; Fort Sisseton. North Dakota (V. Bailey, 1927:125–126): Ludden; Valley City; 10 mi. W Portland; Manvel. Manitoba: Emerson (Anderson, 1947:130).

Geomys bursarius dutcheri Davis

1940. *Geomys breviceps dutcheri* Davis, Texas Agric. Exp. Sta. Bull., 590:12, Oct. 23, type from Fort Gibson, Okla.
1951. *Geomys bursarius dutcheri*, Baker and Glass, Proc. Biol. Soc. Washington, 64:57, April 13.

MARGINAL RECORDS (Davis, 1940:13, unless otherwise noted).—Oklahoma: near Garnett; type locality. Arkansas (Sealander, 1956:272): Mulberry; *Ozark*; 10 mi. N Little Rock; Pine Bluff; El Dorado. Louisiana: Ruston (Lowery, 1943:242); Fishville (*ibid.*); Pineville; Colfax (Lowery, 1943:242); Keithville. Texas: Jefferson; Longview; Decatur; Gainesville. Oklahoma: 3½ mi. E Norman (Baker and Glass, 1951:56); 8 mi. W Red Fork; Tulsa. According to Sealander (1956:272), employees of the Arkansas Game and Fish Commission report pocket gophers from the following counties in Arkansas: *Washington; Cross; Phillips; Chicot; Ashley*; and *Bradley*.

Geomys bursarius hylaeus Blossom

1938. *Geomys lutescens hylaeus* Blossom, Occas. Papers Mus. Zool., Univ. Michigan, 368:1, April 6, type from 10 mi. S Chadron, Dawes Co., Nebraska.
1947. *Geomys bursarius hylaeus*, Villa and Hall, Univ. Kansas Publ., Mus. Nat. Hist., 1:234, November 29.

MARGINAL RECORDS.—Nebraska (Swenk, 1940:9): type locality; Crawford.

Geomys bursarius illinoensis Komarek and Spencer

1931. *Geomys bursarius illinoensis* Komarek and Spencer, Jour. Mamm., 12:405, November 11, type from 1 mi. S Momence, Kankakee Co., Illinois.

MARGINAL RECORDS (Necker and Hatfield, 1941:51, unless otherwise noted).—Illinois: Ottawa [= South Ottawa]; Custer Park. Indiana (Hamilton, 1943:245): Jasper County; [N Wabash River] Tippecanoe Co. Illinois: Clinton; Boody (Mohr, 1946:390); Collinsville (*ibid.*); Havana; Oglesby.

Geomys bursarius industrius Villa and Hall

1947. *Geomys bursarius industrius* Villa and Hall, Univ. Kansas Publ., Mus. Nat. Hist., 1:226, November 29, type from 1¾ mi. N Fowler, Meade Co., Kansas.

MARGINAL RECORDS.—Kansas (Cockrum, 1952:143): Larned, junction Pawnee and Arkansas rivers; Pratt; Rezeau Ranch, 5 mi. N Belvidere; 7 mi. SW Kingsdown, Stephenson Ranch; State Lake and Park (Meade Co.); Cudahy Ash Pit, 7 mi. N Meade; 1 mi. W and 3½ mi. S Kinsley.

Geomys bursarius jugossicularis Hooper

1940. *Geomys lutescens jugossicularis* Hooper, Occas. Papers Mus. Zool., Univ. Michigan, 420:1, June 28, type from Lamar, Prowers Co., Colorado.
1947. *Geomys bursarius jugossicularis*, Villa and Hall, Univ. Kansas Publ., Mus. Nat. Hist., 1:226, November 29.

MARGINAL RECORDS.—Colorado: type locality. Kansas (Cockrum, 1952:142): 1 mi. E Coolidge; 1 mi. E Arkalon. Texas: 15 mi. E Texline (Hall and Kelson, 1952: 364). Kansas: 12 mi. NE Elkhart (Cockrum, 1952:142). Colorado: 4 mi. W Las Animas (60784 MVZ).

Geomys bursarius levisagittalis Swenk

1940. *Geomys lutescens levisagittalis* Swenk, Missouri Valley Fauna, 2:4, February 1, type from Spencer, Boyd Co., Nebraska. Known only from type locality.
1947. *Geomys bursarius levisagittalis*, Villa and Hall, Univ. Kansas Publ., Mus. Nat. Hist., 1:234, November 29.

Geomys bursarius llanensis V. Bailey

1905. *Geomys breviceps llanensis* V. Bailey, N. Amer. Fauna, 25:129, October 24, type from Llano, Texas.
1947. *Geomys bursarius llanensis*, Villa and Hall, Univ. Kansas Publ., Mus. Nat. Hist., 1:234, November 29.

MARGINAL RECORDS.—Texas (Baker, 1950:349): 1 mi. N Pontotoc; 3 mi. W, 1 mi. N Kingsland; 12 mi. S, 8 mi. W Llano; Castell.

Geomys bursarius ludemani Davis

1940. *Geomys breviceps ludemani* Davis, Texas Agric. Exp. Station Bull., 590:19, October 23, type from 7 mi. SW Fannett, Jefferson Co., Texas.
1951. *Geomys bursarius ludemani*, Baker and Glass, Proc. Biol. Soc. Washington, 64:58, April 13.

MARGINAL RECORDS.—Texas: type locality; Double Bayou, 10 mi. S Anahuac (Davis, 1940:20).

Geomys bursarius lutescens Merriam

1890. *Geomys bursarius lutescens* Merriam, N. Amer. Fauna, 4:51, October 8, type from sandhills on Birdwood Creek, Lincoln Co., Nebraska.
1940. *Geomys lutescens vinaceus* Swenk, Missouri Valley Fauna, 2:7, February 1, type from Scottsbluff, Scotts Bluff Co., Nebraska (considered a synonym of *G. b. lutescens* by Russell and Jones, Trans. Kansas Acad. Sci., 58:513, January 23, 1956).

MARGINAL RECORDS.—Wyoming: 23 mi. SW Newcastle, 4500 ft. (20303 KU). South Dakota: Pine Ridge Agency (Merriam, 1895a:129); Rosebud Agency (*ibid.*); Dog Ear Lake (Swenk, 1940:2). Nebraska (Swenk, 1940: 5–6): near Orchard; Battle Creek; Central City; south of Holstein; Campbell. Kansas (Cockrum, 1952:141): Hays State College Campus; 4 mi. S Scott City. Colorado:

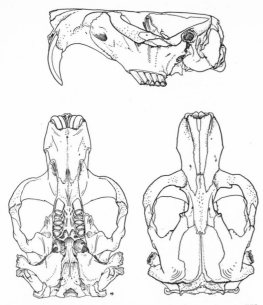

Fig. 261. *Geomys bursarius jugossicularis*, 4 mi. W Las Animas, 4100 ft., Bent Co., Colorado, No. 60784 M.V.Z., ♂, X 1.

Cheyenne Wells (Warren, 1942:167); Pueblo (Cary, 1911:129); Denver (192174 NM); Loveland (Cary, 1911:129). Wyoming: Horse Creek, 5200 ft., 6½ mi. W Meriden (15164 KU); Uva (Swenk, 1940:7); Lusk (*ibid.*); 10 mi. N Hat Creek (20309 KU).

Geomys bursarius major Davis

1940. *Geomys lutescens major* Davis, Texas Agric. Exp. Station Bull., 590:32, October 23, type from 8 mi. W Clarendon, Donley Co., Texas.
1947. *Geomys bursarius major,* Villa and Hall, Univ. Kansas Publ., Mus. Nat. Hist., 1:229, November 29.

MARGINAL RECORDS.—Kansas (Cockrum, 1952:143): 2 mi. S Ellsworth; Smoky Hill River, 1 mi. S, ½ mi. W Lindsborg; ½ mi. E McPherson; 8 mi. W Rosalia; 3 mi. SE Arkansas City. Oklahoma: Ponca Agency (Davis, 1940:33); Stillwater (Blair, 1939:114); 2 mi. E Norman (Baker and Glass, 1951:56); Apache (Davis, 1940:33); 12 mi. S Temple (Blair, 1939:114). Texas (Davis, 1940:33): Brazos; 6 mi. S Waco; Colorado; Stanton; Monahans; 14 mi. S Andrews; 7 mi. W Post. New Mexico (Davis, 1940:33): Mesa Jumanes, near Progresso; Santa Rosa. Texas (Davis, 1940:33): Tascosa; Lipscomb. Kansas (Cockrum, 1952:143): near South Bridge, Sun City; Little Salt Marsh, 15 mi. N, 3 mi. E Stafford.

Geomys bursarius majusculus Swenk

1939. *Geomys bursarius majusculus* Swenk, Missouri Valley Fauna, 1:6, December 5, type from Lincoln, Nebraska.

MARGINAL RECORDS.—South Dakota: southeastern part (Swenk, 1939:6). Iowa: Knoxville (Merriam, 1895a:123). Kansas (Cockrum, 1952:142): Fort Leavenworth; 11 mi. SW Lawrence; 8½ mi. SW Toronto; 4 mi. S, and 14 mi. W Hamilton; 6 mi. S Lincolnville; 3½ mi. W, and ½ mi. S Beloit, 1500 ft. Nebraska (Swenk, 1939:6, unless other-

wise noted): Republican River Valley, Franklin Co. (Swenk, 1940:1); southeastern Hall County (*ibid.*); Hamilton County; Polk County; eastern Platte County; eastern Madison County; Pierce County; Knox County.

Geomys bursarius pratincola Davis

1940. *Geomys breviceps pratincolus* Davis, Texas Agric. Exp. Station Bull., 590:18, October 23, type from 2 mi. E Liberty, Liberty Co., Texas.
1951. *Geomys bursarius pratincolus*, Baker and Glass, Proc. Biol. Soc. Washington, 64:57, April 13.

MARGINAL RECORDS.—Louisiana: Provencal (Lowery, 1943:242); Hutton (*ibid.*); Cravens (*ibid.*); Iowa Station (Davis, 1940:19); *Gum Cove, 15 mi. S Vinton* (*ibid.*). Texas (Davis, 1940:19): 13 mi. NE Sour Lake; 2 mi. E Liberty; 3 mi. W Livingston; Kirbyville.

Geomys bursarius sagittalis Merriam

1895. *Geomys breviceps sagittalis* Merriam, N. Amer. Fauna, 8:134, January 31, type from Clear Creek, Galveston Bay, Galveston Co., Texas.
1951. *Geomys bursarius sagittalis*, Baker and Glass, Proc. Biol. Soc. Washington, 64:57, April 13.

MARGINAL RECORDS.—Texas (Davis, 1940:18, unless otherwise noted): 3 mi. N La Porte; 3 mi. NE Webster; Arcadia; 4 mi. S Altoloma (13198 KU).

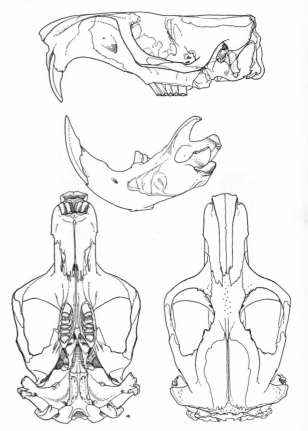

Fig. 262. *Geomys bursarius majusculus*, Lincoln, Lancaster Co., Nebraska, holotype, No. 97913 M.V.Z., ♂, X 1.

Geomys bursarius terricolus Davis

1940. *Geomys breviceps terricolus* Davis, Texas Agric. Exp. Station Bull., 590:17, October 23, type from 1 mi. N Texas City, Galveston Co., Texas. Known only from the type locality.
1951. *Geomys bursarius terricolus,* Baker and Glass, Proc. Biol. Soc. Washington, 64:57, April 13.

Geomys bursarius texensis Merriam

1895. *Geomys texensis* Merriam, N. Amer. Fauna, 8:137, January 31, type from Mason, Mason Co., Texas.
1950. *Geomys bursarius texensis,* Baker, Jour. Mamm., 31: 349, August 21.

MARGINAL RECORDS.—Texas (Baker, 1950:349): 10 mi. W Mason; ½ mi. W Castell; 11 mi. SW Mason.

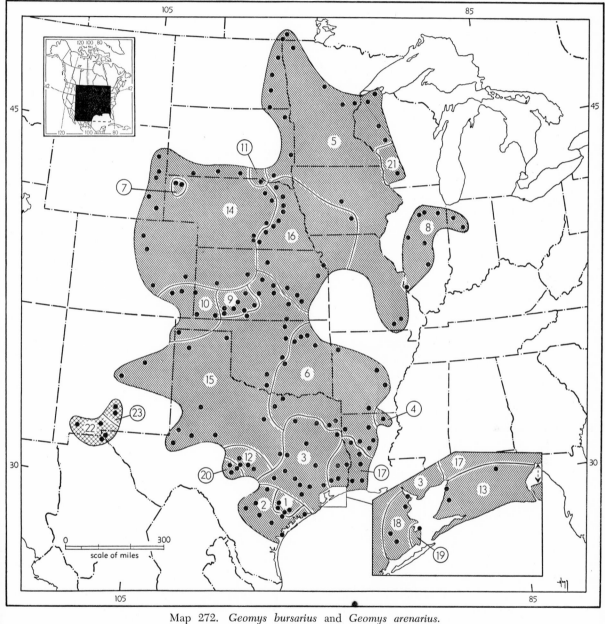

Map 272. *Geomys bursarius* and *Geomys arenarius.*

Guide to kinds	6. *G. b. dutcheri*	12. *G. b. llanensis*	18. *G. b. sagittalis*
1. *G. b. ammophilus*	7. *G. b. hylaeus*	13. *G. b. ludemani*	19. *G. b. terricolus*
2. *G. b. attwateri*	8. *G. b. illinoensis*	14. *G. b. lutescens*	20. *G. b. texensis*
3. *G. b. brazensis*	9. *G. b. industrius*	15. *G. b. major*	21. *G. b. wisconsinensis*
4. *G. b. breviceps*	10. *G. b. jugossicularis*	16. *G. b. majusculus*	22. *G. a. arenarius*
5. *G. b. bursarius*	11. *G. b. levisagittalis*	17. *G. b. pratincola*	23. *G. a. brevirostris*

Geomys bursarius wisconsinensis Jackson

1957. *Geomys bursarius wisconsinensis* Jackson, Proc. Biol. Soc. Washington, 70:33, June 28, type from Lone Rock, Richland Co., Wisconsin. Known only from the type locality.

Geomys arenarius
Desert Pocket Gopher

External measurements: in males, 244–280, 74–95, 30–34; in females, 221–250, 58–84, 27–35. Brown; width of rostrum not exceeding length of basioccipital; squamosal arm of zygoma ending in prominent knob over middle of jugal.

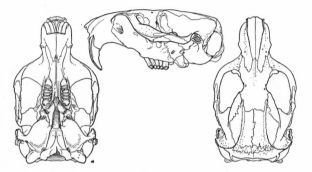

Fig. 263. *Geomys arenarius brevirostris*, E edge [white] sand [9 mi. W Tularosa], Tularosa Hot Springs Road, Otero Co., New Mexico, holotype, No. 50460 M.V.Z., ♀, X 1.

Geomys arenarius arenarius Merriam

1895. *Geomys arenarius* Merriam, N. Amer. Fauna, 8:139, January 31, type from El Paso, El Paso Co., Texas.

MARGINAL RECORDS (Davis, 1940:22).—New Mexico: Deming; Las Cruces. Texas: type locality. Chihuahua: Juárez.

Geomys arenarius brevirostris Hall

1932. *Geomys arenarius brevirostris* Hall, Proc. Biol. Soc. Washington, 45:97, June 21, type from E edge of [white] sand [9 mi. W Tularosa], Tularosa-Hot Springs Road, Otero Co., New Mexico.

MARGINAL RECORDS.—New Mexico (Davis, 1940:23): type locality; 10 mi. SW Tularosa; 12 mi. W Alamogordo.

Geomys personatus
Texas Pocket Gopher

External measurements: in males, 248–326, 72–121, 30–42; in females, 225–305, 59–109, 30–39. Brown; squamosal arm of zygoma lacking prominent knob over middle of jugal.

Geomys personatus fallax Merriam

1895. *Geomys personatus fallax* Merriam, N. Amer. Fauna, 8:144, January 31, type from S side of Nueces Bay, Nueces Co., Texas.

MARGINAL RECORDS.—Texas (Davis, 1940:29, unless otherwise noted): 12 mi. N Beeville (Blair, 1952:240); *Beeville*; 4 mi. SE Edroy; 6 mi. W Corpus Christi; Sandia; 1½ mi. S George West; 5 mi. S Three Rivers.

Geomys personatus fuscus Davis

1940. *Geomys personatus fuscus* Davis, Texas Agric. Exp. Station Bull., 590:30, October 23, type from Fort Clark [Bracketville], Kinney Co., Texas.

MARGINAL RECORDS.—Texas (Davis, 1940:31): Rio Grande at Del Rio; mouth of Sycamore Creek, boundary between Val Verde and Kinney counties; type locality.

Geomys personatus maritimus Davis

1940. *Geomys personatus maritimus* Davis, Texas Agric. Exp. Station Bull., 590:26, October 23, type from Flour Bluff, 11 mi. SE Corpus Christi, Nueces Co., Texas. Known only from the type locality.

Geomys personatus megapotamus Davis

1940. *Geomys personatus megapotamus* Davis, Texas Agric. Exp. Station Bull., 590:27, October 23, type from 4 mi. SE Oilton, Webb Co., Texas.

MARGINAL RECORDS.—Texas (Davis, 1940:28): S side Nueces River, 6 mi. W Cotulla; type locality; 3½ mi. SW Realitos; Falfurrias; Sauz Rancho, near Santa Monica; near Santa Rosa; 1 mi. SW Santa Elena; Carrizo [= Zapata].

Geomys personatus personatus True

1889. *Geomys personatus* True, Proc. U.S. Nat. Mus., 11:159 for 1888, January 5, type from Padre Island, Cameron Co., Texas.

MARGINAL RECORDS.—Texas: 14 mi. SW Port Aransas, Mustang Island (27222 KU); *type locality*.

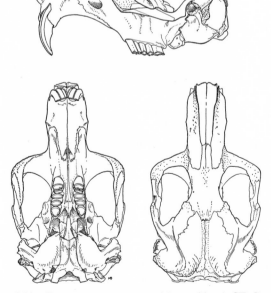

Fig. 264. *Geomys personatus maritimus*, 11 mi. SE Corpus Christi, Nueces Co., Texas, No. 84159 M.V.Z., ♂, X 1.

Geomys personatus streckeri Davis

1940. *Geomys personatus minor* Davis, Texas Agric. Exp. Station Bull., 590:29, October 23, type from Carrizo Springs, Dimmit Co., Texas. Not *Geomys minor* Gidley, 1922, a fossil. Known only from the type locality.

1943. *Geomys personatus streckeri* Davis, Jour. Mamm., 24:508, November 20, a renaming of *Geomys personatus minor* Davis.

Geomys personatus tropicalis Goldman

1915. *Geomys personatus tropicalis* Goldman, Proc. Biol. Soc. Washington, 28:134, June 29, type from Altamira, Tamaulipas. Known only from the type locality.

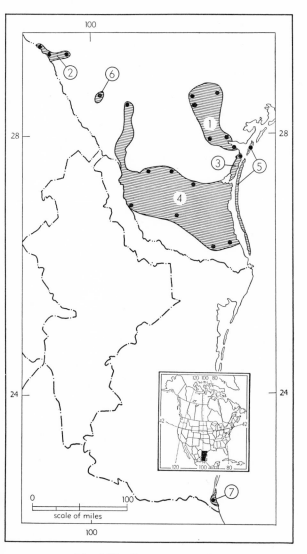

Map 273. *Geomys personatus.*

Guide to subspecies
1. *G. p. fallax*
2. *G. p. fuscus*
3. *G. p. maritimus*
4. *G. p. megapotamus*
5. *G. p. personatus*
6. *G. p. streckeri*
7. *G. p. tropicalis*

Geomys pinetis
Southeastern Pocket Gopher

External measurements: in males, 250–305, 81–96, 33–37; in females, 229–335, 76–82, 30.5–36. Dark brown to black. Width of rostrum more than length of basioccipital; nasals strongly constricted near middle and shaped like an hourglass.

Geomys pinetis austrinus Bangs

1898. *Geomys floridanus austrinus* Bangs, Proc. Boston Soc. Nat. Hist., 28:177, March, type from Belleair, Pinellas Co., Florida.

1952. *Geomys pinetis austrinus*, Harper, Proc. Biol. Soc. Washington, 65:37, January 29.

MARGINAL RECORDS (Hamilton, 1943:250).—Florida: Tarpon Springs; Arcadia, thence westward to the coast and northward along coast to point of beginning.

Geomys pinetis floridanus (Audubon and Bachman)

1853. *Pseudostoma floridanus* Audubon and Bachman, The viviparous quadrupeds of North America, 3:242. Type locality, St. Augustine, St. Johns Co., Florida.

1952. *Geomys pinetis floridanus*, Harper, Proc. Biol. Soc. Washington, 65:37, January 29.

MARGINAL RECORDS.—Florida: near Boulogne (Harper, 1927:339); Rose Bluff (Sherman, 1937:115); Orlando (*ibid.*); 1 mi. W Silver Springs (27151 KU); Gainesville (18513 KU); Chattahoochee (Sherman, 1937:115). Georgia: Springhill Plantation, about 10 mi. SSW Thomasville (Quay, 1949:67). Florida: N of Macclenny (Harper, 1927:339).

Geomys pinetis goffi Sherman

1944. *Geomys tuza goffi* Sherman, Proc. New England Zool. Club, 23:38, August 30, type from Eau Gallie, Brevard Co., Florida.

1952. *Geomys pinetis goffi*, Harper, Proc. Biol. Soc. Washington, 65:37, January 29.

MARGINAL RECORDS.—Florida: type locality; ½ mi. W Eau Gallie (27072 KU).

Geomys pinetis mobilensis Merriam

1895. *Geomys tuza mobilensis* Merriam, N. Amer. Fauna, 8:119, January 31, type from Point Clear, Mobile Bay, Baldwin Co., Alabama.

1952. *Geomys pinetis mobilensis*, Harper, Proc. Biol. Soc. Washington, 65:37, January 29.

MARGINAL RECORDS.—Alabama: Warrior River, near Lock 14 (A. H. Howell, 1921:59); Seale (*op. cit.*:60). Florida: 6 mi. S, ½ mi. W Wausaw (27149 KU); Milton (Sherman, 1937:115). Alabama: 1 mi. N Fairhope (27161 KU).

Geomys pinetis pinetis Rafinesque

1806. *Mus tuza* Barton, Mag. für den neuesten Zustand der Naturkunde (ed. J. H. Voigt), 12(6):488, November, *et auct.* (Type locality restricted to pine barrens near Au-

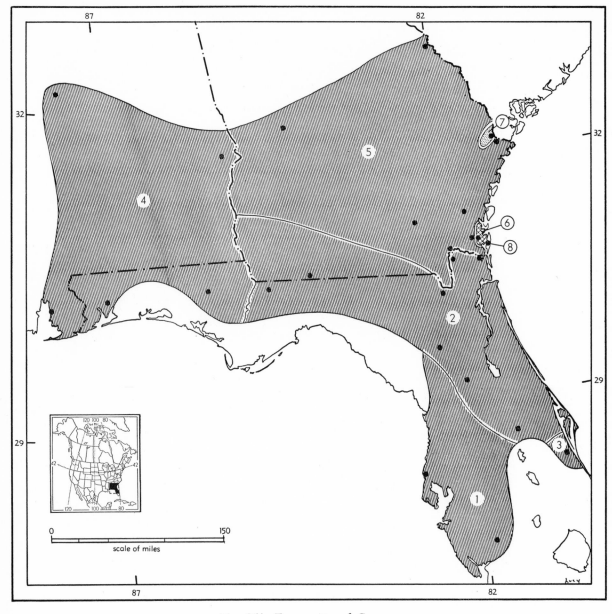

Map 274. Four species of *Geomys*.

Guide
1. *G. pinetis austrinus*
2. *G. pinetis floridanus*

3. *G. pinetis goffi*
4. *G. pinetis mobilensis*
5. *G. pinetis pinetis*

6. *G. colonus*
7. *G. fontanelus*
8. *G. cumberlandius*

gusta, Georgia, by Bangs, Proc. Boston Soc. Nat. Hist., 28:175, March, 1898. According to Harper, Proc. Biol. Soc. Washington, 65:36, January 29, 1952, *tuza* of Barton is of uncertain application and is regarded as not available.)

1817. *Geomys pinetis* Rafinesque, Amer. Monthly Mag., 2(1):45, November. Type locality, Georgia in the region of the pines. (More restrictedly, Screven County according to Harper, Proc. Biol. Soc. Washington, 65:36,

January 29, 1952.) Regarded as identical with *tuza* by Merriam, N. Amer. Fauna, 8:113, January 31, 1895.

MARGINAL RECORDS.—Georgia: Hollywood, 12 mi. S Augusta (Merriam, 1895a:114); Savannah (Hamilton, 1943: 248); Sterling (Sherman, 1940:343); 3 mi. SE Kingsland (Harper, 1927:339); St. Marys River, near Camp Pinckney (Harper, 1927:337); Hebardsville (*ibid.*); Butler (Merriam, 1895a:115).

Geomys colonus Bangs
Colonial Pocket Gopher

1898. *Geomys colonus* Bangs, Proc. Boston Soc. Nat. Hist., 28:178, March, type from Arnot Plantation, about 4 mi. W St. Marys, Camden Co., Georgia.

External measurements: in males, 280–288, 89–100, 34–36; in females (average of 6), 250, 78, 32. Resembles *G. pinetis floridanus* but darker, upper parts being between seal-brown and sepia; palate wider between posterior molars; interpterygoid space broadly U-shaped, nasals shorter and shaped less like an hourglass.

MARGINAL RECORDS.—Georgia (Harper, 1927:341): Arnot (= Arnow) Plantation, approximately 4 mi. W St. Marys; *W of Shingle Swamp, between St. Marys and Kingsland.*

Geomys fontanelus Sherman
Sherman's Pocket Gopher

1940. *Geomys fontanelus* Sherman, Jour. Mamm., 21:341, August 13, type from 7 mi. NW Savannah, Chatham Co., Georgia. Known only from type locality.

External measurements: in males, 222–276, 70–105, 30–34; in females, 232–250, 61–95, 30–34. Described as more nearly related to *G. p. pinetis* than any other species and differing in slightly darker color, auditory bullae larger, presence of a fontanel on each side of skull between parietal and squamosal bones, and in more nearly triangular scapula having more extensive area for insertion of teres major muscle.

Geomys cumberlandius Bangs
Cumberland Island Pocket Gopher

1898. *Geomys cumberlandius* Bangs, Proc. Boston Soc. Nat. Hist., 28:180, March, type from Stafford Place, Cumberland Island, Camden Co., Georgia. Known only from Cumberland Island.

External measurements: Largest male in original series, 324, 114, 35.5; largest female, 283, 96, 34. Resembles *G. p. floridanus*, but tail longer, ascending arms of maxillae narrower, and zygomata less angled at posterior union with skull.

Genus Zygogeomys Merriam

Revised by Merriam, N. Amer. Fauna, 8:195–198, January 31, 1895.

1895. *Zygogeomys* Merriam, N. Amer. Fauna, 8:195, January 31. Type, *Zygogeomys trichopus* Merriam.

External measurements: in males, 343–346, 111–115, 46; in females, 292–322, 92–106, 38–43. Upper premolar with 4 enamel plates, the posterior restricted to lingual ⅓; upper incisor bisulcate; principal sulcus on inner side of median line, minor sulcus on inner convexity. Skull long and narrow; zygomata not widely spreading, slender, and anteroexternal angle rounded rather than expanded; maxillary and jugal roots of zygomata in contact in the arch above the jugal; sagittal crest short, but well developed.

Zygogeomys trichopus
Michoacán Pocket Gopher

Characters as for the genus.

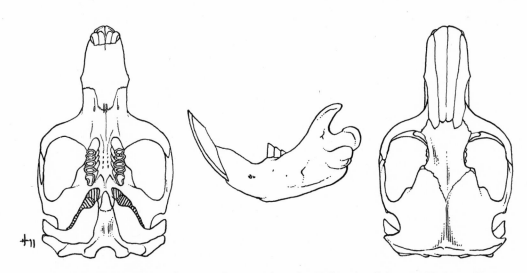

Fig. 265. *Zygogeomys trichopus trichopus*, Nahuatzín, Michoacán, (Merriam, N. Amer. Fauna, No. 8, pl. 6, p. 233), No. 50107 U.S.N.M., ♂, X 1.

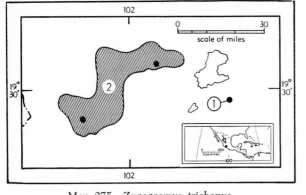

Map 275. *Zygogeomys trichopus.*

1. *Z. t. tarascensis*   2. *Z. t. trichopus*

Zygogeomys trichopus tarascensis Goldman

1938. *Zygogeomys trichopus tarascensis* Goldman, Proc. Biol. Soc. Washington, 51:211, December 23, type from 6 mi. SE Pátzcuaro, 8000 ft., Michoacán. Known only from the type locality.

Zygogeomys trichopus trichopus Merriam

1895. *Zygogeomys trichopus* Merriam, N. Amer. Fauna, 8:196, January 31, type from Nahuatzen, Michoacán.

MARGINAL RECORDS.—Michoacán: type locality; Mt. Tancítaro, 6000 to 10,500 ft. (Hall and Villa, 1949:453).

Genus **Orthogeomys** Merriam
Giant Pocket Gophers

Revised by Merriam, N. Amer. Fauna, 8:172–179, January 3, 1895.

1895. *Orthogeomys* Merriam, N. Amer. Fauna, 8:172, January 31. Type, *Geomys scalops* Thomas.

External measurements: in males, 330–435, 95–140, 44–55; in females, 314–390, 91–121, 38–55. Pelage coarse, hispid or setose. P4 with 3 or 4 enamel plates; M1 and M2 each with 2 enamel plates; I1 unisulcate, sulcus usually slightly medial to mid-line but in some specimens reaching middle. Differs from *Heterogeomys* and *Macrogeomys* (according to Merriam, 1895a:173) in wider interorbital region without evident interorbital constriction, absence of conspicuous postorbital prominences, shape of palatopterygoids (long, narrow and of nearly equal breadth throughout; basal ⅓ or less being palatine), and posterior position of the lateral enamel plates of M3 (both of which normally reach end of heel).

KEY TO NOMINAL SPECIES OF ORTHOGEOMYS

1. Occurring in El Salvador.   *O. pygacanthus*, p. 457
1'. Not occurring in El Salvador.
    2. Total length less than 345.   *O. cuniculus*, p. 457
    2'. Total length more than 345.   *O. grandis*, p. 457

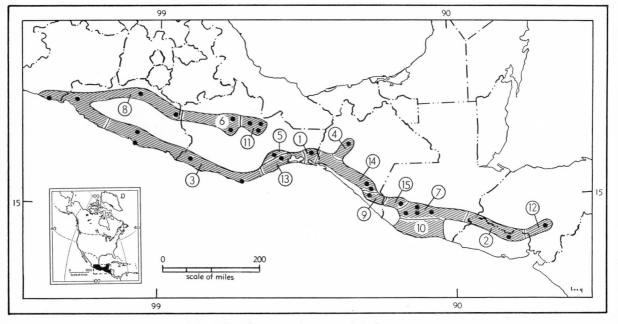

Map 276. The nominal species of *Orthogeomys.*

1. *O. cuniculus*
2. *O. pygacanthus*
3. *O. grandis alleni*
4. *O. grandis annexus*
5. *O. grandis carbo*

6. *O. grandis felipensis*
7. *O. grandis grandis*
8. *O. grandis guerrerensis*
9. *O. grandis huixtlae*
10. *O. grandis latifrons*

11. *O. grandis nelsoni*
12. *O. grandis pluto*
13. *O. grandis scalops*
14. *O. grandis soconuscensis*
15. *O. grandis vulcani*

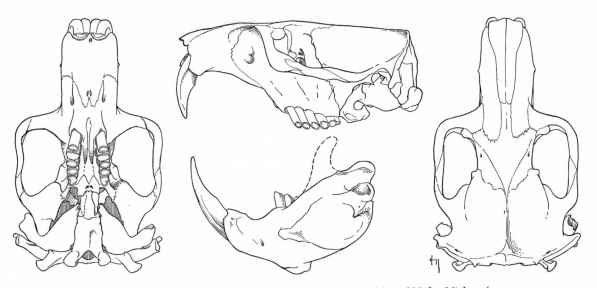

Fig. 266. *Orthogeomys grandis guerrerensis*, ½ mi. E La Mira, 300 ft., Michoacán, No. 39807 K.U., ♀, X 1.

Orthogeomys cuniculus Elliot
Oaxacan Pocket Gopher

1905. *Orthogeomys cuniculus* Elliot, Proc. Biol. Soc. Washington, 18:234, December 9, type from Zanatepec, Oaxaca. (Elliot, Field Columb. Mus., Publ. 115, Zool. Ser., 8:312, March 4, 1907, corrects type locality from Yautepec, Oaxaca, to Zanatepec.) Known only from type locality.

External measurements: in male, 330, 95, 44. According to Nelson and Goldman (1930:317), differs specifically from *O. g. scalops* in smaller size. In adult males: *O. g. scalops*: condylobasal length, 67.4; zygomatic breadth, 41.6; *O. cuniculus*: condylobasal length, 58.3; zygomatic breadth, 36.6.

Orthogeomys pygacanthus Dickey
El Salvador Pocket Gopher

1928. *Orthogeomys pygacanthus* Dickey, Proc. Biol. Soc. Washington, 41:9, February 1, type from Mt. Cacaguatique, 3500 ft., Dept. San Miguel, El Salvador. Known only from the type locality.

External measurements: holotype, male, 341, 104, 54. Externally resembles *O. g. scalops* but smaller, a trifle darker being between Vandyke Brown and Light Seal Brown (*scalops* is Vandyke Brown), and harsher more setose pelage; darker than *grandis,* which is between Bister and Vandyke Brown; skull smaller in all dimensions than in *scalops* or *grandis* except that zygomatic breadth is approximately the same as in *scalops* (after Dickey, 1928:9).

Orthogeomys grandis
Large Pocket Gopher

External measurements: in males, 366–435, 97–140, 49–55; in females, 314–390, 91–121, 38–55. Pelage coarse, hispid or setose.

Orthogeomys grandis alleni Nelson and Goldman

1930. *Orthogeomys grandis alleni* Nelson and Goldman, Jour. Mamm., 11:156, May 9, type from 2000 ft., near Acapulco, Guerrero.

MARGINAL RECORDS.—Guerrero: Río Aguacatillo, 1000 ft., 30 km. N Acapulco (Davis, 1944:389). Oaxaca: Pinotepa (Nelson and Goldman, 1930:157); Puerto Angel (*ibid.*); thence westward along coast to Guerrero: type locality.

Orthogeomys grandis annexus Nelson and Goldman

1933. *Orthogeomys grandis annexus* Nelson and Goldman, Proc. Biol. Soc. Washington, 46:195, October 26, type from Tuxtla Gutiérrez, 2600 ft., Chiapas. Known only from the type locality.

Orthogeomys grandis carbo Goodwin

1956. *Orthogeomys grandis carbo* Goodwin, Amer. Mus. Novit., 1757:5, March 8, type from Escurano, 2500 ft., Cerro de San Pedro, 20 km. W Mixtequilla, Oaxaca. Known only from the type locality.

Orthogeomys grandis felipensis Nelson and Goldman

1930. *Orthogeomys grandis felipensis* Nelson and Goldman, Jour. Mamm., 11:157, May 9, type from Cerro San Felipe, 10 mi. N Oaxaca, Oaxaca.

MARGINAL RECORDS.—Oaxaca: type locality; mountains 15 mi. SW Oaxaca (Nelson and Goldman, 1930:158).

Orthogeomys grandis grandis (Thomas)

1893. *Geomys grandis* Thomas, Ann. Mag. Nat. Hist., ser. 6, 12:270, October, type from Dueñas, Guatemala.
1895. *Orthogeomys grandis*, Merriam, N. Amer. Fauna, 8:175, January 31.

MARGINAL RECORDS.—Guatemala: San Lucas [= Tolimán] (Goodwin, 1934:28); type locality; near Pochuta (Lawrence, 1933:66); Finca Cipres (Goodwin, 1934: 28).

Orthogeomys grandis guerrerensis Nelson and Goldman

1930. *Orthogeomys grandis guerrerensis* Nelson and Goldman, Jour. Mamm., 11:158, May 9, type from El Limón, in valley of Río de las Balsas approximately 20 mi. NW La Unión, Guerrero.

MARGINAL RECORDS.—Guerrero: Río de las Balsas near Mexcala (Nelson and Goldman, 1930:159); Tlalistaquilla near Tlapa (*ibid.*); type locality. Michoacán: ½ mi. E La Mira, 300 ft. (39807 KU).

Orthogeomys grandis huixtlae Villa

1944. *Orthogeomys grandis huixtlae* Villa, Anal. Inst. Biol. Univ. Nac. México, 15(1):319, type from Finca Lubeca, 12 km. NE Huixtla, 850 m., Chiapas. Known only from the type locality.

Orthogeomys grandis latifrons Merriam

1895. *Orthogeomys latifrons* Merriam, N. Amer. Fauna, 8:178, January 31, type from Guatemala; exact locality unknown, probably lowlands of southern part. Known only from Guatemala.
1930. *Orthogeomys grandis latifrons*, Nelson and Goldman, Jour. Mamm., 11:156, May 9.

Orthogeomys grandis nelsoni Merriam

1895. *Orthogeomys nelsoni* Merriam, N. Amer. Fauna, 8:176, January 31, type from Mt. Zempoaltepec, 8000 ft., Oaxaca.
1930. *Orthogeomys grandis nelsoni*, Nelson and Goldman, Jour. Mamm., 11:156, May 9.

MARGINAL RECORDS.—Oaxaca (Merriam, 1895a: 178): Comaltepec; type locality; near Totontepec.

Orthogeomys grandis pluto Lawrence

1933. *Orthogeomys grandis pluto* Lawrence, Proc. New England Zool. Club, 13:66, May 8, type from Cerro Cantoral, north of Tegucigalpa, Honduras. Known only from the type locality.

Orthogeomys grandis scalops (Thomas)

1894. *Geomys scalops* Thomas, Ann. Mag. Nat. Hist., ser. 6, 13:437, May, type from Tehuantepec, Oaxaca. Known only from the type locality.

1930. *Orthogeomys grandis scalops*, Nelson and Goldman, Jour. Mamm., 11:156, May 9.

Orthogeomys grandis soconuscensis Villa

1949. *Orthogeomys grandis soconuscensis* Villa, Anal. Inst. Biol. Univ. Nac. México, 19(1):267, April 8, type from Finca Esperanza, 710 m., 45 km. (by road) NW Huixtla, Chiapas.

MARGINAL RECORDS.—Chiapas: type locality; Finca Liquidámbar, 1210 m. (Villa, 1949:511).

Orthogeomys grandis vulcani Nelson and Goldman

1931. *Orthogeomys grandis vulcani* Nelson and Goldman, Proc. Biol. Soc. Washington, 44:105, October 17, type from Volcán Santa María, 9000 ft., Quezaltenango, Guatemala. Known only from the type locality.

Genus **Heterogeomys** Merriam
Hispid Pocket Gophers

List published by Nelson and Goldman, Proc. Biol. Soc. Washington, 42:147–152, March 30, 1929.

1895. *Heterogeomys* Merriam, N. Amer. Fauna, 8:179, January 31. Type, *Geomys hispidus* Le Conte.

External measurements: in males, 309–343, 74–101, 46–53; in females, 292–335, 75–98, 44–52. Dark brown. P4 with 4 enamel plates, the posterior restricted to inner lingual half; M1 and M2 each with two enamel plates; I1 unisulcate; sulcus wholly on inner side of median line and in some specimens on inner ⅓; sulcus deep and abrupt.

KEY TO SPECIES OF HETEROGEOMYS

1. Occurring at Xuchil, Veracruz; female with total length up to 361 and hind foot up to 54; pelage soft and wooly. . . *H. lanius*, p. 460
1'. Not occurring at Xuchil, Veracruz; female with total length less than 361 and hind foot shorter than 54; pelage harsh and coarse.
H. hispidus, p. 458

Heterogeomys hispidus
Hispid Pocket Gopher

External measurements: in males, 309–343, 74–101, 46–53; in females, 292–335, 75–95, 44–52. Dark brown; pelage harsh and stiff.

Heterogeomys hispidus cayoensis Burt

1937. *Heterogeomys hispidus cayoensis* Burt, Occas. Papers Mus. Zool., Univ. Michigan, 365:1, December 16, type from Mountain Pine Ridge, 12 mi. S El Cayo, British Honduras.

MARGINAL RECORDS.—British Honduras: El Cayo (Burt, 1937:2); type locality.

Heterogeomys hispidus chiapensis Nelson and Goldman

1929. *Heterogeomys hispidus chiapensis* Nelson and Goldman, Proc. Biol. Soc. Washington, 42:151, March 30, type from Tenejapa, 16 mi. NE San Cristóbal, Chiapas.

MARGINAL RECORDS.—Tabasco: Montecristo (Nelson and Goldman, 1929:152). Guatemala: Chipoc (Goodwin, 1934:29); Guatemala City (Nelson and Goldman, 1929: 152); Dueñas (Gaumer, 1917:128). Chiapas: type locality; Ocuilapa (Nelson and Goldman, 1929:152).

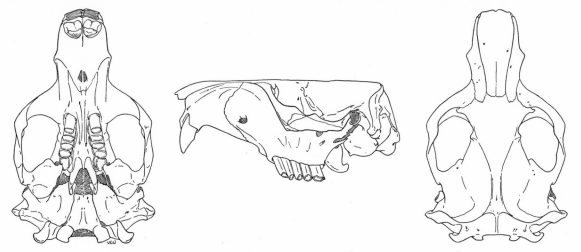

Fig. 267. *Heterogeomys hispidus hispidus*, Potrero Viejo, 7 km. W Potrero, 1700 ft., Veracruz, No. 19355 K.U., ♀, X 1.

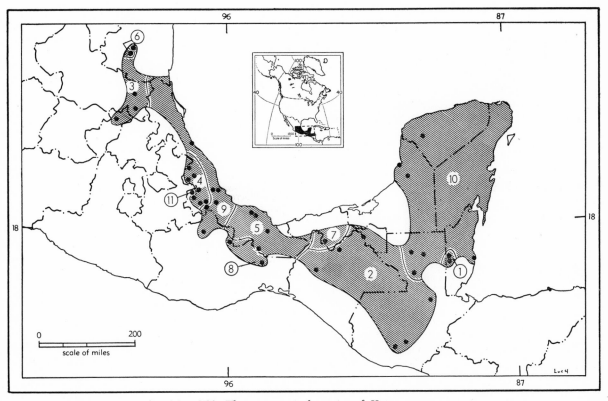

Map 277. The two nominal species of *Heterogeomys*.

Guide to kinds		
1. *H. hispidus cayoensis*	4. *H. hispidus hispidus*	8. *H. hispidus tehuantepecus*
2. *H. hispidus chiapensis*	5. *H. hispidus isthmicus*	9. *H. hispidus torridus*
3. *H. hispidus concavus*	6. *H. hispidus negatus*	10. *H. hispidus yucatanensis*
	7. *H. hispidus teapensis*	11. *H. lanius*

Heterogeomys hispidus concavus Nelson and Goldman

1929. *Heterogeomys hispidus concavus* Nelson and Goldman, Proc. Biol. Soc. Washington, 42:148, March 30, type from Pinal de Amoles, Querétaro.

MARGINAL RECORDS.—Tamaulipas: 70 km. S Ciudad Victoria and 2 km. W El Carrizo (Baker, 1951:211). San Luis Potosí: Valles (Nelson and Goldman, 1929:149); Tancanhuitz (*ibid.*). Querétaro: type locality.

Heterogeomys hispidus hispidus (Le Conte)

1852. *G[eomys]. hispidus* Le Conte, Proc. Acad. Nat. Sci. Philadelphia, 6:158. Type locality, near Jalapa, Veracruz.
1895. *Heterogeomys hispidus*, Merriam, N. Amer. Fauna, 8:181, January 31.

MARGINAL RECORDS.—Veracruz: 4 km. W Tlapacoyan, 1700 ft. (23974 KU); 5 km. N Jalapa, 4500 ft. (19354 KU); 2 km. N Motzorongo, 1500 ft. (19358 KU); 3 km. N Presidio, 1500 ft. (19357 KU); 4 km. WNW Fortín, 3200 ft. (17933 KU); Huatusco (Merriam, 1895a:183); Jico (*ibid.*).

Heterogeomys hispidus isthmicus Nelson and Goldman

1929. *Heterogeomys hispidus isthmicus* Nelson and Goldman, Proc. Biol. Soc. Washington, 42:149, March 30, type from Jaltipan, Veracruz.

MARGINAL RECORDS.—Veracruz: 3 km. E San Andrés Tuxtla, 1000 ft. (23976 KU); Catemaco (Nelson and Goldman, 1929:150); 14 km. SW Coatzacoalcos, 100 ft. (19359 KU); Jesús Carranza, 250 ft. (19361 KU).

Heterogeomys hispidus negatus Goodwin

1953. *Heterogeomys hispidus negatus* Goodwin, Amer. Mus. Novit., 1620:1, May 4, type from Gómez Feras [= Farías], 1300 ft., about 45 mi. S Ciudad Victoria, 10 mi. W Pan American Highway, Tamaulipas. Known only from the type locality.

Heterogeomys hispidus teapensis Goldman

1939. *Heterogeomys hispidus teapensis* Goldman, Jour. Washington Acad. Sci., 29:176, April 15, type from Teapa, Tabasco. Known only from the type locality.

Heterogeomys hispidus tehuantepecus Goldman

1939. *Heterogeomys hispidus tehuantepecus* Goldman, Jour. Washington Acad. Sci., 29:175, April 15, type from mountains 12 mi. NW Santo Domingo and about 60 mi. N Tehuantepec, 1600 ft., Oaxaca.

MARGINAL RECORDS.—Oaxaca: La Gloria (Goodwin, 1956a:5); type locality.

Heterogeomys hispidus torridus Merriam

1895. *Heterogeomys torridus* Merriam, N. Amer. Fauna, 8:183, January 31, type from Chichicaxtle, Veracruz.
1929. *Heterogeomys hispidus torridus*, Nelson and Goldman, Proc. Biol. Soc. Washington, 42:147, March 30.

MARGINAL RECORDS.—Veracruz: 3 km. W Gutiérrez Zamora, 300 ft. (23973 KU); Boca del Río, 10 ft. (Davis, 1944:388); 15 km. W Piedras Negras, 400 ft. (19360 KU). Oaxaca: Reyes [= Pápalo Santos Reyes] (Merriam, 1895a:184). Veracruz: Motzorongo (*ibid.*); type locality.

Heterogeomys hispidus yucatanensis Nelson and Goldman

1929. *Heterogeomys hispidus yucatanensis* Nelson and Goldman, Proc. Biol. Soc. Washington, 42:150, March 30, type from Campeche, Campeche.

MARGINAL RECORDS.—Yucatán: Calcehtok (Hatt and Villa, 1950:234). British Honduras: Stann Creek Valley (referred by Laurie, 1953:386, to *H. h. torridus*; here referred to *H. h. yucatanensis* on geographic grounds). Guatemala: Uaxactún (Murie, 1935:25); Libertad (Nelson and Goldman, 1929:151); Chuntuqui (*ibid.*). Campeche: Apazote (*ibid.*); type locality.

Heterogeomys lanius Elliot
Big Pocket Gopher

1905. *Heterogeomys lanius* Elliot, Proc. Biol. Soc. Washington, 18:235, December 9, type from Xuchil, Veracruz. Known only from the type locality.

External measurements of the type, a female, are: 361, 90, 54. In original description, distinguished from *H. h. hispidus* by larger size and soft wooly coat instead of harsh pelage. The exact geographic position of the type locality Xuchil, needs to be ascertained and a re-examination of the specific *versus* subspecific status of *H. lanius* and *H. hispidus* is desirable.

Genus Macrogeomys Merriam
Central American Pocket Gophers

Revised by Merriam, N. Amer. Fauna, 8:185–195, January 31, 1895.

1895. *Macrogeomys* Merriam, N. Amer. Fauna, 8:185, January 31. Type, *Geomys heterodus* Peters.

External measurements: in males, 177–392, 70–120, 36–53; in females, 170–388, 70–128, 35–52.5. Dark brown to blackish; one species with white transverse band on lumbar region and some other species with white on top of head or rump. P4 with 4 enamel plates; M1 and M2 each with 2 enamel plates; I1 unisulcate; sulcus wholly on inner ⅓ of face, narrow and deep; face of tooth flat on both sides of sulcus; strong postorbital processes and short, broad, palatopterygoids are differences from *Orthogeomys* and *Heterogeomys*.

KEY TO SPECIES OF MACROGEOMYS

1. Occurring in extreme eastern Panamá.
   M. dariensis, p. 462
1'. Not occurring in extreme eastern Panamá.

2. Occurring in Nicaragua. . *M. matagalpae*, p. 463
2'. Not occurring in Nicaragua.
   3. Pelage relatively soft; underparts clearly paler than upper parts. . *M. heterodus*, p. 461
   3'. Pelage harsh and wooly; underparts not (or only slightly) paler than upper parts.
      4. Size large (320–390); color uniformly blackish (dorsal white markings absent). . . . . . . *M. cavator*, p. 461
      4'. Size small (less than 335); dorsal white markings present.
         5. Total length more than 210; white markings present on head and/or rump. . . . . . *M. cherriei*, p. 462
         5'. Total length less than 210; white marking present on lumbar region and less distinctly so across abdomen. . . . . *M. underwoodi*, p. 462

Macrogeomys heterodus
Variable Pocket Gopher

External measurements: in males, 335–392, 72–95, 48–52; in females, 315–380, 70–97, 47–51. Blackish, soft-haired, underparts paler than upper parts.

Macrogeomys heterodus cartagoensis Goodwin

1943. *Macrogeomys heterodus cartagoensis* Goodwin, Amer. Mus. Novit., 1227:2, April 22, type from Paso Ancho, Province of Cartago, Costa Rica.

MARGINAL RECORDS.—Costa Rica (Goodwin, 1946: 377): Rancho Redondo, Volcán Irazú; El Sauce Peralta; Pozo Ancho; Cervantes; San Ramón Tres Ríos.

Macrogeomys heterodus dolichocephalus Merriam

1895. *Macrogeomys dolichocephalus* Merriam, N. Amer. Fauna, 8:189, January 31, type from San José, Costa Rica (probably Zarcero or Palmira according to Goodwin, Bull. Amer. Mus. Nat. Hist., 87:377, December 31, 1946).
1946. *Macrogeomys heterodus dolichocephalus*, Goodwin, Bull. Amer. Mus. Nat. Hist., 87:377, December 31.

MARGINAL RECORDS.—Costa Rica (Goodwin, 1946: 378): Lajas Villa Quesada; Tapesco [= Tapezco].

Macrogeomys heterodus heterodus (Peters)

1865. *Geomys heterodus* Peters, Monatsb. preuss. Akad. Wiss., Berlin, p. 177, type from Costa Rica; exact locality unknown.
1895. *Macrogeomys heterodus*, Merriam, N. Amer. Fauna, 8:186, January 31.

MARGINAL RECORDS.—Costa Rica (Goodwin, 1946: 376): Escazú; Escazú Heights; Sabanilla.

Macrogeomys cavator
Chiriquí Pocket Gopher

External measurements: in males, 370–390, 100–120, 52–53; in females, 320–380, 104–110, 48–51. Dark seal brown, almost blackish; uniformly colored; pelage harsh.

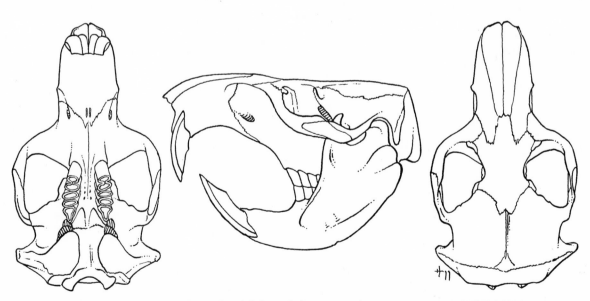

Fig. 268. *Macrogeomys heterodus dolichocephalus*, San José, Costa Rica, No. 36295 U.S.N.M., ♂, X 1. (After Merriam, N. Amer. Fauna, No. 8, pl. 5, p. 231 (B, C, D) and p. 104 (A), January 31, 1895.)

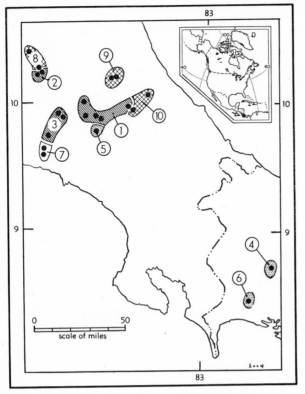

Map 278. Three species of *Macrogeomys*.

1. *M. heterodus*   6. *M. cavator pansa*
   cartagoensis   7. *M. underwoodi*
2. *M. heterodus*   8. *M. cherriei*
   dolichocephalus   *carlosensis*
3. *M. heterodus heterodus* 9. *M. cherriei cherriei*
4. *M. cavator cavator*   10. *M. cherriei*
5. *M. cavator nigrescens*   *costaricensis*

Macrogeomys cavator cavator Bangs

1902. *Macrogeomys cavator* Bangs, Bull. Mus. Comp. Zool., 39:42, April, type from Boquete, 4800 ft., Chiriquí, Panamá. Known only from the type locality.

Macrogeomys cavator nigrescens Goodwin

1943. *Macrogeomys cavator nigrescens* Goodwin, Amer. Mus. Novit., 1227:3, April 22, type from El Muñeco (Río Navarro), 10 mi. S Cartago, Prov. Cartago, 4000 ft., Costa Rica. Known only from the type locality.

Macrogeomys cavator pansa Bangs

1902. *Macrogeomys pansa* Bangs, Bull. Mus. Comp. Zool., 39:44, April, type from Bogava [= Bugaba], 600 ft., Chiriquí, Panamá. Known only from the type locality.
1946. *Macrogeomys cavator pansa*, Goodwin, Bull. Amer. Mus. Nat. Hist., 87:379, December 31.

Macrogeomys dariensis Goldman
Darién Pocket Gopher

1912. *Macrogeomys dariensis* Goldman, Smiths. Miscl. Coll., 60(2):8, September 20, type from Cana, 2000 ft., mountains of eastern Panamá.

External measurements: in males, 358–401, 122–135, 51–53.5; in females, 348–388, 118–128, 48–52.5. Dull brown or black. Resembles *M. c. cavator* but color dull brown or black instead of rich seal brown and skull narrower posteriorly with low and nearly straight (or slightly convex), instead of high and sinuous, lambdoidal crest.

MARGINAL RECORDS.—Panamá (Goldman, 1920: 111): Tacarcuna; Tapalisa; type locality; Boca de Cupe.

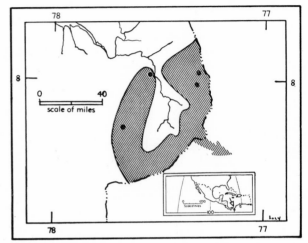

Map 279. *Macrogeomys dariensis*.

Macrogeomys underwoodi Osgood
Underwood's Pocket Gopher

1931. *Macrogeomys underwoodi* Osgood, Field Mus. Nat. Hist., Publ. 295, Zool. Ser. 18(5):143, August 3, type from Alto de Jabillo Pirris, between San Gerónimo and Pozo Azul, western Costa Rica.

External measurements: in males, 277–299, 85–100, 36–38; in females, 280, 92, 35. Dark brown, almost blackish, on upper parts but paler below; transverse band, 13 to 22 mm. wide of all white hair on lumbar region and extending less distinctly across abdomen. Resembles *M. cherriei* but lacks white on head, and rostrum narrower (11–13).

MARGINAL RECORDS.—Costa Rica: San Gerónimo (Goodwin, 1946:382); type locality.

Macrogeomys cherriei
Cherrie's Pocket Gopher

External measurements: in male, 323, 88, 41; in females, 263–280, 70–75, 38.5–44. Mummy brown to blackish brown with white markings on head.

Macrogeomys cherriei carlosensis Goodwin

1943. *Macrogeomys cherriei carlosensis* Goodwin, Amer. Mus. Novit., 1227:3, April 22, type from Cataratos, San Carlos, Alajuela, Costa Rica.

MARGINAL RECORDS.—Costa Rica: type locality; Villa Quesada (Goodwin, 1946:381).

Macrogeomys cherriei cherriei (J. A. Allen)

1893. *Geomys cherriei* J. A. Allen, Bull. Amer. Mus. Nat. Hist., 5:337, December 16, type from Santa Clara, Costa Rica.
1895. *Macrogeomys cherriei,* Merriam, N. Amer. Fauna, 8:194, January 31.

MARGINAL RECORDS.—Costa Rica: type locality; Jiménez (Goodwin, 1946:380).

Macrogeomys cherriei costaricensis Merriam

1895. *Macrogeomys costaricensis* Merriam, N. Amer. Fauna, 8:192, January 31, type from Pacuare, Costa Rica.
1946. *Macrogeomys cherriei costaricensis,* Goodwin, Bull. Amer. Mus. Nat. Hist., 87:380, December 31.

MARGINAL RECORDS.—Costa Rica: type locality; Santa Teresa Perálta (Goodwin, 1946:381).

Macrogeomys matagalpae J. A. Allen
Nicaraguan Pocket Gopher

1910. *Macrogeomys matagalpae* J. A. Allen, Bull. Amer. Mus. Nat. Hist., 28:97, April 30, type from Peña Blanca, Matagalpa, Nicaragua.

External measurements of male: 320, 80, 40. Dark brown with white crown-patch. Resembles *M. c. cherriei* but darker, smaller and with narrower (14 in adult male) rostrum.

MARGINAL RECORDS.—Nicaragua: Matagalpa (J. A. Allen, 1910:97); type locality.

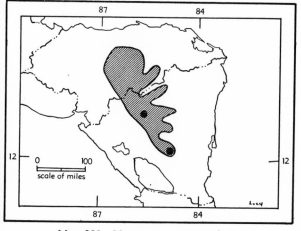

Map 280. *Macrogeomys matagalpae.*

Genus Pappogeomys Merriam

Revised by Merriam, N. Amer. Fauna, 8:145–149, January 31, 1895; Goldman, Jour. Mamm., 20:93–98, February 14, 1939.

1895. *Pappogeomys* Merriam, N. Amer. Fauna, 8:145, January 31. Type, *Geomys bulleri* Thomas.

External measurements: in males, 214–253, 65–84, 28–35; in females, 192–247, 53–82, 27–35. Upper parts dark brown, hair of fine texture; claws on forefeet large as in *Geomys*; P4 with only 3 enamel plates; M1 and M2 each with 2 enamel plates; I1 unisulcate (no second, minor, sulcus as in *Geomys*).

KEY TO SPECIES OF PAPPOGEOMYS

1. Nasal patch white; posterior wall of M1 having enamel entirely across wall. *P. bulleri,* p. 463
1'. Nasal patch cinnamon or buff; posterior wall of M1 lacking enamel on outer three-fourths of wall. . . . . *P. alcorni,* p. 464

Pappogeomys bulleri
Buller's Pocket Gopher

Size of animal, fine texture of fur, and generalized shape of skull all as in some species of *Thomomys*; some cranial details, for example groove on incisor, and large claws of forefeet resembling corresponding parts in *Geomys*. Differs from *P. alcorni* as set forth in the account of that species.

Pappogeomys bulleri albinasus Merriam

1895. *Pappogeomys albinasus* Merriam, N. Amer. Fauna, 8:149, January 31, type from Atemajac, a suburb of Guadalajara, Jalisco.
1939. *Pappogeomys bulleri albinasus,* Goldman, Jour. Mamm., 20:94, February 15.

MARGINAL RECORDS.—Jalisco: W side La Venta, 13 mi. W, 4 mi. N Guadalajara (30995 KU); *2 mi. N, ½ mi. W Guadalajara* (31007 KU); type locality; 10 mi. S, 8 mi. W Guadalajara (31037 KU).

Pappogeomys bulleri amecensis Goldman

1939. *Pappogeomys bulleri amecensis* Goldman, Jour. Mamm., 20:97, February 15, type from mountains near Ameca, 6500 ft., Jalisco.

MARGINAL RECORDS.—Jalisco: Cerro Viejo de Magdalena, 6500 ft. (39803 KU); Cerro Tequila, 10,000 ft., 7 mi. S, 2 mi. E Tequila (33446 KU); type locality.

Pappogeomys bulleri bulleri (Thomas)

1892. *Geomys bulleri* Thomas, Ann. Mag. Nat. Hist., ser. 6, 10:196, type from near Talpa, W slope Sierra de Mascota, 8500 ft., Jalisco.
1895. *Pappogeomys bulleri,* Merriam, N. Amer. Fauna, 8:147, January 31.

MARGINAL RECORDS.—Jalisco: type locality; 5 mi. S Purificación (33453 KU).

Pappogeomys bulleri burti Goldman

1939. *Pappogeomys bulleri burti* Goldman, Jour. Mamm., 20:97, February 15, type from Tenacatita Bay, SW coast of Jalisco.

MARGINAL RECORDS.—Jalisco: type locality. Colima: 4 mi. W, 1 mi. S Santiago, 10 ft. (36675 KU).

Pappogeomys bulleri flammeus Goldman

1939. *Pappogeomys bulleri flammeus* Goldman, Jour. Mamm., 20:95, February 15, type from Milpillas, 5 mi. SW San Sebastián, Jalisco. Known only from the type locality.

Pappogeomys bulleri lagunensis Goldman

1939. *Pappogeomys bulleri lagunensis* Goldman, Jour. Mamm., 20:96, February 15, type from La Laguna, 6500 ft., Sierra de Juanacatlán, Jalisco. Known only from the type locality.

Pappogeomys bulleri nayaritensis Goldman

1939. *Pappogeomys bulleri nayaritensis* Goldman, Jour. Mamm., 20:94, February 15, type from Jalisco (a town), approximately 10 mi. S Tepic, 5000 ft., Nayarit.

MARGINAL RECORDS.—Nayarit: type locality; 6 mi. S Ixtlán del Río, 6800 ft. (39801 KU); 2 mi. WNW Jalcocotán, 3000 ft. (36670 KU).

Pappogeomys bulleri nelsoni (Merriam)

1892. *Geomys nelsoni* Merriam, Proc. Biol. Soc. Washington, 7:164, September 29, type from N slope Sierra Nevada de Colima, 6500 ft., Jalisco. Known only from the type locality.
1939. *Pappogeomys bulleri nelsoni* Goldman, Jour. Mamm., 20:94, February 15.

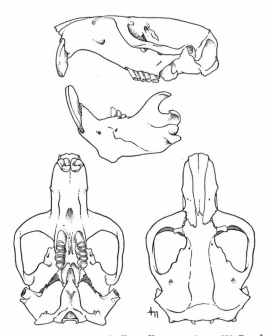

Fig. 269. *Pappogeomys bulleri albinasus*, 4 mi. W Guadalajara, Jalisco, No. 31031 K.U., ♂, X 1.

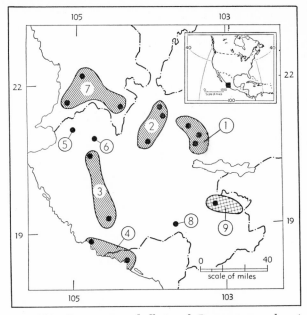

Map 281. *Pappogeomys bulleri* and *Pappogeomys alcorni*.

Guide to kinds
1. *P. b. albinasus*
2. *P. b. amecensis*
3. *P. b. bulleri*
4. *P. b. burti*
5. *P. b. flammeus*
6. *P. b. lagunensis*
7. *P. b. nayaritensis*
8. *P. b. nelsoni*
9. *P. alcorni*

Pappogeomys alcorni Russell
Alcorn's Pocket Gopher

1957. *Pappogeomys alcorni* Russell, Univ. Kansas Publ., Mus. Nat. Hist., 9:359, January 21, type from 4 mi. W Mazamitla, 6600 ft., Jalisco.

External measurements of 2 adult females from the type locality are: 210, 210; 61, 63; 29, 28. Condylobasal length of skull, 38.0, 36.9. Pelage Plumbeous basally and Orange-Cinnamon apically. Resembles *Pappogeomys bulleri* but differs in following respects: nasal patch cinnamon or buffy instead of white; enamel plate of posterior wall of M1 reduced to inner fourth rather than developed completely across posterior wall of tooth; nasals broadly truncate posteriorly instead of narrow and emarginate; anterior palatine foramina short and round instead of long and slitlike.

MARGINAL RECORDS.—Jalisco: Type locality; *3 mi. WSW Mazamitla* (Russell, 1957:360).

Genus Cratogeomys Merriam
Yellow Pocket Gophers

Revised, in part, by Nelson and Goldman, Proc. Biol. Soc. Washington, 47:135–154, June 13, 1934; remainder revised by Goldman, Jour. Mamm., 20:87–93, February 15, 1939.

1895. *Cratogeomys* Merriam, N. Amer. Fauna, 8:150, January 31. Type, *Geomys merriami* Thomas.
1895. *Platygeomys* Merriam, N. Amer. Fauna, 8:162, January 31. Type, *Geomys gymnurus* Merriam. Regarded as inseparable from *Cratogeomys* by Hooper, Jour. Mamm., 27:397–399, November 25, 1946.

External measurements: in males, 226–372, 70–121, 31–53; in females, 210–341, 63–106, 31–50. Upper parts yellowish, brownish, or sometimes (in México) black; P4 with only 3 enamel plates; M1 and M2 with 1 enamel plate each; I1 unisulcate, sulcus median or slightly on inner side of tooth.

At present (1957), this genus is the subject of a revisionary study and the following arrangement of kinds will doubtless be much altered.

KEY TO SPECIES-GROUPS OF CRATOGEOMYS

1. Skull deep and narrow, palatofrontal depth more than 60 per cent of breadth across squamosal processes.
    2. Rostrum broad and heavy; length of maxillary tooth-row more than 11; basioccipital wedge-shaped, abruptly tapering anteriorly; incisors large.
        merriami species-group, p. 469
    2′. Rostrum narrow and lightly constructed; length of maxillary tooth-row less than 11; basioccipital parallel-sided or only slightly tapering anteriorly; incisors small.
        castanops species-group, p. 465
1′. Skull shallow and wide, palatofrontal depth less than 60 per cent of breadth across squamosal processes.
    3. Breadth across squamosal processes greater than zygomatic breadth.
        gymnurus species-group, p. 471
    3′. Breadth across squamosal processes less than zygomatic breadth.
        zinseri species-group, p. 470

castanops-group
Cratogeomys castanops
Yellow-faced Pocket Gopher

External measurements: in males, 226–320, 70–105, 31.5–42.5; in females, 210–298, 63–96, 31–39.5. Yellowish brown or buffy ochraceous. Cranial characters on specific level have not been worked out.

Cratogeomys castanops angusticeps Nelson and Goldman

1934. *Cratogeomys castanops angusticeps* Nelson and Goldman, Proc. Biol. Soc. Washington, 47:139, June 13, type from Eagle Pass, Texas.

MARGINAL RECORDS.—Texas (Nelson and Goldman, 1934:140): Juno; Eagle Pass; Samuels; Langtry; Sanderson.

Cratogeomys castanops bullatus Russell and Baker

1955. *Cratogeomys castanops bullatus* Russell and Baker, Univ. Kansas Publ., Mus. Nat. Hist., 7:597, March 15, type from 2 mi. S, 6½ mi. E Nava, 810 ft., Coahuila.

MARGINAL RECORDS.—Coahuila: 2 mi. S, 12 mi. E Nava, 800 ft. (48496 KU); 9 mi. S, 11 mi. E Sabinas, 1050 ft. (48508 KU); 8 mi. S, 8 mi. E Hda. La Mariposa, 1900 ft. (44844 KU); 10 mi. E Hda. La Mariposa, 2000 ft. (44845 KU).

Cratogeomys castanops castanops (Baird)

1852. *Pseudostoma castanops* Baird, *in* Stansbury, Expl. Surv. . . . Great Salt of Utah . . . , App. C, p. 313, June, type from "Prairie road to Bent's Fort," near present town of Las Animas, Bent Co., Colorado.
1895. *Cratogeomys castanops,* Merriam, N. Amer. Fauna, 8:159, January 31.

MARGINAL RECORDS.—Colorado: 3 mi. W Pueblo (Cary, 1911:130); Olney (Merriam, 1895:160); type locality; Lamar (Cary, 1911:130); Monon (*ibid.*). New Mexico: Chico Springs (Nelson and Goldman, 1934:136).

Cratogeomys castanops clarkii (Baird)

1855. *Geomys clarkii* Baird, Proc. Acad. Nat. Sci. Philadelphia, 7:332, April, type from Presidio del Norte, on the Río Grande, at or near the present town of Ojinaga, Chihuahua. Known only from the type locality.
1934. *Cratogeomys castanops clarkii,* Nelson and Goldman, Proc. Biol. Soc. Washington, 47:140, June 13.

Cratogeomys castanops consitus Nelson and Goldman

1934. *Cratogeomys castanops consitus* Nelson and Goldman, Proc. Biol. Soc. Washington, 47:140, June 13, type from Gallego, 5500 ft., Chihuahua.

MARGINAL RECORDS.—Chihuahua (Nelson and Goldman, 1934:141): Samalayuca. Coahuila: 3 mi. N, 9 mi. E El Pino (54547 KU); 3 mi. NE Sierra Mojada (40866 KU). Chihuahua: Santa Rosalía [= Camargo] (Nelson and Goldman, 1934:141); type locality.

Cratogeomys castanops convexus Nelson and Goldman

1934. *Cratogeomys castanops convexus* Nelson and Goldman, Proc. Biol. Soc. Washington, 47:142, June 13, type from 7 mi. E Las Vacas, Río Grande Valley, Coahuila (opposite Del Rio, Texas).

MARGINAL RECORDS.—Coahuila: Río Grande, 17 mi. S Dryden, Texas (44838 KU); near Río Grande, opposite Samuels, Texas (Nelson and Goldman, 1934:140); type locality; 11 mi. W Hda. San Miguel (35764 KU); Cañon del Cochino, 21 mi. E, 16 mi. N Piedra Blanco (35763 KU).

Cratogeomys castanops excelsus Nelson and Goldman

1934. *Cratogeomys castanops excelsus* Nelson and Goldman, Proc. Biol. Soc. Washington, 47:143, June 13, type from San Pedro, 10 mi. W Laguna de Mayrán, Coahuila.

MARGINAL RECORDS.—Coahuila: 8 mi. E, 2 mi. S Americanos, 3500 ft. (58714 KU); 4 mi. N Acatita, 3600 ft. (40879 KU); 20 mi. S El Hundido (38715 KU); 10

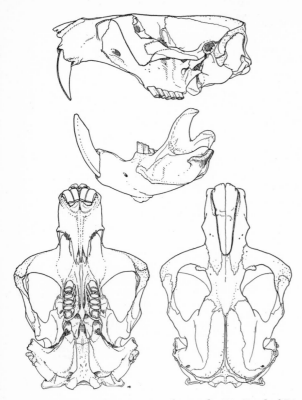

Fig. 270. *Cratogeomys castanops lacrimalis*, Big Bend of Rio Grande, 2000 ft., Brewster Co., Texas, No. 80360 M.V.Z., ♂, X 1.

mi. N, 11 mi. W San Lorenzo (48518 KU). Durango: 4 mi. WSW Lerdo, 3800 ft. (40234 KU); Tlahualilo [= Zaragoza] (Nelson and Goldman, 1934:144).

Cratogeomys castanops goldmani Merriam

1895. *Cratogeomys castanops goldmani* Merriam, N. Amer. Fauna, 8:160, January 31, type from Cañitas, Zacatecas.

MARGINAL RECORDS.—Coahuila: 1½ mi. N Parras (34938 KU). Zacatecas: type locality. Coahuila: Valley Río Aquanaval, 1 mi. S Jimulco (55611 KU).

Cratogeomys castanops hirtus Nelson and Goldman

1934. *Cratogeomys castanops hirtus* Nelson and Goldman, Proc. Biol. Soc. Washington, 47:138, June 13, type from Albuquerque, 5000 ft., New Mexico. Known only from the type locality.

Cratogeomys castanops jucundus Russell and Baker

1955. *Cratogeomys castanops jucundus* Russell and Baker, Univ. Kansas Publ., Mus. Nat. Hist., 7:599, March 15, type from Hermanas, 1205 ft., Coahuila.

MARGINAL RECORDS.—Coahuila: type locality; Hisachalo [= Huiachalo] (58079 KU); Monclova (Nelson and Goldman, 1934:142); 1 mi. N, 13 mi. E Cuatro Ciénegas (48510 KU).

Cratogeomys castanops lacrimalis Nelson and Goldman

1934. *Cratogeomys castanops lacrimalis* Nelson and Goldman, Proc. Biol. Soc. Washington, 47:137, June 13, type from Roswell, 3500 ft., Chaves Co., New Mexico.

MARGINAL RECORDS (Nelson and Goldman, 1934:138, unless otherwise noted).—New Mexico: Santa Rosa; Fort Sumner; 35 mi. N Roswell; type locality; 2 mi. E Carlsbad (7348 KU). Texas: mouth Pine Springs Canyon, 5800 ft. (Davis and Robertson, 1944:267); Kent; Davis Mts., 15 mi. SW Toyahvale; Marathon; Boquillas; Onion Creek, 30 mi. SW Marfa (Merriam, 1895a:160); Valentine; Van Horn; Sierra Blanca; El Paso. New Mexico: White Sands, 18 mi. SW Alamogordo (50478 MVZ); Tularosa; Ancho. (No. 108388 USNM, from Fort Lancaster, Texas, assigned to this subspecies by Nelson and Goldman (*loc. cit.*) is instead *C. c. angusticeps*, *fide* Robert J. Russell.)

Cratogeomys castanops peridoneus Nelson and Goldman

1934. *Cratogeomys castanops peridoneus* Nelson and Goldman, Proc. Biol. Soc. Washington, 47:148, June 13, type from Río Verde, 3000 ft., San Luis Potosí. Known only from the type locality.

Cratogeomys castanops perplanus Nelson and Goldman

1934. *Cratogeomys castanops perplanus* Nelson and Goldman, Proc. Biol. Soc. Washington, 47:137, June 13, type from Tascosa, 3000 ft., Oldham Co., Texas.

MARGINAL RECORDS (Nelson and Goldman, 1934:137, unless otherwise noted).—Texas: type locality; Washburn (Blair, 1954b:246); Hale Center; Big Spring; Stanton. New Mexico: Cuervo.

Cratogeomys castanops planifrons Nelson and Goldman

1934. *Cratogeomys castanops planifrons* Nelson and Goldman, Proc. Biol. Soc. Washington, 47:146, June 13, type from Miquihuana, 5000 ft., Tamaulipas.

MARGINAL RECORDS.—Coahuila: 4 mi. S, 6 mi. E Saltillo, 4500 ft. (35777 KU); 2 mi. E, 2 mi. N San Antonio de las Alazanas, 8700 ft. (35782 KU). Tamaulipas: 4 mi. N Amave (55605 KU); type locality. Coahuila: 12 mi. S, 2 mi. E Arteaga, 7500 ft. (33123 KU).

Cratogeomys castanops rubellus Nelson and Goldman

1934. *Cratogeomys castanops rubellus* Nelson and Goldman, Proc. Biol. Soc. Washington, 47:147, June 13, type from Soledad, 6400 ft., near city of San Luis Potosí, San Luis Potosí.

MARGINAL RECORDS.—San Luis Potosí (Dalquest, 1953b:102): Matehuala; Presa de Guadalupe; type locality.

Cratogeomys castanops subnubilus Nelson and Goldman

1934. *Cratogeomys castanops subnubilus* Nelson and Goldman, Proc. Biol. Soc. Washington, 47:145, June 13, type from Carneros, 6800 ft., Coahuila.

MARGINAL RECORDS.—Coahuila: 1 mi. N Agua Nueva, 5500 ft. (33127 KU); 2 mi. W San Miguel, 5500 ft. (33134 KU); La Ventura (Nelson and Goldman, 1934:146); Domingo Cañon, Sierra Guadalupe, 6700 ft., 11 mi. S, 4 mi. W General Cepeda (55587 KU).

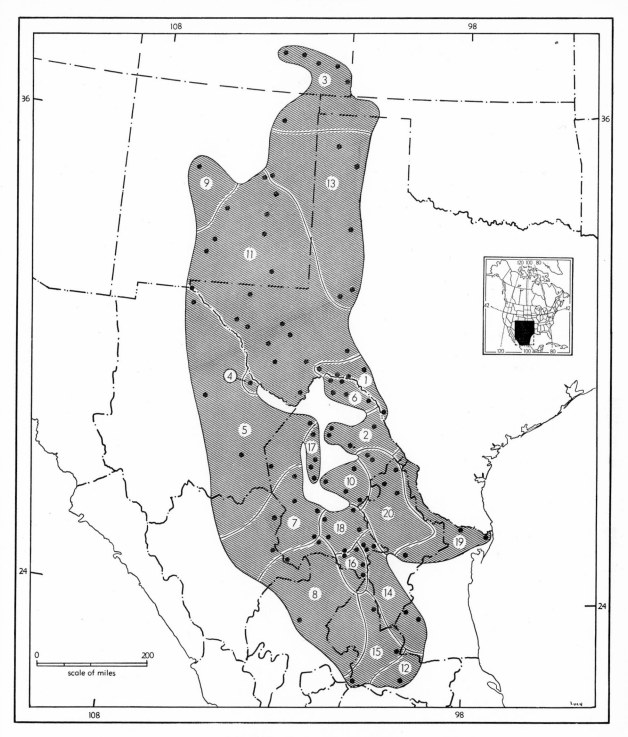

Map 282. *Cratogeomys castanops.*

1. *C. c. angusticeps*
2. *C. c. bullatus*
3. *C. c. castanops*
4. *C. c. clarkii*
5. *C. c. consitus*

6. *C. c. convexus*
7. *C. c. excelsus*
8. *C. c. goldmani*
9. *C. c. hirtus*
10. *C. c. jucundus*

11. *C. c. lacrimalis*
12. *C. c. peridoneus*
13. *C. c. perplanus*
14. *C. c. planifrons*
15. *C. c. rubellus*

16. *C. c. subnubilus*
17. *C. c. sordidulus*
18. *C. c. subsimus*
19. *C. c. tamaulipensis*
20. *C. c. ustulatus*

Cratogeomys castanops sordidulus Russell and Baker

1955. *Cratogeomys castanops sordidulus* Russell and Baker, Univ. Kansas Publ., Mus. Nat. Hist., 7:600, March 15, type from 1½ mi. NW Ocampo, 3300 ft., Coahuila.

MARGINAL RECORDS.—Coahuila: 50 mi. N, 20 mi. W Ocampo, 4150 ft. (48503 KU); 18 mi. S, 14 mi. E Tanque Alvarez, 4000 ft. (48504 KU); 5 mi. N, 19 mi. W Cuatro Ciénegas, 3250 ft. (48512 KU); type locality.

Cratogeomys castanops subsimus Nelson and Goldman

1934. *Cratogeomys castanops subsimus* Nelson and Goldman, Proc. Biol. Soc. Washington, 47:144, June 13, type from Jaral, Coahuila.

MARGINAL RECORDS.—Coahuila: 3 mi. S, 3 mi. E Muralla, 3800 ft. (48513 KU); 2 mi. N Santa Cruz (48517 KU); *17 mi. N, 8 mi. W Saltillo, 5200 ft.* (35756 KU); 10 mi. S, 5 mi. W General Cepeda, 6500 ft. (55586 KU); 12 mi. N, 10 mi. E Parras, 5000 ft. (34937 KU); 21 mi. S, 11 mi. E Australia, 4400 ft. (48716 KU).

Cratogeomys castanops tamaulipensis Nelson and Goldman

1934. *Cratogeomys castanops tamaulipensis* Nelson and Goldman, Proc. Biol. Soc. Washington, 47:141, June 13, type from Matamoros, Tamaulipas.

MARGINAL RECORDS (Nelson and Goldman, 1934: 142).—Tamaulipas: 3 mi. SE Reynosa (58118 KU); type locality. Nuevo León: Montemorelos.

Cratogeomys castanops ustulatus Russell and Baker

1955. *Cratogeomys castanops ustulatus* Russell and Baker, Univ. Kansas Publ., Mus. Nat. Hist., 7:598, March 15, type from Don Martín, 800 ft., Coahuila.

MARGINAL RECORDS.—Coahuila: type locality; 5 mi. SE Don Martín (44308 KU). Nuevo León: 4 mi. N, 1 mi. W Anahuac [= Rodrígues] (56609 KU); Vallecillo, 20 mi. S Río Salado, 100 ft. (55593 KU); 3 mi. N Lampazos (55588 KU).

Cratogeomys perotensis
Perote Pocket Gopher

External measurements: in males, 315–322, 82–94, 40–43; in female, 277, 75, 37. Near Sayal Brown, everywhere finely mixed with black-tipped hairs. Cranial characters on specific level have not been determined.

Cratogeomys perotensis estor Merriam

1895. *Cratogeomys estor* Merriam, N. Amer. Fauna, 8:155, January 31, type from Las Vigas, 8000 ft., Veracruz.
1934. *Cratogeomys perotensis estor*, Nelson and Goldman, Proc. Biol. Soc. Washington, 47:151, June 13.

MARGINAL RECORDS.—Veracruz: 7 km. SE Jalacingo, 8000 ft. (19328 KU); 5 km. E Las Vigas, 8000 ft. (Davis, 1944:388); 2 km. S Sierra de Agua, 8300 ft. (19350 KU).

Cratogeomys perotensis peraltus Goldman

1937. *Cratogeomys perotensis peraltus* Goldman, Jour. Washington Acad. Sci., 27:403, September 15, type from near timber-line, approximately 12,500 ft., Mt. Orizaba, Veracruz. Known only from the type locality.

Cratogeomys perotensis perotensis Merriam

1895. *Cratogeomys perotensis* Merriam, N. Amer. Fauna, 8:154, January 31, type from Cofre de Perote, 9500 ft., Veracruz.

MARGINAL RECORDS.—Veracruz: N slope Cofre de Perote, 10,500 ft. (Davis, 1944:387); *1 km. NW Pescados, 10,500 ft.* (19332 KU).

Cratogeomys fulvescens
Fulvous Pocket Gopher

External measurements: in males, 318–327, 102–105, 43–44; in females, 302–304, 97, 40–41. Yel-

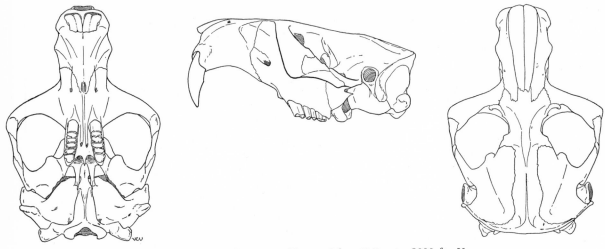

Fig. 271. *Cratogeomys fulvesceus subluteus,* 2 km. E Perote, 8300 ft., Veracruz, No. 19344 K.U., ♂, X 1.

lowish brown. Cranial characters on specific level have not yet been determined.

Cratogeomys fulvescens fulvescens Merriam

1895. *Cratogeomys fulvescens* Merriam, N. Amer. Fauna, 8:161, January 31, type from Chalchicomula, 8200 ft., Puebla. Known only from the type locality.

Cratogeomys fulvescens subluteus Nelson and Goldman

1934. *Cratogeomys fulvescens subluteus* Nelson and Goldman, Proc. Biol. Soc. Washington, 47:152, June 13, type from Perote, 7800 ft., Veracruz.

MARGINAL RECORDS.—Veracruz: 2 km. N Perote, 8000 ft. (30029 KU); 2 km. E Perote, 8300 ft. (19349 KU); 3 km. W Limón, 7500 ft. (19353 KU).

merriami-group
Cratogeomys merriami
Merriam's Pocket Gopher

External measurements: in males, 327–338, 89–95, 46–48; in females, 285–318, 84–102, 42–48. Dull chestnut brown or slate-black. Cranial characters on a specific level have not been determined.

Cratogeomys merriami merriami (Thomas)

1893. *Geomys merriami* Thomas, Ann. Mag. Hist., ser. 6, 12:271, October, type from southern México, probably in the Valley of México.
1895. *Cratogeomys merriami merriami*, Merriam, N. Amer. Fauna, 8:152, January 31.
1895. *Cratogeomys oreocetes*, Merriam, N. Amer. Fauna, 8:156, January 31, type from Mt. Popocatépetl, 11,000 ft., México. Regarded as inseparable from *C. m. merriami* by Davis, Jour. Mamm., 25:386, December 12, 1944.
1895. *Cratogeomys peregrinus* Merriam, N. Amer. Fauna, 8:158, January 31, type from Mt. Iztaccihuatl, 11,000 ft., México. Regarded as inseparable from *C. m. merriami* by Davis, Jour. Mamm., 25:386, December 12, 1944.

MARGINAL RECORDS.—Distrito Federal: Ixtapalapa (Villa, 1953:392). México: Monte Río Frío, 45 km. ESE Mexico City, 10,500 ft. (Davis, 1944:386); N slope Mt. Popocatépetl, 13,500 ft. (*ibid.*). Morelos: 1½ mi. S Huitzilac (Davis and Russell, 1954:73). México: Lerma (Merriam, 1895a:153).

Cratogeomys merriami saccharalis Nelson and Goldman

1934. *Cratogeomys merriami saccharalis* Nelson and Goldman, Proc. Biol. Soc. Washington, 47:149, June 13, type from Atlixco, 5400 ft., Puebla, México. Known only from the type locality.

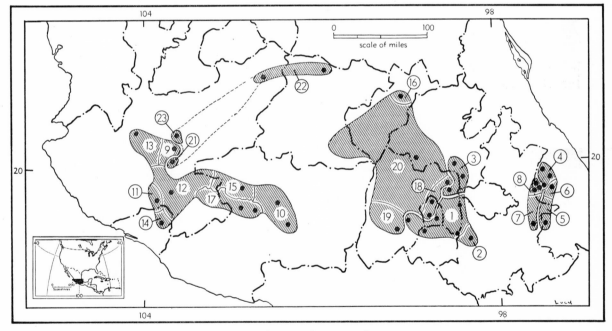

Map 283. Several nominal species of *Cratogeomys*.

Guide to kinds
1. *C. merriami merriami*
2. *C. merriami saccharalis*
3. *C. irolonis*
4. *C. perotensis estor*
5. *C. perotensis peraltus*
6. *C. perotensis perotensis*
7. *C. fulvescens fulvescens*
8. *C. fulvescens subluteus*
9. *C. gymnurus atratus*
10. *C. gymnurus imparilis*
11. *C. gymnurus inclarus*
12. *C. gymnurus gymnurus*
13. *C. gymnurus tellus*
14. *C. fumosus*
15. *C. angustirostris*
16. *C. neglectus*
17. *C. varius*
18. *C. tylorhinus arvalis*
19. *C. tylorhinus planiceps*
20. *C. tylorhinus tylorhinus*
21. *C. zinseri morulus*
22. *C. zinseri zinseri*
23. *C. zinseri zodius*

Cratogeomys irolonis Nelson and Goldman
Iriolonian Pocket Gopher

1934. *Cratogeomys merriami irolonis* Nelson and Goldman, Proc. Biol. Soc. Washington, 47:150, June 13, type from Irolo, 7600 ft., Hidalgo.
1944. *Cratogeomys irolonis,* Davis, Jour. Mamm., 25:387, December 12.

External measurements of females, 318–333, 88–95, 42–43; males probably larger. Rufescent. Resembles *C. m. merriami* but richer (more rufescent) in buffy phase; skull shorter and relatively broader; width of upper incisors 4 instead of 5 mm.; dihedral angle of maxillary plate less than 160° instead of more than 170°; auditory bullae without, instead of with, distinct swelling immediately below glenoid fossa; foramen magnum wider than high instead of reverse; basioccipital distinctly wedge-shaped instead of nearly parallel-sided; hind foot less than 44 (for additional differences see Davis, 1944:387).

MARGINAL RECORDS.—Hidalgo: 9 km. S Pachuca (Villa, 1953:396); type locality. México: 5 km. NW Texcoco, 7600 ft. (Davis, 1944:387); 1½ km. S Tepexpan (Villa, 1953:396).

zinseri-group
Cratogeomys zinseri
Zinser's Pocket Gopher

External measurements: in males, 318–358, 89–115, 41–49; in females, 292–338, 81–106, 39–45. Upper parts dark brown to blackish, but cinnamon on sides. Resembles *C. tylorhinus* but larger, less rufescent, and with more widely spreading zygomata.

Cratogeomys zinseri morulus Russell

1953. *Cratogeomys zinseri morulus* Russell, Univ. Kansas Publ., Mus. Nat. Hist., 5:541, October 15, type from N end Lago Sayula, 4400 ft., 9 mi. N, 2 mi. E Atoyac, Jalisco. Known only from the type locality.

Cratogeomys zinseri zinseri (Goldman)

1939. *Platygeomys zinseri* Goldman, Jour. Mamm., 20:91, February 15, type from Lagos, 6150 ft., Jalisco.
1948. *Cratogeomys zinseri,* Hooper, Jour. Mamm., 29:303, August 31.

MARGINAL RECORDS.—Guanajuato: San Diego de la Unión (Goldman, 1939:92). Jalisco: type locality.

Cratogeomys zinseri zodius Russell

1953. *Cratogeomys zinseri zodius* Russell, Univ. Kansas Publ., Mus. Nat. Hist., 5:540, October 15, type from 13 mi. S, 15 mi. W Guadalajara, Jalisco. Known only from the type locality.

Cratogeomys varius (Goldman)
Uruapan Pocket Gopher

1939. *Platygeomys varius* Goldman, Jour. Mamm., 20:90, February 15, type from Uruapan, 6000 ft., Michoacán.
1948. *Cratogeomys varius,* Hooper, Jour. Mamm., 29:303, August 31.

External measurements of male type: 305, 94, 44. Resembles *C. angustirostris* but Mikado Brown above instead of between cinnamon and orange-cinnamon, smaller, and with relatively narrower braincase.

MARGINAL RECORDS.—Michoacán: 1 mi. S Corupo, approximately 6500 ft. (Hooper, 1947:46); type locality.

Cratogeomys tylorhinus
Taylor's Pocket Gopher

External measurements: in males, 321–372, 87–121, 37–46; in females, 288–337, 76–100, 37–43. Mikado brown. Cranial characters on specific level have not yet been satisfactorily determined.

Cratogeomys tylorhinus arvalis Hooper

1947. *Cratogeomys tylorhinus arvalis* Hooper, Jour. Mamm., 28:45, February 17, type from Colonia de Valle, 2275 m., Distrito Federal.

MARGINAL RECORDS.—México: 1½ km. S Tepexpan (Villa, 1953:394). Distrito Federal: Coyoacán, 2350 m. (Hooper, 1947:46); type locality.

Cratogeomys tylorhinus planiceps (Merriam)

1895. *Platygeomys planiceps* Merriam, N. Amer. Fauna, 8:168, January 31, type from north slope Volcán de Toluca, State of México. Known only from the type locality.
1947. *C[ratogeomys]. t[ylorhinus]. planiceps,* Hooper, Jour. Mamm., 28:46, February 17.

Cratogeomys tylorhinus tylorhinus (Merriam)

1895. *Platygeomys tylorhinus* Merriam, N. Amer. Fauna, 8:167, January 31, type from Tula, Hidalgo.
1947. *C[ratogeomys]. t[ylorhinus]. tylorhinus,* Hooper, Jour. Mamm., 28:46, February 17.

MARGINAL RECORDS.—Hidalgo: Marqués, 8000 ft. (Goldman, 1939:91); *type locality.*

Cratogeomys neglectus (Merriam)
Querétaro Pocket Gopher

1902. *Platygeomys neglectus* Merriam, Proc. Biol. Soc. Washington, 15:68, March 22, type from Cerro de la Calentura, 9000 ft., approximately 8 mi. NW Pinal de Amoles, Querétaro. Known only from the type locality.
1948. *Cratogeomys neglectus,* Hooper, Jour. Mamm., 29:303, August 31.

External measurements of the holotype, said to be an adult male: 310, 96, 42. Resembles *C. t. planiceps* but paler (less chestnut) and smaller; frontal flattened (not channeled) between orbits; zygomatic arches parallel instead of strongly divergent anteriorly.

Cratogeomys angustirostris (Merriam)
Narrow-faced Pocket Gopher

1903. *Platygeomys tylorhinus angustirostris* Merriam, Proc. Biol. Soc. Washington, 16:81, May 29, type from Patambán, Michoacán. Known only from the type locality.
1948. *Cratogeomys angustirostris,* Hooper, Jour. Mamm., 29:303, August 31.

External measurements not published. Brown. Resembles *C. t. tylorhinus* but paler and smaller. Basal length 53.5 and zygomatic breadth anteriorly 38 in holotype. Characterized by original describer as an adult female.

Cratogeomys fumosus (Merriam)
Smoky Pocket Gopher

1892. *Geomys fumosus* Merriam, Proc. Biol. Soc. Washington, 7:165, September 29, type from 3 mi. W Colima City, Colima. Known only from the type locality.
1948. *Cratogeomys fumosus,* Hooper, Jour. Mamm., 29:302, August 31.

External measurements: in males (av. of 7), 288, 82, 42; in females (av. of 3), 277, 75, 40. Slate black. Zygomata bowed out, widest across middle.

gymnurus—group
Cratogeomys gymnurus
Llano Pocket Gopher

External measurements: in males, 344–370, 87–108, 50–53; in females, 299–341, 78–95, 40–50. Reddish brown or black. Posterior part of cranium broad and flat in this and in succeeding species of the genus. This species and the six preceding species

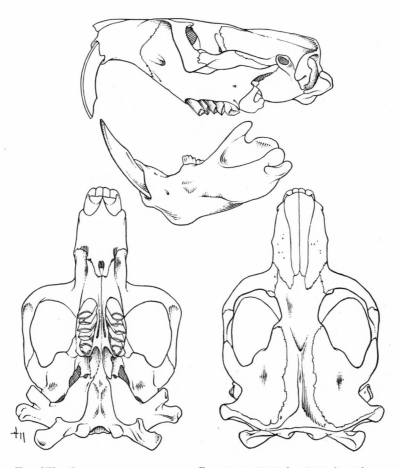

Fig. 272. *Cratogeomys gymnurus tellus,* 3 mi. W Tala, 4300 ft., Jalisco, No. 33454 K.U., holotype, ♀, X 1.

of *Cratogeomys* have much flattened skulls, and until 1946 were placed by most authors in the genus *Platygeomys*, which is now regarded as a synonym of *Cratogeomys*.

Cratogeomys gymnurus atratus Russell

1953. *Cratogeomys gymnurus atratus* Russell, Univ. Kansas Publ., Mus. Nat. Hist., 5:539, October 15, type from top of Cerro Viejo de Cuyutlán, 9700 ft., 19 mi. S, 9 mi. W Guadalajara, Jalisco. Known only from the type locality.

Cratogeomys gymnurus imparilis (Goldman)

1939. *Platygeomys gymnurus imparilis* Goldman, Jour. Mamm., 20:89, February 15, type from Pátzcuaro, 7000 ft., Michoacán.
1948. *Cratogeomys gymnurus imparilis,* Hooper, Jour. Mamm., 29:302, August 31.
MARGINAL RECORDS.—Michoacán: 2 mi. W Pátzcuaro, 7700 ft. (Hall and Villa, 1949:452); *type locality*; 1¾ mi. S Tacámbaro, 5700 ft. (Hall and Villa, 1949:452).

Cratogeomys gymnurus inclarus (Goldman)

1939. *Platygeomys gymnurus inclarus* Goldman, Jour. Mamm., 20:88, February 15, type from N slope Sierra Nevada de Colima, 10,000 ft., Jalisco.
1948. *Cratogeomys gymnurus inclarus,* Hooper, Jour., Mamm., 29:302, August 31.
MARGINAL RECORDS.—Jalisco: type locality; *N slope Sierra de Colima, 6500 ft.* (Goldman, 1939:87).

Cratogeomys gymnurus gymnurus (Merriam)

1892. *Geomys gymnurus* Merriam, Proc. Biol. Soc. Washington, 7:166, September 29, type from Zapotlán, Jalisco. Known only from the type locality.
1947. C[*ratogeomys*]. *gymnurus,* Hooper, Jour. Mamm., 28:46, February 17.

Cratogeomys gymnurus tellus Russell

1953. *Cratogeomys gymnurus tellus* Russell, Univ. Kansas Publ., Mus. Nat. Hist., 5:537, October 15, type from 3 mi. W Tala, 4300 ft., Jalisco.
MARGINAL RECORDS.—Jalisco (Russell, 1953:538): *1 mi. S El Refugio; 1 mi. NE Tala*; type locality.

FAMILY HETEROMYIDAE—Heteromyids

Skull thin, papery, and not strongly modified for fossorial existence; interorbital breadth greater than rostral breadth; nasals produced distally beyond incisors; zygomata slender and threadlike; interparietal reduced; tympanic bullae much inflated, the genera *Microdipodops* and *Dipodomys* constituting the extreme in this respect among American mammals; mastoids inflated and forming part of dorsal surface of skull; occipitals reduced; jaw small and weak; cheek-teeth rooted except in *Dipodomys*, and markedly simplified; molars quadritubercular; incisors thin and compressed.

In spite of the many obvious superficial differences, heteromyids and geomyids are closely related as shown by Hill (1937). This relationship can be shown taxonomically by arranging them as subfamilies of the family Heteromyidae or by according each of them family rank and uniting them under one superfamily name. Both arrangements are in current use, the latter being perhaps the commoner.

There is considerable external variation within the heteromyids, some genera being somewhat murine in appearance (*Liomys* and *Heteromys*) whereas others are highly modified for a saltatorial mode of locomotion (*Dipodomys*). In the last-named genus, the hind limbs are long and powerful and the forelegs reduced.

Geological time range is Oligocene to Recent.

Most heteromyids live in dry, open plains and deserts. Food consists mainly of seeds but some green vegetation is utilized. Most species require little free water and some, none. Heteromyids are nocturnal, dig their own burrows, and many species plug the burrow entrances with moist soil at dawn in order to provide temperature-constant diurnal retreats to their liking.

KEY TO SUBFAMILIES AND GENERA OF HETEROMYIDAE

1. In lower premolars, lophs uniting first at labial side, next at lingual; those of uppers uniting first lingually, then labially; lophs of upper molars, and usually lower molars, uniting at two ends and surrounding a central basin; auditory bullae not inflated. . . . . Heteromyinae, p. 535
   2. Adult pattern of cheek-teeth simplified; enamel islands disappearing with wear; posterior loop in crown of P4 without deep re-entrant anterior fold. . . . . *Liomys*, p. 535
   2'. Adult pattern of cheek-teeth not simplified; enamel islands persisting; posterior loop in crown of P4 with deep re-entrant anterior fold. . . . . *Heteromys*, p. 542
1'. In lower premolars, lophs uniting at center of tooth; those of upper premolars uniting near center of tooth; those of upper molars uniting from lingual toward labial side; those of lower molars uniting primitively from labial edge toward center; pattern lost early in life; auditory bullae well inflated to excessively so.
   3. Cheek-teeth not ever growing, crown pattern not completely simplified in adult; anterior root of zygomatic arch not greatly enlarged. . . . . Perognathinae, p. 473
     4. Mastoids and auditory bullae not greatly inflated; hind foot and hind leg not markedly enlarged.
       Perognathus, p. 473

4'. Mastoids and auditory bullae greatly enlarged; hind foot and hind leg much enlarged for saltatorial locomotion. . . . . *Microdipodops*, p. 508

3'. Cheek-teeth persistently growing, crown pattern markedly simplified in adult; anterior root of zygomatic arch much enlarged; auditory bullae greatly enlarged. . . . . Dipodomyinae, p. 511
Dipodomys, p. 511

Subfamily PEROGNATHINAE

Lophs of upper premolars unite first at or near center of tooth; protoloph usually single-cusped; lophs of upper molars unite progressively from lingual to buccal margins; those of lower premolars unite at center of tooth, giving an x-pattern; lophs of lower molars unite primitively at buccal margin, progressively at center of tooth, forming an H-pattern; cheek-teeth brachydont to hypsodont but always rooted; enamel pattern lost early in life; enamel always complete; $M\frac{3}{3}$ progressively reduced in later kinds; upper incisor smooth or grooved; center of palate between premolars not ridged; ethmoid foramen in frontal; auditory region variable as to degree of inflation; ventral surface of tympanic bullae below level of grinding surface of upper cheek-teeth; no median ventral foramina in caudal vertebrae; astragalus articulating with cuboid (after Wood, 1935:88–89).

Genus Perognathus Wied-Neuwied—Pocket Mice

Revised by Merriam, N. Amer. Fauna, 1:vii + 36 pp., 4 pls., October 25, 1889, and Osgood, N. Amer. Fauna, 18:1–72, 4 pls., 15 figs., September 20, 1900.

1839. *Perognathus* Wied-Neuwied, Nova Acta Phys.-Med. Acad. Caes. Leop.-Carol., 19(pt. 1):368. Type, *Perognathus fasciatus* Wied-Neuwied.
1848. *Cricetodipus* Peale, Mammalia and ornithology, *in* U.S. Explor. Exped. . . . , 8:52. Type, *Cricetodipus parvus* Peale.
1868. *Abromys* Gray, Proc. Zool. Soc. London, May, p. 202. Type, *Abromys lordi* Gray.
1875. *Otognosis* Coues, Proc. Acad. Nat. Sci. Philadelphia, p. 305. Type, *Otognosis longimembris* Coues.

External measurements: 100–230; 44–143; 15–29. Small, slender; posterior limbs appreciably longer than anterior; skull delicate and somewhat flattened; mastoids large; auditory bullae large and well inflated; frontals little constricted; rostrum lightly constricted; nasals long and becoming semi-tubular anteriorly; infraorbital foramen reduced to a lateral opening in maxillae. Molars rooted and tuberculate; upper incisors strongly grooved. Dentition, i. $\frac{1}{1}$, c. $\frac{0}{0}$, p. $\frac{1}{1}$, m. $\frac{3}{3}$

The genus *Perognathus* includes widely different species, which might be placed in different genera were it not for the many structurally intermediate species.

Most pocket mice live in arid to semi-arid situations. They are burrowing animals. So far as known they do not hibernate, but do remain in their burrows during periods of inclement (cold or wet) weather. Food consists mostly of seeds and is supplemented in some species on occasion by bits of green vegetation and small amounts of animal matter. Pocket mice are inveterate harvesters of food, which is then stored in special chambers in the burrow. Each cache may contain from a teaspoonful to a cupful of seeds. Pocket mice probably seldom drink water. Indeed, many individuals undoubtedly never see water in their entire life. Some water is obtained in the food eaten—even comparatively dry food—and still more (metabolic water) is manufactured by body processes. In captivity most species are quite tractable and thrive on a diet of commercial bird seed.

The life span in nature is short, less than 2 months as an average, principally because of predation. In captivity, they sometimes live more than 6 years. Except during the breeding season, pocket mice are solitary. In captivity they are best kept separate, although intraspecific antipathy varies markedly according to species.

Key to Subgenera of Perognathus

1. Pelage soft; soles of hind feet somewhat hairy; mastoids greatly developed, projecting beyond occipital plane; breadth of interparietal less than breadth of interorbital region (rarely equal in *P. longimembris*); audital bullae meeting or nearly so anteriorly.
Perognathus, p. 473

1'. Pelage harsh, sometimes with spiny bristles; soles of hind feet naked; mastoids relatively small, not projecting beyond occipital plane; breadth of interparietal equal to or greater than breadth of interorbital region; audital bullae separated by almost entire width of basisphenoid. . . . . . *Chaetodipus*, p. 492

Subgenus Perognathus Wied-Neuwied

1839. *Perognathus* Wied-Neuwied, Nova Acta Phys.-Med. Acad. Caes. Leop.-Carol., 19(pt. 1):368. Type, *Perognathus fasciatus* Wied-Neuwied.

External measurements: 110–211; 44–118; 15–27. The pelage throughout soft, no spines or bristles.

Soles of hind feet more or less hairy (except in *formosus*). Mastoids greatly developed, projecting beyond plane of occiput; mastoid side of parietal longest. Breadth of interparietal (except rarely) less than breadth of interorbital region. Audital bullae meeting, or almost so, anteriorly. Supra-

occipital without lateral indentations by mastoids (except in *formosus*); ascending branches of supra-occipital slender and threadlike.

Most species of this subgenus live in Sonoran deserts and chaparral and in warmer parts of the pine belts.

KEY TO NOMINAL SPECIES OF SUBGENUS PEROGNATHUS

1. Hind foot more than 20; antitragus lobed; occipitonasal length more than 24.
    2. Ears clothed with white hairs; tail pale.
        3. Dorsal color dark, black predominating. . . . . *P. alticola*, p. 490
        3'. Dorsal color ochraceous buff. . . . . *P. xanthonotus*, p. 491
    2'. Ears not clothed with white hairs; tail dark.
        4. Tail neither crested nor markedly tufted; olivaceous lateral line present; supraoccipital without lateral indentations by mastoid. . . . . *P. parvus*, p. 488
        4'. Tail crested and tufted; olivaceous lateral line absent; supraoccipital with lateral indentations by mastoid. . . . . *P. formosus*, p. 491
1'. Hind foot less than 20 (rarely more in *amplus* and *apache*); antitragus not lobed; occipitonasal length usually more than 24.
    5. Lower premolar distinctly larger than last molar.
        6. Occurs in San Joaquin Valley, California; mastoidal bullae relatively large. . . *P. inornatus*, p. 478
        6.' Not occurring in San Joaquin Valley, California; mastoidal bullae moderate. *P. longimembris*, p. 483
    5'. Lower premolar equal to or smaller than last molar (in some subspecies barely larger).
        7. Total length more than 130 (tail of *P. amplus* rarely less than 130).
            8. Upper parts pinkish buff to ochraceous salmon; tail more than 70% of head-body. *P. amplus*, p. 486
            8'. Upper parts buffy to ochraceous; tail less than 70% of head-body.
                9. Tail 60 or more; hind foot 17 or more; angular process of mandible short and upturned. *P. apache*, p. 481
                9'. Tail less than 60; hind foot less than 17; angular process of mandible long and widespread. . . . . *P. fasciatus*, p. 474
        7'. Total length less than 130.
            10. Tail 57 or more.
                11. Interparietal breadth less than 4.0; dorsal coloration fulvous; occurring south of Colorado (tail of *P. flavus* rarely more than 57). . . . . *P. merriami*, p. 477
                11'. Interparietal breadth more than 4.0; dorsal coloration not fulvous; occurring in Colorado and north and east thereof.
                    12. Lower premolar distinctly smaller than last molar; dorsal coloration buffy, often strongly overlaid with black hairs. . . . . *P. flavescens*, p. 476
                    12'. Lower premolar equal to or but slightly smaller than last molar; dorsal coloration strongly olivaceous. . . . . *P. fasciatus*, p. 474
            10'. Tail 56 or less.
                13. Interparietal less than 4.0 wide; mastoidal breadth more than 80% of basilar length; dorsal coloration yellowish or buffy with large yellow postauricular patches. *P. flavus*, p. 478
                13'. Interparietal more than 4.0 wide; mastoidal breadth less than 80% of basilar length; dorsal coloration olive gray with yellowish spots on ears. . . . . *P. flavescens*, p. 476

fasciatus-group
Perognathus fasciatus
Olive-backed Pocket Mouse

Subspecies reviewed by Jones, Univ. Kansas Publ., Mus. Nat. Hist., 5:515–526, 7 figs. in text, August 1, 1953.

External measurements: 128–135; 59–64; 16–18. Upper parts grayish- or buffy-olivaceous with black hairs intermingled; sides with bright, buffy lateral line; underparts white to buff depending on subspecies. Buffy postauricular spot present. Skull

small with vaulted braincase; interparietal variable in shape, but usually approximately pentagonal and of moderate width; mastoids well developed and slightly projecting; audital bullae barely meeting anteriorly; coronoid processes of mandible long and slender; lower premolar subequal to last molar or slightly smaller.

The olive-backed pocket mouse lives on the high plains, usually in sandy soils. Four to 6 young are born after a gestation period of approximately 4 weeks, usually once a year.

Perognathus fasciatus callistus Osgood

1900. *Perognathus callistus* Osgood, N. Amer. Fauna, 18:28, September 20, type from Kinney Ranch, near Bitter Creek, Sweetwater Co., Wyoming.
1953. *Perognathus fasciatus callistus,* Jones, Univ. Kansas Publ., Mus. Nat. Hist., 5:524, August 1.

MARGINAL RECORDS.—Wyoming: 27 mi. N, 37 mi. E Rock Springs, 6700 ft. (Jones, 1953:525). Colorado: Sunny Peak (Cary, 1911:148); near Snake River, 7 mi. above junction with Bear (Warren, 1942:176). Utah: 15 mi. N Bonanza (Hayward and Killpack, 1956:451); Bridgeport, (*ibid.*). Wyoming: Green River (Osgood, 1900a:28).

Perognathus fasciatus fasciatus Wied-Neuwied

1839. *Perognathus fasciatus* Wied-Neuwied, Nova Acta Phys.-Med. Acad. Caes. Leop.-Carol., 191:369, type from

upper Missouri River near its junction with the Yellowstone, near Buford, Williams Co., North Dakota.

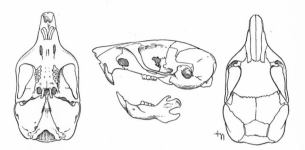

Fig. 273. *Perognathus fasciatus fasciatus,* Buford, North Dakota, No. 168599 U.S.N.M., ♂, X 1½.

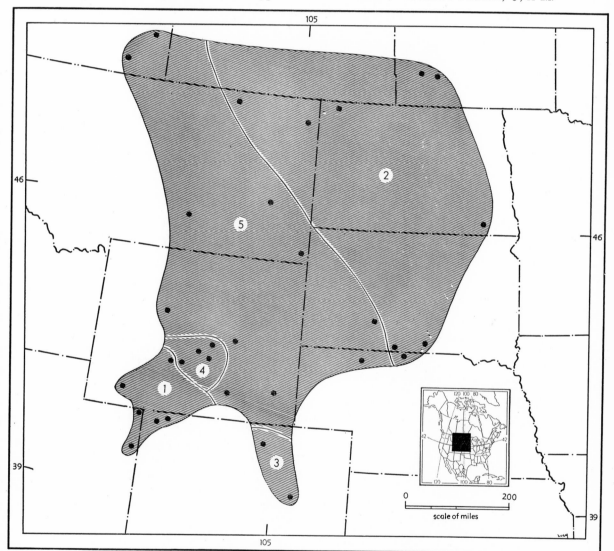

Map 284. *Perognathus fasciatus.*

Guide to subspecies
1. *P. fasciatus callistus*

2. *P. fasciatus fasciatus*
3. *P. fasciatus infraluteus*

4. *P. fasciatus litus*
5. *P. fasciatus olivaceogriseus*

MARGINAL RECORDS (Jones, 1953:519–520, unless otherwise noted).—Manitoba: Oak Lake; Aweme. North Dakota: 7½ mi. E, 1⅛ mi. S Oakes. South Dakota: Colome. Nebraska: Valentine. South Dakota: Rosebud Agency. Montana: Frenchman River (Osgood, 1900a:19); 3 mi. S Medicine Lake. North Dakota: Crosby.

Perognathus fasciatus infraluteus Thomas

1893. *Perognathus infraluteus* Thomas, Ann. Mag. Nat. Hist., ser. 6, 11:406, May, type from Loveland, Larimer Co., Colorado.
1900. *Perognathus fasciatus infraluteus*, Osgood, N. Amer. Fauna, 18:19, September 20.

MARGINAL RECORDS.—Colorado: type locality; 7 mi. N Ramah (Jones, 1953:523).

Perognathus fasciatus litus Cary

1911. *Perognathus fasciatus litus* Cary, Proc. Biol. Soc. Washington, 24:61, March 22, type from Sun, Sweetwater Valley, Natrona Co., Wyoming.

MARGINAL RECORDS.—Wyoming (Jones, 1953:524): 16 mi. S, 11 mi. W Waltman, 6950 ft.; type locality; 27 mi. N Table Rock; Granite Mts.

Perognathus fasciatus olivaceogriseus Swenk

1940. *Perognathus flavescens olivaceogriseus* Swenk, Missouri Valley Fauna, 3:6, June 5, type from Little Bordeaux Creek, sec. 14, T. 33 N, R. 48 W, 3 mi. E Chadron, Dawes Co., Nebraska; see Jones, Univ. Kansas Publ., Mus. Nat. Hist., 5:520–522, August 1, 1953.
1953. *Perognathus fasciatus olivaceogriseus*, Jones, Univ. Kansas Publ., Mus. Nat. Hist., 5:520, August 1.

MARGINAL RECORDS (Jones, 1953:522).—Alberta: Medicine Hat. Montana: 13 mi. E Miles City; Little Missouri River, 8 mi. NE Albion. South Dakota: White River flood plain, 7 mi. S Kadoka. Nebraska: 10 mi. E Gordon. Wyoming: 2½ mi. S Chugwater; Fort Steel; Casper; 40 mi. E Dubois. Montana: Lake Basin. Alberta: Foremost.

Perognathus flavescens
Plains Pocket Mouse

External measurements: 113–130; 47–62; 15–17.3. Upper parts pale grayish buff with wash of dark (sometimes blackish); postauricular spot, lateral line, and eye ring clear buff, principally due to absence of dark wash in these areas; underparts white or nearly so. Skull resembling that of *P. fasciatus* but slightly smaller; interparietal wider; angular process of mandible shorter and wider.

Asdell (1945:231) reports that there are 4 young in a litter.

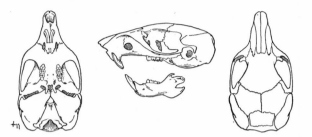

Fig. 274. *Perognathus flavescens flavescens,* Kennedy, Cherry Co., Nebraska, No. 66883, M.V.Z., ♀, X 1½.

Perognathus flavescens cockrumi Hall

1954. *Perognathus flavescens cockrumi* Hall, Univ. Kansas Publ., Mus. Nat. Hist., 7:589, November 15, type from 4½ mi. NE Danville, Harper Co., Kansas.

MARGINAL RECORDS (Hall, 1954:590, unless otherwise noted).—Kansas: ½ mi. S Wilson; Nickerson (Cockrum, 1952:147); type locality. Oklahoma: 6 mi. W, ½ mi. S Canton. Kansas: Cairo.

Perognathus flavescens copei Rhoads

1894. *Perognathus copei* Rhoads, Proc. Acad. Nat. Sci. Philadelphia, for 1893, 46:404, January 27, type from near Mobeetie, Wheeler Co., Texas.
1905. *Perognathus flavescens copei*, V. Bailey, N. Amer. Fauna, 25:143, October 24.

MARGINAL RECORDS.—Oklahoma: 3 mi. N Kenton (Blair, 1939:114). Texas: type locality; 20 mi. N Monahans (V. Bailey, 1905:143).

Perognathus flavescens flavescens Merriam

1889. *Perognathus fasicatus flavescens* Merriam, N. Amer. Fauna, 1:11, October 25, type from Kennedy, Cherry Co., Nebraska.
1900. *Perognathus flavescens*, Osgood, N. Amer. Fauna, 18:20, September 20.

MARGINAL RECORDS.—South Dakota: Rosebud Agency (Osgood, 1900:21). Nebraska: Ewing (Osgood, 1900:21); Neligh (Jones, 1954:483); Adams County (*ibid.*). Kansas (Cockrum, 1952:146): Sand Creek, Cimarron R.; 9 mi. N, 3 mi. E Elkhart. Colorado: Pueblo (Cary, 1911:145); Colorado Springs (Warren, 1942:176); Boulder County (*ibid.*); Greeley (Cary, 1911:145).

Perognathus flavescens perniger Osgood

1904. *Perognathus flavescens perniger* Osgood, Proc. Biol. Soc. Washington, 17:127, June 9, type from Vermillion, Clay Co., South Dakota.

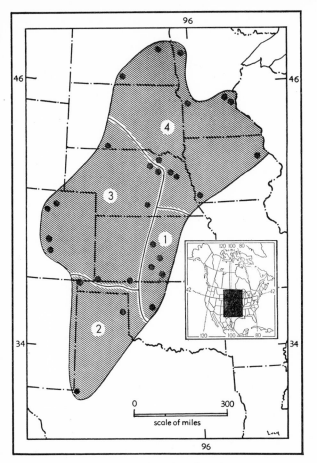

Map 285. *Perognathus flavescens.*

1. *P. f. cockrumi*   3. *P. f. flavescens*
2. *P. f. copei*   4. *P. f. perniger*

MARGINAL RECORDS.—North Dakota: Finley (Fichter, 1939:377). Minnesota (Gunderson and Beer, 1953:95, unless otherwise noted): Polk County; Lac Qui Parle County; near Elk River (B. Bailey, 1929:160); Anoka County. Iowa: Backbone Park, Delaware County (Polder, 1953:723); Randolph (Jones, 1954:483). Nebraska (*ibid.*): Beemer; 1½ mi. S Pilger; Verdigris [= Verdigre]. North Dakota: Parkin [= Bremen] (Fichter, 1939:377).

Perognathus merriami
Merriam's Pocket Mouse

External measurements: 116–122; 57–60; 16–17. Upper parts yellowish- or ochraceous-buff, finely mixed with black; lateral line only faintly expressed; underparts white; postauricular spot clear buff; subauricular spot white; tail buffy above (sometimes dusky) and whitish below. Skull small and comparatively angular; rostrum proportionately broad; zygomatic arches nearly parallel; interparietal relatively wide (compared with, say, that of *P. flavus*).

These delicate little mammals seldom appear in numbers in the collector's trap line, even in areas where they are not uncommon. Most specimens are caught by hand either at night with the aid of a lantern or by frightening them from their burrows in the day. This species occurs most commonly in open, sandy areas, in chaparral, and occasionally in rocky outcroppings or grassy plains. The mice eat seeds and V. Bailey (1905:142) reported that in Texas, juniper berries seemed to be a favored food. Food in limited quantities is stored in the burrows. So far as known, the species does not hibernate; the animals may, however, remain underground when the weather is inclement. Merriam's pocket mice are gentle and are easily maintained in captivity. Little is known of their breeding habits.

Perognathus merriami gilvus Osgood

1900. *Perognathus merriami gilvus* Osgood, N. Amer. Fauna, 18:22, September 20, type from Eddy, near Carlsbad, Eddy Co., New Mexico.

MARGINAL RECORDS.—Texas: Stinnett (Blair, 1954b: 246); Big Springs (V. Bailey, 1905:142); 20 mi. E Rock Springs (*ibid.*); Painted Caves (*ibid.*); N end Mariscal Mtn., 2300 ft. (Borell and Bryant, 1942:23). Coahuila: 2 mi. SSE Castillón (54550 KU). Chihuahua: Casas Grandes Viejo (*ibid.*). New Mexico: 40 mi. W Roswell (V. Bailey, 1932:279); 44 mi. NE Roswell (Borell and Bryant, 1942: 23); about 25 mi. W Tucumcari (V. Bailey, 1932:279).

Perognathus merriami merriami J. A. Allen

1892. *Perognathus merriami* J. A. Allen, Bull. Amer. Mus. Nat. Hist., 4:45, March 25, type from Brownsville, Cameron Co., Texas.
1896. *Perognathus mearnsi* J. A. Allen, Bull. Amer. Mus. Nat. Hist., 8:237, November 21, type from Watson's Ranch, 15 mi. SW San Antonio, Bexar Co., Texas.

MARGINAL RECORDS (Osgood, 1900a:22, unless otherwise noted).—Texas: Wheeler County (Stickel and Stickel, 1948:292); Vernon (Blair, 1954b:246); Ranger (*ibid.*); Austin (V. Bailey, 1905:141); Padre Island (Blair, 1952: 240), thence down coast to Tamaulipas: Altamira; Victoria; Hidalgo. Nuevo León: Linares. Coahuila: 5 mi. N, 2 mi. W Monclova (35794 KU); 11 mi. W Hacienda Miguel (35787 KU); 15 mi. SE Langtry, Texas (Baker, 1956:236). Texas: Comstock (V. Bailey, 1905:141); Kerrville; Mason (V. Bailey, 1905:141); Washburn (*ibid.*).

Fig. 275. *Perognathus merriami merriami*, Benton, Atascosa Co., Texas, No. 4704 K.U., ♂, X 1½.

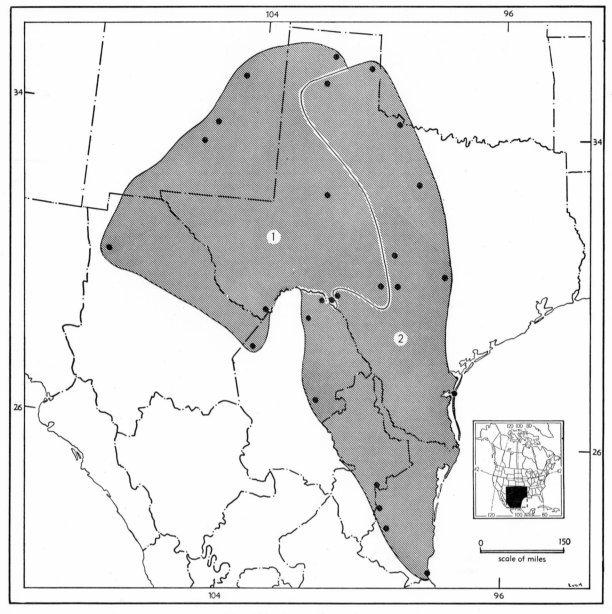

Map 286. *Perognathus merriami.*

1. *Perognathus m. gilvus*   2. *Perognathus m. merriami*

Perognathus flavus
Silky Pocket Mouse

Mexican subspecies reviewed by Baker, Univ. Kansas Publ., Mus. Nat. Hist., 7:339–347, 1 fig. in text, February 15, 1954.

External measurements: 100–119; 44–59; 15–18. Upper parts pale pinkish- or ochraceous-buff, finely lined with black; postauricular patches and ill-defined lateral stripe of buff; underparts white or sometimes with faint tawny suffusion. Skull lightly constructed, comparatively short and broad; auditory bullae well developed; interparietal small and about as long as wide; zygomatic processes of maxillae angular; lower premolar smaller than last molar.

Like *Perognathus merriami*, this beautiful little mammal seldom occurs in a collector's traps in large numbers. Seemingly, it is seldom abundant in nature and is not easily attracted to trap baits.

The diet consists almost exclusively of seeds which usually are shelled and only the inner parts are eaten.

V. Bailey (1932:275) reported that in New Mexico litters contained 2–6 young. In the southern parts of the range of the species, 2 litters a year probably are the rule.

Perognathus flavus bimaculatus Merriam

1889. *Perognathus bimaculatus* Merriam, N. Amer. Fauna, 1:12, October 25, type from Fort Whipple, Yavapai Co., Arizona.
1900. *Perognathus flavus bimaculatus*, Osgood, N. Amer. Fauna, 18:24, September 20.

MARGINAL RECORDS (Hoffmeister, 1956b:57).— Arizona: S rim Grand Canyon (Pasture Wash Ranger Station); near Prescott.

Perognathus flavus bunkeri Cockrum

1951. *Perognathus flavus bunkeri* Cockrum, Univ. Kansas Publ., Mus. Nat. Hist., 5:205, December 15, type from Conard Farm, 1 mi. E Coolidge, Hamilton Co., Kansas. The employment of the name *Perognathus flavus flavus* by Cockrum, Univ. Kansas Publ., Mus. Nat. Hist., 7:148, August 25, 1952, for specimens from Kansas results from the manuscript having been submitted to the printer before the original description was printed.

MARGINAL RECORDS.—Colorado: Loveland (referred to *P.* [*f.*] *flavus* by Osgood, 1900a:24; here referred to *bunkeri* on geographic grounds). Kansas (Cockrum, 1951: 206 (but see under synonymy above): 23 mi. by road NW St. Francis; Vincent Ranch, 4 mi. W, 8 mi. N McAllaster, N fork Smoky River; Wakeeney; Rezeau Ranch, 5 mi. N Belvidere. Oklahoma (*ibid.*): 2 mi. E Eva. Colorado: Salida (Warren, 1942:178; referred by him to *P. flavus* and here referred to subspecies *bunkeri* on geographic grounds).

Perognathus flavus flavus Baird

1855. *Perognatus* [sic] *flavus* Baird, Proc. Acad. Nat. Sci. Philadelphia, 7:332, type from El Paso, El Paso Co., Texas.

MARGINAL RECORDS.—New Mexico: Taos (Osgood, 1900a:24). Oklahoma: 14 mi. S Olustee (Blair, 1939:115). Texas: Alpine (V. Bailey, 1905:140). Chihuahua (Baker, 1954:347): Sierra Almagre, 5300 ft., 12 mi. S Jaco; Escalón, 4200 ft.; 5 mi. E Parral, 5700 ft.; Chihuahua; Gallego. Arizona: near Tumacacori Mission (Burt, 1933:118); Baboquivari Mts. (*ibid.*); SE Pinal County (Hoffmeister, 1956: 56, map, fig. 1); central Graham County (*ibid.*); New Mexico: Zuñi Canyon (Hooper, 1941:27); 1 mi. SE El Rito (7482 KU).

Perognathus flavus fuliginosus Merriam

1890. *Perognathus fuliginosus* Merriam, N. Amer. Fauna, 3:74, September 11, type from cedar belt northeast of San Francisco Mtn., 7000 ft., Coconino Co., Arizona.
1900. *Perognathus flavus fuliginosus*, Osgood, N. Amer. Fauna, 18:25, September 20.

MARGINAL RECORDS (Hoffmeister, 1956b:57–58, unless otherwise noted).—Arizona: Red Horse Wash (Hargrave, 1937:101); Tanner Tank; vicinity of Flagstaff; Bly.

Perognathus flavus goodpasteri Hoffmeister

1956. *Perognathus flavus goodpasteri* Hoffmeister, Proc. Biol. Soc. Washington, 69:55, May 21, type from 2¾ mi. NW Springerville, Apache Co., Arizona.

MARGINAL RECORDS (Hoffmeister, 1956b:57).— Arizona: 3 mi. N Springerville; *type locality*.

Perognathus flavus hopiensis Goldman

1932. *Perognathus flavus hopiensis* Goldman, Proc. Biol. Soc. Washington, 45:89, June 21, type from Oraibi, 6000 ft., Hopi Indian Reservation, Navajo Co., Arizona.

MARGINAL RECORDS.—Colorado: Ashbaugh's Ranch (Goldman, 1932c:90). New Mexico: Fruitland (*ibid.*); Wingate (*ibid.*). Arizona: Holbrook (Osgood, 1900:25); Winslow (*ibid.*); entrance to Wupatki National Monument, along U.S. Highway 89 (Hoffmeister, 1956b:57); SE corner Grand Canyon National Park (*ibid.*). Utah (Durrant, 1952:234): Navajo Mtn. Trading Post, 5 mi. SE Navajo Mtn.; ½ mi. NW Bluff, 4500 ft.

Perognathus flavus medius Baker

1954. *Perognathus flavus medius* Baker, Univ. Kansas Publ., Mus. Nat. Hist., 7:343, February 15, type from 1 mi. S, 6 mi. E Rincón de Romos, 6550 ft., Aguascalientes.

MARGINAL RECORDS (Baker, 1954:344).—Coahuila: 7 mi. S, 4 mi. E Bella Unión, 7200 ft. San Luis Potosí: Jesús María, 6000 ft. Guanajuato: 5 mi. E Celaya, 6000 ft.; 4 mi. N, 5 mi. W León, 7000 ft. Aguascalientes: 3 mi. SW Aguascalientes, 6100 ft. Jalisco: Huejuquilla, 5400 ft. Zacatecas: Valparaiso.

Perognathus flavus mexicanus Merriam

1894. *Perognathus flavus mexicanus* Merriam, Proc. Acad. Nat. Sci. Philadelphia, 46:265, September 27, type from Tlalpan, Distrito Federal, México.

MARGINAL RECORDS (Baker, 1954:343, unless otherwise noted).—Querétaro: 6 mi. E Querétaro, 7400 ft. Hidalgo: Ixmiquilpan, 6000 ft. Veracruz: 2 km. W Perote, 8000 ft. Puebla: 10 km. W San Andrés, 8000 ft.; 7 mi. S, 3 mi. E Puebla, 6850 ft. Morelos: 10 mi. N Cuautla (Davis and Russell, 1954:73).

Perognathus flavus pallescens Baker

1954. *Perognathus flavus pallescens* Baker, Univ. Kansas Publ., Mus. Nat. Hist., 7:345, February 15, type from 1 mi. SW San Pedro de las Colonias, 3700 ft., Coahuila.

MARGINAL RECORDS (Baker, 1954:346).—Coahuila: Cañon del Cochino (35785 KU); ½ mi. E Las Margaritas

(58685 KU); 3 mi. NW Cuatro Ciénegas; La Pastora Rancho, 41 mi. W, 15 mi. N Saltillo; 3 mi. N, 5 mi. W La Rosa; N foot Sierra Guadalupe, 6400 ft., 10 mi. S, 5 mi. W General Cepeda. Durango: 2 mi. N Cuencamé, 5200 ft.; 1 mi. WSW Mapimí, 3800 ft. Coahuila: 3 mi. NE Sierra Mojada, 4100 ft.

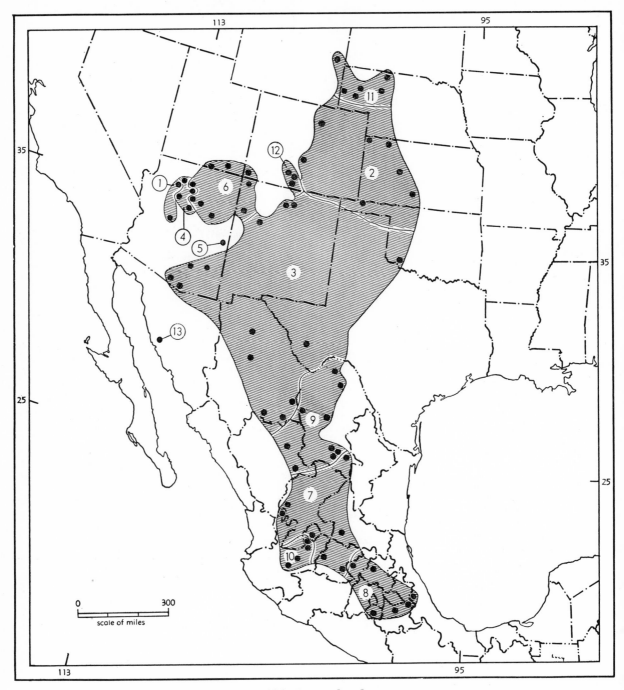

Map 287. *Perognathus flavus.*

Guide
to subspecies
1. *P. flavus bimaculatus*
2. *P. flavus bunkeri*
3. *P. flavus flavus*
4. *P. flavus fuliginosus*
5. *P. flavus goodpasteri*
6. *P. flavus hopiensis*
7. *P. flavus medius*
8. *P. flavus mexicanus*
9. *P. flavus pallescens*
10. *P. flavus parviceps*
11. *P. flavus piperi*
12. *P. flavus sanluisi*
13. *P. flavus sonoriensis*

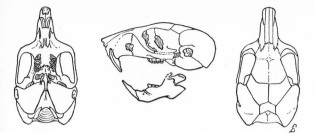

Fig. 276. *Perognathus flavus bunkeri*, 23 mi. (by road) NW St. Francis, Cheyenne Co., Kansas, No. 12092 K.U., ♀, X 1½.

Perognathus flavus parviceps Baker

1954. *Perognathus flavus parviceps* Baker, Univ. Kansas Publ., Mus. Nat. Hist., 7:344, February 15, type from 4 mi. W, 2 mi. S Guadalajara, 5100 ft., Jalisco.

MARGINAL RECORDS (Baker, 1954:345).—Jalisco: 1 mi. NE Villa Hidalgo, 6500 ft.; 3 mi. NW Yahualica; 2 mi. N, ½ mi. W Guadalajara; 21 mi. SW Guadalajara; *4 mi. W Guadalajara*.

Perognathus flavus piperi Goldman

1917. *Perognathus flavus piperi* Goldman, Proc. Biol. Soc. Washington, 30:148, July 27, type from 23 mi. SW Newcastle, Weston Co., Wyoming.

MARGINAL RECORDS (Jones, 1954:484).—Wyoming: type locality. Nebraska: Alliance; Valentine; Kelso; 5 mi. N Bridgeport; 6 mi. N Mitchell.

Perognathus flavus sanluisi Hill

1942. *Perognathus flavus sanluisi* Hill, Amer. Mus. Novit., 1212:1, December 7, type from 9 mi. E Center, Saguache Co. (or 20 mi. NW Alamosa, Alamosa Co.), 7580 ft., Colorado.

MARGINAL RECORDS (Hill, 1942:1).—Colorado: type locality; 3 mi. S Great Sand Dunes National Monument, 24 mi. NE Alamosa; near Fort Garland.

Perognathus flavus sonoriensis Nelson and Goldman

1934. *Perognathus flavus sonoriensis* Nelson and Goldman, Jour. Washington Acad. Sci., 24:267, June 15, type from Costa Rica Ranch, lower Río Sonora, Sonora. Known only from the type locality.

Perognathus apache
Apache Pocket Mouse

External measurements: 130–154; 60–73; 17–21. Upper parts approximating ochraceous buff and varying according to subspecies, finely overlaid with black or blackish hairs; lateral line of clear buffy tone well marked; underparts white; subauricular patch small. Skull short, broad; nasals long; interparietal small, nearly as long as wide; lower premolar smaller than last molar.

This tiny mouse inhabits semi-arid to arid regions and within those regions is usually found in areas with a sparse cover of brush (for example, *Atriplex, Artemisia,* and *Covillea*) or in areas of juniper trees.

Perognathus apache apache Merriam

1889. *Perognathus apache* Merriam, N. Amer. Fauna, 1:14, October 25, type from Keams Canyon, Apache Co., Arizona.

MARGINAL RECORDS (Osgood, 1900a:27, unless otherwise noted).—Utah (Durrant, 1952:237): 1 mi. N Bluff, 4400 ft.; Riverview; Nolands Ranch, N side San Juan River. New Mexico: Chama River near Abiquiu (V. Bailey, 1932:278); Espanola; San Pedro (V. Bailey, 1932:277); Deming; Gallina Mts. (V. Bailey, 1932:277); Fort Wingate. Arizona: Holbrook; Winslow; Walnut [Canyon]. Utah: Navajo Mtn. Trading Post (Durrant, 1952:237).

Perognathus apache caryi Goldman

1918. *Perognathus apache caryi* Goldman, Proc. Biol. Soc. Washington, 31:24, May 16, type from 8 mi. W Rifle, Garfield Co., Colorado.

MARGINAL RECORDS (Durrant, 1952:235, unless otherwise noted).—Utah: Rainbow (Hayward and Killpack, 1956:451). Colorado: type locality; Coventry (Warren, 1942:177). Utah: Johns Canyon, 5150 ft., San Juan River; 2 mi. E Highway 160, 6 mi. S Valley City, 4500 ft.; pump station, 4 mi. N Greenriver, 4100 ft. Browns Corral, 20 mi. S Ouray, 6250 ft.

Perognathus apache cleomophila Goldman

1918. *Perognathus apache cleomophila* Goldman, Proc. Biol. Soc. Washington, 31:23, May 16, type from Winona, 6400 ft., Coconino Co., Arizona. Known only from the type locality.

Perognathus apache gypsi Dice

1929. *Perognathus gypsi* Dice, Occas. Papers Mus. Zool., Univ. Michigan, 203:1, June 19, type from White Sands, 12 mi. SW Alamogordo, Otero Co., New Mexico.
1933. *Perognathus apache gypsi*, Benson, Univ. California Publ. Zool., 40:26, June 13.

MARGINAL RECORDS (Benson, 1933:26).—New Mexico: 14 mi. W Tularosa; 10 mi. SW Tularosa; type locality; 18 mi. SW Alamogordo.

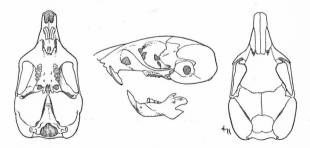

Fig. 277. *Perognathus apache apache*, Wingate, Arizona, No. 137388 U.S.N.M., ♂, X 1½.

Perognathus apache melanotis Osgood

1900. *Perognathus apache melanotis* Osgood, N. Amer. Fauna, 18:27, September 20, type from Casas Grandes, Chihuahua. Known only from the type locality.

Perognathus apache relictus Goldman

1938. *Perognathus apache relictus* Goldman, Jour. Mamm., 19:495, November 14, type from Medano Springs Ranch, 7600 ft., 15 mi. NE Mosca, San Luis Valley, Colorado.

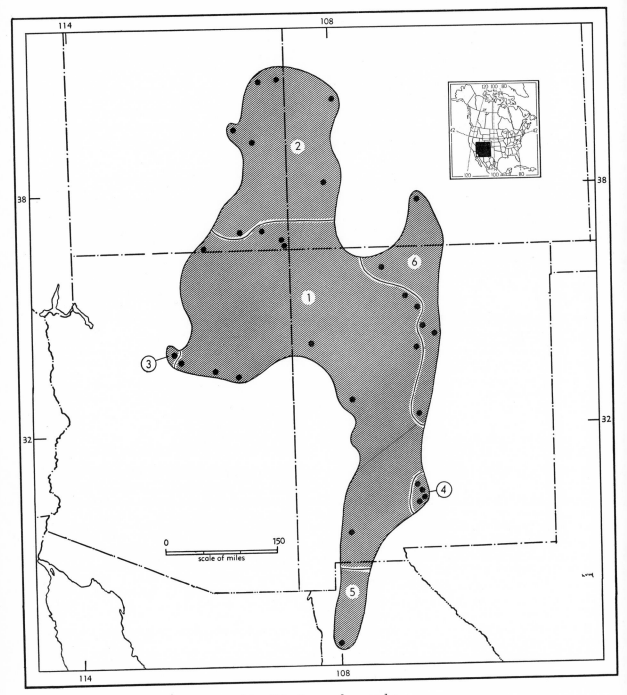

Map 288. *Perognathus apache.*

1. *Perognathus a. apache*
2. *Perognathus a. caryi*
3. *Perognathus a. clemophila*
4. *Perognathus a. gypsi*
5. *Perognathus a. melanotis*
6. *Perognathus a. relictus*

MARGINAL RECORDS.—Colorado: type locality. New Mexico: 3 mi. S Pecos (Goldman, 1938c:496); Gran Quivira (*ibid.*); Santa Fe (V. Bailey, 1932:278); Lake Burford (Goldman, 1938c:496).

longimembris-group
Perognathus longimembris
Little Pocket Mouse

x 1

External measurements: 110–151; 53–86; 15–20. Upper parts approximately pinkish- or ochraceous-buff, the exact shades varying markedly geographically, overlaid with black or blackish hairs to a greater or lesser extent so that some subspecies appear quite dark and others are distinctly buffy in over-all tone; underparts pale tawny to buffy or white, sometimes pectoral region alone is white and remainder tawny or buffy; tail usually bicolored.

This species includes the smallest subspecies of the family, *P. l. pacificus.* The species is often exceedingly numerous on the gravelly or rubble-strewn terraces of desert benchlands, especially where there is a thinly distributed cover of shrubs. The animals are comparatively easily obtained with snap traps baited with rolled oats or seeds. Fluctuation in numbers is a marked characteristic of the species. There is but slight sexual dimorphism.

Although we have no proof, we suppose that the mice of this species hibernate. In Nevada, trapping in cold weather in winter in places where the species occurs has yielded no specimens and indicates that the mice are not then active on the surface of the ground. The seed-filled cheek pouches of trapped specimens suggests that food is stored. Possibly the mice are active in winter, but only underground.

Hall (1946:359) reported that in Nevadan populations the average number of young in a litter is 4.3;

mode, 5; extremes 2–8. The greatest number of pregnant females was taken in May.

Perognathus longimembris aestivus Huey

1928. *Perognathus longimembris aestivus* Huey, Trans. San Diego Soc. Nat. Hist., 5:87, January 18, type from Sangre de Cristo, Valle San Rafael, western base of Sierra Juárez, lat. 31° 52′ N, long. 116° 06′ W, Baja California.

MARGINAL RECORDS.—Baja California: type locality: El Valle de la Trinidad (Huey, 1939:50).

Perognathus longimembris arcus Benson

1935. *Perognathus longimembris arcus* Benson, Univ. California Publ. Zool., 40:451, December 31, type from Rainbow Bridge, San Juan Co., Utah. Known only from the type locality.

Perognathus longimembris arizonensis Goldman

1931. *Perognathus longimembris arizonensis* Goldman, Proc. Biol. Soc. Washington, 44:134, October 17, type from 10 mi. S Jacobs Pools, 4000 ft., Houserock Valley, N side Marble Canyon of Colorado River, Arizona.

MARGINAL RECORDS.—Utah: Kaiparowits Plateau (Durrant, 1952:240). Arizona: type locality; 6 mi. W Colorado River Bridge (Goldman, 1931:135). Utah: Kanab (Durrant, 1952:240).

Perognathus longimembris bangsi Mearns

1898. *Perognathus longimembris bangsi* Mearns, Bull. Amer. Mus. Nat. Hist., 10:300, August 31, type from Palm Springs, Colorado Desert, Riverside Co., California.
1900. *Perognathus panamintinus arenicola* Stephens, Proc. Biol. Soc. Washington, 13:151, June 13, type from San Felipe Narrows, San Diego Co., California.

MARGINAL RECORDS (Huey, 1939:50).—California: Whitewater Ranch; *Borego Springs*; E side San Felipe Narrows.

Perognathus longimembris bombycinus Osgood

1907. *Perognathus bombycinus* Osgood, Proc. Biol. Soc. Washington, 20:19, February 23, type from Yuma, Yuma Co., Arizona.
1929. *Perognathus longimembris bombycinus*, Nelson and Goldman, Proc. Biol. Soc. Washington, 42:104, March 25.

MARGINAL RECORDS.—Arizona: near Ehrenberg (Grinnell, 1914:243); 6 mi. E Yuma (Huey, 1939:50). Sonora: Colonia Lerdo (Osgood, 1907:20). Baja California: San Felipe (Huey, 1939:50). California: 3 mi. W Pilot Knob (*ibid.*).

Perognathus longimembris brevinasus Osgood

1900. *Perognathus panamintinus brevinasus* Osgood, N. Amer. Fauna, 18:30, September 20, type from San Bernardino, San Bernardino Co., California. According to Osgood (Proc. Biol. Soc. Washington, 31:96, June 29, 1918) this is perhaps a synonym of *P. longimembris longimembris.*
1928. *Perognathus longimembris brevinasus*, Huey, Trans. San Diego Soc. Nat. Hist., 5:88, January 18.

MARGINAL RECORDS.—California: San Fernando (Grinnell, 1933:148); type locality; Cabazon (Huey, 1939:50); *Aguanga* (*ibid.*); 2½ mi. N Oak Grove (*ibid.*); Burbank (Osgood, 1900a:31).

Perognathus longimembris gulosus Hall

1941. *Perognathus longimembris gulosus* Hall, Proc. Biol. Soc. Washington, 54:55, May 20, type from near [¼ mi. S] Smith Creek Cave, 5800 ft., Mt. Moriah, White Pine Co., Nevada.

MARGINAL RECORDS.—Utah (Durrant, 1952:238): Kelton, 4225 ft.; 50 mi. W Milford; 55 mi. W of Milford, 5500 ft.; 5 mi. S Garrison, 5400 ft. Nevada (Hall, 1946:364): type locality; 8 mi. S Wendover, 4700 ft.; 13 mi. N Montello, 5000 ft.

Perognathus longimembris internationalis Huey

1939. *Perognathus longimembris internationalis* Huey, Trans. San Diego Soc. Nat. Hist., 9:47, August 31, type from Baja California side of international boundary at Jacumba, San Diego, California.

MARGINAL RECORDS (Huey, 1939:50).—California: La Puerta Valley; *San Felipe Valley*. Baja California: type locality.

Perognathus longimembris kinoensis Huey

1935. *Perognathus longimembris kinoensis* Huey, Trans. San Diego Soc. Nat. Hist., 8:73, August 24, type from Bahía Kino (N end of sand-dune peninsula that borders bay and forms northern arm of estuary), Sonora. Known only from the type locality.

Perognathus longimembris longimembris (Coues)

1875. *O*[*tognosis*]. *longimembris* Coues, Proc. Acad. Nat. Sci. Philadelphia, 27:305, August 31, type from Old Fort Tejon, Tehachapi Mountains, Kern Co., California.
1889. *Perognathus longimembris*, Merriam, N. Amer. Fauna, 1:13, October 25.
1904. *Perognathus elibatus* Elliot, Field Columb. Mus., Publ. 87, Zool. Ser., 3(14):252, January 7, type from Lockwood Valley, near Mt. Piños, Ventura Co., California.
1904. *Perognathus pericalles* Elliot, Field Columb. Mus., Publ. 87, Zool. Ser., 3(14):252, January 7, type from Keeler, Owens Lake, Inyo Co., California.

MARGINAL RECORDS (Grinnell, 1933:147, unless otherwise noted).—California: Marysville Buttes; Three Rivers (Osgood, 1900a:34); Onyx; Little Owen Lake (Osgood, 1900a:30); Olancha (*ibid.*); W side Owens Lake (Bole, 1937:6); W of Independence toward Kearsarge Pass; Laws; 2 mi. SE Keeler (Bole, 1937:6); Lower Centennial Springs, Coso Hills (*ibid.*); vicinity Providence Mts.; Lavic; Lancaster (Bole, 1937:6); Lockwood Valley, 5500 ft., near Mt. Piños; San Emigdio (Osgood, 1900a:34); Huron (*ibid.*); Ripon (*ibid.*); Lodi.

Perognathus longimembris nevadensis Merriam

1894. *Perognathus nevadensis* Merriam, Proc. Acad. Nat. Sci. Philadelphia, 46:264, September 27, type from Halleck, East Humboldt Valley, Elko Co., Nevada.

1933. *Perognathus longimembris nevadensis*, Grinnell, Univ. California Publ. Zool., 40:147, September 26.

MARGINAL RECORDS.—Oregon: Rome (V. Bailey, 1936:249). Nevada (Hall, 1946:360): 36 mi. NE Paradise Valley, 5500 ft.; 3 mi. S Izenhood; 2 mi. NW Halleck, 5200 ft.; 8 mi. E Eureka; Smiths Creek Valley, 3 mi. W Railroad Pass, 5500 ft.; 15 mi. SW Winnemucca; Jackson Creek Ranch, 17 mi. S, 5 mi. W Quinn River Crossing, 4000 ft.; 10 mi. SE Hausen, 4670 ft. California: near Eagleville (Grinnell, 1933:147). Oregon: Tumtum Lake (V. Bailey, 1936:249).

Perognathus longimembris pacificus Mearns

1898. *Perognathus pacificus* Mearns, Bull. Amer. Mus. Nat. Hist., 10:299, August 31, type from Mexican boundary monument No. 258, shore of Pacific Ocean, San Diego Co., California.
1932. *Perognathus longimembris pacificus*, von Bloeker, Proc. Biol. Soc. Washington, 45:128, September 9.
1932. *Perognathus longimembris cantwelli* von Bloeker, Proc. Biol. Soc. Washington, 45:128, September 9, type from Hyperion, Los Angeles Co., California. Regarded as identical with *P. l. pacificus* by Huey, Trans. San Diego Soc. Nat. Hist., 9:48–49, August 31, 1939.

MARGINAL RECORDS.—California: Palisades del Rey (von Bloeker, 1932:129); type locality.

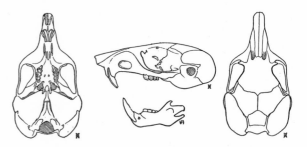

Fig. 278. *Perognathus longimembris panamintinus*, R.38 E, T.6 S, Esmeralda Co., Nevada, No. 38586 M.V.Z., ♀, X 1½.

Perognathus longimembris panamintinus Merriam

1894. *Perognathus longimembris panamintinus* Merriam, Proc. Acad. Nat. Sci. Philadelphia, 46:265, September 27, type from Perognathus Flat, 5200 ft., Panamint Mts., Inyo Co., California.

MARGINAL RECORDS.—Nevada (Hall, 1946:362–363): 1½ mi. N Quinn River Crossing, 4100 ft.; 11 mi. E, 1 mi. N Jungo, 4200 ft.; 9½ mi. E, 1 mi. S Fanning, 4100 ft., Buena Vista Valley; 5 mi. SE Millett P. O., 5500 ft.; Railroad Valley, 2½ to 3¼ mi. S Lock's Ranch, 5000 ft.; 15 mi. WSW Sunnyside; 10 mi. N Seeman Pass, 4600 ft.; Penoyer Valley, 14 mi. NNW Groom Baldy; Belted Range, 2 to 4½ mi. NW Indian Spring, 5700–6300 ft.; Indian Spring Valley, 14 mi. N Indian Spring, 3100 ft.; Mormon Well, 6500 ft.; Boulder City; 12 mi. S, 5 mi. E Searchlight, 2600 ft. California: Wild Rose Canyon, 6300 ft. (Grinnell, 1933:148); Willow Spring (Bole, 1937:6); Lee Flat (*ibid.*); *Grapevine Canyon, 1 mi. W Jackass Springs* (*ibid.*); Oasis (Hall and Kelson, 1952:366); Morans, 5000 ft. (*ibid.*). Nevada (Hall, 1946:362): Mason Valley, 12 mi. E Wellington, 5000 ft.; 3 mi. E Reno; 3½ mi. NW Flanigan, 4200 ft.; Smoke Creek, 9 mi.

E California boundary, 3900 ft.; mouth Little High Rock Canyon, 5000 ft.; Soldier Meadows, 4600 ft.

Perognathus longimembris pimensis Huey

1937. *Perognathus longimembris pimensis* Huey, Trans. San Diego Soc. Nat. Hist., 8:353, June 15, type from 11 mi. W Casa Grande, Pinal Co., Arizona.

MARGINAL RECORDS.—Arizona: Marinette (Huey, 1937:357); type locality.

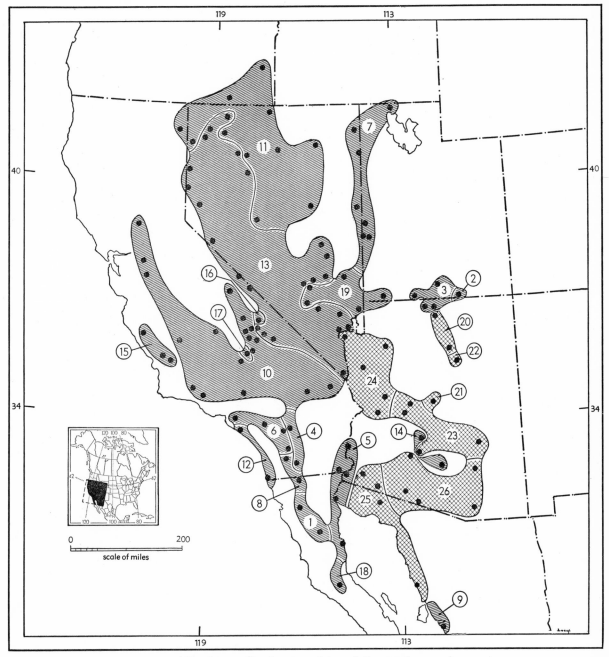

Map 289. *Perognathus longimembris* and *Perognathus amplus.*

Guide to kinds
1. *P. l. aestivus*
2. *P. l. arcus*
3. *P. l. arizonensis*
4. *P. l. bangsi*
5. *P. l. bombycinus*
6. *P. l. brevinasus*
7. *P. l. gulosus*
8. *P. l. internationalis*
9. *P. l. kinoensis*
10. *P. l. longimembris*
11. *P. l. nevadensis*
12. *P. l. pacificus*
13. *P. l. panamintinus*
14. *P. l. pimensis*
15. *P. l. psammophilus*
16. *P. l. salinensis*
17. *P. l. tularensis*
18. *P. l. venustus*
19. *P. l. virginis*
20. *P. a. ammodytes*
21. *P. a. amplus*
22. *P. a. cineris*
23. *P. a. jacksoni*
24. *P. a. pergracilis*
25. *P. a. rotundus*
26. *P. a. taylori*

Perognathus longimembris psammophilus von Bloeker

1937. *Perognathus longimembris psammophilus* von Bloeker, Proc. Biol. Soc. Washington, 50:153, September 10, type from W side Arroyo Seco, 150 ft., 4 mi. S Soledad, Monterey Co., California.

MARGINAL RECORDS (von Bloeker, 1937:154).—California: type locality; Miguel; Sandiego Joe's (= Santiago Springs), 2600 ft.

Perognathus longimembris salinensis Bole

1937. *Perognathus longimembris salinensis* Bole, Sci. Publ. Cleveland Mus. Nat. Hist., 5(2):3, December 4, type from 1 mi. N Salt Camp, 1060 ft., west edge of the salt lake, Saline Valley, Inyo Co., California.

MARGINAL RECORDS.—California: *North Sand Dunes, Saline Valley* (Bole, 1937:6); type locality.

Perognathus longimembris tularensis Richardson

1937. *Perognathus longimembris tularensis* Richardson, Jour. Mamm., 18:510, November 22, type from 1 mi. W Kennedy Meadows, 6000 ft., South Fork Kern River, Tulare Co., California.

MARGINAL RECORDS.—California: type locality; *Chimney Meadows, 6200 ft.* (Richardson, 1937:511).

Perognathus longimembris venustus Huey

1930. *Perognathus longimembris venustus* Huey, Trans. San Diego Soc. Nat. Hist., 6:233, December 24, type from San Agustín, lat. 30° N, long. 115° W, Baja California. Known only from the type locality.

Perognathus longimembris virginis Huey

1939. *Perognathus longimembris virginis* Huey, Trans. San Diego Soc. Nat. Hist., 9:55, August 31, type from St. George, 2950 ft., Washington Co., Utah.

MARGINAL RECORDS.—Nevada: Desert Valley, 20 mi. SW Pioche, 5400–5700 ft. (Hall, 1946:363). Utah: type locality. Nevada (Hall, 1946:363–364): S side Virgin River, ¾ mi. E Mesquite, 1750 ft.; Emigrant Valley, 9 to 9½ mi. S Oak Spring, 4400 ft.; 9 mi. E Wheelbarrow Peak.

Perognathus amplus
Arizona Pocket Mouse

External measurements: 123–170; 72–95; 17–22. Upper parts pinkish buff to pale ochraceous-salmon, overlaid with black which varies in degree so much that some subspecies appear distinctly blackish; underparts white or faintly washed with buff; tail more or less distinctly bicolor according to subspecies and season; lateral line buffy; orbital region usually distinctly paler than remainder of dorsum. Skull large; mastoids excessively developed, but audital bullae not correspondingly large; interparietal small; nasals and rostrum long and slender; zygomatic arches narrower anteriorly than posteriorly.

This species, although possessing a unique combination of cranial characters, is not greatly unlike *P. longimembris* externally. In normal adult specimens *P. amplus* can usually be distinguished from *P. longimembris* by larger size, longer (actually and relatively) tail (more than 75 per cent head-body length in *P. amplus,* less than 75 per cent in *P. longimembris*).

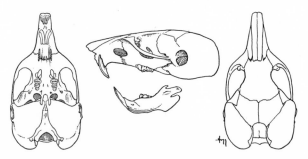

Fig. 279. *Perognathus amplus jacksoni,* 20 mi. SW Phoenix, Maricopa Co., Arizona, No. 7792 K.U., sex ?, X 1½.

Perognathus amplus ammodytes Benson

1933. *Perognathus amplus ammodytes* Benson, Proc. Biol. Soc. Washington, 46:110, April 27, type from 2 mi. S Cameron, Coconino Co., Arizona.

MARGINAL RECORDS.—Arizona: base of northern end Echo Cliffs, S of Grand Canyon Bridge (Benson, 1935:451); type locality.

Perognathus amplus amplus Osgood

1900. *Perognathus amplus* Osgood, N. Amer. Fauna, 18:32, September 20, type from Fort Verde, Yavapai Co., Arizona. Known only from the type locality.

Perognathus amplus cineris Benson

1933. *Perognathus amplus cineris* Benson, Proc. Biol. Soc. Washington, 46:109, April 27, type from near Wupatki Ruins, Wupatki National Monument, 27 mi. NE Flagstaff, Coconino Co., Arizona. Known only from the type locality.

Perognathus amplus jacksoni Goldman

1933. *Perognathus amplus jacksoni* Goldman, Jour. Washington Acad. Sci., 23:465, October 15, type from Congress Junction, 3000 ft., Yavapai Co., Arizona.

MARGINAL RECORDS (Goldman, 1933:466 unless otherwise noted).—Arizona: Kirkland; Rice; 20 mi. SW Phoenix; *Wickenburg;* type locality.

Perognathus amplus pergracilis Goldman

1932. *Perognathus amplus pergracilis* Goldman, Jour. Washington Acad. Sci., 22:387, July 19, type from Hackberry, 3500 ft., Mohave Co., Arizona.

MARGINAL RECORDS.—Arizona: Detrital Valley (Benson, 1933:112); Peach Springs, Hualpai Indian Reservation (Goldman, 1932d:388); 30 mi. E Parker (Hall and Kelson, 1952:366); Signal (Goldman, 1932d:388); Beal Spring, 2 mi. from Kingman (*ibid.*).

Perognathus amplus rotundus Goldman

1932. *Perognathus amplus rotundus* Goldman, Jour. Washington Acad. Sci., 22:387, July 19, type from Wellton, Yuma Co., Arizona.

MARGINAL RECORDS.—Arizona: type locality; Cabeza Prieta Mts. (Halloran, 1947:65). Sonora: Pápago Tanks (Burt, 1938:44); 2 mi. WNW Puerto Libertad (23004 KU).

Perognathus amplus taylori Goldman

1932. *Perognathus amplus taylori* Goldman, Jour. Washington Acad. Sci., 22:488, October 19, type from Santa Rita Range Reserve (near northeast station), 4000 ft., 35 mi. S Tucson, Pima Co., Arizona.

MARGINAL RECORDS.—Arizona: Gila Bend (Goldman, 1932f:489); 5 mi. N Oracle (Dice and Blossom, 1937:26); type locality; Sonoita Valley near Gray's Ranch (Huey, 1942:361); near Bates Well (*ibid.*).

Perognathus inornatus
San Joaquin Pocket Mouse

For present status of subspecies of *Perognathus inornatus* see Osgood, Proc. Biol. Soc. Washington, 31:95–96, June 29, 1918.

External measurements: 128–160; 63–78; 18–21. Upper parts ochraceous-buff to pinkish overlaid with blackish hairs, extent of overlay changing overall tone in the several subspecies; lateral line moderately well marked; underparts white; tail faintly bicolor. Skull in general similar to that of *P. apache* and that of *P. longimembris*; mastoids large; auditory bullae apposed anteriorly; interparietal small, and approximately square; nasals short; coronoid process of mandible large.

This species is easily confused with *P. longimembris*. It is important to obtain fully adult animals on which to base the identification.

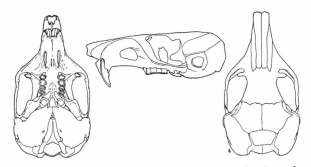
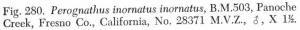

Fig. 280. *Perognathus inornatus inornatus*, B.M.503, Panoche Creek, Fresno Co., California, No. 28371 M.V.Z., ♂, X 1½.

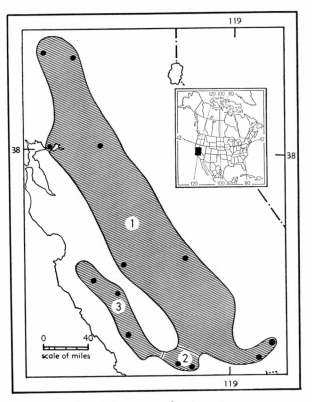

Map 290. *Perognathus inornatus.*

Guide to subspecies   2. *P. inornatus neglectus*
1. *P. inornatus inornatus*   3. *P. inornatus sillimani*

Perognathus inornatus inornatus Merriam

1889. *Perognathus inornatus* Merriam, N. Amer. Fauna, 1:15, October 25, type from Fresno, Fresno Co., California.

MARGINAL RECORDS (Grinnell, 1933:149, unless otherwise noted).—California: Sites; Marysville Buttes; Lodi; type locality; Weldon; Walker Basin; Panoche (Tappe, 1941:145); Benicia (Hooper, 1944:40).

Perognathus inornatus neglectus Taylor

1912. *Perognathus longimembris neglectus* Taylor, Univ. California Publ. Zool., 10:155, May 21, type from McKittrick, 1111 ft., Kern Co., California.
1918. *Perognathus inornatus neglectus*, Osgood, Proc. Biol. Soc. Washington, 31:96, June 29.

MARGINAL RECORDS.—California: Santiago Spring, edge of Carrizo Plain (Grinnell, 1933:149); type locality.

Perognathus inornatus sillimani von Bloeker

1937. *Perognathus inornatus sillimani* von Bloeker, Proc. Biol. Soc. Washington, 50:154, September 10, type from W side Arroyo Seco, 150 ft., 4 mi. S Soledad, Monterey Co., California.

MARGINAL RECORDS (von Bloeker, 1937:155).—California: type locality; mouth Wild Horse Canyon, 500 ft.; Salinas Valley, 2 mi. S San Miguel.

parvus-group
Perognathus parvus
Great Basin Pocket Mouse

External measurements: 148–198; 77–107; 19–27. Weight of 10 adult males and 10 adult females of *P. p. olivaceus* from Nevada (Hall, 1946:367) are, respectively: 25.4 (21.5–31.0), 20.5 (16.5–28.5). Upper parts approximately pinkish buff or ochraceous buff, thinly to heavily overlaid with blackish; underparts white to buffy; tail long, moderately penicillate, bicolored; antitragus lobed. Skull large, slightly rounded in dorsal profile; tympanic bullae well inflated, barely or nearly meeting anteriorly.

Great Basin pocket mice inhabit the Upper Sonoran Life-zone and are often abundant in shrub-covered deserts. Their altitudinal range, however, is wide and the animals are not narrowly restricted ecologically. The diet consists mostly of seeds, but some leaves and tender stems are eaten. The single annual molt is in late spring and early summer, and the young are usually born in the same period. In Nevada, 33 females averaged 5.5 embryos (3–8), with a mode of 5 or 6 (Hall, 1946:366).

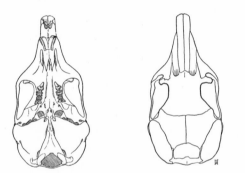

Fig. 281. *Perognathus parvus olivaceus*, Wisconsin Creek, 7800 ft., Nevada, No. 45599 M.V.Z., ♂, X 1½.

Perognathus parvus bullatus Durrant and Lee

1956. *Perognathus parvus bullatus* Durrant and Lee, Proc. Biol. Soc. Washington, 69:183, December 31, type from Ekker's Ranch, Robbers Roost, 25 mi. (airline) E Hanksville, 6000 ft., Wayne Co., Utah.

MARGINAL RECORDS (Durrant and Lee, 1956:186).—Utah: 1 mi. S San Rafael River, from Buckhorn Wash, 5200 ft.; Old Woman Wash, 23 mi. N Hanksville, 5200 ft.; type locality.

Perognathus parvus clarus Goldman

1917. *Perognathus parvus clarus* Goldman, Proc. Biol. Soc. Washington, 30:147, July 27, type from Cumberland, Lincoln Co., Wyoming.

MARGINAL RECORDS.—Idaho (Davis, 1939:265): Lemhi; Birch Creek; 5 mi. E Shelley. Wyoming: type locality; 26 mi. S, 21 mi. W Rock Springs (16931 KU); *2 mi. N Linwood, Utah* (R. D. Svihla, 1931:262); ½ mi. N

junction Henrys Fork and Utah boundary (16935 KU); Mountain View (Goldman, 1917:148); Bear River, 14 mi. N Evanston (*ibid.*). Utah: Laketown (Durrant, 1952:244). Idaho (Davis, 1939:265): 4 mi. N Rupert; Dickey.

Perognathus parvus columbianus Merriam

1894. *Perognathus columbianus* Merriam, Proc. Acad. Nat. Sci. Philadelphia, 46:263, September 27, type from Pasco, Franklin Co., Washington.
1948. *Perognathus parvus columbianus*, Dalquest, Univ. Kansas Publ., Mus. Nat. Hist., 2:299, April 9.

MARGINAL RECORDS.—Washington (Broadbooks, 1954:99): Steamboat Rock; 2 mi. SW Coulee Dam; Sulphur Lake, 7 mi. E Connell; Lyon's Ferry, N side Snake River opposite Perry; type locality; Wenatchee; Waterville.

Perognathus parvus idahoensis Goldman

1922. *Perognathus parvus idahoensis* Goldman, Proc. Biol. Soc. Washington, 35:105, October 17, type from Echo Crater, 20 mi. SW Arco, Butte Co., Idaho.

MARGINAL RECORDS (Davis, 1939:266).—Idaho: mouth Little Cottonwood Creek Canyon, Craters of the Moon; type locality; Sparks Well, 23 mi. N Minidoka; Laidlaw Park, 20 mi. N Kimama.

Perognathus parvus laingi Anderson

1932. *Perognathus laingi* Anderson, Bull. Nat. Mus. Canada, 70:100, November 24, type from Anarchist Mtn., near Osoyoos-Bridesville summit, about 8 mi. E Osoyoos Lake, 3500 ft., lat. 49° 08′ N, long. 119° 32′ W, British Columbia.
1947. *Perognathus parvus laingi*, Anderson, Bull. Nat. Mus. Canada, 102:130, January 24.

MARGINAL RECORDS.—British Columbia: foothills E Okanagan Landing (Anderson, 1947:130); type locality.

Perognathus parvus lordi (Gray)

1868. *Abromys lordi* Gray, Proc. Zool. Soc. London, p. 202, May, type from southern British Columbia.
1939. *Perognathus parvus lordi*, Davis, The Recent mammals of Idaho, p. 266, April 5.

MARGINAL RECORDS (Broadbooks, 1954:99, unless otherwise noted).—British Columbia: Ashcroft; Kamloops; Vernon; Midway (Anderson, 1947:131). Washington: Marcus (Osgood, 1900a:40); Spokane Bridge (Rust, 1947:320); Pullman (Dalquest, 1948:299). Idaho: Lewiston (Rust, 1946:320). Washington: Asotin; Grande Ronde River, 6 mi. S Anatone; Washtucna (Dalquest, 1948:299); Okanogan; Chelan; Conconully (Osgood, 1900a:40). British Columbia: near Keremeos (Anderson, 1947:131).

Cowan and Guiguet (1956:169–170) refer specimens from Ashcroft, British Columbia, to the subspecies *laingi* and state that *lordi* is confined to the arid bottom of the Okanagan and Similkameen rivers.

Perognathus parvus mollipilosus Coues

1875. *P[erognathus]. mollipilosus* Coues, Proc. Acad. Nat. Sci. Philadelphia, 27:296, August 31, type from Fort Crook, Shasta Co., California.
1900. *Perognathus parvus mollipilosus*, Osgood, N. Amer. Fauna, 18:36, September 20.

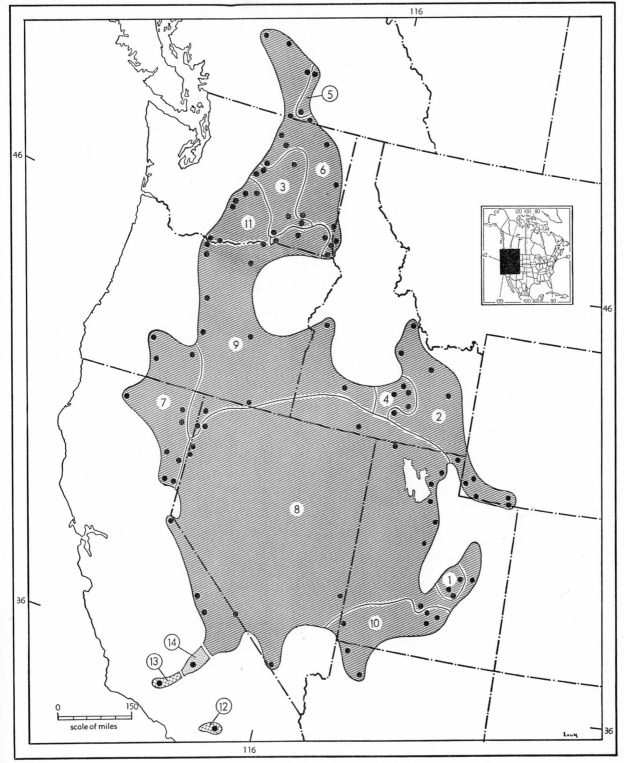

Map 291. *Perognathus parvus* and allies.

Guide to kinds		
1. *P. parvus bullatus*	5. *P. parvus laingi*	10. *P. parvus trumbullensis*
2. *P. parvus clarus*	6. *P. parvus lordi*	11. *P. parvus yakimensis*
3. *P. parvus columbianus*	7. *P. parvus mollipilosus*	12. *P. alticola alticola*
4. *P. parvus idahoensis*	8. *P. parvus olivaceus*	13. *P. alticola inexpectatus*
	9. *P. parvus parvus*	14. *P. xanthonotus*

MARGINAL RECORDS.—Oregon: W edge Wheeler Creek Canyon, 5500 ft., Crater Lake National Park (Huestis, 1942:451); Summer Lake (Osgood, 1900a:37). California: Alturas (*ibid.*); Likely (*ibid.*); Amedee (Grinnell, 1933: 150); Vinton (*ibid.*); Beckwith (reference to source of record misplaced); Susanville (Osgood, 1900a:37); Edgewood (*ibid.*). Oregon: Lost River (V. Bailey, 1936:247).

Perognathus parvus olivaceus Merriam

1889. *Perognathus olivaceus* Merriam, N. Amer. Fauna, 1:15, October 25, type from Kelton, near north end of Great Salt Lake, Boxelder Co., Utah.
1900. *Perognathus parvus olivaceus,* Osgood, N. Amer. Fauna, 18:37, September 20.
1889. *Perognathus olivaceus amoenus* Merriam, N. Amer. Fauna, 1:16, October 25, type from Nephi, Juab Co., Utah.
1900. *Perognathus parvus magruderensis* Osgood, N. Amer. Fauna, 18:38, September 20, type from Mt. Magruder, 8000 ft., Esmerelda Co., Nevada. Regarded as inseparable from *olivaceus* by Hall, Mammals of Nevada, p. 367.
1939. *Perognathus parvus plerus* Goldman, Jour. Mamm., 20:352, August 14, type from north end Stansbury Island, Great Salt Lake, Utah. Regarded as inseparable from *olivaceus* by Durrant, Univ. Kansas Publ., Mus. Nat. Hist., 6:242, August 10.

MARGINAL RECORDS.—Idaho: Salmon Creek, 8 mi. W Rogerson (Davis, 1939:264). Utah (Durrant, 1952:243-244, unless otherwise noted): Clear Creek, 5 mi. SW Nafton, 6500 ft.; Blacksmith Fork (Osgood, 1900:38); Ogden; Millcreek Canyon, 5 mi. SE Salt Lake City, 4700 ft.; Bear Flat, head Slide Canyon, 3 mi. E Provo (J. W. Bee, *in Litt.*); Nephi, 5059 ft.; 7 mi. N Greenriver, 4100 ft.; Otter Creek (Osgood, 1900:38). Nevada (Hall, 1946:368–369); Eagle Valley, 3½ mi. N Ursine, 5900 ft.; N side Potosi Mtn., 5800 ft.; 2½ mi. E, 1 mi. S Grapevine Peak, 6700 ft. California: Little Onion Valley (Grinnell, 1933:150); Bishop Creek (Osgood, 1900:38); Fredericksburg, 5100 ft. (Grinnell, 1933:150). Nevada (Hall, 1946:368): Smoke Creek, 9 mi. E California boundary, 3900 ft.; 17½ mi. W Deep Hole, 4750 ft.; Little High Rock Canyon, 5000 ft.; 1 mi. S Denio, Oregon, 4200 ft.

Perognathus parvus parvus (Peale)

1848. *Cricetodipus parvus* Peale, Mammalia and ornithology, *in* U.S. Explor. Exped. . . . , 8:53, type from Oregon, probably near The Dalles, Wasco Co.
1858. *Perognathus parvus,* Cassin, Mammalia and ornithology, *in* U.S. Explor. Exped. . . . , 8:48.
1858. *Perognathus monticola* Baird, Mammals, *in* Repts. Expl. Surv. . . . , 8(1):422, July 14, type from west of Rocky Mts., St. Marys ? [= St. Marys Mission, Stevensville, Montana]; regarded by Osgood, N. Amer. Fauna, 18:36, September 20, 1900, as having been obtained at The Dalles, Oregon.

MARGINAL RECORDS (Broadbooks, 1954:99, unless otherwise noted).—Washington: [eastern Garfield County] (Dalquest, 1948:298). Oregon: Baker; Harney (Osgood, 1900:36). Idaho (Davis, 1939:263): Crane Creek, 15 mi. E Midvale; 8 mi. N Hammett. Oregon: Denio. Nevada (Hall, 1946:367): 4½ mi. NE Painted Point, 5800 ft.; 1 mi. W Hausen, 4650 ft. Oregon: Fremont; Prineville; Maupin; The Dalles; Umatilla. Washington: Wallula; Prescott.

Perognathus parvus trumbullensis Benson

1937. *Perognathus parvus trumbullensis* Benson, Proc. Biol. Soc. Washington, 50:181, October 28, type from Nixon Spring, 6250 ft., Mt. Trumbull, Mohave Co., Arizona.

MARGINAL RECORDS.—Utah (Durrant, 1955:75): Aquarius Guard Station; Bown's Reservoir; *Steep Creek;* Hall Ranch. Arizona: type locality; 6 mi. N Wolf Hole, 4900 ft. (Benson, 1937:182). Utah: 19 mi. W Enterprise (Durrant, 1955:75).

Perognathus parvus yakimensis Broadbooks

1954. *Perognathus parvus yakimensis* Broadbooks, Jour. Mamm., 35:96, February 10, type from 16 mi. NW Naches, Rocky Flat (or Rocky Prairie), 3800 ft., Yakima Co., Washington.

MARGINAL RECORDS.—Washington (Broadbooks, 1954:99, unless otherwise noted): Ellenburg; Vantage (on geographic grounds; referred to *P. p. parvus* by Dalquest, 1948:298), thence southward and westward along Columbia River to Cliffs; Dallesport; 10 mi. W Wiley City; type locality.

Perognathus alticola
White-eared Pocket Mouse

External measurements: 160–181; 72–97; 21–23. Upper parts olivaceous-buff to near wood brown; underparts white; lateral line usually faintly expressed; tail bicolored or tricolored, above like upper parts proximally, but shading to dusky or black at tip, white below. Skull closely resembles that of *P. parvus* but smaller; ascending branches of supraoccipital exceedingly broad and heavy.

Perognathus alticola alticola Rhoads

1894. *Perognathus alticolus* Rhoads, Proc. Acad. Nat. Sci. Philadelphia, 45:412, January 27, type from Squirrel Inn, near Little Bear Valley, 5500 ft., San Bernardino Mts., San Bernardino Co., California.

MARGINAL RECORDS.—California: type locality; *1 mi. E Strawberry Peak, 5750 ft., San Bernardino Mts.* (Huey, 1926:122).

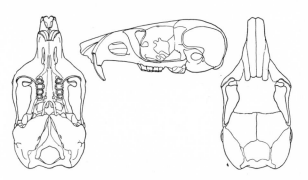

Fig. 282. *Perognathus alticola alticola,* 2 mi. E Strawberry Peak, 5750 ft., San Bernardino Co., California, No. 47408 M.V.Z., ♂, X 1½.

Perognathus alticola inexpectatus Huey

1926. *Perognathus alticola inexpectatus* Huey, Proc. Biol. Soc. Washington, 39:121, December 27, type from 14 mi. W Lebec, 600 ft., Kern Co., California. Known only from the type locality.

Perognathus xanthonotus Grinnell
Yellow-eared Pocket Mouse

1912. *Perognathus xanthonotus* Grinnell, Proc. Biol. Soc. Washington, 25:128, July 31, type from Freeman Canyon, 4900 ft., E slope Walker Pass, Kern Co., California.

Measurements of the type, an adult male, are: 170, 85, 22.5. Upper parts "between ochraceous-buff and cream-buff, almost perfectly clear on sides of body and head, and but slightly obscured mid-dorsally with scanty dusky tippings to the hairs; feet and lower surface white; . . . tail well clothed with hairs, and distinctly penicillate, beneath white, above faint cream-buff with a slight dusky tinge on terminal fifth.

"Skull.—Distinctly smaller than in *olivaceus*, mastoids and audital bullae notably so; closely similar to *alticola*" (Grinnell, 1912:128).

MARGINAL RECORDS (Grinnell, 1912:128).—California: type locality; *W slope Walker Pass, 4600 ft.; head Kelso Valley, 5000 ft.*

formosus-group
Perognathus formosus
Long-tailed Pocket Mouse

External measurements: 172–211; 86–118; 22–26. Ten Nevadan males weighed 21.9 (19.8–24.7); females, 20.2 (16.8–23.3) grams (Hall, 1946:371). Upper parts approximately wood brown but varying geographically; underparts white but sometimes faintly washed with buff; tail distinctly bicolored; tail long, sparsely haired, distinctly crested distally; interparietal markedly wider than long; mastoidal bullae projecting slightly beyond occiput; lower premolar larger than last molar.

This species occurs in the Lower Sonoran Life-zone and in the lower part of the Upper Sonoran Life-zone. The species shows a marked predilection for stony ground and is often common on the dry faces of terraces and benchlands. Hall (1946:371) reported 2 July-taken females containing 6 embryos each.

Perognathus formosus cinerascens Nelson and Goldman

1929. *Perognathus formosus cinerascens* Nelson and Goldman, Proc. Biol. Soc. Washington, 42:105, March 25, type from San Felipe, northeastern Baja California.

MARGINAL RECORDS.—Baja California: type locality; NE El Mármol (Huey, 1954:2).

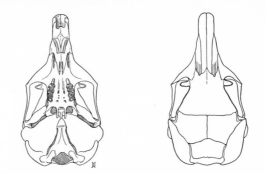

Fig. 283. *Perognathus formosus melanurus*, latitude 40° 28', 6 mi. E California boundary, Nevada, No. 73442 M.V.Z., ♂, X 1½.

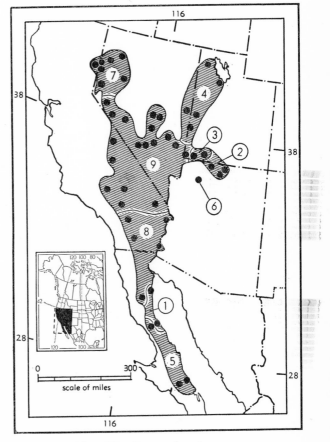

Map 292. *Perognathus formosus.*

Guide to subspecies	5. *P. f. infolatus*
1. *P. f. cinerascens*	6. *P. f. melanocaudatus*
2. *P. f. domisaxensis*	7. *P. f. melanurus*
3. *P. f. formosus*	8. *P. f. mesembrinus*
4. *P. f. incolatus*	9. *P. f. mohavensis*

Perognathus formosus domisaxensis Cockrum

1956. *Perognathus formosus domisaxensis* Cockrum, Jour. Washington Acad. Sci., 46:131, May 7, type from House-rock Valley, 15 mi. W of [the Navajo] bridge, Coconino County, Arizona.

MARGINAL RECORDS (Cockrum, 1956:131).—Arizona: 6 mi. SE Fredonia; *type locality; Soap Creek, 15 mi. SW Lees Ferry*; 2 mi. W Lees Ferry, 3250 ft.; 6 mi. W Grand Canyon Bridge, Marble Canyon, 3800 ft.

Perognathus formosus formosus Merriam

1889. *Perognathus formosus* Merriam, N. Amer. Fauna, 1:17, October 25, type from St. George, Washington Co., Utah.

MARGINAL RECORDS (Durrant, 1952:246).—Utah: Zion National Park; *½ mi. W St. George, 3000 ft.*; 3 mi. SW St. George, 2800 ft.

Perognathus formosus incolatus Hall

1941. *Perognathus formosus incolatus* Hall, Proc. Biol. Soc. Washington, 54:56, May 20, type from 2 mi. W Smith Creek Cave, Mt. Moriah, White Pine Co., Nevada.

MARGINAL RECORDS.—Utah: Groome (Durrant, 1955: 75); 5 mi. S Timpie (*ibid.*); White Valley, 65 mi. W Delta (Durrant, 1952:245); Warm Cove, 55 mi. W Milford, 5500 ft. (*ibid.*). Nevada: type locality; *near* (*within ¼ mi. of*) *Smith Creek Cave, 5800 ft.* (Hall, 1946:373). Utah: *N end Newfoundland Mts.* (Durrant, 1955:75).

Perognathus formosus infolatus Huey

1954. *Perognathus formosus infolatus* Huey, Trans. San Diego Soc. Nat. Hist., 12:1, March 1, type from 7 mi. W San Francisquito Bay, lat. 28° 30′ N, Gulf of California, Baja California.

MARGINAL RECORDS (Huey, 1954:2).—Baja California: 3 mi. W El Mármol; type locality; Barril.

Perognathus formosus melanocaudus Cockrum

1956. *Perognathus formosus melanocaudus* Cockrum, Jour. Washington Acad. Sci., 46:132, May 7, type from lower end of Toroweap Valley (Rim of Grand Canyon), Mohave Co., Arizona. Known only from type locality.

Perognathus formosus melanurus Hall

1941. *Perognathus formosus melanurus* Hall, Proc. Biol. Soc. Washington, 54:57, May 20, type from lat. 40° 28′ N, 4000 ft., 6 mi. E California boundary, Washoe Co., Nevada.

MARGINAL RECORDS (Hall, 1946:372).—Nevada: 10½ mi. W, 6 mi. N Sulphur, 4000 ft.; 3½ mi. NE Toulon, 3950 ft.; N side Truckee River, 10 mi. E Reno, 4500 ft.; 2½ mi. E Flanigan, 4250 ft. California: 4½ mi. WNW Stacy. Nevada: type locality; 1 mi. NE Gerlach, 4000 ft.

Perognathus formosus mesembrinus Elliot

1904. *Perognathus mesembrinus* Elliot, Field Columb. Mus., Publ. 87, Zool. Ser., 3(14):251, January 7, type from Palm Springs, Riverside Co., California.
1929. *Perognathus formosus mesembrinus*, Nelson and Goldman, Proc. Biol. Soc. Washington, 42:106, March 25.

MARGINAL RECORDS.—California: Chemehuevis Valley (Nelson and Goldman, 1929:104); 1 mi. N Potholes (Huey, 1938:36). Baja California: Mattomi (Elliot, 1903: 252). California: San Felipe Canyon (Huey, 1938:36); type locality.

Perognathus formosus mohavensis Huey

1938. *Perognathus formosus mohavensis* Huey, Trans. San Diego Soc. Nat. Hist., 9:35, November 21, type from Bonanza King Mine, Providence Mts., San Bernardino Co., California.

MARGINAL RECORDS (Hall, 1946:373, unless otherwise noted).—Nevada: West Walker River, 12 mi. S Yerington, 4600 ft. (= Wilson Canyon); 2½ mi. NW Blair Junction, 4950 ft.; NW base Timber Mtn., 4200 ft.; ½ mi. S Oak Spring, 5700 ft.; Old Mill, N end Reveille Valley, 6200 ft.; 6½ mi. N Hot Creek, 5900 ft.; 2½ mi. E and N Twin Springs, 5400 ft.; 9 mi. W Groom Baldy, 5500 ft.; Pahroc Spring; 5½ mi. N Elgin, 4000 ft. Utah: 1½ mi. E Beaverdam Wash, 8 mi. N Utah–Arizona border, 3200 ft. (Durrant, 1952:247), thence southward E of Colorado River to California: type locality; Warren Station, near Mohave (on geographic grounds; Grinnell, 1933:151, referred specimens to *P. f. formosus*); Cushenberry Springs (on geographic grounds; Grinnell, see *antea*); 20 mi. S Trona (Huey, 1938:36); Lone Pine (Osgood, 1900a:41); Silver Canyon, White Mts. E of Laws (Grinnell, 1933:151). Nevada: Huntoon Valley, 5700 ft.

Subgenus Chaetodipus Merriam

1889. *Chaetodipus* Merriam, N. Amer. Fauna, 1:5, October 25. Type, *Perognathus spinatus* Merriam.

External measurements: 152–230; 83–143; 22–29. Pelage harsh with spiny bristles on rump; soles of hind feet naked. Mastoids relatively small, not projecting beyond plane of occiput; mastoidal side of parietal equal to or shorter than other sides; interparietal width equal to or greater than interorbital width. Audital bullae separated by nearly full width of basisphenoid; supraoccipital with deep lateral indentations (except in *hispidus*); ascending branches of supraoccipital heavy and laminate.

The species of this subgenus are in general more southern in geographic distribution than those of the subgenus *Perognathus*.

KEY TO NOMINAL SPECIES OF SUBGENUS CHAETODIPUS

1. Rump with distinct spines or bristles.
    2. Lateral line well marked; pelage not markedly hispid; bristles moderate, usually on rump only.
        3. Ear less than 9.
            4. Spines on rump usually weakly developed; interparietal strap-shaped.
                5. Total length more than 180; rostrum and nasals broad and well developed.   *P. nelsoni*, p. 502

5'. Total length less than 180; rostrum and nasals narrow and weakly developed.
P. intermedius, p. 500

4'. Spines on rump strongly developed; interparietal pentagonal with a conspicuous anterior angle.
  6. Total length less than 170; cranium comparatively flattened; rostrum broad and well developed. . . . . *P. anthonyi*, p. 504
  6'. Total length more than 170; cranium moderately arched; rostrum attenuate and narrow.
P. fallax, p. 503

3'. Ear more than 9.
  7. Size large (usually more than 200); ears markedly elongated; bristles strongly developed on rump and flanks; cranium strongly vaulted. . . . . *P. californicus*, p. 504
  7'. Size moderate (usually less than 200); ears more or less circular; bristles not pronounced or not on flanks; cranium slightly vaulted.
    8. Bristles on rump faintly expressed or absent; supraoccipital breadth more than 5.8.
P. artus, p. 503
    8'. Bristles on rump short, stout, and few; supraoccipital breadth less than 5.8.
P. goldmani, p. 502

2'. Lateral line faint or wanting; pelage markedly hispid; bristles pronounced and often present on flanks as well as rump. . . . . *P. spinatus*, p. 506
1'. Rump lacking spines and bristles.
  9. Tail not crested, shorter than head and body; skull with supraorbital bead. . . . *P. hispidus*, p. 494
  9'. Tail crested, longer than head and body; skull without supraorbital bead.
    10. Total length more than 200.
      11. Dorsal coloration distinctly grayish; size usually more than 210; interorbital breadth approximately equal to interparietal breadth. . . . . *P. baileyi*, p. 493
      11'. Dorsal coloration yellowish-brown; size usually less than 210; interorbital breadth less than interparietal breadth. . . . . *P. penicillatus*, p. 497
    10'. Total length less than 200.
      12. Interorbital breadth less than 5.8. . . . . *P. pernix*, p. 499
      12'. Interorbital breadth more than 5.8.
        13. Occurring in southwestern Chihuahua or northwestern Sinaloa. . . . *P. artus*, p. 503
        13'. Not occurring in southwestern Chihuahua or Sinaloa.
          14. Occurring in San Luis Potosí.
            15. Upper parts dull gray, lined with buffy especially on head. . *P. lineatus*, p. 503
            15'. Upper parts not dull gray, usually buffy or ochraceous, sometimes strongly washed with black. . . . . *P. penicillatus*, p. 497
          14'. Not occurring in San Luis Potosí.
            16. Interorbital breadth more than 39 per cent of basilar length; occurring in Baja California except extreme northwestern part. . . . *P. arenarius*, p. 498
            16'. Interorbital breadth less than 39 per cent of basilar length; in Baja California occurring in extreme northwestern part. . . . . *P. penicillatus*, p. 497

baileyi-group
Perognathus baileyi
Bailey's Pocket Mouse

External measurements: 201–230; 110–125; 26–28. Upper parts grayish and washed with yellowish or tawny; underparts white or almost so; tail long, penicillate, and strongly crested, buffy above, whitish below. Skull large and heavily constructed; mastoid side of parietal approximately equal to other long sides; audital bullae barely apposed anteriorly; interparietal relatively large; interparietal breadth approximately equal to least interorbital breadth; lower premolar equal to or slightly smaller than last molar.

Perognathus baileyi baileyi Merriam

1894. *Perognathus baileyi* Merriam, Proc. Acad. Nat. Sci. Philadelphia, 46:262, September 27, type from Magdalena, Sonora.

MARGINAL RECORDS (Burt, 1938:44, unless otherwise noted).—Arizona: New River (Osgood, 1900a:42); Mammoth (Doutt, 1934:262); Florida Canyon, Santa Rita Mts. (*ibid.*). Sonora: 23 mi. S, 8 mi. E Nogales, 3200 ft. (22979 KU); Ures; Obregón; Bahía San Carlos; Hermosilla; 5 mi. N Cornelio (22990 KU); Alamo Wash, 35 mi. NW Magdalena. Arizona: Growler Mine, Organ Pipe Cactus National Monument (Huey, 1942:361).

Perognathus baileyi domensis Goldman

1928. *Perognathus baileyi domensis* Goldman, Proc. Biol. Soc. Washington, 41:204, December 18, type from Castle

Dome, 1400 ft., at base of Castle Dome Peak, Yuma Co., Arizona.

MARGINAL RECORDS.—Arizona: type locality; Cabeza Prieta Game Range (Halloran, 1947:65). Sonora: ½ mi. N Puerto Libertad (22988 KU). Arizona: Tinajas Altas, Gila Mts. (46484 KU).

Perognathus baileyi extimus Nelson and Goldman

1930. *Perognathus baileyi extimus* Nelson and Goldman, Jour. Washington Acad. Sci., 20:223, June 19, type from Tres Pachitas, 700 ft., 36 mi. S La Paz, Baja California.

MARGINAL RECORDS (Nelson and Goldman, 1930: 224).—Baja California: Onyx; Calamahue; San Bruno; Comondú; type locality; Matancita; San Jorge; Punta Prieta.

Perognathus baileyi fornicatus Burt

1932. *Perognathus baileyi fornicatus* Burt, Trans. San Diego Soc. Nat. Hist., 7(16):164, October 31, type from Monserrate Island (lat. 25° 38′ N, long. 111° 02′ W), Gulf of California, Baja California. Known only from type locality.

Perognathus baileyi hueyi Nelson and Goldman

1929. *Perognathus baileyi hueyi* Nelson and Goldman, Proc. Biol. Soc. Washington, 42:106, March 25, type from San Felipe, northeastern Baja California.

MARGINAL RECORDS.—California: Banner (von Bloeker, 1932:279, on geographic grounds, originally referred to *P. b. baileyi*); San Felipe Narrows (Grinnell, 1933:152); Bard (*ibid.*). Baja California: type locality. California: Mountain Spring (Grinnell, 1933:152).

Perognathus baileyi insularis Townsend

1912. *Perognathus baileyi insularis* Townsend, Bull. Amer. Mus. Nat. Hist., 31:122, June 14, type from Tiburón Island, Gulf of California, Sonora. Known only from the type locality.

Perognathus baileyi rudinoris Elliot

1903. *Perognathus baileyi rudinoris* Elliot, Field Columb. Mus., Publ. 74, Zool. Ser., 3(10):167, May 7, type from San Quintín, Baja California.

1903. *Perognathus knekus* Elliot, Field Columb. Mus., Publ. 74, Zool. Ser., 3(10):169, May 7, type from Rosarito, Sierra San Pedro Mártir, Baja California.

MARGINAL RECORDS.—Baja California: type locality; Rosarito (Elliot, 1903:221).

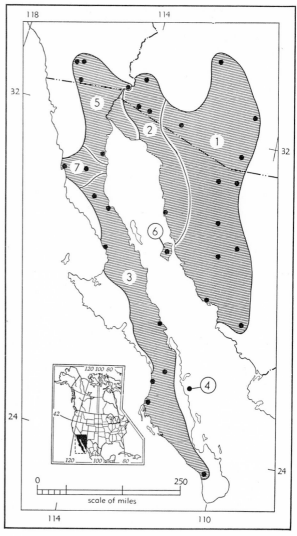

Map 293. *Perognathus baileyi.*

Guide to subspecies
1. *P. b. baileyi*
2. *P. b. domensis*
3. *P. b. extimus*

4. *P. b. fornicatus*
5. *P. b. hueyi*
6. *P. b. insularis*
7. *P. b. rudinoris*

hispidus-group
Perognathus hispidus
Hispid Pocket Mouse

Subspecies reviewed by Glass, Jour. Mamm., 28:174–179, June 1, 1947.

External measurements: 198–223; 90–113; 25–28. Upper parts ochraceous mixed with blackish hairs, sides usually only faintly paler than back; under-

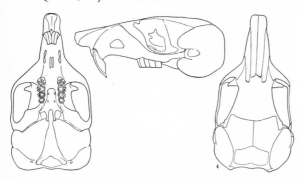

Fig. 284. *Perognathus baileyi hueyi,* Las Palmas Cañon, W side Laguna Salada, U.S.–Mexican boundary, 300 ft., Baja California del Norte, No. 39199 M.V.Z., ♀, X 1½.

X ¾

parts white or nearly so; tail equal to or slightly shorter than head and body, tricolored, white below, buffy laterally, blackish above; lateral line distinct; pelage harsh. Skull large; rostrum robust; interorbital space wide; supraorbital bead conspicuous; mastoids relatively small, not bulging posteriorly; mastoid side of parietal short; interparietal wide; audital bullae usually, but not always, well separated anteriorly; lower premolar approximately equal to last molar.

The hispid pocket mouse usually lives in an open type of habitat; the burrows with their conspicuous piles of earth often are on almost bare ground. In other places these mice are more abundant in prairies covered with a broken rocky pavement. The mice store seeds but eat some animal matter, especially insects. Several litters of 4 to 7 young are born in a season.

Perognathus hispidus hispidus Baird

1858. *Perognathus hispidus* Baird, Mammals, *in* Repts. Expl. Surv. . . . , 8(1):421, July 14, type from Charco Escondido, Tamaulipas.

MARGINAL RECORDS (Glass, 1947:177, unless otherwise noted).—Texas: Jefferson City (117373 BS). Louisiana: Vowell's Mill; Hutton. Texas: 2½ mi. N Hockley; Aransas Refuge; Brownsville. Tamaulipas: Victoria. Coahuila: Sabinas; 3 mi. N Cuatro Ciénegas (Baker, 1956:234); 6 mi. N, 2 mi. E La Babia (35804 KU); Cañon del Cochino, 3200 ft., 16 mi. N, 21 mi. E Piedra Blanca (35798 KU). Texas: 5 mi. NE Cisco; Brazos.

Perognathus hispidus paradoxus Merriam

1889. *Perognathus paradoxus* Merriam, N. Amer. Fauna, 1:24, October 25, type from Banner, Trego Co., Kansas.
1900. *Perognathus hispidus paradoxus*, Osgood, N. Amer. Fauna, 18:44, September 20.
1894. *Perognathus latirostris* Rhoads, Amer. Nat., 28:185, February, type from Rocky Mts.
1894. *Perognathus conditi* J. A. Allen, Bull. Amer. Mus. Nat. Hist., 6:318, November 7, type from San Bernardino Ranch, Cochise Co., Arizona. Regarded by Hoffmeister and Goodpaster (1954:103–104) as a valid subspecies of *P. hispidus.*

MARGINAL RECORDS (Glass, 1947:179, unless otherwise noted).—North Dakota: Wade (V. Bailey, 1927:123).

South Dakota: 2 mi. S, 3 mi. E Fort Thompson, 1470 ft. (41900 KU). Nebraska: 2 mi. SE Niobrara (Jones, 1954:484); Red Cloud. Kansas (Cockrum, 1952:150): 4 mi. E Stockton; 3 mi. N, 2 mi. W Hoisington; Rezeau Ranch, 5 mi. N Belvidere. Oklahoma: 2 mi. W Edith. Texas: ¼ mi. S Chilicothe; 6 mi. NE Coahoma; Fort Stockton; Alpine (108782 BS). Chihuahua: Santa Rosalía; Casas Grandes. Arizona: mouth of Montezuma Canyon (Hoffmeister and Goodpaster, 1954:103); *mouth of Ramsey Canyon (ibid.);* 12 mi. NW Tucson. New Mexico: Dry Creek, between the San Francisco and Gila rivers (V. Bailey, 1932:280); Tularosa; Las Vegas (V. Bailey, 1932:280); 3 mi. SE Cimarron. Colorado: Daniels Park. Wyoming: 2½ mi. S Chugwater (18252 KU); 14 mi. W, 2 mi. N Hulett (32462 KU).

Perognathus hispidus spilotus Merriam

1889. *Perognathus paradoxus spilotus* Merriam, N. Amer. Fauna, 1:25, October 25, type from Gainesville, Cooke Co., Texas.
1937. *Perognathus hispidus spilotus,* Black, 30th Biennial Rept., Kansas State Bd. Agric., p. 183.
1904. *Perognathus hispidus maximus* Elliot, Field Columb. Mus., Publ. 87, Zool. Ser., 3(14):253, January 7, type from Noble, Cleveland Co., Oklahoma.

MARGINAL RECORDS (Glass, 1947:178, unless otherwise noted).—Nebraska (Jones, 1954:484): 9 mi. NW Lincoln; 3 mi. S, 2 mi. E Nebraska City; Peru; 5 mi. SE Rulo. Kansas (Cockrum, 1952:150): Arkansas City. Oklahoma: Garnett; 3 mi. E Wainwright. Texas: type locality; *2 mi. S Marysville* (Russell, 1953:457). Oklahoma: Chattanooga; 1 mi. N Hydro (43876 KU); 5 mi. W Canton (43859 KU); White Horse Springs. Kansas (Cockrum, 1952:150): 6 mi. N Aetna; 1½ mi. S Wilson; 4 mi. E Concordia. Nebraska: 1 mi. S Williams (Jones, 1954:484).

Perognathus hispidus zacatecae Osgood

1900. *Perognathus hispidus zacatecae* Osgood, N. Amer. Fauna, 18:45, September 20, type from Valparaíso, Zacatecas.

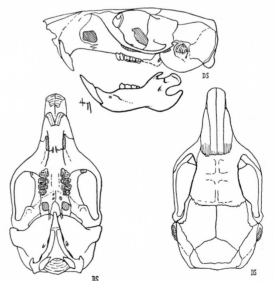

Fig. 285. *Perognathus hispidus paradoxus,* 6 mi. S Atwood, Rawlins Co., Kansas, No. 35092 K.U., ♂, X 1½.

MARGINAL RECORDS.—Coahuila: 3 mi. S and 3 mi. E Bella Unión, 6750 ft. (48665 KU). Hidalgo: 85 km. N Mexico City (9 km. S Pachuca), 8200 ft. (Davis, 1944: 390). Guanajuato: Celaya (Osgood, 1900a:45). Zacatecas: type locality.—Probably occurring more widely than existing records now indicate.

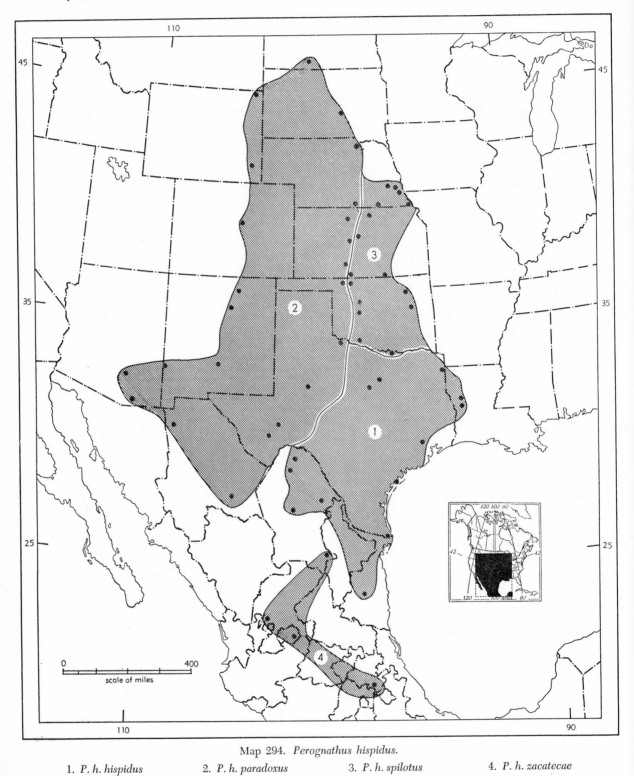

Map 294. *Perognathus hispidus.*

1. *P. h. hispidus*   2. *P. h. paradoxus*   3. *P. h. spilotus*   4. *P. h. zacatecae*

penicillatus-group
Perognathus penicillatus
Desert Pocket Mouse

External measurements: 162–216; 83–129; 22–27. Upper parts yellowish-brown to yellowish-gray; underparts white to buffy; lateral line obscure or absent; tail long, markedly crested, penicillate, white below proximal to tuft; upper side of tail and tuft dusky. Skull of moderate size; rostrum robust and high; mastoid side of parietal equal to squamosal side, other sides much longer; interparietal pentagonal with all angles somewhat rounded; audital bullae widely separated anteriorly.

Desert pocket mice vary to an unusually great degree both individually and microgeographically. Hence identification of individual specimens is often troublesome. The species inhabits brushy or shrubby deserts and is most often found on coarse, sandy soil, less often on fine silts and gravelly soils. Little is known of breeding habits. The species is seldom abundant locally and is of little economic importance.

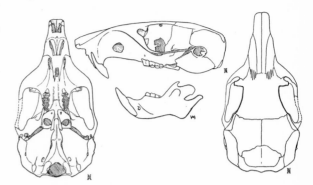

Fig. 286. *Perognathus penicillatus penicillatus*, 14 mi. E Searchlight, Nevada, No. 61569 M.V.Z., ♂, X 1½.

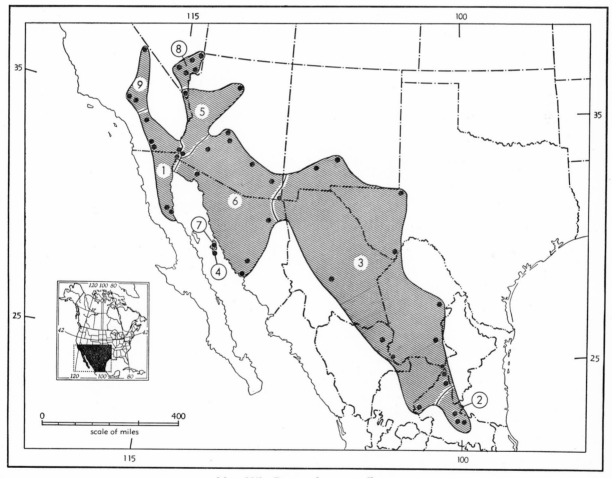

Map 295. *Perognathus penicillatus*.

1. *P. p. angustirostris*	4. *P. p. minimus*	7. *P. p. seri*
2. *P. p. atrodorsalis*	5. *P. p. penicillatus*	8. *P. p. sobrinus*
3. *P. p. eremicus*	6. *P. p. pricei*	9. *P. p. stephensi*

Perognathus penicillatus angustirostris Osgood

1900. *Perognathus penicillatus angustirostris* Osgood, N. Amer. Fauna, 18:47, September 20, type from Carrizo Creek, Colorado Desert, Imperial Co., California.

MARGINAL RECORDS.—California: Cabezon (Grinnell, 1933:153); vicinity Bard (4018 KU). Arizona: 4 mi. S Gadsden (22285 KU). Baja California: San Felipe (Elliot, 1907:339); Buena Vista Camp (*ibid.*). California: Coyote Wells (Osgood, 1900a:47); Vallecitos (Grinnell, 1933:153).

Perognathus penicillatus atrodorsalis Dalquest

1951. *Perognathus penicillatus atrodorsalis* Dalquest, Jour. Washington Acad. Sci., 41:362, November 14, type from 7 km. W Presa de Guadalupe, San Luis Potosí.

MARGINAL RECORDS.—San Luis Potosí (Dalquest, 1953b:110, unless otherwise noted): type locality; *Presa de Guadalupe*; 10 mi. NW Ciudad del Maíz; 2 mi. NW Tepeyac, 3400 ft., 14 mi. N, 29 mi. W Ciudad del Maíz (39941 KU); *7 km. SE Presa de Guadalupe.*

Perognathus penicillatus eremicus Mearns

1898. *Perognathus (Chaetodipus) eremicus* Mearns, Bull. Amer. Mus. Nat. Hist., 10:300, August 31, type from Fort Hancock, Hudspeth Co., Texas.
1900. *Perognathus penicillatus eremicus,* Osgood, N. Amer. Fauna, 18:48, September 20.

MARGINAL RECORDS (Osgood, 1900a:49, unless otherwise noted).—New Mexico: Tularosa (V. Bailey, 1932:281). Texas: Monahans (V. Bailey, 1905:138); Boquillas (Borell and Bryant, 1942:24). Coahuila (Baker, 1956: 240–241): 1 mi. S Hermanas; Hda. El Tulillo, 5 km. S Hipólito; *4 mi. NNW Saltillo*; La Ventura. San Luis Potosí (Dalquest, 1953b:109): 3 km. E Illescas; 6 km. S Matehuala; Hernández. Coahuila: Jimulco. Durango: Mapimí. Chihuahua: Santa Rosalía. Arizona: San Bernardino Ranch, Mexican boundary. New Mexico: Garfield (V. Bailey, 1932:281).

Perognathus penicillatus minimus Burt

1932. *Perognathus penicillatus minimus* Burt, Trans. San Diego Soc. Nat. Hist., 7:164. October 31, type from Turners Island, lat. 28° 43′ N, long. 112° 19′ W, Gulf of California, Sonora. Known only from type locality.

Perognathus penicillatus penicillatus Woodhouse

1852. *Perognathus penecillatus* [sic] Woodhouse, Proc. Acad. Nat. Sci. Philadelphia, 6:200, December, type from San Francisco Mtn., Coconino Co., Arizona.
1853. *Perognathus penicillatus* Woodhouse, *in* Sitgreaves, Rept. Exped. Zuni and Colorado rivers, U.S. Senate, 32 Cong., 2 Sess., Exec. No. 54, p. 49, pl. 3.

MARGINAL RECORDS.—Arizona: type locality; Norton (Osgood, 1900a:46). Nevada: Colorado River, Jap Ranch, 14 mi. E Searchlight, 500 ft. (Hall, 1946:377).

Perognathus penicillatus pricei J. A. Allen

1894. *Perognathus pricei* J. A. Allen, Bull. Amer. Mus. Nat. Hist., 6:318, November 7, type from Oposura, Sonora.
1900. *Perognathus penicillatus pricei,* Osgood, N. Amer. Fauna, 18:47, September 20.

MARGINAL RECORDS.—Arizona (Osgood, 1900a:48): New River; Phoenix; Mammoth; Fort Bowie. Sonora (Burt, 1938:44): type locality; Ortiz; Batamotal, thence northward along coast to Sierra Pinacate, 41 mi. W Sonoyta. Arizona: Sentinel (Osgood, 1900a:48).

Perognathus penicillatus seri Nelson

1912. *Perognathus penicillatus goldmani* Townsend, Bull. Amer. Mus. Nat. Hist., 31:122, June 14, type from Tiburón Island, Gulf of California, Sonora. Not *Perognathus goldmani* Osgood, 1900, type from Sinaloa, Sinaloa. Known only from type locality.
1912. *Perognathus penicillatus seri* Nelson, Proc. Biol. Soc. Washington, 25:116, June 29, a renaming of *goldmani* Townsend.

Perognathus penicillatus sobrinus Goldman

1939. *Perognathus penicillatus seorsus* Goldman, Proc. Biol. Soc. Washington, 52:34, March 11, type from sand flat along Virgin River, 7 mi. above Bunkerville, Clark Co., Nevada. [Regarded as Mohave County, Arizona, by Hardy, Jour. Mamm., 30:435, November 17, 1949.] Not *Perognathus spinatus seorsus* Burt, 1932, type from Danzante Island, Baja California.
1939. *Perognathus penicillatus sobrinus* Goldman, Jour. Mamm., 20:257, May 15, a renaming of *seorsus* Goldman.

MARGINAL RECORDS (Hall, 1946:376). Nevada: type locality; island in "Boulder" Lake at mouth Virgin River; near mouth Vegas Wash; Vegas Valley; 5 mi. SE Overton, 1200 ft.

Perognathus penicillatus stephensi Merriam

1894. *Perognathus (Chaetodipus) stephensi* Merriam, Proc. Acad. Nat. Sci. Philadelphia, 46:267, September 27, type from Mesquite Valley, northwest arm of Death Valley, Inyo Co., California.
1913. *Perognathus penicillatus stephensi,* Grinnell, Proc. California Acad. Sci., ser. 4, 3:333, August 28.

MARGINAL RECORDS.—California: type locality; Victorville (Grinnell, 1933:153); near Peck's Butte (*ibid.*).

Perognathus arenarius
Little Desert Pocket Mouse

External measurements: 136–182; 70–103; 20–23. Upper parts approximately buffy drab finely mixed with black; underparts white; lateral line usually absent; tail slightly exceeding head and body; skull small and relatively broad; braincase vaulted; nasals slender, zygomatic arches fragile; lower premolar larger than last molar; pelage soft and without bristles.

Perognathus arenarius albescens Huey

1926. *Perognathus arenarius albescens* Huey, Proc. Biol. Soc. Washington, 39:67, July 30, type from San Felipe, Baja California. Known only from the type locality.

Perognathus arenarius albulus Nelson and Goldman

1923. *Perognathus penicillatus albulus* Nelson and Goldman, Proc. Biol. Soc. Washington, 36:159, May 1, type from Magdalena Island, Baja California. Known only from Magdalena Island.
1926. *Perognathus arenarius albulus*, Huey, Proc. Biol. Soc. Washington, 39:68, July 30.

Perognathus arenarius ambiguus Nelson and Goldman

1929. *Perognathus arenarius ambiguus* Nelson and Goldman, Proc. Biol. Soc. Washington, 42:108, March 25, type from Yubay, 30 mi. SE Calamahué, Baja California.

MARGINAL RECORDS (Nelson and Goldman, 1929: 107, unless otherwise noted).—Baja California: San Fernando; Pozo San Augustín, 20 mi. E San Fernando; mouth Calamahué Canyon; type locality; Pozo Altimirano; 20 mi. W San Ignacio; Turtle (San Bartolomé) Bay; San Andrés; 25 mi. N Punta Prieta (Huey, 1939:58).

Perognathus arenarius ammophilus Osgood

1907. *Perognathus penicillatus ammophilus* Osgood, Proc. Biol. Soc. Washington, 20:20, February 23, type from Santa Margarita Island, Baja California. Known only from Santa Margarita Island.
1926. *Perognathus arenarius ammophilus*, Huey, Proc. Biol. Soc. Washington, 39:68, July 30.

Perognathus arenarius arenarius Merriam

1894. *Perognathus arenarius* Merriam, Proc. California Acad. Sci., ser. 2, 4:461, September 25, type from San Jorge, near Comondú, Baja California. Known only from the type locality.

Perognathus arenarius helleri Elliot

1903. *Perognathus helleri* Elliot, Field Columb. Mus., Publ. 74, Zool. Ser., 3(10):166, May 7, type from San Quentín, Baja California. Known only from the type locality.
1929. *Perognathus arenarius helleri*, Huey, Proc. Biol. Soc. Washington, 39:68, July 30.

Perognathus arenarius mexicalis Huey

1939. *Perognathus arenarius mexicalis* Huey, Trans. San Diego Soc. Nat. Hist., 9:57, August 31, type from Los Muertos Canyon fan, lat. 32° 27′ N, long. 115° 53′ W, Gaskill's Tank, near Laguna Salada, Baja California.

MARGINAL RECORDS.—Baja California: De Mara's Well, Laguna Salada (Huey, 1939:58); type locality.

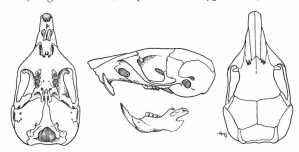

Fig. 287. *Perognathus arenarius arenarius*, San Jorge, Baja California, No. 146016 U.S.N.M., ♀, X 1½.

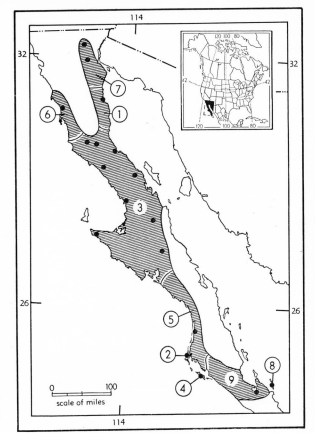

Map 296. *Perognathus arenarius.*

Guide to subspecies	
1. *P. a. albescens*	5. *P. a. arenarius*
2. *P. a. albulus*	6. *P. a. helleri*
3. *P. a. ambiguus*	7. *P. a. mexicalis*
4. *P. a. ammophilus*	8. *P. a. siccus*
	9. *P. a. sublucidus*

Perognathus arenarius siccus Osgood

1907. *Perognathus penicillatus siccus* Osgood, Proc. Biol. Soc. Washington, 20:20, February 23, type from Ceralbo Island, Baja California. Known only from Ceralbo Island.
1929. *Perognathus arenarius siccus*, Nelson and Goldman, Proc. Biol. Soc. Washington, 42:108, March 25.

Perognathus arenarius sublucidus Nelson and Goldman

1929. *Perognathus arenarius sublucidus* Nelson and Goldman, Proc. Biol. Soc. Washington, 41:109, March 25, type from La Paz, Baja California. Known only from the type locality.

Perognathus pernix
Sinaloan Pocket Mouse

External measurements: 162–175; 94–97; 22–24. Upper parts above lateral line hair brown; underparts white or almost so; lateral line buffy and well marked; tail long, thinly haired, faintly crested,

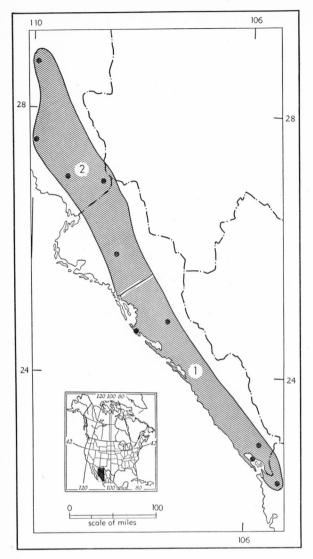

Map 297. *Perognathus pernix.*

1. *P. p. pernix*   2. *P. p. rostratus*

brownish black above, whitish below; skull small, narrow, and elongate; mastoids small; interorbital breadth narrow; nasals comparatively broad and flattened; interparietal wide and produced anteriorly; molariform teeth small; lower premolar larger than last molar; pelage slightly hispid.

Perognathus pernix pernix J. A. Allen

1898. *Perognathus pernix* J. A. Allen, Bull. Amer. Mus. Nat. Hist., 10:149, April 12, type from Rosario, Sinaloa.

MARGINAL RECORDS (Osgood, 1900a:51, unless otherwise noted).—Sinaloa: Culiacán; type locality. Nayarit: Acaponeta. Sinaloa: Hacienda Island, a few miles W Escuinapa (J. A. Allen, 1906:211); Altata.

Perognathus pernix rostratus Osgood

1900. *Perognathus pernix rostratus* Osgood, N. Amer. Fauna, 18:51, September 20, type from Camoa, Río Mayo, Sonora.

MARGINAL RECORDS.—Sonora (Burt, 1938:45): Tecoripa; Guirocoba. Sinaloa: Sinaloa (Osgood, 1900a:52). Sonora (Burt, 1938:45): Chinobampo; Obregon.

intermedius-group
Perognathus intermedius
Rock Pocket Mouse

External measurements: 152–180; 83–103; 19–24. Upper parts highly variable ranging from pale buffy gray (almost white) to nearly black, usually near drab; sides usually paler than back; underparts varying from buffy white to much darker; tail long, crested, and usually much darker distally than proximally, lighter below than above; skull with well-arched braincase; rostrum slender, depressed; interparietal wide, straplike; pelage hispid, weak spines often present on rump.

As the name suggests, the rock pocket mouse shows a strong predilection for rocky situations. Burrows are usually in sandy soils and the entrance to a burrow is under a rock.

Perognathus intermedius ater Dice

1929. *Perognathus intermedius ater* Dice, Occas. Papers Mus. Zool., Univ. Michigan, 203:2, June 19, type from Malpais Spring, 4150 ft., 15 mi. W Three Rivers, Otero Co., New Mexico.

MARGINAL RECORDS.—New Mexico: 8⅓ mi. N, 1 mi. W Carrizozo (Bradt, 1932:325); near Carrizozo (Dice, 1929:3); type locality.

Perognathus intermedius crinitus Benson

1934. *Perognathus intermedius crinitus* Benson, Proc. Biol. Soc. Washington, 47:199, October 2, type from 2.6 mi. W Wupatki Ruins, Coconino Co., Arizona.

MARGINAL RECORDS.—Utah: Rainbow Bridge, 4000 ft. (Durrant, 1952:247). Arizona: Moa Ave (Benson, 1934:200); type locality; S end Grand Canyon Bridge (Benson, 1934:200).

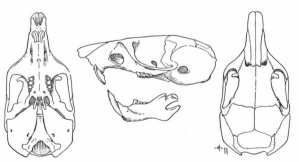

Fig. 288. *Perognathus intermedius lithophilus,* ½ mi. N Puerto Libertad, Sonora, No. 23006 K.U., ♂, X 1½.

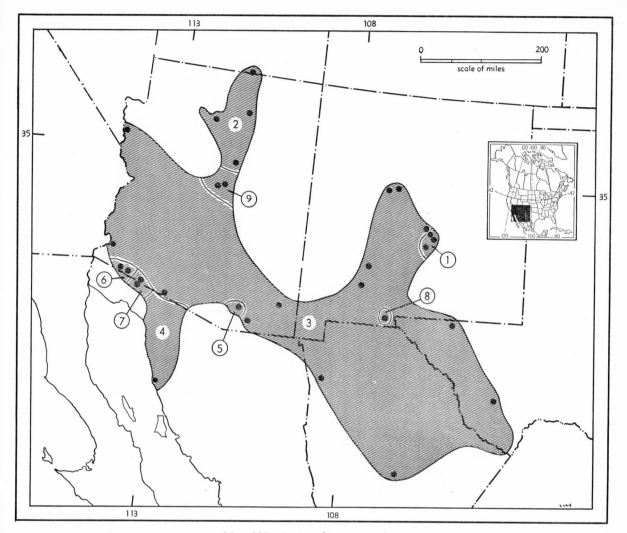

Map 298. *Perognathus intermedius.*

1. *P. i. ater*	4. *P. i. lithophilus*	7. *P. i. pinacate*
2. *P. i. crinitus*	5. *P. i. nigrimontis*	8. *P. i. rupestris*
3. *P. i. intermedius*	6. *P. i. phasma*	9. *P. i. umbrosus*

Perognathus intermedius intermedius Merriam

1889. *Perognathus intermedius* Merriam, N. Amer. Fauna, 1:18, October 25, type from Mud Spring, Mohave Co., Arizona.

1889. *Perognathus obscurus* Merriam, N. Amer. Fauna, 1:20, October 25, type from Camp Apache, Hidalgo Co., New Mexico.

MARGINAL RECORDS.—Arizona: type locality; Fort Bowie (Cahalane, 1939:430). New Mexico (V. Bailey, 1932:282, unless otherwise noted): Lake Valley; Las Palomas; Rio Puerco; Isleta; 8⅓ mi. N, 1 mi. W Carrizozo (Bradt, 1932:325). Texas: 7 mi. N Pine Springs, 5300 ft. (Davis and Robertson, 1944:268); Alpine (Osgood, 1900a:53). Chihuahua: Chihuahua (Osgood, 1900a:53); Casas Grandes (*ibid.*). Arizona: Fort Huachuca (Cahalane, 1939:430); Quitovaquita (Huey, 1942:361); 5 mi. NE Laguna

(Grinnell, 1914:248), thence northward east of the Colorado River to point of beginning.

Perognathus intermedius lithophilus Huey

1937. *Perognathus intermedius lithophilus* Huey, Trans. San Diego Soc. Nat. Hist., 8:355, June 15, type from Puerto Libertad (1½ mi. NW of the freshwater spring on the beach), Sonora. Known only from the type locality.

Perognathus intermedius nigrimontis Blossom

1933. *Perognathus intermedius nigrimontis* Blossom, Occas. Papers Mus. Zool., Univ. Michigan, 265:1, June 21, type from Black Mtn., 10 mi. S Tucson, Pima Co., Arizona. Known only from the type locality.

Perognathus intermedius phasma Goldman

1918. *Perognathus intermedius phasma* Goldman, Proc. Biol. Soc. Washington, 31:22, May 16, type from Tinajas Altas, 1400 ft., Gila Mts., Yuma Co., Arizona.

MARGINAL RECORDS.—Arizona: type locality; Tule Wells (Goldman, 1918a:23).

Perognathus intermedius pinacate Blossom

1933. *Perognathus intermedius pinacate* Blossom, Occas. Papers Mus. Zool., Univ. Michigan, 273:4, October 31, type from Pápago Tanks, Pinacate Mts., Sonora.

MARGINAL RECORDS.—Arizona: Pinacate lava (Blossom, 1933:5). Sonora: type locality.

Perognathus intermedius rupestris Benson

1932. *Perognathus intermedius rupestris* Benson, Univ. California Publ. Zool., 38:337, April 14, type from that part of the lava beds nearest to Kenzin, Dona Ana Co., New Mexico. Known only from the type locality.

Perognathus intermedius umbrosus Benson

1934. *Perognathus intermedius umbrosus* Benson, Proc. Biol. Soc. Washington, 47:200, October 2, type from Camp Verde, Yavapai Co., Arizona.

MARGINAL RECORDS (Benson, 1934:201).—Arizona: 5 mi. NE Camp Verde; type locality; *1 mi. W Camp Verde.*

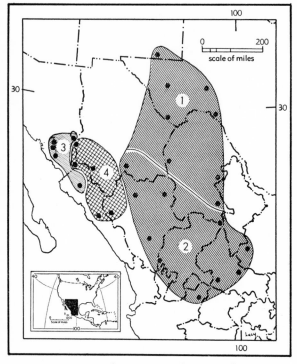

Map 299. Three species of *Perognathus.*

1. *P. nelsoni canescens*   3. *P. goldmani*
2. *P. nelsoni nelsoni*   4. *P. artus*

Perognathus nelsoni
Nelson's Pocket Mouse

External measurements: 182–193; 104–117; 22–23. Upper parts dark brown; underparts white or almost so; lateral line fawn colored, well marked; tail heavily crested, blackish above, whitish below; pelage harsh; skull similar to that of *P. intermedius;* premaxillary tongues extending posterior to nasals.

On the Mexican tableland this is one of the commonest pocket mice; its relationships to *P. lineatus* are not well understood but seem to be close.

Perognathus nelsoni canescens Merriam

1894. *Perognathus (Chaetodipus) intermedius canescens* Merriam, Proc. Acad. Nat. Sci. Philadelphia, 46:267, September 27, type from Jaral, Coahuila.
1900. *Perognathus nelsoni canescens,* Osgood, N. Amer. Fauna, 18:54, September 20.
1938. *Perognathus collis* Blair, Occas. Papers Mus. Zool., Univ. Michigan, 381:1, June 20, type from Limpia Canyon, 4800 ft., about 1 mi. NW Fort Davis, Texas. Regarded as synonym of *canescens* by Borell and Bryant, Univ. California Publ. Zool., 48:25, August 7, 1942.
1938. *Perognathus collis popei* Blair, Occas. Papers Mus. Zool., Univ. Michigan, 381:3, June 20, type from Pinnacle Spring, Brewster Co., Texas. Regarded as inseparable from *canescens* by Borell and Bryant (*loc. cit.*).

MARGINAL RECORDS.—New Mexico: 4 mi. W White City (Webb, 1954:453). Texas: Sheffield (V. Bailey, 1905:140); Comstock (Borell and Bryant, 1942:25). Coahuila: Pánuco, 1220 ft. (56632 KU); 17 mi. N, 8 mi. W Saltillo (35819 KU); 3 mi. NE Sierra Mojada, 4100 ft. (40886 KU). Texas (Borell and Bryant, 1942:25): Pinnacle Spring; 1 mi. NW Fort Davis.—For Coahuila see Baker (1956:238 and fig. 34) for modification of range as here given.

Perognathus nelsoni nelsoni Merriam

1894. *Perognathus (Chaetodipus) nelsoni* Merriam, Proc. Acad. Nat. Sci. Philadelphia, 46:266, September 27, type from Hacienda La Parada, about 25 mi. NW C. San Luis Potosí, San Luis Potosí.

MARGINAL RECORDS.—Chihuahua: 5 mi. E Parral, 5700 ft. (40882 KU). Durango: Mapimí (Osgood, 1900a:53). Coahuila: 8 mi. N La Ventura, 5500 ft. (33137 KU). Tamaulipas: Jaumave (Miller, 1924:284). San Luis Potosí: 2 mi. NW Tepeyac, 3400 ft., 14 mi. N, 29 mi. W Ciudad del Maíz (39930 KU); Jesús María (Osgood, 1900a:53). Jalisco: Lagos (Osgood, 1900a:53). Zacatecas: Hda. San Juan Capistrano (*ibid.*). Durango: 4 mi. W Durango, 6200 ft. (38386 KU); Indé (Osgood, 1900a:53).—For Coahuila see Baker (1956:239 and fig. 34) for modification of range as here given.

Perognathus goldmani Osgood
Goldman's Pocket Mouse

1900. *Perognathus goldmani* Osgood, N. Amer. Fauna, 18:54, September 20, type from Sinaloa, Sinaloa.

External measurements of the type, an adult female: 202, 108, 28. Upper parts distinctly brown across shoulders and anterior part of dorsum, becoming darker—almost blackish—on rump; underparts whitish; lateral line pinkish buff, distinct; tail moderately long and heavily crested; sharply bicolor, blackish above, whitish below; skull large and especially robust; mastoids, compared to those of *P. nelsoni*, smaller and more sculptured; nasals larger; braincase higher and narrower; pelage hispid with a few short bristles on rump; ears large and orbicular.

MARGINAL RECORDS (Burt, 1938:46, unless otherwise noted).—Chihuahua: near Carimechi (Burt and Hooper, 1941:6). Sinaloa: type locality. Sonora: Chinobampo; Tesia; Camoa (Laurie, 1953:386).

Perognathus artus Osgood
Narrow-skulled Pocket Mouse

1900. *Perognathus artus* Osgood, N. Amer. Fauna, 18:55, September 20, type from Batopilas, Chihuahua.

Average external measurement of 5 adult topotypes: 191, 106, 24.6. Color as in *P. goldmani*. "The skins of *artus* are similar to those of *goldmani* except for slightly smaller size, less hairy tail, and broader dorsal tail stripe. The skulls differ in having a broader supraoccipital (least width 6.0, 6.4 mm. in two adult *artus*, and 5.7 mm. in one adult *goldmani*), smaller, more rugose and more prominently ridged mastoids, and greater extensions of the premaxillae beyond the posterior borders of the nasals (less than 1 mm. in *goldmani*, more than 1 mm. in *artus*)" (Burt and Hooper, 1941:6).

MARGINAL RECORDS.—Chihuahua: near Carimechi (Burt and Hooper, 1941:6); type locality. Durango: Chacala (Osgood, 1900a:55). Sinaloa: Culiacán (*ibid.*). Sonora: Guirocoba (Burt, 1938:46).

Perognathus lineatus Dalquest
Lined Pocket Mouse

1951. *Perognathus lineatus* Dalquest, Jour. Washington Acad. Sci., 41:362, November 14, type from 1 km. S Arriaga, San Luis Potosí.

External measurements (average of 8 males and 7 females, respectively) are: 174, 174; 95, 98; 23, 23. Upper parts "dull gray, finely but distinctly lined with buffy, especially on head; general appearance of upper parts near Light Drab or Drab Gray; sides more grayish; underparts white separated from gray of sides by faint, indistinct line of pale buffy; tail dusky above and white beneath" (Dalquest, 1951: 362). Skull larger and broader than in neighboring subspecies of *P. penicillatus*.

MARGINAL RECORDS (Dalquest, 1953b:111).—San Luis Potosí: 6 km. S Matehuala; 10 km. NW Villar; Bledos; type locality; Cerro Peñón Blanco.

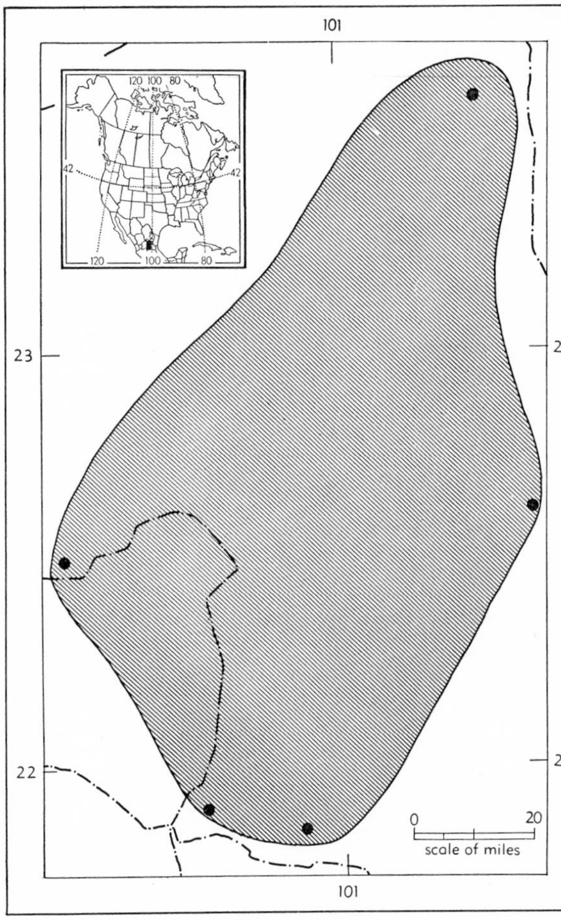

Map 300. *Perognathus lineatus*.

Perognathus fallax
San Diego Pocket Mouse

External measurements: 176–200; 88–118; 23. Upper parts rich brown, becoming blackish over rump; underparts white or whitish; lateral line buffy; tail long, crested, distinctly bicolor; skull with arched braincase; interparietal wide, anterior angle obsolete; mastoids large; pelage harsh, with spines on rump.

Perognathus fallax fallax Merriam

1889. *Perognathus fallax* Merriam, N. Amer. Fauna, 1:19, October 25, type from Reche Canyon, 1250 ft., 3 mi. SE Colton, San Bernardino Co., California.

MARGINAL RECORDS.—California: 3 mi. N Claremont, 1600 ft. (Vaughan, 1954:548); type locality; Banning, 2500 ft. (Grinnell, 1933:153); Jacumba (*ibid.*). Baja California (Elliot, 1907:341): San Matías Spring; Mattomi; San Quentín, thence up the coast to California: San Onofre (Grinnell, 1933:153); *Riverside* (Osgood, 1900a:56).

Perognathus fallax inopinus Nelson and Goldman

1929. *Perognathus fallax inopinus* Nelson and Goldman, Proc. Biol. Soc. Washington, 42:110, March 25, type from Turtle (San Bartolomé) Bay, Baja California. Known only from the type locality.

Perognathus fallax pallidus Mearns

1901. *Perognathus fallax pallidus* Mearns, Proc. Biol. Soc. Washington, 14:135, August 9, type from Mountain Spring, half way up the east slope of the Coast Range Mountains, on the Mexican boundary, Imperial Co., California.

MARGINAL RECORDS (Grinnell, 1933:153, unless otherwise noted).—California: 2 mi. E Valyermo, 4500 ft. (Vaughan, 1954:549); Oro Grande; Twenty-nine Palms; type locality; San Felipe Canyon (Mearns, 1901:136); Cabezon.

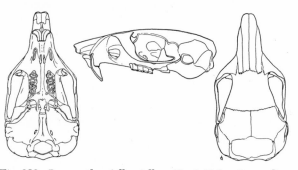

Fig. 289. *Perognathus fallax fallax*, 4¾ mi. N San Bernardino, 1600 ft., San Bernardino Co., California, No. 77119 M.V.Z., ♀, X 1½.

Perognathus anthonyi Osgood
Anthony's Pocket Mouse

1900. *Perognathus anthonyi* Osgood, N. Amer. Fauna, 18: 56, September 20, type from South Bay, Cerros (Cedros) Island, Baja California. Known only from the type locality.

External measurements of type, adult female, are: 168, 92, 23.5. Upper parts grayish fawn mixed with black; underparts whitish; tail long, dusky above, whitish below; lateral line brownish fawn. "Skull.—Similar to *P. fallax*; cranium less arched; rostrum heavier; mastoids smaller; interparietal smaller and shorter; zygomatic breadth greater anteriorly" (Osgood, 1900a:56).

californicus-group
Perognathus californicus
California Pocket Mouse

External measurements: 190–235; 103–143; 24–29. Upper parts brownish gray flecked with fulvous; underparts yellowish white; tail crested, bicolor; braincase markedly vaulted; mastoids especially small; mastoid breadth reduced; occiput greatly produced posteriorly; interparietal approximately twice as long as broad; lower premolar but little larger than last molar; pelage markedly hispid; strong spines present on rump and flanks; ears much elongated.

Perognathus californicus bensoni von Bloeker

1938. *Perognathus californicus bensoni* von Bloeker, Proc. Biol. Soc. Washington, 51:197, December 23, type from Stonewall Creek, 1300 ft., about 6.3 mi. NE Soledad, Monterey Co., California.

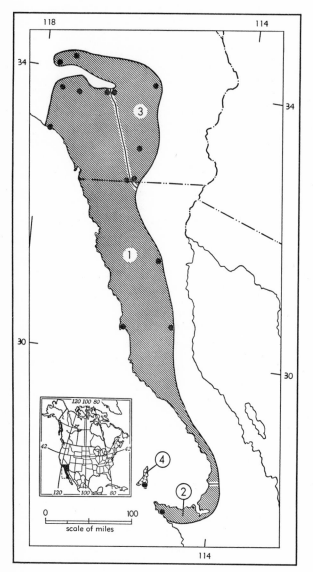

Map 301. *Perognathus fallax* and *Perognathus anthonyi*.

1. *P. fallax fallax*
2. *P. fallax inopinus*
3. *P. fallax pallidus*
4. *P. anthonyi*

MARGINAL RECORDS (von Bloeker, 1938:198–199). —California: 10 mi. W Gustine; Sweeney's Ranch, 1200 ft., Herrero Canyon, 22 mi. S Los Baños; Waltham Creek, 1850 ft., 4½ mi. SE Priest Valley; Carrizo Plains, 2000 ft., 7 mi. SE Simmler; Santa Margarita, 996 ft.; Jolon, 1100 ft.; E base Sierra de Salinas, 250 ft., 2½ mi. W Soledad Mission.

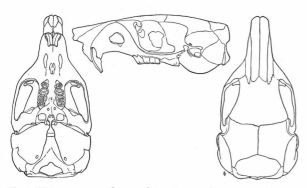

Fig. 290. *Perognathus californicus californicus,* N side Claremont Canyon, 600 ft., Alameda Co., California, No. 65120 M.V.Z., ♂, X 1½.

Perognathus californicus bernardinus Benson

1930. *Perognathus californicus bernardinus* Benson, Univ. California Publ. Zool., 30:449, September 6, type from 2 mi. E. Strawberry Peak, 5750 ft., San Bernardino Mts., San Bernardino Co., California.

MARGINAL RECORDS (Benson, 1930:450).—California: Big Pines, 6860 ft.; Seven Oaks, 5100 ft.; Strawberry Valley, 6000 ft.

Perognathus californicus californicus Merriam

1889. *Perognathus californicus* Merriam, N. Amer. Fauna, 1:26, October 25, type from Berkeley, Alameda Co., California.
1889. *Perognathus armatus* Merriam, N. Amer. Fauna, 1:27, October 25, type from Mt. Diablo, Contra Costa Co., California.

MARGINAL RECORDS.—California: E and S of San Francisco Bay from Sommersville (Hooper, 1944:41); Gilroy (Osgood, 1900a:58); Portola (Elliot, 1907:343); Redwood City (Grinnell, 1933:154), northward to point of beginning.

Perognathus californicus dispar Osgood

1900. *Perognathus californicus dispar* Osgood, N. Amer. Fauna, 18:58, September 20, type from Carpenteria, Santa Barbara Co., California.

MARGINAL RECORDS (Osgood, 1900a:59, unless otherwise noted).—California: (eastern segment of range) Auburn (Grinnell, 1933:154); Hume (*ibid.*); Dunlap (*ibid.*) (western segment of range) San Luis Obispo; Santa Paula; San Fernando; Santa Monica, thence up coast to point of beginning. Note: the separated segments of the geographic range of this subspecies are undoubtedly the result of failure of some taxonomists to take cognizance of earlier published records of occurrence. The eastern segment of the range is occupied by animals probably sub-

specifically distinct from those occurring along the coast. We have not attempted to solve the problem because S. B. Benson at Berkeley is using the pertinent specimens in completing his monograph of *Perognathus.*

Perognathus californicus femoralis J. A. Allen

1891. *Perognathus (Chaetodipus) femoralis* J. A. Allen, Bull. Amer. Mus. Nat. Hist., 3:281, June 30, type from Dulzura, San Diego Co., California.
1913. *Perognathus californicus femoralis,* Grinnell, Proc. California Acad. Sci., ser. 4, 3:335, August 28.

MARGINAL RECORDS.—California: mouth of Santa Margarita River (von Bloeker, 1931:432); Banner (Grinnell, 1933:155). Baja California: Hanson Lagoon, Hanson Laguna Mts. (Elliot, 1907:342). California: type locality.

Perognathus californicus marinensis von Bloeker

1938. *Perognathus californicus marinensis* von Bloeker, Proc. Biol. Soc. Washington, 51:199, December 23, type

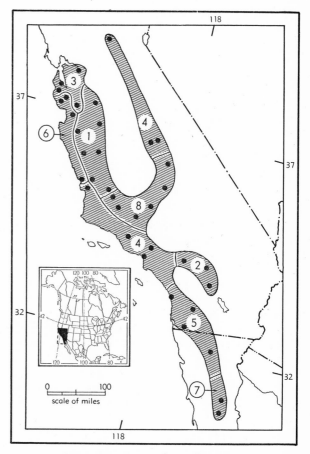

Map 302. *Perognathus californicus.*

1. *P. c. bensoni*	5. *P. c. femoralis*
2. *P. c. bernardinus*	6. *P. c. marinensis*
3. *P. c. californicus*	7. *P. c. mesopolius*
4. *P. c. dispar*	8. *P. c. ochrus*

from Indian Harbor, 50 ft., 1½ mi. S Marina, Monterey Co., California.

MARGINAL RECORDS (von Bloeker, 1938:199–200). —California: Black Mountain; N end Gabilan Mts., 500 ft., 3½ mi. W San Juan Bautista; 4½ mi. S Morro; Bear Creek, 650 ft., 2–4½ mi. NE Boulder Creek.

Perognathus californicus mesopolius Elliot

1903. *Perognathus femoralis mesopolius* Elliot, Field Columb. Mus., Publ. 74, Zool. Ser., 3(10):168, May 7, type from Piñon, 5000 ft., Sierra San Pedro Mártir, Baja California.
1955. *Perognathus californicus mesopolius,* Miller and Kellogg, Bull. U.S. Nat. Mus., 205:280, March 3.

MARGINAL RECORDS (Elliot, 1907:342).—Baja California: *type locality; Agua de las Fresas*; Santa Eulalia; Santa Rosa.

Perognathus californicus ochrus Osgood

1904. *Perognathus californicus ochrus* Osgood, Proc. Biol. Soc. Washington, 17:128, June 9, type from Santiago Spring, 16 mi. SW McKittrick, Kern Co., California.

MARGINAL RECORDS.—California: Jordan Hot Springs (Grinnell, 1933:154); Onyx (Osgood, 1904:128); Tehachapi (*ibid.*); Cuddy Canyon (Grinnell, 1933:154); Cayama Valley (Osgood, 1904:128); Painted Rock, 25 mi. SE Simmler (*ibid.*).

spinatus-group
Perognathus spinatus
Spiny Pocket Mouse

External measurements: 164–225; 89–128; 20–28. Upper parts brownish to pale buffy yellow; underparts white or buffy-white; lateral line usually obsolete, and pale ecru when present; tail long, crested, brownish above, white below; skull comparatively slender and flattened; mastoids small (smaller, for example, than in *P. fallax* and *P. intermedius*); interparietal broad and anterior angle faintly expressed; supraorbital ridge usually slightly trenchant; lower premolar and last molar approximately equal in size.

In the arid parts of southern California and Baja California this is one of the commoner pocket mice. It occurs usually in only the most arid habitats. For the most part the subspecies are, for pocket mice, strongly differentiated, possibly because so many are insular.

Perognathus spinatus bryanti Merriam

1894. *Perognathus bryanti* Merriam, Proc. California Acad. Sci., ser. 2, 4:458, September 25, type from San José Island, Gulf of California, Baja California. Known only from the type locality.
1930. *P[erognathus]. s[pinatus]. bryanti,* Benson, Univ. California Publ. Zool., 30:452, September 6.

Perognathus spinatus evermanni Nelson and Goldman

1929. *Perognathus evermanni* Nelson and Goldman, Proc. Biol. Soc. Washington, 42:111, March 25, type from Mejía Island, near N end Angel de la Guarda Island, Baja California. Known only from Mejía Island.
1932. *Perognathus spinatus evermanni,* Burt, Trans. San Diego Soc. Nat. Hist., 7:165, October 31.

Perognathus spinatus guardiae Burt

1932. *Perognathus spinatus guardiae* Burt, Trans. San Diego Soc. Nat. Hist., 7:165, October 31, type from Puerto Refugio, 30 ft., N end Angel de la Guarda Island, Gulf of California, Baja California. Known only from the type locality.

Perognathus spinatus lambi Benson

1930. *Perognathus spinatus lambi* Benson, Univ. California Publ. Zool., 32:452, September 6, type from San Gabriel, Espíritu Santo Island, Baja California. Known only from the type locality.

Perognathus spinatus latijugularis Burt

1932. *Perognathus spinatus latijugularis* Burt, Trans. San Diego Soc. Nat. Hist., 7:168, October 31, type from San Francisco Island, lat. 24° 50′ N, long. 110° 34′ W, Gulf of California, Baja California. Known only from the type locality.

Perognathus spinatus magdalenae Osgood

1907. *Perognathus spinatus magdalenae* Osgood, Proc. Biol. Soc. Washington, 20:21, February 23, type from Magdalena Island, Baja California. Known only from the type locality.

Perognathus spinatus marcosensis Burt

1932. *Perognathus spinatus marcosensis* Burt, Trans. San Diego Soc. Nat. Hist., 7:166, October 31, type from San Marcos Island, lat. 27° 13′ N, long. 112° 05′ W, Gulf of California, Baja California. Known only from the type locality.

Perognathus spinatus margaritae Merriam

1894. *Perognathus margaritae* Merriam, Proc. California Acad. Sci., ser. 2, 4:459, September 25, type from Margarita Island, Baja California. Known only from the type locality.
1930. *P[erognathus]. s[pinatus]. margaritae,* Benson, Univ. California Publ. Zool., 32:452, September 6.

Perognathus spinatus occultus Nelson

1912. *Perognathus spinatus nelsoni* Townsend, Bull. Amer. Mus. Nat. Hist., 31:122, June 14, type from Carmen Island, Gulf of California, Baja California. Not *Perognathus (Chaetodipus) nelsoni* Merriam, 1894, type from Hacienda La Parada, San Luis Potosí. Known only from the type locality.

1912. *Perognathus spinatus occultus* Nelson, Proc. Biol. Soc. Washington, 25:116, June 29, a renaming of *nelsoni* Townsend.

Perognathus spinatus peninsulae Merriam

1894. *Perognathus spinatus peninsulae* Merriam, Proc. California Acad. Sci., ser. 2, 4:460, September 25, type from San José del Cabo, Baja California.

MARGINAL RECORDS.—Baja California (Huey, 1930: 233): From San Ignacio and Llano de San Bruno southward to the tip of the peninsula.

Perognathus spinatus prietae Huey

1930. *Perognathus spinatus prietae* Huey, Trans. San Diego Soc. Nat. Hist., 6:232, December 24, type from 25 mi. N Punta Prieta, lat. 29° 24' N, long. 114° 24' W, Baja California.

MARGINAL RECORDS (Huey, 1930:233).—Baja California: San Agustín; Cataviña; type locality.

Perognathus spinatus pullus Burt

1932. *Perognathus spinatus pullus* Burt, Trans. San Diego Soc. Nat. Hist., 7:166, October 31, type from Coronados Island, lat. 26° 06' N, long. 111° 18' W, Gulf of California, Baja California. Known only from the type locality.

Perognathus spinatus rufescens Huey

1930. *Perognathus spinatus rufescens* Huey, Trans. San Diego Soc. Nat. Hist., 6:231, December 24, type from mouth Palm Canyon, Borego Valley, San Diego Co., California.

MARGINAL RECORDS.—California: Palm Springs (Huey, 1930:233); San Felipe Canyon (*ibid.*); Mountain Spring (Grinnell, 1933:156); Vallecitos (Elliot, 1907:344).

Perognathus spinatus seorsus Burt

1932. *Perognathus spinatus seorsus* Burt, Trans. San Diego Soc. Nat. Hist., 7:167, October 31, type from Danzante Island, lat. 25° 47' N, long. 111° 11' W, Gulf of California, Baja California. Known only from the type locality.

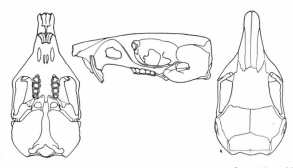

Fig. 291. *Perognathus spinatus spinatus*, Chocolate Mts., 11 mi. NE Niland, Imperial Co., California, No. 77285 M.V.Z., ♀, X 1½.

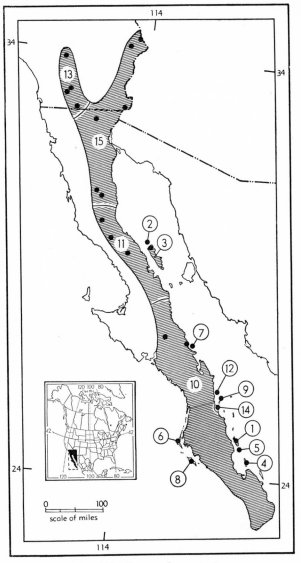

Map 303. *Perognathus spinatus.*

Guide to subspecies
1. *P. s. bryanti*
2. *P. s. evermanni*
3. *P. s. guardiae*
4. *P. s. lambi*
5. *P. s. latijugularis*
6. *P. s. magdalenae*
7. *P. s. macrosensis*
8. *P. s. margaritae*
9. *P. s. occultus*
10. *P. s. peninsulae*
11. *P. s. prietae*
12. *P. s. pullus*
13. *P. s. rufescens*
14. *P. s. seorsus*
15. *P. s. spinatus*

Perognathus spinatus spinatus Merriam

1889. *Perognathus spinatus* Merriam, N. Amer. Fauna, 1:21, October 25, type from 25 mi. below The Needles, Colorado River, San Bernardino Co., California.

MARGINAL RECORDS.—California: type locality; Pilot Knob, 200 ft. (Grinnell, 1933:155). Baja California: Mattomi (Elliot, 1907:344); Parral (*ibid.*); Cocopah Mts. (Osgood, 1900a:60). California: Horn Mine, 1000 ft., E base Turtle Mts. (Grinnell, 1933:155).

Genus **Microdipodops** Merriam
Kangaroo Mice

Revised by Hall, Field Mus. Nat. Hist., Zool. Ser., 27: 233–277, December 8, 1941.

1891. *Microdipodops* Merriam, N. Amer. Fauna, 5:115, July 30. Type, *Microdipodops megacephalus* Merriam.

External measurements: 130–180; 64–103; 22.3–27. Weight, 10.2–16.8 grams; basal length of skull (measured from anterior faces of upper incisors), 17.3–19.2; greatest breadth of skull, 17.7–20.8. Tail averaging slightly longer than head and body; tail short-haired, lacking terminal tuft and of greater diameter in middle than at base or tip; sole of hind foot densely covered with long hair; no dermal gland on back between shoulders; auditory bullae more highly inflated than in any other heteromyid, reaching below level of grinding surface of cheek-teeth and in many individuals extending anteriorly beyond glenoid fossae; bullae meeting in a symphysis across ventral face of basisphenoid; anterolateral face of zygomatic process of maxilla not much expanded, resulting in hamular process of lacrimal projecting free of maxilla; cheek-teeth hypsodont but each with more than one root, except M3 and m3; molars with H-pattern; P4 as in *Perognathus*, p4 with 5 or 6 cusps; cusps soon worn away with result that occlusal face of each cheek-tooth is an area of dentine completely surrounded by enamel; no pit behind m3; manus long and slender; tibia and fibula fused throughout almost three-fifths of their length; cervical vertebrae mostly fused; caudal vertebrae lacking median ventral foramen.

In this genus the number of embryos, in 54 *M. megacephalus* and 56 *M. pallidus*, ranged from 1 to 7 in the former and 1 to 6 in the latter. In each species the mean was 3.9 and the mode, 4.0.

KEY TO SPECIES OF MICRODIPODOPS

1. Upper parts blackish; top of tail distally tipped with black; incisive foramina widest posteriorly or at middle; premaxillae extending but little posteriorly to nasals.
   M. megacephalus, p. 508
1'. Upper parts near (*e*) Light Pinkish Cinnamon; top of tail not black distally but same color as base; incisive foramina parallel-sided; premaxillae extending far behind nasals. . . . . *M. pallidus*, p. 510

Microdipodops megacephalus
Dark Kangaroo Mouse

Upper parts brownish, blackish or grayish; top of distal 6th to half of tail ordinarily darker than back; hair of underparts plumbeous and white-tipped; hind foot, 23–25; anterior palatine foramina wide posteriorly and tapering to sharp point anteriorly; nasals extending posteriorly quite, or almost, as far as premaxillae. The few areas in which some of the above mentioned characters do not hold are far removed from the geographic range of the other species, *M. pallidus*.

Microdipodops megacephalus albiventer Hall and Durrant

1937. *Microdipodops pallidus albiventer* Hall and Durrant, Jour. Mamm., 18:357, August 14, type from Desert Valley, 5300 ft., 21 mi. W Panaca, Lincoln Co., Nevada. Known only from the type locality.
1941. *Microdipodops megacephalus albiventer*, Hall, Field Mus. Nat. Hist., Zool. Ser., 27:263, December 8.

Microdipodops megacephalus ambiguus Hall

1941. *Microdipodops megacephalus ambiguus* Hall, Field Mus. Nat. Hist., Zool. Ser., 27:252, December 8, type from 1¼ mi. S Sulphur, 4050 ft., Humboldt Co., Nevada.

MARGINAL RECORDS (Hall, 1946:391, except as otherwise noted).—Nevada: ½ mi. W Quinn River Crossing, 4100 ft.; 6 mi. N Golconda; 10 mi. NNW Golconda; 7 mi. N Winnemucca, 4400 ft.; 3 mi. SW Winnemucca, 4500 ft.; 15 mi. SW Winnemucca; 1 mi. W Humboldt, 4180 ft.; ¾ mi. S Sulphur, 4050 ft.; 1 mi. SE Wadsworth, 4200 ft.; 3½ mi. E Flanigan, 4200 ft. California: 1 mi. SW Warm Spring, 4000 ft. (Hall, 1941:255). Nevada: Smoke Creek, 9 mi. E California boundary, 3900 ft.; 2½ mi. E, and 13 mi. N Gerlach, 4050 ft.

Microdipodops megacephalus californicus Merriam

1901. *Microdipodops californicus* Merriam, Proc. Biol. Soc. Washington, 14:128, July 19, type from Sierra Valley, near Vinton, Plumas Co., California.
1941. *Microdipodops megacephalus californicus*, Hall, Field Mus. Nat. Hist., Zool. Ser., 27:250, December 8.

MARGINAL RECORDS.—Nevada (Hall, 1946:389): 2¾ mi. SW Pyramid, 4300 ft.; 3½ mi. E Carson City, 4700 ft.; Junction House, 4500 ft. California: type locality.

Microdipodops megacephalus leucotis Hall and Durrant

1941. *Microdipodops megacephalus leucotis* Hall and Durrant, Murrelet, 22:6, April 30, type from 18 mi. SW Orr's Ranch, 4400 ft., Tooele Co., Utah. Known only from the type locality.

Microdipodops megacephalus medius Hall

1941. *Microdipodops megacephalus medius* Hall, Field Mus. Nat. Hist., Zool. Ser., 27:256, December 8, type from 3 mi. S Vernon, 4250 ft., Pershing Co., Nevada.

MARGINAL RECORDS.—Nevada (Hall, 1946:392): 3 mi. SW Vernon, 4300 ft.; type locality; 21 mi. W, 2 mi. N Lovelock, 4000 ft.

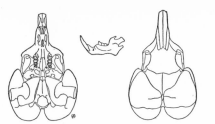

Fig. 292. *Microdipodops megacephalus megacephalus,* Winzell, Nevada, No. 70942 M.V.Z., ♀ (except lower jaw, which is No. 58077 M.V.Z., ♂, from 6½ mi. N Fish Lake, 6700 ft., Fish Spring Valley, Nye Co., Nevada), X 1.

Microdipodops megacephalus megacephalus Merriam

1891. *Microdipodops megacephalus* Merriam, N. Amer. Fauna, 5:116, July 30, type from Halleck, Elko Co., Nevada.

MARGINAL RECORDS.—Nevada (Hall, 1946:393–394): 9 mi. NE San Jacinto, 5300 ft.; Cobre, 6100 ft.; 5 mi. SE Greens Ranch, Steptoe Valley, 5900 ft.; 7 mi. SW Osceola, Spring Valley, 6275 ft.; 4 mi. S Shoshone, Spring Valley, 5900 ft.; 3 mi. S. Geyser Pass, Duck Valley, 6050 ft.; Old Mill, N end Reveille Valley, 6200 ft.; 2½ mi. E, N Twin Spring, S end Hot Creek Valley, 5400 ft.; 3½ mi. E Hot Creek, Hot Creek Valley, 5650 ft.; 6½ mi. N Fish Lake, Fish Spring Valley, 6700 ft.; 15½ mi. NE Tonopah, Ralston Valley, 5800 ft.; 5 mi. N Belmont, Monitor Valley; 30 mi. N Belmont, Monitor Valley; Dutch Flat Schoolhouse, Reese River, 6715 ft.; 6 mi. ENE Smiths Creek Ranch, 5550 ft.; Winzell, 3–5 mi. W Halleck, 5200–5300 ft.; Marys River, 22 mi. N Deeth, 5800 ft.; 15 mi. S Contact, 5800 ft.

Microdipodops megacephalus nasutus Hall

1941. *Microdipodops megacephalus nasutus* Hall, Field Mus. Nat. Hist., Zool. Ser., 27:251, December 8, type from Fletcher, 6098 ft., Mineral Co., Nevada. Known only from the type locality.

Microdipodops megacephalus nexus Hall

1941. *Microdipodops megacephalus nexus* Hall, Field Mus. Nat. Hist., Zool. Ser., 27:257, December 8, type from 3 mi. S Izenhood, Lander Co., Nevada.

MARGINAL RECORDS.—Nevada (Hall, 1946:392): 5 mi. NE Golconda; Izenhood; type locality.

Microdipodops megacephalus oregonus Merriam

1901. *Microdipodops megacephalus oregonus* Merriam, Proc. Biol. Soc. Washington, 14:127, July 19, type from Wild Horse Creek, 4 mi. NW Alvord Lake, Harney Co., Oregon.

MARGINAL RECORDS.—Oregon: Becker Ranch, Powell Butte (Hall, 1941:249); 1 mi. S Narrows, 4200 ft. (*ibid.*); head of Crooked Creek (V. Bailey, 1936:241); White Horse Sink (*ibid.*); 1½ mi. E Denio, 4200 ft. (Hall, 1941: 249). Nevada (Hall, 1946:388): 1 mi. E mouth Little High Rock Canyon, 5000 ft.; 10 mi. SE Hausen, 4675 ft.

California: 6 mi. N Observation Peak, 5300 ft. (Hall, 1941: 250); Sand Creek (Hall, 1941:249). Oregon: NE edge Alkali Lake, 4200 ft. (*ibid.*).

Microdipodops megacephalus paululus Hall and Durrant

1941. *Microdipodops megacephalus paululus* Hall and Durrant, Murrelet, 22:5, April 30, type from Pine Valley, ½ mi. E headquarters building of Desert Range Exp. Station, U.S. Forest Service, sec. 33, T. 25 S, R. 17 W, Salt Lake B.M., Millard Co. Utah.

MARGINAL RECORDS.—Utah (Durrant, 1952:252): 4 mi. S Gandy, 5000 ft.; White Valley, 60 mi. W Delta; type locality; 5 mi. S Garrison, 5400 ft.

Microdipodops megacephalus polionotus Grinnell

1914. *Microdipodops polionotus* Grinnell, Univ. California Publ. Zool., 12:302, April 15, type from McKeever's Ranch, 2 mi. S Benton Station, 5200 ft., Mono Co., California.

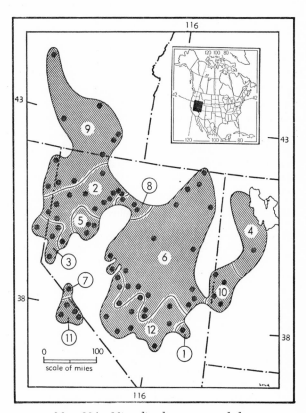

Map 304. *Microdipodops megacephalus.*

1. *M. m. albiventer*	7. *M. m. nasutus*
2. *M. m. ambiguus*	8. *M. m. nexus*
3. *M. m. californicus*	9. *M. m. oregonus*
4. *M. m. leucotis*	10. *M. m. paululus*
5. *M. m. medius*	11. *M. m. polionotus*
6. *M. m. megacephalus*	12. *M. m. sabulonis*

1941. *Microdipodops megacephalus polionotus*, Hall, Field Mus. Nat. Hist., Zool. Ser., 27:251, December 8.

MARGINAL RECORDS.—California (Hall, 1941:252): E side Mono Lake; Pellisier Ranch, 5600 ft., 5 mi. N Benton; Taylor Ranch, 5300 ft., 2 mi. S Benton Station; Taylor Valley, 7000 ft., 25 mi. W Benton Station.

Microdipodops megacephalus sabulonis Hall

1941. *Microdipodops megacephalus sabulonis* Hall, Proc. Biol. Soc. Washington, 54:59, May 20, type from 5 mi. SE Kawich P.O., 5400 ft., Kawich Valley, Nye Co., Nevada.

MARGINAL RECORDS.—Nevada (Hall, 1946:395): 4 mi. SE Millet, 5500 ft.; 13 mi. NE San Antonio; 9 mi. W, 3 mi. S Tybo, 6200 ft.; 34 mi. E, 1 mi. N Tonopah, 5650 ft.; 16½ mi. WSW Sunnyside, White River Valley, 5500 ft.; 10 mi. N Seeman Pass, 4650 ft., Coal Valley; 15 mi. S Groom Baldy; 11½ mi. SW Silverbow, Cactus Flat, 5400 ft.; 14 mi. SE Goldfield, Stonewall Flat, 4700 ft.; 13½ mi. NW Goldfield, 4850 ft.

Microdipodops pallidus
Pale Kangaroo Mouse

Upper parts near Light Pinkish Cinnamon, lightly marked with buffy or blackish; upper parts of tail approximately same color as upper parts of body and lacking black tip; hair of underparts everywhere white to base; hind foot averaging more than 25 mm. long; anterior palatine foramina parallel-sided; premaxillae extending well behind nasals.

This species has been found only on fine sand that supports some plant growth.

Microdipodops pallidus ammophilus Hall

1941. *Microdipodops pallidus ammophilus* Hall, Field Mus. Nat. Hist., Zool. Ser., 27:273, December 8, type from Able Spring, 12½ mi. S Lock's Ranch, Railroad Valley, 5000 ft., Nye Co., Nevada.

MARGINAL RECORDS.—Nevada (Hall, 1946:402): Railroad Valley, 5000 ft., 2½ mi. S Lock's Ranch; 9½ mi. E New Reveille, Railroad Valley, 5100 ft.

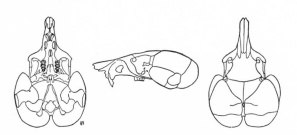

Fig. 293. *Microdipodops pallidus pallidus*, 8 mi. SE Blair, Nevada, No. 59344 M.V.Z., ♀, X 1.

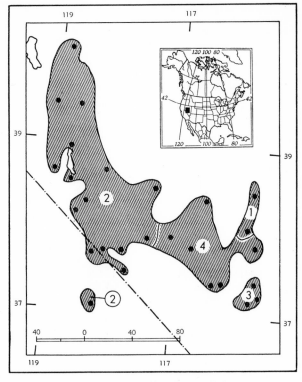

Map 305. *Microdipodops pallidus.*

1. *M. p. ammophilus*   3. *M. p. purus*
2. *M. p. pallidus*   4. *M. p. ruficollaris*

Microdipodops pallidus pallidus Merriam

1901. *Microdipodops pallidus* Merriam, Proc. Biol. Soc. Washington, 14:127, July 19, type from Mountain Well, Churchill Co., Nevada.
1926. *Microdipodops megacephalus lucidus* Goldman, Proc. Biol. Soc. Washington, 39:127, December 27, type from 8 mi. SE Blair, 4500 ft., Esmeralda Co., Nevada.
1927. *Microdipodops megacephalus dickeyi* Goldman, Proc. Biol. Soc. Washington, 40:115, September 26, type from 3 mi. SE Oasis, 5150 ft., Mono Co., California.

MARGINAL RECORDS (Hall, 1946:399, except as otherwise noted).—Nevada: 21 mi. W, 2 mi. N Lovelock, 4000 ft.; type locality; Fingerrock Wash, Stewart Valley, 5400 ft.; 5½ mi. NE San Antonio, 5700 ft.; 13½ mi. NW Goldfield, 4850 ft.; 8 mi. SE Blair, 4500 ft.; 2 mi. SE Dyer, 4900–4950 ft.; mouth Palmetto Wash, 5350 ft. California (Hall, 1941:271): Deep Spring Valley, 4900–5000 ft.; 4½ to 5½ mi. SE Oasis, 5300 ft. Nevada: Huntoon Valley, 5700 ft.; Marietta, 4900 ft.; Cat Creek, 4 mi. W Hawthorne, 4500 ft.; 3 mi. S Schurz, 4100 ft.; 11¾ mi. S, 2¾ mi. E Yerrington, 4650 ft.; 9 mi. W Fallon, 4000 ft.

Microdipodops pallidus purus Hall

1941. *Microdipodops pallidus purus* Hall, Field Mus. Nat. Hist., Zool. Ser., 27:273, December 8, type from 14½ mi. S Groom Baldy, Lincoln Co., Nevada.

MARGINAL RECORDS.—Nevada (Hall, 1946:403): Desert Valley, 8 mi. SW Hancock Summit, 5300 ft.; 5½ mi. N Summit Spring, 4700 ft.; 15 mi. S Groom Baldy.

Microdipodops pallidus ruficollaris Hall

1941. *Microdipodos* [misspelling for *Microdipodops*] *pallidus ruficollaris* Hall, Proc. Biol. Soc. Washington, 54:60, May 20, type from 5 mi. SE Kawich P.O., 5400 ft., Kawich Valley, Nye Co., Nevada.

MARGINAL RECORDS.—Nevada (Hall, 1946:402): 9 mi. W, 3 mi. S Tybo, 6200 ft.; 17 mi. N Groom Baldy, Penoyer Valley; 5⁷⁄₁₀ mi. SE Kawich P.O., Kawich Valley, 5400 ft.; 6 mi. SW Kawich P.O., Gold Flat, 5100 ft.; 11½ mi. SW Silverbow, Cactus Flat, 5400 ft.; N shore Mud Lake, S end Ralston Valley, 5300 ft.

Subfamily DIPODOMYINAE

Cheek-teeth as in Perognathinae, except that H-pattern is always present; cheek-teeth progressively hypsodont in geologically later kinds, which show progressive loss of enamel with result that cheek-teeth of *Dipodomys* are almost ever-growing; in adults, enamel limited to anterior and posterior plates; M$\frac{3}{3}$ small; increased height of crown not affecting pattern, which is rapidly destroyed, leaving only an oval of enamel; p4 never more than 5-cusped, the 5th appearing in center of metalophid; ventral surface of tympanic bullae rarely reaching level of grinding surface of cheek-teeth, never appreciably below that level; no ethmoid foramen in frontal; zygomatic root of maxilla expanded anteroposteriorly; center of palate between premolars ridged; pterygoid fossae double; caudal vertebrae with median ventral foramina; calcaneo-navicular or calcaneo-cuneiform articulation present (after Wood, 1935:117).

Genus Dipodomys Gray—Kangaroo Rats

Arranged according to the list published by Setzer, Univ. Kansas Publ., Mus. Nat. Hist., 1:494–496, December 27, 1949.

1841. *Dipodomys* Gray, Ann. and Mag. Nat. Hist., ser. 1, 7:521, August. Type, *Dipodomys phillipsii* Gray.

1867. *Perodipus* Fitzinger, Sitzungsber. k. Akad. Wiss., Wien, Math-Nat., Abth. 1, 56:126. Type, *Dipodomys agilis* Gambel. For taxonomic status, see Grinnell, Proc. Biol. Soc. Washington, 32:203, December 31, 1919.
1890. *Dipodops* Merriam, N. Amer. Fauna, 3:71, September 11. Type, *Dipodomys agilis* Gambel.

External measurements: 208–365; 100–212; 34–58; weight, 33.8–138.0 grams; basal length of skull (measured from front of upper incisors), 23.7–32.5; breadth of skull across auditory bullae, 21.3–31.9. Underparts, upper lips, spot above each eye, spot behind each ear, forelegs (except in some individuals, which have pigmented hairs on outer sides of forelegs), forefeet and antiplantar faces of hind feet white; white stripe extending from flank to base of tail and isolating patch of pigmented hair on each hind leg, this patch being some shade of buff or brownish like upper parts; tail white all around at base and having white stripes for entire length on each side; dark stripe extending down top of tail and in most species a second dark stripe on underside of tail; tail tufted in most species; fur silky, plumbeous basally on upper parts and white to base on underparts. Sleekness may result from secretion of dermal gland on back between shoulders. Hind legs large and 5th toe on large hind feet vestigial or wanting. Cervical vertebrae compressed, resulting in short neck.

Among American mammals, the huge auditory bullae are exceeded in size, relative to the remainder of the skull, only by members of the genus *Microdipodops*. The tail is longer than the head and body except that in *Dipodomys ordii* occasional individuals of the subspecies from southern Texas and northern Tamaulipas have the tail barely shorter than the head and body.

Dale (1939:730) points out that the environmental factors favoring *Dipodomys* are (1) arid or semiarid climate, (2) proper drainage, (3) any combination of soil and climatic factors to provide an abundance of seed plants with light ground cover, (4) some provision for shelter, and (5) the availability of dusting places for at least a part of the year.

KEY TO SPECIES OF DIPODOMYS

1. Four toes on each hind foot.
    2. Occurring in northern Texas and southwestern Oklahoma. . . . . *D. elator*, p. 529
    2'. Not occurring in northern Texas and southwestern Oklahoma.
        3. Occurring in southern Oregon and northern California north of a line from Suisun Bay to Lake Tahoe. . . . . *D. heermanni*, p. 525
        3'. Occurring in California south of the mentioned line as well as in states east of California; also in México.
            4. Hind foot less than 42.

5. Interorbital breadth more than half of basal length; tail-tip dusky or blackish brown.
   6. Occurring in San Joaquin Valley of California; Margarita and San José islands of Baja California.
      7. Occurring in San Joaquin Valley of California. . . . . . . *D. nitratoides*, p. 533
      7'. Not occurring in San Joaquin Valley of California.
         8. Occurring on Margarita Island, Baja California. . . . . *D. margarita*, p. 533
         8'. Occurring on San José Island, Baja California. . . . . *D. insularis*, p. 533
   6'. Not occurring in San Joaquin Valley of California or on Margarita or San José islands of Baja California. . . . . *D. merriami*, p. 530
5'. Interorbital breadth less than half of basal length; tail-tip pure white following an all black segment, or rarely, instead, distal 4th or more of tail all jet black.
   9. Occurring in Aguascalientes and adjoining parts of Zacatecas and Jalisco; interorbital region narrow. . . . . *D. ornatus*, p. 529
   9'. Occurring south of Aguascalientes on southern part of Mexican Plateau; interorbital region broad. . . . . *D. phillipsii*, p. 529
4'. Hind foot more than 42.
   10. Upper parts pale ochraceous buff; ventral dark tail-stripe absent, or pale if present; no black band in front of white tip of tail; hind foot, 50–58. . . . . . . *D. deserti*, p. 534
   10'. Upper parts brownish; ventral tail-stripe well defined; tail with subterminal blackish band and tipped with white; hind foot, 45–51.
      11. White tip of tail shorter than 25, or absent altogether. . . . . . *D. nelsoni*, p. 529
      11'. White tip of tail longer than 25. . . . . *D. spectabilis*, p. 527
1'. Five toes on each hind foot (5th is half way up inside of foot and little more than the claw is exposed).
12. Head and body usually longer than 130; greatest width across maxillary roots of zygomatic arches more than 25.5. . . . . *D. ingens*, p. 527
12'. Head and body usually shorter than 130; greatest width across maxillary roots of zygomatic arches less than 25.5.
   13. Occurring east of Sierra Nevada-Tehachapi-Southern Coast Range Mountains.
      14. Lower incisors chisellike (anterior faces flat). . . . . *D. microps*, p. 518
      14'. Lower incisors awllike (anterior faces rounded).
         15. Total length ordinarily more than 280.
            16. Hind foot ordinarily less than 42.5; San Jacinto Valley and vicinity (western Riverside and southern San Bernardino counties, California). . *D. stephensi*, p. 520
            16'. Hind foot ordinarily more than 42.5; north of San Jacinto Valley but wholly within California and western Nevada. . . . . *D. panamintinus*, p. 520
         15'. Total length ordinarily less than 280. . . . . *D. ordii*, p. 513
   13'. Occurring west of Sierra Nevada-Tehachapi-Southern Coast Range Mountains.
      17. Posteroexternal angle of maxillary root of zygomatic arch prominent and sharp; width across maxillary roots of zygomatic arches more than 54.8 per cent of greatest length of skull.
         18. Occurring in California. . . . . *D. heermanni*, p. 525
         18'. Occurring in Baja California. . . . . *D. gravipes*, p. 527
      17'. Posteroexternal angle of maxillary root of zygomatic arch weakly angled; width across maxillary roots of zygomatic arches less than 54.8 per cent of greatest length of skull.
         19. Width of maxillary arch at middle averaging more than 5; pinna of ear averaging 15.5 or more from crown.
            20. Color of upper parts close to cinnamon buff; ear mostly brownish; dark ventral tail-stripe half way toward end narrower than lateral white stripe; pinna of ear averaging more than 16.7 from crown. . . . . . . *D. elephantinus*, p. 521
            20'. Color of upper parts light cinnamon brown to deep cinnamon brown; ear mostly blackish; dark ventral tail-stripe half way toward end wider than lateral white stripe; pinna of ear averaging less than 16.7 from crown. *D. venustus*, p. 522
         19'. Width of maxillary arch at middle averaging less than 5 (5 in *D. peninsularis australis*); pinna of ear averaging 15.4 or less from crown.
            21. Occurring north of lat. 29° 30'; dorsal coloration darker than ochraceous.
               22. General outline of skull nearer that of an acute triangle than that of an equilateral triangle. . . . . *D. agilis*, p. 522
               22'. General outline of skull nearer that of an equilateral triangle than that of an acute triangle. . . . . *D. paralius*, p. 523
            21'. Confined to Baja California, principally south of lat. 28° 30'; dorsal coloration ochraceous. . . . . *D. peninsularis*, p. 524

ordii-group
Dipodomys ordii
Ord's Kangaroo Rat

x ½

Revised by Setzer, Univ. Kansas Publ., Mus. Nat. Hist., 1:473–573, December 27, 1949.

External measurements: 208–281; 100–163; 35–45. Five toes on each hind foot. The only other 5-toed kangaroo rats with which *Dipodomys ordii* shares parts of its range are *D. panamintinus* and *D. microps*. In *D. ordii* each of the lower incisors is awl-shaped instead of chisel-shaped as in *D. microps*. The hind foot of *D. ordii* is shorter than 44 mm. in the part of its range that is shared with the longer-footed, larger, *D. panamintinus*. In 80 pregnant females from Nevada the embryos averaged 3.5 with extremes of 1 and 6. The mode was 4.

Dipodomys ordii attenuatus Bryant

1939. *Dipodomys ordii attenuatus* Bryant, Occas. Papers Mus. Zool., Louisiana State Univ., 5:65, November 10, type from mouth Santa Helena Canyon, 2146 ft., Big Bend of the Rio Grande, Brewster Co., Texas.

MARGINAL RECORDS.—Texas (Setzer, 1949:555): 6 mi. S Marathon; Cooper's Well, 47 mi. S Marathon; 10 mi. W San Vicente; mouth Santa Helena Canyon.

Dipodomys ordii celeripes Durrant and Hall

1939. *Dipodomys ordii celeripes* Durrant and Hall, Mammalia, 3:10, March, type from Trout Creek, 4600 ft., Juab Co., Utah.

MARGINAL RECORDS.—Nevada (Setzer, 1949:550): 13 mi. N Montello, 5000 ft. Utah (Durrant, 1952:254): Clifton Flat, 7 mi. SW Gold Hill, 6149 ft.; 35 mi. W Delta; 20 mi. SW Nephi; E side Clear Lake, 4600 ft.; Hendry Creek, 17 mi. S Gandy, 5000 ft. Nevada (Setzer, 1949:550): Hendry Creek, 8 mi. SE Mt. Moriah, 6200 ft.; Cobre, 6100 ft.

Dipodomys ordii chapmani Mearns

1890. *Dipodomys chapmani* Mearns, Bull. Amer. Mus. Nat. Hist., 2:291, February 21, type from Fort Verde, Yavapai Co., Arizona.

1921. *Dipodomys ordii chapmani*, Grinnell, Jour. Mamm., 2:96, May 2.

MARGINAL RECORDS.—Arizona (Setzer, 1949:537): lower end Prospect Valley, 4500 ft., Grand Canyon; Bill Williams Mtn.; ½ mi. S Camp Verde; Kirkland; Kingman.

Dipodomys ordii cinderensis Hardy

1944. *Dipodomys ordii cinderensis* Hardy, Proc. Biol. Soc. Washington, 57:53, October 31, type from approximately 4000 ft., immediately N of the northern of two large cinder cones, Diamond Valley, 10 mi. N St. George, Washington Co., Utah.

MARGINAL RECORDS.—Utah (Durrant, 1952:266): 11 mi. SE Lund; 4½ mi. NW Summit, 6 mi. W Parowan; Cedar City; type locality; N end Mountain Meadows.

Dipodomys ordii cineraceus Goldman

1939. *Dipodomys ordii cineraceus* Goldman, Jour. Mamm., 20:352, August 14, type from Dolphin Island, Great Salt Lake, 4250 ft., Boxelder Co., Utah. Known only from the type locality.

Dipodomys ordii columbianus (Merriam)

1894. *Perodipus ordi columbianus* Merriam, Proc. Biol. Soc. Washington, 9:115, June 21, type from Umatilla, at mouth of Umatilla River, Plains of Columbia, Umatilla Co., Oregon.

1921. *Dipodomys ordii columbianus*, Grinnell, Jour. Mamm., 2:96, May 2.

MARGINAL RECORDS (Setzer, 1949:545–546, unless otherwise noted).—Washington: 4 mi. E Burbank; Wallula. Idaho: Payette; Hammett; Arco; 5 mi. E Shelley; 3 mi. S Blackfoot; 5 mi. NW Michaud; 6 mi. SW American Falls; 8 mi. W Rogerson. Nevada: Marys River, 22 mi. N Deeth; 5 mi. SE Greens Ranch, Steptoe Valley; 4 mi. S Shoshone; Bells Ranch, Reese River, 6890 ft.; 2½ mi. NE Smiths Creek Ranch; 5 mi. N Beowawe; 1 mi. SE Tuscorara, 5900 ft.; 2 mi. SW Quinn River Crossing (Setzer, 1949:544); 2½ mi. E, 11 mi. S Gerlach (*ibid.*); Fox Canyon, 6 mi. S Pahrum Peak, 4800 ft.; 2¾ mi. SW Pyramid, 4300 ft. California: Beckwith; Dransfield, 6 mi. E Ravendale, 5300 ft.; 2 mi. W Red Rock P.O.; Eagleville. Oregon: 9 mi. S Adel, mouth 20 mile Creek; Fort Rock; 2 mi. NE Prineville; 7 mi. E Madras; Arlington.

Dipodomys ordii compactus True

1889. *Dipodomys compactus* True, Proc. U.S. Nat. Mus., 11:160, January 5, type from Padre Island, Cameron Co., Texas.

1942. *Dipodomys ordii compactus*, Davis, Jour. Mamm., 23:332, August 13.

MARGINAL RECORDS.—Texas: type locality. Tamaulipas: Bagdad (Hall, 1951a:41).

Dipodomys ordii cupidineus Goldman

1924. *Dipodomys ordii cupidineus* Goldman, Jour. Washington Acad. Sci., 14:372, September 19, type from Kanab Wash, at southern boundary of Kaibab Indian Reservation, Mohave Co., Arizona.

MARGINAL RECORDS.—Utah (Durrant, 1952:268): mouth Calf Creek, Escalante River; Willow Tank Springs. Arizona (Setzer, 1949:562): 2 mi. W Lees Ferry; 10 mi. S Jacobs Pools, Houserock Valley; 5 mi. S Trumbull Spring; 20 mi. S Wolf Hole; 6 mi. N Wolf Hole. Utah (Durrant, 1952:268): near Short Creek Road, south of town of Virgin; Cottonwood Canyon, 8 mi. NW Kanab, 4800 ft.

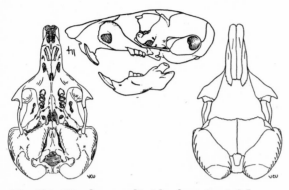

Fig. 294. *Dipodomys ordii richardsoni*, 1 mi. S Lamar, Prowers Co., Colorado, No. 15995 K.U., ♀, X 1.

Dipodomys ordii durranti Setzer

1949. *Dipodomys ordii fuscus* Setzer, Univ. Kansas Publ., Mus. Nat. Hist., 1:555, December 27, type from Jaumave, Tamaulipas. Not *Dipodomys agilis fuscus* Boulware, 1943, type from 2½ mi. N La Purisima Mission, Santa Barbara Co., California.
1952. *Dipodomys ordii durranti* Setzer, Jour. Washington Acad. Sci., 42:391, December 17, a renaming of *D. o. fuscus* Setzer, 1949.

MARGINAL RECORDS (Setzer, 1949:556, unless otherwise noted).—Coahuila: 11 mi. W Hda. San Miguel, 2200 ft. (35812 KU). Tamaulipas: Nuevo Laredo; type locality; Tula. San Luis Potosí: 6 km. S Matehuala (Dalquest, 1953b:113). Zacatecas: Lulú. Coahuila: San Juan Nepomuceno, 5 mi. N La Ventura; 17 mi. N, 8 mi. W Saltillo, 5200 ft. (35843 KU); 5 mi. N, 2 mi. W Monclova (35825 KU).

Dipodomys ordii evexus Goldman

1933. *Dipodomys ordii evexus* Goldman, Jour. Washington Acad. Sci., 23:468, October 15, type from Salida, 7000 ft., Chaffee Co., Colorado.

MARGINAL RECORDS.—Colorado: type locality; Pueblo (Setzer, 1949:519).

Dipodomys ordii extractus Setzer

1949. *Dipodomys ordii extractus* Setzer, Univ. Kansas Publ., Mus. Nat. Hist., 1:534, December 27, type from 1 mi. E Samalayuca, 4500 ft., Chihuahua. Known only from the type locality.

Dipodomys ordii fetosus Durrant and Hall

1939. *Dipodomys ordii fetosus* Durrant and Hall, Mammalia, 3:14, March, type from 2 mi. N Panaca, 4800 ft., Lincoln Co., Nevada.

MARGINAL RECORDS.—Utah (Durrant, 1952:264, unless otherwise noted): 5 mi. S Garrison, 5400 ft. (Setzer, 1949:542); Desert Range Experiment Station, 50 mi. W Milford, 5252 ft. Nevada (Setzer, 1949:542): type locality; 10 mi. E Crystal Spring, 5000 ft.; 15 mi. S Groom Baldy; Garden Valley; 8½ mi. NE Sharp; White River Valley, 15 mi. WSW Sunnyside, 5500 ft.

Dipodomys ordii fremonti Durrant and Setzer

1945. *Dipodomys ordii fremonti* Durrant and Setzer, Bull. Univ. Utah, 35(26):21, June 30, type from Torrey, 7000 ft., Wayne Co., Utah.

MARGINAL RECORDS.—Utah: type locality; ¼ mi. N Grover (Durrant, 1952:265).

Dipodomys ordii idoneus Setzer

1949. *Dipodomys ordii idoneus* Setzer, Univ. Kansas Publ., Mus. Nat. Hist., 1:546, December 27, type from San Juan, 12 mi. W Lerdo, 3800 ft., Durango.

MARGINAL RECORDS.—Coahuila: 4 mi. N Acatita, 3600 ft. (40993 KU); ½ mi. S, 1 mi. E Jaral, 4 mi. S, 2 mi. W Hipolite (35831 KU). Durango: 5 mi. SE Lerdo, 3800 ft. (40519 KU); type locality; 1 mi. WSW Mapimí, 3800 ft. (40509 KU).—Baker (1956:248 and fig. 38) assigned specimens from 3 mi. NE Mojada in Coahuila to this subspecies after our account and Map 306 were prepared.

Dipodomys ordii inaquosus Hall

1941. *Dipodomys ordii inaquosus* Hall, Proc. Biol. Soc. Washington, 54:58, May 20, type from 11 mi. E and 1 mi. N Jungo, 4200 ft., Humboldt Co., Nevada.

MARGINAL RECORDS.—Nevada (Setzer, 1949:553): 18 mi. NE Iron Point, 4600 ft.; Izenhood; 23 mi. NW Battle Mountain; 15 mi. SW Winnemucca; 8 mi. E, 1 mi. N Jungo, 4200 ft.; 7 mi. N Winnemucca, 4400 ft.

Dipodomys ordii largus Hall

1951. *Dipodomys ordii largus* Hall, Univ. Kansas Publ., Mus. Nat. Hist., 5:40, October 1, type from Mustang Island, 14 mi. SW Port Aransas, Aransas Co., Texas. Known only from the type locality.

Dipodomys ordii longipes (Merriam)

1890. *Dipodops longipes* Merriam, N. Amer. Fauna, 3:72, September 11, type from foot of Echo Cliffs, Painted Desert, Coconino Co., Arizona.
1921. *Dipodomys ordii longipes*, Grinnell, Jour. Mamm., 2:96, May 2.
1933. *Dipodomys ordii cleomophila* Goldman, Jour. Washington Acad. Sci., 23:469, October 15, type from 5 mi. NE Winona, 6200 ft., Coconino Co., Arizona.

MARGINAL RECORDS.—Utah (Durrant, 1952:269): Hatch Trading Post, Montezuma Creek, 25 mi. SE Blanding, 4500 ft. New Mexico (Setzer, 1949:558): Ship Rock; Blanco; Chama Canyon; 1 mi. S Bernardo; Riley; 10 mi. S Quemado. Arizona (ibid.): 3 mi. SE Springerville; Holbrook; Winslow; 5 mi. NE Winona; Deadmans Flat, 6400 ft., NE San Francisco Mtn.; 20 mi. NE Lees Ferry. Utah (Durrant, 1952:269): Johns Canyon, San Juan R., 5150 ft.

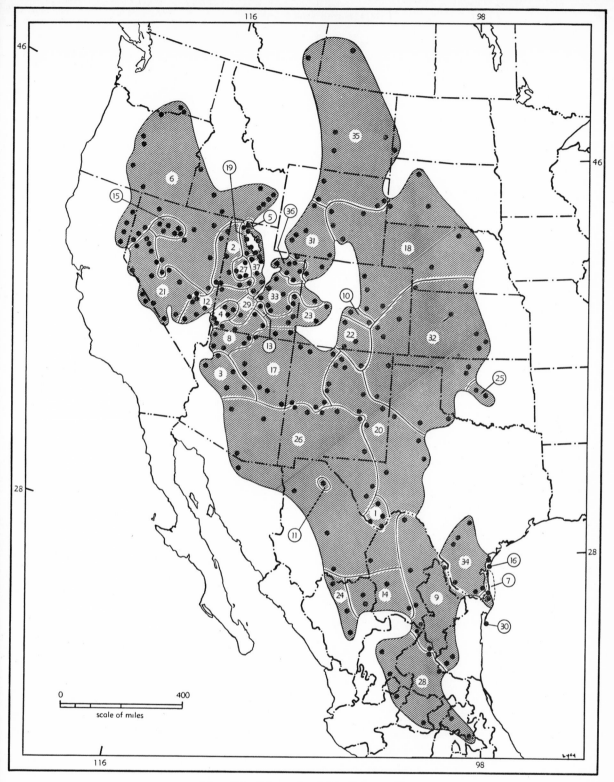

Map. 306. Subspecies of *Dipodomys ordii.*

1. *attenuatus*	7. *compactus*	12. *fetosus*	17. *longipes*	22. *montanus*	27. *pallidus*	32. *richardsoni*
2. *celeripes*	8. *cupidineus*	13. *fremonti*	18. *luteolus*	23. *nexilis*	28. *palmeri*	33. *sanrafaeli*
3. *chapmani*	9. *durranti*	14. *idoneus*	19. *marshalli*	24. *obscurus*	29. *panguitchensis*	34. *sennetti*
4. *cinderensis*	10. *evexus*	15. *inaquosus*	20. *medius*	25. *oklahomae*	30. *parvabullatus*	35. *terrosus*
5. *cineraceus*	11. *extractus*	16. *largus*	21. *monoensis*	26. *ordii*	31. *priscus*	36. *uintensis*
6. *columbianus*						37. *utahensis*

Dipodomys ordii luteolus (Goldman)

1917. *Perodipus ordii luteolus* Goldman, Proc. Biol. Soc. Washington, 30:112, May 23, type from Casper, Natrona Co., Wyoming.
1921. *Dipodomys ordii luteolus,* Grinnell, Jour. Mamm., 2:96, May 2.

MARGINAL RECORDS (Setzer, 1949:534, unless otherwise noted).—South Dakota: 9 mi. N Bison; 20 mi. SSE Philip (in Haakon Co.). Nebraska: Perch; Neligh; Birdwood Creek. Colorado: Hugo; Colorado Springs; 6 mi. E, 1 mi. N Denver; Loveland. Wyoming: Fort Steele; Granite Mtn.; 2½ mi. W Shoshoni; 12 mi. N, 6 mi. W Bill, 4800 ft. (32467 KU). South Dakota: Elk Mtn.

Handley (1953:264) records bones of *Dipodomys ordii luteolus* from an Indian archaeological site in South Dakota: 6³⁄₁₀ mi. NW of Pierre. This occurrence is not shown on our Map 306.

Dipodomys ordii marshalli Goldman

1937. *Dipodomys ordii marshalli* Goldman, Proc. Biol. Soc. Washington, 50:223, December 28, type from Bird Island, Great Salt Lake, 4300 ft., Utah.

MARGINAL RECORDS.—Utah (Durrant, 1952:257, unless otherwise noted): Kelton, 4300 ft.; type locality; *Carrington Island, Great Salt Lake, 4300 ft.*; Stansbury Island, Great Salt Lake, 4300 ft.; 14 mi. W Salt Lake Ctiy, 4300 ft.; 2 mi. W Grantsville (Setzer, 1949:552).

Dipodomys ordii medius Setzer

1949. *Dipodomys ordii medius* Setzer, Univ. Kansas Publ., Mus. Nat. Hist., 1:519, December 27, type from Santa Rosa, Guadalupe Co., New Mexico.

MARGINAL RECORDS (Setzer, 1949:520).—New Mexico: Rio Alamosa, 15 mi. N Ojo Caliente; Rinconada; Santa Rosa; 4 mi. W, 2¾ mi. N Clovis. Texas: 9 mi. SW Muleshoe; 7 mi. E Post; Colorado; Monahans. New Mexico: 15 mi. NE Roswell; 44 mi. NW Roswell; Pajarito; 12 mi. NW Alameda, 5500 ft.; 2 mi. SE El Rito.

Dipodomys ordii monoensis (Grinnell)

1919. *Perodipus monoensis* Grinnell, Univ. California Publ. Zool., 21:46, March 29, type from Pellisier Ranch, 5600 ft., 5 mi. N Benton Station, Mono Co., California.
1921. *Dipodomys ordii monoensis* Grinnell, Jour. Mamm., 2:96, May 2.

MARGINAL RECORDS (Setzer, 1949:529–530).—Nevada: 21 mi. W, 2 mi. N Lovelock, 4000 ft.; ½ mi. NE Toulon; 1 mi. W Mountain Well, 5350 ft.; Eastgate, 4400 ft.; Fingerrock Wash, Stewart Valley, 5400 ft.; 2 mi. S Millett P.O., 5500 ft.; Fish Spring Valley, ½ mi. N Fish Lake, 6500 ft.; Railroad Valley, 2½ mi. S Lock's Ranch, 5000 ft.; Big Creek, Quinn Canyon Mts.; 5 mi. W White Rock Spring, 6950 ft., Belted Range; 1 mi. N Beatty; 2 mi. NW Palmetto. California: Deep Springs Valley; type locality. Nevada: West Walker River, Smith's Valley, 4700 ft.; ½ mi. S Pyramid Lake, 3950 ft.

Dipodomys ordii montanus Baird

1855. *Dipodomys montanus* Baird, Proc. Acad. Nat. Sci. Philadelphia, 7:334, April, type from Fort Massachusetts (now Fort Garland), Costilla Co., Colorado.

1921. *Dipodomys ordii montanus,* Grinnell, Jour. Mamm., 2:96, May 2.

MARGINAL RECORDS (Setzer, 1949:540).—Colorado: Saguache; type locality. New Mexico: 4 mi. SW Cimmaron. Colorado: Antonito.

Dipodomys ordii nexilis Goldman

1933. *Dipodomys ordii nexilis* Goldman, Jour. Washington Acad. Sci., 23:470, October 15, type from 5 mi. W Naturita, Montrose Co., Colorado.

MARGINAL RECORDS.—Utah (Durrant, 1952:263): Cisco. Colorado (Setzer, 1949:561): Hotchkiss; Coventry. Utah (Durrant, 1952:263, unless otherwise noted): Blanding; Snyders Pond, 22 mi. ENE Monticello; Castle Valley, 18 mi. NE Moab, 6000 ft. (Kelson, 1951:73).

Dipodomys ordii obscurus (J. A. Allen)

1903. *Perodipus obscurus* J. A. Allen, Bull. Amer. Mus. Nat. Hist., 19:603, November 12, type from Río Sestín, northwest Durango.
1921. *Dipodomys ordii obscurus,* Grinnell, Jour. Mamm., 2:96, May 2.

MARGINAL RECORDS.—Durango (Setzer, 1949:521): Rosario; *Villa Ocampo*; Río del Bocas; Mt. San Gabriel; *type locality.*

Dipodomys ordii oklahomae Trowbridge and Whitaker

1940. *Dipodomys oklahomae* Trowbridge and Whitaker, Jour. Mamm., 21:343, August 13, type from north bank South Canadian River, 2¼ mi. S Norman, Cleveland Co., Oklahoma.
1942. *Dipodomys ordii oklahomae,* Davis, Jour. Mamm., 23:332, August 13.

MARGINAL RECORDS.—Oklahoma (Setzer, 1949:515): 4 mi. N Minco; type locality.

Dipodomys ordii ordii Woodhouse

1853. *D[ipodomys]. ordii* Woodhouse, Proc. Acad. Nat. Sci. Philadelphia, 6:224. Type locality, El Paso, El Paso Co., Texas.

MARGINAL RECORDS (Setzer, 1949:530–532, unless otherwise noted).—New Mexico: Gran Quivira, Mesa Jumanes; 40 mi. N Roswell; 2 mi. E Carlsbad. Texas: 5 mi. E Toyahvale; 14½ mi. S Fort Davis. Coahuila: 3 mi. NE Sierra Mojada, 4100 ft. (40989 KU—See Baker's [1956:248 and fig. 38] identification as *D. o. idoneus* after our Map 306 was prepared). Chihuahua: 5 mi. E Parral, 5700 ft. (40978 KU); Chihuahua; 4³⁄₁₀ mi. W Casas Grandes Viejo, 5000 ft. Sonora: Alamo Wash, 35 mi. NW Magdalena. Arizona: La Osa; Marinette; 20 mi. NE Calva. New Mexico: Mangos Valley; Gallina Mts.; 10 mi. NE Socorro.

Dipodomys ordii pallidus Durrant and Setzer

1945. *Dipodomys ordii pallidus* Durrant and Setzer, Bull. Univ. Utah, 35(26):24, June 30, type from Old Lincoln Highway, 18 mi. SW Orr's Ranch, Skull Valley, 4400 ft., Tooele Co., Utah.

MARGINAL RECORDS.—Utah (Durrant, 1952:260): type locality; 1 mi. N Lynndyl, 4768 ft.; Hinckley, 4600 ft.; *7 mi. S Fish Springs, 4400 ft.*; Fish Springs, 4400 ft.

Dipodomys ordii palmeri (J. A. Allen)

1881. *Dipodops ordii palmeri* J. A. Allen, Bull. Mus. Comp. Zool., 8(9):187, March, type from San Luis Potosí, State of San Luis Potosí.
1921. *Dipodomys ordii palmeri*, Grinnell, Jour. Mamm., 2:96, May 2.

MARGINAL RECORDS (Setzer, 1949:563, unless otherwise noted).—Zacatecas: Cañitas. San Luis Potosí: Potrero Santa Ana, 7⁹⁄₁₀ mi. S. Matehuala; Tepeyac (Dalquest, 1953b:113). Hidalgo: Ixmiquilpan; Irolo. Guanajuato: Celaya. Jalisco: 9 mi. N Encarnación, 1900 m. Zacatecas: Berriozábal.

Dipodomys ordii panguitchensis Hardy

1942. *Dipodomys ordii panguitchensis* Hardy, Proc. Biol. Soc. Washington, 55:90, June 25, type from 1 mi. S Panguitch, 6666 ft., Garfield Co., Utah. Known only from the type locality.

Dipodomys ordii parvabullatus Hall

1951. *Dipodomys ordii parvabullatus* Hall, Univ. Kansas Publ., Mus. Nat. Hist., 5:38, October 1, type from 88 mi. S and 10 mi. W Matamoros, Tamaulipas.

MARGINAL RECORDS.—Tamaulipas: type locality; *90 mi. S, 10 mi. W Matamoros* (Hall, 1951a:39).

Dipodomys ordii priscus Hoffmeister

1942. *Dipodomys ordii priscus* Hoffmeister, Proc. Biol. Soc. Washington, 55:167, December 31, type from Kinney Ranch, 21 mi. S Bitter Creek, 7100 ft., Sweetwater Co., Wyoming.

MARGINAL RECORDS (Setzer, 1949:548, unless otherwise noted).—Wyoming: Wind River; 1½ mi. N Baggs (25684 KU). Colorado: Bear River; W side White River, 1 mi. N Rangeley. Utah (Durrant, 1952:259): N(E) side Green River, 1 mi. E Hideout Trail Bridge, Hideout Canyon, 6400 ft. Wyoming: 10 mi. SW Granger; 27 mi. N, 37 mi. E Rock Springs, 6700 ft. (37582 KU); Eden.

Dipodomys ordii richardsoni (J. A. Allen)

1891. *Dipodops richardsoni* J. A. Allen, Bull. Amer. Mus. Nat. Hist., 3:277, June 30, type from one of the sources of Beaver River, probably Harper Co., Oklahoma.
1921. *Dipodomys ordii richardsoni*, Grinnell, Jour. Mamm., 2:96, May 2.

MARGINAL RECORDS (Setzer, 1949:513, unless otherwise noted).—Nebraska: Bladen. Kansas (Cockrum, 1952: 154): Ellis; Medora; Wichita; 4½ mi. NE Danville. Oklahoma: 4 mi. SE Cherokee; 3 mi. S Cleo Springs. Texas: Vernon; 6 mi. S, 1 mi. W Quitaque. New Mexico: 2 mi. W, 1 mi. S Conchas Dam, 4250 ft. (41907 KU); Clayton. Colorado: 18 mi. S La Junta; Olney; Chivington. Nebraska: Haigler.

Dipodomys ordii sanrafaeli Durrant and Setzer

1945. *Dipodomys ordii sanrafaeli* Durrant and Setzer, Bull. Univ. Utah, 35(26):26, June 30, type from 1½ mi. N Price, 5567 ft., Carbon Co., Utah.

MARGINAL RECORDS.—Utah (Durrant, 1952:262): 12 mi. NE Price; pump station, 4 mi. N Greenriver, 4100 ft. Colorado: Grand Junction (Setzer, 1949:527). Utah (Durrant, 1952:262–263): 3 mi. W Arches National Monument; King Ranch, 4800 ft.; Notom; 4 mi. E Mt. Alice, between Emery and Loa, 7450 ft.; 5 mi. S Castle Dale, 5600 ft.

Dipodomys ordii sennetti (J. A. Allen)

1891. *Dipodops sennetti* J. A. Allen, Bull. Amer. Mus. Nat. Hist., 3:226, April 29, type from Santa Rosa, 85 mi. SW Corpus Christi, Cameron Co., Texas. (See V. Bailey, N. Amer. Fauna, 25:146, October 24, 1905.)
1942. *Dipodomys ordii sennetti*, Davis, Jour. Mamm., 23: 332, August 13.

MARGINAL RECORDS.—Texas (Setzer, 1949:518, unless otherwise noted): Somerset; 5 mi. S Port Aransas (Blair, 1952:241); 28 mi. E Raymondville; 17 mi. NW Edinburg (Blair, 1952:241); 5 mi. E Zapata (*ibid.*); 8 mi. E Encinal; 8 mi. NE Los Angeles.

Dipodomys ordii terrosus Hoffmeister

1942. *Dipodomys ordii terrosus* Hoffmeister, Proc. Biol. Soc. Washington, 55:165, December 31, type from Yellowstone River, 5 mi. W Forsyth, 2750 ft., Rosebud Co., Montana.

MARGINAL RECORDS (Setzer, 1949:524, unless otherwise noted).—Saskatchewan: near Shackelton, 45 to 50 mi. NW Swift Current. Montana: Glendive. North Dakota: 10 mi. N Marmarth (35440 KU). Wyoming: Newcastle; 23 mi. SW Newcastle; Wilson's Ranch, Sheep Creek, S base Owl Creek Mts.; Greybull. Montana: Billings; 24 mi. N Roundup, 8 mi. SW Flatwillow. Alberta: near Medicine Hat.

Dipodomys ordii uintensis Durrant and Setzer

1945. *Dipodomys ordii uintensis* Durrant and Setzer, Bull. Univ. Utah, 35(26):27, June 30, type from Red Creek, 6700 ft., 2 mi. N Fruitland, Duchesne Co., Utah.

MARGINAL RECORDS.—Utah (Durrant, 1952:261, unless otherwise noted): 15 mi. W Vernal; Vernal; *E side Green River, 3 mi. S Jensen*; 20 mi. E Ouray (Setzer, 1949: 526); Brown Corral, 20 mi. S Ouray, 6250 ft.; 20 mi. S Myton; type locality.

Dipodomys ordii utahensis (Merriam)

1904. *Perodipus montanus utahensis* Merriam, Proc. Biol. Soc. Washington, 17:143, July 14, type from Ogden, Weber Co., Utah.
1921. *Dipodomys ordii utahensis*, Grinnell, Jour. Mamm., 2:96, May 2.

MARGINAL RECORDS.—Utah (Durrant, 1952:256, unless otherwise noted): 15 mi. E Park Valley, Raft River Mts., 5500 ft.; Ogden, 4293 ft. (Setzer, 1949:544); 4 mi. N Draper, 4500 ft.; Provo, 4510 ft. (Setzer, 1949:544); Spring City (*ibid.*); 1 mi. W Aurora, 5190 ft.; Nephi; St. John, 4300 ft.

Dipodomys microps
Chisel-toothed Kangaroo Rat

Revised by Hall and Dale, Occas. Papers Mus. Zool., Louisiana State University, 4:47–63, November 10, 1939.

External measurements: 254–297; 134–175; 39.0–46.4. Five toes on each hind foot. The only other 5-toed kangaroo rats with which *Dipodomys microps* shares its range are *Dipodomys panamintinus* and *Dipodomys ordii*. In *D. microps* the lower incisors are flat on their anterior faces and chisellike, whereas in *D. ordii* they are rounded and awllike. The hind foot of *D. microps* is shorter than 44 mm. in the part of its range that it shares with the longer-footed *D. panamintinus*. In 39 pregnant females from Nevada the embryos averaged 2.3 with extremes of 1 and 4. The mode was 2.

Dipodomys microps alfredi Goldman

1937. *Dipodomys microps alfredi* Goldman, Proc. Biol. Soc. Washington, 50:221, December 28, type from Gunnison Island, 4300 ft., Great Salt Lake, Utah. Known only from Gunnison Island.

Dipodomys microps aquilonius Willett

1935. *Dipodomys microps aquilonius* Willett, Jour. Mamm., 16:63, February 14, type from 3 mi. E Eagleville, Modoc Co., California.

MARGINAL RECORDS.—California: 6 mi. E Cedarville, 4500 ft. (Hall and Dale, 1939:56). Nevada (Hall, 1946: 421): 1 mi. W Hausen, 5650 ft.; 12 mi. N and 2 mi. E Gerlach, 4000 ft.; 1 mi. NE Gerlach, 4000 ft.; ½ mi. S Pyramid Lake, 3950 ft. California (Hall and Dale, 1939:56): 9 mi. E Amedee; type locality.

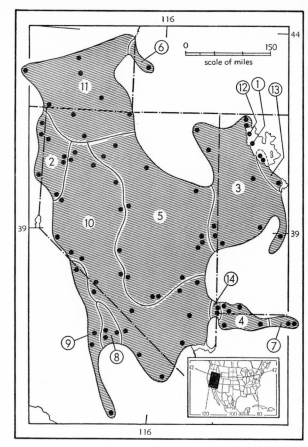

Map 307. *Dipodomys microps.*

1. *D. m. alfredi*	8. *D. m. levipes*
2. *D. m. aquilonius*	9. *D. m. microps*
3. *D. m. bonnevillei*	10. *D. m. occidentalis*
4. *D. m. celsus*	11. *D. m. preblei*
5. *D. m. centralis*	12. *D. m. russeolus*
6. *D. m. idahoensis*	13. *D. m. subtenuis*
7. *D. m. leucotis*	14. *D. m. woodburyi*

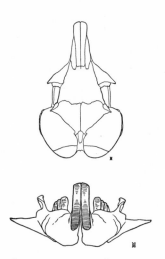

Fig. 295. *Dipodomys microps aquilonius*, 3½ mi. E Flanigan, Nevada, No. 73616 M.V.Z., ♂, X 1, but front view of lower incisors X 2.

Dipodomys microps bonnevillei Goldman

1937. *Dipodomys microps bonnevillei* Goldman, Proc. Biol. Soc. Washington, 50:222, December 28, type from Kelton, 4300 ft., Boxelder Co., Utah.

MARGINAL RECORDS.—Utah (Durrant, 1952:271): Hardup; type locality; Old Lincoln Highway, 18 mi. SW Orr's Ranch, Skull Valley, 4400 ft.; Aurora; 2 mi. E Clear Lake, 4600 ft.; Pine Valley, sec. 33, T. 25 S, R. 17 W, Salt Lake B.M., 50 mi. W Milford, 5500 ft. Nevada (Hall, 1946: 424): 1 mi. N Baker; 2 mi. W Smith Creek Cave, Mt. Moriah, 6300 ft.; Cobre, 6100 ft.; 15 mi. S Contact, 5800 ft.

Dipodomys microps celsus Goldman

1924. *Dipodomys microps celsus* Goldman, Jour. Washington Acad. Sci., 14:372, September 19, type from 6 mi. N Wolf Hole, 3500 ft., Arizona.

MARGINAL RECORDS.—Utah (Durrant, 1952:276): 1½ mi. NW Diamond Valley; 5 mi. NW St. George; Gould's Ranch, Hurricane. Arizona (Goldman, 1924:372): Kanab Wash, near S boundary Kaibab Indian Reservation; type locality.

Dipodomys microps centralis Hall and Dale

1939. *Dipodomys microps centralis* Hall and Dale, Occas. Papers Mus Zool., Louisiana State Univ., 4:52, November 10, type from 4 mi. SE Romano, Diamond Valley, Eureka Co., Nevada.

MARGINAL RECORDS.—Nevada (Hall, 1946:421–422): 18 mi. NE Iron Point, 4600 ft.; ½ mi. S Beowawe; 5 mi. SE Greens Ranch, Steptoe Valley, 5900 ft.; 7 mi. SW Osceola, Spring Valley, 6100 ft.; 5½ mi. NW Shoshone P.O., 6100 ft.; Duck Valley, 3 mi. S Geyser, 6050 ft.; Coal Valley, 10 mi. N Seeman Pass, 4650 ft.; 9 mi. W Groom Baldy, 5500 ft.; 9 mi. E Wheelbarrow Peak; 1 mi. SW Cactus Spring, Cactus Range; San Antonio, 5400 ft.; Reese River Valley, 7 mi. N Austin; 15 mi. SW Winnemucca.

Dipodomys microps idahoensis Hall and Dale

1939. *Dipodomys microps idahoensis* Hall and Dale, Occas. Papers Mus. Zool., Louisiana State Univ., 4:53, November 10, type from 5 mi. SE Murphy, Owyhee Co., Idaho.

MARGINAL RECORDS.—Idaho (Hall and Dale, 1939: 54): *10 mi. E Murphy*; type locality.

Dipodomys microps leucotis Goldman

1931. *Dipodomys microps leucotis* Goldman, Proc. Biol. Soc. Washington, 44:135, October 17, type from 6 mi. W Colorado River Bridge, 3700 ft., Houserock Valley, N[= W] side Marble Canyon of Colorado River, Arizona.

MARGINAL RECORD.—Arizona: type locality; ½ mi. E Navajo Bridge (Hardy, 1949:435).

Dipodomys microps levipes (Merriam)

1904. *Perodipus microps levipes* Merriam, Proc. Biol. Soc. Washington, 17:145, July 14, type from Perognathus Flat, 5200 ft., Emigrant Gap, Panamint Mts., Inyo Co., California.
1931. *Dipodomys microps levipes*, Hall, Univ. California Publ. Zool., 37:5, April 10.

MARGINAL RECORDS.—California (Hall and Dale, 1939:61): 15 mi. N Darwin, 5200 to 5300 ft.; type locality; Darwin, 4800 ft.

Dipodomys microps microps (Merriam)

1904. *Perodipus microps* Merriam, Proc. Biol. Soc. Washington, 17:145, July 14, type from Lone Pine, Owens Valley, Inyo Co., California.
1921. *Dipodomys microps*, Grinnell, Jour. Mamm., 2:96, May 2.

MARGINAL RECORDS.—California (Hall and Dale, 1939:62): Pellisier Ranch, 5600 ft., 5 mi. N Benton Station; 2½ mi. NE Lone Pine; Victorville; 1½ mi. SW Olancha, 3900 ft.

Dipodomys microps occidentalis Hall and Dale

1939. *Dipodomys microps occidentalis* Hall and Dale, Occas. Papers Mus. Zool., Louisiana State Univ., 4:56, November 10, type from 3 mi. S Schurz, 4100 ft., Mineral Co., Nevada.

MARGINAL RECORDS.—Nevada (Hall, 1946:423): 9½ mi. N Sulphur, 4050 ft.; 1 mi. W Humboldt, 4180 ft.; S slope Granite Peak, East Range; Smiths Creek Valley, 5550 ft.; 2 mi. W Railroad Pass; N shore Mud Lake, 5300 ft., S end Ralston Valley; 8½ mi. NE Springdale, 4250 ft.; 9½ mi. NW Crystal Spring, 4800 ft., Pahranagat Valley; Desert Valley, 5300 ft., 21 mi. W Panaca; Coyote Spring, 2800 ft.; 4 mi. NW Las Vegas. California: SE side Clark Mtn., 5100 ft. (Johnson *et al.*, 1948:362); 2 mi. E Greenwater, 3900 ft. (Hall and Dale, 1939:57); Salt Creek, northwest arm Death Valley, −91 ft. (*ibid.*); N end Deep Spring Valley, 5300 ft. (*ibid.*). Nevada (Hall, 1946:423): 2½ mi. N Dyer, 4850 ft.; Huntoon Valley, 5700 ft.; Fletcher, 6098 ft.; Smiths Valley, 7½ mi. NE Wellington, 4900 ft.; 1½ mi. N Wadsworth, 4100 ft.; 10 mi. W and 6 mi. N Sulphur, 4000 ft.

Dipodomys microps preblei (Goldman)

1921. *Perodipus microps preblei* Goldman, Jour. Mamm., 2:233, November 29, type from Narrows, Malheur Lake, Harney Co., Oregon.
1939. *Dipodomys microps preblei*, Hall and Dale, Occas. Papers Mus. Zool., Louisiana State Univ., 4:54, November 10.

MARGINAL RECORDS.—Oregon (Hall and Dale, 1939: 55): type locality; Buena Vista, 25 mi. S Narrows, 4300 ft.; White Horse Sink. Nevada (Hall, 1946:420): 36 mi. NE Paradise Valley, 5500 ft.; Jackson Creek Ranch, 4000 ft., 17½ mi. S and 5 mi. W Quinn River Crossing; Virgin Valley. Oregon (Hall and Dale, 1939:55): 8 mi. S Adel, E of mouth of Twenty Mile Creek; Summer Lake.

Dipodomys microps russeolus Goldman

1939. *Dipodomys microps russeolus* Goldman, Jour. Mamm., 20:353, August 14, type from Dolphin Island, 4250 ft., Great Salt Lake, Utah. Known only from the type locality.

Dipodomys microps subtenuis Goldman

1939. *Dipodomys microps subtenuis* Goldman, Jour. Mamm., 20:354, August 14, type from Carrington Island, 4250 ft., Great Salt Lake, Utah.

MARGINAL RECORDS.—Utah (Durrant, 1952:275): type locality; *Badger Island*; Stansbury Island, 4250 ft.; Chimney Rock Pass, lat. 40° 04′ N, long. 111° 56′ W, Cedar Valley.

Dipodomys microps woodburyi Hardy

1942. *Dipodomys microps woodburyi* Hardy, Proc. Biol. Soc. Washington, 55:89, June 25, type from Beaverdam Slope, approximately 3500 ft., W of Beaverdam Mts., Washington Co., Utah.

MARGINAL RECORDS.—Utah (Durrant, 1952:277): type locality; near Ed Terry Ranch, Beaverdam Wash.

panamintinus-group
Dipodomys panamintinus
Panamint Kangaroo Rat

External measurements: 285–334; 156–202; 42–48. Five toes on each hind foot; pinna of ear and auditory bullae small; broad across maxillary processes of zygomatic arches.

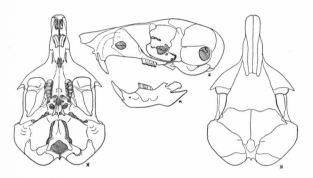

Fig. 296. *Dipodomys panamintinus leucogenys,* Junction House, Nevada, No. 49012 M.V.Z., ♂, X 1.

Dipodomys panamintinus argusensis Huey

1945. *Dipodomys mohavensis argusensis* Huey, Trans. San Diego Soc. Nat. Hist., 10(10):131, March 9, type from Junction Ranch, 5725 ft., Argus Mts., Inyo Co., California. Known only from the type locality.
1955. *Dipodomys panamintinus argusensis,* Miller and Kellogg, Bull. U.S. Nat. Mus., 205:387, March 3.

Dipodomys panamintinus caudatus Hall

1946. *Dipodomys panamintinus caudatus* Hall, Mammals of Nevada, p. 409, July 1, type from 6 mi. S Granite Well, 3800 ft., Providence Mts., San Bernardino Co., California.

MARGINAL RECORDS.—Nevada (Hall, 1946:410): 9 mi. W and 3½ mi. S Searchlight, 4300 ft. California (Johnson *et al.,* 1948:362): Purdy; 2 mi. ESE Rock Spring; type locality; 5 mi. NE Granite Well.

Dipodomys panamintinus leucogenys (Grinnell)

1919. *Perodipus leucogenys* Grinnell, Univ. California Publ. Zool., 21:46, March 29, type from Pellisier Ranch, 5600 ft., 5 mi. N Benton Station, Mono Co., California.
1946. *Dipodomys panamintinus leucogenys,* Hall, Mammals of Nevada, p. 407, July 1.

MARGINAL RECORDS.—Nevada (Hall, 1946:409): ½ mi. S Pyramid Lake, 3950 ft.; 6 mi. NE Virginia City, 6000 ft.; 2 mi. SW Pine Grove, 7250 ft.; Lapon Canyon, Mt. Grant, 8900 ft.; Huntoon Valley, 5700 ft.; Endowment Mine, Excelsior Mts., 6930 ft. California: type locality; Taylor Ranch, 5300 ft., 2 mi. S Benton Station (Grinnell, 1922: 63); Walters Ranch, 3900 ft., 2 mi. NNW Independence (*ibid.*); 9 mi. W Bishop (*ibid.*); Dry Creek, 6700–6900 ft., near Mono Lake (*ibid.*). Nevada (Hall, 1946:409): N end Topaz Lake; 6½ mi. S Minden, 4900 ft.; 5½ mi. S Carson City, 4700 ft.; 3½ mi. E Carson City, 4700 ft.; 10 mi. S Reno; 8 mi. NE Reno.

Dipodomys panamintinus mohavensis (Grinnell)

1918. *Perodipus mohavensis* Grinnell, Univ. California Publ. Zool., 17:428, April 25, type from ½ mi. E of Railway Station at Warren, 3275 ft., about 5 mi. N Mohave, Kern Co., California.
1946. *D[ipodomys]. panamintinus mohavensis,* Hall, Mammals of Nevada, p. 408, July 1.

MARGINAL RECORDS.—California: vicinity Lone Pine (Grinnell, 1933:159; Hesperia (Huey, 1945:132); Rock Creek (*ibid.*); Fairmont, Antelope Valley (*ibid.*); 7 mi. W Mohave (Grinnell, 1922:62); Isabella (Grinnell, 1933: 159); Fay Creek, 4100 ft. (Grinnell, 1922:62); Walker Pass, 4500 ft. (Huey, 1945:132); Little Lake, 3150 ft. (Grinnell, 1922:62); Olancha, 3645–3900 ft. (*ibid.*).

Dipodomys panamintinus panamintinus (Merriam)

1894. *Perodipus panimintinus* Merriam, Proc. Biol. Soc. Washington, 9:114, June 21, type from head Willow Creek, Panamint Mts., Inyo Co., California.
1921. *Dipodomys panamintinus,* Grinnell, Jour. Mamm., 2:95, May 2.

MARGINAL RECORDS.—California: type locality; 1 mi. S Lee Pump, 6100 ft., Panamint Mts. (Grinnell, 1922:65).

Dipodomys stephensi (Merriam)
Stephens' Kangaroo Rat

1907. *Perodipus stephensi* Merriam, Proc. Biol. Soc. Washington, 20:78, July 22, type from San Jacinto Valley [a little west of present town of Winchester toward Menifee], Riverside Co., California.
1921. *Dipodomys stephensi,* Grinnell, Jour. Mamm., 2:95, May 2.

External measurements: 277–300; 165–180; 41–43. Closely related to *Dipodomys panamintinus* and possibly only subspecifically distinct from it. Differs from *D. panamintinus* in larger auditory bullae and, on the average, in shorter hind foot.

MARGINAL RECORDS.—California: Reche Canyon, 4 mi. SE Colton (Grinnell, 1933:160); 6 mi. NW San Jacinto (Grinnell, 1922:67); type locality; Temescal (*ibid.*).

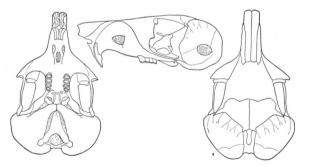

Fig. 297. *Dipodomys stephensi,* Perris, Riverside Co., California, No. 33570 M.V.Z., ♀, X 1.

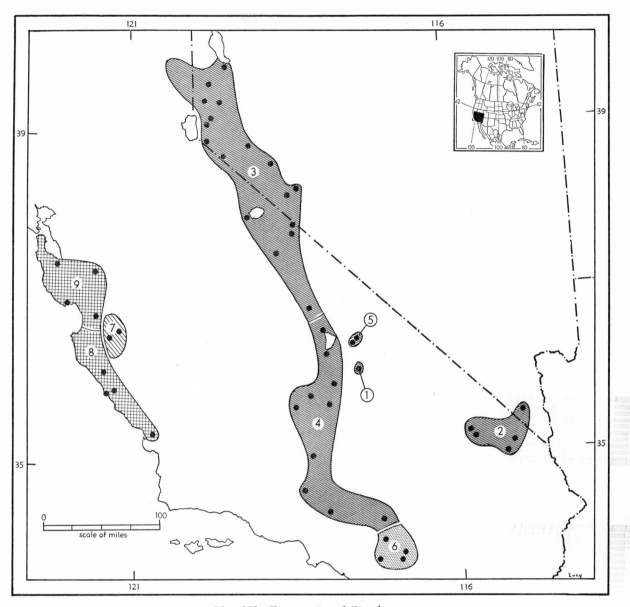

Map 308. Four species of *Dipodomys*.

1. *D. panamintinus argusensis*	4. *D. panamintinus mohavensis*	7. *D. elephantinus*
2. *D. panamintinus caudatus*	5. *D. panamintinus panamintinus*	8. *D. venustus santiluciae*
3. *D. panamintinus leucogenys*	6. *D. stephensi*	9. *D. venustus venustus*

heermanni-group
Dipodomys elephantinus (Grinnell)
Big-eared Kangaroo Rat

1919. *Perodipus elephantinus* Grinnell, Univ. California Publ. Zool., 21:43, March 29, type from 1 mi. N Cook P. O., 1300 ft., Bear Valley, San Benito Co., California.
1921. *Dipodomys elephantinus* Grinnell, Jour. Mamm., 2:96, May 2.

External measurements: 305–336; 183–210; 44–50. The big-eared kangaroo rat is closely related to, and possibly only subspecifically distinct from, *Dipodomys venustus* but differs from *D. venustus* in greater width (averaging 4.9) of rostrum near its end.

MARGINAL RECORDS.—California: type locality; Stonewall Creek, 1300 ft., 6 mi. NE Soledad (Grinnell, 1922: 102).

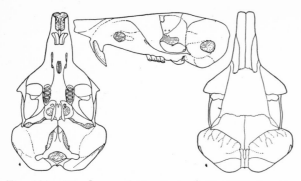

Fig. 298. *Dipodomys elephantinus,* Cook, 1300 ft., Bear Valley, San Benito Co., California, No. 28509 M.V.Z., ♀, X 1.

Dipodomys venustus
Narrow-faced Kangaroo Rat

External measurements: 293–332; 175–203; 44–47. This large, dark, 5-toed kangaroo rat with large external ears is narrow across the maxillary processes of the zygomatic arches of the skull. In this latter feature resemblance is shown to the species *Dipodomys agilis* from which *D. venustus* eventually may be found to be only subspecifically distinct.

Dipodomys venustus sanctiluciae Grinnell

1919. *Dipodomys sanctiluciae* Grinnell, Proc. Biol. Soc. Washington, 32:204, December 31, type from 1 mi. SW Jolon, Monterey Co., California.
1921. *Dipodomys venustus sanctiluciae* Grinnell, Jour. Mamm., 2:96, May 2.

MARGINAL RECORDS.—California (Grinnell, 1922: 101): Santa Lucia Peak, 5900 ft.; type locality; Santa Margarita; Chalk Peak, 3000 ft.

Dipodomys venustus venustus (Merriam)

1904. *Perodipus venustus* Merriam, Proc. Biol. Soc. Washington, 17:142, July 14, type from Santa Cruz, Santa Cruz Co., California.
1919. *Dipodomys venustus,* Grinnell, Proc. Biol. Soc. Washington, 32:204, December 31.

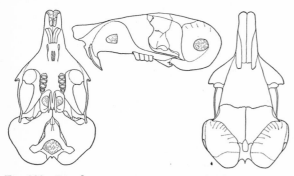

Fig. 299. *Dipodomys venustus venustus,* Doyle Gulch, 9 mi. E Santa Cruz, Santa Cruz Co., California, No. 46777 M.V.Z., ♂, X 1.

MARGINAL RECORDS.—California: Jasper Ridge, near Stanford Univ. (Grinnell, 1922:99); Mt. Hamilton (Grinnell, 1933:164); Fremont Peak (*ibid.*); type locality.

Dipodomys agilis
Agile Kangaroo Rat

External measurements: 265–319; 155–197; 40–46. Five toes on each hind foot; external ear of medium to large size; color dark; skull narrow across maxillary processes of zygomatic arches.

Dipodomys agilis agilis Gambel

1848. *Dipodomys agilis* Gambel, Proc. Acad. Nat. Sci. Philadelphia, 4:77, type from Los Angeles, Los Angeles Co., California.
1853. *D[ipodomys]. wagneri* Le Conte, Proc. Acad. Nat. Sci. Philadelphia, 6:224, January, type from an unknown locality.

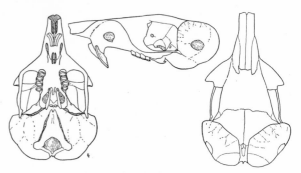

Fig. 300. *Dipodomys agilis agilis,* Mint Canyon, 2400 ft., Los Angeles Co., California, No. 47175 M.V.Z., ♂, X 1.

MARGINAL RECORDS.—California: Schoolhouse Canyon (Grinnell, 1933:163); Matilija (Grinnell, 1922:91); Elizabeth Lake, 3400 ft. (*ibid.*); N base Sugarloaf Mtn., 7500 ft., San Bernardino Mts. (Grinnell, 1922:92); near Banning (*ibid.*); Schain's Ranch, 4900 ft., San Jacinto Mts. (*ibid.*); Kenworthy (Grinnell, 1933:163); mouth Trabuco Canyon, 1500 ft. (Grinnell, 1922:92), thence northward along coast to point of beginning.

Dipodomys agilis cabezonae (Merriam)

1904. *Perodipus cabezonae* Merriam, Proc. Biol. Soc. Washington, 17:144, July 14, type from Cabezon, San Gorgonio Pass, Riverside Co., California.
1921. *Dipodomys agilis cabezonae,* Grinnell, Jour. Mamm., 2:96, May 2.

MARGINAL RECORDS.—California: type locality; near Dos Palmos Spring (Grinnell, 1922:96); vicinity Mountain Spring (Grinnell, 1933:163). Baja California (Huey, 1951: 234): Tres Piños Mine, near Juárez; 3 mi. NE Neji. California (Grinnell, 1922:96): Banner, 2700 ft.; Warner Pass, 3000 ft.

Dipodomys agilis fuscus Boulware

1943. *Dipodomys agilis fuscus* Boulware, Univ. California Publ. Zool, 46:393, September 16, type from 2½ mi. N La Purisima Mission, 600 ft., Santa Barbara Co., California.

MARGINAL RECORDS.—California: *C. A. Davis Ranch, 2 mi. NNW Lompoc, 400 ft.* (Boulware, 1943:393); type locality.

Dipodomys agilis martirensis Huey

1927. *Dipodomys agilis martirensis* Huey, Trans. San Diego Soc. Nat. Hist., 5:7, February 20, type from La Grulla (east side of valley), 7500 ft., Sierra San Pedro Mártir, Baja California.

MARGINAL RECORDS.—Baja California (Huey, 1951: 240, unless otherwise noted): Laguna Hanson; *1 mi. E Laguna Hanson*; Diablito Spring, summit San Matías Pass; type locality; Rosarito Divide (Hall and Kelson, 1952:366); Rosarito (*ibid.*); Aquaito Spring, el Valle de la Trinidad; Sangre de Cristo.

Dipodomys agilis perplexus (Merriam)

1907. *Perodipus perplexus* Merriam, Proc. Biol. Soc. Washington, 20:79, July 22, type from Walker Basin, 3400 ft., Kern Co., California.
1921. *Dipodomys agilis perplexus,* Grinnell, Jour. Mamm., 2:96, May 2.

MARGINAL RECORDS.—California: Trout Creek, toward head of S. Fork Kern River (Grinnell, 1933:163); Rip Rap Mine, Piute Mts. (Grinnell, 1922:97); 1½ mi. N Tehachapi (*ibid.*); 10½ mi. S, 13½ mi. E Victorville, 5200 ft., San Bernardino Mts. (63624 KU); Cajon Wash, ½ mi. SW Devore, 200 ft. (Vaughan, 1954:553); 1 mi. S, 2 mi. W Big Pines, 7400 ft. (*ibid.*); head Piru Creek (Grinnell, 1933: 163); S side Mt. Piños, 5500–6500 ft. (Grinnell, 1922:97); Kern River at Bodfish, 2400 ft. (*ibid.*).

Dipodomys agilis plectilis Huey

1951. *Dipodomys agilis plectilis* Huey, Trans. San. Diego Soc. Nat. Hist., 11:240, April 30, type from mouth of canyon San Juan de Díos, lat. 30° 07′ N, Baja California.

MARGINAL RECORDS.—Baja California (Huey, 1951: 240): type locality; 3 mi. W El Marmol; 4 mi. N Santa Catarina Landing; 1 mi. E El Rosario.

Dipodomys agilis simulans (Merriam)

1904. *Perodipus streatori simulans* Merriam, Proc. Biol. Soc. Washington, 17:144, July 14, type from Dulzura, San Diego Co., California.
1921. *Dipodomys agilis simulans,* Grinnell, Jour. Mamm., 2:96, May 2.
1925. *Dipodomys agilis latimaxillaris* Huey, Proc. Biol. Soc. Washington, 38:84, May 26, type from 2 mi. W Santo Domingo Mission, 30° 45′ N, 115° 58′ W, Baja California. Regarded as identical with *simulans* by Huey, Trans. San Diego Soc. Nat. Hist., 11:234, April 30, 1951.

MARGINAL RECORDS.—California: Bonsall (Grinnell, 1933:163); Santa Ysabel (*ibid.*); type locality. Baja California (Huey, 1951:239, unless otherwise noted): 3 mi. E Ojos Negros; Rancho San Pablo, 10 mi. SE Alamo; San José; Valledares (Hall and Kelson, 1952:367); San Quintín (Huey, 1951:234), thence northward along coast to point of beginning.

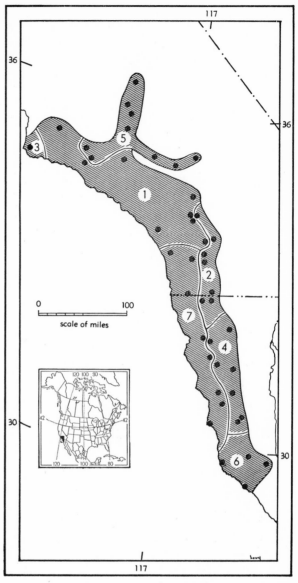

Map 309. *Dipodomys agilis.*

Guide to subspecies	
1. *D. a. agilis*	4. *D. a. martirensis*
2. *D. a. cabezonae*	5. *D. a. perplexus*
3. *D. a. fuscus*	6. *D. a. plectilis*
	7. *D. a. simulans*

Dipodomys paralius Huey
Santa Catarina Kangaroo Rat

1951. *Dipodomys paralius* Huey, Trans. San Diego Soc. Nat. Hist., 10:241, April 30, type from Santa Catarina Landing, lat. 29° 31′ N, Baja California.

External measurements: 255–280; 145–170; 38–41. Greatest length of skull, 37.2–39.2; breadth across bullae, 24.2–24.7. From its near relative, *Dipodomys agilis plectilis,* which occurs in the same geographic area, *D. paralius* differs in paler upper parts, lesser size, relatively more flattened auditory bullae, and more angular and more widely spreading zygomatic arches. The general outline of the skull is more nearly that of an equilateral triangle than that of an acute triangle, according to the original description.

MARGINAL RECORDS.—Baja California (Huey, 1951: 241): Rancho La Ramona, 8 mi. N Santa Catarina; type locality.

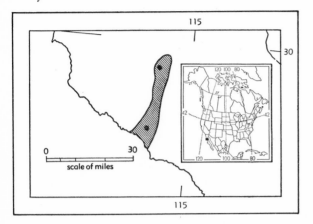

Map 310. *Dipodomys paralius*.

Dipodomys peninsularis
Baja California Kangaroo Rat

External measurements: 270–302; 158–189; 40–44. Greatest length of skull, 38.0–41.5; breadth across bullae, 24.1–26.9. Five toes on each hind foot. Closely resembles *Dipodomys agilis*, but differs in more inflated tympanic bullae, heavier-boned tail, and brighter, more buffy, coloration. For a taxonomic treatment of the subspecies of this species see Huey (1951:244–249) who deals similarly with all of the other kinds of kangaroo rats known from Baja California (*op. cit.*).

Dipodomys peninsularis australis Huey

1951. *Dipodomys peninsularis australis* Huey, Trans. San Diego Soc. Nat. Hist., 11:249, April 30, type from Santo Domingo, Magdalena Plain, lat. 25° 30′ N, Baja California.

MARGINAL RECORDS.—Baja California (Huey, 1951: 249): San Jorgé; type locality; 9 mi. S El Refugio.

Dipodomys peninsularis eremoecus Huey

1951. *Dipodomys peninsularis eremoecus* Huey, Trans. San Diego Soc. Nat. Hist., 11:248, April 30, type from 7 mi. W San Francisquito Bay, lat. 28° 30′ N, Baja California.

MARGINAL RECORDS.—Baja California: type locality; Santa Teresa Bay (Huey, 1951:249).

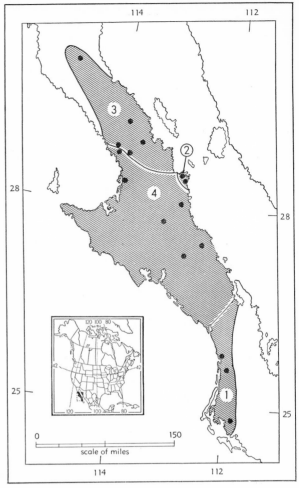

Map 311. *Dipodomys peninsularis*.

1. *D. p. australis*	3. *D. p. pedionomus*
2. *D. p. eremoecus*	4. *D. p. peninsularis*

Dipodomys peninsularis pedionomus Huey

1951. *Dipodomys peninsularis pedionomus* Huey, Trans. San Diego Soc. Nat. Hist., 11:247, April 30, type from 2 mi. N Chapala Dry Lake, on Llano de Santa Ana, lat. 29° 30′ N, long. 114° 35′ W, Baja California.

MARGINAL RECORDS.—Baja California (Huey, 1951: 248): San Agustín; type locality; El Valle de Agua Amargá; San Borjas Mission; Punta Prieta.

Dipodomys peninsularis peninsularis (Merriam)

1907. *Perodipus simulans peninsularis* Merriam, Proc. Biol. Soc. Washington, 20:79, July 22, type from Santo Domingo (Santo Domingo Landing), lat. 28° 51′ N, long. 114° W, Baja California.

1951. *Dipodomys peninsularis peninsularis*, Huey, Trans. San Diego Soc. Nat. Hist., 11:246, April 30.

MARGINAL RECORDS.—Baja California (Huey, 1951: 247): 11 mi. S Punta Prieta; Santa Gertrudis Mission; Valle de Yaqui, 10 mi. W Santa Rosalía; San Ignacio; Poso Altimisano; La Lomita María.

Dipodomys heermanni
Heermann's Kangaroo Rat

External measurements: 250–340; 160–200; 38–47. Four or 5 toes on each hind foot, depending on the subspecies; external ear of moderate length; auditory bullae small to medium; skull broad across maxillary processes of zygomatic arches.

Tappe (1941:117–148) studied this species in the San Joaquin Valley and learned that each individual dug one main burrow in which it spent the daylight hours and one or more subsidiary burrows that were used chiefly as places of temporary refuge at night when danger threatened. Seeds were the principal food but in the seasons of plant growth large amounts of green grass and other plants were eaten. The number of embryos varied from 2 to 5; the average was 3.7. Young ventured from the burrows first when approximately 6 weeks old.

Dipodomys heermanni arenae Boulware

1943. *Dipodomys heermanni arenae* Boulware, Univ. California Publ. Zool., 46:392, September 16, type from 2 mi. NNW Lompoc, 400 ft., Santa Barbara Co., California.

MARGINAL RECORDS.—California (Boulware, 1943: 393): 2¾ mi. S Oceano, 10–50 ft.; 2⅝ mi. W Buellton, 350 ft.; type locality.

Dipodomys heermanni berkeleyensis Grinnell

1919. *Dipodomys berkeleyensis* Grinnell, Proc. Biol. Soc. Washington, 32:204, December 31, type from head of Dwight Way, Berkeley, Alameda Co., California.
1921. *Dipodomys heermanni berkeleyensis* Grinnell, Jour. Mamm., 2:95, May 2.

MARGINAL RECORDS.—California: type locality; Mt. Diablo (Hooper, 1944:44); vicinity Livermore (*ibid.*).

Dipodomys heermanni californicus Merriam

1890. *Dipodomys californicus* Merriam, N. Amer. Fauna, 4:49, October 8, type from Ukiah [W edge of main road

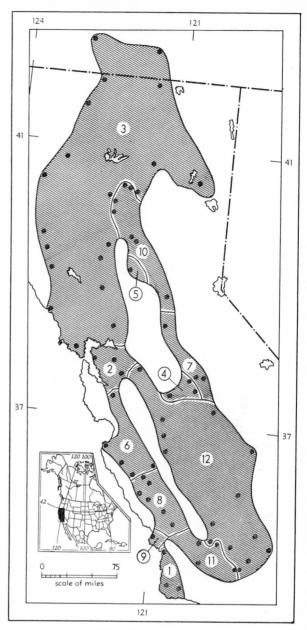

Map 312. *Dipodomys heermanni.*

1. *D. h. arenae*	7. *D. h. heermanni*
2. *D. h. berkeleyensis*	8. *D. h. jolonensis*
3. *D. h. californicus*	9. *D. h. morroensis*
4. *D. h. dixoni*	10. *D. h. saxatilis*
5. *D. h. eximius*	11. *D. h. swarthi*
6. *D. h. goldmani*	12. *D. h. tularensis*

running S from Ukiah and about 1 mi. S of the then center of town], Mendocino Co., California.
1921. *Dipodomys heermanni californicus*, Grinnell, Jour. Mamm., 2:95, May 2.
1899. *Dipodomys californicus pallidulus* Bangs, Proc. New England Zool. Club, 1:65, July 31, type from Sites, Colusa Co., California.

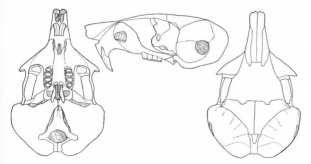

Fig. 301. *Dipodomys heermanni tularensis*, 6 mi. E Panoche, 1400 ft., Fresno Co., California, No. 72724 M.V.Z., ♀, X 1.

1916. *Dipodomys californicus trinitatis* L. Kellogg, Univ. California Publ. Zool., 12:366, January 27, type from Helena, 1405 ft., Trinity Co., California.

1925. *Dipodomys heermanni gabrielsoni* Goldman, Proc. Biol. Soc. Washington, 38:33, March 12, type from Brownsboro, Jackson Co., Oregon. Regarded as inseparable from *californicus* by Grinnell and Linsdale, Univ. California Publ. Zool., 30:457, June 15, 1929.

MARGINAL RECORDS.—Oregon (V. Bailey, 1936:240–241): Brownsboro; Swan Lake Valley. California (Grinnell, 1922:41, unless otherwise noted): E side Tule Lake (Grinnell, 1933:156); Petes Valley (*ibid.*); Hat Creek, 15 mi. S Cassel; Lyman's, 3300 ft. (Grinnell, Dixon and Linsdale, 1930:500); 10 mi. N Red Bluff, 500 ft. (*ibid.*); Willows; Sites; Rumsey; Vacaville (Hooper, 1944:42); Lagunitas; 7 mi. W Cazadero; type locality; near Willets; 6 mi. SW Laytonville; Mad River; Helena (Grinnell and Linsdale, 1929:457); Scott Valley, 4 mi. S Fort Jones; Hornbrook (Grinnell, 1933:156).

Dipodomys heermanni dixoni (Grinnell)

1919. *Perodipus dixoni* Grinnell, Univ. California Publ. Zool., 21:45, March 29, type from Delhi, near Merced River, Merced Co., California.

1921. *Dipodomys heermanni dixoni* Grinnell, Jour. Mamm., 2:95, May 2.

MARGINAL RECORDS.—California: 3 mi. S Lagrange (Grinnell, 1922:51); [1½ mi. S] Merced Falls (Grinnell, 1933:157); type locality.

Dipodomys heermanni eximius Grinnell

1919. *Dipodomys californicus eximius* Grinnell, Proc. Biol. Soc. Washington, 32:205, December 31, type from Marysville Buttes, 300 ft., 3 mi. NW Sutter Co., California. Known only from the type locality.

1921. *Dipodomys heermanni eximius* Grinnell, Jour. Mamm., 2:95, May 2.

Dipodomys heermanni goldmani (Merriam)

1904. *Perodipus goldmani* Merriam, Proc. Biol. Soc. Washington, 17:143, July 14, type from Salinas, mouth of Salinas Valley, Monterey Co., California.

1921. *Dipodomys heermanni goldmani*, Grinnell, Jour. Mamm., 2:95, May 2.

MARGINAL RECORDS.—California: vicinity of San Jose (Hooper, 1944:45); Bear Valley, vicinity of Cook P. O. (Grinnell, 1933:158); Arroyo Seco, S of Paraiso Springs (Grinnell, 1922:54); Jamesburg, Valley of Carmel River (*ibid.*); Seaside (Hooper, 1944:46).

Dipodomys heermanni heermanni Le Conte

1853. *D*[*ipodomys*]. *heermanni* Le Conte, Proc. Acad. Nat. Sci. Philadelphia, 6:224. Type locality, Sierra Nevada, California, probably in the Upper Sonoran Life-zone on Calaveras River, Calaveras Co.; see Grinnell, Univ. California Publ. Zool., 24:47, June 17, 1922.

1894. *Perodipus streatori* Merriam, Proc. Biol. Soc. Washington, 9:113, June 21, type from Carbondale, Amador Co., California.

MARGINAL RECORDS.—California (Grinnell, 1933:157): Carbondale; [6 mi. E] Coulterville; vicinity Calaveras River, foothill district.

Dipodomys heermanni jolonensis Grinnell

1919. *Dipodomys jolonensis* Grinnell, Proc. Biol. Soc. Washington, 32:203, December 31, type from floor of valley 1 mi. SW Jolon, Monterey Co., California.

1921. *Dipodomys heermanni jolonensis* Grinnell, Jour. Mamm., 2:95, May 2.

MARGINAL RECORDS.—California (Grinnell, 1922:56, unless otherwise noted): vicinity King City (Grinnell, 1933:158); San Lucas; Creston (Grinnell, 1933:158); 2 mi. S San Miguel; Pleyto; type locality.

Dipodomys heermanni morroensis (Merriam)

1907. *Perodipus morroensis* Merriam, Proc. Biol. Soc. Washington, 20:78, July 22, type from 4 mi. S Morro, San Luis Obispo Co., California. Known only from the type locality.

1943. *Dipodomys heermanni morroensis*, Boulware, Univ. California Publ. Zool., 46:393, September 16.

Dipodomys heermanni saxatilis Grinnell and Linsdale

1929. *Dipodomys heermanni saxatilis* Grinnell and Linsdale, Univ. California Publ. Zool., 30:453, June 15, type from near Dale's, N side Paine's Creek, 700 ft., Tehama Co., California.

MARGINAL RECORDS.—California: near Longs, 1 mi. S junction N and S forks Battle Creek (Dale, 1939:704); Inskip Forebay, 6 mi. SW Manton (*ibid.*); Limekiln, 1200 ft. (Grinnell and Linsdale, 1929:455); 8 mi. SE Chico, 450 ft. (*ibid.*); 4 mi. SE Chico, 450 ft. (*ibid.*); 2½ mi. NE Tehama, 400 ft. (Grinnell, *et al.*, 1930:505); type locality.

Dipodomys heermanni swarthi (Grinnell)

1919. *Perodipus swarthi* Grinnell, Univ. California Publ. Zool., 21:44, March 29, type from 7 mi. SE Simmler, Carrizo Plain, San Luis Obispo Co., California.

1921. *Dipodomys heermanni swarthi* Grinnell, Jour. Mamm., 2:95, May 2.

MARGINAL RECORDS.—California (Grinnell, 1933:158): type locality; vicinity McKittrick; San Emigdio; extreme northern Santa Barbara Co. [Cuyama Valley].

Dipodomys heermanni tularensis (Merriam)

1904. *Perodipus agilis tularensis* Merriam, Proc. Biol. Soc. Washington, 17:143, July 14, type from Alila, now Earlimart, Tulare Co., California.

1921. *Dipodomys heermanni tularensis*, Grinnell, Jour. Mamm., 2:95, May 2.

MARGINAL RECORDS.—California: Tracy (Hooper, 1944:46); Raymond (Grinnell, 1922:49); Dunlap (*ibid.*); Tipton (*ibid.*); 8 mi. NE Bakersfield (*ibid.*); mouth Caliente Creek Wash (Tappe, 1941:126); about 20 mi. S Bakersfield (*op. cit.*: 117); lower San Emigdio Creek Wash, 450 ft. (Grinnell, 1922:49); Taft (von Bloeker, 1930:237); Temblor Mts. [12 mi.], W McKittrick (Grinnell, 1933:157); near Lost Hills (Tappe, 1941:135); 4½ mi. E and 1 mi. N Panoche (*op. cit.*: 119); 22 mi. S Los Baños (Grinnell, 1922:49); Los Baños (*ibid.*).

Dipodomys gravipes Huey
San Quintín Kangaroo Rat

1925. *Dipodomys gravipes* Huey, Proc. Biol. Soc. Washington, 38:83, May 26, type from 2 mi. W Santo Domingo Mission, Baja California, lat. 30° 45′ N, long. 115° 58′ W.

External measurements: 286–310; 157–180; 43–44. "A large-sized, heavy bodied, small-eared animal, with thick tail of medium length, belonging to the *heermanni* group" (Huey, 1925:83).

MARGINAL RECORDS.—Baja California (Huey, 1951: 255): 3 mi. S San Telmo; type locality; 1 mi. S San Ramón. See Map 314.

Dipodomys ingens (Merriam)
Giant Kangaroo Rat

1904. *Perodipus ingens* Merriam, Proc. Biol. Soc. Washington, 17:141, July 14, type from Painted Rock, 20 [= 12] mi. SE Simmler, Carrizo Plain, San Luis Obispo Co., California.
1921. *Dipodomys ingens,* Grinnell, Jour. Mamm., 2:95, May 2.

External measurements: 311–348; 157–198; 46–55. Weight, 131–180 grams and hence the heaviest of all kangaroo rats. Five toes on each hind foot. Tail and ear short in relation to length of head and body. Skull broad across maxillary processes of zygomatic arches.

Shaw (1934:275–286) found that in March and April one of these rats constructed as many as 875 surface-of-the-ground caches. Each was approximately 1 in. in depth and diameter, in solid ground

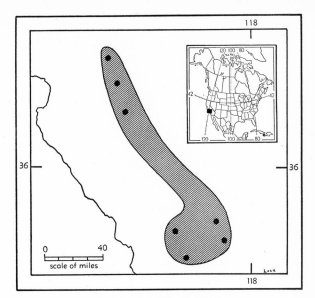

Map 313. *Dipodomys ingens.*

and shaped like the closed end of a test tube. Each pit was filled with semigreen seeds. These caches were covered with loose dry soil. By May many of the rats had moved this food material into dens; 9 underground caches in one den contained approximately 33 quarts of seeds and other plant materials. The number of embryos in 4 pregnant females was 5, 5, 5, and 6.

MARGINAL RECORDS.—California: near mouth of Laguna Seca Creek (Grinnell, 1933:160); Buttonwillow (Grinnell, 1922:69); near Buena Vista Lake (Grinnell, 1933:160); extreme northern Santa Barbara Co. (*ibid.*); Carrizo Plain, near Santiago Spring (Grinnell, 1922:69); Panoche Creek, foothills of Coast Range, about 50 mi. W Fresno (Shaw, 1934:275); about 12 mi. S Los Baños (Grinnell, 1932:316).

spectabilis-group
Dipodomys spectabilis
Banner-tailed Kangaroo Rat

External measurements: 310–349; 180–208; 47–51; weight 98–132 grams. Four toes on each hind foot. Distal 40 mm. of tail white; proximal to this white area, tail black all round; lateral white stripes present on only proximal half of tail. In Arizona Vorhies and Taylor (1922) found that this species inhabited firmer (less sandy) soils than *D. deserti,* and constructed a mound, 6 ins. to 4 ft. high and 5 to 15 ft. in diameter. In each mound the rat had several entrances to the underground burrow system in which seeds were stored, sometimes to the amount of 12½ lbs. In 67 females the number of embryos ranged from 1 to 3, 2 being the mode.

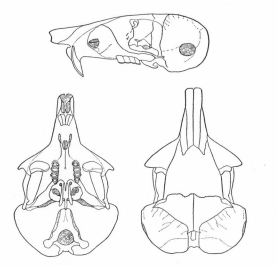

Fig. 302. *Dipodomys ingens,* Panoche Creek, 2 mi. SE Panoche, 1200 ft., Fresno Co., California, No. 72763 M.V.Z., ♀, X 1.

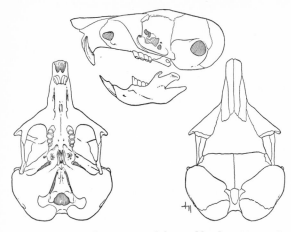

Fig. 303. *Dipodomys spectabilis perblandus*, 30 mi. S Tucson, Pima Co., Arizona, No. 7680 K.U., ♂, X 1.

Dipodomys spectabilis baileyi Goldman

1923. *Dipodomys spectabilis baileyi* Goldman, Proc. Biol. Soc. Washington, 36:140, May 1, type from 40 mi. W Roswell, Chaves Co., New Mexico.

MARGINAL RECORDS.—New Mexico: 1 mi. W Santa Fe Municipal Airport, Santa Fe (353, Santa Fe Field Sta., U.S. Publ. Health Surv.); Mesa Jumanes (Vorhies and Taylor, 1922:9); 12 mi. NW Carrizozo (Blair, 1941:223); type locality; E side Pecos River, 15 mi. NE Roswell (Vorhies and Taylor, 1922:9); 8 or 10 mi. N Santa Rosa (V. Bailey, 1932:260); Pecos Valley, 30 mi. E Carlsbad (*op. cit.*:259). Texas: Odessa (V. Bailey, 1905:147); Grand Falls (*ibid.*); 4 mi. SW Fort Davis, 5000 ft. (Blair, 1940: 29); 7 mi. NE Marfa (*ibid.*); Valentine (V. Bailey, 1905: 147); Sierra Blanca (*ibid.*); lower edge Franklin Mts. (Vorhies and Taylor, 1922:9). New Mexico (Vorhies and Taylor, 1922:9): Rio Alamosa; Gallina Mts.; Juan Tofoya, about 10 mi. NE Cebolleta (Hooper, 1941:27).

Dipodomys spectabilis clarencei Goldman

1933. *Dipodomys spectabilis clarencei* Goldman, Jour. Washington Acad. Sci., 23:467, October 15, type from Blanco, San Juan Co., New Mexico.

MARGINAL RECORDS.—New Mexico (Goldman, 1933: 468): Fruitland; type locality; 15 mi. NW Gallup.

Dipodomys spectabilis cratodon Merriam

1907. *Dipodomys spectabilis cratodon* Merriam, Proc. Biol. Soc. Washington, 20:75, July 22, type from Chicalote, Aguascalientes.

MARGINAL RECORDS.—San Luis Potosí (Dalquest, 1953b:118): 2 km. E Illescas; 4 km. E Salinas. Aguascalientes: type locality.

Dipodomys spectabilis perblandus Goldman

1933. *Dipodomys spectabilis perblandus* Goldman, Jour. Washington Acad. Sci., 23:466, October 15, type from Calabasas, 3500 ft., Santa Cruz Co., Arizona.

MARGINAL RECORDS (Goldman, 1933:467, unless otherwise noted).—Arizona: between Florence and Tucson, U.S. Highway 80 (Doutt, 1934:262; recorded as *D. s. spectabilis*); Oracle; N base Santa Rita Mts.; type locality. Sonora: Cerro Blanco (Burt, 1938:46); Noria (*ibid.*); 2 mi. S Sasabe (*ibid.*). Arizona: *75 mi. SW Tucson*; Ajo (Vorhies and Taylor, 1922:9); Indian Oasis [=Sells, Pima Co.].

Dipodomys spectabilis spectabilis Merriam

1890. *Dipodomys spectabilis* Merriam, N. Amer. Fauna, 4:46, October 8, type from Dos Cabezos, Cochise Co., Arizona.

MARGINAL RECORDS.—New Mexico (V. Bailey, 1932: 249): Silver City; Deming. Chihuahua: 15 mi. W, 6 mi. S Coyame, 5500 ft. (55826 KU); 38 mi. N, 18 mi. E Chihuahua, 4700 ft. (55825 KU); *4 mi. N, 2 mi. W Chihuahua* (54684 KU) Gallego (Vorhies and Taylor, 1922:9). Arizona: San Bernardino Ranch (J. A. Allen, 1895:213); mouth of Montezuma Canyon (Hoffmeister and Goodpaster, 1954: 108); *8 mi. SE Fort Huachuca* (*ibid.*); *7 mi. ESE Fort Huachuca* (*ibid.*); type locality; SW slopes Graham Mts., near Fort Grant (Vorhies and Taylor, 1922:8). New Mexico: Lordsburg (V. Bailey, 1932:249).

Dipodomys spectabilis zygomaticus Goldman

1923. *Dipodomys spectabilis zygomaticus* Goldman, Proc. Biol. Soc. Washington, 36:140, May 1, type from Parral, southern Chihuahua.

MARGINAL RECORDS.—Chihuahua: type locality; *5 mi. E Parral, 5700 ft.* (40915 KU).

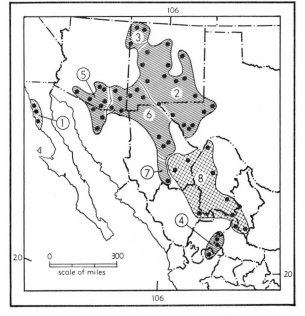

Map 314. Three species of *Dipodomys*.

1. *D. gravipes*
2. *D. spectabilis baileyi*
3. *D. spectabilis clarencei*
4. *D. spectabilis cratodon*
5. *D. spectabilis perblandus*
6. *D. spectabilis spectabilis*
7. *D. spectabilis zygomaticus*
8. *D. nelsoni*

Dipodomys nelsoni Merriam
Nelson's Kangaroo Rat

1907. *Dipodomys nelsoni* Merriam, Proc. Biol. Soc. Washington, 20:75, July 22, type from La Ventura, Coahuila.

External measurements: 310–330; 177–204; 45–50. Four toes on each hind foot. Averages slightly smaller than *D. spectabilis* and with shorter (20 mm.) terminal white area on tail, or tip of tail black. This rat closely resembles *D. spectabilis*, but the two have not been shown to intergrade and therefore are arranged as separate species.

MARGINAL RECORDS.—Coahuila: 7 mi. S, 2 mi. E Boquillas, 1800 ft. (44875 KU); 2½ mi. S, 21 mi. E Ocampo, 3500 ft. (56636 KU); Treviño (50176 BS). Nuevo León: Dr. Arroyo (Merriam, 1907:75). San Luis Potosí: 6 km. S Matehuala (Dalquest, 1953b:119). Coahuila: type locality. Durango: 2 mi. E Pedriceña, 4300 ft. (40539 KU). Chihuahua: Santa Rosalía [= Camargo] (Merriam, 1907:75); 1 km. W San Francisco, 4325 ft. (54685 KU). See Map 314.

merriami-group
Dipodomys elator Merriam
Texas Kangaroo Rat

1894. *Dipodomys elator* Merriam, Proc. Biol. Soc. Washington, 9:109, June 21, type from Henrietta, Clay Co., Texas.

External measurements: 317, 196, 46. Four toes on each hind foot. Superficially, in size and color pattern, resembling *D. spectabilis*. Skull narrow interorbitally; interparietal wide; orbit large.

Grinnell (1921:95) and Setzer (1949:495) consider this species to be more closely allied to *D. phillipsii* than to *D. spectabilis* but Davis (1942: 329) takes the opposite view and points out that some features ally *D. elator* with *D. merriami*. All three authors seem to agree that *D. elator* is a species, and not subspecifically linked to any other named kind of *Dipodomys*.

MARGINAL RECORDS.—Oklahoma: Chattanooga (Blair, 1949:201). Texas: type locality; 3 mi. W Gatesville (Blair, 1954b:248); about 15 mi. S Vernon (Blair, 1949:201).

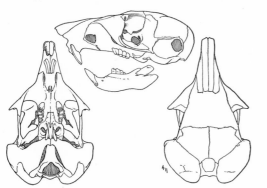

Fig. 304. *Dipodomys elator*, Henrietta, Texas, No. 107244 U.S.N.M., ♀, X 1.

Dipodomys ornatus Merriam
Ornate Kangaroo Rat

1894. *Dipodomys ornatus* Merriam, Proc. Biol. Soc. Washington, 9:110, June 21, type from Berriozábal, Zacatecas.

External measurements: 270–274; 162–167; 39. Closely resembling *Dipodomys phillipsii* and possibly only subspecifically different. Top of cranium almost flat.

MARGINAL RECORDS.—Zacatecas: type locality. San Luis Potosí (Dalquest, 1953b:117): 1 km. N Arenal; Bledos. Aguascalientes: 5 mi. NNE Rincón de Romos, 6400 ft. (34348 KU).

Dipodomys phillipsii
Phillips' Kangaroo Rat

External measurements: 265–271; 162–168; 40–41. Four toes on each hind foot; arietiform facial markings black and extensive; dark stripes on tail uniting in distal 3rd; tip of tail white or black; auditory bullae small.

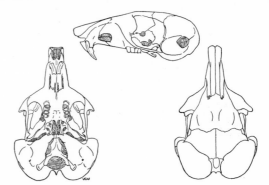

Fig. 305. *Dipodomys phillipsii perotensis*, 2 km. E Perote, 8300 ft., Veracruz, No. 19380 K.U., ♀, X 1.

Dipodomys phillipsii oaxacae Hooper

1947. *Dipodomys phillipsii oaxacae* Hooper, Jour. Mamm., 28:48, February 17, type from Teotitlán, 950 m., Oaxaca. Known only from the type locality.

Dipodomys phillipsii perotensis Merriam

1894. *Dipodomys perotensis* Merriam, Proc. Biol. Soc. Washington, 9:111, June 21, type from Perote, Veracruz.
1944. *Dipodomys phillipsii perotensis*, Davis, Jour. Mamm., 25:391, December 12.

MARGINAL RECORDS.—Veracruz: type locality. Puebla: W base Mt. Orizaba, 9000 ft. (Merriam, 1893:87). Tlaxcala: Huamantla (*ibid.*).

Dipodomys phillipsii phillipsii Gray

1841. *Dipodomys philipii* [*sic*] Gray, Ann. Mag. Nat. Hist., ser. 1, 7:522, August, type from Valley of Mexico, México.
1893. *Dipodomys phillipsi*, Merriam, Proc. Biol. Soc. Washington, 8:91, July 18.

MARGINAL RECORDS.—Hidalgo: 85 km. N Mexico City, 9 km. S Pachuca, 8200 ft. (Davis, 1944:390). México (Merriam, 1893:86): W base Mt. Popocatépetl, near Amecameca; near peak of Huitzilac, near Cruz del Marquez, 9000 ft.

Dipodomys merriami
Merriam's Kangaroo Rat

External measurements of 20 adults (10 of each sex) from Searchlight, in southern Nevada: 240–259; 140–161; 36–41; weight, 38.4–46.9 grams. Four toes on each hind foot; hind feet and tail slender; auditory bullae large; skull narrow across maxillary processes of zygomatic arches; interorbital breadth of skull more than half of basal length.

In Nevada, there seem to be 2 litters per year. In 72 pregnant females the number of embryos varied from 1 to 5; the mean and mode both were 3. Pregnant females were trapped as early as March and as late as August.

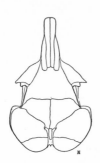

Fig. 306. *Dipodomys merriami merriami*, 14 mi. E Searchlight, Nevada, No. 61580 M.V.Z., ♂, X 1.

Dipodomys merriami annulus Huey

1951. *Dipodomys merriami annulus* Huey, Trans. San Diego Soc. Nat. Hist., 11:224, April 30, type from Barril, Gulf of California, lat. 28° 20′ N, long. 112° 50′ W, Baja California.

MARGINAL RECORDS.—Baja California: Las Flores near Los Angeles Bay (Huey, 1951:225); type locality.

Dipodomys merriami arenivagus Elliot

1904. *Dipodomys m[erriami]. arenivagus* Elliot, Field Columb. Mus., Publ. 87, Zool. Ser., 3(14):249, January 7, type from San Felipe, Baja California.

MARGINAL RECORDS.—Baja California (Huey, 1951:222): De Mara's Well, W side Laguna Salada; 40 mi. N San Felipe; type locality; Gaskill's Tank, E base Sierra Juárez.

Dipodomys merriami atronasus Merriam

1894. *Dipodomys merriami atronasus* Merriam, Proc. Biol. Soc. Washington, 9:113, June 21, type from Hacienda La Parada, about 25 mi. NW San Luis Potosí, State of San Luis Potosí.

MARGINAL RECORDS.—San Luis Potosí (Dalquest, 1953b:115): 3 km. S Matehuala; Tepeyac; 1 km. W Bledos. Zacatecas: 2 mi. ESE Trancoso, 7000 ft. (39996 KU). San Luis Potosí: 3 km. E Illescas (Dalquest, 1953b:115).—Baker (1956:242 and fig. 36) referred specimens from SE Coahuila to *atronasus* after our account and Map 315 were prepared.

Dipodomys merriami brunensis Huey

1951. *Dipodomys merriami brunensis* Huey, Trans. San Diego Soc. Nat. Hist., 11:225, April 30, type from Llano de San Bruno, Baja California.

MARGINAL RECORDS.—Baja California (Huey, 1951:226): El Valle de Yaqui, NW of Santa Rosalía; Canipolé.

Dipodomys merriami llanoensis Huey

1951. *Dipodomys merriami llanoensis* Huey, Trans. San Diego Soc. Nat. Hist., 11:226, April 30, type from Buena Vista, Magdalena Plain, lat. 24° 50′ N, long. 111° 50′ W, Baja California.

MARGINAL RECORDS.—Baja California (Huey, 1951:227): San Jorge; 9 mi. S El Refugio.

Dipodomys merriami mayensis Goldman

1928. *Dipodomys merriami mayensis* Goldman, Proc. Biol. Soc. Washington, 41:141, October 15, type from Alamos, Sonora.

MARGINAL RECORDS.—Sonora (Burt, 1938:47): Camoa; type locality; Guirocoba; Chinobampo.

Dipodomys merriami melanurus Merriam

1893. *Dipodomys merriami melanurus* Merriam, Proc. California Acad. Sci., ser. 2, 3:345, June 5, type from San José del Cabo, Baja California.

MARGINAL RECORDS.—Baja California (Huey, 1951:226): La Paz; Tres Pachitas, and southward over rest of Baja California.

Dipodomys merriami merriami Mearns

1890. *Dipodomys merriami* Mearns, Bull. Amer. Mus. Nat. Hist., 2:290, February 21, type from New River, between Phoenix and Prescott, Maricopa Co., Arizona.
1890. *Dipodomys ambiguus* Merriam, N. Amer. Fauna, 4:42, October 8, type from El Paso, El Paso Co., Texas. Regarded as identical with *merriami* by Davis, Jour. Mamm., 22:194, May 13, 1941. Regarded as a valid subspecies by Blair, Jour. Mamm., 30:388, November 17, 1949.
1894. *Dipodomys merriami nevadensis* Merriam, Proc. Biol. Soc. Washington, 9:111, June 21, type from Pyramid Lake, Washoe Co., Nevada. Regarded as identical with *merriami* by Hall, Mammals of Nevada, p. 424, July 1, 1946.
1894. *Dipodomys merriami nitratus* Merriam, Proc. Biol. Soc. Washington, 9:112, June 21, type from Keeler, east side of Owens Lake, Inyo Co., California. Regarded as identical with *merriami* by Grinnell, Jour. Mamm., 2:97, May 2, 1921.
1904. *Dipodomys merriami mortivallis* Elliot, Field Columb. Mus., Publ. 87, Zool. Ser., 3(14):250, January 7, type from Furnace Creek, Death Valley, Inyo Co., California. Regarded as identical with *merriami* by Grinnell, Jour. Mamm., 2:97, May 2, 1921.

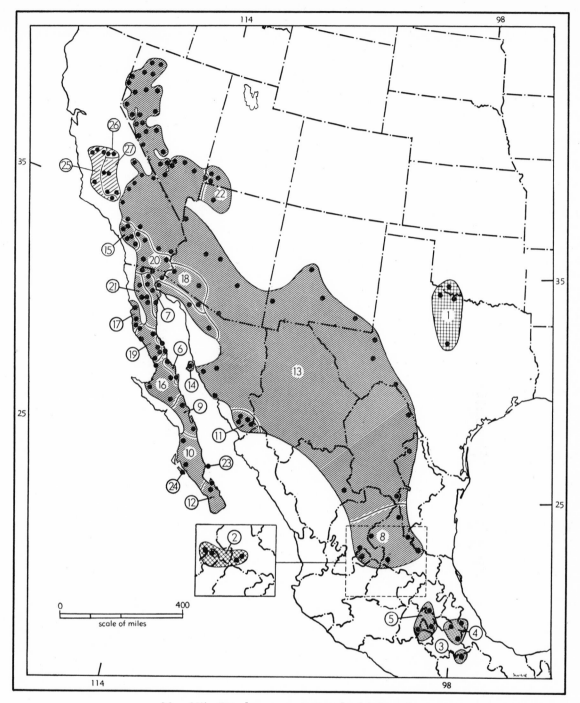

Map 315. *Dipodomys merriami* and related species.

1. *D. elator*	10. *D. merriami llanoensis*	19. *D. merriami semipallidus*
2. *D. ornatus*	11. *D. merriami mayensis*	20. *D. merriami simiolus*
3. *D. phillipsii oaxacae*	12. *D. merriami melanurus*	21. *D. merriami trinidadensis*
4. *D. phillipsii perotensis*	13. *D. merriami merriami*	22. *D. merriami vulcani*
5. *D. phillipsii phillipsii*	14. *D. merriami mitchelli*	23. *D. insularis*
6. *D. merriami annulus*	15. *D. merriami parvus*	24. *D. margaritae*
7. *D. merriami arenivagus*	16. *D. merriami platycephalus*	25. *D. nitratoides brevinasus*
8. *D. merriami atronasus*	17. *D. merriami quintinensis*	26. *D. nitratoides exilis*
9. *D. merriami brunensis*	18. *D. merriami regillus*	27. *D. nitratoides nitratoides*

1907. *Dipodomys merriami kernensis* Merriam, Proc. Biol. Soc. Washington, 20:77, July 22, type from Onyx, W end Walker Pass, Kern Co., California. Regarded as identical with *merriami* by Grinnell, Jour. Mamm., 2:97, May 2, 1921.

1929. *Dipodomys merriami olivaceus* Swarth, Proc. California Acad. Sci., ser. 4, 18:356, April 26, type from Fairbank, Cochise Co., Arizona. Regarded as identical with *merriami* by Benson, Proc. Biol. Soc. Washington, 47:183, October 2, 1934.

MARGINAL RECORDS.—Nevada (Hall, 1946:428): Quinn River Crossing; 1¼ mi. N Sulphur, 4050 ft.; 3½ mi. NE Toulon, 4500 ft.; 9½ mi. E and 1 mi. S Fanning, Buena Vista Valley, 4100 ft.; Eastgate, 4400 ft.; 2 mi. E Hawthorne, 4300 ft.; Marietta, 4900 ft.; 3½ mi. SE Coaldale, 4850 ft.; Gold Flat, 6 mi. W Kawich P.O., 5150 ft.; NW base Timber Mtn., 4200 ft.; 9 mi. E Wheelbarrow Peak; NW base Skull Mtn., 3500 ft.; ½ mi. N Oak Spring, 6500 ft.; 9 mi. W Groom Baldy, 5500 ft.; 3 mi. N Crystal Spring, 4000 ft.; Meadow Valley, 21 mi. S Caliente, 3200 ft. Utah: 1½ mi. E Beaverdam Wash, 8 mi. N Utah-Arizona border, 2800 ft. (Durrant, 1952:279). Arizona: Hardyville (Bole, 1936:2); Wickenburg (*ibid.*); New River, N of Phoenix (Grinnell, 1933:160); 5 mi. N Oracle (Dice and Blossom, 1937:31). New Mexico: Redrock (V. Bailey, 1932:264); Socorro (*ibid.*); near Salinas (Blair, 1941:223); Carlsbad (Blair, 1943a:29). Texas (V. Bailey, 1905:149–150): Monahans; Fort Stockton; Langtry. Coahuila: 15 mi. N and 8 mi. W Piedras Negras (35823 KU). Nuevo León: Lampazos (25632/33025 BS). Coahuila: 8 mi. N La Ventura, 5500 ft. (34966 KU—but Baker, 1956, Map 36 and p. 242 identified it as *D. m. atronasus* after our account and Map 315 were completed). Durango: 3 mi. NNW Cuencamé, 5400 ft. (40472 KU). Sonora (Burt, 1938:47): Guaymas; Costa Rica Ranch, 45 mi. SW Hermosillo; Hermosillo. Arizona: Baboquivari Mts. (Burt, 1933:119). California: Blythe (Grinnell, 1933:160); 53 mi. E Mecca (*ibid.*); Doble, 7000 ft., San Bernardino Mts. (Grinnell, 1922:79); Hesperia (*ibid.*); 7 mi. W Mohave (Grinnell, 1933:160); Weldon, S. Fork Kern River (*ibid.*); Little Lake (Grinnell, 1922:79); Old Camp Independence (Bole, 1936:2); 15 mi. N Darwin (Grinnell, 1922:79); Furnace Creek Ranch, Death Valley (Grinnell, 1933:160). Nevada (Hall, 1946:428): Dyer; Huntoon Valley, 5700–6000 ft.; Cat Creek, 4 mi. W Hawthorne; 8 mi. SE Schurz, 4100 ft.; West Walker River, 6 mi. S Yerington, 4500 ft.; 3½ mi. E Carson City, 4700 ft.; 2¼ mi. S Pyramid Lake; 4 mi. NW Flanigan, 4200 ft.; Smoke Creek, 9 mi. E California boundary, 3900 ft.; 12 mi. N and 2 mi. E Gerlach, 4000 ft.; Soldier Meadows, 4600 ft.

Dipodomys merriami mitchelli Mearns

1897. *Dipodomys mitchelli* Mearns, Proc. U. S. Nat. Mus., 19:719, July 30, type from Tiburón Island, Gulf of California, Sonora. Known only from Tiburón Island.

1938. *Dipodomys merriami mitchelli*, Burt, Misc. Publ. Mus. Zool., Univ. Michigan, 39:48, February 15.

Dipodomys merriami parvus Rhoads

1894. *Dipodomys parvus* Rhoads, Amer. Nat., 28:70, January, type from Reche Canyon, 4 mi. SE of Colton, San Bernardino Co., California. (See Grinnell, Univ. California Publ. Zool., 24:82, June 17, 1922.)

1901. [*Dipodomys merriami*] *parvus*, Elliot, Field Columb. Mus., Publ. 45, Zool. Ser., 2:234, March 6.

MARGINAL RECORDS.—California: 4 mi. NW San Bernardino (Huey, 1927:66); Vallevista (Grinnell, 1933:161); Aquanga (Huey, 1951:220); 4 mi. SW Perris (*ibid.*); Reche Canyon, 1250 ft., 3 mi. SE Colton (Grinnell, 1933:161).

Dipodomys merriami platycephalus Merriam

1907. *Dipodomys platycephalus* Merriam, Proc. Biol. Soc. Washington, 20:76, July 22, type from Calmallí, Baja California.

1927. *Dipodomys merriami platycephalus*, Huey, Trans. San Diego Soc. Nat. Hist., 5:66, July 6.

MARGINAL RECORDS.—Baja California (Huey, 1951:224): San Francisquito; Yubay, 30 mi. S Calamahué; 1 mi. E Rancho Lagunitas; Valle de Agua Amarga; mainland on S side Scammons Lagoon; La Lomita María (Miller's Landing).

Dipodomys merriami quintinensis Huey

1951. *Dipodomys merriami quintinensis* Huey, Trans. San Diego Soc. Nat. Hist., 11:222, April 30, type from 5 mi. E San Quintín, Baja California.

MARGINAL RECORDS.—Baja California (Huey, 1951:223): Santo Domingo, lat. 30° N; type locality; 8 mi. E Rosario.

Dipodomys merriami regillus Goldman

1937. *Dipodomys merriami regillus* Goldman, Proc. Biol. Soc. Washington, 50:75, June 22, type from Tule Well, Tule Desert between Cabeza Prieta Mountains, Yuma Co., Arizona.

MARGINAL RECORDS (Goldman, 1937:76).—Arizona: 3 mi. E Dome; 10 mi. N Ajo. Sonora: Sonoyta; Colorado River, 10 mi. S U.S. boundary.

Dipodomys merriami semipallidus Huey

1927. *Dipodomys merriami semipallidus* Huey, Trans. San Diego Soc. Nat. Hist., 5:65, July 6, type from 7 mi. N Santa Catarina, Baja California, lat. 29° 45′ N.

MARGINAL RECORDS.—Baja California (Huey, 1951:223): San Fernando; Onyx; 13 mi. NW Chapala; 25 mi. N Punta Prieta; San Andrés; Santa Catarina Landing.

Dipodomys merriami simiolus Rhoads

1894. *Dipodomys simiolus* Rhoads, Proc. Acad. Nat. Sci. Philadelphia, 45:410, January 27, type from Agua Caliente, now Palm Springs, Riverside Co., California.

1897. *Dipodomys merriami simiolus*, Mearns, Proc. U.S. Nat. Mus., 19:720, July 30.

1894. *Dipodomys similis* Rhoads, Proc. Acad. Nat. Sci. Philadelphia, 45:411, January 27, type from Whitewater, Riverside Co., California.

MARGINAL RECORDS (Grinnell, 1933:161, unless otherwise noted).—California: Cabezon; Coachella (Grinnell, 1922:81); Palo Verde. Sonora: about 5 mi. E Pitiquito (Dice and Blossom, 1937:31); Sierra Pinacate, 40 mi. W Sonoyta (Burt, 1938:47); El Doctor (*ibid.*). Baja California: SE base Signal Mt. (Huey, 1951:220); a few yards S international boundary near Jacumba (*ibid.*). California: La Puerta.

Dipodomys merriami trinidadensis Huey

1951. *Dipodomys merriami trinidadensis* Huey, Trans. San Diego Soc. Nat. Hist., 11:220, April 30, type from Aquajito Spring, El Valle de la Trinidad, Baja California.

MARGINAL RECORDS.—Baja California: Sangre de Cristo (Huey, 1951:221); Diablito Spring, summit of San Matías Pass (*ibid.*); Cañon Esperanza (on geographic grounds from Elliot, 1903:250, originally referred to *D. m. simiolus*); type locality.

Dipodomys merriami vulcani Benson

1934. *Dipodomys merriami vulcani* Benson, Proc. Biol. Soc. Washington, 47:181, October 2, type from lower end Toroweap Valley, about ½ mi. E Vulcan's Throne, Mohave Co., Arizona.
1936. *Dipodomys merriami frenatus* Bole, Sci. Publ. Cleveland Mus. Nat. Hist., 5(1):1, January 17, type from Toquerville, Washington Co., Utah. Regarded as identical with *vulcani* by Durrant and Setzer, Bull. Univ. Utah, 35(26):31–32, June 30, 1945.

MARGINAL RECORDS (Durrant, 1952:278).—Utah: Veyo; Toquerville. Arizona: type locality. Utah: 5 mi. NW St. George.

Dipodomys insularis Merriam
San José Island Kangaroo Rat

1907. *Dipodomys insularis* Merriam, Proc. Biol. Soc. Washington, 20:77, July 22, type from San José Island, Gulf of California, Baja California. Known only from San José Island.

External measurements of 5 specimens average 249, 146, 39.6. Closely allied to *D. merriami*, this insular rat is described as paler than its relatives of the nearby mainland.

Dipodomys margaritae Merriam
Margarita Island Kangaroo Rat

1907. *Dipodomys margaritae* Merriam, Proc. Biol. Soc. Washington, 20:76, July 22, type from Santa Margarita Island, Baja California. Known only from Santa Margarita Island.

External measurements of three specimens average: 240; 149; 38.2. Closely allied to *D. merriami*, this insular rat is described as differing in smaller auditory bullae and smaller size generally.

Dipodomys nitratoides
Fresno Kangaroo Rat

External measurements: 211–253; 120–152; 33–37. Rostrum short, narrow at base and its sides nearly parallel. The morphological differences between the species *D. nitratoides* and *D. merriami* are slight; it is principally because intergradation does not occur between them that they are treated as

distinct species. The Tehachapi Mountains isolate the small 4-toed kangaroo rats in the San Joaquin Valley from *D. merriami* which occurs widely to the east and south.

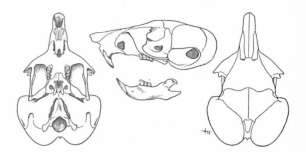

Fig. 307. *Dipodomys nitratoides brevinasus*, 7 mi. SE Simmler, San Luis Obispo Co., California, No. 10747 K.U., ♀, X 1.

Dipodomys nitratoides brevinasus Grinnell

1920. *Dipodomys merriami brevinasus* Grinnell, Jour. Mamm., 1:179, August 24, type from Hayes Station, 19 mi. SW Mendota, Fresno Co., California.
1921. *Dipodomys nitratoides brevinasus* Grinnell, Jour. Mamm., 2:96, May 2.

MARGINAL RECORDS.—California: near Mendota (Grinnell, 1933:162); 21½ mi. W Fresno (Boolootian, 1954:573—recorded as subspecies *exilis* but see remarks beyond under *exilis*); near Wheeler Ridge, 600 ft. (Grinnell, 1922:86); 7 mi. SE Simmler (10747 KU); 11 mi. E Llanado (Boolootian, 1954:571); *type locality*.

Dipodomys nitratoides exilis Merriam

1894. *Dipodomys merriami exilis* Merriam, Proc. Biol. Soc. Washington, 9:113, June 21, type from Fresno, San Joaquin Valley, Fresno Co., California.
1921. *Dipodomys nitratoides exilis*, Grinnell, Jour. Mamm., 2:96, May 2.

MARGINAL RECORDS.—California: type locality (according to Grinnell, 1933, p. 161, this is 4 mi. N of the railway station of the town of Fresno, the specimens having been trapped along the Southern Pacific right of way); immediately S Kerman, 210 ft. (Culbertson, 1934:161). [Boolootian, 1954:570–577, referred specimens from 21½ mi. W Fresno to the subspecies *exilis* and used these specimens in comparison that led him to conclude that *exilis* was not subspecifically distinct from the subspecies *nitratoides*. S. B. Benson, *in verbis*, in the spring of 1955, pointed out that specimens from 21½ mi. W Fresno are not subspecies *exilis* but instead are referable to the subspecies *brevinasus*. For the present, therefore, *exilis* is retained as a recognizable subspecies.]

Dipodomys nitratoides nitratoides Merriam

1894. *Dipodomys merriami nitratoides* Merriam, Proc. Biol. Soc. Washington, 9:112, June 21, type from Tipton, San Joaquin Valley, Tulare Co., California.
1921. *Dipodomys nitratoides nitratoides*, Grinnell, Jour. Mamm., 2:96, May 2.

MARGINAL RECORDS.—California (Grinnell, 1933: 161, unless otherwise noted): type locality; Caliente Wash; N side Buena Vista Lake; 15 mi. S Corcoran.

deserti-group
Dipodomys deserti
Desert Kangaroo Rat

External measurements: 305–377; 180–215; 50–58; weight, 83–138 grams. Upper parts pale ochraceous buff and remainder of body white; ventral dark stripe on tail lacking in most specimens; distal 3rd of tail crested; long hair forming crest dusky, except that distal 25 mm. of tail white; 4 toes on hind foot; inflation of auditory bullae maximum for genus; enlargement of mastoidal bullae so restricting space for interparietal and supraoccipital that these bones are barely visible on dorsal surface of skull.

D. deserti is a species of the Lower Sonoran Life-zone and wherever found by us lived in wind-drifted sand 20 or more inches deep. Well-beaten trails often lead away from burrows.

Dipodomys deserti arizonae Huey

1955. *Dipodomys deserti arizonae* Huey, Trans. San Diego Soc. Nat. Hist., 12:99, February 10, type from 3 mi. SE Picacho, Pinal Co., Arizona.

MARGINAL RECORDS (Huey, 1955:100).—Arizona: 10 mi. S Gila Bend; 11 mi. W Casa Grande; type locality; 7 mi. E Papago Well.

Dipodomys deserti deserti Stephens

1887. *Dipodomys deserti* Stephens, Amer. Nat., 21:42, January, type from Mohave River [3 to 4 mi. from, and opposite, Hesperia], San Bernardino Co., California.
1904. *Dipodomys deserti helleri* Elliot, Field Columb. Mus., Publ. 87, Zool. Ser., 3:249, January 7, type from Keeler, Owens Lake, Inyo Co., California. Regarded as identical with *deserti* by Grinnell, Univ. California Publ. Zool., 24:106, June 17, 1922.

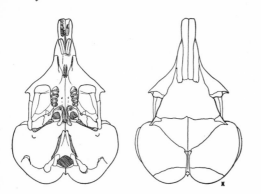

Fig. 308. *Dipodomys deserti deserti*, 21 mi. W, 2 mi. N Lovelock, 4000 ft., Nevada, No. 73694 M.V.Z., ♂, X 1.

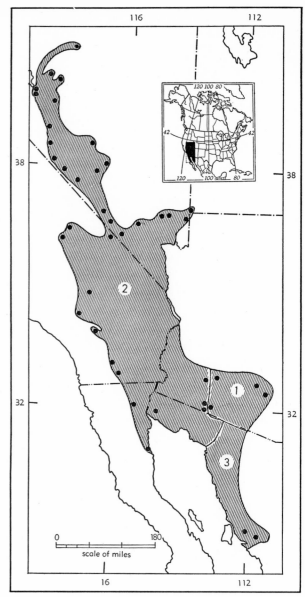

Map 316. *Dipodomys deserti.*

Guide to subspecies
1. *D. d. arizonae*
2. *D. d. deserti*
3. *D. d. sonoriensis*

MARGINAL RECORDS.—Nevada (Hall, 1946:431): 8 mi. E and 1 mi. N Jungo, 4200 ft.; 21 mi. W and 2 mi. N Lovelock, 4000 ft.; 3¼ mi. NNE Toulon, 3900 ft.; 4 mi. W Fallon, 4000 ft.; San Antonio, 5400 ft.; 34 mi. E and 1 mi. N Tonopah, Ralston Valley, 5650 ft.; N shore Mud Lake, 5300 ft.; 1 mi. N Beatty, 3400 ft.; Amargosa Desert, 20 mi. SE Beatty, 2500 ft.; 3½ mi. N Pahrump, 2667 ft.; Indian Spring Valley, 14 mi. N Indian Springs, 3100 ft.; Coyote Spring, 2800 ft.; Carp. Utah: 8 mi. N Utah–Arizona border, 2800 ft., Beaverdam Wash (Durrant, 1952:280). Nevada: Mesquite (Hall, 1946:431). Arizona: Sentinel (J. A. Allen, 1895:212); Growler Valley, about 3 mi. SW Growler Mine (Huey, 1942:361); 1 mi. E Quitovaquita,

Abra Valley (*ibid.*). Sonora: El Doctor (Burt, 1938:49). Baja California (Huey, 1951:253): San Felipe, Gulf of California; De Mara's Well, W side Laguna Salada, 35 mi. below international boundary. California: Carrizo Creek (Grinnell, 1922:110); Borego Spring (Grinnell, 1933:165); Whitewater (*ibid.*); type locality; Barstow (Grinnell, 1922: 110); Olancha (*ibid.*); Keeler (Grinnell, 1933:165); Kelley's Well, Amargosa River (Grinnell, 1922:110. Nevada (Hall, 1946:431): 8 mi. SE Blair; 7 mi. N Arlemont, 5500 ft.; Huntoon Valley, 5700 ft.; Cat Creek, 4 mi. W Hawthorne, 4500 ft.; 8 mi. SE Schurz, 4100 ft.; ½ mi. SE Wadsworth, 4200 ft.; 4½ mi. N and 2½ mi. W Nixon.

Dipodomys deserti sonoriensis Goldman

1923. *Dipodomys deserti sonoriensis* Goldman, Proc. Biol. Soc. Washington, 36:139, May 1, type from La Libertad Ranch, 30 mi. E Sierra Seri, Sonora.

MARGINAL RECORDS.—Sonora: Costa Rica Ranch (Burt, 1938:50); type locality.

SUBFAMILY HETEROMYINAE

Lophs of lower premolars first unite, when worn, at buccal side, next at lingual side; stylids progressively present on p4 in geologically later kinds, developing at any point on tooth; lophs of upper premolars unite first at lingual side, then at buccal side; protoloph of P4 formed of more than 1 cusp; lophs of upper molars always, and of lowers usually, unite at 2 ends, surrounding central basin; external cingulum of lower teeth migrates to anterior side, internal cingulum of upper teeth migrates to posterior side, developing secondary connection with middle of adjacent loph, forming Y-shaped crest; cheek-teeth rooted but progressively high-crowned; in later hypsodont kinds, entire crown increasing so that pattern is long retained; 2 pairs of pits for pterygoid muscles; ethmoid foramen present in dorsal part of orbit; ventral surface of tympanic bullae never reaching level of grinding surface of upper cheek-teeth; median ventral foramina at anterior end of centra of caudal vertebrae; masseteric crest ending above, not behind, mental foramen; astragalo-cuboid articulation (after Wood, 1935:165).

Genus Liomys Merriam—Spiny Pocket Mice

Revised by Goldman, N. Amer. Fauna, 34:32–63, September 7, 1911.

1902. *Liomys* Merriam, Proc. Biol. Soc. Washington, 15:44, March 5. Type, *Heteromys alleni* Coues.

Resembling *Heteromys*; pelage hispid; tail usually well haired; skull usually broad; rostrum narrow; interpterygoid fossa U-shaped, broad and rounded anteriorly; angle of mandible strongly everted; posterior molars decidedly narrower than premolars; posterior loop in crown of upper premolar with anterior border concave or slightly notched, but without deep re-entrant angle (after Goldman, 1911:32).

KEY TO NOMINAL SPECIES OF LIOMYS

pictus-group
Liomys pictus
Painted Spiny Pocket Mouse

External measurements: 202–262; 105–146; 24–33. Upper parts variable from buffy to grayish, usually richly buffy; lateral line distinct, buffy to orange; underparts white or nearly so. Skull slender with subtriangular interparietal.

These animals are burrowers. The burrows are usually placed under a log, rock, or other shelter, and are easily overlooked. A definite mound of earth at the entrance of the burrow is usually lacking. The painted spiny pocket mice are essentially herbivorous and utilize both seeds and tender herbaceous parts of plants depending upon season and locality. Most members of this species live in arid to semiarid habitats. Four (3–5) young are born at any time of year but usually in spring and early summer.

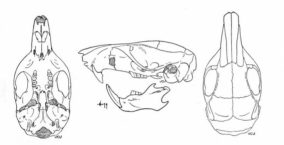

Fig. 309. *Liomys pictus veraecrucis*, 3 km. E San Andrés Tuxtla, 1000 ft., Veracruz, No. 24029 K.U., ♂, X 1.

Liomys pictus escuinapae (J. A. Allen)

1906. *Heteromys pictus escuinapae* J. A. Allen, Bull. Amer. Mus. Nat. Hist., 22:211, July 25, type from Esquinapas [= Escuinapa], Sinaloa.
1911. *Liomys pictus escuinapae*, Goldman, N. Amer. Fauna, 34:35, September 7.

MARGINAL RECORDS (Goldman, 1911:36).—Sinaloa: Mazatlán; Plomosas. Nayarit: Pedro Pablo; Amatlán. Jalisco: Estancia. Nayarit: Tepic.

Liomys pictus isthmius Merriam

1902. *Liomys pictus isthmius* Merriam, Proc. Biol. Soc. Washington, 15:46, March 5, type from Tehuantepec, Oaxaca.

MARGINAL RECORDS (Goldman, 1911:42).—Chiapas: Tuxtla Gutiérrez; San Bartolomé. Guatemala: Nentón. Chiapas: Tonalá. Oaxaca: Huilotepec; San Bartolo; Chicapa.

Liomys pictus obscurus Merriam

1902. *Liomys obscurus* Merriam, Proc. Biol. Soc. Washington, 15:48, March 5, type from Carrizal, Veracruz.

1911. *Liomys pictus obscurus,* Goldman, N. Amer. Fauna, 34:44, September 7.
1903. *Heteromys paralius* Elliot, Field Columb. Mus., Publ. 80, Zool. Ser., 3:233, September 3, type from San Carlos, Veracruz.

MARGINAL RECORDS.—Veracruz: San Carlos (Goldman, 1911:45); Boca del Río, 10 ft. (30043 KU); Otatitlán (Goldman, 1911:45); 2 km. N Paraje Nuevo, 1700 ft. (24016 KU); type locality.

Liomys pictus parviceps Goldman

1904. *Liomys parviceps* Goldman, Proc. Biol. Soc. Washington, 17:82, March 21, type from La Salada, 40 mi. S Uruapan, Michoacán.
1911. *Liomys pictus parviceps* Goldman, N. Amer. Fauna, 34:38, September 7.

MARGINAL RECORDS.—Michoacán: type locality; 1 mi. E, 2½ mi. S Tacámbaro, 4700 ft. (Hall and Villa, 1949: 454). Guerrero: Río Balsas (Goldman, 1911:39); 2 km. E Zihuatanejo (35325 KU); El Limón (Goldman, 1911:39). Michoacán: Apatzingán, 1040 ft. (Hall and Villa, 1949: 454).

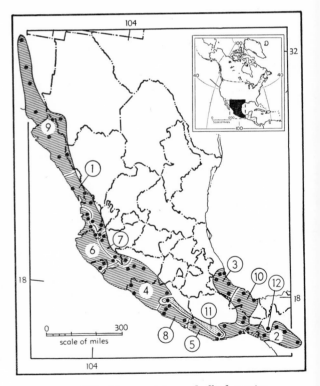

Map 317. *Liomys pictus* and allied species.

1. *L. pictus escuinapae*
2. *L. pictus isthmius*
3. *L. pictus obscurus*
4. *L. pictus parviceps*
5. *L. pictus phaeurus*
6. *L. pictus pictus*
7. *L. pictus plantinarensis*
8. *L. pictus rostratus*
9. *L. pictus sonoranus*
10. *L. pictus veraecrucis*
11. *L. annectens*
12. *L. pinetorum*

Liomys pictus phaeurus Merriam

1902. *Liomys phaeura* Merriam, Proc. Biol. Soc. Washington, 15:48, March 5, type from Pinotepa, Oaxaca.
1911. *Liomys pictus phaeurus,* Goldman, N. Amer. Fauna, 34:40, September 7.

MARGINAL RECORDS (Goldman, 1911:41).—Oaxaca: Llano Grande; type locality; Puerto Angel.

Liomys pictus pictus (Thomas)

1893. *Heteromys pictus* Thomas, Ann. Mag. Nat. Hist., ser. 6, 12:233, September, type from Mineral San Sebastián, 4300 ft., Jalisco.
1911. *Liomys pictus,* Goldman, N. Amer. Fauna, 34:33, September 7.
1897. *Heteromys hispidus* J. A. Allen, Bull. Amer. Mus. Nat. Hist., 9:56, March 15, type from Compostela, Nayarit.

MARGINAL RECORDS (Goldman, 1911:35, unless otherwise noted).—Nayarit: Santiago; Navar[r]ete; Compostela; 1 mi. E Ixtlán del Río, 3700 ft. (39840 KU). Jalisco: Arroyo de Platanar. Colima: Colima; Armería, thence up coast to point of beginning.

Liomys pictus plantinarensis Merriam

1902. *Liomys plantinarensis* Merriam, Proc. Biol. Soc. Washington, 15:46, March 5, type from Plantinar, Jalisco.
1911. *Liomys pictus plantinarensis,* Goldman, N. Amer. Fauna, 34:37, September 7.

MARGINAL RECORDS.—Jalisco: 2 mi. ESE Tequila, 4000 ft. (33459 KU). Michoacán: Los Reyes (Hall and Villa, 1949:454). Jalisco: type locality; Ameca (Goldman, 1911:38).

Liomys pictus rostratus Merriam

1902. *Liomys pictus rostratus* Merriam, Proc. Biol. Soc. Washington, 15:46, March 5, type from near Ometepec, Guerrero.

MARGINAL RECORDS.—Guerrero: Acahuizotla (Goldman, 1911:40); type locality; Acapulco (Goldman, 1911:40); Río Aguacatillo, 30 km. N Acapulco (Davis, 1944:390).

Liomys pictus sonoranus Merriam

1902. *Liomys sonorana* Merriam, Proc. Biol. Soc. Washington, 15:47, March 5, type from Alamos, Sonora.
1911. *Liomys pictus sonorana,* Goldman, N. Amer. Fauna, 34:36, September 7.

MARGINAL RECORDS (Goldman, 1911:37, unless otherwise noted).—Sonora: 23 mi. S, 5 mi. E Nogales, 3200 ft. (22978 KU); Ures (Burt, 1938:43); Tecoripa (*ibid.*). Sinaloa: Sierra de Choix, 50 mi. NE Choix. Chihuahua: near Batopilas. Durango: Chacala. Sinaloa: Culiacán; Sinaloa. Sonora: Chinobampo (Burt, 1938:43).

Liomys pictus veraecrucis Merriam

1902. *Liomys veraecrucis* Merriam, Proc. Biol. Soc. Washington, 15:47, March 5, type from San Andrés Tuxtla, Veracruz.
1911. *Liomys pictus veraecrucis,* Goldman, N. Amer. Fauna, 34:42, September 7.

1902. *Liomys orbitalis* Merriam, Proc. Biol. Soc. Washington, 15:48, March 5, type from Catemaco, Veracruz.

MARGINAL RECORDS.—Veracruz: 3 km. E San Andrés Tuxtla, 1000 ft. (24017 KU); 14 km. SW Coatzacoalcos, 100 ft. (19366 KU). Oaxaca: Guichicovi (Goldman, 1911:43); Laguna (*ibid.*). Veracruz: Jimba, 350 ft. (19365 KU).

Liomys annectens (Merriam)
Pluma Spiny Pocket Mouse

1902. *Heteromys annectens* Merriam, Proc. Biol. Soc. Washington, 15:43, March 5, type from Pluma Hidalgo, Oaxaca.
1911. *Liomys annectens,* Goldman, N. Amer. Fauna, 34:45, September 7.

Average external measurements of 4 adults: 281, 156, 32. Upper parts dark gray; lateral line rich orange-buff; underparts white; tail dusky above, whitish below, becoming darker distally. Cranially this nominal species closely resembles *L. pictus* and differs chiefly in larger size.

MARGINAL RECORDS.—Guerrero: Omilteme (Goldman, 1911:45). Oaxaca: type locality.

Liomys pinetorum Goodwin
Chiapan Spiny Pocket Mouse

1956. *Liomys pinetorum* Goodwin, Amer. Mus. Novit., 1791:2, September 28, type from San Miguel, about 4000 ft., 24 km. NE Tonalá, Cerro Tres Picos, District of Tonalá, Chiapas. Known only from the type locality.

External measurements of the adult female holotype are: 214; 142; 28; 12.5. Greatest length of skull, 33.4; zygomatic breadth, 15.5; interorbital breadth, 7.9; alveolar length of maxillary tooth-row, 5.5. From *L. pictus isthmius,* according to the original description, *pinetorum* differs in richer color, larger skull, and less crowded dentition—and from *L. annectens* in shorter tail, smaller foot, and more buffy coloration—but is a member of the *L. pictus* group.

crispus-group
Liomys crispus
Rough Spiny Pocket Mouse

External measurements: 208–225; 97–112; 25–30. Upper parts grayish to drab or brownish according to subspecies, darkest in mid-line; lateral line absent; underparts white; tail dusky above, pale ecru below, but not sharply bicolored. Skull small and, for the genus, delicate; ascending branches of premaxillae slender; zygomatic arches almost parallel-sided; interparietal irregularly ovoid with slight posterior emargination; dentition much as in *L. pictus,* but never forming central enamel island on crown by wear of ends of enamel loops.

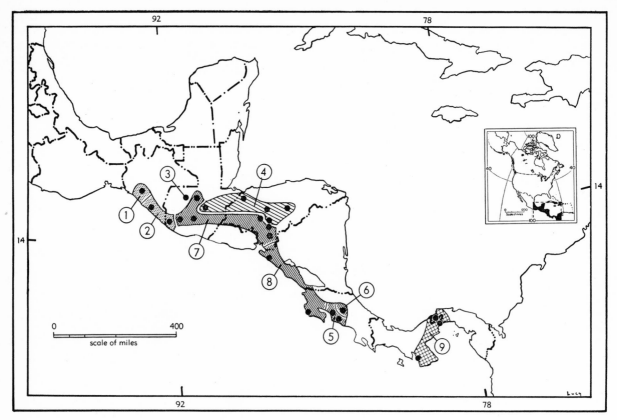

Map 318. Five species of *Liomys*.

1. *L. crispus crispus*	4. *L. heterothrix*	7. *L. salvini salvini*
2. *L. crispus setosus*	5. *L. salvini aterrimus*	8. *L. salvini vulcani*
3. *L. anthonyi*	6. *L. salvini nigrescens*	9. *L. adspersus*

Liomys crispus crispus Merriam

1902. *Liomys crispus* Merriam, Proc. Biol. Soc. Washington, 15:49, March 5, type from Tonalá, Chiapas. Known only from the type locality.

Liomys crispus setosus Merriam

1902. *Liomys crispus setosus* Merriam, Proc. Biol. Soc. Washington, 15:49, March 5, type from Huehuetán, Chiapas.

MARGINAL RECORDS.—Chiapas: Estación Vieja, 1 km. S Mapastepec, 46 m. (Villa, 1949:511). Guatemala: Hda. California (Goodwin, 1934:32).

Liomys anthonyi Goodwin
Anthony's Spiny Pocket Mouse

1932. *Liomys anthonyi* Goodwin, Amer. Mus. Novit., 528:2, May 23, type from Sacapulas, 4500 ft., Guatemala. Known only from the type locality.

External measurements: 240–260; 116–135; 30–32. Upper parts hair brown mixed with ochraceous buff; underparts, forelimbs, hind feet, lips, and cheek pouches creamy white; tail dark brown above, white below. Cranially resembling *L. salvini* but with more evenly rounded braincase, and narrower and relatively longer nasals.

Liomys heterothrix Merriam
Honduran Spiny Pocket Mouse

1902. *Liomys heterothrix* Merriam, Proc. Biol. Soc. Washington, 15:50, March 5, type from San Pedro Sula, Honduras.

External measurements: 210–255; 100–126; 25–31. Upper parts between drab and hair brown, washed with ochraceous buff; underparts, forelimbs, and feet creamy white; tail dusky above, paler below. Skull resembling that of *L. c. setosus*; nasals more wedge-shaped, tapering posteriorly; ascending branches of premaxillae broader, reaching posteriorly beyond nasals, as in *setosus*; maxillary root of zygoma narrower and weaker, owing to greater anterior development of frontal along intermaxillary suture; interparietal more evenly oval, without small posterior emargination present in *setosus* and *crispus*; dentition as in *crispus* (after Goldman, 1911: 49).

MARGINAL RECORDS.—Honduras: type locality; El Caliche Orica (Goodwin, 1942:156); Catacamas (*ibid.*); La Cueva Archaga (*ibid.*). Guatemala: Progresso [*sic*] (Goodwin, 1934:33).

Liomys salvini
Salvin's Spiny Pocket Mouse

The type specimen of *Liomys salvini salvini* is recorded as measuring: head and body, 115; imperfect tail, 95+?; hind foot, 26.5. Those of the type of *L. s. nigrescens* are: head and body, 127; tail broken; hind foot without claws, 25. Measurements of the type of *L. s. vulcani* are 220, 110, and 25. Upper parts slaty to blackish, sometimes faintly washed with yellow; lateral line absent; underparts white; tail dusky above, white below; outer surface of forelimb with slate gray edging (except in *L. s. vulcani*).

Liomys salvini aterrimus Goodwin

1938. *Liomys salvini aterrimus* Goodwin, Amer. Mus. Novit., 987:4, May 13, type from Sabanilla de Pirrís, about 3730 ft., 10 mi. S Puriscal, San José, Costa Rica.

MARGINAL RECORDS.—Costa Rica: San Francisco, Esparta (Goodwin, 1946:374); type locality.

Liomys salvini nigrescens (Thomas)

1893. *Heteromys salvini nigrescens* Thomas, Ann. Mag. Nat. Hist., ser. 6, 12:234, September, type from Costa Rica, probably Escazú (Goodwin, Bull. Amer. Mus. Nat. Hist., 87:374, December 31, 1946).
1911. *Liomys salvini nigrescens*, Goldman, N. Amer. Fauna, 34:51, September 7.

MARGINAL RECORDS (Goodwin, 1946:374).—Costa Rica: Los Higuerones, Escazú; *Villa Colón*.

Liomys salvini salvini (Thomas)

1893. *Heteromys salvini* Thomas, Ann. Mag. Nat. Hist., ser. 6, 11:331, April, type from Dueñas, Guatemala.
1911. *Liomys salvini*, Goldman, N. Amer. Fauna, 34:50, September 7.

MARGINAL RECORDS.—Guatemala: La Primavera (Goodwin, 1934:34). Honduras (Goodwin, 1942:156): Monte Redondo; La Flor Archaga; *Hatillo*; El Zapote. Guatemala (Goodwin, 1934:34): Antigua; Volcán San Lucas.

Liomys salvini vulcani (J. A. Allen)

1908. *Heteromys vulcani* J. A. Allen, Bull. Amer. Mus. Nat. Hist., 24:652, October 13, type from Volcán de Chinandega, about 4000 ft., Nicaragua.

1946. *Liomys salvini vulcani,* Goodwin, Bull. Amer. Mus. Nat. Hist., 87:374, December 31.

MARGINAL RECORDS.—Nicaragua: type locality. Costa Rica: San Juanillo (Goodwin, 1946:375).

Liomys adspersus (Peters)
Panamá Spiny Pocket Mouse

1874. *Heteromys adspersus* Peters, Monatsb. preuss. Akad. Wiss., Berlin, p. 357, May, type from Panamá, by restriction (Goldman, Smiths. Miscl. Coll., 69(5):118, April 26, 1920), Panama City.
1911. *Liomys adspersus,* Goldman, N. Amer. Fauna, 34:51, September 7.

External measurements of type, taken dry, are: head-body, 145; tail, 95; hind foot, 30. Upper parts dark grayish drab lightly flecked with ochraceous buff; underparts creamy white; tail thinly haired, coarsely annulated, indistinctly bicolored, brownish above, white below.

MARGINAL RECORDS.—Panamá: Empire, Canal Zone (Goldman, 1920:119); Balboa, Canal Zone (*ibid.*); Paracote (Bole, 1937:165).

irroratus-group
Liomys irroratus
Mexican Spiny Pocket Mouse

External measurements: 202–295; 105–163; 25–35. Upper parts mouse gray, usually sprinkled with tawny or ochraceous hairs; underparts white; lateral line absent or only faintly expressed; tail dusky above, white below, but tip usually dark above and below. Skull robust; rostrum slender; zygomatic arches widely spreading; interparietal broadly ovoid; audital bullae well inflated; dentition heavy.

The *irroratus* group is closely knit and eventually *L. bulleri* and *L. guerrerensis* probably will be found to be subspecies of *L. irroratus*. According to Goldman (1911:54) the group belongs mainly to the Sonoran zones, but the ranges of several representatives extend a short distance into the Arid and Humid Tropical zones.

Liomys irroratus acutus Hall and Villa

1948. *Liomys irroratus acutus* Hall and Villa, Univ. Kansas Publ., Mus. Nat. Hist., 1:253, July 26, type from 2 mi. W Pátzcuaro, 7700 ft., Michoacán.

MARGINAL RECORDS (Hooper and Handley, 1948: 15–17, unless otherwise noted).—Michoacán: 4 mi. S Cuitzeo, 5900 ft.; 15 mi. E Morelia, 7000 ft. México: Temascaltepec, 5000 ft. Michoacán: 5 mi. S Pátzcuaro, 7800 ft. (Hall and Villa, 1949:455); 3 mi. NW Pátzcuaro, 6700 ft. (*ibid.*); 4½ mi. NE Terequato, 6600 ft. (62607 KU). Jalisco: 4 mi. W Mazamitla, 6600 ft. (39906 KU).

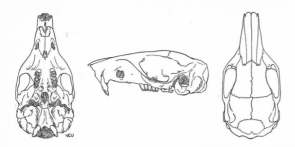

Fig. 310. *Liomys irroratus acutus*, 2 mi. W Pátzcuaro, 7700 ft., Michoacán, No. 100171 M.V.Z., ♀, X 1.

Liomys irroratus alleni (Coues)

1881. *Heteromys alleni* Coues, Bull. Mus. Comp. Zool., 8: 187, March, type from Río Verde, San Luis Potosí.
1911. *Liomys irroratus alleni*, Goldman, N. Amer. Fauna, 34:56, September 7.

MARGINAL RECORDS (Goldman, 1911:57, unless otherwise noted).—Nuevo León: Monterrey; Cerro de la Silla; Río Ramos, 20 km. NW Montemorelos, 1000 ft. (Davis, 1944:389). Tamaulipas: Jaumave, 2600–3300 ft. (Hooper and Handley, 1948:19). San Luis Potosí: 4 km. NE C. Valles (17953 KU); Paso de San Antonio (Dalquest, 1953b:120). Querétaro: Pinal de Amoles. Hidalgo: Zimapán, 6200 ft. (Hooper and Handley, 1948:19). Veracruz: 10 km. SW Jacales, 6500 ft. (30039 KU). Puebla: San Martín [Texmelucán]. Michoacán: Queréndaro (Hall and Villa, 1949:455). Jalisco: Ocotlán. Aguascalientes: Chicolote. Zacatecas: Berriozábal. San Luis Potosí (Dalquest, 1953b:120): Cerro Peñón Blanco; Villar.

Liomys irroratus canus Merriam

1902. *Liomys canus* Merriam, Proc. Biol. Soc. Washington, 15:44, March 5, type from near Parral, Chihuahua.
1911. *Liomys irroratus canus*, Goldman, N. Amer. Fauna, 34:60, September 7.

MARGINAL RECORDS (Goldman, 1911:60).—Chihuahua: Santa Rosalía [= Camargo]. Durango: Indé. Zacatecas: Valparaíso; Hda. San Juan Capistrano. Durango: Durango. Chihuahua: type locality.

Liomys irroratus irroratus (Gray)

1868. *Heteromys irroratus* Gray, Proc. Zool. Soc. London, p. 205, May, type from near Oaxaca, Oaxaca.
1911. *Liomys irroratus*, Goldman, N. Amer. Fauna, 34:53, September 7.
1868. *Heteromys albolimbatus* Gray, Proc. Zool. Soc. London, p. 205, May, type from La Parada, Oaxaca.

MARGINAL RECORDS (Hooper and Handley, 1948:11, unless otherwise noted).—Guerrero: Chilpancingo, 4500 ft.; Agusinapa (Hall and Kelson, 1952:364). Oaxaca: Sierra Juárez, Ixtlán, 8000 ft.; Yalalag; Cerro Zempoaltepec; Miahuatlán, 5000 ft.; Sola de la Vega. Guerrero: 15 mi. S Chilpancingo (on geographic grounds from Davis, 1944: 389, referred by him to *L. i. torridus*).

Liomys irroratus jaliscensis (J. A. Allen)

1906. *Heteromys jaliscensis* J. A. Allen, Bull. Amer. Mus. Nat. Hist., 22:251, July 25, type from Las Canoas, 7000 ft., about 20 mi. W Zapotlán, Jalisco.

1911. *Liomys irroratus jalicensis* [*sic*], Goldman, N. Amer. Fauna, 34:60, September 7.

MARGINAL RECORDS.—Jalisco: Etzatlán, 4500 ft. (Hooper and Handley, 1948:17); Atemajac (*ibid.*); 3 mi. NW Chapala, 5100 ft. (*ibid.*). Michoacán: Zamora (Hall and Villa, 1949:454). Jalisco: ½ mi. NW Mazamitla (Hooper, 1955:9). Michoacán: S bank Río de Tepalcatepec, 800 ft., 17 mi. S Spatzingán (39909 KU). Jalisco: Zapotlán (Goldman, 1911:61).

Liomys irroratus minor Merriam

1902. *Liomys torridus minor* Merriam, Proc. Biol. Soc. Washington, 15:45, March 5, type from Huajuapan, Oaxaca.
1911. *Liomys irroratus minor*, Goldman, N. Amer. Fauna, 34:56, September 7.
1903. *Heteromys exiguus* Elliot, Field Columb. Mus., Publ. 71, Zool. Ser., 3(8):146, March 20, type from Puente de Ixtla, Morelos.

MARGINAL RECORDS.—Morelos (Davis and Russell, 1954:73): 1½ mi. SE Huitzilac; Yautepec. Oaxaca: type locality. Guerrero (Hall and Kelson, 1952:365); Tlalixtaquilla; Tlapa. Morelos (Davis and Russell, 1954:73): Huajintlán; 2 mi. SW Michapa.

Liomys irroratus pretiosus Goldman

1911. *Liomys irroratus pretiosus* Goldman, N. Amer. Fauna, 34:58, September 7, type from Metlatoyuca, Puebla.

MARGINAL RECORDS.—San Luis Potosí: El Salto (Dalquest, 1954:121). Veracruz: La Mar, 20 ft. (30034 KU); Nautla (Hooper and Handley, 1948:20); 4 km. S Tlapacoyan, 1700 ft. (24010 KU). Puebla: Pahuatlán, 3600 ft. (Hooper and Handley, 1948:20). Querétaro: Jalpan (Goldman, 1911:58). San Luis Potosí (Dalquest, 1953b:121): Xilitla at Apetsco; 4 km. N Valles; *10 mi. E, 2 mi. N Ciudad del Maíz.*

Liomys irroratus pullus Hooper

1947. *Liomys irroratus pullus* Hooper, Jour. Mamm., 28: 47, February 17, type from Tlalpan, 2250 m., Distrito Federal, México.

MARGINAL RECORDS.—México: Hda. Córdoba, 8500 ft. (Hooper and Handley, 1948:15). Morelos (Davis and Russell, 1954:73): 10 mi. N Cuautla; 2 mi. SW Tepoztlán. Distrito Federal: Contreras, 8500 ft. (Hooper and Handley, 1948:15); Cerro Xaltepec, 1½ mi. NNW Zapotitlán, 3380 m. (Villa, 1953:405).

Liomys irroratus texensis Merriam

1902. *Liomys texensis* Merriam, Proc. Biol. Soc. Washington, 15:44, March 5, type from Brownsville, Cameron Co., Texas.
1911. *Liomys irroratus texensis*, Goldman, N. Amer. Fauna, 34:59, September 7.

MARGINAL RECORDS (Goldman, 1911:59, unless otherwise noted).—Texas: about 10 mi. NW Raymondville (Blair, 1952:241); type locality. Tamaulipas: Altamira;

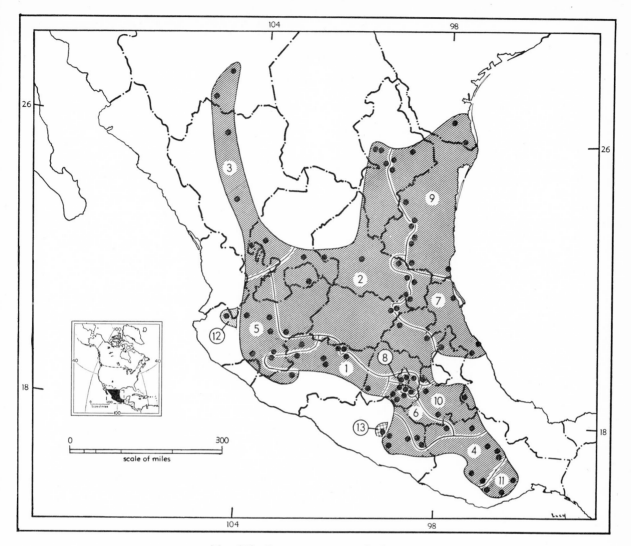

Map 319. *Liomys irroratus* and relatives.

Guide to kinds	4. *L. irroratus irroratus*	9. *L. irroratus texensis*
1. *L. irroratus acutus*	5. *L. irroratus jaliscensis*	10. *L. irroratus torridus*
2. *L. irroratus alleni*	6. *L. irroratus minor*	11. *L. irroratus yautepecensis*
3. *L. irroratus canus*	7. *L. irroratus pretiosus*	12. *L. bulleri*
	8. *L. irroratus pullus*	13. *L. guerrerensis*

Antiguo Morelos, 1000 ft. (Hooper and Handley, 1948:22); *Gómez Farías* (Goodwin, 1954:9); 53 km. N El Limón, 12 km. S Río Guayalejo (17949 KU); Victoria; Hidalgo. Nuevo León: Montemorelos; 20 km. NW General Terán, 900 ft. (Hooper and Handley, 1948:21–22); China (Miller, 1924: 271).

Liomys irroratus torridus Merriam

1902. *Liomys torridus* Merriam, Proc. Biol. Soc. Washington, 15:45, March 5, type from Cuicatlán, Oaxaca.
1911. *Liomys irroratus torridus*, Goldman, N. Amer. Fauna, 34:55, September 7.

MARGINAL RECORDS.—Puebla: Atlixco (Goldman, 1911:55). Veracruz: Acultzingo, 7000 ft. (Hooper and Handley, 1948:13). Oaxaca: type locality. Puebla: Acatlán (Goldman, 1911:55).

Liomys irroratus yautepecus Goodwin

1956. *Liomys irroratus yautepecus* Goodwin, Amer. Mus. Novit., 1757:7, March 8, type from Rancho Sauce, 5000 ft., San Pedro Jilotepec, Oaxaca.

MARGINAL RECORDS.—Oaxaca (Goodwin, 1956a:7): type locality; Santo Tomás Téipan, 7000 ft.; Santo Tomás Quieri, 6000 ft.

Liomys bulleri (Thomas)
Buller's Spiny Pocket Mouse

1893. *Heteromys bulleri* Thomas, Ann. Mag. Nat. Hist., ser. 6, 11:330, April, type from Laguna, Sierra de Juanacatlán, Jalisco. Known only from the type locality.
1911. *Liomys bulleri,* Goldman, N. Amer. Fauna, 34:61, September 7.

External measurements of an adult topotype: 250, 128, 32. Upper parts mouse gray mixed with blackish along mid-line, sprinkled with ochraceous hairs; lateral line pale ochraceous; underparts and feet white; tail brownish above, creamy below. Skull broad and flattened; interparietal small, subtriangular; nasals concave proximally.

Liomys guerrerensis Goldman
Guerreran Spiny Pocket Mouse

1911. *Liomys guerrerensis* Goldman, N. Amer. Fauna, 34: 62, September 7, type from Omilteme, Guerrero. Known only from the type locality.

Measurements of the type: 255; 127; 34. Upper parts black or almost so, sprinkled with ochraceous; underparts white; tail black above, but white below except for black tip. Skull short, broad, massive.

Genus Heteromys Desmarest—Spiny Pocket Mice

Revised by Goldman, N. Amer. Fauna, 34:14–32, September 7, 1911.

1817. *Heteromys* Desmarest, Nouv. Dict. Hist. Nat., 14: 181. Type, *Mus anomalus* Thompson.

External measurements: 272–357; 128–201; 31–44. "Pelage composed of flattened, anteriorly grooved bristles or spines . . . , mingled with slender hairs; tail usually longer than head and body, not conspicuously crested or penciled at tip. . . . Skull elongated; mastoids rather small, appearing externally entirely posterior to auditory meatus; audital bullae not overlapped by pterygoids; interpterygoid fossa V-shaped, narrowing gradually to a rather acute point anteriorly. . . . Molar crowns in early life completely divided by a transverse sulcus into two parallel enamel loops, the grinding surface becoming flat, and the loops uniting first at inner ends of upper row and outer ends of lower row, and continued wear obliterating sulcus or leaving a central enamel island" (Goldman, 1911: 14–15).

KEY TO SUBGENERA OF HETEROMYS

1. Posterior molars narrower than premolars; pelage with numerous stiff bristles or spines.
   Heteromys, p. 542
1'. Posterior molars equal to or broader than premolars; pelage harsh but bristles soft.
   Xylomys, p. 546

Subgenus Heteromys Desmarest

1817. *Heteromys* Desmarest, Nouv. Dict. Hist. Nat., 14:181. Type, *Mus anomalus* Thompson.

Characters are those of the genus.

KEY TO NOMINAL SPECIES OF SUBGENUS HETEROMYS

1. Soles of hind foot hairy from posterior tubercle to heel; occurring on Peninsula of Yucatán.
   H. gaumeri, p. 545
1'. Soles of hind foot naked posteriorly; not occurring on Peninsula of Yucatán.
   2. Parietals not extending laterally across temporal ridges. . . . . *H. temporalis,* p. 544
   2'. Parietals reaching laterally across temporal ridges.
      3. Zygomatic breadth usually less than 14; tail usually less than 140; occurring only in extreme eastern Panamá below 3000 ft. . . . . *H. australis,* p. 545
      3'. Zygomatic breadth usually more than 14; tail usually more than 140; not occurring as above.
         4. Nasals broadly expanded distally and abruptly narrowing posteriorly. . *H. longicaudatus,* p. 544
         4'. Nasals neither broadly expanded distally nor abruptly narrowing posteriorly.
            5. Upper parts lacking a pronounced sprinkling of slender, ochraceous hairs.
               H. goldmani, p. 544
            5'. Upper parts with pronounced sprinkling of slender buffy or ochraceous hairs.
               6. Upper parts distinctly blackish; occurring in southern Veracruz and adjoining parts of north-central Oaxaca. . . . . *H. lepturus,* p. 544
               6'. Upper parts grayish to brownish or, if not grayish to brownish, not in Veracruz or Oaxaca.
                  7. In Sierra de Choapan and Sierra de los Mije. . . . . . *H. nigricaudatus,* p. 546
                  7'. Not recorded from Sierra de Choapan and Sierra de los Mije.
                     H. desmarestianus, p. 543

desmarestianus-group
Heteromys desmarestianus
Desmarest's Spiny Pocket Mouse

External measurements: 255–345; 130–190; 31–42. Upper parts mouse gray to blackish, darker shades usually limited to middorsal region, sprinkled with slender, ochraceous hairs; underparts white; lateral line sometimes present, but when present usually not pronounced, buffy or ochraceous; tail longer than head and body, sparsely haired, dusky above, white below; outer surface of forelegs usually washed with ochraceous. Skull large in most subspecies (greatest length *circa* 35); cranium vaulted; interparietal variable; bullae small; interpterygoid fossa V-shaped. Pelage thin.

This species is usually found at high elevations but in some places, especially in southern Central America, is found near sea level. The habitat is tropical rain forest, especially in areas where rocky outcroppings occur.

This species-group presents some perplexing taxonomic problems; the current nomenclatural arrangement is unsatisfactory and the keys are correspondingly unsatisfactory.

Heteromys desmarestianus chiriquensis Enders

1938. *Heteromys desmarestianus chiriquensis* Enders, Proc. Acad. Nat. Sci. Philadelphia, 90:141, September 20, type from Cerro Pando, between Río Chiriquí Viejo and its tributary Río Colorado, about 10 mi. from Volcán de Chiriquí, Panamá.

MARGINAL RECORDS.—Panamá: type locality. Costa Rica: Agua Buena, Puntarenas (Goodwin, 1946:370).

Heteromys desmarestianus crassirostris Goldman

1912. *Heteromys crassirostris* Goldman, Smiths. Miscl. Coll., 60(2):10, September 20, type from near head of Río Limón, 5000 ft., Mt. Pirri, eastern Panamá.
1920. *Heteromys desmarestianus crassirostris* Goldman, Smiths. Miscl. Coll., 69(5):117, April 24.

MARGINAL RECORDS.—Panamá: Mt. Tacarcuna (Goldman, 1920:118); type locality.

Heteromys desmarestianus demarestianus Gray

1868. *Heteromys desmarestianus* Gray, Proc. Zool. Soc. London, p. 204. May, type from Cobán, Guatemala.
1928. *Heteromys desmarestianus psakastus* Dickey, Proc. Biol. Soc. Washington, 41:10, February 1, type from Los Esesmiles, 8000 ft., Chalatenango, El Salvador. Stated by Goldman (Jour. Washington Acad. Sci., 27:419, October 15, 1937) and reaffirmed by Goodwin (Bull. Amer. Mus. Nat. Hist., 87:371, December 31, 1946) to be identical with *H. d. desmarestianus*, but not, by them, so arranged nomenclatorially.

MARGINAL RECORDS.—Yucatán (Laurie, 1953:387): Chichén-Itzá; Tekom. British Honduras (*ibid.*): Belize.

Guatemala: Puebla (Goodwin, 1934:30). El Salvador: Los Esesmiles, 8000 ft. (Hayman, 1940:475). Guatemala: Volcán San Lucas (Goodwin, 1934:30). Chiapas: Ocuilapa (Goldman, 1911:22). Tabasco: Teapa (*ibid.*). Chiapas: 6 mi. SE Palenque (Kuns and Tashian, 1954:101). Guatemala (Goodwin, 1934:30): Chamá; Secanquim. British Honduras (Laurie, 1953:387): Double Falls; Kate's Lagoon. Not found: X-Cala-Koop, Yucatán (Laurie, 1953:387). That part of range in Yucatán and British Honduras is based on record-stations from which the specimens were identified only to species by Laurie (*loc. cit.*).

Heteromys desmarestianus fuscatus J. A. Allen

1908. *Heteromys fuscatus* J. A. Allen, Bull. Amer. Mus. Nat. Hist., 24:652, October 13, type from Tuma, Nicaragua.
1920. *Heteromys desmarestianus fuscatus*, Goldman, Smiths. Miscl., Coll., 69(5):115, footnote, April 26.

MARGINAL RECORDS.—Honduras (Goodwin, 1942:155): La Mica; Cerro Cantoral. Nicaragua (Goldman, 1911:29): type locality; Chontales; Matagalpa. Honduras (Goodwin, 1942:155): Monte Linderos; Cerro Pucca.

Heteromys desmarestianus griseus Merriam

1902. *Heteromys griseus* Merriam, Proc. Biol. Soc. Washington, 15:42, March 5, type from mountains near Tonalá, Chiapas.
1911. *Heteromys desmarestianus griseus*, Goldman, N. Amer. Fauna, 34:22, September 7.

MARGINAL RECORDS.—Oaxaca: Guichicovi (Goldman, 1911:23). Chiapas: type locality.

Heteromys desmarestianus panamensis Goldman

1912. *Heteromys panamensis* Goldman, Smiths. Miscl. Coll., 56(36):9, February 19, type from Cerro Azul, near headwaters of Río Chagres, 2800 ft., Panamá.
1920. *Heteromys desmarestianus panamensis* Goldman, Smiths. Miscl. Coll., 69(5):117, April 24.

MARGINAL RECORDS.—Panamá: Cerro Brujo (Goldman, 1920:117); type locality.

Heteromys desmarestianus planifrons Goldman

1937. *Heteromys desmarestianus planifrons* Goldman, Jour. Washington Acad. Sci., 27:418, October 15, type from San Gerónimo Pirrís, Costa Rica.

MARGINAL RECORDS (Goodwin, 1946:371): Costa Rica: Hda. Santa María; Cataratos, San Carlos; El General; type locality.

Heteromys desmarestianus repens Bangs

1902. *Heteromys repens* Bangs, Bull. Mus. Comp. Zool., 39:45, April, type from Boquete, S slope of Volcán de Chiriquí, 4000 ft., Panamá.
1920. *Heteromys desmarestianus repens*, Goldman, Smiths. Miscl. Coll., 69(5):115, April 24.

MARGINAL RECORDS.—Panamá: type locality; Boquerón (Goldman, 1911:28).

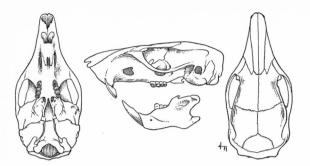

Fig. 311. *Heteromys desmarestianus subaffinis,* 5 km. SE Turrialba, 1950 ft., Prov. Cartago, Costa Rica, No. 26965 K.U., ♀, X 1.

Heteromys desmarestianus subaffinis Goldman

1937. *Heteromys desmarestianus subaffinis* Goldman, Jour. Washington Acad. Sci., 27:420, October 15, type from Angostura, 1980 ft., S side Río Reventazón, opposite Turrialba, Costa Rica.

MARGINAL RECORDS.—Costa Rica: Suerre (Goodwin, 1946:372); type locality; *5 km. SE Turrialba* (26965 KU).

Heteromys desmarestianus underwoodi Goodwin

1943. *Heteromys desmarestianus underwoodi* Goodwin, Amer. Mus. Novit., 1227:1, April 22, type from Escazú, about 3000 ft., about 7 mi. SW San José, San José, Costa Rica.

MARGINAL RECORDS.—Costa Rica: Isla Nievo Irazú (Goodwin, 1946:373); type locality.

Heteromys desmarestianus zonalis Goldman

1912. *Heteromys zonalis* Goldman, Smiths. Miscl. Coll., 56(36):9, February 19, type from Río Indio, near Gatún, Canal Zone, Panamá.
1920. *Heteromys desmarestianus zonalis* Goldman, Smiths. Miscl. Coll., 69(5):116, April 24.

MARGINAL RECORDS.—Panamá: type locality; Maxon Ranch, Río Trinidad (Goldman, 1920:116).

Heteromys goldmani Merriam
Goldman's Spiny Pocket Mouse

1902. *Heteromys goldmani* Merriam, Proc. Biol. Soc. Washington, 15:41, March 5, type from Chicharras, Chiapas.

External measurements: 300–350; 170–201; 35–41. Goldman (1911:24–25) characterized the skull as follows: "In general form similar to that of *H. desmarestianus,* but larger; rostrum less decurved, flatter above; premaxillae narrower and more tapering posteriorly . . . zygomata more spreading anteriorly."

MARGINAL RECORDS.—Chiapas: Catarina, 1300 m. (Hooper, 1947:46); type locality. Guatemala: Zunil, 5000

ft. (Goodwin, 1934:31). Chiapas: Huehuetán (Goldman, 1911:25).

Heteromys longicaudatus Gray
Long-tailed Spiny Pocket Mouse

1868. *Heteromys longicaudatus* Gray, Proc. Zool. Soc. London, p. 204, May, type from México. Known precisely only from Montecristo, Tabasco (Goldman, 1911:24).

An adult female from Montecristo, Tabasco, measures 295, 170, 37. Upper parts approximately mouse gray, with sprinkling of buffy hairs; underparts and feet white; buffy lateral line present but faint; tail dusky above, white below. Skull large, broad, robust; rostrum short, robust; nasals, frontals, premaxillae broad; zygomata and interparietal narrow.

Heteromys lepturus Merriam
Santo Domingo Spiny Pocket Mouse

1902. *Heteromys goldmani lepturus* Merriam, Proc. Biol. Soc. Washington, 15:42, March 5, type from mountains near Santo Domingo (a few miles west of Guichicovi), Oaxaca
1911. *Heteromys lepturus,* Goldman, N. Amer. Fauna, 34:25, September 7.

The type measures: 340, 191, 39. This "species" is closely related to *H. desmarestianus* and *H. longicaudatus.* It is said (Goldman, 1911:26) to differ from *longicaudatus* in longer and more decurved rostrum, more highly arched braincase, broader and—with reference to the nasals—more posteriorly extended premaxillae, more widely spreading zygomata anteriorly; broader frontals, more strongly developed supraorbital shelves, wider interparietal, less sharply incurved temporal ridges; decidedly broader basioccipital.

MARGINAL RECORDS (Goldman, 1911:26, unless otherwise noted).—Veracruz: San Andrés Tuxtla; 25 km. SE Jesús Carranza (32144 KU). Oaxaca: type locality; Choapam [= Choapan]; Tuxtepec.

Heteromys temporalis Goldman
Motzorongo Spiny Pocket Mouse

1911. *Heteromys temporalis* Goldman, N. Amer. Fauna, 34:26, September 7, type from Motzorongo, Veracruz.

The type measures: 320, 180, 37. The species closely resembles *H. goldmani* in most aspects but is unique in the genus in that the temporal ridges follow the parietosquamosal suture rather than cross the parietal.

MARGINAL RECORDS.—Veracruz: 2 km. N Motzorongo, 1800 ft. (19363 KU); *type locality.*

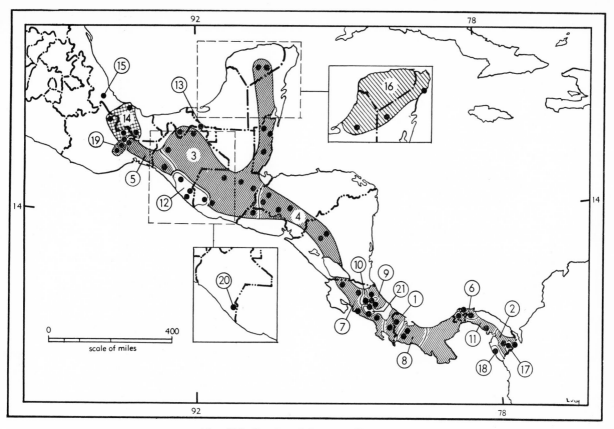

Map 320. Species of the genus *Heteromys*.

1. *H. desmarestianus chiriquensis*
2. *H. desmarestianus crassirostris*
3. *H. desmarestianus desmarestianus*
4. *H. desmarestianus fuscatus*
5. *H. desmarestianus griseus*
6. *H. desmarestianus panamensis*
7. *H. desmarestianus planifrons*

8. *H. desmarestianus repens*
9. *H. desmarestianus subaffinis*
10. *H. desmarestianus underwoodi*
11. *H. desmarestianus zonalis*
12. *H. goldmani*
13. *H. longicaudatus*
14. *H. lepturus*

15. *H. temporalis*
16. *H. guameri*
17. *H. australis conscius*
18. *H. australis pacificus*
19. *H. nigricaudatus*
20. *H. nelsoni*
21. *H. oesterus*

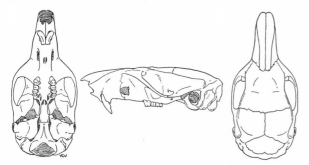

Fig. 312. *Heteromys temporalis*, 2 km. N Motzorongo, 1500 ft., Veracruz, No. 19363 K.U., ♂, X 1.

Heteromys gaumeri J. A. Allen and Chapman
Gaumer's Spiny Pocket Mouse

1897. *Heteromys gaumeri* J. A. Allen and Chapman, Bull. Amer. Mus. Nat. Hist., 9:9, February 23, type from Chichén-Itzá, Yucatán.

Three adults from Tunkás, Yucatán, measured: 295–300; 160–166; 34–35. "Skull rather long and angular, with supraorbital ridges strongly developed laterally as overhanging shelves" (Goldman, 1911:30). The species resembles *H. longicaudatus* and *H. desmarestianus* but, unlike those species, has the soles of the hind feet hairy posteriorly.

MARGINAL RECORDS.—Quintana Roo: Puerto Morelos (Goldman, 1911:30). Esmeralda (Hatt and Villa R., 1950:234). Yucatán: Xlac (Gaumer, 1917:131). Campeche: Apazote (Goldman, 1911:30), thence along coast to point of beginning.

anomalus-group
Heteromys australis
Southern Spiny Pocket Mouse

Measurements of the type of *H. australis conscius* are: 260, 133, 32. Two adult topotypes of *conscius* measure: 240, 251; 120, 131; 31, 33.5. Upper parts slaty black finely grizzled with gray hairs; underparts variable, but usually white; tail brownish above, lighter below, but not sharply bicolor. Skull short, broad; braincase well inflated; rostrum short, massive; audital bullae small.

The species lives in the tropical rain forests of Colombia and eastern Panamá below 2100 ft. altitude, whereas *H. desmarestianus* occurs in the same area of Panamá but at higher elevations.

Heteromys australis conscius Goldman

1913. *Heteromys australis conscius* Goldman, Smiths. Miscl. Coll., 60(22):8, February 28, type from Cana, 2000 ft., mountains of eastern Panamá. Known only from the type locality.

Heteromys australis pacificus Pearson

1939. *Heteromys australis pacificus* Pearson, Not. Naturae, Acad. Nat. Sci. Philadelphia, 6:4, June 8, type from Amagal, 1000 ft., S of Guayabo Bay, Darién, Panamá. Known only from the type locality.

Heteromys nigricaudatus Goodwin
Goodwin's Spiny Pocket Mouse

1956. *Heteromys nigricaudatus* Goodwin, Amer. Mus. Novit., 1791:4, September 28, type from Mazatlán, about 1500 ft., Oaxaca.

The type, an adult female, measured: 283; 153; 36.5. Upper parts approximately mummy brown; underparts white; no lateral line; tail short, blackish and nearly unicolor; skull short and broad (greatest length, 36; zygomatic breadth, 17).

MARGINAL RECORDS (Goodwin, 1956b:4).—Oaxaca: type locality; Ixcuintepec.

Subgenus Xylomys Merriam

1902. *Xylomys* Merriam, Proc. Biol. Soc. Washington, 15:43, March 5. Type, *Heteromys nelsoni* Merriam.

Xylomys can readily be distinguished from the subgenus *Heteromys* as follows: markedly greater development of posterior part of tooth-row; more intricate enamel folds in posterior upper molars; greater lateral extension of parietals along lambdoidal crest (they reach, or almost reach, mastoids); comparatively soft pelage.

KEY TO SPECIES OF SUBGENUS XYLOMYS

1. Ears edged with white; premaxillary tongues extending posterior to nasals. *H. oresterus*, p. 546
1'. Ears without white edge; premaxillary tongues coterminous with nasals. *H. nelsoni*, p. 546

Heteromys nelsoni Merriam
Nelson's Spiny Pocket Mouse

1902. *Heteromys (Xylomys) nelsoni* Merriam, Proc. Biol. Soc. Washington, 15:43, March 5, type from Pinabete, 8200 ft., Chiapas. Known only from the type locality.

Measurements of type are: 356, 195, 43.5. Upper parts mouse gray to blackish; underparts white; tail dusky above, whitish below except for dusky tip. Skull long, slender; nasals markedly broadened, especially distally; premaxillary tongues and nasals crowded well forward by anterior extension of frontals.

Heteromys oresterus Harris
Mountain Spiny Pocket Mouse

1932. *Heteromys oresterus* Harris, Occas. Papers Mus. Zool., Univ. Michigan, 248:4, August 4, type from El Copey de Dota, Cordillera de Talamanca, 6000 ft., Costa Rica.

Average external measurements of 8 adult topotypes are: 340, 174, 40. Upper parts blackish gray with sprinkling of ochraceous or buffy hairs; underparts white; ears edged with white; tail blackish above, white below except for black basal area, white tipped. Skull resembling that of "*repens* but with longer rostrum more inflated anteriorly; premaxillae reaching posteriorly beyond the nasals; palate narrower; bullae less inflated" (Harris, 1932:4).

MARGINAL RECORDS.—Costa Rica: El Muñeco (Goodwin, 1946:373); type locality.

INDEX TO VERNACULAR NAMES

INDEX TO TECHNICAL NAMES

A **bold faced** number refers to the page of the principal account of a taxon.
Names in legends for maps, and names in addenda at end of volume, are not indexed.

A

abaconis,
  Geocapromys, **796**
abbotti,
  Thomomys, **416**
abbreviata,
  Neotoma, **689**, 691
abbreviatus,
  Microtus, 722, **747**
abditus,
  Microtus, **737**
aberti,
  Sciurus, 369, **384**, 386
abieticola,
  Martes, **898**
  Mustela, 898
  Sciurus, 399
  Tamiasciurus, **399**
abietinoides,
  Martes, **898**
abietorum,
  Napaeozapus, **778**
  Peromyscus, **613**
  Vulpes, **855**
  Zapus, 778
ablusus,
  Citellus, 343
  Spermophilus, **343**
abrasus,
  Eumops, 210, **211**,
  212
Abromys, 473
  lordi, 473, 488
absarokus,
  Ursus, **869**
absonus,
  Thomomys, **418**
abstrusus,
  Thomomys, **418**
Abusticola, 722
acadicus,
  Castor, **548**
  Meriones, 772
  Microtus, **724**
  Neosorex, 38
  Sorex, **25**, 26, 27, 38
  Zapus, **772**
acapulcensis,
  Cervus, 1008
  Dama, **1008**
  Odocoileus, 1008
Achlis, 1017
achradophilus,
  Artibeus, 144, 145
Acinonyx, 951
acraia,
  Neotoma, **702**
  Teonoma, 702
Acratocnus, 235, 236
  comes, **236**
  major, 236

Acratocnus (*Continued*)
  odontrigonus, 235, **236**
acrirostratus,
  Thomomys, **418**
Acrocodia, 991
acrus,
  Eutamias, **317**
actuosa,
  Martes, **898**
  Mustela, 898
actuosus,
  Thomomys, **418**
acuminata,
  Phocaena, 831
acuticornis,
  Panolia, 999
acutorostrata,
  Balaenoptera, 834,
  836
acuto-rostrata,
  Balaenoptera, 836
acutus,
  Delphinus, 824
  Lagenorhynchus, 823,
  824
  Liomys, **539**, 540
Adelonycteris, 184
  gaumeri, 187
aderrans,
  Thomomys, 421
admiraltiae,
  Microtus, **724**
adocetus,
  Citellus, 357
  Microtus, **744**
  Spermophilus, 352, **357**
adolphei,
  Macroxus, 379
  Sciurus, **379**
adsitus,
  Eutamias, **318**
adspersus,
  Heteromys, 539
  Liomys, 535, **539**
adustus,
  Canis, 842
aedium,
  Plagiodontia, 796, **797**,
  798
Aegoceros,
  argali, 1030
Aëllo, 95
  cuvieri, 95
Aeluropus, 865
aenobarbus,
  Vespertilio, 177
Aeorestes, 159
  albescens, 159
  nigricans, 159
  villosissimus, 159
aequalidens,
  Thomomys, **437**

aequatorialis,
  Alouata, 222
  Alouatta, **222**
  Nyctinomus, 209
aequivocatus,
  Microtus, **731**
aereus,
  Scalops, 72
  Scalopus, **72**
aestivus,
  Perognathus, **483**
aestuans,
  Sciurus, 394
aestuarina,
  Mustela, **916**
aestuarinus,
  Microtus, **731**
Aesurus, 893
aethiops,
  Cercopithecus, **233**
afer,
  Homo, **234**
affinis,
  Eutamias, **303**
  Globiocephalus, 828
  Hesperomys, **628**
  Neotoma, 699
  Ototylomys, **577**
  Peromyscus, **628**
  Promops, 209
  Tamias, 303
  Thomomys, **419**
  Vespertilio, 161
africana,
  Orca, 825
africanus,
  Armadillo, 243
Agaphelus, 833
  glaucus, 833
agilis,
  Dipodomys, 511, 512, **522**,
  524
  Mustela, 913
  Putorius, 913
  Vespertilio, 174
Agouti, **787**
  nelsoni, 788
  paca, 787, **788**
  virgatus, **788**
Agoutinae, 787
agrestis,
  Campicola, 722
  Microtus, 724, 728
  Mus, 722
  Thomomys, **437**
Agricola, 722
agricolaris,
  Thomomys, **419**
aguti,
  Dasyprocta, **789**
  Mus, 788, 789
Ailurinus, 952

Ailurogale, 952
Ailuropoda, 878
Ailurus, 878
akeleyi,
  Peromyscus, 616
Akodon,
  apricus, 669
  irazu, 670
  xerampelinus, 669
alacer,
  Lepus, 260
  Sylvilagus, **260**
alascanus,
  Callorhinus, 974
alascensis,
  Dicrostonyx, 767
  Evotomys, 712
  Lemmus, 759, **760**
  Mustela, **905**
  Myotis, 160
  Putorius, 905
  Sorex, 23, **31**
  Ursus, **869**
  Vulpes, **856**
  Zapus, 773
alaskanus,
  Sorex, **40**
alba,
  Diplostoma, 448,
  449
  Ectophylla, **135**
  Mustela, 903
  Ondatra, 755
albata,
  Ochotona, **248**
albatus,
  Ochotona, 248
  Thomomys, **419**
albertae,
  Citellus, 342
alberti,
  Sciurus, 384
albescens,
  Aeorestes, 159
  Felis, **960**, 961
  Myotis, 159, **177**,
  178
  Onychomys, **662**
  Perognathus, **498**
  Reithrodontomys, **582**,
  583
  Vespertilio, 177
albibarbis,
  Neosorex, 38
  Sorex, 38
albicauda,
  Phoca, 982
albicaudatus,
  Thomomys, 413,
  419
albicinctus,
  Myotis, 160

11

avia,
 Mephitis, **934**
avicennia,
 Sciurus, **387**
avius,
 Peromyscus, **605**
awahnee,
 Thomomys, **420**
azteca,
 Carollia, 123, **124**
 Felis, **956**
aztecus,
 Artibeus, **140**
 Arvicola, 724
 Caluromys, **17**
 Hesperomys, 633
 Lepus, 260
 Microtus, **724**
 Molossus, **216**
 Myotis, **170**
 Oryzomys, **557**
 Peromyscus, **633**
 Philander, 17
 Potos, **894**
 Reithrodontomys, **585**
 Sylvilagus, **260**
azuerensis,
 Ateles, **228**
 Oryzomys, 554, **559**
azulensis,
 Peromyscus, **654**

B

bachmani,
 Lepus, 256
 Musaraneus, 29
 Sciurus, **387**
 Sylvilagus, 252, **256,**
  258
 Thomomys, **435**
badia,
 Felis, 952
Badiofelis, 952
badius,
 Peromyscus, **652**
 Spermophilus, 347
 Thomomys, 445
Baeodon, 158, **197**
 alleni, **197**
bahamensis,
 Eptesicus, **184**
 Nyctinomus, 205
 Tadarida, **205**
 Vespertilio, 184
baileyi,
 Canis, **847**
 Castor, **548**
 Dipodomys, **528**
 Lepus, 266
 Lynx, **969**
 Microtus, **737**
 Myotis, 167
 Neotoma, **683**
 Odocoileus, 1008
 Perognathus, **493, 494**
 Sciurus, 399
 Sigmodon, **672**

baileyi (*Continued*)
 Sylvilagus, **266**
 Tamiasciurus, **399**
 Thomomys, 413, **435**
Baiomys, 553, **659**
 allex, **659**
 ater, **659**
 brunneus, **661**
 grisescens, **661**
 infernatis, **661**
 musculus, 659, **661,** 662
 nigrescens, **661**
 pallidus, **662**
 paulus, **659**
 subater, **659**
 taylori, **659, 660**
Baiosciurus, 369
bairdi,
 Gulo, **924**
 Microtus, **744**
 Peromyscus, 618
 Sorex, **31**
 Tapirus, 993
 Ursus, **872**
bairdii,
 Berardius, **807**
 Delphinus, 820, **821**
 Elasmognathus, 991, 993
 Hesperomys, 622
 Lepus, **273**
 Mus, 618, 622
 Peromyscus, 612, 613,
  618, 619, 622
 Tapirus, 992, **993**
balaclavae,
 Peromyscus, **619**
Balaena, 839, **840**
 ampullata, 811
 antarctica, 838
 antiquorum, 835
 arctica, 835
 australis, 839, 840
 biscayensis, 839
 boops, 834, 835, 837,
  838
 britannica, 839
 cisarctica, 839
 gibbosa, 833, 834
 glacialis, 839
 Japonica, 840
 japonica, 840
 lalandii, 837, 838
 longimana, 838
 musculus, 834, 836, 837
 mysticetus, **840**
 nodosa, 838
 nordcaper, 839
 novae angliae, 837, 838
 physalus, 834, 835
 pitlekajensis, 840
 robusta, 835
 rostrata, 811, 834, 835,
  836
 roysii, 840
 Sieboldii, 840
 sulcata, 835
 tarentina, 839
Balaenidae, 832, **839**

Balaenoptera, **834**
 acutorostrata, 834, **836**
 acuto-rostrata, 836
 aragous, 835
 arctica, 835
 australis, 838
 blythii, 835
 borealis, 834, **835**
 capensis, 838
 carolinae, 837
 copei, 835
 davidsoni, 836
 edeni, 836
 eschrichtii, 836
 gibbar, 835
 gigas, 837
 indica, 837
 jubartes, 837
 laticeps, 834, 835
 leucopteron, 838
 mediterraneensis, 835
 patachonica, 837
 physalus, **835**
 robusta, 833
 rorqual, 835
 swinhoii, 834, 835
 syncondylus, 838
 tenuirostris, 835
 velifera, 835
Balaenoptère,
 poeskop, 838
Balaenopteridae, 832, **834**
Balantiopteryx, 80, **84**
 io, 84, **85**
 ochoterenai, 85
 pallida, **85**
 plicata, 84, **85**
baliolus,
 Peromyscus, 627
 Sciurus, **378**
balteatus,
 Delphinus, 820
baltica,
 Halichoerus, 984
banderanus,
 Peromyscus, 611, 612,
  652
bangsi,
 Felis, 956, 960
 Glaucomys, **408**
 Mustela, **906**
 Pecari, 996
 Perognathus, **483**
 Sciuropterus, 408
 Sciurus, **379**
 Tayassu, **996**
 Vulpes, **856**
bangsii,
 Lepus, **278**
banksianus,
 Canis, 847
barabensis,
 Glis, 320
barang,
 Leptonyx, 944
Barangia, 944
barbara,
 Eira, 919

barbara (*Continued*)
 Galictis, 920
 Mustela, 919
 Tayra, 921
barbata,
 Phoca, 982, 983
barbatus,
 Erignathus, 982, **983**
barberi,
 Sciurus, **384**
barnesi,
 Ochotona, **248**
barrowensis,
 Spermophilus, 343
basilicae,
 Thomomys, **420**
Bassaricyon, 878, **895,** 896
 gabbii, 895, **896**
 lasius, 896, **897**
 orinomus, **896**
 pauli, 896, **897**
 richardsoni, **896,** 897
Bassaris, 879
 astuta, 879
 monticola, 883
 raptor, 881
 sumichrasti, 879, 883
 variabilis, 883
Bassariscus, 878, **879**
 albipes, 879
 arizonensis, **879**
 astuta, 882
 astutus, **879,** 880
 bolei, **880**
 campechensis, **882**
 consitus, **880**
 flavus, **880**
 insulicola, **880**
 macdougalli, **880**
 nevadensis, **880**
 notinus, **882**
 oaxacensis, **882**
 octavus, **881**
 oregonus, 881
 palmarius, **881**
 raptor, **881**
 saxicola, **882**
 sumichrasti, 879, **882,** 883
 variabilis, **883**
 willetti, **882**
 yumanensis, **882**
Bassariscyon,
 orinomus, 896
bassi,
 Scalopus, **74**
battyi,
 Didelphis, **5**
 Lepus, **285**
 Odocoileus, 1008
Bdeogale, 841
beatae,
 Peromyscus, 635
beaufortiana,
 Phoca, **981,** 982
bechsteinii,
 Vespertilio, 158
bedfordi,
 Proedomys, 722

evexus (*Continued*)
  Thomomys, **424**
evides,
  Peromyscus, **635**
evotis,
  Myotis, 160, **168, 169,** 170
  Notiosorex, **64**
  Sorex, 64
  Vespertilio, 169
Evotomys, 711
  alascensis, 712
  athabascae, 713
  brevicaudus, 713
  californicus, 717
  carolinensis, 713
  caurinus, 717
  dawsoni, 712
  fuscodorsalis, 713
  galei, 713
  gapperi, 713, 714, 716
  idahoensis, 714
  insularis, 712
  limitis, 714
  loringi, 714
  mazama, 717
  nivarius, 717
  obscurus, 717
  occidentalis, 718
  ochraceus, 714
  orca, 712
  phaeus, 715
  proteus, 716
  pygmaeus, 718
  rhoadsii, 716
  saturatus, 716
  smithii, 711
  ungava, 716
  wrangeli, 716
excelsifrons,
  Rangifer, 1020
excelsus,
  Cratogeomys, **465**
  Procyon, **886**
exiguus,
  Heteromys, 540
  Peromyscus, **620**
  Sylvilagus, **257**
  Vespertilio, 177
exilipes,
  Blarina, 58
exilis,
  Dipodomys, **533**
  Grampidelphis, 826
  Vespertilio, 174
eximius,
  Blarina, 58
  Dipodomys, **526**
  Mephitis, **937**
  Microsorex, **50**
  Microtus, **732**
  Sorex, 50
  Thomomys, **424**
  Ursus, **872**
Exochurus, 158
  horsfieldii, 158
  macrodactylus, 158
  macrotarsus, 158

exoristus,
  Neofiber, 754
exsputus,
  Sigmodon, **674**
exsul,
  Dicrostonyx, 765, **767**
extenuatus,
  Thomomys, **424**
extera,
  Lutra, **945**
exterus,
  Peromyscus, **620**
extimus,
  Ammospermophilus, **332,** 334
  Perognathus, **494**
  Sciurus, **370**
  Thomomys, **424**
extractus,
  Dipodomys, **514**
extremus,
  Myotis, **176**

F

falcatus,
  Arctibeus, 143, 144
  Phyllops, **144**
Falcifer, 237
falcifer,
  Thomomys, **440**
fallax,
  Geomys, **452**
  Neotoma, **695,** 696
  Perognathus, 493, **503,** 504, 506
fallenda,
  Mustela, **906**
familiaris,
  Canis, 842
fannini,
  Ovis, 1034
fasciata,
  Lynx, 971
  Phoca, 979, **980,** 982
fasciatus,
  Lynx, **970**
  Perognathus, 473, **474, 475,** 476
fatuus,
  Synaptomys, 762
Felidae, 841, 842, **950,** 951
felina,
  Lutra, 944
felinus,
  Nyctipithecus, 219
felipensis,
  Neotoma, **691**
  Orthogeomys, **457**
  Peromyscus, **644**
Felis, 841, **951,** 952, 966
  albescens, **960,** 961
  apache, 966
  arizonensis, 954
  arundivaga, 956
  aurata, 951
  azteca, **956**

Felis (*Continued*)
  aztecus, 956
  badia, 952
  bangsi, 956, 960
  bengalensis, 951
  bieti, 952
  braccata, 952
  browni, **956**
  buffoni, 961
  cacomitli, **966**
  californica, **956**
  californicus, 956
  canescens, 961
  caracal, 966
  carrikeri, 964
  catus, 951
  celidogaster, 951
  centralis, 955
  chaus, 951
  concolor, 951, 952, **955,** 956, 959
  cooperi, **962**
  coryi, **956**
  costaricensis, **956,** 960
  couguar, **956,** 959
  emeritae, 964
  floridana, 956
  fossata, **966**
  geoffroyi, 951
  glaucula, **962**
  goldmani, 955
  griffithii, 961
  guigna, 951
  hernandesii, 952, 955
  himalayanus, 951
  hippolestes, 956, 959
  improcera, **957**
  kaibabensis, **958**
  limitis, 960
  ludoviciana, 960
  lynx, 966
  macrocelis, 951
  maculata, 971
  maculatus, 971
  margarita, 952
  marmorata, 951
  maul, 951
  mayensis, **958**
  mearnsi, **960**
  megalotis, 951
  mexicana, 961, 962
  minimus, 961
  missoulensis, **959**
  moormensis, 951
  neglecta, 951
  nelsoni, **961**
  nicaraguae, **962**
  nigripes, 952
  oaxacensis, **962**
  ocelot, 961
  olympus, 959
  onca, 951, **952**
  oncilla, 952, **964**
  oregonensis, **959**
  pajeros, 951
  pallida, 952
  panamensis, **966**

Felis (*Continued*)
  pardachrous, 951
  pardalis, 951, 952, **959, 961**
  pardina, 966
  pardinoides, 952, 964
  pardus, 951
  pirrensis, **962,** 963
  planiceps, 951, 952
  pseudopardalis, 961
  rufa, 971
  ruffus, 971
  salvinia, **963**
  schorgeri, **959**
  serval, 951, 952
  sonoriensis, **961**
  stanleyana, **959**
  strigilata, 951
  temmincki, 951, 952
  tigrina, 952, **964**
  tigris, 951, 952
  tolteca, **966**
  uncia, 951
  vancouverensis, **959**
  veraecrucis, **955**
  viverrina, 951
  vulgaris, 971
  wiedii, 951, 952, **961**
  yagouaroundi, 952, **964**
  yaguarundi, 951
  youngi, 959
  yucatanica, **963**
Felix,
  oregonensis, 959
felix,
  Eutamias, **304**
  Tamias, 304
femoralis,
  Perognathus, **505**
femorosacca,
  Tadarida, 204, **207,** 208
femorosaccus,
  Nyctinomus, 204, 207
femurvillosum,
  Artibeus, 138
fenestratus,
  Dasypus, **244**
fenisex,
  Ochotona, **249**
Feresa, 816, **830**
  attenuata, 830
  occulta, **830**
ferox,
  Molossus, 213
  Ursus, 865
ferreus,
  Monophyllus, **117**
  Sciurus, **385**
ferruginea,
  Neotoma, **696**
  Tadarida, **207**
ferrugineiventris,
  Sciurus, 372
ferruginiventris,
  Sciurus, 372
fervidus,
  Caluromys, **18**

martinensis (*Continued*)
  Peromyscus, 620
  Thomomys, **427**
martinus,
  Mustela, 899
martirensis,
  Dipodomys, **523**
  Lepus, **284**
  Neotoma, **700**
  Peromyscus, **640**
  Sitomys, 640
  Spilogale, **932**
  Thomomys, **427**
marylandica,
  Taxidea, 928
mascotensis,
  Sigmodon, **675**
mastivus,
  Noctilio, **88**
  Vespertilio, 88
matacus,
  Loricatus, 243
matagalpae,
  Alouatta, 223
  Macrogeomys, 460,
    463
  Sciurus, **382**
matecumbi,
  Sciurus, **371**
maul,
  Felis, 951
maurus,
  Clethrionomys, **714**
  Eumops, 210, **212**
  Molossus, 212
  Mus, 769
  Vesperugo, 180
maximiliani,
  Centronycteris, **84**
  Vespertilio, 84
maximus,
  Perognathus, 495
  Pipistrellus, **181**
mayensis,
  Blarina, 61
  Cryptotis, 56, **61**
  Dipodomys, **530**
  Felis, **958**
  Marmosa, **14**
  Oryzomys, **568**
maynardi,
  Procyon, 884, **889**, 890
Mazama, 999, 1003, **1012**
  americana, **1012**
  cerasina, **1013**
  dorsata, 1026, 1027
  gouazoubira, 1012, **1013**
  hemionus, 1007
  pandora, **1014**
  peninsulae, 1007
  permira, **1014**
  pita, 1012
  reperticia, **1013**
  sericea, 1027
  tema, 1013
  temama, **1013**
mazama,
  Clethrionomys, **717**

mazama (*Continued*)
  Evotomys, 717
  Thomomys, **446**
mcguirei,
  Rangifer, 1020
mcilhennyi,
  Dama, **1010**
  Odocoileus, 1010
mcmurtrii,
  Centurio, 146
mearnsi,
  Canis, 844, **846**
  Conepatus, **940**
  Felis, **960**
  Neotoma, **686**
  Perognathus, 477
  Sciurus, 405
  Tamiasciurus, **405**
  Thomomys, **435**
mearnsii,
  Lepus, 262
  Sylvilagus, 260, **262**
  Vesperimus, 631
Medatus, 136
medioximus,
  Synaptomys, **764**
mediterraneensis,
  Balaenoptera, 835
mediterraneus,
  Delphinus, 817
  Petrorhynchus, 810
medius,
  Dipodomys, **516**
  Microdipodops, **508**
  Perognathus, **479**
  Peromyscus, 620
  Thomomys, **442**
megacephalus,
  Microdipodops, **508,
    509**
  Peromyscus, **633**
  Sitomys, 633
Megaceros, 1014
  hibernicus, 999
Megachiroptera, 147
megadon,
  Oryzomys, **561**
Megadontomys, 601, **655**
  flavidus, 656
megalodous,
  Procyon, **888**
Megalomys, 553, **570**
  audreyae, 570
  desmarestii, **570** 571
  luciae, 570, **571**
  majori, 570
Megalonychidae, **235**
Megalonychoidea, **235**
megalophylla,
  Mormoops, 95, **96**
megalops,
  Peromyscus, 610, 611,
    612, **653, 654**
megalotis,
  Felis, 951
  Hesperomys, 642
  Micronycteris, 97, **98**, 99
  Nyctinomus, 209

megalotis (*Continued*)
  Phyllophora, 97
  Reithrodon, 579, 582, 587
  Reithrodontomys, 580,
    581, 582, 583, **584,
    587,** 591
  Vespertilio, 200
Megamys, 570
Meganeuron, 812
megapotamus,
  Geomys, **452**
Megaptera, 834, **837**
  americana, 838
  bellicosa, 838
  gigas, 838
  indica, 838
  kurzira, 838
  longimana, 838
  longipinna, 837
  morrei, 838
  novaeangliae, **838**
  osphyia, 838
Megascapterus, 412
Megasorex, 64
mejiae,
  Peromyscus, **608**
mekisturus,
  Peromyscus, 610, **645**
melaena,
  Globicephala, **828**
melampeplus,
  Mustela, **918**
  Putorius, 918
melania,
  Macroxus, 380
  Sciurus, **380**
melanocarpus,
  Peromyscus, 610, **654**
melanocaudus,
  Perognathus, **492**
melanochir,
  Ateles, 228
melanogaster,
  Cynalicus, 864
melanogenys,
  Sorex, 32
Melanomys, 553, **568**
melanonotus,
  Sciurus, 390
melanophrys,
  Hesperomys, 644
  Onychomys, **665**
  Peromyscus, 612, **644,**
    646
  Vesperimus, 644
melanops,
  Eptesicus, 183
  Monodelphis, 18, **19**
  Peramys, 19
  Thomomys, **442**
  Vespertilio, 186
melanopterus,
  Eptesicus, 184
  Vesperus, 184
melanopus,
  Arctomys, 321
melanorhinus,
  Myotis, **175**

melanorhinus (*Continued*)
  Vespertilio, 175
melanorhyncha,
  Mustela, 903
melanotis,
  Lepus, **284**
  Oryzomys, 554, **560, 561**
  Perognathus, **482**
  Peromyscus, 610, **627,** 679
  Sigmodon, **677**
  Thomomys, **427**
melanura,
  Neotoma, 682, **688**
melanurus,
  Capromys, 793, **794, 795**
  Dipodomys, **530**
  Perognathus, 491, **492**
  Peromyscus, **654**
  Tamias, 302
melanus,
  Procyon, 887
melas,
  Delphinus, 827, 828
  Neotoma, **688**
Meles,
  americanus, 928
  jeffersonii, 928
  labradorius, 925
  taxus, 928
Melictis, 864
  beskii, 864
Mellivora, 841
mellonae,
  Phoca, **980**
melvillensis,
  Ovibos, 1030
mendocinensis,
  Ursus, **873**
mephitica,
  Mephitis, 935
  Viverra, 936
Mephitis, 897, 929, **933, 939**
  americana, 936
  avia, **934**
  bivirgata, 936
  chilensis, 939
  concolor, 939
  dentata, 937
  edulis, 939
  elongata, **935**
  estor, **935**
  eximius, **937**
  fetidissima, 936
  foetulenta, 937
  frontata, 936
  holzneri, **936**
  hudsonica, **936**
  intermedia, 939
  interrupta, 929, 931
  longicaudata, 939
  luconata, 939, 942
  macroura, 933, 934, **937,
    938, 939**
  major, 934, **936**
  mephitica, 935
  mephitis, **934, 936**, 937
  mesoleuca, 941
  mesomelas, **936**

navus,
Neotoma, 696
Oryzomys, 566
Thomomys, 428
nayaritensis,
Cryptotis, 58
Pappogeomys, 464
Sciurus, 392
Neacomys, 552, 571
pictus, 571
nebracensis,
Canis, 844
nebrascensis,
Hesperomys, 622
Peromyscus, 622
Pteromys, 407
Reithrodontomys, 585
nebulicola,
Citellus, 343
Spermophilus, 343
nebulosus,
Thomomys, 442
necator,
Vulpes, 855, 857
Nectomys, 553, 571, 572
alfari, 572
dimidiatus, 572, 573
efficax, 572
negatus,
Heterogeomys, 460
neglecta,
Felis, 951
Taxidea, 926, 928
neglectus,
Arvicola, 732
Ateles, 230
Citellus, 359
Cratogeomys, 470
Eutamias, 301, 302
Macroxus, 387
Microtus, 732, 733
Perognathus, 487
Platygeomys, 470
Spermophilus, 359
Tamias, 301
Thomomys, 429
Ursus, 873
negligens,
Sciurus, 381, 382
Nelomys, 802
armatus, 802
blainvillei, 802
nelsoni,
Agouti, 788
Ammospermophilus, 331, 334
Blarina, 61
Cervus, 1001, 1003
Conepatus, 941
Cryptotis, 56, 61
Dama, 1010
Dicrostonyx, 766
Didelphis, 8
Dipodomys, 512, 529
Felis, 961
Geomys, 464
Heteromys, 546

nelsoni (Continued)
Nasua, 891 893
Neotoma, 682, 688
Odocoileus, 1010
Orthogeomys, 458
Oryzomys, 554, 559
Ovis, 1032, 1033
Pappogeomys, 464
Pecari, 997
Perognathus, 492, 502, 503, 506
Peromyscus, 655, 656
Reithrodontomys, 594
Romerolagus, 253
Sciurus, 375
Spermophilus, 334
Sylvilagus, 262
Tayassu, 997
Thomomys, 435
Ursus, 873
Vampyrum, 112
Vampyrus, 112
Xenomys, 707
Nelsonia, 552, 707
goldmani, 708
neotomodon, 707, 708
nemoralis,
Microtus, 750
Sciurus, 374
Nemorhoedus,
palmeri, 1032
nemorigavus,
Cervus, 1012
Neoaschizomys, 711
sikotanensis, 711
Neodon, 722
sikimensis, 722
Neofelis, 951
Neofiber, 711, 753, 754, 755
alleni, 753, 754
apalachicolae, 754
exoristus, 754
nigrescens, 754
struix, 754
Neogale, 904
neomexicana,
Mustela, 912
Vulpes, 858
neomexicanus,
Putorius, 912
Sciurus, 402
Sorex, 32
Sylvilagus, 266
Vulpes, 858
Neomys,
fodiens, 23
panamensis, 575
Neopsomys, 803
Neoromicia, 184
Neosciurus, 369, 386
Neosorex, 23, 40
acadicus, 38
albibarbis, 38
navigator, 23, 39
palustris, 38
Neotamias, 296, 306, 398

Neotoma, 552, 680, 681, 699, 705, 706, 707, 708
abbreviata, 689, 691
acraia, 702
affinis, 699
albigula, 681, 682, 686, 689, 699
alleni, 705
alticola, 702
angustapalata, 682, 699
angusticeps, 686
annectens, 699
anthonyi, 681, 693
apicalis, 704
arenacea, 691
arizonae, 702
atrata, 695
attwateri, 683
aureotunicata, 691
auripila, 691
baileyi, 683
bella, 692
bensoni, 691
brevicauda, 686
bryanti, 681, 693
bullata, 695
bullatior, 699
bunkeri, 681, 694
californica, 691
campestris, 683
canescens, 685
chamula, 695, 699
chrysomelas, 682, 698, 699
cinerea, 701, 702
cinnamomea, 702
cnemophila, 701
columbiana, 704
cumulator, 688
desertorum, 692
devia, 691
dispar, 701
distincta, 695
drummondii, 704
durangae, 686
egressa, 691
eremita, 695
fallax, 695, 696
felipensis, 691
ferruginea, 696
flava, 691
floridana, 681, 682, 683
fulviventer, 698
fusca, 704
fuscipes, 681, 682, 699
gilva, 691
goldmani, 682, 694
grandis, 688
grangeri, 704
grinnelli, 692
griseoventer, 696
guerrerensis, 705
haematoreia, 683
harteri, 692
illinoensis, 683
inopinata, 696

Neotoma (Continued)
inornata, 696
insularis, 692
intermedia, 692
isthmica, 696
laplataensis, 686
latifrons, 682, 688
latirostra, 692
lepida, 681, 682, 686, 689, 691, 692, 693, 694
leucodon, 686
leucophaea, 685
littoralis, 682, 685
luciana, 700
lucida, 704
macrodon, 704
macropus, 685
macrotis, 694, 700
madrensis, 696
magister, 681, 683, 684
marcosensis, 692
marshalli, 692
martinensis, 681, 694
martirensis, 700
mearnsi, 686
melanura, 682, 688
melas, 688
mexicana, 681, 682, 695, 696, 699
micropus, 681, 682, 685, 686, 699
mohavensis, 701
molagrandis, 692
monochroura, 700, 701
monstrabilis, 692
montezumae, 682, 689
navus, 696
nelsoni, 682, 688
nevadensis, 692
notia, 693
nudicauda, 693
occidentalis, 704, 705
ochracea, 696
orizabae, 698
orolestes, 704
osagensis, 683, 685
palatina, 682, 689
parvidens, 696
pennsylvanica, 684
perpallida, 693
perplexa, 701
petricola, 693
phenax, 706, 707
picta, 698
pinetorum, 698
planiceps, 686
pretiosa, 693
pulla, 704
ravida, 693
relicta, 694
riparia, 701
robusta, 688
rubida, 685
rupicola, 704
sanrafaeli, 693
saxamans, 705

pseudocrinitus,
  Peromyscus, 601, **604**
pseudopardalis,
  Felis, 961
Pseudorca, 816, **827**
  crassidens, **827**
Pseudostoma, 449
  castanops, 465
  floridanus, 453
psilotis,
  Chilonycteris, 89, **91**
psora,
  Procyon, 886, **888**
Pternopterus, 158
Pterobalaena, 834
  bergensis, 836
  gryphus, 837
  minor, 836
Pteroderma, 136
  perspicillatum, 136
Pteromys,
  alpinus, 408
  americana, 407
  canadensis, 411
  cucullatus, 407
  nebrascensis, 407
  oregonensis, 410
  virginianus, 407
  volans, 407
Pteronotus, 89, **93**
  centralis, 95
  davyi, **93**, **94**, 95
  fulvus, **94**
  suapurensis, 93, **94**, 95
Pteropidae, 147
Pteropteryx,
  canina, 83
pucheranii,
  Macroxus, 394
pueblensis,
  Cryptotis, **58**
puertae,
  Thomomys, **431**
pugetensis,
  Thomomys, **443**
pugeti,
  Microtus, **734**
pugnax,
  Ursus, **868**
pulchellus,
  Ursus, **874**
pulcher,
  Onychomys, **667**
  Scalopus, 72
pulchra,
  Mustela, **914**
pulla,
  Neotoma, **704**
pullatus,
  Microtus, 724, **727**
pullus,
  Liomys, **540**
  Perognathus, **507**
  Peromyscus, **607**
  Thomomys, **431**
Puma, 951

pumila,
  Brachyphylla, 129, **130**
pumilus,
  Microtus, 720
  Procyon, **888**
punctata,
  Dasyprocta, 789, 790, **791**, **792**
punctulatus,
  Cariacus, 1004
  Sorex, **40**
punensis,
  Myotis, 177
punukensis,
  Microtus, **736**
purus,
  Microdipodops, **510**
Pusa, 949, **981**
  hispida, 981
  orientalis, 949, 950
  pygmaea, 981
pusilla,
  Eucervus, 1004
  Mustela, 906
pusillum,
  Phyllostoma, 133
pusillus,
  Chilonycteris, **93**
  Thomomys, **432**
putida,
  Mephitis, 936
Putorius, **914**, 916
  agilis, 913
  alascensis, 905
  alleghemiensis, 908
  alleni, 910
  arcticus, 906, 907
  arizonensis, 910
  audax, 906
  energumenos, 916
  eskimo, 908
  frenatus, 912
  goldmani, 912
  haidarum, 906
  imperii, 907
  kadiacensis, 907
  leptus, 907
  leucoparia, 912
  longicauda, 913
  lutensis, 918
  macrophonius, 912
  melampeplus, 918
  mexicanus, 910
  microtis, 907
  mundus, 912
  muricus, 907
  neomexicanus, 912
  nigrescens, 919
  nigripes, 914
  notius, 913
  Noveboracensis, 913
  noveboracensis, 913
  occisor, 913
  oregonensis, 913
  oribasus, 913
  peninsulae, 913
  perdus, 913

Putorius (*Continued*)
  polaris, 907
  richardsoni, 905
  rixosus, 909
  saturatus, 914
  spadix, 914
  streatori, 908
  tropicalis, 914
  vison, 916, 918
  vulgivagus, 919
  washingtoni, 914
  xanthogenys, 912
putorius,
  Mustela, 914
  Spilogale, **929**, **931**, 933
  Viverra, 931
pygacanthus,
  Orthogeomys, 456, **457**
pygmaea,
  Pusa, 981
  Spilogale, **933**
pygmaeus,
  Evotomys, 718
  Macrotus, 98
  Molossus, 217
  Procyon, 884, **889**
  Thomomys, 412, **443**
Pygoderma, 128, **145**
  bilabiatum, **145**, 146
pyladei,
  Macroxus, 381
Pyrofelis, 952
pyrrotrichus,
  Cynomys, 365

Q

quadratus,
  Thomomys, **443**, 445
quadricincta,
  Tatusia, 243
quadridens,
  Lobostoma, 91
quadrimaculatus,
  Eutamias, 297, 309, **314**, 316
  Tamias, 314
quadrivatatus,
  Tamias, 302
quadrivittatus,
  Eutamias, 297, 298, **311**, **312**, 316, 318
  Sciurus, 312
  Tamias, 303, 312
quarterlinearis,
  Mephitis, 931
quasiater,
  Arvicola, 751
  Microtus, 723, **751**
quebecensis,
  Myotis, 190
  Tamias, **295**
Quemisia, **786**
  gravis, **787**
querceti,
  Glaucomys, **407**
  Sciuropterus, 407

quercinus,
  Myotis, 174
  Sciurus, 374
  Thomomys, **432**
quica,
  Didelphis, 10
quintinensis,
  Dipodomys, **532**
quixensis,
  Vespertilio, 177

R

raceyi,
  Marmota, **329**
rafinesquei,
  Zapus, 773
rafinesquii,
  Corynorhinus, 198, **200**
  Plecotus, 200
rafiventer,
  Sciurus, 372
rainieri,
  Aplodontia, **292**
ramona,
  Onychomys, **667**
randi,
  Euarctos, 869
  Ursus, **869**
Rangifer, 999, **1017**
  arcticus, **1018**
  asiaticus, 1020
  caboti, **1018**
  caribou, **1018**, 1021
  cylindricornis, 1021
  dawsoni, **1018**
  eogroenlandicus, **1019**
  excelsifrons, 1020
  fortidens, **1019**
  granti, **1020**
  grönlandicus, 1018, **1020**
  mcguirei, 1020
  montanus, 1019, **1020**
  osborni, **1020**
  pearyi, **1020**
  selousi, 1020
  sibiricus, **1020**
  stonei, **1020**
  sylvestris, **1020**, 1021
  tarandus, **1017**, **1021**
  terraenovae, **1021**
  transuralensis, 1020
rangifer,
  Tarandus, 1020
raptor,
  Bassaris, 881
  Bassariscus, **881**
  Rheomys, 708, **710**
ratticeps,
  Microtus, 735
Rattus, 77, 289, **768**, 770, 950
  alexandrinus, 768, 769
  frugivorus, 768
  norvegicus, 575, 767, 768, **769**
  rattus, 573, 767, **768**, 769